DESIGN OF STEEL STRUCTURES

Third Edition

Edwin H. Gaylord, Jr.

Professor Emeritus of Civil Engineering
University of Illinois at Urbana–Champaign

Charles N. Gaylord

Late Professor of Engineering
University of Virginia

James E. Stallmeyer

Professor of Civil Engineering
University of Illinois at Urbana–Champaign

McGraw-Hill, Inc.

New York   St. Louis   San Francisco   Auckland   Bogotá   Caracas
Lisbon   London   Madrid   Mexico   Milan   Montreal   New Delhi
Paris   San Juan   Singapore   Sydney   Tokyo   Toronto

This book was set in Times Roman.
The editors were B. J. Clark and David A. Damstra;
the production supervisor was Louise Karam.
The cover was designed by Carla Bauer.
R. R. Donnelley & Sons Company was printer and binder.

Cover: The Smith Avenue High Bridge, St. Paul, Minn.
(photo by Neil Kueberg–MNDOT).

DESIGN OF STEEL STRUCTURES

1 2 3 4 5 6 7 8 9 0 DOC DOC 9 0 9 8 7 6 5 4 3 2 1

ISBN 0-07-023054-4

Library of Congress Cataloging-in-Publication Data

Gaylord, Edwin Henry.
    Design of steel structures/Edwin H. Gaylord, Jr.,
  Charles N. Gaylord, James E. Stallmeyer.—3rd ed.
       p.   cm.
    Includes indexes.
    ISBN 0-07-023054-4.
    1. Building, Iron and steel.   2. Aluminum construction.
  I. Gaylord, Charles N.   II. Stallmeyer, James E.   III. Title.
  TA684.G3   1992
  624.1'821—dc20   91–14984

ABOUT THE AUTHORS

Edwin H. Gaylord, Jr. is professor emeritus of civil engineering at the University of Illinois at Urbana-Champaign. He is a graduate of Wittenberg University, Case Western Reserve University, and the University of Michigan. He has been involved in teaching, research, and consulting in structural engineering, particularly in the area of steel structures. In addition to his coauthorship of "Design of Steel Structures" he is coauthor, with Charles N. Gaylord, of "Design of Steel Bins for Storage Bulk Solids," coeditor, with Charles N. Gaylord, of "Structural Engineering Handbook," and coeditor of the volume "Criteria and Loading" published by the Council on Tall Buildings and Urban Habitat.

He was a member of the American Institute of Steel Construction Committee on Specifications from 1959 to 1986 and in 1988 received the Institute's Special Citation Award for outstanding contribution to the art of building with structural steel. He is a life member of the Structural Stability Research Council and served as its chairman from 1962 to 1966. In 1971 he received the American Society of Engineering Education's Westinghouse Electric Fund Award for excellence in teaching. He also received in 1990 the American Society of Civil Engineers Shortridge Hardesty Award in recognition of his contributions in applying fundamental results of research to solutions of practical engineering problems in the field of structural stability.

James E. Stallmeyer is professor of civil engineering at the University of Illinois at Urbana-Champaign. He is a graduate of the University of Illinois. He has been involved in teaching, research and consulting in structural engineering; particularly in the area of steel structures.

He has been a member of American Railway Engineering Association's Committee on Steel Structures since 1962 and has been a member of committees of the American Association of State Highway and Transportation Officials and the American Iron and Steel Institute. In 1964 he was awarded the Adams Memorial Membership Award by the American Welding Society for teaching activities in welding technology. He received the Everitt Award for teaching excellence in 1981.

CONTENTS

8 Connections

9 Plastic Analysis and Design

10   Stability and Strength of Flat Plates   679

11   Steel Bridges   711

12   Buildings   757

Appendix

Indexes

PREFACE

This book deals with the design of steel structural members, and their connections, with emphasis on their use in bridges and buildings. Discussion of theory and behavior under the various combinations of loads such members must resist is followed by a discussion of applications according to standard specifications for load-and-resistance factor design and allowable-stress design. Discussions of these two types of specifications are presented in separately numbered articles followed by worked-out examples. This will facilitate matters for those who may wish to cover only load-and-resistance factor design, only allowable-stress design, or both.

In addition to a number of worked-out examples there are 32 design problems (labeled DP), which was a feature of previous editions. These examples help to show structural members as components of real-world structures rather than as isolated elements. Practically all DPs and worked-out examples are presented in both load-and-resistance factor design and allowable-stress design. DPs are especially useful in helping the student prepare flow diagrams and computer programs relating to the portion of the standard specifications they depend on for design. The authors believe that in this way the student will learn the fundamentals of the design procedure and the sequence of the calculations involved much better than if they are presented in the form of flow charts and computer programs. It has been the authors' experience that students who rely on flow diagrams and computer programs prepared by others do not develop a capacity for critical evaluation of the procedures and their resulting output. Another feature is the presentation and discussion of the design calculations for the truss spans and composite-beam approach spans of a highway bridge in Maryland.

Discussion and applications of the AISC specifications are based on the Specification for Structural Steel Buildings: Allowable Stress Design and Plastic Design, June 1, 1989 and the Load and Resistance Factor Design Specification for Structural Steel Buildings, September 1, 1991. Discussion and applications of the AASHTO Standard Specification for Highway Bridges are based on the 1989 edition. References to AREA Specifications for Steel Railway Bridges are to the 1990 edition.

The authors suggest that the first course in steel structures be based on Chapters 1 to 3; Articles 4-1 to 4-16; Articles 5-1 to 5-9, 5-11, and 5-13 to 5-18 of Chapter 5; and either Articles 6-1 to 6-3 and 6-6 to 6-9 of Chapter 6 or Articles 8-1 to 8-5 and 8-16 to 8-19 of Chapter 8.

Special thanks are extended to Prof. W. J. Hall, for his support and encouragement during the preparation of this edition. Suggestions by Profs. Hall and Scott Schiff, who used parts of the manuscript for their classes, and the assistance of Scott Greer in the preparation of examples in Chapter 6, are gratefully acknowledged. We are also grateful to Nestor Iwankiw of the American Institute of Steel Construction for alerting us to forthcoming changes in the Institute's specifications.

McGraw-Hill would like to thank Terry Hand, U.S. Military Academy and Ralph Mozingo, Penn State University for their many helpful comments and suggestions in reviewing the manuscript.

Edwin H. Gaylord, Jr.
James E. Stallmeyer

NOTATION

Abbreviations

kcf	kips per cubic foot
klf	kips per lineal foot
kli	kips per lineal inch
ksf	kips per square foot
ksi	kips per square inch
mph	miles per hour
pcf	pounds per cubic foot
plf	pounds per lineal foot
pli	pounds per lineal inch
psf	pounds per square foot
psi	pounds per square inch
AASHTO	American Association of State Highway and Transportation Officials
AISC	American Institute of Steel Construction
AISI	American Iron and Steel Institute
ANSI	American National Standards Institute
AREA	American Railway Engineering Association
ASCE	American Society of Civil Engineers
ASTM	American Society for Testing and Materials
AWS	American Welding Society
BBC	Basic Building Code
BOCA	Building Officials and Code Administrators National Building Code
NIST	National Institute of Standards and Technology
RCSC	Research Council for Structural Connections
SSBC	Southern Standard Building Code
SSRC	Structural Stability Research Council

UBC   Uniform Building Code
WRC   Welding Research Council

Nomenclature

A area

A_b area of bolt

A_e effective net area

A_f area of beam flange

A_g gross area

A_n net area of tension member

A_s area of steel section in composite beam; area of longitudinal stiffener; shear area of bolts in connection

A_{sc} cross-sectional area of stud shear connector

A_{st} area of transverse stiffener

A_w area of beam or plate-girder web

a length of plate; distance between vertical stiffeners

B bending factor (area of cross section divided by section modulus)

B_1, B_2 amplification factor

b spacing of stringers in bridge floor; width of flange; width of plate; length of bearing on beam web; effective width of concrete flange of composite beam

b_e effective width of plate or web for determining postbuckling strength

C compressive force; fundamental period coefficient

C_D drag coefficient

C_L lift coefficient

C_1, C_2 lateral-torsional buckling coefficients

C_b moment-gradient coefficient for lateral-torsional buckling of beams

C_c column slenderness ratio dividing elastic and inelastic buckling

C_m coefficient of bending term in beam-column interaction formula

C_s shape factor determining effective wind pressure

C_v ratio of critical shear stress to yield shear stress

C_w warping constant of cross section

c distance from neutral axis to extreme fiber of beam

D, DL dead load

d diameter of hole; diameter of rocker; depth of cross section; diameter of bolt

d_c column-web depth between fillets; web depth between fillets

d_s diameter of stud shear connector

E modulus of elasticity (Young's modulus)

E_c modulus of elasticity of concrete

E_r double modulus (also called reduced modulus)

E_s strain-hardening modulus

E_t tangent modulus

e eccentricity of load; natural logarithm base

F_a allowable axial compressive stress

F_b allowable bending stress

$F_{b,cr}$ critical bending stress

F_c allowable web-crippling stress

F_{cr} critical compressive stress

F_E Euler column stress

$F_{E'}$ allowable Euler column stress

F_{EXX} weld electrode strength

F_p allowable bearing stress; proportional-limit stress

F_r allowable fatigue stress; residual stress

F_s axial force in stiffener

F_{sr} range of stress for fatigue loading

F_t allowable tensile stress

F_u ultimate stress

F_v allowable shear stress

$F_{v,cr}$ elastic critical shear stress

$F_{v(cr)i}$ inelastic critical shear stress

F_{vp} proportional-limit shear stress

F_{vu} ultimate shear stress

F_{vy} shear yield stress

F_y yield stress

f calculated stress

f_a calculated axial compressive stress

f_b calculated bending stress

f_c calculated compressive stress

$f_{c'}$ specified 28-day compressive strength of concrete

f_e postbuckling edge stress in plate

f_p calculated bearing stress

f_t calculated tensile stress

f_v calculated shear stress

G modulus of elasticity in shear (modulus of rigidity); center of gravity; ratio of sum of column stiffnesses to sum of beam stiffnesses at joint in frame

G_t tangent modulus in shear

g gage (transverse spacing of fastener lines); distance from shear center to point of application of load; acceleration of gravity

h depth of web of beam or plate girder; depth of section

I impact ratio; moment of inertia; occupancy importance factor

I_{eff} effective moment of inertia

I_p polar moment of inertia

I_{pG} polar moment of inertia with respect to centroid

I_{pS} polar moment of inertia with respect to shear center

I_s moment of inertia of stiffener

I_{xy} product of inertia

J torsion constant of cross section

K spring constant; effective-length coefficient

K' effective-length coefficient of laced or battened column

K_1, K_2, K_3, K_4 net-section efficiency coefficients

k distance from flange outside face to toe of web fillet; coefficient in plate-buckling formula; $\sqrt{P/EI}$; weld geometry parameter

k_c flange local-buckling parameter

L length; story height

L, LL basic live load

L_c length of channel shear connector

L_b spacing of braces

L_0 center-to-center spacing of battens

l length

M moment

M_1 smaller of end moments on unbraced length

M_2 larger of end moments on unbraced length

M_{cr} critical moment

M_{lt} moment due to lateral translation

M_m critical moment in plastic design

M_n nominal resisting moment

M_{nt} moment with no lateral translation

M_0 moment due to transverse loads on beam column

M_p plastic moment

M_r limiting elastic-buckling moment

M_s simple-beam moment

M_u ultimate moment; factored moment

M_y yield moment

N bolt pretension; cycles to failure; normal force; length of bearing

n factor of safety; number of fasteners; shape factor for cross section in shear; E/E_c

P load

P_{cr} column critical load

P_D drag component of wind

P_E Euler column load

P_L lift component of wind

P_n probability that an event will be exceeded at least once in n years

P_r column double-modulus load

P_T column twist-buckling load

P_t column tangent-modulus load

P_u ultimate load; factored axial load

P_u ultimate load

P_y plastic axial load

p pressure per unit of area; allowable bearing pressure of rocker on bearing plate

Q shear; prying force; first moment of area in shear-stress formula

Q, Q_a, Q_s coefficients used in evaluating postbuckling allowable loads

Q_u static strength of shear connector

q velocity pressure (also called dynamic pressure or stagnation pressure); allowable load on shear connector; shear per lineal inch

q_u static strength of shear connector

R reaction; shear force on fastener; return period (also called recurrence interval) of snow, wind, etc.; reduction in live load on building floors, percent; ratio of maximum stress to minimum stress (in fatigue formula); member resistance

R_e reduction factor for hybrid girder

R_{PG} reduction factor for post-bend buckling

R_{ult} strength of fastener; strength of weld element

R_w structural system coefficient

r radius of gyration; rate of reduction of live load; radius of hole

r_{eq} equivalent radius of gyration for lateral-torsional buckling

r_0 radius of gyration of chord of battened column

r_{pS} polar radius of gyration with respect to shear center

r_T radius of gyration of section consisting of compression flange and one-third the compression web area

r_t equivalent radius of gyration for torsional buckling

r_{tb} equivalent radius of gyration for twist-bend buckling

S elastic section modulus; shear center; effective span of bridge floor slab; site coefficient; fatigue strength

S_{xc} compression-flange section modulus

S_{xt} tension-flange section modulus

s pitch (distance, in the direction of the gage lines, between two successive holes)

T tensile force; torsional moment; fundamental period of vibration

T_b specified pretension of high-strength bolt

T_e effective throat of fillet weld or partial-penetration groove weld

T_v St. Venant torsional resistance

T_w torsional resistance due to nonuniform warping

t thickness

t_f flange thickness

t_w web thickness

U reduction coefficient

V shear; velocity; coefficient of variation

V_{cr} critical shear in plate-girder web

V_h shear force in composite concrete slab

V_n factored shear force

V_t shear component of plate-girder web tension field

V_u shear strength of beam or plate-girder web

v velocity

W load on beam, kips

W_e external work during virtual displacement

W_i internal work during virtual displacement

WL wind load

w distributed load on beam, kips per foot; unit weight of concrete

w_g gross width of part in tension

w_n net width of part in tension

x_0 distance from shear center to centroid

y_0 deflection due to transverse loads on beam columns; distance from shear center to centroid

Z plastic section modulus; zone factor

α angle of inclination

β angle of twist; reliability index

Δ beam deflection

Δ_i fastener deformation; weld deformation

Δ_{oh} story translational deflection

δ displacement; deflection of column at midlength

δ_0 midlength displacement due to initial crookedness

ϵ unit strain

ϵ_r residual strain

ϵ_s strain at onset of strain hardening

ϵ_y yield strain

θ rotation of joint in frame or of beam at support; angle of twist per unit length; angle of plate-girder panel diagonal with horizontal; mechanism angle; acute angle between shear force and weld axis

λ slenderness parameter

λ_c column slenderness parameter

λ_p slenderness parameter to attain M_p

λ_r slenderness parameter to attain M_r

μ Poisson's ratio; coefficient of friction

ρ radius of curvature; mass density of air

σ standard deviation

τ ratio of tangent modulus to Young's modulus

τ_u shear strength

ϕ inclination of tension field in plate-girder web; rotation at end of beam; resistance factor

ϕ_b resistance factor for bending

ϕ_c resistance factor for columns

CHAPTER
1

LOADS AND
STRUCTURES

1-1 ENGINEERED STRUCTURES

Engineered structures are of such variety that they defy any attempt to enumerate them except in a general way. The countless problems which arise in their design have prompted engineers to specialize in the design of particular structures or groups of related structures, and it is profitable to study design somewhat according to customary areas of specialization. Although the complete design of many structures is the result of the coordinated efforts of several branches of engineering, we refer sometimes to the design of a structure having in mind only that part of the design which comes within the province of one of the branches.

Among the structures that are designed by civil engineers are bridges, buildings, transmission towers, storage vessels, dams, retaining walls, docks, wharves, highway pavements, and aircraft landing strips. Even this group of structures is too large for convenient study as a unit. In this book we will limit ourselves to a study of structural members in metal and the methods by which they are usually connected, together with applications to the design of bridges and buildings.

1-2 THE DESIGN PROCEDURE

The first and often the most difficult problem in design is the development of a plan that will enable the structure to fulfill effectively the purpose for which it is to be built. If the structure is a building, for example, the designer must create a plan which is adapted to the site; which provides a suitable arrangement of rooms, corridors, stairways, elevators, etc.; which will be aesthetically acceptable; and which can be built at a price the client is prepared to pay. This phase of design, sometimes called *functional planning*, calls for a designer with a high order of skill and imagination.

Although the structural scheme is never independent of the functional plan, it is convenient for the purposes of this discussion to think of its development as a second major step in the design procedure. The extent to which the scheme must be developed during the functional-planning stage depends upon the structure. For example, the location of the columns in a building usually must be worked out with the functional plan, and sufficient space must be anticipated between finished ceiling and finished floor of adjacent stories to accommodate the floor construction. The functional plan and structural scheme of a highway bridge usually are not so interdependent. The roadway grade and alignment of a highway bridge are influenced principally by clearance requirements with respect to whatever is to be bridged and the necessity of providing adequate approaches to collect and disperse traffic, while the width depends upon the number of lanes required to accommodate the expected traffic. Many different types of bridge structure can be adapted to a given functional plan.

It is usually necessary to make tentative cost estimates for several preliminary structural layouts. Sometimes this may have to be done while the functional plan is being developed; sometimes it can be done later. Selection of structural materials must be based upon consideration of availability of specific materials and the corresponding skilled labor, relative costs, and wage scales, and the suitability of the materials for the structure. Successful development of an efficient structural scheme hinges on the engineer's familiarity with the many types of supporting structure which have been developed in the past. On the other hand, the designer who leans too heavily on tradition may fail to see the possibilities in new and better solutions.

The third stage of the design is a structural analysis. Although design specifications and building codes usually prescribe the nature and magnitude of the loads to which the structure may be subjected, at times the engineer must make the decision. Once the loads are defined, a structural analysis must be made to determine the internal forces which will be produced in the various members of the framework. Although this is a fairly routine procedure, simplifying assumptions must invariably be made before the principles of mechanics can be applied. The designer must be conscious of his or her assumptions to ensure that the structure as designed can be expected to behave accordingly.

In the fourth phase of the design the engineer proportions the members of the structural system. They must be chosen so that they will be able to resist, with an appropriate margin of safety, the forces which the structural analysis has disclosed. Familiarity with the methods and processes of fabrication (and their limitations) and with the techniques of construction (and their limitations) is indispensable.

The four steps in structural design discussed above are seldom, if ever, distinct, and in many cases they must be carried along more or less simultaneously. Furthermore, they assume varying degrees of importance relative to one another.

Design is necessarily a trial-and-error procedure. Most structures are statically indeterminate and require that member properties be specified before the analysis for the load effects can be carried out. After the member forces have been determined, the validity of the member selection must be evaluated. If changes in member properties are required, a reanalysis must be carried out. The procedure must be repeated until the members selected and the resultant member forces are in acceptable agreement. The development of the computer has greatly facilitated this phase of the design process, but the judgment and experience of the designer are impossible to build into a completely logical system as required by the computer.

Development of procedures for translating design specifications into computer programs continues to receive the attention of engineers in many specialties. Some special application packages are available. Such programs should be utilized only after the engineer has a thorough understanding of the requirements of the specifications, the method of analysis employed in the program, and the behavior of the many types of structural members.

1-3 LOADS

The weight of a structure is called *dead load*. It can be determined with a high degree of precision, although not until after the structure has been designed. For this reason it is necessary to estimate dead load before a structural analysis is made so that the part of the internal forces due to weight can be taken into account. Experienced designers can often estimate the weight of a structure or its parts with good accuracy. The actual weight should be determined and compared with the estimated weight and correction made if the difference is significant. The designers of the ill-fated first Quebec bridge across the St. Lawrence River neglected this point. After the collapse of the bridge during erection, with the resulting death of more than 100 workmen, investigation disclosed dead loads 20 to 30 percent larger than those assumed for the design. Although this discrepancy was not the cause of the failure, it would have handicapped the bridge had it been possible to complete it as originally designed.

Live loads may be steady or unsteady; they may be fixed, movable, or moving; they may be applied slowly or suddenly; and they may vary considerably in magnitude. The history of some live loads—notably the weights of the heaviest highway trucks—is one of more or less continual increase in magnitude. The following loads usually must be considered:

1. The weight of the structure
2. The weight of people, furniture, machinery, and goods in a building
3. The weight of traffic on a bridge
4. The weight of snow

5. Dynamic forces resulting from moving loads
6. Dynamic forces induced by wind and earthquakes
7. The pressure of liquids in storage vessels
8. Forces resulting from temperature change if expansion and contraction are impeded
9. The pressure of earth, as on retaining walls and column footings

The primary effect of gravity loads on structures is calculated from their weight; i.e., they are considered to be static loads. However, live loads in motion may produce forces that are considerably greater than those resulting from the same loads at rest. These are the dynamic forces mentioned in category 5 above. Dynamic force caused by motion is called *impact* if the effect is equivalent to additional gravity load and *lateral* or *longitudinal force* (depending upon its direction relative to the path of the vehicle) when the result is equivalent to load in the horizontal plane. Lateral force may result from motion in a curved path (centrifugal force) or from the nosing of a train on a straight track. Longitudinal forces are caused by acceleration and deceleration of moving vehicles.

The determination of the loads for which a given structure or class of structure should be proportioned is one of the most difficult problems in design. Several questions must be answered: What loads may the structure be called upon to support during its lifetime? In what combinations may these loads occur? To what extent should a possible but highly improbable load or combination of loads be allowed to dictate the design? The probability that a specific live load will be exceeded at some time during the life of the structure usually depends on the period of exposure (life) of the structure and the magnitude of the design load. For example, if the roof of a building is designed for a snow load of 30 psf, the chance that this load might be exceeded at some time during the life of the building is greater if the building stands for 50 years than if the building stands for only 10 years. This is because the maximum snowfall varies from year to year, and a given seasonal maximum can be expected to occur at a given locality only once in so many years in the long run. This period is called a *mean return period* or *mean recurrence interval*. Such return periods can be determined by statistical analysis of snowfall records. Of course, extremes of other natural phenomena such as wind or flood also occur infrequently, and return periods for specific extremes can be determined similarly.

The reciprocal of the recurrence interval of an extreme snowfall, wind velocity, etc., is the probability that the extreme value will be exceeded in any one year. Thus if the return period R of a wind speed of, say, 90 mph at a certain locality is 100 years, the probability that there will be a wind speed greater than 90 mph in any one year is $1/R = 1/100 = 0.01$. However, the probability which is of interest in choosing a wind velocity for design purposes is not the probability that the design speed will be exceeded in any one year but rather the probability that it will be exceeded during the life of the structure. This probability can be determined as follows.[1] Since $1/R$ is the probability that the specified velocity will be exceeded in any year, $1 - 1/R$ is the probability that it will *not* be exceeded. Then the probability that it will *not* be exceeded during n years, where n is the life of the structure, is $(1 - 1/R)^n$. Therefore, the probability P_n that it *will* be exceeded at least once in the n years is

$$P_n = 1 - \left(1 - \frac{1}{R}\right)^n \tag{1-1}$$

As an example, suppose a structure which is expected to have a life of 50 years is to be built in the locality mentioned above, where the mean recurrence interval of a wind speed of 90 mph is 100 years. The probability that the structure will encounter a wind speed exceeding 90 mph during its life is

$$P_{50} = 1 - (1 - 0.01)^{50} = 1 - 0.60 = 0.40$$

That is, there is a 40 percent chance that the structure will be exposed to a wind exceeding 90 mph. If this is an acceptable risk, it is sufficient to design the building to resist the pressures from a 90 mph wind. There will be a margin of safety in the design, of course, and so the structure would not be expected to collapse under a wind of this velocity.

1-4 LIVE LOADS ON BUILDING FLOORS

Buildings serve such diverse purposes and present such random arrangements of physical equipment and persons as to make it extremely difficult to estimate suitable design loads. Although a number of systematic surveys have been made, there is still a lack of adequate data. Many municipalities assume responsibility for the public safety by controlling the design of buildings through building codes which specify live-load requirements as well as other factors pertaining to design, and several organizations have issued codes for national or regional use. Among the latter are the following:

Uniform Building Code, sponsored since 1972 by the International Conference of Building Officials, Pasadena, California. This code is used widely in the western states.

Southern Standard Building Code, sponsored since 1945 by the Southern Building Code Congress, Birmingham, Alabama. This code is used in the southern and southeastern states.

BOCA National Building Code, sponsored since 1950 by the Building Officials and Code Administrators International, Chicago. This code is used in the eastern and north central states.

Live-load recommendations are also published by the American Society of Civil Engineers, New York, in Building Code Requirements for Minimum Design Loads for Buildings and Other Structures, ASCE 7-88 (formerly American National Standards Institute ANSI A58.1-1982).

Buildings may be classified according to occupancy as follows:

1. Residential (including hotels)
2. Institutional (hospitals, sanatoriums, jails)
3. Assembly (theaters, auditoriums, churches, schools)
4. Business (office-type buildings)
5. Mercantile (stores, shops, salesrooms)
6. Industrial (manufacturing, fabrication, assembly)
7. Storage (warehouses)

Except for studies of combustible contents made in connection with fire-resistance classifications, apparently there are no published reports of residential live loads which are the results of an actual weighing of contents. Building Materials and Structures Report 92, Fire-Resistance Classifications of Building Constructions (U.S. Department of Commerce), reports average combustible contents of about 4 psf of floor area, with a maximum of 7.3 psf except in one portion which served as a library. These figures are probably good approximations of total contents excluding persons. A residential room containing 1 person to every 6 ft²—surely adequate allowance for a crowd—would average, say, 25 psf. At the most, then, we might expect residential live loads to be 35 psf over relatively small areas, with an average of about 10 psf over an entire building. The 40 psf design requirement found in most building codes is ample.

Live loads for institutional occupancy may be expected to be about the same as those for residential occupancy. Several surveys of crowded hospital wards have been made, and even those wards which contained 1 bed for every 30 ft² supported average live loads of only 9 psf. Building codes are in substantial agreement on 40 psf as a minimum live load for institutional private rooms.

There have been a number of investigations of live loads due to crowds of people. At the University of Iowa, students packed for the purpose of testing dynamic loads on balcony construction resulted in a load of 116 psf. Observations of normal loading conditions on the elevators of Grand Central Terminal in New York City showed live loads of about 100 psf. In a test by the Milwaukee Board of Education in 1920, a room normally intended for 48 pupils was crowded with 258 pupils, filling all seats double and all aisles and open space. The resulting live load, including furniture, was 41.7 psf. The range of minimum-live-load requirements for assembly occupancy, as specified by various building codes, is given in Table 1-1. The table is not intended to be complete but rather to show representative loads.

The U.S. Public Buildings Administration sponsored live-load studies of the Internal Revenue Building and the Veterans Administration Building in Washington.[2] In the former building, 20 psf or less of actual average live load was found on 70 percent of its area, 40 psf or less on 88 percent, and 60 psf or less on 96.5 percent. The maximum average live load of 106 psf occupied 825 ft² (0.5 percent of the total area). In the latter building, 95 percent of the floor area

TABLE 1-1

Live loads for typical assembly occupancies

Range in values required by building codes

Type of space	Live load, psf
School classrooms (fixed seats)	40–60
School classrooms (movable seats)	40–100
Assembly halls (fixed seats)	50–60
Assembly halls (movable seats)	100
Theaters (not necessarily balconies)	50–60
Dance halls	100–120

supported an average load of 20 psf or less, 97.8 percent supported 40 psf or less, and 99.5 percent supported 60 psf or less. The maximum average live load of 90 psf was found on 1176 ft^2 of the tenth floor (0.5 percent of the total area). Somewhat similar prior studies of the Equitable Building in New York City disclosed average loads of 11.6 psf over three selected floors. The maximum load was 78.3 psf, the minimum 0.87. The National Institute of Standards and Technology (formerly the National Bureau of Standards) surveyed their Administration Building and the U.S. Civil Service Commission Building.[3] The largest load intensity found was 72.5 psf. Building-code requirements for office-space buildings range from 50 to 80 psf.

Studies, similar to those mentioned above, of mercantile, industrial, and storage occupancies are reported in Ref. 4. The studies included two department stores, two mattress factories, one men's clothing factory, one dress factory, two furniture factories, one newspaper plant, one printing plant, and two warehouses. As might be expected, wide variations in live load were found. For example, the maximum live load in one of the mattress factories was only 41 psf on 0.3 percent of the total floor area, while in the other it was 101 psf on 11.1 percent of the area. The latter load is somewhat misleading, because it was in a cotton storage area. Maximums for the furniture factories were 98 and 120 psf. The largest load in the printing plant was 168 psf on 1 percent of its area. The range of loads in one of the department stores is shown in Fig. 1-1. The ordinates of this diagram give the percentage of area occupied by loads varying in increments of 5 psf. The lightest load was 21 psf, and the heaviest 61 psf. In one warehouse, 0.4 percent of its area carried a load of 257 psf; in the other, 0.7 percent of the area supported

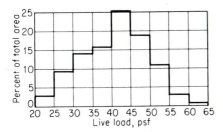

FIGURE 1-1

TABLE 1-2

Live loads for various occupancies

Range in values required by building codes

Occupancy	Live load, psf
Residential	40
Libraries (reading rooms)	60
Libraries (stacks)	125
Mercantile	75–125
Light manufacturing	75–125
Heavy manufacturing	125–150
Light storage	120–125
Heavy storage	250 minimum

304 psf. The usual range of building-code requirements for the occupancies discussed in this paragraph is given in Table 1-2, which is not intended to be complete.

The load surveys mentioned above involve observations of load intensity at an instant of time, i.e., at the time of the observation. However, floor loads in a particular structure vary randomly with time, and it is important to know what the peak lifetime loads may be. Very little information of this kind is available.

The tendency of average building live loads to decrease with an increase in the floor area considered poses a question with respect to the design of various kinds of supporting members. For example, it would be unrealistic to assume all the floor areas supported by a column to have loads of the same intensity as that supported by a joist. Similarly, because the maximum expected load is not likely to be realized on all floors simultaneously (except perhaps for some types of warehouse), it would be unrealistic to assume the same uniform load on all the floors supported by a lower column as on the floors supported by a column higher in the building. Building codes make varying provisions for this contingency. The Uniform Building Code and the BOCA National Building Code permit a reduction in the basic design live load on any member supporting more than 150 ft², except for floors in places of public assembly, in accordance with the formula

$$R = r(A - 150) \tag{1-2}$$

where R = reduction, percent

r = rate of reduction = 0.08 percent for floors

A = area supported by floor or member (contributory area)

The reduction cannot exceed 40 percent for members receiving load from one level only, 60 percent for other members, nor R as determined from

$$R = 23.1\left(1 + \frac{D}{L}\right) \tag{1-3}$$

where D = dead load, psf

L = basic live load, psf

The maximum reduction according to Eq. (1-3) is prescribed so that the structure designed for the reduced load would still be safe if the total area were to be subjected to the full live load. Should this happen the maximum load would be 30 percent greater than the load for which the structure was designed. For example, if $D/L = \frac{1}{3}$ the maximum reduction according to Eq. (1-3) is 30.8 percent. The contributory area corresponding to this reduction can be obtained from Eq. (1-2) as

$$30.8 = 0.08(A - 150)$$

which yields $A = 535$ ft^2. The structure would be designed for

$$535D + 535(1 - 0.308)L$$

Substituting $D = 0.33L$ yields

$$535 \times 0.33L + 535(1 - 0.308)L = 548.5L$$

Should the structure receive full live load over the entire area, the total load would be

$$535 \times 0.33L + 535L = 713.3L$$

The maximum load, 713.3L, is 1.3 times the design load 548.5L. For allowable stress design (Art. 1-12), this is acceptable since the factor of safety in these specifications is at least 1.6 or 1.67. But for load-factor design and load-and-resistance-factor design (Art. 1-12), the ratio of maximum possible load to the design load is not constant. In these cases the ratio is a function of the relative values of dead load and live load and the load factors applied to them. For the case illustrated above ($D/L = \frac{1}{3}$, $A = 535$ ft^2, $R = 30.8$ percent) the result is as follows. The design load is

$$535[1.2 \times 0.33L + 1.6 \times (1 - 0.308)L] = 806.4L$$

If the entire area should experience the full live load, the total load would be

$$535[0.33L + 1.0L] = 713.3L$$

The ratio of the design load to maximum possible load is 806.4/713.3 = 1.13. For the extreme cases the results are as follows. If $D/L = 0$, the ratio of design load to maximum possible load is 1.23. However, for the case where D/L produces the maximum reduction of 40 percent from Eq. (1-3), the ratio of design load to maximum possible load is only 1.06. (The maximum reduction of 40 percent corresponds to a ratio of dead load to live load of 0.73.) Although specifications for load-factor design and load-and-resistance-factor design (Art. 1-12) provide so-called resistance factors by which predicted member strengths are multiplied to obtain design strengths, these factors are not intended to allow in any way for differences between design loads and possible maximum loads. Consequently, for structures designed according to specifications of this type, the designer might want to consider in some cases somewhat smaller load-reduction factors than those of Eq. (1-2).

No reduction is allowed in the Uniform Building Code for roof loads or live loads in excess of 100 psf, except that in the latter case column live loads may be reduced by 20 percent. Special conditions apply to loads and reduction permitted on roofs. Reductions are dependent upon the slope of the roof and the loaded area.

The possibility of failure because of overload is a hazard which is often overlooked. The design live load should be conspicuously posted in commercial and industrial buildings, and the occupant should be held responsible for keeping the actual loads within the specified limit. Failures due to overload are not uncommon. Many such failures are the result of the conversion of buildings or portions of them to purposes for which they were not designed.

1-5 LIVE LOADS ON BRIDGE FLOORS

Highway traffic is made up of four principal kinds of vehicles: the truck-tractor with semitrailer, the truck, the bus, and the passenger car. These units vary widely in weight, and their average weights are considerably less than the weights of the heaviest units. The heaviest truck which is used to any considerable extent at present weighs about 50,000 lb when fully loaded, and since it is about 40 ft long, it represents an average load of, say, 1250 plf of traffic lane. An average passenger car weighs perhaps 4000 lb fully loaded, while the heaviest car may weigh something less than 10,000 lb, with corresponding intensities of 200 to 500 plf. The distance between vehicles in the same traffic lane is obviously important in its effect on load intensity. This distance may range from 25 to 50 ft center to center at speeds of 10 mph to upward of 200 ft at 60 mph.

Because of the widely variable character and distribution of highway traffic, it is expedient to adopt a conventionalized loading. Nearly all highway bridges in the United States are designed for one of the four classes of load recommended by the American Association of State Highway and Transportation Officials (AASHTO). These loads consist of a system of concentrated loads to represent a truck or of a load distributed uniformly along the traffic lane, together with a concentrated load, to represent a long line of medium-weight traffic with a heavy vehicle somewhere in the line. The two systems are necessary because of the differences in length of traffic responsible for maximum forces in various parts of a bridge. A stringer will usually be of such length that it can support only one or two axles of a truck, and since the effect of one or two concentrated loads on a beam is quite different from the effect of an equal amount of load distributed uniformly, the actual concentrations must be considered. On the other hand, the force in a chord member of a simple truss span will be largest when the full length of the bridge is loaded. A relatively small error results from the substitution of a uniform load for a large number of concentrated loads; hence the lane load may be used, with considerable simplification in calculations. Since exceptionally heavy trucks usually operate at respectable distances from one another, a

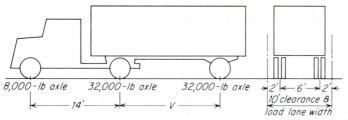

8,000-lb axle   32,000-lb axle   32,000-lb axle

|←———— 14' ————→|←———— V ————→|

2'|← 6' →|2'
10' clearance &
load lane width

V = variable spacing, 14' to 30'. Use value which produces maximum stress.

(a)

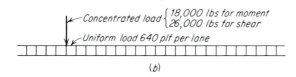

Concentrated load $\begin{cases} 18,000 \text{ lbs for moment} \\ 26,000 \text{ lbs for shear} \end{cases}$

Uniform load 640 plf per lane

(b)

FIGURE 1-2
HS20-44 load.

line of traffic is considered to have only one such vehicle (two in the case of continuous spans) represented by the concentrated load mentioned above. The heaviest loading of the AASHTO specifications is the HS20-44, pictured in Fig. 1-2.

Although it is not an accurate representation of modern locomotives, the system of loads used in the design of most railroad bridges is one whose makeup was proposed a few years prior to 1890 by Cooper. The Cooper load (Fig. 1-3*a*) is intended to represent two locomotives followed by a uniformly loaded train. Although from time to time load systems intended to be closer approximations to the steam locomotives typical of the era preceding the advent of the diesel have been proposed, they have never been adopted. For comparison with the Cooper

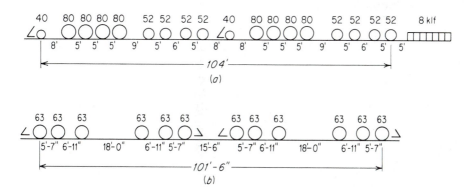

FIGURE 1-3
(*a*) Cooper E-80 train load. Axle load in kips. (*b*) Typical diesel locomotive (two units). Axle load in kips.

load, Fig. 1-3*b* shows the axle loads and spacing for two units of one of the heavier diesel locomotives.

Bridge specifications of the American Railway Engineering Association (AREA) recommend that main-line bridges be designed for the Cooper E-80 train shown in Fig. 1-3*a*. In his original specifications, Cooper recommended three classes of load, which he called A, B, and C. The locomotive driving-axle loads for these three classes were 24, 22, and 25 kips, respectively, as compared with the 80-kip axles of the E-80 load.

1-6 IMPACT

The meaning of the word *impact* as it is used in structural design may be illustrated by describing two different ways in which a spring may be loaded. If one attaches a 20-lb weight to a suspended spring and supports the weight while it is being lowered to the position where it is supported by the spring, the maximum force in the spring is 20 lb. On the other hand, if the weight is released after it is fastened to the spring, the maximum elongation of the spring will be almost double that required to support the weight in its position of static equilibrium and the corresponding force in the spring will be almost 40 lb. The 20 lb of force in excess of the 20-lb static force is called *impact*. It is customary to express impact as a percentage of the static force, and in this case, therefore, the impact factor is almost 100 percent.

The impact of moving live loads is a much more complex phenomenon than the one just described. The speed of a moving vehicle, its mass relative to the mass of a bridge, and irregularities in the track or floor and in the wheels of the vehicle are significant factors. Pulsating loads are particularly critical if the frequency of the pulses happens to be coincident, or nearly so, with the period of a fundamental mode of vibration of a structure.

Design-specification provisions for impact are frankly empirical and do not attempt to account for all the variables. The AASHTO specifications require impact allowance given by the equation

$$I = \frac{50}{L + 125} \tag{1-4}$$

but not to exceed 0.3. In this formula, I is the ratio of impact to static load and L is the length in feet of the part of the span which is loaded. The AREA specifications make similar but more severe provision for impact. Impact allowance for moving loads such as elevators, traveling cranes, and reciprocating machinery is usually specified as a fixed percentage of the load.

The effect of impact is taken into account in the calculation of the load effects. For example, if the impact is 25 percent, the live load is multiplied by 1.25 in the calculation of the forces.

Since most building-floor live loads are essentially static, the values discussed in Art. 1-4 are considered to be sufficiently on the safe side to cover any impact likely to occur. One exception to this statement is an AISC stipulation that the live load on hangers supporting floor and balcony construction be increased by one-third for impact.

1-7 SNOW LOADS

Freshly fallen dry snow weighs 5 to 6 pcf, packed snow about 10 pcf. A number of studies of records of the National Weather Service have been made in an attempt to set reasonable snow loads for various sections of the country. In 1939 the Service published data from 166 weather stations on the greatest depth of snow in sheltered areas such as clearings in forests. The results disclosed snow loads ranging from zero in the southernmost parts of the southern tier of states, through about 5 psf for the remainder of the south; 10 psf for the central tier of states; 15 psf through southern New York, the southern Great Lakes region, and the northern Plains states; and up to 20 to 25 psf for the Lake Superior and New England areas. Exceptions to these values occur in mountainous regions, where the values may run about 5 psf higher than in the lower altitudes of the same section, and along the Pacific coast to Seattle, where snow rarely falls.

A map published by the National Weather Service gives ground snow loads having a 50-year mean recurrence interval (Fig. 1-4). These loads were based on the maximum annual water equivalents of snow on the ground. Except for the southern states, these loads tend to be higher than those discussed in the preceding paragraph. They range from 5 psf in the southern coastal states to 40 to 50

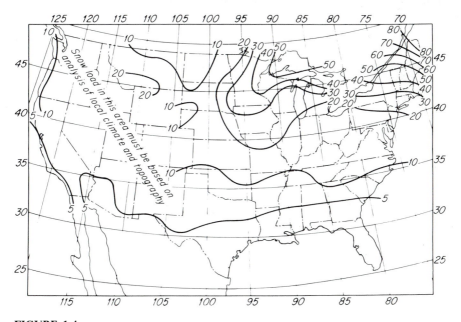

FIGURE 1-4

Snow load on the ground, 50-year mean recurrence interval. (*United States Weather Bureau Map 12158, January 1969*).

psf in the northern Great Lakes region to 70 to 80 psf in northeastern Maine. Data on the Rocky Mountain states are not given.

The snow load on a roof is usually less than that on the ground. Based on a comprehensive study of roof loads relative to ground loads, the National Building Code of Canada specifies for flat roofs a basic snow load of 80 percent of the sum of the weights of the 30-year ground snowpack and the maximum 1-day rainfall in late winter or early spring. The weight of snowpack plus rain runs to as much as 120 psf in the Canadian Rocky Mountains.[5] ASCE 7-88 specifies a basic snow load of 80 percent of the 50-year return ground snow. A further reduction (to 60 percent) is allowed in both codes for roofs that have a clear exposure to winds of sufficient intensity to remove snow. Still further reductions are allowed for sloping roofs, since they accumulate less snow than flat roofs. On the other hand, valleys of adjoining gabled roofs of multibay buildings may accumulate more than normal amounts of snow. Projections, such as penthouses on flat roofs, may also cause drifting. The Canadian Building Code recommends that snow loads near projections from a roof be increased by 50 percent for a width three times the height of the projection, but not to exceed 15 ft.

Based on a study of the weights of seasonal snowpacks having a mean recurrence interval of 10 years, the loads in Table 1-3 were suggested for the design of roofs.[6] It should be noted, however, that the mountain areas defined in this table were not included in the study because of extreme local variations in depths of snow. Therefore, the suggested 40 psf for flat roofs will be excessive for many localities in these areas and too low in others. For example, the 10-year-return snowpacks in Reno and Salt Lake City were 20 and 30 psf, respectively, but these cities are in an excluded area. On the other hand, measurements of the snowpack on the roof of a building at 10,000 ft in the Rocky Mountains in Colorado, where the winter-long accumulation was 7 ft deep at the valley and 5 ft

TABLE 1-3
Suggested minimum snow or other live load for roofs*

On horizontal projection, psf

Region	Slope of roof			
	3 in 12 or less	6 in 12	9 in 12	12 in 12 or more
Southern states	20	15	12	10
Central states	25	20	15	10
Northern states	30	25	17	10
Great Lakes, New England, and mountain areas†	40	30	20	10

* From Ref. 6. These loads are based in part on weights of seasonal snowpacks, 10-year mean recurrence interval; see Art. 1-7.

† Great Lakes and New England areas include northern portions of Minnesota, Wisconsin, Michigan, New York, and Massachusetts and the states of Vermont, New Hampshire, and Maine. Mountain areas include Appalachians above 2000-ft elevation, Pacific coastal ranges above 1000-ft elevation, and Rocky Mountains above 4000-ft elevation; however, see Art. 1-7.

deep at the eaves of the V-shaped roof, disclosed densities of 8, 16, and 25 pcf at depths of 3, 5, and 7 ft. Thus, the average density was about 16 pcf, and the roof load at the 7-ft depth was about 100 psf (Ref. 7).

The live load suggested in Table 1-3 for flat roofs in the southern states (20 psf) exceeds the 10 psf (or less) 10-year-return snowpack. This load was chosen because it conformed with the value commonly specified for this region by various building codes. It is intended to provide for live loads other than snow, such as those incidental to construction and maintenance. In many cases, of course, the minimum live load prescribed by a governing building code may differ from the value in Table 1-3.

Snow load need not be considered in the design of bridges, since a fall heavy enough to be of consequence would make the bridge impassable or else compel traffic to move at such a pace as to reduce the dynamic effect.

1-8 WIND LOADS

The evaluation of the effects of wind on an object in its path is a complex problem in aerodynamics. If we consider air to be nonviscous and incompressible, which is a reasonable assumption for velocities of the magnitudes for which civil engineering structures are designed, Bernoulli's equation for streamline flow can be used to determine the local pressure at the stagnation point as a column of air strikes (at 90°) an immovable body. Thus,

$$q = \tfrac{1}{2}\rho v^2 \tag{a}$$

where q = pressure
ρ = mass density of air
v = velocity of air

This pressure is called *velocity* pressure, *dynamic* pressure, or *stagnation* pressure. It is important to note that this equation is based on steady flow and does not account for the dynamic effects of gusts or the dynamic response of the body.

The resultant wind pressure on a body depends upon the pattern of flow around it. Pressures vary from point to point on the surface, depending upon the local changes in velocity, which depend in turn upon the shape and size of the body. The resultant pressure P is expressed in terms of the drag component P_D and the lift component P_L:

$$P_D = C_D A \frac{\rho v^2}{2} \qquad P_L = C_L A \frac{\rho v^2}{2} \tag{b}$$

The drag coefficient C_D and the lift coefficient C_L depend on the shape of the body and its orientation with respect to the wind. A is a characteristic area of the body, usually the projection of the body's surface on a plane.

The terms *drag* and *lift* are not ordinarily used in describing wind pressures on buildings, bridges, and the like. Instead, the pressure p per square foot, normal to the surface, is expressed in terms of a shape factor C_s (also called *pressure coefficient*):

$$p = C_s q = C_s \frac{\rho v^2}{2} \qquad (c)$$

Air at a temperature of 15°C (59°F) at sea level weighs 0.0765 pcf. Substituting the corresponding mass density 0.0765/32.2 into Eq. (c) gives $p = 0.00119 C_s v^2$. With the symbol V to denote velocity in miles per hour, this gives

$$p = 0.00256 C_s V^2 \qquad (1\text{-}5)$$

It will be noted that a velocity of 100 mph will induce a pressure of 26 psf when $C_s = 1$. Shape factors are discussed later in this article.

Measured wind velocities are necessarily averages of the fluctuating velocities which are encountered during a finite interval of time. The usual reported value in the United States is the average of the velocities which are recorded during the time it takes a horizontal column of air 1 mi long to pass a fixed point (the measuring anemometer). For example, if a 1-mi column of air is moving at an average velocity of 60 mph, it passes a fixed point in 60 s; the reported velocity is the average of the velocities recorded during these 60 s. The *fastest mile* is the highest velocity in 1 day. The *annual extreme mile* is the largest of the daily maximums. Furthermore, since the annual extreme mile varies from year to year, wind pressures to be used in design should be based on a wind velocity having a specific mean recurrence interval. Charts of annual-extreme-mile velocities with mean recurrence intervals of 2, 10, 25, 50, and 100 years have been published.[8] These are based on statistical analysis of records from 138 stations, the average record covering a period of 21 years. The 50-year map is shown in Fig. 1-5. This recurrence interval has been suggested for all "permanent" structures except those that might have a high degree of sensitivity to wind and an unusually high loss of life and property in case of failure.[9] For the latter, a 100-year recurrence interval is suggested.* Furthermore, in recognition of the smaller risk with short periods of exposure, velocities of only 75 percent of the 50-year velocities are suggested for temporary structures, such as those used during construction.[9] The 50-year recurrence interval is also prescribed (with exceptions subject to the judgment of the engineer or authority having jurisdiction) by ASCE 7-88.

The velocities shown in Fig. 1-5 are "open-country" velocities; i.e., they obtain where surface friction is relatively uniform for a fetch of about 25 mi. If the exposure is elevated, subject to channeling of the wind, etc., the map values must be adjusted accordingly. Locations with unobstructed exposure to large bodies of water may experience extreme winds 30 mph (or more) greater than for locations a short distance inland. However, this effect has been taken into account in Fig. 1-5.

---

* On the average, the 100-year velocity in the United States is about 8 percent higher than the 50-year velocity.

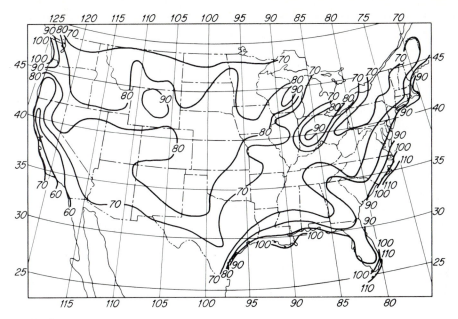

FIGURE 1-5
Annual extreme fastest-mile wind speed 30 ft above ground, 50-year mean recurrence interval. (*From Ref. 8.*)

The National Building Code of Canada recommends pressures based on the 30-year *hourly* wind speed (average of the velocities measured during 1 h). The hourly speed is the only speed measured at most weather stations in Canada.

Variation of wind velocity with height must be considered in the design of tall structures. The flow of air close to the ground is slowed by surface roughness, which is dependent on the density, size, and height of buildings, trees, vegetation, etc., on the ground. Figure 1-6 shows velocity profiles and the corresponding exponential variation with height, according to Davenport.[10] Various other exponents have been suggested. However, the $\frac{1}{7}$-power law of Fig. 1-6 is generally accepted for flat open country. Velocity at 30 ft above ground is used as the basic value for design purposes, and increases with height are provided for by specifying velocities (or wind pressures) for various height zones. Table 1-4 gives suggested velocities for various height zones for several basic wind velocities. Intermediate values can be interpolated. Velocity increases for inland areas are based on the $\frac{1}{7}$-power law. It will be noted that the velocity profiles for inland areas and coastal areas differ considerably. This is in agreement with Fig. 1-6.

Since measured wind velocities are average values, it is necessary to consider the effects of fluctuations in velocity (gusts). The response of a structure to such fluctuations is a dynamic one and depends on the size of the structure, its natural period of vibration, and its damping characteristics. The dynamic effect is usually accounted for by multiplying the wind velocity by a *gust factor* and computing the corresponding pressure by Eq. (1-5), which is to say that the response

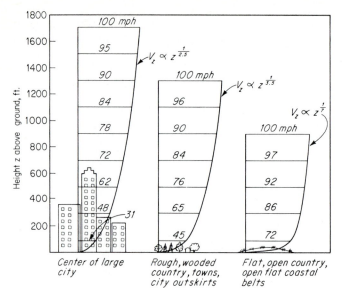

FIGURE 1-6
Velocity profiles over terrain with three different roughness characteristics for uniform-gradient wind velocity of 100 mph. (*From Ref. 10.*)

is evaluated as a static one. The gust factor depends on the wind velocity and the size of the structure, because the wind pressures are not fully developed until the structure is enveloped in the moving mass of air. For this reason, a massive structure is relatively insensitive to gusts of short duration, while a sign is not. A gust factor of 1.3 will account for a 1-s gust in a 90 mph basic wind. Such a gust would have a downwind length of 130 ft and would be adequate for signs and small structures.[11] A gust factor of 1.1 will account for a 10-s gust in a 90 mph

TABLE 1-4
Fastest mile of wind for various zones above ground*

Zone height, ft	Design velocity, inland areas, mph			Zone height, ft	Design velocity, coastal areas,† mph			
0–50	60‡	80‡	100‡	0–50	60‡	80‡	100‡	130‡
50–150	70	95	120	50–150	85	105	125	150
150–400	80	110	140	150–400	115	135	155	180
400–700	90	120	150	400–600	140	165	185	195
700–1000	100	130	160	600–1500	150	170	190	200
1000–1500	105	135	165					

* From Ref. 9.
† Area to 30 mi inland from well-defined coast line along oceans or other large bodies of water.
‡ Basic velocity, i.e., velocity at 30 ft, from Fig. 1-5 or other source.

basic wind, which would have a downwind length of about 1300 ft. This gust factor has been suggested for structures on the order of 125 ft wide transverse to the wind.[11] A method for evaluating the gust factor as a function of wind velocity and the characteristics of the structure has been developed.[12] It should be noted that the gust factors discussed in this paragraph do not provide for dynamic effects such as flutter or vortex shedding. These effects are discussed in Ref. 13.

Design wind pressures can be determined for the velocities of Table 1-4 by Eq. (1-5). The shape factor C_s varies considerably with the proportions of the structure and the horizontal angle of incidence of the wind. The shape factor for the windward face of a flat-roofed rectangular building is about 0.9, regardless of the proportions of the building. There is negative pressure (suction) on the rear face, for which the shape factor varies from about -0.3 to -0.6, depending on the proportions of the building. Thus, the resultant pressure on such a building can be determined by using a shape factor ranging from 1.2 to 1.5 in Eq. (1-5). The value 1.3 is commonly used. It is not necessary to divide this force into pressure and suction when dealing with wind bracing of buildings. Sidewalls experience suction, for which C_s ranges from about -0.4 to -0.8. The roof also experiences suction, for which C_s ranges from about -0.5 to -0.8 for the average over the roof. However, the suction is larger on the windward side, and the average coefficient for the windward half may be as much as twice that on the leeward half.

The preceding discussion applies to an airtight building. Air leakage through small openings around doors, windows, etc., gives rise to internal pressures, with C_s as large as 0.25 if the openings are chiefly on the windward face, and to internal suctions, with C_s as large as -0.35 if the openings are predominantly leeward. The following internal wind pressures were suggested in Ref. 14:

1. For buildings which are nominally airtight, a pressure or suction of 4.5 psf normal to the walls and roof
2. For buildings which have 30 percent or more of the wall surfaces open or subject to being opened or broken open, a pressure of 12 psf or a suction of 9 psf
3. For buildings which have wall openings between 0 and 30 percent of the wall area, pressures or suctions varying linearly between the values recommended in 1 and 2

The pressures in items 1 to 3 above are for a velocity which produces a resultant pressure (sum of windward-wall pressure and leeward-wall suction) of 20 psf, so it would be consistent to increase (or decrease) them proportionately for larger (or smaller) basic pressures. When openings are large, as in hangars, internal wind pressures may be quite large.

Wind pressures on sloping roofs depend on the exposure, the slope, and the proportions of the building. For wind normal to a side parallel to the ridge, the leeward roof surface is always subjected to suction. There is suction on the windward surface for slopes less than about 30° and pressure for larger slopes. These pressures are not uniform but have maximum values at the eaves. The following pressures for single-ridged roofs are given in Ref. 9:

$$\text{For the windward surface:} \quad p = \begin{cases} -0.7q & 0 \leq \alpha \leq 20° \\ (0.07\alpha - 2.1)q & 20° \leq \alpha \leq 30° \\ (0.03\alpha - 0.9)q & 30° \leq \alpha \leq 60° \\ 0.9q & 60° \leq \alpha \end{cases}$$

For the leeward surface: $\quad p = -0.7q \qquad 0 \leq \alpha \leq 90°$

Negative values of p in these formulas denote suction, q is the velocity pressure from Eq. (a), and α is the angle of inclination with the horizontal.

Wind forces on trussed structures, such as bridges and transmission towers, and on beam bridges, girder bridges, etc., are at least as difficult to assess as those on enclosed structures. A complicating factor in this evaluation is the shielding of leeward parts of the structure. The amount of shielding depends principally on the distance between trusses or girders and on the angle of incidence of the wind. Shielding is discussed in Ref. 9.

A comprehensive tabulation of pressure coefficients for a wide variety of structures is given in Ref. 15 (reprinted in part in Refs. 9 and 16). Recommended coefficients for walls of buildings, gabled roofs, arched roofs, roofs over unenclosed structures (such as stadiums), chimneys, tanks, signs, transmission towers, etc., are also given in ASCE 7-88.

It is important to note that wind pressures specified by building codes include allowances for gust factors and shape factors, except where these factors are specified separately. For example, the BOCA National Building Code wind pressures on vertical surfaces (Table 1-5) include allowances for a gust factor of 1.3 and a shape factor of 1.3 (rectangular buildings). This code also specifies wind

TABLE 1-5

BOCA National Building Code wind requirements

Horizontal wind pressure on vertical surfaces, psf

Height zone, ft	Windstorm area		
	Minimum	Moderate	Severe*
Less than 30	15	25	35
30–49	20	30	45
50–99	25	40	55
100–499	30	45	70
500–1199	35	55	80
1200 and up	40	60	90

* Recommended for use within 50 mi of the Gulf coast, and the Atlantic coast from the southernmost part of Florida to Chesapeake Bay.

pressures on signs which differ from those for vertical surfaces because of the differences in shape factor. On the other hand, ASCE 7-88 specifies shape factors separately for various structures.

Until 1957 AASHTO specified wind pressures on trusses at 50 psf on $1\frac{1}{2}$ times the exposed area of one truss. The exposed area of one truss is the area seen in elevation normal to the length of the bridge. Thus, the leeward truss was considered to be shielded to the extent that only half its area was effective. This was changed in 1957 to 75 psf on the exposed area of one truss, which gives the same result. Since the shape factor of the H cross section commonly used for truss members is about 2, a pressure of 50 psf corresponds to a wind velocity of about 100 mph, including the effect of gusts [Eq. (1-5)]. The corresponding AREA requirement is 50 psf on the exposed area of the windward truss plus all the exposed area of all parts of the leeward truss not shielded by the floor. In both AASHTO and AREA specifications these are pressures on an unloaded bridge, and smaller intensities are prescribed when wind pressure on both the structure and the live load is considered.

The dynamic response of long-span bridges to wind forces is a significant consideration. The failure in 1940 of the Tacoma suspension bridge only 6 months after it was opened to traffic stimulated research on the problems of aerodynamic instability. There have been several spectacular failures of bridges due to wind. In addition to the collapse of the Tacoma bridge, it is of interest to recall the failure in 1879 of a railroad bridge across Scotland's Firth of Tay. Two years after its completion, 13 of the 84 truss spans of this bridge were blown from their piers, carrying with them a train and its seventy-odd passengers. The shock of the disaster was so great that its designer and builder, Sir Thomas Bouch, died within the year.

1-9 EARTHQUAKE LOADS

Earthquakes may happen in any part of the world, but they are more frequent and generally more violent in two great belts of the earth, of which one almost encircles the Pacific Ocean and the other stretches across southern Asia into the Mediterranean region. Although earthquakes of destructive or near-destructive proportions have occurred in almost every one of the United States, they have been far more frequent and disastrous on the Pacific coast, particularly in California. Seismologists distinguish three types of waves set in motion by earthquakes. The type that seems to be most destructive travels over the earth's surface much like the waves generated by a stone dropped into water, except that they are not as regular. Major wave movements may last from a few seconds to several minutes. These waves cause the ground beneath the structure to move rapidly back and forth and impart accelerations into the base of the structure. The period and intensity of these acceleration pulses change rapidly, and their magnitudes vary from very small values to more than that of gravity. The corresponding amplitude of ground motion may vary from a fraction of an inch to 9 in or more.

Transient accelerations as high as 1.7*g* have been recorded. During the San Fernando, California, earthquake of February 9, 1971, ground intensities larger than those for any earthquake ever recorded occurred. A ground acceleration of 1.25*g* was recorded at Pacoima Dam. Interpolation and examination of damage close to the center indicated ground accelerations of 0.25 to 0.50*g*. In the El Centro, California, earthquake of May 18, 1940, which covered a much larger area, the recorded accelerogram showed a maximum ground acceleration of 0.32*g*. The maximum ground velocity, determined by integrating the accelerogram, was 13.7 in/s, and the maximum ground displacement, determined by integrating the velocity diagram, was 8.3 in.

The Mexico City earthquake of 1985 had a peak ground acceleration of about 0.18*g*, which is not particularly high. Nevertheless it produced extensive damage. The records of ground accelerations revealed a significant number of ground pulses of this magnitude, spaced at regular intervals of about 2 s. This period corresponds to the natural frequency of structures from 8 to 15 stores in height, and such structures suffered substantial damage.

A structure's response to an earthquake primarily depends upon its location in the affected region, its orientation relative to the direction of the most violent motion of the earth, its natural periods of vibration, its damping characteristics, the physical properties of the structural material, and the nature of the foundation material which supports it. Computer programs have been developed which enable these factors to be considered in an analysis of the complete response of the structure to ground motion. However, it is generally unnecessary to make these calculations in the design of a multistory building. The Uniform Building Code recommendations are, in general, consistent with forces and displacements determined by more elaborate procedures. A structure designed according to these recommendations will remain elastic, or nearly so, under moderate earthquakes of frequent occurrence but must be able to yield locally without serious consequences to resist an El Centro–type earthquake. Thus, design for the required ductility is an important consideration.[17]

The 1988 UBC recommends that the minimum total lateral seismic force V, assumed to act nonconcurrently in the direction of each of the main axes of the building, be determined by

$$V = \frac{ZICW}{R_W} \tag{1-6}$$

where Z = zone factor, which depends on expected severity of earthquake in various regions of the United States

I = occupancy importance factor

C = coefficient related to the fundamental elastic period of vibration of the structure [Eq. (1-7)]

W = total dead load plus (*a*) weight of permanent equipment, (*b*) at least 25 percent of floor live load in storage and warehouse occupancies, (*c*) at least 10 psf if partition loads are used in floor design, (*d*) snow load if it exceeds 30 psf

R_W = tabular coefficient which depends on type of basic structural system and lateral-load-resisting system

The coefficient I has assigned values of 1.0 and 1.25, depending on the building use. The highest value is assigned to hazardous facilities and to essential facilities which must be safe and usable for emergency purposes after an earthquake to preserve the health and safety of the general public. Included in the essential-facility category are hospitals, fire and police stations, and centers required to handle disaster operations and communications. The value of 1.0 is assigned to various types of structures with capacities of 50 to 5000 persons and to structures with occupancies not specifically listed.

The coefficient C is given by

$$C = \frac{1.25S}{T^{2/3}} \tag{1-7}$$

except that it need not exceed 2.75. Also, a minimum value $C/R_W = 0.075$ is specified. In Eq. (1-7), T is the fundamental period of vibration, in seconds, in the direction considered. In the absence of properly substantiated technical data for the structure, T is determined from

$$T = C_1 h_n^{3/4} \tag{1-8}$$

where h_n = height, above base, of uppermost level in main portion of structure, ft
C_1 = 0.035 for steel moment-resisting frames, 0.030 for reinforced concrete moment-resisting frames, 0.20 for all other buildings

S (called the *site coefficient*) in Eq. (1-7) reflects the extent to which the vibration characteristics of the structure and the site may produce resonance in the structural response. It ranges from 1 for soil profiles with rocklike materials and stiff or dense soils less than 200 ft deep to 2 for soil profiles containing more than 40 ft of soft clay.

According to the specification the lateral force V is to be distributed over the height of the structure in the following manner:

A force F_t at the uppermost level n given by

$$F_t = 0.07TV \tag{1-9}$$

F_t need not exceed $0.25V$ and may be taken as 0 if T is 0.7 s or less.

A force F_x at each level x, including the uppermost level n, given by

$$F_x = \frac{(V - F_t)w_x h_x}{\sum\limits_{i=1}^{n} w_i h_i} \tag{1-10}$$

where w_x, w_i = portion of W located at or assigned to level x, i
h_x, h_i = height of level x, i above the base, ft

Codes usually specify much larger coefficients for parts and appendages than for the structure itself, because such parts may experience accelerations much larger than those of the earthquake motion. The cantilevered parapet wall is an example. For such elements, the UBC specifies the force

$$F_p = ZIC_p W_p \qquad (1\text{-}11)$$

where W_p is the weight of the part. Values of C_p range from 0.75 to 2. The value of I is the value for the building, except $I = 1.5$ for anchorage of machinery and equipment required for life-safety systems and for tanks and vessels containing quantities of highly toxic or explosive substances sufficient to be hazardous to the safety of the general public.

Overturning moments for buildings of low or medium height can be determined with fair accuracy by assuming the building to be a cantilever beam loaded with the lateral earthquake forces acting simultaneously in the same direction.

1-10   SAFETY OF STRUCTURES

Although it goes without saying that the strength and performance characteristics of any member of a structure must be greater than what is expected of it over the life of the structure, it is not easy to decide what this relationship should be. Strength refers to a limit state under which the structure or any component is considered to have failed in its capacity to carry load. Performance characteristics refer to the ability of the structure to respond so as not to impair its function. These are sometimes called *serviceability* limits. The ratio of the ultimate strength or resistance of a structure or member to the force to which it is expected to be subjected is called the *factor of safety*. In view of the variability of the strength of a member or structure and the loads to which it may be subjected, considerable effort has been devoted to the concept of reliability or probability of failure in recent years.

The development of design specifications to provide suitable values of the margin of safety, reliability, and probability of failure must take into consideration the following factors:

1. Variability of the material with respect to strength and other pertinent physical properties
2. Uncertainty in the expected loads in regard to possible future change as well as with respect to present magnitude
3. Precision with which the internal forces in the various parts of a structure are determined
4. Possibility of deterioration due to corrosion and other causes
5. The extent of damage and loss of life which might result from failure
6. Quality of workmanship

Since no two specimens of a given structural material will have identical strengths, it is important to know the pattern of variation in strength with respect to the average of a large number of specimens. Even steel, whose manufacture is carefully controlled, exhibits an occasional relatively large deviation in strength from the average. Concrete is more variable than steel, and carefully selected samples of the same wood may vary widely in strength and other properties. Strength is therefore a statistical quantity, and we can determine only the probability that it will not be less than a specified value. As an illustration, results of 73 tensile tests on structural silicon-steel shapes for the towers of the Golden Gate Bridge are presented in Fig. 1-7. The ordinates of this figure show the relative frequency of the various tensile strengths (shown as abscissas) revealed by the tests. Strengths ranges from a low of 80.3 ksi to a high of 104.5 ksi, with an average of 88.79 ($\bar{f}_t$ on the figure). The points marked "observed frequencies" represent the number of test specimens having tensile strengths between the values of the abscissas of the vertical boundaries of the corresponding rectangles. The graph of a theoretical probability function chosen to fit the experimental data is labeled "theoretical frequencies." One of the properties of a probability curve is that the area lying under the curve and between any two ordinates gives the probability that the event will lie between the corresponding abscissas. For example, the crosshatched portion marked $P_0 = 3$ percent is an indication that there are only 3 chances in 100 that any specimen of this particular steel will have a tensile strength less than 80 ksi. Other physical properties, such as yield point, modulus of elasticity, and weight, show similar distributions of values about a mean. Extensive data and statistical analysis of these properties are reported by Galambos and Ravindra.[22]

Most live loads are amenable to statistical analysis. For example, the similarity of Fig. 1-1, depicting variations in department-store live loads, to Fig. 1-7 suggests that if adequate data were available, we could predict the probability of occurrence of a department-store live load of any prescribed intensity. Statistical analysis of records of wind and snowfall to determine mean recurrence intervals was discussed in Arts. 1-3, 1-7, and 1-8. Because extreme intensities of such live loads can be assessed only in terms of their probabilities of occurrence, it is clear that the margin of safety must bear some relationship to the live-load intensity. Thus, assuming that the probability of failure of structures of a given use or

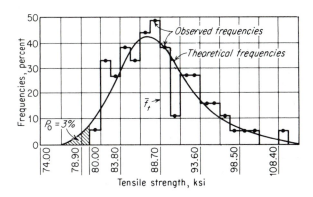

FIGURE 1-7
(*From Ref. 18.*)

occupancy should be about the same, it would be inconsistent to use the same margins of safety for, say, snow loads based on return periods of 10 years and those based on return periods of 100 years.

Occasionally certain live loads may be more or less rigidly restricted. For example, the amount of water in a storage tank cannot exceed the capacity of the tank. Airplane passenger, baggage, and freight loadings are also controlled, although in a different sense. The railroad can control the loads on its bridges, since they are used exclusively by the railroad. Many live loads are not subject to control, however, and there are obstacles to the control of some which might be restricted in theory. Uncertainty with respect to future increases makes the problem of predicting highway-bridge loadings even more difficult than it might otherwise be.

The internal forces in most structures can be determined with varying degrees of precision, and in general greater precision is attained only as the result of more detailed (and therefore usually more costly) analysis. Other things being equal, smaller margins of safety may be used with more precise knowledge of the forces in a structure. However, it is no advantage to the owner to pay for refined design procedures that do not produce at least an equal reduction in the cost of the structure or, as in the aircraft industry, greater revenue as a result of increased payloads or improved performance made possible by reduced dead load. In any case, there is a limit to the reduction in margin of safety which can accompany more precise evaluation of internal forces, unless it is feasible to verify the predicted structural behavior by tests. The aeronautical structural engineer designs many airplane components for a factor of safety of only 1.5 with respect to failure but also substantiates many of the designs by tests and subjects the completed ship to extensive flight tests before it is put into service. A comparable program would serve no useful purpose in the case of most civil engineering structures—in the interests of economy it is cheaper to use larger margins of safety. To be sure, these arguments dodge the larger question of what might be in the best interests of the nation and the world with respect to conservation of our natural resources.

Loss of strength as a result of corrosion sometimes must be considered. This is particularly true with steel. The designer must evaluate the hazards, not only with respect to exposure, but also with respect to preventive maintenance. Thin parts are more susceptible to severe damage from corrosion than thick parts. Corrosion hazards are greater for structures located near bodies of salt water. Exposure to chemical wastes, e.g., the sulfurous products of the combustion of coal, increases the danger of corrosion.

Probability of failure should not necessarily be the same for all parts of a structure or for all structures of a given class. For example, the failure of one of the floor-beam hangers of a suspension bridge would be less serious than the failure of one of the suspension cables. Localized damage would result from failure of the hanger, but failure of the cable would almost certainly precipitate a collapse of the entire floor. Similarly, the failure of a small highway bridge would not ordinarily be so disastrous as the failure of a Golden Gate Bridge. Furthermore, abandonment of the smaller bridge at some later time as a result of its having insufficient reserve to support loads which may have turned out to be heavier than predicted would not be so economically significant as abandonment of a Verrazano-Narrows Bridge.

1-11 PROBABILISTIC CONSIDERATIONS OF SAFETY

The factor of safety was defined in Art. 1-10 as the ratio of resistance to induced force. However, it was also shown that there is an element of uncertainty in resistance in the sense that there is a range of values which cluster around a mean (Fig. 1-7). Furthermore, it is clear that no absolute minimum tensile strength of any particular grade of steel can ever be known. Similarly, it was shown in preceding articles that most of the live loads for which structures are designed are also uncertain (Fig. 1-1). Again, no absolute maximum value can be determined for loads of this type. Because of these uncertainties, the reliability of a structure (conversely, the probability that it will fail) is difficult to determine. Probabilistic evaluation of structural safety will be discussed briefly in this article.

Figure 1-8 shows the frequency distributions of load L (or of the load effect, such as an induced force in a structural member) and of member resistance R (such as yield strength and tensile strength). Suppose L_q is the load effect caused by, say, the annual extreme wind speed for which the mean return period is 50 years. Points on x to the right of L_q represent effects of winds of higher velocity (return period greater than 50 years), and the shaded area q is the probability that L_q will be exceeded in any one year. Similarly, let R_p be the member resistance which is chosen for purposes of design. The area p gives the probability that the resistance will be less than R_p. By definition, the factor of safety n is R_p/L_q. This factor of safety must be determined so that the probability of failure is acceptably small.

The probability of failure p_f can be determined as follows.[19] The probability that the load effect L will be between the values x and $x + dx$ (Fig. 1-9) is $f_L(x)\, dx$, where $f_L(x)$ is the ordinate at x of the frequency distribution. The probability that the resistance R will be less than x is the shaded area $p(x)$ of the frequency distribution of R. Since these two events are independent, the probability that they occur simultaneously is the product of the probability of each. Therefore, the probability $R \le L$ for $L = x$ is given by $p(x)f_L(x)\, dx$. Summing this for all values of L gives

$$p_f = \int_0^\infty p(x)f_L(x)\, dx \qquad (a)$$

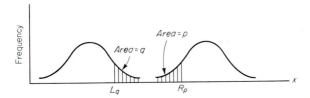

FIGURE 1-8

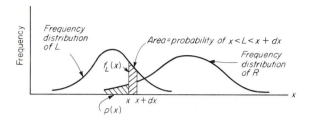

FIGURE 1-9

If the frequency distributions are known, p_f can be evaluated. A variety of formulas are available for this purpose.

The probability p_f given by Eq. (*a*) is the probability of failure under a single application of load and is not a direct measure of the safety of a structure which must withstand repeated applications of load. Therefore, the probability of failure under a single application of load is of interest largely to the extent that it can be used to determine the probability that a structure can survive a random sequence of loads during its life. This probability is called the *probability of survival*. Procedures for evaluating it have been developed.[19,20]

An additional complicating factor in evaluating the safety of structures has to do with a significant difference in the failure modes of statically determinate and statically indeterminate structures. A statically determinate structure can be expected to collapse if one of its members fails. On the other hand, a statically indeterminate structure does not necessarily collapse if one or more of its members fail. This problem is discussed briefly in Ref. 20.

Evaluations of probabilities of failure and of survival are very difficult to implement. Calculated probabilities are extremely sensitive to variations in the extreme values, i.e., the rare large values of L and the rare small values of R. Furthermore, there are other uncertainties and unknowns, some of which are not statistical or probabilistic. These difficulties have been summarized by Freudenthal, as follows:[21]

1. The existence of nonrandom phenomena affecting structural safety which cannot be included in a probabilistic approach
2. The impossibility of observing the relevant random phenomena within the ranges that are significant for safety analysis and the resulting necessity of extrapolation far beyond the range of actual observation
3. The assessment and justification of a numerical value for the "acceptable risk" of failure
4. The codification of the results of the rather complex probabilistic safety analysis in a simple enough form to be usable in actual design

The probability concepts discussed above can be presented in a different form, as follows. Figure 1-10*a* shows the frequency distribution of the difference $R - L$ between resistance R and load effect L. Mean values are denoted by the subscript m. The distance from the origin to $(R - L)_m$ is expressed in the form

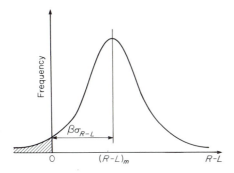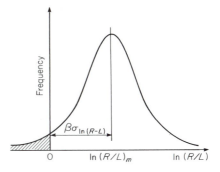

FIGURE 1-10

$\beta\sigma_{R-L}$, where σ_{R-L} is the standard deviation. Thus β is a measure of the probability that $R - L$ will be negative, i.e., that the load effect will be greater than the resistance. Therefore, the shaded area to the left of zero equals the probability of failure. For this reason, β is called the *reliability index* (also the *safety index*).

An alternative presentation is shown in Fig. 1-10*b*, where with some approximations the reliability index is given by

$$\left(\ln \frac{R}{L}\right)_m \approx \ln \frac{R_m}{L_m}$$

and the standard deviation by

$$\sigma_{\ln R/L} \approx \sqrt{V_R^2 + V_L^2}$$

where V_R and V_L are the coefficients of variation of R and L, respectively. With these approximations, β is given by

$$\beta = \frac{\ln (R_m/L_m)}{\sqrt{V_R^2 + V_L^2}}$$

The reliability index is a measure of the probability of a limit state being exceeded. It serves to evaluate the relative safety of various design alternatives, although a consistent value cannot be achieved for all members or for all load combinations. This is the basis for the probability-based design criteria presented by Galambos and Ravindra.[22] Additional studies of the relationship between loadings, strength, and design have been reported by Ellingwood, Galambos, MacGregor, and Cornell.[23]

1-12 FACTOR OF SAFETY, LOAD FACTORS, AND RESISTANCE FACTORS

The design safety of structures may be evaluated in either of two ways:

1. The expected resistance of the structural member, or other component, usually expressed as a tensile stress, compressive stress, etc., is divided by a factor of safety to obtain an *allowable* or *working* stress, and the part is then chosen so that the stress induced by the expected service load, or service-load combination, is equal to or less than the allowable value. This procedure is called *allowable-stress design* or *working-stress design*, but because the force analysis is usually by methods based on Hooke's law, it is sometimes (and less accurately) called *elastic design*. Allowable stresses usually depend on the load combination; for example, allowable stresses for combinations of wind or earthquake forces with dead- and live-load forces are usually larger than those for dead and live load alone. This is in recognition of the lower probability of occurrence of the combinations with wind or earthquake.

2. The structural member or other component is chosen so that its resistance, multiplied by a *resistance factor*, equals or exceeds the service load, or service-load combination, multiplied by *load factors*. With this procedure it is a simple matter to account for differing reliabilities in the prediction of load and member resistance. For example, dead load, which can usually be determined with good precision, can be multiplied by a smaller number than that for live load. This procedure is called by various names: *load-factor design*, *load-and-resistance-factor design*, *limit-states design*, and (in American reinforced-concrete practice) *strength design*.

1-13   CODES AND SPECIFICATIONS

Standard design specifications and building codes have been developed as a means of supplying the engineer with a digest of the collective knowledge, judgment, and experience of the profession. They are intended to convey the pertinent information relative to service loads and member resistance. In addition, they attempt to cover in a general way the questions of form and proportion of a structure and its members, together with their connections, and acceptable methods of analysis, fabrication, erection, and construction. Specification writers evaluate the implications of the various clauses with a view to public safety, utility, and economy. Finally, codes provide the building official with an enforceable document.

The AREA specification for steel structures uses only the allowable-stress procedure. Both allowable-stress design and load-factor design are used in the AASHTO specifications.

The AISC Specification for Structural Steel Buildings contains requirements for allowable-stress design based on force analysis by elastic behavior and for load-factor design with the force analysis based on plastic behavior.

The AISC Load and Resistance Factor Design Specification for Structural Steel Buildings covers load-and-resistance-factor design, using either elastic analysis or plastic analysis. Probabilistic methods discussed in Art. 1-11 were used to determine load factors and resistance factors. The following combinations of load are prescribed:

$$1.4D \tag{a}$$

$$1.2D + 1.6L + 0.5(L_r \text{ or } S \text{ or } R) \tag{b}$$

$$1.2D + 1.6(L_r \text{ or } S \text{ or } R) + (0.5L \text{ or } 0.8W) \tag{c}$$

$$1.2D + 1.3W + 0.5L + 0.5(L_r \text{ or } S \text{ or } R) \tag{d}$$

$$1.2D + 1.5E + (0.5L \text{ or } 0.2S) \tag{e}$$

$$0.9D - (1.3W \text{ or } 1.5E) \tag{f}$$

where D = dead load due to weight of structural elements and permanent features on the structure

L = live load due to occupancy and movable equipment

L_r = roof live load

W = wind load

S = snow load

E = earthquake load

R = load due to initial rainwater or ice exclusive of the ponding contribution

The load factors in the equations above were developed for a 50-year life of the structure. Because lifetime maximums of the various types of load are extremely unlikely to occur simultaneously, it is assumed that the maximum of a combination of loads will occur when one of the loads is at its lifetime maximum while the others are at values that can be expected to act at any time (called *point-in-time* or *anytime* loads).[24] This is consistent with the fact that many failures have occurred when *one* of the loads was at an extreme value and explains why many of the load factors in these equations are less than unity. Thus, for the load $0.5S$ in load combination (b), S is the *maximum* snow load to be expected during a 50-year life of the structure, while $0.5S$ is the point-in-time load. In the case of wind load, the point-in-time load is taken to be the maximum *daily* wind load. In general, the anytime load is on the order of 0.24 to 0.4 times the mean maximum lifetime load for many occupancies.

Resistance factors ϕ in the LRFD specification vary from 0.6 to 1. Examples are $\phi = 0.90$ for tension-member yield, 0.90 for beams (except that $\phi = 0.85$ for composite beams), 0.85 for compression members, and 0.75 for tension-member fracture. Thus, member design is controlled by only three resistance factors. Resistance factors for bolts and welds vary from 0.75 to 1.

The factor of safety in AISC allowable-stress design has been quite constant at $\frac{5}{3}$ for over 50 years, and since this has produced generally acceptable results, reliabilities in the LRFD specification were calibrated so as to give about the same reliability as is inherent in structures designed according to the 1978 AISC specifications at a ratio of live load to dead load of about 3. Typical reliability indexes, computed for a ratio of live load to dead load of 1, are the following:[24]

Tension-member yield	3.0
Tension-member fracture	4.1
Beams and plate girders in flexure	2.5–2.9
Beams and plate girders in shear	3.3–3.4
Columns	2.7–3.6
High-strength bolts	4.8–6.0
Fillet welds	4.4

The reliability index is fairly constant over a wide range of the ratio of live load L to dead load D. LRFD is likely to give lighter beam designs for $L/D \leq 3$ but somewhat heavier ones if $L/D \geq 3$.

REFERENCES

1. Thom, H. C. S.: Distributions of Extreme Winds in the United States, *J. Struct. Div. ASCE*, April 1960.
2. Dunham, J. W.: Design Live Loads in Buildings, *Trans. ASCE*, vol. 112, 1947.
3. Bryson, J. O., and D. Gross: Techniques for the Survey and Evaluation of Live Floor Loads and Fire Loads in Modern Office Buildings, *Nat. Bur. Stand. Build. Sci. Ser.* 16, 1967.
4. Dunham, J. W., G. N. Brekke, and G. N. Thompson: Live Loads on Floors in Buildings, *Nat. Bur. Stand. Build. Mater. Struct. Rep.* BMS133, December 1952.
5. Climatic Information for Building Design in Canada, *Nat. Res. Counc. Ottawa, Suppl.* 1 to *Nat. Building Code of Canada*, 1961.
6. Snow Load Studies, *Housing Home Finance Agency Washington, Housing Res. Pap.* 19, May 1952.
7. Andersen, A. E.: Snow Loads for Roofs, *Civ. Eng.*, July 1965.
8. Thom, H. C. S.: New Distributions of Extreme Winds in the United States, *J. Struct. Div. ASCE*, July 1968.
9. Wind Force on Structures, Final Report, Task Committee on Wind Forces, Committee on Loads and Stresses, Structural Division, ASCE, *Trans. ASCE*, vol. 126, 1961, pt. II.
10. Davenport, A. G.: Wind Loads on Structures, *Nat. Res. Counc. Canada, Div. Build. Res., Tech. Pap.* 88, 1960.
11. Sherlock, R. H.: Gust Factors for the Design of Buildings, *Int. Assoc. Bridge Struct. Eng., Zurich, Publ.* vol. 8, 1947.
12. Vellozzi, J., and E. Cohen: Gust Response Factors, *J. Struct. Div. ASCE*, June 1960.
13. Scruton, C.: Aerodynamics of Structures, paper no. 4 in "Wind Effects on Buildings and Structures," Univ. of Toronto Press, 1968.
14. Wind Bracing in Steel Buildings, Final Report of Subcommittee 31, Committee on Steel of the ASCE Structural Division, *Trans. ASCE*, vol. 105, 1940.
15. Standards of the Swiss Association of Engineers and Architects on Load Assumptions, Acceptance and Supervision of Buildings, *Schweiz. Ing. Architek, Ver., Tech. Normen* 160, 1956.
16. McGuire, W.: "Steel Structures," Prentice-Hall, Englewood Cliffs, N.J., 1968.
17. Hall, W. J.: Earthquake-Resistant Building Design, sec. 3 in E. H. Gaylord and C. N. Gaylord (eds.), "Structural Engineering Handbook," 3d ed., McGraw-Hill, New York, 1990.
18. Freudenthal, A. M.: The Safety of Structures, *Trans. ASCE*, vol. 112, p. 125, 1947.
19. Freudenthal, A. M., J. M. Garrelts, and M. Shinozuka: The Analysis of Structural Safety, *J. Struct. Div. ASCE*, February 1966.
20. Ang, A. H.-S, and M. Amin: Reliability of Structures and Structural Systems, *J. Eng. Mech. Div. ASCE*, April 1968.
21. Freudenthal, A. M.: Critical Appraisal of Safety Criteria and Their Basic Concepts, *Prelim. Publ., 8th Congr. IABSE*, New York, 1968.
22. Ravindra, M. K., and T. V. Galambos: Load and Resistance Factor Design for Steel, *J. Struct. Div. ASCE*. 1978.
23. Ellingwood, B., T. V. Galambos, J. G. MacGregor, and C. A. Cornell: Development of a Probability Based Load Criterion for American National Standard A58, *Nat. Bur. Stand., Spec. Publ.* 577, June 1980.
24. Galambos, T. V.: Reliability of Structural Steel Systems, Structural Engineering Report No. 88-06, Univ. of Minnesota, August 1988.

CHAPTER

2

STRUCTURES, METALS, AND FASTENERS

The supporting systems used in buildings, bridges, transmission towers, radio towers, observation towers, airplanes, ships, storage vessels, and various other structures may be classified broadly into three categories: (1) framed systems, (2) suspension systems, and (3) shell systems. Examples of these systems are discussed in following articles. In many cases, structures are supported by combinations of supporting systems.

2-1 BUILDINGS

In addition to their function of partitioning space, walls in *bearing-wall* construction furnish reactions for the beams and joists which support the floors and roof. *Frame construction* uses a stable system of structural members to support *curtain walls* as well as the floor and roof construction. Frames may be classified as *rigid*, *semirigid*, and *simple*, depending upon the stiffness of the beam-to-column connections. In the AISC/ASD specification, these framing systems are designated Type 1, Type 3, and Type 2, respectively. In the AISC/LRFD specification, rigid frames are designated fully restrained (FR), while semirigid and simple frames are combined in a single system designated partially restrained (PR). Framed buildings are also called *tier* buildings.

Simple-frame construction is illustrated in Fig. 2-1. Floors and roof in such buildings are supported on joists which are supported by beams framing into the columns. Beam-to-column connections in simple frames are essentially rotationally unrestrained.

Because of the varied uses to which they are put, commercial and industrial buildings are framed in a number of ways. Frequently they have only a ground

FIGURE 2-1
Simple frame with open-web steel joists.

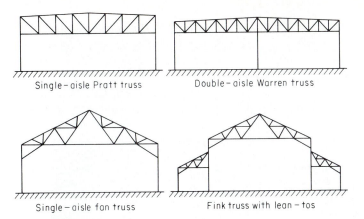

Single—aisle Pratt truss

Double—aisle Warren truss

Single—aisle fan truss

Fink truss with lean—tos

FIGURE 2-2
Types of industrial-building bents.

floor with the roof supported on beams or trusses. The latter may be supported by masonry walls or by columns. Sheet siding may be used instead of masonry. Industrial buildings often have two lines of columns forming a single-aisle structure. However, they may have one or more duplicate aisles, or additional aisles in the form of lean-tos.

Trusses which support flat roofs are usually of the Warren or Pratt type. Pitched roofs may be supported on Fink or fan trusses. A truss and its supporting columns is called a *bent*, and the space between successive bents is called a *bay*. The longitudinal beams which support the roof covering are called *purlins*. Some types of building bents are shown in Fig. 2-2.

Rigid frames may be single-span or multispan and single-story or multistory. The transverse member in the single-story frame may be straight, V-shaped, or arched. Single-story rigid frames are used in assembly halls, churches, gymnasiums, field houses, hangars, industrial buildings, etc., and have been built with spans of over 200 ft (Fig. 2-3). Steel arches are usually used for longer spans and, in general, for the same types of building. Arches may be trussed or of solid-webbed I or box cross section. They have been built with spans exceeding 350 ft.

Steel-framed domes may take a number of forms. The ribbed dome has radial members which frame into a compression ring at the crown and a tension ring or foundation at the perimeter (Fig. 2-4). The ribs may be solid-webbed or trussed. Domed structures may also be latticed. In the lamella dome secondary framing members parallel to the main ribs extend from the perimeter to their intersections with the ribs, forming a diamond-shaped pattern. Domed roofs have been built with spans exceeding 400 ft.

Cable-supported roofs may be suspended from a series of cables supported by towers and abutments, as in a suspension bridge. Another type consists of radial cables stretched between a central tension ring and an exterior compression ring, with a precast or cast-in-place concrete roof deck supported on the

FIGURE 2-3

FIGURE 2-4
Athletic and Convocation Center, University of Notre Dame. (*American Institute of Steel Construction.*)

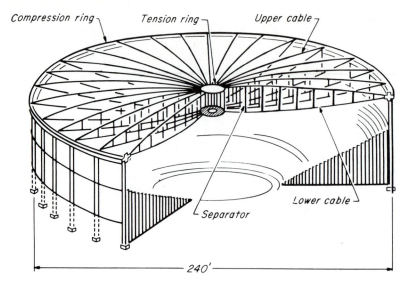

FIGURE 2-5
Utica Municipal Auditorium. Gehron & Seltzer, Architects. Lev Zetlin Associates, Inc., Structural Engineers, New York.

cables. These roofs may develop oscillatory motions, usually called *flutter*, from the effect of dynamic forces. Flutter may be controlled by tying the roof to the ground with cables or by using a system of interconnected cables which are internally self-damping. The Municipal Auditorium in Utica, New York (Fig. 2-5), is an example of the internally self-damping system. Suspension roofs have been built with diameters of over 350 ft. Cables may be also used to support cantilever roofs (Fig. 2-6).

Shells may be built with standard cold-formed steel roof-deck panels. The *folded plate* and the *hyperbolic paraboloid* are suitable for this type of structure. In the folded-plate roof, flat or inclined light-gage steel panels span between ridge and valley members. The panels and ridge and valley members act together as

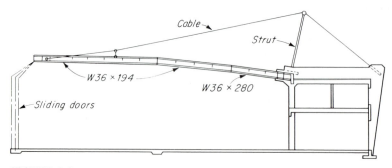

FIGURE 2-6
Framing system for TWA hangar, Philadelphia International Airport.

FIGURE 2-7
Folded-plate roof. Marple Township Library, Pennsylvania. (*American Institute of Steel Construction.*)

longitudinal beams or girders. In addition, the panels themselves act as transverse beams to support snow or other live load (Fig. 2-7). Hyperbolic paraboloids are doubly curved shells made up of two families of straight generators intersecting at right angles. The steel panels are laid in the direction of one set of generators, which requires a slight warping of the individual panel (Fig. 2-8).

2-2 FIXED BRIDGES

Most bridges are built for the transportation of highway or railway traffic across natural or artificial obstacles. A *deck bridge* supports the roadway on its top chords or flanges, while a *through bridge* supports the floor system at or near the lower chords or flanges so that traffic passes through the supporting structure.

The rolled-beam bridge supports its roadway directly on the top flanges of a series of rolled beams placed parallel to the direction of traffic and extending from abutment to abutment. It is simple and economical. It may also be used for multiple spans where piers or intermediate bents can be built economically. Beam bridges may be economical for spans up to about 60 ft. A typical beam bridge for highway traffic is illustrated in Fig. 2-9.

For crossings greater than those which can be spanned economically by a rolled-beam bridge, deck or through plate-girder bridges may be used. In its

(*a*)

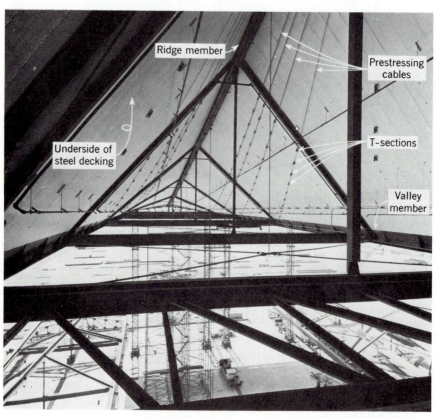

(*b*)

FIGURE 2-8
American Airlines superbay hangar, San Francisco. Lev Zetlin Associates, Inc., Consulting Engineers, New York.

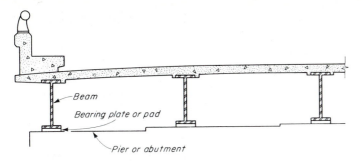

FIGURE 2-9
Beam bridge.

simplest form, a plate girder consists of three plates welded together to form an I. Ties and rails for railway bridges rest directly on the top flanges of the deck plate-girder bridge. When clearance below the structure is limited, a through girder span is used. The floor system may consist of a single line of stringers under each rail, supported by floor beams framing into the girders just above their lower flanges. If an open floor is objectionable, ballast may be laid on concrete or steel-plate decking supported by closely spaced floor beams without stringers. Knee braces are used to support the top flanges of through bridges, as illustrated in Fig. 2-10. Highway plate-girder bridges are usually of the deck type. The floor slab is usually supported directly on the girders, as in the beam bridge of Fig. 2-9.

Plate girders may also take the form of a box, as shown in Fig. 2-11. Cross sections *a* and *b* consist of steel plates for the entire cross section, whereas in *c* the top flange consists of a reinforced concrete section attached to the steel flange plates to act as a composite section. Such cross sections have substantially greater torsional resistance than the conventional I cross section. Their fabrication requires careful control, and erection procedures must receive special consideration. The latter is especially important for cross section *c*, which may be very unstable until the concrete deck is in place. Girders of type *a* and *b* have

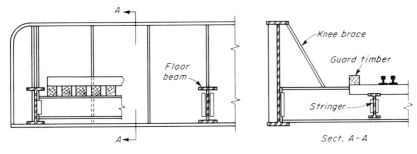

FIGURE 2-10
Plate-girder railroad bridge.

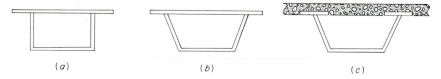

(a)   (b)   (c)

FIGURE 2-11
Box girder cross sections.

been employed for continuous girders of highway bridges with spans in excess of
700 ft. Type *c* has been widely used for bridges crossing interstate highways.

In orthotropic steel-deck-plate construction the floor consists of a steel deck
plate stiffened in two mutually perpendicular directions by a system of longitudinal and transverse ribs welded to it (Fig. 2-12). The deck structure
functions as the top flange of the main girders and floor beams. This system
makes efficient and economical use of materials, particularly for long-span
construction.

When the crossing is too long to be spanned economically by plate girders,
a through or deck truss bridge may be used. Deck bridges are more economical
than through bridges because the trusses can be placed closer together so that the
span of the floor beam is shortened. For multiple spans there is also a saving in
the height of the piers.

Figure 2-13 shows the common types of simple-span bridge trusses. By
varying the depth of a truss throughout its length (Fig. 2-13*c*), forces in the chord
members can be more nearly equalized and the forces in the web reduced.

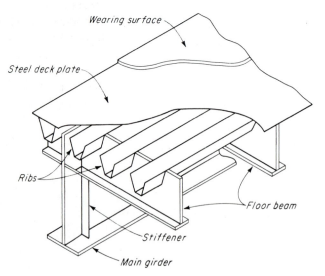

FIGURE 2-12
Elements of steel-deck bridges.

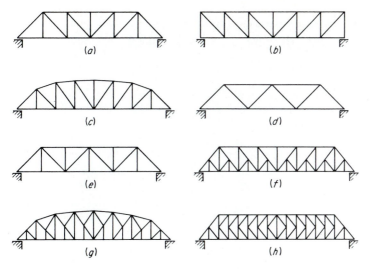

FIGURE 2-13
Common types of bridge trusses: (*a*) Pratt truss through bridge; (*b*) Pratt truss deck bridge; (*c*) curved-chord Pratt truss; (*d*) Warren truss; (*e*) Warren truss with verticals; (*f*) subdivided Pratt truss (Baltimore truss); (*g*) Petit or Pennsylvania truss; (*h*) K truss.

Trusses of economical proportions usually result if the angle between diagonals and verticals ranges from 45 to 60°. However, if long-span trusses are made deep enough for adequate rigidity as well as for economy, a suitable slope of the diagonals may produce panels too long for an economical floor system. The subdivided panels of the Baltimore and Petit trusses (Fig. 2-13*f* and *g*) solve this problem. Certain objections to subdivided panels were overcome with the invention of the K truss (Fig. 2-13*h*).

Cantilever bridges, continuous bridges (Fig. 2-14), arch bridges (Fig. 2-15), and suspension bridges are common types of structures suitable for long spans. A cantilever bridge consists of two shore, or anchor, spans flanked by cantilever arms supporting a suspended simple span. Positive bending moments are decreased because of the shorter simple span, while the cantilever and anchor arms are subjected to negative moments. Positive bending moments in continuous bridges are reduced because of the negative moments at the piers. Arch bridges may be fixed, single-hinged, two-hinged, or three-hinged. The principal supporting elements of the suspension-bridge superstructure are the cables which pass over the towers to be anchored in foundations at each end.

Since 1950 a new form for bridge structures called the *cable-stayed bridge* has been developed (Fig. 2-16). Such structures take advantage of the tensile strength of wire cables as well as the advantages which accrue when the roadway consists of a continuous structure over multiple supports with corresponding reduction in the moments. The towers at the interior supports may take a variety of forms, and the cables may assume a fan configuration as in *a* or a parallel configuration as in *b*.

FIGURE 2-14
Rio Grande Gorge Bridge, Taos County, New Mex. New Mexico State Highway Commission. (*American Institute of Steel Construction.*)

FIGURE 2-15
Satsop River Bridges, Satsop, Wash. Washington State Highway Commission. (*American Institute of Steel Construction.*)

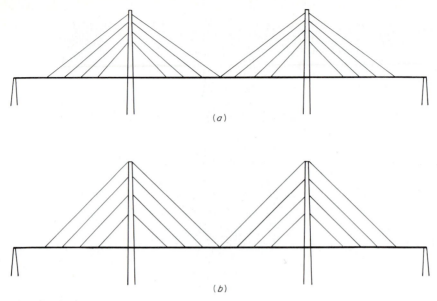

FIGURE 2-16
Typical cable-stayed bridge forms.

2-3 TOWERS

Towers are used to support transmission lines, radio and television antennas, radar and microwave equipment, tanks, bridges, etc. Freestanding towers (such as transmission towers and some radio and television towers) are usually rectangular in plan. The tall towers used in the electronic industry are usually guyed. The plan is usually an equilateral triangle, with the legs at the vertices. Most steel-tower members are hot-dipped galvanized for weather protection.

Aluminum towers are usually made of alloy 6061-T6, which is corrosion-resistant in all climates without surface protection. It can be extruded to produce optimum shapes for resisting stress and simplifying joints. Because of their lighter weight, aluminum towers can be flown by helicopter to relatively inaccessible sites.

2-4 MECHANICAL PROPERTIES OF STRUCTURAL METALS

The design of structures which support calculated loads at specified stresses is based on the assumption that certain mechanical properties of structural materials can be depended upon to meet definite requirements. The most widely used standards for structural materials are those of the American Society for Testing and Materials (ASTM).

ASTM specifications for structural steels generally identify the process by

which the steel is to be made, the chemical composition, and the tensile requirements. Specification A6 outlines the General Requirements For Rolled Steel
Plates, Shapes, Sheet Piling, and Bars For Structural Use. Specification A370
outlines the procedures for Mechanical Testing of Steel Products. A6 contains
requirements for manufacture, heat treatment, chemical analysis, metallurgical
structure, surface and edge condition, repair procedures, testing requirements,
dimensional tolerances, and other criteria essential to quality control. Additional
requirements may be specified by the purchaser if they are necessary. A370 contains detailed procedures for the mechanical tests used to determine the properties required in the product specification.

The yield point, ultimate strength, and elongation specified for structural
materials are determined according to the procedures of ASTM A370. Standard
specimens, generally called *coupons*, are used in the tensile test to establish the
properties of the material. Flat specimens of the dimensions shown in Fig. 2-17a
or round specimens of the dimensions shown in Fig. 2-17b are the standard specimens used for this purpose. The dimensions of the specimens are established to
ensure that failure occurs within the designated gage length. Substandard specimens are permitted in special cases, and the results of tests on such specimens
have been correlated with the corresponding results for the standard coupon. On
different structural sections the location from which the sample or coupon is to
be taken is also specified. If the design situation warrants it, the engineer may
specify tests in addition to those required by A6.

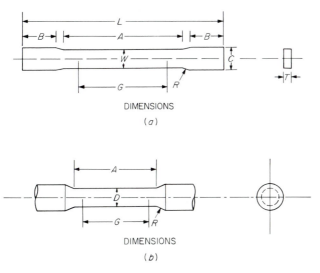

FIGURE 2-17
Standard coupon specimens. (a) Flat specimens: G = gage length; W = width; T = thickness;
R = radius of fillet, min; L = overall length; A = length of reduced section; B = length of grip
section; C = width of grip section. (b) Round specimens: G = gage length; D = diameter; R = radius
of fillet, A = length of reduced section.

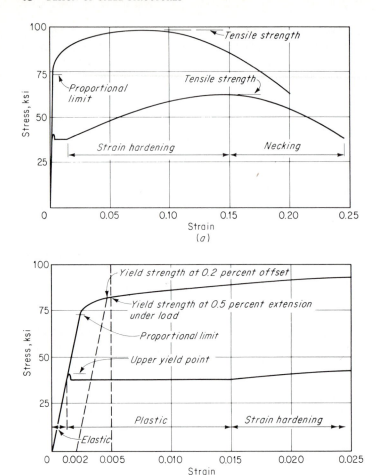

FIGURE 2-18

Two typical stress-strain curves for structural-steel coupons tested in tension are shown in Fig. 2-18a. The tensile strength is the highest stress, based on the original cross-sectional area. After reaching this maximum stress, a localized reduction in area, called *necking*, begins, and elongation continues with diminishing load until the specimen breaks.

The *yield point* is the stress at which there is a marked increase in strain with no increase in load. The increase in strain may be as large as 1.5 or 2 percent; this is sometimes called *plastic strain*. The subsequent increase in stress, which continues until the tensile strength is reached, is called *strain hardening*. Yielding is sometimes accompanied by an abrupt decrease in load, as shown in the lower curves of Fig. 2-18, which results in *upper* and *lower* yield points. The upper yield point is influenced considerably by the shape of the test specimen and by the testing machine itself and is sometimes completely suppressed. The lower yield point is much less sensitive and is considered to be more representative. Stress-strain curves of this type are typical of low-carbon (mild) steels. Both upper and lower yield points tend to increase with increase in speed of loading (strain rate). The lower yield stress at zero strain rate is called the *static yield level*. It may be as much as 10 or 15 percent lower than the yield stress reported in rolling-mill acceptance tests.

High-carbon steels do not usually have a pronounced yield point. Instead, after a range of linearly elastic behavior which ends at the *proportional limit*, the rate of increase in stress begins to drop and continues to fall until the tensile strength is reached (upper curve of Fig. 2-18a). In this case, yielding is defined arbitrarily by a *yield strength*, which is usually taken to be that stress which leaves the specimen with a permanent set (plastic elongation) of 0.2 percent when the specimen is unloaded (Fig. 2-18b). However, yield strength may also be defined (ASTM Specification A370) as the stress corresponding to a 0.5 percent elongation under load (Fig. 2-18b).

The term *yield stress* is commonly used to mean either yield point or yield strength when it is not necessary to make the distinction.

Steel in compression has the same modulus of elasticity as in tension. The lower yield stress is also the same, and there is about the same length of level yielding (contraction).

The horizontal portion of the lower curve in Fig. 2-18b is not strictly a stress-strain curve for the material. This is because the unrestricted yielding which it represents is not a continuous process in the sense that the elongation is distributed uniformly over the length of the specimen. Instead, yielding is a discontinuous phenomenon. In a tension test, it generally begins with the sudden appearance in the specimen of one or more narrow slipbands, which are also called *Lüders' lines*, *flow lines*, or *yield lines*. These lines are usually inclined at about 45° to the direction of the tension. They result from sliding along the inclined planes, which are planes of maximum shearing stress. The strains in these planes of sliding increase suddenly from the yield strain to values of the order of 0.02 to 0.04. Flow lines are easily detected on a specimen whose surface has been polished. They are also revealed by the flaking of mill scale on members of hot-rolled steel. They can be detected more readily if the specimen is whitewashed, in which case they appear as dark lines or bands (Fig. 7-5).

Slipbands are plastic regions which are separated from one another by completely elastic regions. Thus, the elongation which is measured over a region yielded in tension is actually the sum of a sequence of alternating layers of elastic and plastic strains. Once they start, slipbands spread and increase in thickness until the yielded region is completely strain-hardened, at which stage stress begins to increase again.

Aluminum alloys do not have a pronounced yield point, so the stress-strain curve is similar to the upper curve of Fig. 2-18a. The elongations of the aluminum alloys commonly used for structural purposes are roughly only half that of the structural steels (compare Tables 2-2 and 2-5). The modulus of elasticity is about 10,000 ksi as compared to 29,000 ksi for steel. Thus, the elastic deformation of an aluminum structure will be three times that of an identically loaded steel structure of the same dimensions.

Stainless steels also do not have a pronounced yield. The initial modulus is approximately the same as for structural steel, but the proportional limit is generally quite low. For some stainless steels the stress-strain curve may be different in tension and compression and the results may also be different in the longitudinal and transverse direction depending upon the method by which they are produced. Consequently the application of these materials in compression requires knowledge of the stress-strain curve.

Ductility implies a large capacity for inelastic deformation without rupture (opposite of *brittleness*). It is usually measured by the elongation, in percent, of a specific length, called the *gage length*, or by the reduction, in percent, of the cross-sectional area. It is also measured by a cold-bend test, which consists in bending a specimen 180° around a pin. The diameter of the pin is related to the thickness of the specimen and also varies with the steel. Ductility is an extremely important property, but there is no generally accepted minimum which is required of steels for structures.

Other important properties of structural metals are fatigue strength, resistance to brittle fracture, and toughness. *Fatigue* is a progressive, localized permanent damage under fluctuating stress that usually results in cracks which may eventually lead to complete fracture (Art. 2-15). *Brittle fractures* are usually catastrophic, low-ductility fractures that propagate rapidly at relatively low stresses. They often initiate at nominal stresses equal to or less than the yield strength and propagate at stresses as low as 20 percent of the yield strength (Art. 2-16). *Toughness* denotes the capacity of a material to resist fracture under impact loading. The area under the stress-strain curve is a measure of toughness, so both strength and ductility contribute to toughness. Thus, because its modulus of elasticity is only one-third that of steel, an aluminum structural member can absorb three times as much energy, for the same stress, as a steel member of the same dimensions, provided the stress does not exceed the proportional limit.

Strain rate and strain aging are sometimes important in assessing the suitability of metals for structural purposes. Both yield stress and tensile strength increase with increase in strain rate. These increases can be substantial under tension impact. Strain aging has to do with a change in properties during a rest period following unloading of a specimen which has been stressed into the inelastic range. Such an unloading path is parallel to the elastic loading path of the material (*AB* of Fig. 2-19). If the specimen is immediately reloaded, it retraces the unloading path to the level of stress at which unloading began and, if strain continues, follows the path it would have taken had no unloading occurred (*BAC* of Fig. 2-19). However, if the specimen is allowed to "age" at room temperature for a few days after it is unloaded, it may reload along *BADE*. Aging for 1 or 2 weeks may result in marked increases in the proportional limit, the yield strength, and the ultimate strength.[1] It will be noted that these increases are accompanied by a loss in ductility (*BF* compared with *BG* in Fig. 2-19).

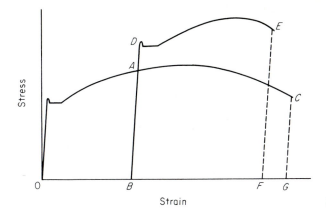

Strain

FIGURE 2-19

2-5 STRUCTURAL METALS

A wide variety of steels is produced for the construction of bridges, buildings, towers, tanks, and other structures. They are made by either the open-hearth, basic-oxygen, or electric furnace process. They may be rimmed, semikilled, or killed. Rimmed steels are only slightly deoxidized and are characterized by a rim of low-carbon steel which freezes upon initial contact of the molten metal with the ingot mold, a strong evolution of carbon monoxide gas upon solidification, and a higher-carbon core. In semikilled steels the evolution of gas is controlled by limited addition of deoxidizing agents such as silicon and aluminum. Killed steels are those in which the carbon-oxygen reaction is completely stopped by the addition of silicon or aluminum.

Rimmed steels are subject to segregation in the ingot mold and generally exhibit considerable variation in physical properties. Their use as structural materials is therefore restricted. Semikilled and killed steels are usually deoxidized by the addition of either silicon or aluminum. Killed steel provides the most homogeneous structure in the finished steel. Structural steels used regularly in bridges and buildings are described in Table 2-1. Tensile properties are given in Tables 2-2 to 2-4. Producers have given many of these steels brand names, some of which are not covered by ASTM specifications. Only ASTM steels are discussed here.

Steels for structural purposes can be classified in various ways but are commonly called carbon steels, high-strength steels, high-strength low-alloy steels, and quenched and tempered steels. This terminology is somewhat confusing and inconsistent, however. All steels contain carbon, which is the most important element except for the ferrite itself, but carbon steels are generally understood to mean steels whose properties are controlled largely by controlling the carbon content. Most of the high-strength steels are really of intermediate strength compared to the quenched and tempered steels. It will be noted that the yield stresses in Table 2-2 range from 36 to 42 ksi for carbon steel, 42 to 65 ksi for the high-strength steels, and 90 to 100 ksi for quenched and tempered steels.

TABLE 2-1
Steel for structural purposes

ASTM designation	Product	Use
A36	Carbon-steel shapes, plates, and bars	Welded, riveted, and bolted construction; bridges, buildings, towers, and general structural purposes
A53	Welded or seamless pipe, black or galvanized	Welded, riveted, and bolted construction; primary use in buildings, particularly columns and truss members
A242	High-strength low-alloy shapes, plates, and bars	Welded, riveted, and bolted construction; bridges, buildings, and general structural purposes; atmospheric-corrosion resistance about four times that of carbon steel; a weathering steel
A441	High-strength low-alloy manganese-vanadium steel shapes, plates, and bars	Welded, riveted, or bolted construction but intended primarily for welded construction; bridges, buildings, and other structures; atmospheric-corrosion resistance double that of carbon steel
A446	Zinc-coated (galvanized) sheets in coils or cut lengths	Cold-formed structural members for buildings, especially standardized buildings; welded, cold-riveted, bolted, and metal-screw construction
A500	Cold-formed welded or seamless tubing in round, square, rectangular, or special shapes	Welded, riveted, or bolted construction; bridges, buildings, and general structural purposes
A501	Hot-formed welded or seamless tubing in round, square, rectangular, or special shapes	Welded, riveted, or bolted construction; bridges, buildings, and general structural purposes
A514	Quenched and tempered plates of high yield strength	Intended primarily for welded bridges and other structures; welding techniques must not affect properties of the plate, especially in heat-affected zone
A529	Carbon-steel plates and bars $\frac{1}{2}$ in thick	Buildings, especially standardized buildings; welded, riveted, or bolted construction
A570	Hot-rolled carbon-steel sheets and strip in coils or cut lengths	Cold-formed structural members for buildings, especially standardized buildings; welded, cold-riveted, bolted, and metal-screw construction
A572	High-strength low-alloy columbium-vanadium steel shapes, plates, sheet piling, and bars	Welded, riveted, or bolted construction of building in all grades; welded bridges in grades 42, 45, and 50 only

TABLE 2-1—(*continued*)

ASTM designation	Product	Use
A588	High-strength low-alloy steel shapes, plates, and bars	Intended primarily for welded bridges and buildings; atmospheric-corrosion resistance about four times that of carbon steel; a weathering steel
A606	High-strength low-alloy hot- and cold-rolled sheet and strip	Intended for structural and miscellaneous purposes where savings in weight or added durability are important
A611	Carbon-steel sheets, cold-rolled	Cold-formed structural members for buildings, especially standardized buildings; welded, cold-riveted, bolted, and metal-screw connections
A606	High-strength low-alloy, cold- or hot-rolled sheets and strip	Cold-formed structural members for buildings, especially standardized buildings; welded, cold-riveted, bolted, and metal-screw connection; atmospheric-corrosion resistance double or quadruple that of carbon steel
A607	High-strength low-alloy columbium or vanadium, cold- or hot-rolled sheets and strip	Cold-form structural members for buildings, especially standardized buildings; welded, cold-riveted, bolted, and metal-screw connections. Class 2 has greater weldability and formability than Class 1
A709	Structural steel for bridges	Intended for use in bridges. Three strength levels, enhanced corrosion resistance, and stringent impact test requirements

Structural steel is produced in the form of shapes and flat-rolled products. Flat-rolled steel is called *bar*, *plate*, *sheet*, or *strip*, depending on its width and thickness, and may be either cold-rolled or hot-rolled. Specified tensile properties of the steels furnished in shapes, plates, and bars are given in Table 2-2; properties of structural pipe and tubing are given in Table 2-3 and of sheet and strip steels in Table 2-4. All the steels in these three tables are listed in Table 2-1. It will be noted that both yield stress and tensile strength are specified as "minimum values." Since the specification requires that test specimens conform to these values, rolling mills control the manufacture of the product so that the average yield stress and average tensile strength are well above the specified minimums. Figure 2-20 shows the yield-stress distribution of 3974 mill-test specimens taken from 33,000 tons of A7 steel* on nine projects erected between 1938 and

---

* A carbon steel with a minimum yield stress of 33 ksi which was used extensively from 1936 to about 1965. It was discontinued in 1967.

TABLE 2-2
Minimum tensile properties of structural steels

ASTM designation	Yield, ksi	Strength, ksi	Elongation, % (in 8 in unless noted)
Carbon steels:			
A36	36	58–80	20
A529	42	60–85	19
High-strength steels:			
A242, A441:			
To $\frac{3}{4}$ in thick	50	70	18
Over $\frac{3}{4}$ in to $1\frac{1}{2}$ in	46	67	19
Over $1\frac{1}{2}$ in to 4 in	42	63	16
A572:			
Grade 42, to 4 in incl.	42	60	20
Grade 50, to $1\frac{1}{2}$ in incl.	50	65	18
Grade 60, to 1 in incl.	60	75	16
Grade 65, to $\frac{1}{2}$ in incl.	65	80	15
A588:			
To 4 in thick	50	70	19–21*
Over 4 in to 5 in	46	67	19–21*
Over 5 in to 8 in	42	63	19–21*
Quenched and tempered steels:			
A514:			
To $2\frac{1}{2}$ in thick	100	110–130	18*
Over $2\frac{1}{2}$ in to 4 in	90	100–130	17*

* In 2 in.

TABLE 2-3
Minimum tensile properties of structural pipe and tubing

ASTM designation	Yield, ksi	Strength, ksi	Elongation, % (in 8 in unless noted)
Welded or seamless pipe:			
A53:			
Grade A	30	48	*
Grade B	35	60	*
Welded or seamless tubing:			
A500 (cold-formed):			
Round, Grade A	33	45	25†
Round, Grade B	42	58	23†
Round, Grade C	46	62	21
Shape, Grade A	39	45	25†
Shape, Grade B	46	58	23†
Shape, Grade C	50	62	21
A501 (hot-formed), shaped	36	58	20

* Varies, see specification.

† In 2 in.

TABLE 2-4
Minimum tensile properties of sheet and strip steels

ASTM designation	Yield, ksi	Strength, ksi	Elongation, % (in 8 in unless noted)
Carbon steels:			
A570:			
Grade 30	30	49	19
Grade 33	33	52	18
Grade 36	36	53	17
Grade 40	40	55	16
Grade 45	45	60	14
Grade 50	50	65	12
A611:			
Grade A	25	42	26*
Grade B	30	45	24*
Grade C	33	48	22*
Grade D	40	52	20*
Grade E	80	82	‡
Low-alloy steels:			
A374	45	65	20–22*
A607:			
Class 1			
Grade 45	45	50	22–25*
Grade 50	50	65	20–22*
Grade 55	55	70	18–20*
Grade 60	60	75	16–18*
Grade 65	65	80	14–16*
Grade 70	70	85	12–14*
Class 2			
Grade 45	45	55	22–25*
Grade 50	50	60	20–22*
Grade 55	55	65	18–20*
Grade 60	60	70	16–18*
Grade 65	65	75	15–16*
Grade 70	70	80	12–14*
Zinc-coated (galvanized):			
A446:			
Grade A	33	45	20*
Grade B	37	52	18*
Grade C	40	55	16*
Grade D	50	65	12*
Grade E†	80	82	‡

* In 2 in.

† This grade is a full-hard product for roofing and similar applications. Properties are obtained by cold working.

‡ Not specified.

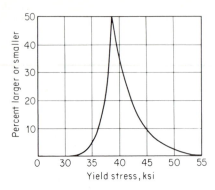

FIGURE 2-20
Yield-stress frequency distribution.

1951 (Ref. 2). The figure shows that about 5 percent of the specimens tested less than 35 ksi, with possibly 2 percent below the specified minimum of 33 ksi. More than one-third had yield points in excess of 40 ksi.

Extensive data on yield stress and modulus of elasticity for different structural materials have been analyzed statistically by Galambos and Ravindra.[3] They report mean values of the ratio of mill yield stress to specified yield value from U.S. mills of approximately 1.20 with a coefficient of variation of 0.10. Since mill tests are taken from the webs of rolled shapes and the yield stress of the flanges is usually smaller than that of the web, and because mill tests are performed at loading rates higher than occur in most structures, the values are adjusted to reflect these facts. The adjusted ratio of mean yield stress to specified yield stress varies from 1.04 to 1.11.

The most important factor affecting mechanical properties of the steels is the chemical composition. Some of the other factors are the total reduction from ingot to finished product, finishing temperatures, and rate of cooling. Because thin plates involve a larger reduction in the ingot than thick plates, which requires more passes through the rolls, they have higher yield stresses. However, yield stress may be kept independent of thickness by varying the chemical composition with the thickness of shape to be rolled. This is done with A36 steel for thicknesses to 8 in. On the other hand, the chemical composition of A242 and A441 is held constant, so the yield stress of these steels is smaller for thicker material (Table 2-2).

Steel which will be concealed (as in buildings) usually needs only one coat of paint, but steel which will be exposed requires additional paint after erection. However, certain corrosion-resistant steels that produce a tight, dense, hard, protective skin during oxidation have been developed. Only about 0.002 in of metal is lost through erosion by wind and rain in the process. The film is deep russet in color and pleasing in texture. It does not crack or flake, and it retards further corrosion so that painting is unnecessary except where the steel may be exposed to concentrated industrial fumes or to salt spray and fog. The protective coating is darker in color and forms faster (18 to 36 months) in an industrial atmosphere. These steels are called *weathering steels*. They have been used in bridges and in buildings with exposed frames. A242 and A588 are weathering steels. They have about four times the atmospheric-corrosion resistance of A36 steel.

ASTM Specification A36 covers weldable structural carbon steel with a minimum yield point of 36 ksi. It is available in all the standard rolled shapes and in plates to 8 in thick. It is also furnished in plates over 8 in thick, up to 15 in, but only with a yield point of 32 ksi. Copper can be specified as an alloying element in an amount which doubles the resistance to atmospheric corrosion. A529 is also a weldable structural carbon steel. It has a minimum yield stress of 42 ksi. It is available in plates and bars to $\frac{1}{2}$ in thick and in the lighter standard shapes. It has the same atmospheric-corrosion resistance as copper-bearing A36 steel. It is used principally in standardized steel buildings.

A242, A572, and A588 are called high-strength steels. A242 and A441 have the same minimum yield points (Table 2-2). A242 steel is suitable for riveted, bolted, and welded construction. It is not as economical as A441 and is not used unless corrosion is a factor. Vanadium and silicon are the principal alloying elements of A441 steel, which is produced for welded construction. A572 covers steels available in four different yield stresses. Each is classified as a "grade," with the grade number denoting the yield stress. Grades 42 and 50 are intended for riveted, bolted, or welded construction of bridges, buildings, and other structures. Grades 60 and 65 are also intended for riveted, bolted, and welded construction of buildings and other structures but only for riveted and bolted construction in bridges. A588 is a high-strength low-alloy steel with 50 ksi minimum yield point in thicknesses to 4 in. It is also available in larger thicknesses at smaller yield stresses (Table 2-2). It is suitable for welded, riveted, and bolted construction but is intended primarily for welded bridges and buildings. There are five grades, all with the same yield stress. Each grade is a proprietary steel, and each is produced by a different company. The A709 specification for structural steel for bridges applies to three different yield points and also provides for enhanced corrosion resistance. The strength of this material is comparable to that of A36, A572, A588, and A514. The most significant difference is that this specification requires testing for impact resistance. These requirements vary for fracture-critical and non-fracture-critical members. This concept is discussed in Art. 2-16. The required toughness of these materials is related to the ambient temperature to which the structure will be exposed.

Quenched and tempered alloy steel plate is covered by A514. This steel is furnished in 16 types, each under a proprietary brand name. It has the highest yield stress of the structural steels. It has outstanding toughness and is intended primarily for use in welded bridges and other structures.

Although all the steels in Table 2-2 are classified as weldable, this does not mean that identical welding procedures can be used for all. The ASTM specification usually cautions the user that welding procedures must be suitable for the steel and the intended service. Weldability of many of these steels is discussed in Ref. 4.

Steel pipe and tubing is often used in building construction (Table 2-3). A53 covers welded and seamless pipe. However, only Grade B of this specification,

TABLE 2-5
Minimum tensile properties of aluminum alloys

Alloy and temper	Yield, ksi	Strength, ksi	Elongation, % in 2 in
6061-T6*	35	38–42	10
6062-T6*	35	38–42	10
6063-T5	16	22	8
6063-T6	25	30	8
2014-T6	53	60	7

* May be used interchangeably.

which is electric-resistance welded, is permitted by the AISC specifications. It has about the same tensile properties as A36 steel (Table 2-2). This pipe is furnished in standard sizes ranging in outside diameter from $\frac{1}{2}$ to 24 in. Carbon-steel structural tubing in round, square, rectangular, or special shapes may be cold-formed, welded, or seamless (A500) or hot-formed, welded, or seamless (A501). Properties of these steels are given in Table 2-3. Common sizes of the square tube range from 3 × 3 in to 12 × 12 in. The rectangular tube ranges from 3 × 2 in to 12 × 6 in.

The sheet and strip steels (Table 2-4) are used for cold-formed structural members and find wide application in standardized steel buildings. Yield stresses range from 30 to 80 ksi. A606 is intended for service requiring greater strength and atmospheric-corrosion resistance equal to or greater than that of plain copper-bearing steel. A446 is produced with eight classes of hot-dip zinc coatings so that sheets with coating consistent with forming hazards and expected service life will be available.

The aluminum alloys usually used for structural work are known commercially as 2014-T6, 6061-T6, 6062-T6, 6063-T5, and 6063-T6 (Table 2-5). The number in these designations identifies the composition of the alloy, T means that the metal has been heat-treated, and the final numeral indicates the type of heat treatment. Although these alloys weigh only about 36 percent as much as steel, they can compete only when their higher initial cost is offset by such advantages as light weight, resistance to corrosion, reduced maintenance, and appearance.

2-6 STRUCTURAL SHAPES

A wide variety of structural-steel shapes is manufactured. Round and square bars are extruded. Flat steel is rolled from the ingot and is classified according to width and thickness as bars, plates, and bearing plates. The common rolled shapes are the angle, the tube, the channel, and the I. The I is available in two classifications. The most widely used is the W shape (formerly WF, meaning "wide flange"). The other, once called the American Standard Beam, is called the

S shape. Miscellaneous column and beam shapes used for lightweight construction are rolled by a few mills. Wide-flange shapes can be produced by passing an assembly of two flange plates and a web plate through submerged-arc welding machines which simultaneously weld both flanges to one side of the web. The section is turned over to weld the flanges to the other side. The structural tee is obtained by splitting the web of an I, generally by the use of rotary shears. There is a more or less constant demand for all these shapes, and therefore they are readily procurable. A group of special shapes such as subway columns, special channels, bearing piles, tees, and zees are rolled only by arrangement with the mills and should not be used unless the quantity needed is sufficient to warrant a rolling. All these shapes are manufactured to certain tolerances with respect to dimensional variations such as camber, cross section, diameter, squareness, flatness, length, straightness, sweep, thickness, weight, and width. The specific limitations are contained in ASTM A6.

Rolled section properties which are to be used in structural design calculations are presented in part 1 of the AISC Manuals.[5,6] Structural shapes are identified by a letter designator which indicates the particular cross section. Typical indicators are:

W	Wide flange beam
M	Miscellaneous beam
S	American standard beam
C	American standard channel
MC	Miscellaneous channel
L	Angle
WT	Structural tee cut from W
MT	Structural tee cut from M
ST	Structural tee cut from S

The letter designators are followed by numbers which identify the particular section, for example, W18 × 50, C12 × 30, MC8 × 8.5, WT18 × 80. The first numeral indicates the depth of the section and the second its weight in pounds per foot. In the case of W, M, and S shapes and tees cut from them the depth designation is the nominal depth, whereas for the C and MC shapes the indicated depth is the exact depth of the section. Angles are designated by the leg sizes and thickness, $L6 \times 6 \times \frac{1}{2}$ or $L7 \times 5 \times \frac{1}{2}$, with the long leg designated first and the thickness last. Part I of the Manuals also tabulates the properties of many commonly used built-up sections.

Cross-sectional properties utilized in design calculations are listed in the tables of the Manuals. Particular note should be taken of the fact that for the flange width, flange thickness, and web thickness two values are given, one in decimals and the other in fractions. The fractional value is used in detailing. All design calculations employ the decimal values.

Aluminum structural shapes are produced by rolling or by extrusion. Standard angles, channels, I's, tees, and zees are available in a wide range of sizes.

Limited selections of wide-flange shapes are also available. Hollow tubular shapes, interlocking shapes, sections with integral backup strips and bevels for welding, structural shapes with stiffening lips or bulbs to support outstanding flanges, and stiffened sheet panels are a few of the sections readily extruded.

Cold-formed steel shapes are formed in rolls or brakes from sheet or strip steel. Because of the great variety which can be produced, shapes of this type, unlike hot-rolled shapes, have not been standardized. Although a number of fabricators have developed their lines of members, the designer may devise special shapes for particular jobs. While shapes up to thicknesses of $\frac{1}{2}$ and even $\frac{3}{4}$ in can be formed, cold-formed steel construction is usually restricted to thicknesses ranging from 30 gage (0.012 in) to 4 (0.224 in). Shapes such as channels, zees, and angles in the thinner gages usually require lips or other edge stiffeners. I shapes are made by spot-welding two or more shapes, e.g., two channels or a channel and two angles.

Wire rope is made of a number of strands laid helically around a core, which may be a fiber rope, another steel strand, or a small wire rope. A strand is made of a number of wires laid helically around a center wire. Strand itself may be used as an individual load-carrying tension member where flexibility or bending is not a major requirement. Wire rope provides increased flexibility. For structural purposes it usually consists of six strands plus the central core.

Bridge strand is approximately four times as strong as A36 steel but costs only about twice as much per pound. A large portion of the cost of suspension members is in the fittings, connections, and anchorage members.

2-7 RIVETS

The components which make up the completed metal member or structure are fastened together by means of rivets, bolts, or welds. Rivets are rarely used in the types of steel structures discussed in this book. They are made from rivet bar stock in a machine which forms one head and shears the rivet to the desired length. Rivet heads are usually of a rounded shape called a buttonhead. The head may be flattened when clearance is limited. When very little clearance is available, countersunk heads are used. Countersunk heads are chipped flush if no clearance is available. Information concerning conventional signs for riveting, sizes of heads, weights, lengths, and other data are given in the AISC Steel Construction Manuals.

Steel rivets are almost always heated before driving. In the shop the rivet is heated to a minimum temperature identified by a light cherry-red color. Most shop rivets are driven by pressure-type riveters which complete the riveting operation in one stroke. Riveting guns are portable hand tools, operated by compressed air, which drive the rivet by a rapid succession of blows.

Rivets are made from steel conforming to the specifications for rivet steel, ASTM A502. This specification covers two grades of steel. Grade 1 is a carbon steel for general purposes. Grade 2 is a carbon-manganese steel for riveting high-strength alloy structural steels. Rivet heads are marked to identify the manufacturer and with a numeral 1 or 2 to identify the grade; the manufacturer may omit the numeral 1.

Rivets used in fabricating structures of aluminum alloys may be driven either hot or cold. Cold-driven rivets for structures of alloys 6061-T6 and 6062-T6 are made from alloy 6061-T6 and for structures of 6063-T5 and 6063-T6 from alloy 6053-T61. Cold-driven rivets for structures of alloy 2014-T6 are made from alloy 2117-T3. Hot-driven rivets for the five alloys are made from alloy 6061-T43.

2-8 STRUCTURAL BOLTS

The two commonly used types of bolts for steel structures are the *unfinished bolt* (A307) and the *high-strength bolt* (A325, A449, and A490).

The A307 bolt is known by a variety of names—unfinished, rough, common, ordinary, and machine. It is furnished in two grades, A and B, the former for general purposes and the latter for joints in pipe systems. They are made of low-carbon steel with a minimum tensile strength of 60 ksi. They are tightened by using long-handled manual wrenches, so the induced tension is relatively small and unpredictable. They are satisfactory for use in building frames not subject to shock or vibration and are used in both hot-rolled and cold-formed steel construction. Castellated nuts with cotter pins, jam nuts, and various types of locknuts can be used to prevent loosening where shock and vibration are a consideration.

The A325 bolt (Fig. 2-21a) is made of medium-carbon steel. It is also used in both hot-rolled and cold-formed steel construction. The tensile strength of this

(a)   (b)

(c)   (d)

FIGURE 2-21
Structural bolts: (a) A325 bolt, (b) A490 bolt, (c) interference-body bolt, (d) ribbed bolt.

TABLE 2-6
Properties of structural bolts

ASTM designation	Bolt diameter, in	Tensile strength, ksi*		Minimum yield strength, ksi,* 0.2% offset	Proof load; length measurement, ksi*
		Minimum	Maximum		
Low-carbon steel:					
A307:					
Grade A	All	60			
Grade B	All	60	100		
High-strength structural bolts:					
Medium-carbon steel:					
A325 and A449S	$\frac{1}{2}$–1	120	...	92	85
A325 and A449	$1\frac{1}{8}$–$1\frac{1}{2}$	105	...	81	74
A449	$1\frac{3}{4}$–3	90	...	58	55
Alloy steel:					
A490	$\frac{1}{2}$–$1\frac{1}{2}$	150	180	130	120

* On the area $\dfrac{\pi}{4}\left(D - \dfrac{0.9743}{n}\right)^2$, where D = nominal size and n = threads per inch.

bolt decreases with increase in diameter of the bolt, so two ranges of diameter are specified (Table 2-6). The A449 bolt, also of medium-carbon steel, is furnished in three ranges of diameter. The A490 bolt is made of alloy steel in one tensile-strength grade. It should be noted that the tensile properties are based on the "stress area." This is larger than the section at the root of the thread but smaller than the unthreaded area. The tensile strength of the bolt, based on this area, is about the same as the coupon strength.

High-strength bolts can be tightened to large tensions, which produce high clamping forces between the connected parts. The Research Council on Structural Connections (RCSC) Specifications for Structural Joints Using ASTM A325 or A490 Bolts[7] prescribes four tightening procedures for control of the pretension:

1. Turn-of-the-nut method
2. Calibrated-wrench tightening
3. Installation of alternate design bolts
4. Direct-tension-indicator tightening

Ordinary spud wrenches or standard-power impact wrenches can be used in the turn-of-the-nut method. Bolt elongation, and thus the tension, is controlled in this method. After the bolts in a connection have been tightened to the *snug-tight* condition, they are given an additional one-third turn if the bolt length is less than four diameters, one-half turn if the bolt length is greater than four diameters but less than eight diameters, and two-thirds turn if the bolt length is greater than eight diameters but less than twelve diameters. For lengths greater than twelve diameters special calibration is required. The snug-tight condition is defined as the tightness that exists when all plies in a joint are in firm contact. One full turn from a *finger-tight* condition corresponds approximately to the one-half turn from the snug-tight condition.

Manual torque wrenches or adjustable-power impact wrenches are used in the calibrated-wrench-method of tightening. Wrenches are calibrated by tightening, in a hydraulic tension-measuring device, a minimum of three bolts of the same diameter. Impact wrenches are set to stall when the prescribed bolt tension is reached. Manual torque wrenches have a torque-indicating device so that the torque required to produce the initial tension is measured. The calibration should be checked at least once a day or when the wrench is to be used on a bolt of different size. A hardened washer must be used under the nut or the head, whichever is turned in tightening. This requirement was added to the specification in 1985 to ensure the development of consistent and reliable pretensioning of the bolt. Without the hardened washer the friction between the nut or head and the connected material is likely to vary considerably from one connection to another, or even from one bolt to another.

Alternate design bolts are fasteners which incorporate design features intended to indirectly indicate the bolt tension or to automatically provide the required tension. Some are provided with a special appendage beyond the normal thread of the bolt which shears off when the correct bolt tension has been obtained. The direct-tension indicator is a device, usually a special washer, which is placed under the nut and has properties such that its deformation is correlated with the bolt tension. Special qualification procedures for such installations are required by the specification.

Not all the specifications (AISC, AASHTO, and AREA) permit all the tightening procedures defined by the RCSC. Each of the specifications has different requirements for the use of washers, which are dependent upon the yield point of the connected material and the tightening procedure employed. The AISC has special requirements in both ASD and LRFD when oversize or slotted holes are used. The designer should be aware of variations among the specifications.

Other fasteners are used occasionally. The high-strength, interference-body bearing bolt (Fig. 2-21c) has relatively hard, rolled, serrated ribs which produce a solid bearing for the full thickness of the connected parts. This bolt gives the strength and clamping force of the A325 bolt and, because it fills the hole, prevents slip should shear loads exceed the frictional resistance of the joint. Another type of interference fastener is the ribbed bolt (Fig. 2-21d). It is made of carbon steel and has strength equal to or greater than that of the A502 Grade 1 rivet of the same diameter. It has a standard rivet head, a fluted shank with triangular-shaped ribs, and a self-locking nut. These fasteners are especially useful where it is impractical to use power tools.

A394 galvanized steel bolts and nuts are the common fasteners for towers and similar structures. These bolts are available with hexagonal or square heads and nuts. A nonloosening connection is provided by lock washers, jam nuts, or locknuts.

Aluminum bolts and nuts are recommended for aluminum structures, although steel fasteners can be used. Steel bolts should be aluminized, hot-dip galvanized, electrogalvanized, or of stainless steel to prevent galvanic corrosion that might result from direct contact between steel and aluminum. Alloy 2024-T4 is the common alloy for aluminum bolts, while the nuts are usually of alloy 6061-T6 or 6062-T6.

2-9 BOLTED AND RIVETED CONNECTIONS

The behavior of joints with mechanical fasteners (rivets or bolts) is shown in Fig. 2-22, where tension T is plotted against joint displacement Δ. At initial application of load the forces are transferred from one element to the other by friction along the contact (faying) surfaces. The load at which slip occurs (A, B, or C) depends upon the magnitude of the clamping force and the coefficient of friction on the contact surfaces. There will be a slight increase in the load as slipping progresses because various fasteners will come into bearing at different amounts of slip as a result of variations in the location of the fastener within the hole. After slip is complete (D, E, or F), the load is transferred from one element to the other by bearing of the fastener on the hole and by shear on the bolt at the plane of slip.

In riveted connections the magnitude of the clamping force is quite variable. The clamping force is a function of the length of the rivet and the magnitude of the shrinkage which takes place after the head is formed. This shrinkage is a function of the temperature at which the driving is completed. The magnitude of the slip depends upon the extent to which the rivet fills the hole.

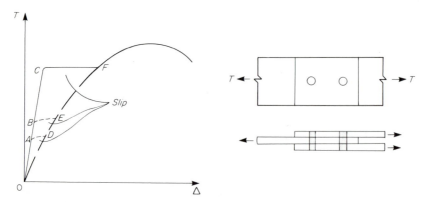

FIGURE 2-22
Behavior of mechanically connected joints.

High-strength bolts may be tightened to a specific installation tension. In this case the clamping force is controlled, and if the condition of the faying surface is known, the load at which slip occurs can be calculated. The clamping forces are sufficient to produce a significantly higher slip load than would be the case for a similar riveted connection.

Two types of connection are recognized. In the *slip-critical connection* the force which the fastener is permitted to transmit is small enough to provide a margin of safety with respect to slip of the joint. Thus, the connection transmits the force by friction produced between the faying surfaces by the clamping action of the bolts. The condition of the faying surfaces must be taken into account. Slip-critical connections are recommended for joints subjected to stress reversal, severe stress fluctuation, impact, vibration, or where slip is objectionable.

In the *bearing-type connection* the load is transferred by shear and bearing on the bolt. The capacity in shear depends on whether the shear plane intersects the body of the bolt or the threaded portion. Tests of bearing connections show that the strength of single-shear joints is increased by 40 to 45 percent if threads are excluded from the shear plane. Of course, this is a consequence of the difference in area.

The RCSC specification requires that slip-critical joints be tightened enough to ensure the minimum clamping force given in Table 2-7. In bearing joints it is only required to bring the connectors to the snug-tight condition. Slip-critical connections and connections subjected to direct tensions must be identified on the construction drawings.

Both slip-critical and bearing-type connections are proportioned on the basis of the calculated shear on the gross area of the bolt. The permitted force provides a margin of safety against slip in the case of the slip-critical joint and a

TABLE 2-7

Minimum installation tension*, ksi, for high-strength bolts in slip-critical connections and connections in direct tension

Bolt size, in	A325	A490
$\frac{1}{2}$	12	15
$\frac{5}{8}$	19	24
$\frac{3}{4}$	28	35
$\frac{7}{8}$	39	49
1	51	64
$1\frac{1}{8}$	56	80
$1\frac{1}{4}$	71	102
$1\frac{3}{8}$	85	121
$1\frac{1}{2}$	103	148

* $0.7 \times$ tensile strength.

margin of safety against failure of the fastener in the case of the bearing-type joint.

The different types of failure that may occur in bolted or riveted joints with the fasteners in shear are illustrated in Fig. 2-23. Failure in which the fastener is sheared along the plane of slip is illustrated in Fig. 2-23a and b. The area subjected to shear is the cross-sectional area of the fastener. For the lap joint a, failure is on one plane, and the fastener is in single shear. For the butt joint b, failure occurs on two planes, and the fastener is in double shear.

Failure of the plate at a hole, caused by compression between the cylindrical surface of the plate hole and the fastener, is shown in Fig. 2-23c. This is called a *bearing failure*. The variation of the compressive stresses around the perimeter of the hole is unknown. For design purposes the stress distribution is assumed uniform over the rectangular area equal to the thickness of the plate times the nominal diameter of the fastener.

Failure may also occur in the plate between the hole and the end of the plate by shearing in the direction of the load, as illustrated in Fig. 2-23d, or by transverse tension, as in Fig. 2-23e. These failures are unlikely to occur if the fastener is placed at a distance from the end sufficient to make the shearing strength of the plate equal to the shearing strength of the fastener. For structural metals this requires a distance from the center of the hole to the end of the plate of 1.25 to 2 times the diameter of the fastener.

Owing to the eccentricity of the applied forces, the plates of a lap joint tend to bend, as shown in Fig. 2-24a. This bending produces some tension in the fastener and nonuniform bearing of the fastener on the plate, as shown in Fig. 2-24b. However, tests indicate that the bearing strength of the fastener is about the same for single-shear and double-shear bearing. Nevertheless, some specifi-

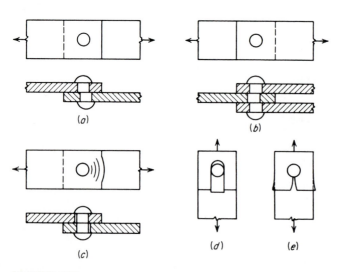

FIGURE 2-23

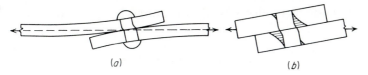

FIGURE 2-24

cations allow a larger unit stress for bearing in double shear than for bearing in single shear.

Tests have demonstrated[8] that failure by tearing through the free edge of the material will not occur if the distance L_e measured parallel to the line of the applied force (Fig. 2-25) is not less than the diameter of the bolt multiplied by the ratio of the bearing stress to the tensile strength of the connected part. This relationship has been established from tests on finger-tight bolts.

The relationship between bearing stress and tearing out of the hole can be evaluated by considering the situation shown in Fig. 2-25. If the bolt tears out, the failure planes will be along the dashed lines shown in the figure. It is conservative to use the solid straight lines as the failure planes. The force P transmitted by the bolts is given by

$$P = f_p Dt \tag{a}$$

where f_p = bearing stress
D = diameter of bolt
t = plate thickness

The force to cause failure along the two shear planes is

$$P = 2\left(L_e - \frac{D}{2}\right)t\tau_u \tag{b}$$

where τ_u is the ultimate shear strength of the plate material, which is taken as

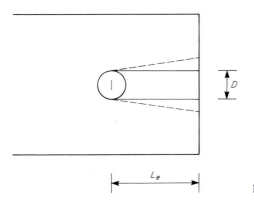

FIGURE 2-25

$0.7F_u$, where F_u is the tensile strength of the plate material. This equation can be rewritten in the form

$$P = 2D\left(\frac{L_e}{D} - \frac{1}{2}\right)t \times 0.7F_u = 1.4DtF_u\left(\frac{L_e}{D} - \frac{1}{2}\right) \tag{c}$$

Equating (a) and (c) and solving for L_e/D gives

$$\frac{L_e}{D} = \frac{f_p Dt}{1.4DtF_u} + \frac{1}{2} = \frac{0.714f_p}{F_u} + \frac{1}{2} \tag{d}$$

This equation agrees quite well with experimental data,[8] but there is some divergence as L_e/D increases. As L_e/D increases, the failure mechanism changes from shearing out of the plate material to piling it up at the edge of the hole. For values of f_p/F_u between 1 and 3 (the practical range), Eq. (d) is closely approximated by

$$\frac{L_e}{D} \approx \frac{f_p}{F_u}$$

from which

$$L_e = \frac{f_p D}{F_u} = \frac{f_p Dt}{F_u t} = \frac{P}{F_u t} \tag{2-1}$$

In the AISC/LRFD specification this relationship appears in the form

$$L_e = \frac{P}{\phi F_u t} \tag{2-2}$$

where the resistance factor ϕ is taken to be 0.75. With a factor of safety of 2, Eq. (2-1) becomes

$$L_e = \frac{2P}{F_u t} \tag{2-3}$$

which is the form used in AISC/ASD specification. For spacing between holes these values are increased by one-half the hole diameter d_h, so

$$L = \frac{P}{\phi F_u t} + \frac{d_h}{2} \tag{2-4}$$

in LRFD notation and

$$L = \frac{2P}{F_u t} + \frac{d_h}{2} \tag{2-5}$$

in ASD notation.

In addition to this requirement most specifications provide for a minimum edge distance for all fasteners in any direction toward an edge. The requirements are shown in Table 2-8. The edge distances in this table, which are for standard holes, must be increased if oversized or slotted holes are used. Specifications

TABLE 2-8
AISC minimum edge distance (standard hole)

Nominal fastener diameter, in	Sheared edge	Rolled edge or gas-cut edge*
$\frac{1}{2}$	$\frac{7}{8}$	$\frac{3}{4}$
$\frac{5}{8}$	$1\frac{1}{8}$	$\frac{7}{8}$
$\frac{3}{4}$	$1\frac{1}{4}$	1
$\frac{7}{8}$	$1\frac{1}{2}$†	$1\frac{1}{8}$
1	$1\frac{3}{4}$†	$1\frac{1}{4}$
$1\frac{1}{8}$	2	$1\frac{1}{2}$
$1\frac{1}{4}$	$2\frac{1}{4}$	$1\frac{5}{8}$
Over $1\frac{1}{4}$	$1\frac{3}{4}$ × diameter	$1\frac{1}{4}$ × diameter

* All distances in this column may be reduced $\frac{1}{8}$ in if the hole is at a point where the stress in the element is less than 25 percent of the maximum allowed stress.

† These may be $1\frac{1}{4}$ in at the ends of beam connection angles.

which permit the use of oversized or slotted holes contain provisions to cover this case.

Allowable stresses for high-strength bolts according to the RCSC are given in Tables 2-9 and 2-10. The values in Table 2-9 are based on strength and those in Table 2-10 on prevention of slip. Slip-critical connections must be checked for both criteria to provide adequate strength in the event of premature slip. For

TABLE 2-9
Allowable working stress* on fasteners or connected material (ksi)

Load condition	A325	A490
Applied static tension†‡	44	54
Shear on bolt with threads in shear plane	21	28
Shear on bolt without threads in shear plane	30	40
Bearing on connected material with single bolts in line of force in a standard or short slotted hole		$1.0F_u$‡§
Bearing on connected material with two or more bolts in line of force in standard or short slotted holes		$1.2F_u$‡§
Bearing on connected material in long slotted holes		$1.0F_u$‡§

* Ultimate failure load divided by factor of safety.

† Bolts must be tensioned to requirements of Table 2-7.

‡ F_u = specified minimum tensile strength of connected part.

§ Tabulated values apply when the distance L parallel to the line of force from the center of the bolt to the edge of the connected part is not less than $1\frac{1}{2}d$ and the distance from the center of a bolt to the center of an adjacent bolt is not less than $3d$.

Source: Ref. 7.

TABLE 2-10
Allowable load for slip-critical connections (slip load per unit of bolt area, ksi)

	Hole type and direction of load application							
	Any direction				Transverse		Parallel	
	Standard		Oversize and short slot		Long slots		Long slots	
Contact surface of bolted parts	A325	A490	A325	A490	A325	A490	A325	A490
Class A (slip coefficient 0.33): clean mill scale and blast-cleaned surfaces with Class A coatings*	17	21	15	18	12	15	10	13
Class B (slip coefficient 0.50): blast-cleaned surfaces and blast-cleaned surfaces with Class B coatings*	28	34	24	29	20	24	17	20
Class C (slip coefficient 0.40): hot-dip galvanized and roughened surfaces	22	27	19	23	16	19	14	16

* Coatings classified as Class A or Class B include those coatings which provide a mean slip coefficient not less than 0.33 or 0.50, respectively, as determined by testing method prescribed by RCSC.
Source: Ref. 7.

example, A325 bolts in slip-critical connections for Class B conditions are permitted to be stressed to 28 ksi (Table 2-10). The strength criterion for this bolt is 21 ksi if the threads are in the shear plane and 30 ksi if they are excluded (Table 2-9). Therefore, if the threads are in the shear planes, the bolts must be proportioned on the basis of 21 ksi (the strength criterion), but if they are excluded from the shear planes, they are proportioned on the basis of 28 ksi.

Allowable stresses for high-strength structural bolts specified by AISC, AASHTO, and AREA are presented in Table 2-11. It should be noted that allowable tension is independent of the size of the bolt, even though tensile properties vary with the size (Table 2-6). In assessing the factors of safety which these allowable stresses provide, it will be noted that the ASTM tensile properties are based on the stress area, while the allowable stresses in structural specifications are based for convenience on the unthreaded ("nominal") area of the bolt. Thus, for a 1-in bolt the stress area is 0.606 in^2, while the nominal area is 0.785 in^2. The recommended allowable tensile stress of 44 ksi for A325 bolts gives a factor of safety for 1-in bolts of

$$\text{F.S.} = 120 \times \frac{0.606}{44} \times 0.785 = 2.11$$

Factors of safety for the sizes listed in Table 2-6 range from 1.76 to 2.35 for buildings.

TABLE 2-11
Specification allowable stresses* for high-strength structural bolts (ksi)

Condition	A325			A490		
	AISC/ASD	AASHTO	AREA	AISC/ASD	AASHTO	AREA
Tension	44	39.5	44	54	48.5	54
Shear, slip-critical connection†						
Standard hole	17	16	17.5	22	20	22
Oversize hole	15	13.5	15§	19	17	19§
Shear, bearing-type connection:						
Threads in shear plane	21	19.5	...	28	25	
No threads in shear plane	30	27	...	40	36	
Bearing	$1.2F_u$‡	$1.35F_u$‡	$1.5F_u$‡	$1.2F_u$‡	$1.35F_u$‡	$1.5F_u$‡

* On unthreaded-body area, also called nominal area.
† Class A surface, clean mill scale.
‡ Ultimate strength of lowest-strength connected material.
§ Special permission by the engineer required.

Results of numerous tests show that the shear strength of a single A325 bolt is 65 to 70 ksi. Thus, the factor of safety for a single bolt at the allowable stress for a bearing-type connection, 30 ksi, is about 2.3. However, if there are a number of bolts in the line of stress, as in a long connection, this factor of safety is reduced if the shear is assumed to be divided equally among the bolts, as is customary (Art. 3-10). AISC/ASD, AISC/LRFD, and AASHTO require that for bearing-type connections in tension members the tabulated values be reduced by 20 percent if the length of the connection in the direction of stress exceeds 50 in.

The allowable bearing stresses in Table 2-11 appear to exceed the ultimate strength of the connected material. However, it must be remembered that this is not a true stress on the surface in bearing; instead, it is a fictitious stress on the projected area of the surface. Tests have shown that the strength of the net section of a tension member is not affected if the bearing stress is not larger than 2.25 times the net-section stress.

The factor of safety against slip is easily evaluated by assuming that the slip resistance equals the coefficient of friction multiplied by the specified pretension force. For example, the ASD capacity of the bolt is its area multiplied by the allowable shear stress, so the factor of safety against slip is

$$\text{F.S.} = \frac{\mu N}{A_b F_v}$$

where μ = coefficient of friction
    N = specified pretension in bolt
    A_b = cross-sectional area of bolt
    F_v = specified allowable shear stress on bolt

Assuming $\mu = 0.33$ (Class A) and the appropriate values of N, A_b, and F_v, the calculated factor of safety for A325 connections varies from 1.06 to 1.22, while for A490 bolt connections it varies from 1.17 to 1.26.

Kulak, Fisher and Struik[8] discuss the factor of safety on the basis of the probability of slip, method of installation of the bolts, and a fabrication factor related to the size of the holes. In any joint there will be variations in the clamping force and the coefficient of friction. Based on their evaluation there is about a 10 percent probability of slip for A325 connections when the allowable stresses of AISC/ASD are used.

Table 2-12 gives allowable stresses for A502 rivets according to AISC/ASD, AASHTO, and AREA. Although there are no tensile requirements for A502 rivets (hardness is specified instead), Grade 1 corresponds to a former ASTM designation, A141, for which the specified tensile properties were 28 ksi yield and 52 to 62 ksi tensile strength. Thus, it would appear that the allowable tension for Grade 1 rivets, 23 ksi, gives a low factor of safety relative to yield. However, the yield stress of the in-place rivet exceeds that of the undriven rivet because of the work hardening caused by driving. Furthermore, allowable stresses are based on the area of the undriven rivet, which is smaller than that of the driven rivet because rivet holes are $\frac{1}{16}$ in larger than the nominal diameter of the rivet. The combination of these two effects gives an effective yield stress 20 to 25 percent more than that of the rivet stock. Thus, the allowable tension of 23 ksi gives a factor of safety with respect to yield on the order of 1.5. The factor of safety with respect to tensile ultimate of the undriven rivet is at least 2.5. The Grade 2 rivet also corresponds to a former ASTM designation, A195, for which the tensile properties were 38 ksi yield and 68 to 82 ksi tensile strength. The ratio of the allowable tensions for the two grades, 29/23, and the ratio of the yield stresses, 38/28, differ only slightly.

Tensile-strength and shear-strength criteria of the AISC/LRFD specification are presented in Table 2-13. Allowable stresses in bearing recommended by the RCSC, presented in Table 2-9, have been adopted in the AISC/ASD specification. If deformation around the hole is permitted, they may be increased to $1.5F_u$. In the AISC/LRFD specification the ASD values are multiplied by 2.

TABLE 2-12
Allowable stresses (ksi) for A502 rivets

Condition	Grade 1			Grade 2	
	AISC	AASHTO	AREA	AISC	AASHTO
Tension	23	...	...	29	
Shear	17.5	13.5	13.5	22	20
Bearing	$1.2F_u$*	40	27†	...	40
			36‡		

* Stress of connected part.
† Rivet in single shear.
‡ Rivet in double shear.

TABLE 2-13
AISC/LRFD design strength of fasteners

Description of fasteners	Tensile strength		Shear strength in bearing-type connections	
	Resistance factor	Nominal strength, ksi	Resistance factor	Nominal strength,[a] ksi
A307 bolts	0.75	45.0[b]	0.75	24.0[c,e]
A325 bolts, when threads are not excluded from shear planes	0.75	90.0	0.75	48.0[e]
A325 bolts, when threads are excluded from shear planes	0.75	90.0	0.75	60.0[e]
A490 bolts, when threads are not excluded from shear planes	0.75	113.0	0.75	60.0[e]
A490 bolts, when threads are excluded from the shear planes	0.75	113.0[e]	0.75	75.0[e]
Threaded parts meeting the requirements for materials approved by AISC, when threads are not excluded from the shear planes	0.75	$0.75F_u$[b,d]	0.75	$0.40F_u$
Threaded parts meeting the requirements for materials approved by AISC, when threads are excluded from the shear planes	0.75	$0.75F_u$[b,d]	0.75	$0.50F_u$
A502, Grade 1, hot-driven rivets	0.75	45.0[b]	0.75	25.0[e]
A502, Grades 2 and 3, hot-driven rivets		60.0[b]	0.75	33.0[e]

[a] Values in this column are approximately 80 percent of the ultimate shear strength. See Art. 3-11.

[b] Static loading only.

[c] Threads permitted in shear planes.

[d] The nominal tensile strength of the threaded portion of an upset rod, based upon the cross-sectional area at its major thread diameter. A_b shall be larger than the nominal body area of the rod before upsetting, times F_y.

[e] When bearing-type connections used to splice tension members have a fastener pattern whose length, measured parallel to the line of force, exceeds 50 in, tabulated values shall be reduced by 20 percent.

Source: Adapted from the 1991 AISC/LRFD Specification.

Example 2-9-1 (AISC/ASD). Determine the number of bolts required, and an appropriate layout, to transmit a dead-load force of 80 kips and a live-load force of 240 kips through two C10 × 30 to a 1-in gusset plate (Fig. 2-26). All material is A36. Bolts are $\frac{3}{4}$-in A325 (standard holes) in a bearing-type connection with threads excluded from the shear planes. Use three lines of bolts across the web of the channel.

Solution

$$\text{Design force} = DL + LL = 320 \text{ kips}$$

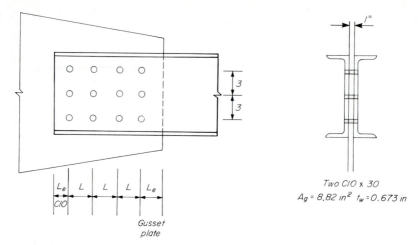

Two C10 x 30
$A_g = 8.82$ in^2 $t_w = 0.673$ in

Gusset
plate

FIGURE 2-26

For $\frac{3}{4}$-in bolt,

$$A = 0.4418 \text{ in}^2$$

$$F_v = 30 \text{ ksi} \qquad \text{(Table 2-13)}$$

$$R_v = 0.4418 \times 30 = 13.25 \text{ kips/shear surface}$$

Two shear surfaces per bolt. Number of bolts required is

$$\frac{320}{2 \times 13.25} = 12.1 \qquad \text{Use } 12$$

Bearing. Use

$$F_p = 1.2F_u = 1.2 \times 58 = 69.6 \text{ ksi}$$

This requires that the end distance be $1\frac{1}{2}d$ and the between-fastener spacing $3d$ (Table 2-9).

Channel

$$R_p = dtF_p = \tfrac{3}{4} \times 0.673 \times 69.6 = 35.13 \text{ kips}$$

There are 24 bearing surfaces, so

$$\text{Capacity} = 24 \times 35.13 = 843 \text{ kips} > 320$$

Gusset

$$R_p = dtF_p = \tfrac{3}{4} \times 1 \times 69.6 = 52.2 \text{ kips}$$

There are 12 bearing surfaces, so

$$\text{Capacity} = 12 \times 52.2 = 626 \text{ kips} > 320$$

Spacing

End distance, sheared edge: $1\frac{1}{4}$ in minimum.

End spacing: $1\frac{1}{2}d = 1.13$ in $\leq 1\frac{1}{4}$ in.

Center-to-center spacing for $F_p = 1.2F_u$ is $3d = 2\frac{1}{4}$ in.

Since R_p for both the channel and the gusset is considerably larger than required, consider the minimum end distance of $1\frac{1}{4}$ in and the minimum between-connector spacing of 2 in. Then, from Eqs. (2-3) and (2-5) we get

Channel

$$1.25 = \frac{2P}{F_u t} = \frac{2P}{58 \times 0.673} \qquad\qquad P = 24.4 \text{ kips [Eq. (2-3)]}$$

$$2 = \frac{2P}{F_u t} + \frac{d}{2} = \frac{2P}{58 \times 0.673} + \frac{\frac{3}{4}}{2} \qquad P = 31.7 \text{ kips [Eq. (2-5)]}$$

$$\text{Capacity} = 2(3 \times 24.4 + 9 \times 31.71) = 717 \text{ kips}$$

Gusset

$$1.25 = \frac{2P}{F_u t} = \frac{2P}{58 \times 1} \qquad\qquad P = 36.25 \text{ kips [Eq. (2-3)]}$$

$$2 = \frac{2P}{F_u t} + \frac{d}{2} = \frac{2P}{58 \times 1} + \frac{\frac{3}{4}}{2} \qquad P = 47.13 \text{ kips [Eq. (2-5)]}$$

$$\text{Capacity} = 3 \times 36.25 + 9 \times 47.13 = 533 \text{ kips}$$

Therefore, 12 bolts in three rows of four are adequate with end distance of $1\frac{1}{4}$ in and center-to-center spacing of 2 in.

Although the calculations show that the minimum spacings may be used, most designers would use the end distance of $1\frac{1}{2}d$ and between-fastener spacing of $3d$, which permits a bearing strength of $1.2F_u$. The minimum spacing would ordinarily be used only in special situations.

Example 2-9-2   (AISC/LRFD). Determine the number of bolts required, and an appropriate layout, to transmit a dead-load force of 80 kips and a live-load force of 240 kips through two C10 × 30 to a 1-in gusset plate (Fig. 2-26). All material is A36. Bolts are $\frac{3}{4}$-in A325 (standard holes) in a bearing-type connection with threads excluded from the shear planes. Use three lines of bolts across the web of the channel.

Solution

$$\text{Design force} = 1.2DL + 1.6LL = 1.2 \times 80 + 1.6 \times 240 = 480 \text{ kips}$$

For $\frac{3}{4}$-in bolts,

$$A = 0.4418$$

$$\text{Resistance factor } \phi = 0.75 \qquad \text{(Table 2-13)}$$

$$\text{Nominal shear strength} = 60 \text{ ksi} \qquad \text{(Table 2-13)}$$

Bolts are in double shear. Therefore, shear capacity per bolt is

$$R_b = 2 \times 0.4418 \times 0.75 \times 60 = 39.76 \text{ kips}$$

Number of bolts required is

$$\frac{480}{39.76} = 12.1 \qquad \text{Use } 12$$

Bearing and spacing

End distance, sheared edge: $1\frac{1}{4}$ in minimum (Table 2-8)
End distance: $1\frac{1}{2}d = 1.13$ in $\leq 1\frac{1}{4}$
Center-to-center spacing: $3d = 2.25$ in

When end distance is $1\frac{1}{2}d$ and center-to-center spacing is $3d$, the bearing strength is $2.4F_u$.

Bearing
Channel

$$R_n = 2.4dtF_u$$
$$= 2.4 \times \tfrac{3}{4} \times 0.673 \times 58 = 70.26 \text{ kips}$$
$$\phi = 0.75$$
$$\phi R_n = 52.7 \text{ kips}$$

There are 24 bearing surfaces, so

$$\text{Capacity} = 24 \times 52.7 = 1265 \text{ kips} > 480 \text{ kips}$$

Gusset plate

$$R_n = 2.4dtF_u$$
$$= 2.4 \times \tfrac{3}{4} \times 1 \times 58 = 104.4 \text{ kips}$$
$$\phi = 0.75$$
$$\phi R_n = 78.3 \text{ kips}$$

There are 12 bearing surfaces, so

$$\text{Capacity} = 12 \times 78.3 = 940 > 480 \text{ kips}$$

Spacing between connectors could be reduced by satisfying Eq. (2-4). If the minimum spacing of $2\frac{2}{3}d$ is used instead of $3d$, the following calculations are required.

Channel. End distance L_e, Eq. (2-2). For this case ϕ is 0.75.

$$1\frac{1}{4} = \frac{P}{\phi F_u t} = \frac{P}{0.75} \times 58 \times 0.673$$

$$P = 36.59 \text{ kips}$$

Between connectors L, Eq. (2-4).

$$2 = \frac{P}{\phi F_u t} + \tfrac{1}{2}d_h$$

$$= \frac{P}{0.75 \times 58 \times 0.673} + \tfrac{1}{2}(\tfrac{3}{4} + \tfrac{1}{8})$$

$$P = 45.74 \text{ kips}$$

$$\text{Capacity} = 2(3 \times 36.59 + 9 \times 45.74) = 1043 \text{ kips}$$

Gusset. End distance L_e, Eq. (2-2).

$$1\tfrac{1}{4} = \frac{P}{\phi F_u t} = \frac{P}{0.75} \times 58 \times 1$$

$$P = 54.38 \text{ kips}$$

Between connectors L, Eq. (2-4).

$$2 = \frac{P}{\phi F_u t} + \tfrac{1}{2}d_h$$

$$= \frac{P}{0.75 \times 58 \times 1} + \tfrac{1}{2}(\tfrac{3}{4} + \tfrac{1}{8})$$

$$P = 67.97 \text{ kips}$$

$$\text{Capacity} = 2(3 \times 54.38 + 9 \times 67.97) = 775 \text{ kips}$$

Therefore, 12 bolts in three rows of four are adequate with end distance of $1\tfrac{1}{4}$ in and center-to-center spacing of 2 in.

Although the calculations show that the minimum spacings may be used, most designers would use the end distance of $1\tfrac{1}{2}d$ and between-fastener spacing of $3d$, which permits a bearing strength of $2.4F_u$. The minimum spacing would ordinarily be used only in special situations.

Allowable stresses for aluminum rivets according to the Specifications for Aluminum Structures of the Aluminum Association[9] are given in Table 2-14. It will be noted that tension is not mentioned, which means, of course, that connections should be designed to avoid tension on the rivets as much as possible. Contrary to the practice of evaluating steel rivets in terms of their undriven diameters, tests on aluminum rivets are interpreted in terms of the diameter of the hole. Diameters and areas of rivets and the recommended diameters of the corresponding holes are given in Tables 2-15 and 2-16. The allowable shear stresses in Table 2-14 are based on factors of safety, with respect to shear strength, of about 2.25 for buildings and 2.65 for bridges. The allowable bearing stresses are based on factors of safety, with respect to bearing yield strength, of about 1.65 for buildings and 1.85 for bridges.

TABLE 2-14
Allowable stresses for aluminum rivets*

These values apply for a ratio of edge distance to rivet diameter of 2 or greater. For smaller ratios, multiply the allowable stress by the ratio (edge distance)/(2 × rivet diameter).

Designation after driving	Driving procedure	Designation of alloy fabricated	Shear, ksi		Bearing, ksi	
			Bridges	Buildings	Bridges	Buildings
6061-T6	Cold, as received	6061-T6	10	11	30	34
6053-T61	Cold, as received	6063-T5	7.5	8.5	†	16
		6063-T6	7.5	8.5	22	24
6061-T43	Hot, 990–1050°F	6061-T6	8	9	30	34
		6063-T5	8	9	†	16
		6064-T6	8	9	22	24

* From Ref. 9. These allowable stresses do not apply to material within 1 in of a weld. See Ref. 9 for reductions in heat-affected zone of weld.
† Not used in bridges.

TABLE 2-15
Hot-driven aluminum rivets

Rivet diameter, in	Hole diameter, in	Rivet area, in²
$\frac{3}{8}$	0.397	0.124
$\frac{7}{16}$	0.469	0.173
$\frac{1}{2}$	0.531	0.222
$\frac{9}{16}$	0.594	0.277
$\frac{5}{8}$	0.656	0.338
$\frac{3}{4}$	0.781	0.479
$\frac{7}{8}$	0.922	0.668
1	1.063	0.888

TABLE 2-16
Cold-driven aluminum rivets

Rivet diameter, in	Hole diameter, in	Rivet area, in²
$\frac{3}{8}$	0.386	0.117
$\frac{7}{16}$	0.453	0.161
$\frac{1}{2}$	0.516	0.209
$\frac{9}{16}$	0.578	0.262
$\frac{5}{8}$	0.641	0.323
$\frac{3}{4}$	0.766	0.461
$\frac{7}{8}$	0.891	0.624
1	1.016	0.811

2-10 WELDING PROCESSES

Most specifications require that the provisions of ANSI/AWS D1.1 Structural Welding Code be satisfied. That code contains detailed provisions for design, qualification, workmanship, inspection, and quality control.

Welding is a process of joining metal parts by means of heat and pressure, which causes fusion of the parts (resistance welding), or by heating the metal to the fusion temperature, with or without the addition of weld metal (fusion welding). Fusion welding usually employs either an electric arc or an oxyacety-lene flame to heat the metal to the fusion temperature. The electric arc is used for most structural welding.

Welds are classified according to their type as groove, fillet, plug, and slot. A groove weld is made in the opening (called a groove) between two parts being

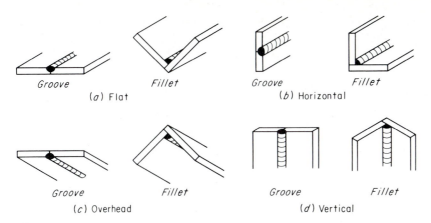

FIGURE 2-27
Welding positions.

joined, while the fillet weld, which is triangular in shape, joins surfaces which are at an angle with one another (Fig. 2-27). A plug weld is made by depositing weld metal in a circular hole in one of two lapped pieces. The hole must be filled completely. A slot weld is similar, the only difference being that the hole is elongated. Holes and slots can also be fillet-welded around the circumference, but these are not plug or slot welds.

Welds are classified according to the position of the weld during welding as flat (also called downhand), horizontal, vertical, and overhead. Welding in the flat position is executed from above, the weld face being approximately horizontal (Fig. 2-27a). The horizontal position is similar, but the weld is harder to make (Fig. 2-27b). Work in the overhead position is from the underside of the joint; this is the most difficult weld to make (Fig. 2-27c). The longitudinal axis of the weld is vertical in vertical-position welding (Fig. 2-27d).

In metal-arc welding the arc is a sustained spark between a metallic electrode and the work to be welded. At the instant the arc is formed, the temperature of the work and the tip of the electrode are brought to the melting point. Only that portion of the work at the arc is melted. As the tip of the electrode melts, tiny globules of molten metal form and are forced across the arc to be deposited in the molten base metal. It is because these globules are actually impelled across the arc that the process can be used in overhead welding. The molten metal, when exposed to the air, combines chemically with oxygen and nitrogen to form oxides and nitrides which tend to embrittle it and make it less resistant to corrosion. Tough, ductile welds that are more resistant to corrosion are produced if the molten pool is shielded by an inert gas which completely envelops the molten metal and the tip of the electrode. This shielding can be provided in a variety of ways, and the manner in which it is obtained can usually be determined from the name or designator used to indicate the process to be used.

Many types of welding processes are used in arc welding. They are *manual* or *automatic*. Other terminology, such as shielded-metal-arc welding (SMAW) or submerged-arc welding (SAW), is also used.

Most manual welding (stick welding) is performed with the shielded-metal-arc process. In this process the electrode is placed in an electrode holder to establish electrical contact and positioned by the welder. Shielding is obtained by the use of electrodes heavily coated with a material of such composition that large quantities of gas are produced in the heat of the arc. The coating burns at a slower rate than the metal core does, thus directing and concentrating the arc stream as it protects it from the atmosphere. The coating also forms a slag which floats on top of the molten metal and protects it from the atmosphere while cooling. The slag is easily removed after the weld has cooled. Figure 2-28 illustrates the shielding of the arc and the slag protection of the weld metal.

Automatic arc-welding processes produce high-quality welds at very high welding speeds. They are commonly used in construction and fabrication. One process is called submerged-arc welding (SAW). In this process (also called hidden-arc) a bare wire is fed automatically through the welding head at a rate to maintain a constant arc length. The welding is shielded by a blanket of granular, fusible material which is fed onto the work area by gravity in an amount sufficient to submerge the arc completely (Fig. 2-29). Some of the granular material fuses to form a covering over the weld. In addition to protecting the weld from the atmosphere, the covering aids in controlling the rate of cooling of the weld. Multiple-electrode welding uses two or more small weld wires, instead of the single wire, for increased speed at reduced cost. Submerged-arc welding must be performed downhand. Welding speeds for one-pass groove welds range from 30 in/min in $\frac{1}{4}$-in plate to 8 in/min in $1\frac{1}{2}$-in plate. The high currents used cause considerable melting of the base metal, so less filler metal is required and the joint opening may be less than that necessary for other types of welding.

In flux-cored arc welding (FCAW), shielding is provided by a flux contained within a tubular electrode and may be supplemented by an externally applied gas. In both applications the electrode core material produces a relatively thin slag covering to protect the solidifying weld metal. Flux-cored arc welding is usually a semiautomatic process where the gun, which controls the rate of feed, is held and manipulated by the welder. The process may be used in machine welding, in which the operator monitors the arc during the mechanized travel.

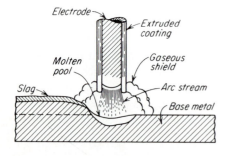

FIGURE 2-28
Shielded-metal-arc welding. (*Lincoln Electric Company.*)

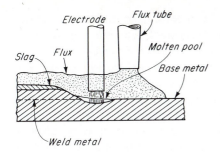

FIGURE 2-29
Submerged-metal-arc welding.

Inert-gas shielded-arc welding is usually performed without flux. The arc and the weld region are shielded from the atmosphere by a gas or gas mixture or by a combination of a gas and a flux. In addition to the inert gases argon and helium, carbon dioxide, which is heavier than air, may also be used. Carbon dioxide is popular because of its low cost. Since they are completely protected from atmospheric elements, the welds are stronger, more ductile, and more corrosion-resistant. High welding speeds with thorough penetration of the weld and little distortion are obtained because of the intense arc heat. In gas-shielded metal-arc welding (called *Mig*, for metal-arc, inert-gas), a bare-wire consumable electrode is fed automatically into the arc and deposited as weld metal. In the tungsten-arc process (*Tig*, for tungsten-arc, inert-gas), an arc is struck between a virtually nonconsumable tungsten electrode and the base metal. Filler metal, if required, is added by feeding a welding rod into the weld pool.

The basic elements of the electroslag welding process are shown in Fig. 2-30. Heat is generated by passing an electric current through molten flux which melts the electrode and the edges of the base metal. Welding is usually done in a

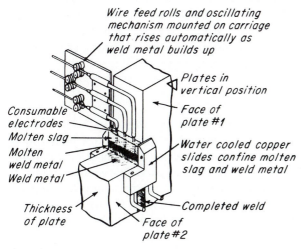

FIGURE 2-30
Electroslag welding.

vertical position. The cavity formed between the water-cooled molding shoes and the edges of the base metal contains the molten flux pool, the molten weld metal, and the solidified weld metal. Joint preparation is simple since only square, oxygen-cut edges are necessary. Plates 18 in thick can be welded in a single pass. A starting tab is needed to build up the proper depth of flux to ensure complete fusion of the base metal. A runoff tab is required at the top because the slag depth must be carried beyond the base metal. The slag bath is $1\frac{1}{2}$ to 2 in deep.

Although similar in its basic elements to the electroslag process, the electro-gas welding process uses an open electric arc instead of a molten flux to melt the base metal and electrode. Since the arc causes instantaneous fusion and no flux bath is required, starting and runoff tabs are not necessary. Joint thicknesses of $\frac{1}{2}$ to 3 in can be produced with a single pass.

Electroslag or electrogas welding produces relatively large grain sizes as a result of the slow cooling rate of the weld. This condition also produces carbon migration from the portion of the weld which cools first to that part which cools last. As a result, the center section of such welds may consist of material with a relatively large grain size and increased carbon content. In addition, fairly large residual stresses may be present as a result of the constraint of the thick pieces being joined. Under these conditions the weld could be susceptible to brittle fractures. This condition is more critical in the presence of a flaw. Brittle fracture is discussed in Art. 2-16.

Electroslag or electrogas welding of ASTM A514 steel is not permitted unless the weldment is quenched and tempered after welding.

Aluminum alloys can be joined by arc welding, resistance welding, gas welding, or brazing. The most commonly used procedures are Mig and Tig welding. They can be used on metal $\frac{1}{16}$ in or more thick. Tig welding is generally used for material thicknesses from 0.05 to 0.25 in. The commonly used structural aluminum alloys are all readily weldable. Butt joints made in aluminum alloys which are in the annealed condition are usually 100 percent efficient. With alloys in the strain-hardened or heat-treated tempers, however, the heat of welding affects the metal on each side of the weld so that it is not as strong as the parent metal.

2-11 WELDED JOINTS

Welded joints are classified as butt, lap, tee, corner, and edge (Fig. 2-31). The butt joint is groove-welded, while the lap joint is fillet-welded. The tee joint can be groove-welded, as shown, or it can be fillet-welded with one fillet on each side. Groove-welded joints can be *complete-penetration* or *partial-penetration* joints. In some cases the penetration is intentionally partial in that the weld is less in depth than the thickness of the part joined, while in other cases it is partial because the welding procedure does not produce effective penetration in what might appear otherwise to be a complete-penetration joint.

A number of joints can be used without qualification, which means that no tests are required to demonstrate their adequacy. Some of the manual shielded-

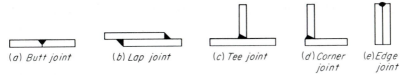

FIGURE 2-31
Types of welded joints.

metal-arc joints for buildings, prequalified by the American Welding Society, are shown in Fig. 2-32. Two of them, *a* and *b*, are complete-penetration joints but are limited in use to the thicknesses shown. Four, *c* to *f*, are complete-penetration joints of unlimited thickness. The last four, *g* to *j*, are partial-penetration joints.

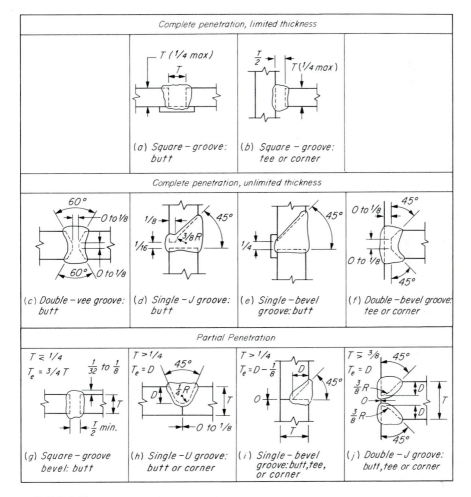

FIGURE 2-32
Typical prequalified shielded-metal-arc joints for buildings. (*From ANSI/AWS D1.1, 1988.*)

The square-groove joints, *a*, *b*, and *i*, require no preparation of the edges of the parts to be joined. The type of groove for other than square-butt joints depends in part upon the thickness of the material and the position of the weld and whether one side or both sides are accessible for welding. Single grooves, such as the bevel and the V, J, and U, are cheaper to form but require more weld metal than the double-grooved joints. For example, the single-V joint requires approximately twice as much weld metal as the double-V. The choice between single and double grooves is usually a question of whether the higher cost of preparation is offset by the saving in weld metal. Bevel or V joints are usually preferred for horizontal welds because it is difficult to make a good U or J joint in this position.

The part of a weld which is assumed to be effective in transferring stress is called the *throat*. The throat thickness of each of the complete-penetration welds in Fig. 2-32 is denoted by T. The effective throats of the partial-penetration welds, denoted by T_e, are also shown in the figure. Five of the joints in the figure (*a*, *e*, *g*, *h*, and *i*) are welded from only one side of the joint. However, *a* and *g* are welded against backing strips, which accounts for their being complete-penetration joints. Weld *g* is partial-penetration because it is welded from one side without backup. In the remaining complete-penetration joints, the root of the weld deposited first must be "gouged" before welding from the other side, which means that it must be cleaned.

The fillet weld is quite common in structural connections. The faces of the weld which are in contact with the parts joined are called its legs. The size of an *equal-legged* fillet weld is given by the length of the side of the largest isosceles right triangle that can be inscribed within the weld cross section. This triangle is called the diagrammatic fillet weld. The throat is the shortest distance from the root of the weld to the hypotenuse. For the equal-legged fillet weld this dimension is $0.707s$, where s is the leg size. (In the case of the submerged-arc weld, there is an exception to this definition in the AISC specification, discussed in Art. 2-13.) The legs are usually equal, but conditions sometimes require unequal legs. Large fillet welds made manually require two or more passes, as indicated in Fig. 2-33. Each pass must cool, and the slag must be removed, before the next pass is made. Therefore, the most efficient fillet welds are those which can be made in one pass. The largest size that can be made in one pass depends on the welding position and should not exceed the following:

$\frac{5}{16}$ in in the horizontal or overhead position

$\frac{3}{8}$ in in the flat position

$\frac{1}{2}$ in in the vertical position

Efficiency of welding is also affected by the amount of filler metal required, which increases by the square of the leg size as the throat dimension increases linearly. For example, a $\frac{5}{16}$-in fillet weld has a throat only 25 percent greater than that of a $\frac{1}{4}$-in weld, but its volume is 56 percent greater.

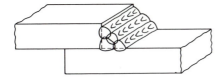

FIGURE 2-33
Multiple-pass fillet weld.

The most commonly used fillet welds increase in size by sixteenths of an inch from $\frac{1}{8}$ to $\frac{1}{2}$ and by eighths of an inch for sizes greater than $\frac{1}{2}$ in. To ensure full throat thickness, the size of the weld should be less than the thickness of the edge of the connected part. The maximum size of fillet permitted by the AWS along the edges of material $\frac{1}{4}$ in or more in thickness is $\frac{1}{16}$ in less than the thickness of the material. When it is impracticable to obtain a sufficient connection with these maximum sizes, the specifications permit a weld of the same thickness as the edge, provided this information is designated on the drawings. Along the edges of material less than $\frac{1}{4}$ in thick, the weld size may be equal to the thickness of the material.

A fillet weld that is too small compared with the thickness of the material being welded is affected adversely during cooling. The amount of heat required to deposit a small weld is not sufficient to produce appreciable expansion of the thick material, and as the hotter weld contracts during cooling it is restrained by being attached to the cooler material. Thus, a lengthwise tensile stress is produced in the weld. Furthermore, conduction of heat by the relatively cold material accelerates the rate of cooling of the weld, and this tends to cause brittleness. The weld may actually crack because of the combination of the two effects. To help control this situation, specifications limit the size of the weld which may be deposited on the basis of the maximum thickness of the parts to be joined, as given in Table 2-17.

Groove-welded joints are more efficient than fillet-welded joints and because of their greater resistance to repeated stress and impact are to be preferred for dynamically loaded members. Groove welds not only require less weld metal than fillet welds of equal strength, they also frequently eliminate the need for extra metal in the form of connecting plates or other structural shapes. Nevertheless, fillet welds are often used in structural work, partly because many con-

TABLE 2-17
Fillet-weld sizes

Size of fillet weld, in	Maximum thickness of part, in
$\frac{1}{8}$	To $\frac{1}{4}$
$\frac{3}{16}$	Over $\frac{1}{4}$ to $\frac{1}{2}$
$\frac{1}{4}$	Over $\frac{1}{2}$ to $\frac{3}{4}$
$\frac{5}{16}$	Over $\frac{3}{4}$

nections are more easily made with fillet welds and partly because groove welds require the member of a structure to be cut to rather close tolerances.

Cold-formed members are usually shop-fabricated by spot welding (resistance welding). In this process the parts to be welded are clamped between two electrodes. Resistance of the metal to a strong current passed through the electrodes generates sufficient heat to melt a small area of the metal. Fusion of the parts between the electrodes is effected by pressure. Fusion welds are used for on-site welding to connect cold-formed members to other cold-formed members or to hot-rolled framing members. Shapes of welds and welding techniques are often different from those in ordinary structural welding. For example, the puddle weld, which is the standard way of connecting floor or roof deck to structural framing, is made by burning through the deck and then filling the hole with weld metal. This is analogous to the plug weld.

Standard welding symbols are shown in Fig. 2-34. The fillet weld is shown by a triangle and the groove weld by a symbol denoting the type of groove. The symbol for the type of weld is drawn on a reference line which has an arrow pointing to the joint. If the symbol is on the near side of the reference line, the weld is to be deposited at the side of the joint to which the arrow points. This is shown in Fig. 2-34a. Dimensions of the weld are to be specified as shown. In this case, the instruction is to deposit a $\frac{3}{8}$-in fillet weld, 6 in long, at the arrow side of the joint. If the symbol is on the far side of the reference line, the weld is to be made on the other side of the joint, as shown in Fig. 2-34b. Similarly, a weld symbol on both sides of the reference line is an instruction to weld both sides of the joint (Fig. 2-34c).

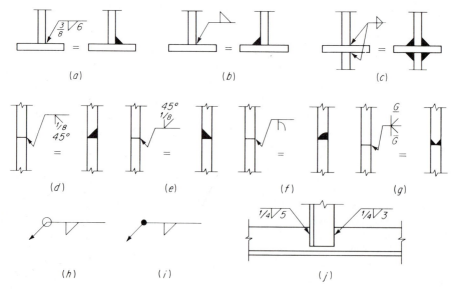

FIGURE 2-34
Welding symbols.

The arrow for a bevel or J-groove welding symbol points with a definite break toward the member which is to be chamfered (Fig. 2-34*d*). The root opening and the groove angle are specified as shown. The horizontal lines above and below the weld symbol in Fig. 2-34*g* mean that the weld is to be flush. If it is to be finished, a letter denoting the type of finish (G = grind, M = machine, etc.) is added. A weld which is to be made all around the joint is denoted by an open circle (Fig. 2-34*h*). The blacked-in circle in *i* signifies a weld to be made in the field.

A common situation in structural drawings is shown in Fig. 2-34*j*, which represents two angles (vertical) welded to a tee, as in a truss. The weld symbols are shown for the angle which is seen in the drawing, in this case the angle on the near side of the tee. It is understood that the duplicate angle on the far side is to be welded identically, and it would be incorrect to try to indicate this by using triangles on both sides of the weld reference line. In other words, the weld symbol can point to only one joint. On the other hand, if duplicate parts on opposite sides of a piece appear on the drawing, as in Fig. 2-34*c*, the required welding for both parts is shown.

These and other standard weld symbols and notations are described in detail in Ref. 10.

2-12 STRESSES IN WELDS

The groove weld may be stressed in tension, compression, shear, or a combination of tension, compression, and shear, depending upon the direction and position of the load relative to the weld. For example, the groove weld in the tee joint shown in Fig. 2-35*a* is in tension, while those in Fig. 2-35*b* are in shear. In either case, the stress is assumed to be distributed uniformly over the area of the throat. Thus for the weld in Fig. 2-35*a*, the tensile stress f_t is given by

$$f = \frac{P}{LT_e} \qquad (a)$$

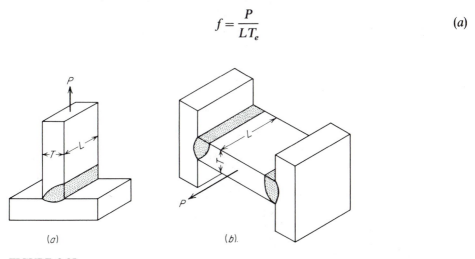

FIGURE 2-35

where L is the length of the weld and T_e is the effective throat thickness. If the weld is full-penetration, $T_e = T$. In the connection of Fig. 2-35b, the shearing stress f for each weld is

$$f = \frac{P/2}{LT_e} \tag{b}$$

where $T_e = T$ for full-penetration welds.

The load P in Fig. 2-36a is resisted by a shearing force $P/2$ on the throat of each fillet weld. Therefore, the shearing stress is

$$f = \frac{P/2}{LT_e} \tag{c}$$

where T_e is the thickness of the throat (the minimum dimension across the diagrammatic weld). In the usual case of the manually deposited 45° fillet, $T_e = 0.707T$, where T is the width of the leg. The superior penetration of the submerged-arc fillet weld justifies a more liberal definition of the throat. Only the AISC specifications make such an allowance, however. In these specifications the throat for submerged-arc fillet welds is

$$T_e = \begin{cases} T & T \leq \frac{3}{8} \text{ in} \\ 0.707T + 0.11 & T \geq \frac{3}{8} \text{ in} \end{cases}$$

It is customary to take the force on a fillet weld as a shear on the throat irrespective of the direction of the load relative to the throat. Thus, in Fig. 2-36b the load P produces on the throat of each weld both a shearing component and a tensile component, each equal to $P\frac{\sqrt{2}}{4}$. In spite of this fact the stress is determined from Eq. (c).

Tests have shown that a fillet weld transverse to the load, as in Fig. 2-36b, is much stronger than a fillet weld of the same size parallel to the load, as in Fig. 2-36a (Art. 2-13). The explanation probably lies in the fact that the force on the throat of the transverse weld has both a shearing component and a normal com-

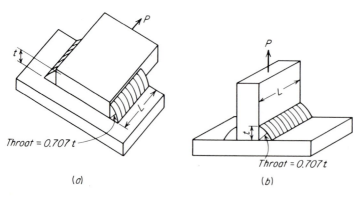

(a)   (b)

FIGURE 2-36

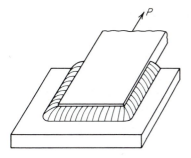

FIGURE 2-37

ponent, as was shown above. Therefore, it is reasonable to expect the strength of the transverse weld to be intermediate between the shearing and the tensile strengths of the weld metal, which is actually the case. It is also well known that at working loads the shearing stress is not uniform over the length of a longitudinal weld and that for long welds it may be considerably larger at the ends than at the center of the weld. However, since the more highly stressed portions yield first under increasing load, it is probable that the stress approaches a uniform distribution at failure under static loading.

Figure 2-37 shows a lap joint with two longitudinal fillet welds and one transverse fillet weld. A portion of the load P will be transmitted by each weld, but it is impossible to determine by statics alone how the load will be divided among the three welds. However, it is customary to assume that the stress is distributed among the welds in proportion to their lengths, if all welds are the same size. If the weld on the end of the member is different in size from the welds along the sides, the load is assumed to be distributed in proportion to the area of the welds.

Any abrupt discontinuity or change in the section of a member, such as a notch or a sharp reentrant corner, interrupts the transmission of stress along smooth lines. The magnitude of the stress concentration increases as the sharpness of the notch or the abruptness of the discontinuity increases. These concentrations, including those at the ends of longitudinal welds discussed above, are of no consequence for static loads or for cases where only a few thousand repetitions of maximum stress are likely to occur. However, they are significant where fatigue is involved (Art. 2-15). Figure 2-38a illustrates a transverse joint in which the weld is elongated in the direction of the load to produce a more uniform transfer of stress than in the conventional weld of Fig. 2-38b. Specifications do not permit an increase in the allowable unit stress for such a weld.

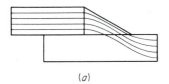
(a)

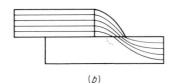
(b)

FIGURE 2-38

2-13 SPECIFICATIONS FOR WELDED CONNECTIONS

Welding electrodes are classified on the basis of the mechanical properties of the weld metal, the welding position, the type of coating, and the type of current required. Electrodes for shielded-metal-arc welding (SMAW) are covered by AWS A5.1-81 and AWS A5.5-81. Each electrode is identified by a code number EXXXXX, where E stands for electrode and each X represents a number. The first two (or three) numbers indicate the tensile strength (kips per square inch) of the weld metal. The next number denotes the position in which the electrode can be used, the number 1 meaning all positions, the number 2 flat and horizontal fillet welds, and the number 3 flat welding only. The last number denotes the type of covering, the type of current (alternating or direct), and the polarity (straight or reversed). Straight polarity means that the electrode is negative. For example, an E7018 electrode has a tensile strength of 70 ksi, the number 1 means that it can be used in all positions, and the number 8 means that it is an iron powder, low-hydrogen electrode which can be used with either alternating or direct current but only in reverse polarity.

Combinations of flux and electrodes for submerged-arc welding (SAW) are covered by AWS A5.23-80. A flux is designated by the letter F followed by two digits denoting the tensile strength and Charpy V-notch impact strength of the test weld. This is followed by a set of letters and numbers denoting the electrode used to classify the flux. For example, the letters EL in EL8 signify a low-manganese electrode, while the number 8 denotes the chemical composition in percent of carbon, manganese, and silicon. Electrodes for gas metal-arc welding are covered by AWS A5.26-78 and are identified by similar notation. Thus, E70S-X and E70-U1 are solid and emissive electrodes, respectively, where the last number identifies the chemical composition.

The mechanical properties of electrodes are given in Table 2-18. For the full-penetration groove weld, most specifications prescribe tensile stresses equal to those for the base metal and require that "matching" weld metal must be used. In compression the allowable stress is the same as for the base metal, but the weld metal may have a strength equal to or less than the matching weld metal. Shear must be checked on both the base metal and weld metal. Filler-metal requirements are given in Table 2-19.

Partial-penetration groove welds and fillet welds may be made with filler metals whose tensile properties are less than those of the base metal. The permissible stresses for this situation are based on test results evaluated according to the assumptions as to stress distribution which were discussed in Art. 2-12. Figure 2-39 shows the results of 168 tests on fillet-welded joints.[11] Weld sizes were $\frac{1}{4}$, $\frac{3}{8}$, and $\frac{1}{2}$ in, base metals A36, A441, and A514, and electrode classifications E60, 70, 90, and 110. The combinations of base metal and electrode tested are given in Table 2-20. Combinations of strong weld metal with weaker base metal, and vice versa, showed that the effect of dilution upon weld strength was quite small. For example, the strength of $\frac{1}{4}$-in fillet welds made with E110

TABLE 2-18
Mechanical properties of electrodes

| Welding process | | | | Mechanical properties | | | |
Shielded metal-arc	Submerged arc	Gas metal-arc	Flux-cored arc	Minimum tensile strength, ksi	Minimum yield point, ksi	Minimum elongation in 2 in, %	Minimum impact strength, ft · lb at 0°F
E60XX				67	50	17–25	*
	F6X-EXXX			62–80	50	25	*
E70XX				70	57	17–22	*
	F7X-EXXX			70–95	60	22	*
		E70S-X		72	60	20–22	*
E80XX				80	67	16–19	*
	F8X-EXXX	E80S		80	67	18	20†
			E80T	80–95	68	18	20†
E100XX				100	87	13–16	*
	F10X-EXXX			100–130	88	16	20†
		E100S		100	90	16	20†
			E100T	100–115	88	16	20†
E110XX				110	97	15	*
	F11X-EXXX			110–130	98	15	20†
		E110S		110	98	15	20†
			E110T	110–125	98	15	20†

* Not required.
† Applicable only to bridges.

TABLE 2-19
Filler-metal requirements for complete-penetration groove welds*

Lower specified minimum yield point of base metals being joined	Welding process			
	Shielded metal-arc	Submerged arc	Gas metal-arc	Flux-cored arc
A36, A53 Grade B, A500, A501, A529, A570, A709 Grade 36	E60XX or E70XX*†	F6X or F7X-EXXX	E705-X or E70U-1	E60T-X or E70T-X
A242, A441, A572 Grades 42 to 55, A588, A709 Grade 50‡	E70XX§	F7X-EXXX	E70S-X or E70U-1	E70T-X
A572 Grades 60 and 65	E80XX§	F8X-EXXX	Grade E80S	Grade E80T
A514, A709 Grade 100:				
$t \leq 2\frac{1}{2}$ in	E110XX§	F11X-EXXX	Grade E110S	Grade E110T
$t > 2\frac{1}{2}$ in	E100XX§	F10X-EXXX	Grade E100S	Grade E100T

* Use of same type filler metal having next-higher mechanical properties is permitted.

† Low-hydrogen electrodes must be used for welding A36 steel more than 1 in thick for bridges.

‡ For architectural exposed bare unpainted applications, the deposited weld metal and the base metal must have similar atmospheric-corrosion resistance and coloring characteristics. Follow steel manufacturer's recommendation.

§ Low-hydrogen classifications.

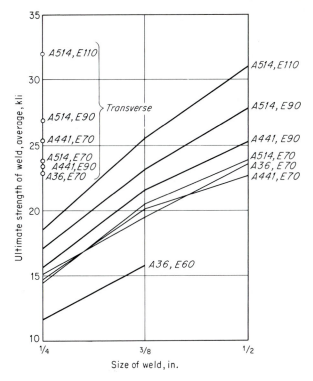

FIGURE 2-39
Strength of fillet welds. (*From AWS-AISC Fillet Weld Study, Report to AISC by Testing Engineers, Inc., Oakland, Calif., 1968.*)

TABLE 2-20
Base metal and electrodes for tests of Fig. 2-39

	E60XX Weld size		E70XX Weld size			E90XX Weld size			E110XX Weld size		
Base metal	$\frac{1}{4}$	$\frac{3}{8}$	$\frac{1}{4}$	$\frac{3}{8}$	$\frac{1}{2}$	$\frac{1}{4}$	$\frac{3}{8}$	$\frac{1}{2}$	$\frac{1}{4}$	$\frac{3}{8}$	$\frac{1}{2}$
Longitudinal fillet welds											
A36	×	×	×	×	×	×					
A441			×	×	×	×	×	×	×		
A514			×	×	×	×	×	×	×	×	×
Transverse fillet welds											
A36			×								
A441			×			×					
A514			×			×			×		

electrodes on A441 steel, whose average tensile strength was 79 ksi, was only 8 percent less than that of the same electrode on A514 steel with an average tensile strength of 118 ksi. Conversely, the strength of $\frac{1}{4}$-in welds of E70 electrodes on A514 steel was only 2 percent greater than that of the same electrodes on A441 steel.

The 36 transverse-shear tests were made only on joints with $\frac{1}{4}$-in welds. It will be noted (Fig. 2-39) that weld strength is considerably greater in transverse shear. For example, the E110 electrode on A514 steel produced a weld which was $32/18.6 = 1.72$ times as strong when tested transverse to the load as it was in the direction of the load. Similarly, the E70 weld on A36 steel was $22.8/15 = 1.52$ times stronger transversely. Specification values for fillet welds and partial-penetration groove welds are based on the results for longitudinal welds.

The superior penetration of the submerged-arc fillet weld justifies a more liberal definition of the throat. Only the AISC specification makes such an allowance, however. It defines the throat thickness T_e as the leg size for $\frac{3}{8}$-in and smaller fillets, and 0.11 in more than the theoretical throat for larger welds.

AISC/ASD. Allowable stresses in welded connections are given in Table 2-21. Shear stress for complete-penetration groove welds, partial-penetration groove welds, fillet welds, and plug and slot welds is limited to 0.3 times the nominal tensile strength of the weld metal.

AISC/LRFD. Design strengths of welds are given in Table 2-22. The shear strength of complete-penetration groove welds, partial-penetration groove welds, fillet welds, and plug and slot welds is 0.6 times the nominal tensile strength of the weld metal. The resistance factor $\phi = 0.80$ for complete-penetration groove welds, while $\phi = 0.75$ for the other three cases.

AASHTO. Allowable stresses in this specification are more conservative than the AISC specifications. The allowable stress on fillet welds is $0.27F_u$, where F_u is the tensile strength of the electrode classification but not greater than the tensile strength of the connected part. For plug welds the allowable shear stress is 12,400 psi.

AREA. Allowable shear stresses on fillet welds in this specification are given as a function of the base material and the strength of the weld metal. They are

   A36. Electrode or electrode-flux combinations with:

60,000 psi tensile strength	16,500 psi
70,000 psi tensile strength	19,500 psi

but not to exceed 12,500 psi shear stress on base material.

   A441, A572, A588. Electrode or electrode-flux combinations with:

70,000 psi tensile strength	19,000 psi
80,000 psi tensile strength	22,000 psi

but not to exceed $0.35F_y$ shear stress on base material.

TABLE 2-21
AISC/ASD allowable stress on welds

Type of weld and stress	Allowable stress	Required weld strength
Complete penetration groove welds		
Tension normal to effective area	Same as base metal	Matching weld must be used
Compression normal to effective area	Same as base metal	
Tension or compression parallel to axis of weld	Same as base metal	Weld metal with a strength level equal to or less than matching weld metal may be used
Shear on effective area	0.30 × nominal tensile strength of weld metal (ksi)	
Partial-penetration groove welds		
Compression normal to effective area	Same as base metal	
Tension or compression parallel to axis of weld	Same as base metal	
Shear parallel to axis of weld	0.30 × nominal tensile strength of weld metal (ksi)	Weld metal with a strength level equal to or less than matching weld metal may be used
Tension normal to effective area	0.30 × nominal tensile strength of weld metal (ksi), except tensile stress on base metal shall not exceed 0.60 × yield strength of base metal	
Fillet welds		
Shear on effective area	0.30 × nominal tensile strength of weld metal (ksi)	Weld metal with a strength level equal to or less than matching weld metal may be used
Tension or compression parallel to axis of weld	Same as base metal	
Plug and slot welds		
Shear parallel to faying surfaces (on effective area)	0.30 × nominal tensile strength of weld metal (ksi)	Weld metal with a strength level equal to or less than matching weld metal may be used

Source: Adapted from 1989 AISC/LRFD Specification.

TABLE 2-22
AISC/LRFD design strength of welds

Type of weld and stress	Material	Resistance factor ϕ	Nominal strength F_{BM} or F_W	Required weld strength level
Complete-penetration groove welds				
Tension normal to effective area	Base	0.90	F_y	Matching weld must be used
Compression normal to effective area	Base	0.90	F_y	Weld metal with a strength level equal to or less than matching weld metal may be used
Tension or compression parallel to axis of weld	Base	0.90	F_y	
Shear on effective area	Base	0.90	$0.60F_y$	
	Weld electrode	0.80	$0.60F_{EXX}$	
Partial-penetration groove welds				
Compression normal to effective area	Base	0.90	F_y	Weld metal with a strength level equal to or less than matching weld metal may be used
Tension or compression parallel to axis of weld	Base	0.90	F_y	
Shear parallel to axis of weld	Base			
	Weld electrode	0.75	$0.60F_{EXX}$	
Tension normal to effective area	Base	0.90	F_y	
	Weld electrode	0.80	$0.60F_{EXX}$	
Fillet welds				
Stress on effective area	Base			Weld metal with a strength level equal to or less than matching weld metal may be used
	Weld electrode	0.75	$0.60F_{EXX}$	
Tension or compression parallel to axis of weld	Base	0.90	F_y	
Plug or slot welds				
Shear parallel to faying surfaces (on effective area)	Base			Weld metal with a strength level equal to or less than matching weld metal may be used
	Weld electrode	0.75	$0.60F_{EXX}$	

Example 2-13-1 (AISC/ASD). Design and detail the welded end connection required to transmit a dead-load force of 80 kips and a live-load force of 300 kips through two C10 × 30 to a 1-in gusset plate (Fig. 2-40). All material is A36. Welds are to be deposited manually using E60XX electrodes.

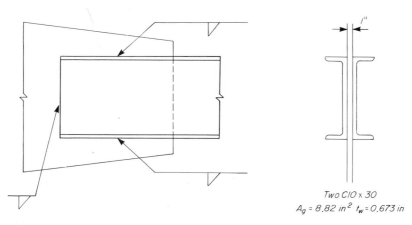

Two C10 × 30
$A_g = 8.82$ in^2 $t_w = 0.673$ in

FIGURE 2-40

Solution

$$\text{Design force} = DL + LL = 380 \text{ kips or } 190 \text{ kips per channel}$$

$$\text{Minimum weld size} = \tfrac{5}{16} \text{ in} \qquad \text{(Table 2-17)}$$

$$\text{Maximum weld size along web} = 0.673 - \tfrac{1}{16} = 0.610 \text{ in}$$

Use $\tfrac{5}{16}$-in weld, which requires only a single pass. The weld throat is

$$0.707 \times \tfrac{5}{16} = 0.221 \text{ in}$$

$$F_v = 0.3 \times F_{\text{EXX}} = 0.3 \times 60 = 18 \text{ ksi}$$

Therefore the capacity of 1 in of $\tfrac{5}{16}$-in weld is $q = 0.221 \times 18 = 3.98$ kips and the required length L is $190/3.98 = 47.8$ in. Use 10 in at the end of the channel and 19 in along each flange for a total of 48 in.

The shear capacity of the gusset plate must also be checked. The procedure for this check is discussed in Art. 3-4 and presented in Example 3-4-1 (AISC/ASD).

The length of the overlap of the channel can be reduced by using a larger weld, which can be accomplished in a variety of ways. For example, a $\tfrac{7}{16}$-in weld would require only 35.2 in of weld. Overlap could then be reduced to 13 in for a total of 36 in of fillet weld.

Example 2-13-2 (AISC/LRFD). Design and detail the welded end connection required to transmit a dead-load force of 80 kips and a live-load force of 300 kips through two C10 × 30 to a 1-in gusset plate (Fig. 2-40). All material is A36. Welds are to be deposited manually using E60XX electrodes.

Solution

Design force $= 1.2DL + 1.6LL$

$$= 1.2 \times 80 + 1.6 \times 300 = 576 \text{ kips or } 288 \text{ kips per channel}$$

Minimum weld size $= \frac{5}{16}$ in   (Table 2-17)

Maximum weld size along web $= 0.673 - \frac{1}{16} = 0.610$ in

Use $\frac{5}{16}$-in weld, which requires only a single pass. The weld throat is

$$0.707 \times \frac{5}{16} = 0.221 \text{ in}$$

$$F_v = 0.6 \times F_{\text{EXX}} = 0.6 \times 60 = 36 \text{ ksi}$$

$$\phi = 0.75$$

Therefore the capacity of 1 in of $\frac{5}{16}$-in weld is $q = 0.221 \times 0.75 \times 36 = 5.97$ kips and the required length L is $288/5.97 = 48.3$ in. Use 10 in at the end of the channel and $19\frac{1}{2}$ in along each flange for a total of 49 in.

The shear capacity of the gusset plate must also be checked. The procedure for this check is discussed in Art. 3-4 and presented in Example 3-4-2 (AISC/LRFD).

The length of the overlap of the channel can be reduced by using a larger weld, which can be accomplished in a variety of ways. For example, a $\frac{7}{16}$-in weld would require only 35.3 in of weld. Overlap could then be reduced to 13 in for a total of 36 in of fillet weld.

2-14   WELDING QUALITY CONTROL

The production of sound welds is governed by many factors. The type of joint, its preparation and fit-up, the root opening, etc., are important, as are the welding position, the welding current and voltage, the arc length, and the rate of travel. Accessibility for the welding operation is also important, as the quality of a weld is determined to a considerable degree by the position of the electrode. For a fillet weld, the electrode ordinarily should bisect the angle between the two legs of the weld. Furthermore, it must lean about 20° in the direction of travel. The joints in Fig. 2-41a and b emphasize the significance of inclination in the direction of travel. The welding procedure was identical for these two joints except that the electrode leaned about 45° in the direction of travel in Fig. 2-41a and 20° in Fig. 2-41b. The defective weld in Fig. 2-41a shows incomplete penetration, slag inclusion at the root, and a slight undercutting at the upper edge. This weld is also likely to be brittle.

The defective weld in Fig. 2-41c is shown to emphasize the importance of current. Too much current relative to the rate of travel of the electrode was used in producing these welds. The excessive penetration results in a weld with a large inner portion that cools more slowly than the rest. Shrinkage of the outer portion may cause cracking, as in the weld at the left. The pear-shaped weld at the right in Fig. 2-41d shows a similar crack.

The American Welding Society publishes weld qualification procedures. Procedure qualification deals with properties of the metals, type of groove and

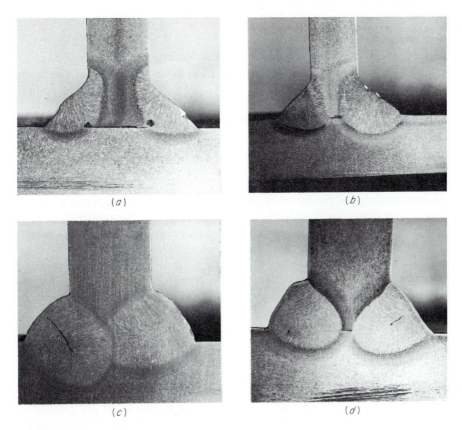

(a)

(b)

(c)

(d)

FIGURE 2-41
Effect of welding technique on quality of weld. (*State of California, Department of Public Works, Division of Highways.*)

position of welding, electrode type and size, current and voltage, and requirements for preheating the base metal. The operator must also be qualified by welding prescribed test specimens, which must demonstrate the required strength and ductility. However, qualification of the procedure and the operator are not enough to guarantee satisfactory welds, and inspection is important. In addition to visual inspection, nondestructive tests can be used to determine the types and distribution of weld defects.[12]

Magnetic-particle inspection (magnaflux) is based on inducing a strong magnetic field in a short section of ferromagnetic material. Poles develop where there are leakages in the field, which occur at discontinuities in the weld, and iron powder sprinkled on the test area migrates to the poles. The resulting pattern tends to outline the discontinuities.

In dye-penetrant inspection a dye is brushed or sprayed on the surface of the weld. It seeps into surface irregularities. A developer that is sprayed on is stained red by the dye, which rises from the surface defects by capillary action. A similar procedure is based on using a fluorescent liquid which detects surface imperfections upon exposure to black light.

Radiographic inspection uses shortwave radiations, such as x-rays or gamma rays, to discover surface and subsurface flaws in the weld. The beam encounters less resistance at a defect, and when the radiation is recorded on film, the defect is disclosed.

Ultrasonic inspection is also effective in locating subsurface weld defects as well as those on the surface. High-frequency sound waves sent through the area to be inspected are reflected by discontinuities and density differences. The reflected sound waves are monitored by a receiver, converted to electric energy, and displayed as visual patterns on an oscilloscope screen.

In interpreting the results of inspection of a weld, it is important to assess the severity of a defect as it relates to service requirements. Some defects may be relatively unimportant, while others may be critical in specific service situations.

2-15 FATIGUE

Fracture of metals is not always preceded by yielding and the subsequent elongation described in Art. 2-4. Instead, it may occur at stresses even less than the yield stress if a load is repeated a large number of times. This kind of failure is called *fatigue*. It is progressive in nature and is believed to begin with a dislocation or slip in the crystalline structure of the metal, followed by the development of a crack which gradually increases in size. Crack initiation is brittle, rather than ductile, and almost always occurs at a point of stress concentration such as a hole, weld, notch, or even a scratch. These stress raisers are usually on the surface, but they can also be internal, as at a defect in a weld. Because there is no plastic deformation of the material, fatigue cracks are hard to detect even on the surface of a member. They usually propagate very slowly and intermittently.

Fatigue failure of a laboratory specimen consisting of two plates joined by a groove weld is shown in Fig. 2-42. The specimen was tested in repeated tension in the longitudinal direction of the weld. Cracking began at an irregularity at the surface of the weld and propagated radially into the plate. This progressive cracking usually results in the "oystershell" or "beach" markings visible in the photograph.

Behavior under repeated load is evaluated in rotating-beam tests, flexure tests, and axial-load tests. In the rotating-beam test a round, polished specimen supported as a simple beam is rotated at constant speed while being subjected to a bending moment so that every fiber of the specimen alternates sinusoidally between tension and compression. A polished specimen is also used in the flexure test, but it is tested by bending in one plane. In the axial-load test, the specimen is subjected to alternating axial stress. Test data are plotted with the maximum stress S (*fatigue strength*) as ordinate and the number of cycles N to failure (*fatigue life*) as abscissa. The result is called an *S-N* curve. Figure 2-43 shows *S-N* curves for axially stressed polished specimens of A514 steel for three different conditions. Axially loaded specimens are subjected to stress cycles ranging from a

FIGURE 2-42
Typical fatigue fracture in a welded plate. (*Department of Civil Engineering, University of Illinois.*)

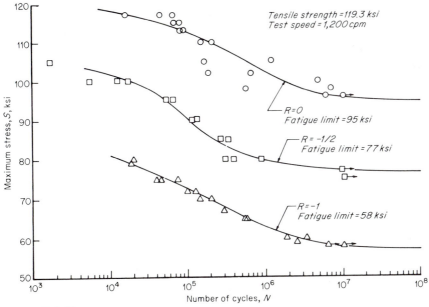

FIGURE 2-43
S-N diagrams for polished specimens of T1 steel in axial fatigue. (*From "USS Steel Design Manual,"* U.S. Steel Corporation, November 1968.)

minimum value to a maximum. R denotes the ratio of minimum to maximum stress. Thus, $R = 0$ (upper curve) denotes stress ranging from zero to tension; $R = -\frac{1}{2}$ (middle curve) denotes stress alternating between tension and compression equal to half the tension, etc. The total excursion from the minimum stress in the cycle to the maximum is called the range of stress. A positive value of R signifies a stress alternating between a lesser and a maximum tension. A negative value of R indicates a reversal of the sign of the stress during the fatigue cycle. The data in the figure are plotted with the maximum stress in the cycle as the ordinate. S-N curves tend to become horizontal at large values of N; the corresponding strength is called the *fatigue limit*. The fatigue limit is generally considered to correspond to a fatigue life of about 2 million cycles.

It will be noted that the fatigue limit for $R = -1$ in Fig. 2-43 is about one-half the tensile strength of the steel. Although this is a good approximation for polished specimens, severe stress concentrations and exposure to corrosion may produce drastic reductions, as in Fig. 2-44. This figure shows that these reductions can be so large as to make high-strength steels little, if any, better in fatigue than low-strength steels.

The data in Fig. 2-43 are presented in Fig. 2-45 in a form which is better adapted to design. This figure, called a *modified Goodman diagram*, is a variation of a diagram published by Goodman in 1899. Each curve is the locus of all the points corresponding to a given fatigue life, and the diagram covers the full range of stress ratios $-1 \le R \le 1$. Minimum stresses are plotted as abscissas and maximum stress as ordinate. Radial lines from the origin correspond to the various stress ratios. Since $R = 1$ denotes no reversal of stress, the ray $R = 1$ corresponds to static tension and all the curves for a given steel join at the intersection of $R = 1$ with the ordinate corresponding to the tensile strength of the steel.

Taking the yield stress as the limiting useful strength, it will be seen that the curves in Fig. 2-45 can be represented quite closely by the straight lines AB and

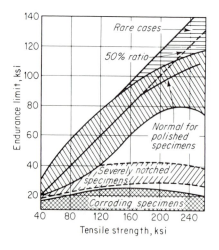

FIGURE 2-44

Relationship between fatigue limit and ultimate tensile strength of various steels. (*From Ref. 13.*)

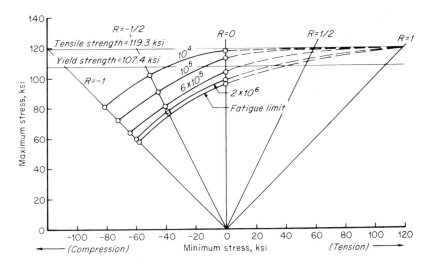

FIGURE 2-45
Modified Goodman diagram for specimens of Fig. 2-43. (*From "USS Steel Design Manual," U.S. Steel Corporation, November 1968.*)

BC of Fig. 2-46. This enables fatigue-design criteria to be put in the form of simple equations. Allowable-stress formulas are obtained by applying a factor of safety to *ABC* to get *DEF*. This factor of safety can be smaller than the factor of safety for static load because of the smaller probability of occurrence of the much larger number of cycles of service-load magnitude needed to cause a fatigue failure.

Specifications for fatigue loading prescribe an allowable *range of stress*, $F_{sr} = f_{max} - f_{min}$. These criteria are based on evaluations of extensive laboratory fatigue data. Data have been obtained on small specimens, specimens which simulate actual structural components, and on actual components. Most of these experiments are conducted under stress amplitudes of constant magnitude, but few structures are subjected to stress cycles of this type. Variations in the loading conditions over the life of a structure will produce stress cycles of varying magnitudes. Laboratory studies which employ variable-amplitude loading under controlled conditions have been conducted.

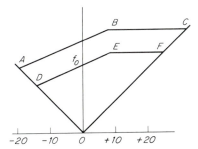

FIGURE 2-46

Specification provisions are presented in the AISC ASD and LRFD Manuals and in the AASHTO and AREA specifications for a variety of structural configurations and loading conditions. Some of these details are shown in Fig. 2-47. They are defined in a tabular format to assist the designer in the evaluation of specific details (Table 2-23). The table describes the various details and correlates them with the illustrative examples. It also states the kind of stress and defines the stress category (A, B, C, etc.). The allowable stress ranges for four loading conditions, based on the anticipated number of loading cycles, are given in Table 2-24.

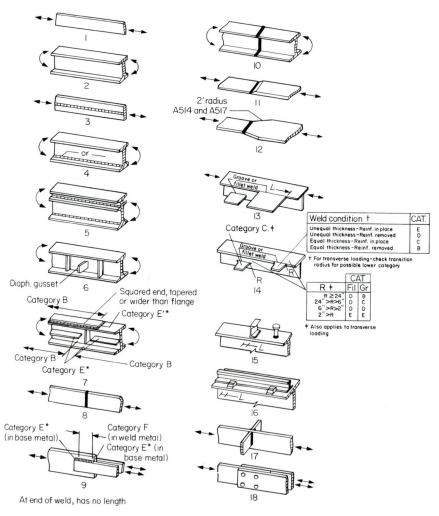

FIGURE 2-47
Fatigue examples.

TABLE 2-23
AASHTO fatigue categories

General condition	Situation	Kind of stress	Stress category	Illustrative example (Fig. 2-47)
Plain material	Base metal with rolled or cleaned surfaces; flame-cut edges with ASA smoothness of 1000 or less	T or Rev*	A	1, 2
Built-up members	Base metal and weld metal in members without attachments, built-up plates, or shapes connected by continuous full- or partial-penetration groove welds or by continuous fillet welds parallel to the direction of applied stress	T or Rev	B	3–5, 7
	Calculated flexural stress at toe of transverse stiffener welds on girder webs or flanges	T or Rev	C	6
	Base metal at end of partial-length welded cover plates having square or tapered ends, with or without welds across the ends (a) Flange thickness < 0.8 in (b) Flange thickness > 0.8 in	T or Rev T or Rev	E E'	7 7
Groove welds	Base metal and weld metal at full-penetration groove-welded splices of rolled and welded sections having similar profiles when welds are ground flush and weld soundness established by nondestructive inspection	T or Rev	B	8, 10, 14
	Base metal and weld metal in or adjacent to full-penetration groove-welded splices at transitions in width or thickness, with welds ground to provide slopes no steeper than 1 to $2\frac{1}{2}$, with grinding in the direction of applied stress, and weld soundness established by nondestructive inspection	T or Rev	B	11, 12
	Base metal and weld metal in or adjacent to full-penetration groove-welded splices, with or without transitions having slopes no greater than 1 to $2\frac{1}{2}$ when reinforcement is not removed and weld soundness is established by nondestructive inspection	T or Rev	C	8, 10–12, 14
	Base metal at details attached by groove welds subject to longitudinal loading when the detail length L parallel to the line of stress is between 2 in and 12 times the plate thickness but less than 4 in	T or Rev	D	13
	Base metal at details attached by groove welds subject to longitudinal loading when the detail length L is greater than 12 times the plate thickness or greater than 4 in long	T or Rev	E	13
Fillet†-welded connections	Base metal at intermittent fillet welds	T or Rev	E	

TABLE 2-23—(*continued*)

General condition	Situation	Kind of stress	Stress category	Illustrative example (Fig. 2-47)
	Base metal adjacent to fillet-welded attachments with length L in direction of stress less than 2 in and stud-type shear connectors	T or Rev	C	13, 15–17
	Base metal at details attached by fillet welds with detail length L in direction of stress between 2 in and 12 times the plate thickness but less than 4 in	T or Rev	D	13, 15, 16
	Base metal at attachment details with detail length L in direction of stress (length of fillet weld) greater than 12 times the plate thickness or greater than 4 in	T or Rev	E	7, 9, 13, 16

* T signifies range in tensile stress only; Rev signifies a range of stress involving both tension and compression during a stress cycle.

† Gusset plates attached to girder flanges with only transverse fillet welds, not recommended.

Source: AASHTO Standard Specifications for Highway Bridges.

It should be noted that fatigue is not often a factor in the design of buildings, except for crane runways and the like. For example 100,000 cycles of load correspond to 10 applications of maximum service load daily for 25 years, and buildings ordinarily do not experience such a pattern of load. On the other hand, it is obvious that bridges may well experience many more daily cycles of maximum service load.

The importance of details, such as splices and connections, must be appreciated in situations where fatigue is a factor. For example, the fatigue strength of a complete-penetration groove-welded butt splice in a tension member will usually be increased if the weld is ground flush with the surface of the connecting parts. This eliminates the stress concentrations that would arise in the as-welded condition.

The following suggestions should be kept in mind when designing structures subject to fatigue:[14]

1. Avoid details of design that produce severe stress concentrations of poor stress distribution.
2. Provide gradual changes in the section, and avoid reentrant, notchlike corners.
3. Avoid abrupt changes of section or stiffness in members or components.
4. Align parts to eliminate eccentricities or reduce them to a minimum.
5. Avoid making attachments on parts subjected to severe fatigue loadings.
6. Use continuous welds rather than intermittent welds.
7. Avoid details that introduce high, localized constraint.

TABLE 2-24
AASHTO allowable fatigue stress range

Category (see Table 2-23)	Allowable range of stress F_{sr}, ksi*			
	For 100,000 cycles	For 500,000 cycles	For 2,000,000 cycles	For over 2,000,000 cycles
Redundant load-path structures†				
A	60	36	24	24
B	45	27.5	18	16
C	32	19	13	10
				12‡
D	27	16	10	7
E	21	12.5	8	5
E′	16	9.4	5.8	2.6
Nonredundant load-path structures				
A	36	24	24	24
B	27.5	18	16	16
C	19	13	10	9
			12‡	11‡
D	16	10	7	5
E§	12.5	8	5	2.5

* The range of stress is defined as the algebraic difference between the maximum stress and the minimum stress. Tension stress is considered to have the opposite algebraic sign for compression stress.

† Structure types with multiload paths where a single fracture in a member cannot lead to collapse. For example, a simply supported single-span multibeam bridge or a multielement eye-bar truss member has redundant load paths.

‡ For transverse stiffener welds on girder webs or flanges.

§ Partial-length welded cover plates shall not be used on flanges more than 0.8 in thick for nonredundant load-path structures.

8. Provide suitable inspection to guarantee proper riveting, adequate clamping in high-strength bolts, and the deposition of sound welds.

9. Provide for suitable inspection during the fabrication and erection of structures.

10. When fatigue cracks are discovered, take immediate steps to prevent their propagation.

2-16 BRITTLE FRACTURE

Steel structures sometimes fail suddenly and without warning in the form of excessive deformation. These failures are often catastrophic in the sense that the structure is more or less completely destroyed. Fatigue failures develop over some time as a result of repeated cycles of loads of varying magnitude, usually all within the permissible load for the structure, but brittle fractures occur as a result of some critical combination of stress, temperature, flaw size, and toughness of the metal. Most brittle fractures occur under static load at stress levels which are not excessive, but they can result from a dynamic application of load or some overload.

One of the best-known brittle fractures occurred in Boston in a riveted steel tank 90 ft in diameter and 50 ft high which contained 2 million gal of molasses. The tank fractured in an explosive manner on January 15, 1919. The failure resulted in the death of 12 people from drowning in molasses or from other injuries. Forty people were injured, and several horses drowned. Damage to houses and a portion of the Boston Elevated Railway was extensive.

Similar sudden failures of steel water tanks, oil tanks, transmission lines, ships, plate-girder bridges, etc., have occurred. Historical surveys of failures can be found in Shank[15] and Parker.[16] Most of these failures occurred under normal service conditions, rather than overload, and originated at a point of concentration of stress such as a defect or a geometrical stress raiser. Furthermore, most of the structures were welded and failed at low temperatures.

There is little or no plastic deformation in advance of brittle fracture. In effect, this is another way of saying that the sliding on planes of maximum shear stress described in Art. 2-4, which is the source of the plastic deformation that precedes fracture, is somehow inhibited. This may happen because the material's resistance to sliding exceeds its resistance to separation (cleavage) or because sliding is prevented.

The relation between resistance to sliding and resistance to cleavage is not constant for a given material but depends on the speed of deformation and on the temperature. Resistance to sliding increases with increase in speed of deformation, while resistance to separation is affected to a smaller degree. Asphalt is a good example of sensitivity to strain rate; it may flow under its own weight over a long period of time, but it is brittle under suddenly applied forces. Again, both kinds of resistance increase with decrease in temperature, but in steel the difference between the two tends to become smaller and may finally disappear. Therefore, a material that may fail in a ductile manner at one temperature may fail in a brittle manner at a lower temperature.

Sliding in a ductile material may be inhibited by local geometry of the member, such as a hole or notch. For example, in a tensile test of a notched specimen, such as that shown in Fig. 2-48a, sliding that would ordinarily develop in the notched portion is restrained by the larger, lower-stressed portions on either side of the notch. The smaller the length d of the notch in relation to its depth and to the size of the specimen, the more the sliding is inhibited. This may increase resistance to sliding to the point where it exceeds resistance to separation so that the specimen fails in a brittle manner on the reduced area. An analogous situation may develop at a small notch in a plate, as in Fig. 2-48b. In this case, there are tensile stresses f_x in the region of the notch, distributed somewhat as shown by the curve abc, in addition to the tensile stresses f_y, which are distrib-

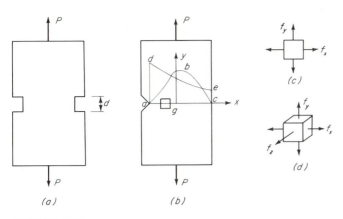

FIGURE 2-48

uted as shown by the curve *de*. Therefore, an element such as the one at *g* is in the biaxial state of stress shown in Fig. 2-48c. When the load *P* reaches the value at which yielding would normally begin at *a*, the necessary contraction, which must be largely in the direction of the thickness of the plate (*z* axis), is restrained by the adjacent less highly stressed portions, in a manner similar to the restraint in the specimen of Fig. 2-48a. As a consequence, sliding is inhibited, and a brittle fracture may initiate at point *a*. Once it begins, such a fracture propagates rapidly, and in mild steel it may travel at a speed of 4000 to 5000 fps at stress levels as low as 6 to 8 ksi (Ref. 17). The resulting fracture surface is granular in appearance, in contrast to the silky or fibrous appearance of a shear-failure surface, and usually has a herringbone or chevron appearance, with the apexes of the chevrons pointing toward the point of fracture initiation (Fig. 2-49).

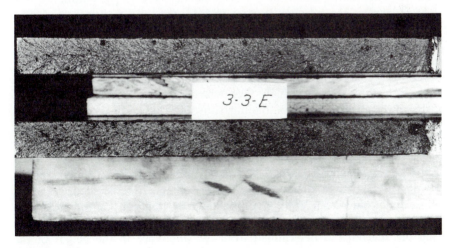

FIGURE 2-49
Brittle fracture of structural steel. (*Department of Civil Engineering, University of Illinois.*)

It will be noted that the restraint of contraction in Fig. 2-48b is accompanied by a tensile stress in the direction of the thickness of the plate, so an element in the interior of the plate near the notch is in the triaxial state of stress shown in Fig. 2-48d. Brittle fracture can also be explained in terms of this condition. Assuming $f_z \leq f_x \leq f_y$, the maximum shear stress is $(f_y - f_z)/2$, which acts on the section through the x axis that bisects the angle between the y and z axes. Therefore, if f_z approaches f_y in magnitude, the shear stress becomes very small, so fracture may be by cleavage rather than by sliding.

Although failures typical of brittle fracture have been traced back to 1879, the subject did not receive great attention until a large number of failures occurred in welded ships during World War II. As a result of investigations conducted at that time certain design changes were implemented. For welded ships these changes involved the use of crack arrestors, improved work quality, and restrictions on chemical composition of ship steels. Despite these improvements ship failures were reported in the early 1950s. Although the number of failures has been reduced, they continue to be reported. During the severe cold wave that swept through the midwest during the winter of 1977, several spectacular failures occurred in bridge structures in Illinois, Minnesota, and Pennsylvania. On January 22, 1988, several brittle failures occurred in a bridge in Providence, Rhode Island.

Control of brittle fractures as well as of fatigue failures has been improved by application of fracture mechanics, whose basic concepts were developed between 1946 and 1966. Modifications and extensions have continued to the present time.

Extensive research on brittle fracture has shown that service temperature, material toughness, constraint, residual stress, presence of flaws, etc., contribute to such failures. Many of these parameters have been studied using a variety of test specimens and testing conditions. These include the Charpy V-notch (CVN) impact test, drop-weight nil-ductility test (NDT), dynamic tear test, explosion bulge test, wide plate test, Battelle drop-weight tear test, and many others.

Fracture mechanics has shown that material toughness, crack size, and stress are the primary factors which determine the susceptibility to brittle fracture. Fracture mechanics principles provide a methodology to correlate material toughness with the stress and flaw size which would cause brittle fracture. Knowledge of the effect of speed of loading, shown in Figs. 2-50 and 2-51, permits extension of this methodology to various types of structures. Most of the structures of interest to the civil engineer are subjected to relatively slow loading conditions. A more detailed discussion is given by Barsom and Rolfe.[18]

The Charpy V-notch test (ASTM E23) is commonly used to evaluate the behavior of a metal as it is affected by an abrupt change in cross section. In this test, a rectangular bar with a V notch at midlength is simply supported as a beam and struck by a pendulum released from a fixed height. The energy absorbed in fracturing the specimen is determined from the difference in the height of the pendulum before release and the height to which it returns after impact. In the case of steel, it turns out that energy-absorbing capacity in the notched specimen

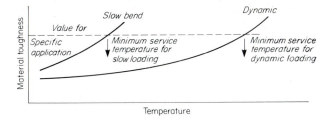

FIGURE 2-50
Schematic showing the effect of temperature and loading rate on material toughness. (*From S. T. Rolfe, Fracture and Fatigue Control in Steel Structures; AISC Eng. J., 1st quarter, 1977.*)

is not uniformly related to properties determined by the standard tension test. In other words, a steel that is ductile in the tension test might break in a brittle manner at a notch. Furthermore, the energy-absorbing capacity of a notched specimen may be drastically reduced at low temperatures. On the other hand, aluminum and many other nonferrous materials show consistent behavior; i.e., if they are ductile (or brittle) in the standard tension test, they are ductile (or brittle) in their notch behavior independently of temperature.

Variations in energy-absorbing capacity with temperature is determined from notched-specimen tests covering a range of temperatures. Figure 2-52 shows a typical plot of absorbed energy vs. temperature. There is a range of temperature in which fracture is largely by cleavage (separation), another in which it is largely by shear, and an intermediate zone of transition from one type of fracture to the other. The lower-temperature boundary of the transition zone is called the *ductility transition* and the higher-temperature boundary the *plastic-fracture transition*. The corresponding temperatures are called *transition temperatures*. A value

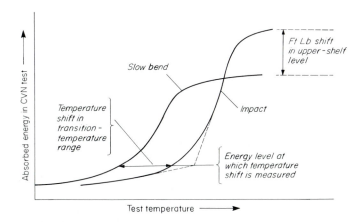

FIGURE 2-51
Schematic representation of shift in CVN transition temperature and upper-shelf level due to rate of loading. (*From S. T. Rolfe, Fracture and Fatigue Control in Steel Structures; AISC Eng. J., 1st quarter, 1977.*)

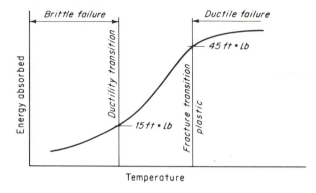

FIGURE 2-52
Transition from ductile to brittle behavior of mild structural steel.

of 15 ft·lb generally is used to define the lower transition temperature, and 45 ft·lb has sometimes been specified for the higher one.[17] The difference between the two is generally about 120°F. If the temperature is above the ductility-transition temperature, there will be appreciable plastic flow at the root of a notch before cracking begins.

Brittle-fracture behavior is affected by the chemistry of the steel. Small increases in carbon lower the energy-absorbing capacity and raise the transition temperature.[17] The size of the piece is also a factor. Thick plates have higher transition temperatures than thin plates, because they require less rolling than thin plates. They also cool more slowly. Residual stress (Art. 3-1) is another important factor. Most low-temperature low-stress brittle fractures have been in situations where there were large residual stresses, usually because of welding, in addition to notches. Cold work is also detrimental because of the resultant lowering of ductility.

Charpy V-notch 15 ft·lb transition temperatures are on the order of +30°F for A36 and A441 steels. On the other hand, A514 steel has a 15 ft·lb transition temperature of about −50°F. It is important to note that A36 and A441 steels have been used successfully and extensively in bridges, transmission towers, and other exposed structures in riveted, bolted, and welded construction throughout the continental United States with little or no history of brittle-fracture problems. Therefore, it is clear that a low 15 ft·lb transition temperature is not a necessary prerequisite to successful, low-temperature applications of these steels in these structures. Thus, the best guide to avoidance of brittle fracture is experience with structures and steels of various types. It must be kept in mind, however, that the lower the expected service temperatures, the more important it becomes to avoid conditions conducive to brittle fracture. In other words, an exposed structure is much more likely to tolerate poor detail geometry (notches, abrupt changes in section, etc.), weld flaws (inclusions, undercut, incomplete fusion, etc.), residual stresses, cold working during fabrication, etc., in a warm climate than in a cold one. Guides to protecting against brittle fracture in structures for which there is no adequate specification or experience are discussed in Ref. 17.

The AASHTO and AREA specifications contain provisions developed as a fracture-control program. Both specify special criteria for materials to be used in critical members. The AASHTO specification requires that material used in main load-carrying member components subjected to tensile stress satisfy supplemental impact properties. The AREA specification contains special requirements for materials, fabrication, welding, inspection, and testing for fracture-critical members in steel bridges. Fracture-critical members are defined as any tension member or component thereof whose failure would be expected to result in the collapse of the bridge or inability to perform its design function. Impact-test requirements in the form of Charpy V-notch results are prescribed for three different service temperatures.

2-17 CORROSION

Corrosion may be defined as the deterioration of a metal by chemical or electrochemical reaction with its environment. In its most familiar form it appears as rust on the surface of exposed steel structures and results in the gradual loss of metal. The natural consequence is a reduction of the cross section of the member and a resulting increase in stress in the remaining material. Protection is normally provided by painting the exposed structure. There are, however, other types of corrosion and other effects of corrosion, which are called direct attack, that may be more serious. The extent of direct attack depends on the solubility of the corrosion product. If the film of corrosive products adheres to the metal, it will isolate the metal from the corrosive agent and reduce the rate of corrosion, but in some cases the corrosive product may not adhere, so a protective layer is not maintained.

In the case of electrochemical attack, corrosion is accompanied by electric currents flowing through the metal. The situation is comparable to the action in a battery with spatially separated anodic and cathodic areas. Iron covered with mill scale can suffer severe attack at small interruptions in the scale when placed in salt water. The mill scale acts as the cathode, and the exposed iron at the discontinuity acts as the anode. In this case the attack is more intense because the anode is small compared to the cathode. The effect is concentrated at the small anode, and the attack can produce serious pitting at the breaks in the scale.

Corrosion in the presence of stress can produce failure called *stress-corrosion cracking*. If the crack size, stress, and temperature correspond to the conditions for brittle fracture discussed in Art. 2-16, failure may occur. The failure in 1967 of the Silver Bridge across the Ohio River, with the loss of 40 lives, has been attributed to this effect. That structure employed eyebars with large pin connections which were not accessible for inspection. A very small crack in one of the eyebars caused a fracture, resulting in subsequent failure of other eyebars as a result of overload and subsequent complete collapse of the structure.

Stainless steel is subject to a type of corrosion which progresses along the grain boundaries and results in a crack. Failure of a suspended ceiling over a swimming pool in Switzerland in 1985 resulted from this type of attack. The chlorine in the air above the pool produced corrosion of the stainless steel hangers supporting the suspended ceiling. Stainless steel is especially sensitive to this type of attack when halides are present in the corrosive environment.

Reference 19 contains a comprehensive discussion of corrosion for a wide range of materials.

REFERENCES

1. Chajes, A., S. J. Britvec, and G. Winter: Effects of Cold-Straining on Structural Steel Sheets, *J. Struct. Div. ASCE*, April 1963.
2. Julian, O. G.: Synopsis of First Progress Report of Committee on Factors of Safety, *J. Struct. Div. ASCE*, July 1957.
3. Galambos, T. V., and M. K. Ravindra, Properties of Steel for Use in LRFD, *ASCE, Jour. of Struc. Div.*, vol. 104, No. ST9, September 1978.
4. Stout, R. D.: "Weldability of Steels," 4th ed., American Welding Society, Miami, 1987.
5. Manual of Steel Construction, Allowable Stress Design, 9th ed., American Institute of Steel Construction, Chicago, 1989.
6. Manual of Steel Construction, Load and Resistance Factor Design, American Institute of Steel Construction, Chicago, 1986.
7. Research Council on Structural Connections: Specification for Structural Joints Using ASTM A325 or A490 Bolts, 1988.
8. Kulak, G. L., Fisher, J. W., and Struik, J. H. A.: "Guide to Design Criteria for Bolted and Riveted Joints," 2nd ed., Wiley, New York, 1987.
9. "Specifications for Aluminum Structures," The Aluminum Association, Washington, D.C., April 1982.
10. "Standard Welding Symbols," American Welding Society, Miami, 1968.
11. Higgins, T. R., and F. R. Preece: Proposed Working Stresses for Fillet Welds in Building Construction, *Weld. J.*, October 1968.
12. "Structural Welding Code-Steel," American Welding Society, Miami, 1988.
13. Battelle Memorial Institute: "Prevention of Failure of Metals under Repeated Stress," Wiley, New York, 1946.
14. Designing and Making Welded Structural Steel Members for Cyclic Loading, Welding Research Council Committee on Fatigue of Welded Joints, *Weld. J.*, vol. 38, August 1954.
15. Shank, M. E.: A Critical Review of Brittle Failure in Carbon Steel Structures Other Than Ships, Ship Structure Committee Report, Serial No. SSC-65, National Academy of Sciences, National Research Council, Washington, D.C., December 1953.
16. Parker, E. R.: "Brittle Behavior of Engineering Structures," Wiley, New York, 1957.
17. Munse, W. H.: Fatigue and Brittle Fracture, sec. 4 in E. H. Gaylord and C. N. Gaylord (eds.), "Structural Engineering Handbook," 3d ed., McGraw-Hill, New York, 1990.
18. Barsom, J. M., and Rolfe, S. T.: "Fracture and Fatigue Control in Structures," 2d ed., Prentice-Hall, Englewood Cliffs, N.J., 1987.
19. "Corrosion," vol. 13: "Metals Handbook": American Society for Metals International, Metals Park, OH, 1987.

CHAPTER

3

TENSION MEMBERS

3-1 EFFECT OF RESIDUAL STRESSES

Tension members are efficient carriers of load and are used in many types of structures. In general, their response to load is much the same as that of the tensile-test coupon used to determine the basic material properties, but it is not identical. The stress-strain curves shown in Fig. 2-18 are typical of coupon results. Member behavior may differ from coupon behavior for various reasons, such as slip in bolted and riveted connections, nonlinear behavior of the connections, and residual stresses in the member. Residual stresses result principally from nonuniform cooling of hot-rolled or welded shapes and from cold straightening of bent members.

The rolled I or H shape will be used to explain the manner in which stresses arise from nonuniform cooling after rolling (Fig. 3-1a). Because they have more surface exposure per unit of volume, the flange tips tend to cool faster than the flange-to-web junctures. Similarly, the central portion of the web tends to cool faster than the junctures. Therefore, the metal at the junctures continues to contract as it cools after the flange tips and web interior have cooled to the temperature of the surrounding atmosphere. This contraction is partially restrained by the cooler metal, so tensile stresses develop in the regions of the junctures and

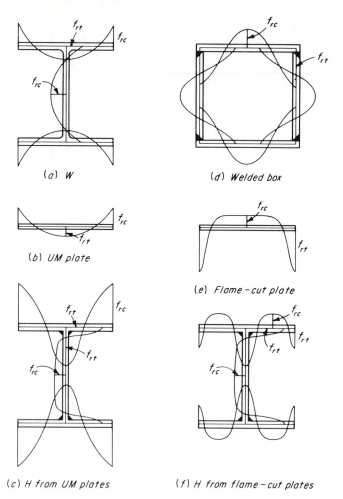

(a) W

(d) Welded box

(b) UM plate

(e) Flame – cut plate

(c) H from UM plates

(f) H from flame – cut plates

FIGURE 3-1
Thermal residual stresses.

compressive stresses in the remainder of the cross section. These stresses are called *residual* stresses. Figure 3-1a shows a typical distribution of residual stress in a standard W shape. These stresses also vary across the thickness, so the pattern shown represents averages of the across-thickness values. Variation across the thickness is discussed in Art. 4-7 (see Fig. 4-18).

Both magnitude and distribution of thermal residual stress are influenced to a considerable degree by the geometry of the cross section. Thus, in one investigation of W sections, the flange-tip stress f_{rc} of Fig. 3-1a varied from 4.1 to 18.7 ksi, the average being 12.8 ksi (Ref. 1). The residual stress at the center of the web varied even more, ranging from 41 ksi compression to 18.2 ksi tension. This means that some W's developed residual tension over the entire web, instead of the pattern shown in Fig. 3-1*a*. Only one of the 20 cross sections in this investigation was thicker than 1 in, and since residual stresses tend to increase in magnitude with increase in thickness, these values are not representative of W's with thick flanges and webs.

Because of the high concentration of heat, tensile residual stresses at the weld in welded members usually equal the yield strength of the weld metal itself, which may be as much as 50 percent higher than that of the parent metal. Residual stresses in welded shapes are determined by the section geometry and the method of preparation of the components. Thus, a welded H may be fabricated from universal-mill (rolled edge) plates or from plates flame-cut to width. The residual stress in the universal-mill plate is distributed as shown in Fig. 3-1*b*, where the magnitudes depend on both width and thickness and where f_{rc}, the residual stress in compression, may vary from as little as 4 or 5 ksi (for relatively thin plates) to as much as F_y for very thick plates, and f_{rt}, the residual stress in tension, from 2 or 3 to 15 or 16 ksi. The residual-stress distribution in a welded H composed of such plates will be about as shown in Fig. 3-1*c*. Cooling after welding increases both the residual tension and the residual compression in the flange plate. In the case of the flame-cut plate, cooling after cutting leaves a residual-stress distribution such as that shown in Fig. 3-1*e*, where f_{rt} may equal F_y. The residual-stress distribution in a welded H formed from such plates will approximate that shown in Fig. 3-1*f*.

Large residual tensions develop at the corners of the welded box (Fig. 3-1*d*). On the other hand, residual stresses in the hot-rolled square box are very low and in one investigation averaged less than 5 ksi.

Because they are quenched and tempered, A514 rolled steel shapes are partially stress-relieved, so residual stresses are small. In one investigation of A514 W shapes the maximum residual stress was about 7 ksi, except for one flange tip where it reached about 10 ksi.

Thermal residual stresses extend almost the full length of a member. Of course, they must vanish at the ends. However, they build up quite rapidly, so they attain the values indicated in Fig. 3-1 at relatively short distances from the ends.

Fabricating operations such as cambering and straightening by cold bending also induce residual stresses. These stresses are superimposed on the thermal residual stresses. They are of about the same magnitude as thermal residual stresses but differ in distribution. If the member is straightened by rotorizing, which is a continuous straightening procedure, the residual-stress distribution will be changed along the entire length of the member. If it is straightened by gagging, which concentrates the straightening at a few points, thermal residual stresses may remain essentially unchanged over much of the length.

The effect of residual stress on the behavior of a tension member can be demonstrated by considering the idealized (webless) H shown in Fig. 3-2*b*. The residual-stress distribution has also been idealized as linear to simplify the discussion. The stress-strain curve for the steel is shown in *a*, the assumed residual-stress pattern in *c*, and the corresponding residual-strain pattern in *d*. The $\int f\,dA$

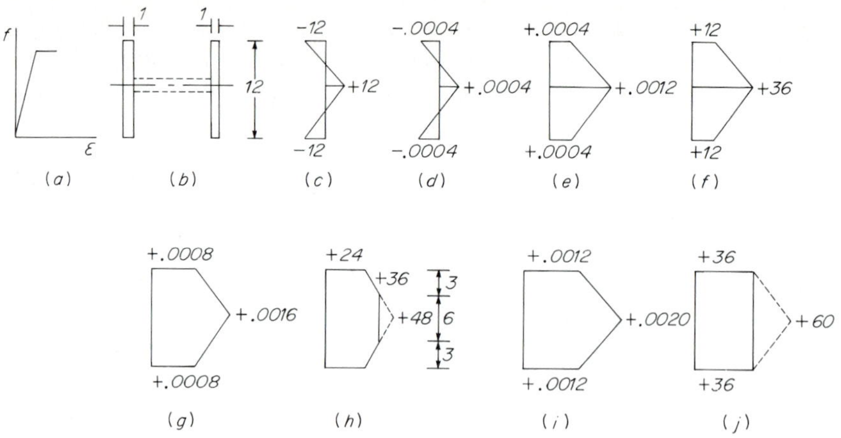

FIGURE 3-2

over the cross section reveals that the resultant P is zero, as it must, since the internal residual stresses are in equilibrium. If the member is subjected to a gradually increasing uniform tensile strain, all fibers will remain elastic for a strain of 0.0008. The strain distribution when a strain of 0.0008 has been applied is shown in e and the corresponding stress distribution in f. The load is $P = 2(24 \times 12 \times 1) = 576$ kips, and the average stress on the cross section is $f = \frac{576}{24} = 24$ ksi. This gives point A on the stress-strain curve for the member (Fig. 3-3).

If the strain is increased by an additional 0.0004, the resulting strain distribution will be as shown in Fig. 3-2g. The stress distribution is shown in h, where each flange is yielded over a length of 6 in. The load is

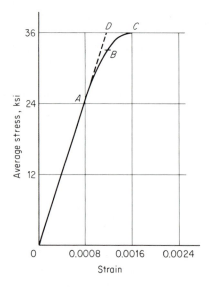

FIGURE 3-3

$P = 2 \times 36 \times 6 \times 1 + 30 \times 6 \times 1 = 792$ kips, and the average stress on the cross section is $f = \frac{792}{24} = 33$ ksi. This gives point B in Fig. 3-3. If an additional strain of 0.0004 is applied, the resulting strain and stress distribution are as shown in i and j. The entire flange cross section is now fully yielded, and the average stress is 36 ksi. This gives point C in Fig. 3-3. Further straining produces no increase in stress until the metal at the juncture of the flange and web begins to strain-harden.

If this member were free of residual stress, the stress-strain curve in the elastic region would be OAD. Thus, although the residual stresses do not affect the yield strength of the member, they do lower the proportional limit (point A) and increase the strain at initiation of overall yielding. However, they are of no consequence in regard to the static strength of the member. (They can be important if fatigue is involved.) On the other hand, residual stresses have a pronounced effect on the strength of columns (Arts. 4-6 and 4-7).

Additional discussion of residual stresses is presented in Art. 3-19.

3-2 TYPES OF TENSION MEMBERS

The form of a tension member is governed to a large extent by the type of structure of which it is a part and by the method of joining it to connecting portions of the structure. Some of the more common types are described in the following paragraphs.

The simplest tension members are made of wire rope or cable, round and square bars, and rectangular bars or plate. Wire rope is used for guy wires, floor suspenders in suspension bridges, hoisting lines, etc. Bridge strand (Art. 2-6) is used for small suspension bridges, suspended roofs, and similar structures. Rope and cable are attached to other members or to anchorages by various kinds of sockets. Main cables of large suspension bridges consist of parallel wires which are strung individually, squeezed together, and wrapped.

Rods and bars are used principally in bracing systems, as in towers and sag rods for purlins in sloping roofs. Round bars may be threaded at the ends and held in place by nuts. Standard clevises are available to fit threaded ends so that the bar can be pin-connected. The end of an unthreaded bar can be bent back along itself and welded to form a loop for a pin connection. Loop rods and rods with clevises are usually made in two sections joined with a turnbuckle which is adjusted to tighten the member in place. Standard dimensions and details of plain and upset rods, loop rods, and clevises are tabulated in the AISC Manuals.

Eyebars are members of rectangular cross section with enlarged heads at each end which are bored for pin connections. They were used extensively in early bridge trusses and are still used occasionally as hangers.

Single shapes, such as an angle, the plate, the W and S shapes, and the tee, may be used as tension members. However, two or more shapes are often combined to form a "built-up" member, of which some of the more common are shown in Fig. 3-4. In this figure, shapes which extend full length are shown in solid lines, while intermittent connections whose function is to hold the shapes in

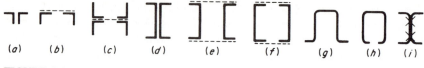

(a)   (b)   (c)   (d)   (e)   (f)   (g)   (h)   (i)

FIGURE 3-4

line are shown in dashed lines. In welded structures, connections to adjoining members can usually be made directly by butting or lapping, while in riveted or bolted structures the connection must usually be made to a plate called a *gusset plate*. A single plate at each joint is sufficient for the lighter roof trusses (single-plane truss), but two parallel gusset plates are required in bridge trusses and large roof trusses (double-plane truss).

Single-angle members are used extensively in towers. Single-angle and double-angle members are common in roof trusses. Single angles, and double angles as in Fig. 3-4a, may be riveted or bolted to a single gusset plate at each end, or they may be welded directly to the webs or flanges of tee or I chord members. Two-angle members as in Fig. 3-4b usually require two gusset plates— one at each outstanding leg—although occasionally the other two legs may be connected to a single gusset plate. The four-angle section c usually connects to two gusset plates. Two channels may be arranged as in Fig. 3-4d to connect to a single gusset plate which fits between the webs or as in Fig. 3-4e to connect to a gusset plate at each web. Two channels may also have their flanges turned inward, as in Fig. 3-4f. Various shapes may be made up of plates welded together. For example, three plates welded in the form of an I are often used in trusses, and two plates in the form of an angle have been used for transmission towers.

Aluminum shapes are produced in the same forms as steel and, by extrusion, in some different forms (Art. 2-6). Cold-formed steel tension members may be of angle, channel, or other shape. The cross sections shown in Fig. 3-4g and h are used as chord members in trusses. Cold-formed shapes can also be built-up, as in i, which shows two channels spot-welded together to form an I.

3-3 DESIGN STRESSES FOR BASE MATERIAL

Tension members are simple in principle, and their design is usually based on the assumption that stress is distributed uniformly over the cross section. Except for a few simple forms of member, however, this condition can be realized only if the member has no abrupt changes in cross section and is fully groove-welded to rigid connecting parts at each end.

Two hazards must be considered in establishing margins of safety: (1) excessive elongation at service loads and (2) fracture. Except for unusual situations, elongations less than those at the beginning of yield are tolerable. For example, an A36-steel tension member 10 ft long which is stressed just short of the yield point elongates 120(36/30,000) = 0.144 in. However, the elongation *after* yielding may be as much as 12 times the initial-yield value (1.8 in, say) before strain hardening begins. Obviously, then, there must be a margin of safety with respect to yielding at service loads. On the other hand, this margin of safety need not be as large as the margin with respect to fracture of the member because of the possible differences in the consequences.

Although the stress is assumed to be uniformly distributed on the member cross section, there will usually be nonuniform distributions at and near the ends where it is connected to another member or to gusset plates. There are no provisions in the AASHTO and AREA specifications to account for this effect.

In the AISC specifications, stress at yielding of the member is assumed to be uniformly distributed over the gross area A_g, that is, $P = F_y A_g$, while the ultimate stress F_u at fracture of the member is assumed to be uniformly distributed over an *effective* area A_e, that is, $P = F_u A_e$. The effective area for bolted and riveted connections is given by

$$A_e = U A_n \qquad (3\text{-}1a)$$

and for welded connections by

$$A_e = U A_g \qquad (3\text{-}1b)$$

where U = reduction coefficient
A_n = net area (Art. 3-6)
A_g = gross area

Values of U, described somewhat differently here than in the specifications, are as follows.

a. For W, M, or S shapes with flange widths not less than two-thirds the depth and structural tees cut from them, connected by the flanges, and for bolted and riveted connections with at least three fasteners per line in the direction of the stress, $U = 0.90$.

b. For W, M, or S shapes not meeting the conditions specified in a, for structural tees cut from them, and for all other shapes including built-up sections, and for bolted and riveted connections with at least three fasteners per line in the direction of the stress, $U = 0.85$.

c. For all members with bolted or riveted connections with only two fasteners per line in the direction of stress, $U = 0.75$.

d. If all the elements of a member cross section are connected, $U = 1$.

If the load is transmitted by transverse welds to only some of the cross-sectional elements, A_e is taken to be the area of the directly connected elements. The AISC specifications also contain a clause which requires the center of gravity of groups of welds or bolts at the end of any axial-force member to coincide with the center of gravity of the member unless the eccentricity is taken into account, but which excepts statically loaded single angles, double angles, and similar members from the requirement. The exception is based on the fact that this has been the practice for bolted and riveted connections for many years, and that tests show that it applies to welded connections as well.

Both AISC and AASHTO specify requirements based on both F_y and F_u. In AISC/ASD the allowable stress F_t is $0.6F_y$ on the gross area and $0.5F_u$ on the effective net area. AISC/LRFD specifies a design strength $\phi_t P_n$, which for yielding of the gross section is

$$\phi_t P_n = \phi_t F_y A_g = 0.9 F_y A_g \qquad (3\text{-}2a)$$

and for fracture of the net section is

$$\phi_t P_n = \phi_t F_u A_e = 0.75 F_u A_e \qquad (3\text{-}2b)$$

where P_n = nominal axial strength and ϕ_t = resistance factor for tension. For members without holes, fully connected by welds, A_e is the smaller of the gross area of the member and the effective area of the welds.

For members with no holes for high-strength bolts or rivets the allowable stresses according to the AASHTO specification are $0.55F_y$ for A36, A572 Grade 50, and A588, and $0.46F_u$ for A514 and A517. In members with holes for high-strength bolts or rivets two criteria apply to A36, A572 Grade 50, and A588: $0.55F_y$ on the gross section and $0.50F_u$ on the net section. Such members fabricated from A514 and A517 are designed on the basis of $0.46F_u$ on the net section. The AREA specifies only $0.55F_y$ on the net section. However, only 36 and 50 ksi materials are applicable under this specification, and for them $0.55F_y$ is always less than $0.46F_u$.

Factors of safety for structural members of aluminum are suggested in Ref. 2. For buildings and similar structures comparable to those to which the AISC specifications apply, the factors of safety are 1.65 on yield strength and 1.95 on tensile strength. For bridge structures, the recommended factors of safety are 1.85 on yield strength and 2.2 on tensile strength.

3-4 MEMBER CONNECTIONS

The proportioning of tension members with welded connections is relatively simple. Welded joints were discussed in Art. 2-11. For butt-welded connections deposited with matching electrode the deposited weld metal is at least as strong as the base metal, so no calculations for the weldment are needed. To allow for the case where a member may have excess cross-sectional area, the AISC specifications allow partial-penetration welds. For this case, of course, the capacity of the weldment need only equal, or exceed, the member design load.

The principal problem in welded connections is in deciding what form or forms of member are best-suited and how the connections can be arranged to assure good welding position. In general, welds should be distributed in such a manner that the center of gravity of the resisting forces coincides with the center of gravity of the member. Computations to determine the required welds and their arrangement for concentricity are usually simple. For symmetrical members concentricity is easily achieved by distributing the required welds symmetrically. In the case of an I-shaped member connected to gusset plates or to another member by welds on the flanges, it is only necessary to divide the required length of weld equally along the four flange tips.

The design of tension members with bolted or riveted connections is more complicated than that of members with welded connections because of the loss of cross section due to the holes for the fasteners. There may be several net sections on which fracture may occur, and the problem is to make sure that the critical section has been found (Art. 3-9).

Connecting elements (gusset plates, splice plates, etc.) may determine the usable strength of a tension member. In Fig. 3-5a the gusset plate may fail in tension on the net area of section *a-a*, and in Fig. 3-5c by tension on the gross area of section *a-a*. The angle member in Fig. 3-5a may also separate from the gusset plate by shear on the net area 1-2 combined with tension on the net area 2-2, as shown in Fig. 3-5b. A similar fracture of the welded connection of Fig. 3-5c is shown in Fig. 3-5d. Fracture of a gusset plate for a double-angle member,

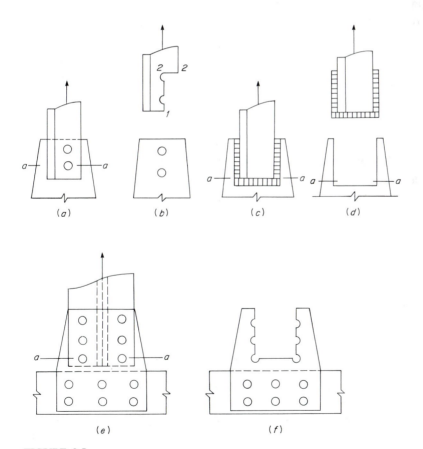

FIGURE 3-5

or of one of the gusset plates for a W shape (Fig. 3-5e), is shown in Fig. 3-5f. The gusset plate in Fig. 3-5d may also fail on the net section a-a. The failures shown in Fig. 3-5b, d, and f are called *block-shear* failures.

AISC/ASD. Connecting-element allowable stresses where failure may be by shear on a plane through the fasteners, or by a combination of such a shear with tension on a perpendicular plane, are the following (sec. J5.2).
  On the net shear area,

$$F_v = 0.30F_u \tag{3-3a}$$

and on the net tension area,

$$F_t = 0.50F_u \tag{3-3b}$$

Allowable block shear is the sum of the total shear on the net shear area and the total tension on the net tension area. The specification also requires the net failure path on the periphery of welded connections to be checked. Hardash and Bjorhovde[3] have shown that this evaluation of block shear is conservative and that the AISC/LRFD evaluation [Eqs. (3-6)] is in better agreement with available test results.

AISC/LRFD. For connecting elements statically loaded in tension (for example, section a-a of Fig. 3-5a) the design strengths ϕR_n are the following (sec. J5.2).
  For yielding on the gross section,

$$\phi R_n = \phi A_g F_y = 0.9 A_g F_y \tag{3-4a}$$

and for fracture of the net section,

$$\phi R_n = \phi A_n F_u = 0.75 A_n F_u \tag{3-4b}$$

where A_g = gross area of connecting element
  A_n = net area of connecting element, but not to be taken larger than $0.85 A_g$

Equations (3-4) are the same as Eqs. (3-2) for $\phi_t P_n$ except for the limiting value of the net area. The reason for the limiting value is discussed in Art. 3-6.
  If the design of a connecting element involves shear on the element, the design strength ϕR_n is given by

$$\phi R_n = \phi(0.7 A_g F_y) = 0.80 \times 0.7 A_g F_y \tag{3-5}$$

  If block shear is involved, the specification states (sec. J5.2) that the resistance is to be taken as the sum of the shear resistance on the shear-failure path, or paths, and the tensile resistance on the perpendicular path. Furthermore, when the resistance of a section is taken to be its *ultimate* strength in shear (or tension) on the *net* section, the resistance of the perpendicular section is taken to be the *yield* strength in tension (or shear) on the *gross* section, with $\phi = 0.75$ for both.

This leads to the following formulas for the design strength ϕR_n:

$$\phi R_n = \begin{cases} 0.75(0.6F_y A_{gv} + F_u A_{nt}) & \text{(3-6a)} \\ 0.75(0.6F_u A_{nv} + F_y A_{gt}) & \text{(3-6b)} \end{cases}$$

where A_{gv} = gross area in shear
A_{gt} = gross area in tension
A_{nv} = net area in shear
A_{nt} = net area in tension

The factor $0.6F_y$ in Eq. (3-6a) is a rounded value of the yield stress in shear according to the maximum-strain-energy theory, namely, $F_y/\sqrt{3} = 0.577F_y$. The ultimate shear stress is assumed in Eq. (3-6b) to be $F_u/\sqrt{3} \approx 0.6F_u$.

Only one of Eqs. (3-6) applies to a given connection, namely, the one in which the fracture term is larger than the yield term. This is explained by noting that, as the tensile-force area 2-2 in Fig. 3-5b approaches zero, Eq. (3-6a) would indicate failure by shear yielding on the gross area 1-2 rather than on shear fracture of the net section as it should. Therefore, Eq. (3-6b) applies for this case. A similar argument shows that for a connection such as Fig. 3-5e with, say, a single row of fasteners perpendicular to the member force, Eq. (3-6a) would apply. Thus the correct formula in a given situation is that one in which the fracture term is larger than the yield term. If the fracture plane is not readily identified, the correct value can be determined by using both equations and choosing the *larger* value of R.

No net areas are involved in the block-shear failure of the welded connection of Fig. 3-5c. Therefore, in applying Eq. (3-6a) to this case the second term should be $F_u A_{gt}$ and the first term in Eq. (3-6b) should be $0.6F_u A_{gv}$.

Example 3-4-1 (AISC/ASD). Design an A36-steel double-angle tension member 15 ft long to transmit 40 kips dead load and 110 kips live load. Connection to a gusset plate is by fillet welds deposited with E70XX electrodes.

Solution. Allowable stresses are $0.6F_y = 0.6 \times 36 \approx 22$ ksi on the gross area and $0.5F_u = 0.5 \times 58 = 29$ ksi on the effective net area. Since the connection is welded, the net area equals the gross area. The value of U is 0.85 for this connection, so $A_e = 0.85A_g$. Therefore,

$$T = 22 \times A_g$$

$$T = 29 \times 0.85A_g = 24.65 \times A_g$$

The smaller of the allowables determines the required gross area.

$$\text{Load per angle} = \frac{40 + 110}{2} = 75 \text{ kips}$$

$$A_g = \tfrac{75}{22} = 3.41 \text{ in}^2$$

For a $5 \times 3\frac{1}{2} \times \frac{7}{16}$ angle, $A = 3.53$ in². Use two angles with long legs back to back (Fig. 3-6).

From tables in the AISC Manual, $r_x = 1.59$ in and, with a $\frac{3}{8}$-in gusset plate, $r_y = 1.47$ in.

$$\frac{L}{r} = \frac{15 \times 12}{1.47} = 123 \le 300 \qquad \text{(The specification preferred upper limit is 300.)}$$

Use E70XX $\frac{5}{16}$-in welds, for which the allowable shear is $21 \times 0.707 \times \frac{5}{16} = 4.64$ kips/in. The required length of weld is $75/4.64 = 16.2$ in per angle. If the angle is welded at the heel (weld L_1 in Fig. 3-6) and at the toe (weld L_2), the required lengths for concentricity with the center of gravity of the member can be determined by taking moments. For weld L_2, with moments about the heel,

$$5 \times 4.64 L_2 = 1.63 T = 1.63 \times 16.2 \times 4.64$$

$$L_2 = 5.28 \text{ in}$$

Subtraction gives the length of weld along the heel:

$$L_1 = 16.2 - 5.3 = 10.9 \text{ in}$$

If each angle is also welded along its end with a $\frac{5}{16}$-in weld, each of these lengths may be reduced by half the length of the weld at the end. This is proved by taking the moment about the heel:

$$4.64 \times 5 L_2 = 4.64 \times 16.2 \times 1.63 - 4.64 \times 5 \times 2.5$$

$$L_2 = 5.3 - 2.5 = 2.8 \text{ in}$$

Thus, the connection may be made concentric with $L_1 = 8.4$ in, $L_2 = 2.8$ in, and 5 in of weld at the end, or with $L_1 = 10.9$ in, $L_2 = 5.3$ in, and no weld at the end.

Gusset plate. To prevent yield or rupture on section a-a of Fig. 3-6, the area on this section must equal the area of the angles if the gusset plate is of the same steel. For example, if the width on section a-a is 10 in, the required gusset-plate thickness t_g is $2 \times 3.53/10 = 0.706$ in.

Shear stress in the gusset plate along the welds must be checked. The allowable shear is $F_v = 0.4 F_y = 0.4 \times 36 = 14.4$ ksi. Two welds transfer the shear along L_1 and L_2. Equating the gusset-plate shear per inch to the weld shear per inch gives

$$1 \times 14.4 t_g = 1 \times 4.64 \times 2$$

$$t_g = 0.64 \text{ in}$$

The required thickness to prevent a block-shear failure (Fig. 3-5d) is found by

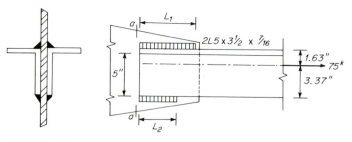

FIGURE 3-6

equating the member load to the sum of the tension on the gusset-plate section adjacent to the transverse weld and the shears on the sections adjacent to the longitudinal welds. The allowable shear is $F_v = 0.3F_u = 0.3 \times 58 = 17.4$ ksi (Eq. 3-3a), which is greater than the allowable shear 14.4 ksi in the calculation above. Therefore, block shear need not be checked.

Based on the two computed values of t_g, 0.64 and 0.706 in, use a $\frac{3}{4}$-in gusset plate.

Example 3-4-2 (AISC/LRFD). Design an A36-steel double-angle tension member 15 ft long to transmit 40 kips dead load and 110 kips live load. Connection to a gusset plate is by fillet welds deposited with E70XX electrodes.

Solution. The factored load is $1.2DL + 1.6LL = 1.2 \times 40 + 1.6 \times 110 = 224$ kips. For members of this type $U = 0.85$, so $A_e = 0.85A_g$. From Eqs. (3-2):

$$0.90 \times 36A_g = 224$$

$$A_g = 6.91 \text{ in}^2 = 3.46 \text{ in}^2 \text{ per angle}$$

$$0.75 \times 58 \times 0.85A_g = 224$$

$$A_e = 6.04 \text{ in}^2 = 3.02 \text{ in}^2 \text{ per angle}$$

For a $5 \times 3\frac{1}{2} \times \frac{7}{16}$ angle, $A = 3.53$ in^2. Use two angles with long legs back to back (Fig. 3-6).

From tables in the AISC Manual, $r_x = 1.59$ in and, with a $\frac{3}{8}$-in gusset plate, $r_y = 1.47$ in.

$$\frac{L}{r} = \frac{15 \times 12}{1.47} = 123 \le 300 \qquad \text{(The specification preferred upper limit is 300.)}$$

Use E70XX $\frac{5}{16}$-in welds, for which the design strength is ϕF_w, where $\phi = 0.75$ and $F_w = 0.6F_{EXX}$ (Table 2-22). The design strength of 1 in of weld is

$$0.75 \times 0.6 \times 70 \times 0.707 \times \tfrac{5}{16} = 6.96 \text{ kips/in}$$

The required length of weld is $(\frac{224}{2})/6.96 = 16.1$ in per angle. If the angle is welded at the heel (weld L_1 in Fig. 3-6) and at the toe (weld L_2), the required lengths for concentricity with the center of gravity of the member can be determined by taking moments. For weld L_2, with moments about the heel,

$$5 \times 6.96L_2 = 1.63T = 1.63 \times 16.1 \times 6.96$$

$$L_2 = 5.25 \text{ in}$$

Subtraction gives the length of weld along the heel:

$$L_1 = 16.1 - 5.2 = 10.9 \text{ in}$$

If each angle is also welded along its end with a $\frac{5}{16}$-in weld, each of these lengths may be reduced by half the length of the weld at the end. This is proved by taking the moment about the heel:

$$6.96 \times 5L_2 = 6.96 \times 16.1 \times 1.63 - 6.96 \times 5 \times 2.5$$

$$L_2 = 5.2 - 2.5 = 2.7 \text{ in}$$

Thus, the connection may be made concentric with $L_1 = 8.4$ in, $L_2 = 2.7$ in, and 5 in of weld at the end, or with $L_1 = 10.9$ in, $L_2 = 5.2$ in, and no weld at the end.

Gusset plate. To prevent yield or rupture on section a-a of Fig. 3-6, the area on this section must equal the area of the angles if the gusset plate is of the same steel. For example, if the width on section a-a is 10 in, the required gusset-plate thickness t_g is $2 \times 3.53/10 = 0.706$ in.

Shear in the gusset plate along the welds must be checked. The shear design strength is given by Eq. (3-5). The design strength of a 1-in-long section through the plate $(1 \times t_g)$ is

$$0.8 \times 0.7 \times 1 \times t_g \times 36 = 20.2t_g \text{ kips/in}$$

Equating the gusset-plate shear per inch to the weld shear per inch gives

$$20.2t_g = 1 \times 6.96 \times 2$$

$$t_g = 0.69 \text{ in}$$

The required thickness to prevent a block-shear failure (Fig. 3-5d) is found by equating the factored load, 224 kips, to the *larger* of ϕR_n by Eqs. (3-6). Since the member is welded to the gusset plate, no net areas are involved, so A_{nt} and A_{nv} in these equations should be taken to be the corresponding gross areas. Using the weldment with $L_1 = 8.4$ in, $L_2 = 2.7$ in, and a 5-in weld at the end of the angle, Eq. (3-6a) yields

$$\phi R_n = 0.75[0.6 \times 36(L_1 + L_1)t_g + 58 \times 5t_g] = 490t_g$$

and from Eq. (3-6b)

$$\phi R_n = 0.75[0.6 \times 58(L_1 + L_1)t_g + 36 \times 5t_g] = 584t_g$$

Therefore

$$584t_g = 224$$

$$t_g = 0.38 \text{ in}$$

Note that L_2 does not enter into this calculation, because a shear rupture of the gusset plate along the toe of the angle runs for the full length of the contact with the toe, 8.4 in, instead of only the length L_2.

Based on the three values of t_g, 0.38, 0.69, and 0.706 in, use a $\frac{3}{4}$-in gusset plate.

3-5   ECCENTRIC CONNECTIONS

In Examples 3-4-1 (AISC/ASD) and 3-4-2 (AISC/LRFD) the distribution of the welds is established by writing the equation of moments in terms of the length of the weld on the assumption that all the welds are the same size. The distribution may also be determined by writing the equation of moments in terms of the forces. Figure 3-7 shows a single angle connected to a gusset plate with welds at the heel, toe, and end. The corresponding forces are designated as F_h, F_t, and F_e. The force T is located at the centroid of the angle at a distance y from the heel.

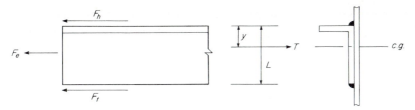

FIGURE 3-7

Taking moments about the heel gives

$$Ty - \frac{F_e L}{2} - F_t L = 0$$

where L is the width of the angle leg attached to the gusset plate. If no weld is placed along the end of the angle, $F_e = 0$ and

$$F_t = \frac{Ty}{L}$$

$$F_h = T - F_t = T\left(1 - \frac{y}{L}\right)$$

If it is necessary to reduce the overlap of the angle on the gusset plate, the weld size at the heel of the angle can be increased.

In the case of a single-angle member connected by one leg to a gusset plate (Fig. 3-8), it is impossible to arrange the welds so that the centroid of the weld forces coincides with that of the member. Eccentricity in the plane of the welds can be avoided by arranging the welds as described in Examples 3-4-1 and 3-4-2, but there remains the eccentricity e shown in the figure. Consequently, stress in the member will not be uniformly distributed, so the member cross section is not fully effective. Both AASHTO and AREA provide for this condition by allowing only one-half the unconnected leg to be counted in computing the cross-sectional area to be used in determining the capacity.

With certain exceptions to be discussed in this paragraph, AASHTO, AISC, and AREA all require that the centroid of the forces in the connecting welds on an axially loaded member be coincident with the centroid of the member cross section, and if this condition cannot be realized, the eccentricity must be taken

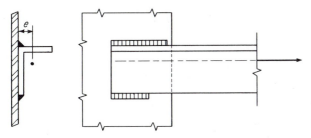

FIGURE 3-8

into account. There is no exception to this requirement in the AASHTO specifications. The exception in the AISC specifications concerns double-angle members, single-angle members, and the like, for which disposition of the fillet welds at the connections to avoid the eccentricity discussed in the preceding paragraph is not required, provided there is no question of fatigue (ASD Sec. J1.9, LRFD Sec. J1.6). Therefore, in the connection of Examples 3-4-1 and 3-4-2, AISC specifications would permit $L_1 = L_2$, so the shortest connection with E70 $\frac{5}{16}$-in welds would be $L_1 = L_2 = 6$ in with 5 in of weld at the end. The exception in the AREA specifications concerns a single-angle member such as that of Fig. 3-8, in which case the eccentricity can be ignored if the welds are proportioned so that their force resultant lies between the centroid of the angle and the middle of the connected leg.

It will be shown in Art. 3-8 that an axially loaded member may not be 100 percent efficient even if the centroid of the weld-force resultant coincides with the centroid of the member cross section.

3-6   THE NET SECTION

Holes for bolts or rivets in tension members affect the member in two ways: (1) they reduce the area of the cross section, and (2) they result in nonuniform strain on cross sections in the neighborhood of the hole (Fig. 3-13b).

The areas used in the calculation of member capacity are called the *net areas*. The net area is defined as the gross section minus the area which is lost because of the holes. The effective net area according to the AISC specification is the area obtained by multiplying the net area by a coefficient to account for its reduced effectiveness if not all the member elements are connected (Art. 3-4). Failure paths may occur on sections normal to the axis of the member, or they may include zigzag sections if the fasteners are staggered. Thus, for the case shown in Fig. 3-9, failure may occur on the path 1-2-5 or on the path 1-2-3-4, depending on the relative values of the gage g, the pitch s, and the hole diameter d. (Note that gage refers to the distance between the longitudinal fastener lines, while pitch refers to the distance between transverse rows.) If g is large relative to s, failure would be expected along 1-2-3-4, while if it is small, failure is more likely along 1-2-5. On the other hand, for fixed values of g and s we see that failure along the zigzag section becomes more likely as the size of the holes increases.

Design procedure is based on simple empirical formulas which have been proposed from time to time. The method prescribed by most specifications is

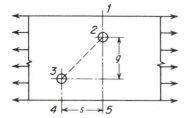

FIGURE 3-9

based on the assumption that the effect of the zigzags in any failure path can be accounted for by deducting from the area of the section the areas lost by the holes in the failure path and adding the quantity $(s^2/4g)t$ for each zigzag. For section 1-2-3-4 this procedure gives

$$A_n = A_g - 2dt + \frac{s^2 t}{4g} \tag{3-7}$$

where A_n = net area
A_g = gross area on 1-2-5
t = thickness of plate
d = diameter of the hole

If the plate thickness is uniform, we can divide each term of Eq. (3-7) by t to get

$$w_n = w_g - 2d + \frac{s^2}{4g} \tag{3-8}$$

where w_n is the net width and w_g the gross width along 1-2-5. The formula shows that the net width is found by deducting from the gross width the sum of the diameters of both holes in the chain and adding the quantity $s^2/4g$ for the staggered hole.

The net-width concept is useful when elements of uniform thickness are being evaluated. For rolled shapes and other cross sections which have elements of different thicknesses, Eq. (3-7) must be used.

To account for additional holes in the chain, the procedure just described is continued from one hole to the next, so for any zigzag section the net width is determined by deducting from the gross width the sum of the deductions for all the holes in the chain and adding the quantity $s^2/4g$ for each gage space in the failure path. Values of $s^2/4g$ must be computed in sequence from one hole to the next. This method of determining the net section, called the $s^2/4g$ rule, was proposed in 1922 (Ref. 4). A limit analysis published in 1955 suggests that the rule is a reasonable one.[5] It is used in all standard specifications.

The standard hole in the AISC, AASHTO, and AREA specifications is $\frac{1}{16}$ in larger than the diameter of the connector. AISC and RCSC permit the use of oversize, short-slotted, and long-slotted holes. Special provisions apply when holes other than the standard hole are used. AISC, AASHTO, and AREA specify that the net section be calculated on the basis of a deduction $\frac{1}{16}$ in larger than the dimension of the hole or slot perpendicular to the direction of the stress. For the standard hole this means that the deduction is $\frac{1}{8}$ in larger than the diameter of the connector. This procedure makes some allowance for damage to the material adjacent to the hole caused by the punching or drilling operation. However, suggested specifications for aluminum structures require only $\frac{1}{32}$ in be added to the hole dimension if the hole is punched. These specifications also recognize the lesser damage by drilling and require deduction of only the actual hole diameter for a drilled or subpunched-and-reamed hole.[2]

Example 3-6-1. A $7 \times 4 \times \frac{3}{4}$ angle is connected by two rows of $\frac{3}{4}$-in bolts in the 7-in leg and one row in the 4-in leg (Fig. 3-10). Standard holes are used.

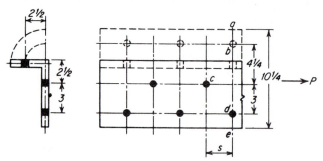

FIGURE 3-10

Solution

(a) Determine the pitch s so that only two holes for $\frac{3}{4}$-in fasteners need be deducted in computing the net area.

The fastener gages shown in the figure are the usual values for a 7×4 angle. For the purpose of computing the cross-sectional area, the width of the angle and the distances between gage lines must be measured along the mid-thickness line of the cross section. Thus the gross width of the angle is the sum of the widths of the two legs less their thickness, or $7 + 4 - 0.75 = 10.25$ in. The distance between the gage line in the 4-in and the adjacent line in the 7-in leg is $2.5 + 2.5 - 0.75 = 4.25$ in. The net width for the section $abcde$ must be not less than the gross width less the sum of the diameters of the two holes which are allowed.

Net width across section $abcde$ is

$$10.25 - (3 \times 0.875) + \frac{s^2}{4 \times 3} + \frac{s^2}{4 \times 4.25}$$

Net width across section $abde$ is

$$10.25 - 2 \times 0.875$$

Equating these and solving for s yields $s = 2.48$ in. Use 2.50 in.

$$A_n = (10.25 - 2 \times 0.875)0.75 = 6.38 \text{ in}^2$$

(b) Determine the net area of the 7×4 angle if the pitch s is 2 in.

$$A_n = \left(10.25 - 3 \times 0.875 + \frac{2^2}{4 \times 3} + \frac{2^2}{4 \times 4.25}\right)0.75 = 6.15 \text{ in}^2$$

Example 3-6-2. Calculate the net sections on the possible failure paths of the C12 × 30 channel shown in Fig. 3-11. For bolt patterns symmetrical about the axis of the member, only failure paths symmetrical about the axis need be considered.

Solution. There are three possible failure planes: $abcd$, $abgcd$, and $efghi$. All other symmetrical failure planes farther along the connection will be repetitions of $abgcd$ or $efghi$.

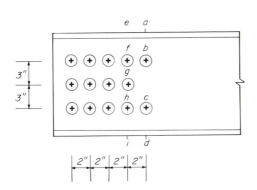

FIGURE 3-11

The C12 × 30 has a gross area of 8.82 in² and a web thickness t_w of 0.510 in. Holes are to be standard for $\frac{3}{4}$-in bolts.

Failure path *abcd*

$$A_g \qquad\qquad\qquad = \quad 8.82$$

$$\text{Holes} \quad 2(\tfrac{3}{4} + \tfrac{1}{8})0.510 = -0.89$$

$$\overline{7.93}$$

Failure path *abgcd*

$$A_g \qquad\qquad\qquad = \quad 8.82$$

$$\text{Holes} \quad 3(\tfrac{3}{4} + \tfrac{1}{8})0.510 = -1.34$$

$$\text{Zigzags} \quad 2\left(\frac{2^2}{4 \times 3}\right)0.510 = +0.34$$

$$\overline{7.82}$$

Failure path *efghi*

$$A_g \qquad\qquad\qquad = \quad 8.82$$

$$\text{Holes} \quad 3(\tfrac{3}{4} + \tfrac{1}{8})0.510 = -1.34$$

$$\overline{7.48}$$

Note that in the calculation for the reduction of area due to the holes the term $\frac{3}{4}$ in parentheses is the size of the connector, in, while the $\frac{1}{8}$ in consists of $\frac{1}{16}$ in to account for the $\frac{13}{16}$-in hole plus $\frac{1}{16}$ in additional which is required by most specifications.

Example 3-6-3. Calculate the net sections on the possible failure paths of the C12 × 30 attached to the gusset plate as shown in Fig. 3-12. For bolt patterns symmetrical about the axis of the member, only failure paths symmetrical about the axis need be considered.

Solution. The possible failure paths are *abcd*, *abgcd*, and *efghi*. All other failure paths along the member will be repetitions of *abgcd* or *efghi*. This connection is identical to that used in Example 3-6-2 except that angles have been connected to the flanges as shown.

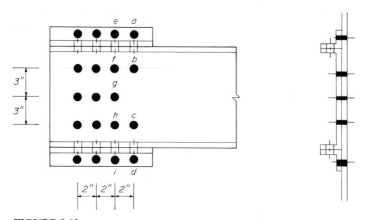

FIGURE 3-12

The C12 × 30 has a gross area of 8.82 in², a web thickness t_w of 0.510 in, and a flange thickness t_f of 0.501 in. Standard holes are provided for $\frac{3}{4}$-in diameter connectors.

Failure path *abcd*

$$A_g \qquad\qquad\qquad\qquad = \quad 8.82$$

Flange holes $\quad 2(\frac{3}{4} + \frac{1}{8})0.501 = -0.88$

Web holes $\qquad 2(\frac{3}{4} + \frac{1}{8})0.510 = -0.89$

$$\overline{\qquad 7.05}$$

Failure path *abgcd*

$$A_g \qquad\qquad\qquad\qquad\qquad 8.82$$

Flange holes $\quad 2(\frac{3}{4} + \frac{1}{8})0.501 = -0.88$

Web holes $\qquad 3(\frac{3}{4} + \frac{1}{8})0.510 = -1.34$

Zigzags $\qquad 2\left(\dfrac{2^2}{4 \times 3}\right)0.510 \ = +0.34$

$$\overline{\qquad 6.94}$$

Failure path *efghi*

$$A_g \qquad\qquad\qquad\qquad\qquad 8.82$$

Flange holes $\quad 2(\frac{3}{4} + \frac{1}{8})0.501 = -0.88$

Web holes $\qquad 3(\frac{3}{4} + \frac{1}{8})0.510 = -1.34$

$$\overline{\qquad 6.60}$$

In Example 3-6-1 the $s^2/4g$ rule was applied to an angle in which the zigzag went from a hole in one leg to a hole in the other leg. For that situation the dimension g, taken along the centerline of the member, is $g_1 + g_2 - t$.

Occasionally the failure path may involve a zigzag which goes from a hole in one element to a hole in another element where the thicknesses of the two elements are different. In this case the values of g and t to be used in evaluating $(s^2/4g)t$ are unclear.

For purposes of discussion assume that g_1 is the gage of the hole in element 1 with a thickness t_1 and that g_2 is the gage of the hole in element 2 with a thickness t_2. If the gage is determined along the midthickness line of the elements, the result is

$$g = g_1 + g_2 - \tfrac{1}{2}t_1 - \tfrac{1}{2}t_2$$

Alternatively the gage can be defined as $g = g_1 + g_2 - t_1$ or $g = g_1 + g_2 - t_2$. The value of the thickness to be used is also undefined. It could be taken as t_1 or t_2 or the average of the two. It could also be evaluated on the basis of a weighted average. This would require development of the zigzag to determine the lengths of the failure paths in the two elements. With this information it would be possible to arrive at an average thickness over the total zigzag path. Because $(s^2/4g)t$ is empirical and generally small compared with the other terms involved, the complexity of these calculations is not justified. It is conservative to use the largest value of g with the smallest thickness along the path. The largest value of g is obtained if the smaller thickness is subtracted from the sum of the gages. Therefore, a conservative value of $(s^2/4g)t$ is obtained if the smaller thickness is used in evaluating both g and t.

3-7 DISTRIBUTION OF STRESS ON NET SECTION

Nonuniform strain in the vicinity of the hole in a uniformly stretched sheet of rubber is shown in Fig. 3-13. The unloaded sheet, upon which an orthogonal grid was drawn, is shown in Fig. 3-13a, while the stretched sheet is shown in Fig. 3-13b. It will be noted that the strains at the edge of the elongated hole (at the ends of the minor diameter) are much larger than those elsewhere in the sheet. The disturbance is highly localized, however. Whether the corresponding stresses are nonuniform or not depends on the stress-strain relationship of the material. According to the theory of elasticity, the distribution of stress on the net section of an infinitely wide plate containing a hole at its centerline is given by[6]

$$f = f_1 \left[1 + \frac{1}{2}\left(\frac{r}{x}\right)^2 + \frac{3}{2}\left(\frac{r}{x}\right)^4 \right] \qquad (3\text{-}9)$$

where f_1 = stress that would exist if there were no hole
  r = radius of hole
  x = distance from center of hole to any point on the transverse section

Because of the highly localized disturbance in stress, this equation can be applied with good accuracy to a plate of finite width. The results for a plate of the dimensions of that in Fig. 3-13a, subjected to a uniformly distributed tension of 12 ksi,

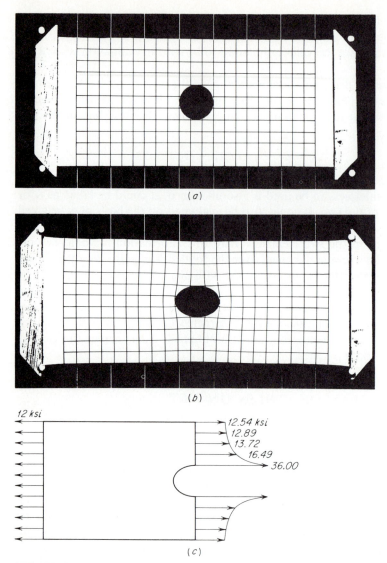

FIGURE 3-13

are shown in Fig. 3-13c. It will be noted that the stress at the edge of the hole is equal to the yield stress of A36 steel.

Equation (3-9) is valid only if the stress at the edge of the hole does not exceed the proportional limit. If the load continues to increase after the proportional limit is reached, the stress distribution will depend on the nature of the stress-strain curve of the metal. The metal immediately adjacent to a hole in a plate of a flat-yielding steel will deform without increase in stress, but if the plate is of a steel with no definite yield, the stress at the edge of the hole will increase, although at a slower rate than at points on the cross section farther from the hole. In either case, stresses at points away from the edge of the hole will be greater than the value given by Eq. (3-9).

Stress concentrations at holes are usually neglected in structural design, and stress is calculated on the assumption that it is uniformly distributed over the net area of the cross section. This assumption is justified because structural metals are sufficiently ductile to equalize the stress over the area in most cases. For example, in a test of an A440 steel hanger 2.25×0.263 in in cross section connected to a gusset plate with $\frac{3}{4}$-in bolts in $\frac{13}{16}$-in holes (actual diameter 0.817 in), the member broke on the net section at a load of 29.75 kips. The net area was $(2.25 - 0.817) \times 0.263 = 0.377$ in^2. Thus, the average stress at fracture was $29.75/0.377 = 78.9$ ksi. A test of a standard coupon cut from the hanger showed a tensile strength of 77.8 ksi and a yield stress of 55.6 ksi. Corresponding ASTM values for the steel are 70 and 50 ksi.

3-8 NET-SECTION EFFICIENCY

Tests have shown that tension members do not always develop a net-section average stress equal to the tensile strength, as was the case for the $\frac{1}{4} \times 2\frac{1}{4}$ in hanger described in Art. 3-7. Reductions in strength can be expressed in terms of the *efficiency* of the net section, i.e., the ratio of the average stress at fracture to the coupon strength. Net-section efficiency depends on (1) the ductility of the metal, (2) the method of making the holes, (3) the ratio of the gage g to the fastener diameter d, (4) the ratio of the net area in tension to the area in bearing on the fastener (called the *bearing ratio*), and (5) the distribution of the cross-sectional material relative to the gusset plates or other elements to which the member is connected.

Because of the nonuniform stress distribution which was discussed in Art. 3-7, it is not surprising that the efficiency of the net section is dependent on the ductility of the metal. Investigation of a large number of tests showed that the net section in a highly ductile material may be 15 to 20 percent stronger than the same section in a material with relatively low ductility.[7] This effect can be expressed by a net-section efficiency coefficient K_1, which is a function of the percent reduction R in the area of a standard test coupon (2-in gage length), as follows:

$$K_1 = 0.82 + 0.0032R \leq 1 \qquad (3\text{-}10)$$

Since values of R are not prescribed by ASTM specifications, data for evaluating K_1 are not readily available. However, R is 50 percent or more for A36 steel, which makes this steel 100 percent efficient as regards ductility. Also, it will be noted that efficiency is still high ($K_1 = 0.90$) even if R is only 25 percent.

Punched holes may reduce the efficiency of the net section by as much as 15 percent compared with drilled holes.[7] This effect can be expressed by an efficiency coefficient K_2, using $K_2 = 0.85$ for punched holes and $K_2 = 1$ for holes that are drilled, or subpunched and reamed.

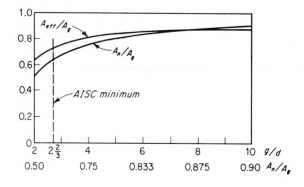

FIGURE 3-14
Effect of g/d ratio on net-section efficiency.

Tests show that the net section is more efficient if the ratio of the gage g to the diameter d is small than if it is large. The increase for close transverse spacing is explained by the suppression of contraction, which was discussed in Art. 2-16 (Fig. 2-48a). Reduction in area at yielding of the metal on the net section between holes is restrained by the metal on the adjacent parallel gross cross sections. Therefore, a condition of biaxial stress develops, and there is an increase in tensile strength. On the other hand, a wide spacing of fasteners (large values of g/d) reduces the efficiency. This is because the concentrated forces applied to the member by the widely spaced fasteners produce nonuniform straining of such a nature that fracture begins before stress can be equalized over the net section. The following efficiency coefficient K_3 has been proposed to evaluate this effect:[8]

$$K_3 = 1.6 - 0.7 \frac{A_n}{A_g} \tag{3-11}$$

where A_n and A_g are the net area and the gross area, respectively. This equation was derived by fitting a curve to test results. Figure 3-14 shows a comparison of the net area of a plate, whose fastener lines are at a uniform gage g, with the effective area obtained by multiplying the net area by K_3. The horizontal scale in this figure is given in terms of both A_n/A_g and g/d. There is a direct relationship between these parameters for a plate with equally spaced fastener lines:

$$\frac{A_n}{A_g} = \frac{(g-d)t}{gt} = 1 - \frac{d}{g}$$

The dashed line at $g/d = 2\frac{2}{3}$ corresponds to the minimum distance between fasteners according to the AISC specifications. At this value of g/d, $K_3 = 1.16$. At $A_n/A_g = \frac{6}{7}$, which corresponds to $g/d = 7$ (a fairly wide spacing of fasteners), $K_3 = 1$. For still larger values of g/d, K_3 becomes less than unity and approaches 0.9 as a limit. This is in agreement with tests, which show that, except for members with all elements connected, the *effective* net section will not exceed 85 to 90 percent of the gross area no matter how widely fasteners are spaced in an attempt to increase it. This is recognized in the AREA specifications, which limits the value of the net area to be used in the computations to not more than $0.85A_g$.

In the AISC specifications, however, single angles, double angles and the like which are connected by only one leg are excepted (Art. 3-3).

It is difficult to isolate the effect of bearing pressure from the effect of the spacing of the fastener gage lines. In the case of a plate with uniform gage spacing, the bearing ratio and the fastener spacing are directly related, as is shown by

$$\frac{A_n}{A_g} = \frac{(g - d)t}{dt} = \frac{g}{d} - 1$$

Test data suggest that the strength of a connection is not impaired by bearing pressure so long as adequate spacing is provided to preclude the failure modes discussed earlier.

Net-section efficiency is also influenced by the position of the shear planes of the fasteners relative to the cross section of the member. This is shown by a series of tests on truss-type members reported in Ref. 8. The specimens consisted of four $5 \times 3 \times \frac{3}{8}$ in angles riveted to a $\frac{1}{2} \times 16$ in web plate and connected at each end to two gusset plates (Fig. 3-15). Holes were drilled. Eight of these members were tested (Table 3-1). The two specimens with riveted connections, 1 and 2, were among a number of truss-type members of various types of cross section which had been tested in an earlier investigation of riveted connections. With the intent of verifying the greater shear strength of A325 bolts as compared to rivets, two specimens fabricated to receive seven bolts per line (3 and 4 in

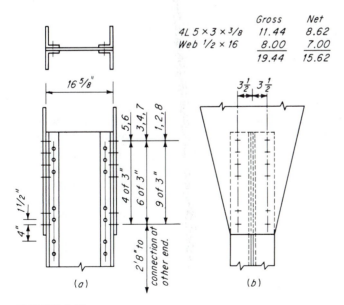

	Gross	Net
4L 5 × 3 × 3/8	11.44	8.62
Web 1/2 × 16	8.00	7.00
	19.44	15.62

FIGURE 3-15
Test member reported in Table 3-1.

TABLE 3-1

Tests on truss-type tension members

Specimen	Fasteners per line	P_u, kips	$f_n = P/A_n$, ksi	$f_g = P/A_g$, ksi	Member properties		$\dfrac{f_n}{F_u}$	$\dfrac{f_g}{F_y}$
					F_u, ksi	F_y, ksi		
1	10*	872	55.8	44.8	62.1	38.4	0.90	1.17
2	10*	902	57.6	46.2	62.5	39.4	0.92	1.17
3	7	866	55.4	44.5	64.8	39.4	0.86	1.13
4	6†	870	55.7	44.7	66.4	40.2	0.84	1.11
5	5	706	45.2	36.4	63.0	38.7	0.72	0.94
6	5	722	46.2	37.1	62.8	38.6	0.74	0.96
7	7	815	52.1	41.8				
8	5‡	796	51.0	40.9				

* $\frac{7}{8}$-in rivets, all others $\frac{7}{8}$-in high-strength bolts. Drilled holes.

† Last hole (at end of member) in each line empty.

‡ Last five holes (at end of member) in each line empty.

Table 3-1) were tested. The first of these failed, at 866 kips, on the same net section as specimens 1 and 2. The fracture was through the net section of the angles in the legs connected to the gusset plates, at the first row of bolts (the bottom row in Fig. 3-15b), and thence through the net section of the other legs (Fig. 3-16). This specimen failed at 870 kips and on the same net section as specimen 3.

In an attempt to force a shear failure of the bolts, two specimens which had been fabricated for 10 fasteners per line were shortened by flame cutting so that there were only five bolts per line (specimens 5 and 6 in Table 3-1). However, instead of failing by shearing the bolts, both members broke on the same net section as the others had, one at 706 kips and one at 722 kips. It is of interest to note that this represented a reduction in the strength of the net section of about 18 percent. Thus, it is clear that the strength of the net section is influenced by the makeup of the connection. In this case, the evidence points to the length of the connection as a determinant. Strain measurements showed that the webs of specimens 3 (seven bolts per line), 4 (six bolts per line), and 6 (five bolts per line) were only 54, 52, and 38 percent effective, respectively, at the AISC (1963) allowable load of 312 kips for this member and 88, 82, and 70 percent effective at twice this load. Effectiveness in this case is expressed as the ratio of the load corresponding to the measured strains to that corresponding to uniform stress over the entire net section.

Specimens 7 and 8 were tested with high-strength bearing bolts. Specimen 8 had been fabricated for ten fasteners per line and was tested with only five per line without removing the excess length of member. It failed at 796 kips. This increase in strength in comparison with specimens 5 and 6 is due to the stiffening effect of the excess length, which results in more nearly uniform strain in the web at the section where the first transfer of stress from the gusset plates to the

FIGURE 3-16
Net-section failure of truss-type member. (*From Ref. 8.*)

member occurs. Figure 3-17 shows the local buckling which developed in the outstanding legs of this specimen, demonstrating that tension was being carried into the portion of the web beyond the last row of bolts and was being reacted by the compression in the angles.

Average stresses at failure of the eight specimens in this series of tests are given in Table 3-1. The average net-section stress f_n is based on the net area by the $s^2/4g$ rule, which is 15.62 in^2 (Fig. 3-15). Also shown are the weighted averages of the coupon properties F_u and F_y of the angles and web plate. The decreasing efficiency of the net section with decrease in length of the connection is shown in the next-to-last column. It will be noted (last column) that the first four specimens exceeded the coupon yield on the gross section before breaking while the last two did not.

Figure 3-18 shows the variation of load with overall deformation for the members of Table 3-1. Overall deformation is measured in the length of the specimen, including both joints. Calculated values based on $\Delta = PL/AE$ are also shown, one based on net area, the other on gross. It is of interest to note that nonlinear behavior of the specimens began at a load somewhat less than the AISC (1963) allowable load for members 5 and 6. It should also be noted that

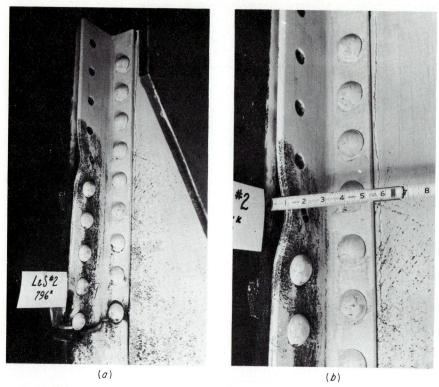

(*a*)   (*b*)

FIGURE 3-17
Net-section failure of truss-type member. (*From Ref. 8.*)

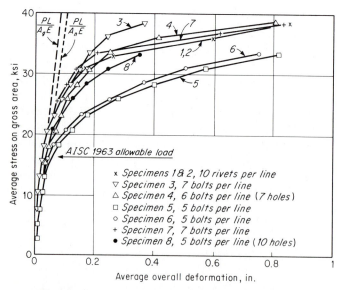

FIGURE 3-18
Load-deformation curves for member of Fig. 3.15. (*From Ref. 8.*)

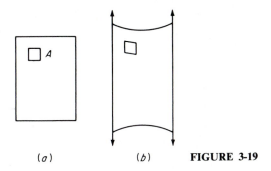

(a)   (b)   **FIGURE 3-19**

these plots stop short of the ultimate load. Thus, the plot for specimen 5 stops at about 33 ksi, but failure was at 36.4 ksi.

The phenomenon of nonuniform straining of the web in the test specimens discussed in this article is called *shear lag*. Figure 3-19, which shows the web of the test specimens in the unloaded and the loaded state, helps to explain the significance of this name. The four forces shown in Fig. 3-19*b* are the resultants of the bolt shears in the connections. Since the ends of the web are free, the distortion will be as shown. Therefore, an element such as that at *A* in the unloaded web will be deformed as shown in Fig. 3-19*b* when the member is loaded. This is a shear deformation, and the stress in the web is said to lag because of it. The shear-lag phenomenon can be analyzed by considering this deformation.[9]

Since shear lag reduces the effectiveness of tension-member components that are not connected directly to a gusset plate or other anchorage, the efficiency of a member can be increased by reducing the areas of such components relative to the area of the member as a whole. The distance from a fastener plane (gusset plate) to the center of gravity of the area tributary to it is a convenient measure of the distribution of the cross-sectional area of a member. For example, the tributary area of the single-angle member of Fig. 3-20*a* is the entire area of the angle, and the coordinate $\bar{x}$ from the fastener plane to the centroid of the area is a measure of the efficiency of the cross section. Similarly, in the double-plane member of Fig. 3-20*b*, the area tributary to each fastener plane is the area of half the cross section, and the coordinate $\bar{x}$ from each fastener plane to the centroid of each half cross section measures the relative importance of the unconnected web. Shear lag is also influenced by the length of the connection. This was seen to be

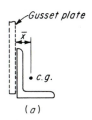

(a)

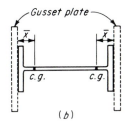

(b)   **FIGURE 3-20**

the case for the members of Table 3-1, where net-section effectiveness decreased with a decrease in the length of the fastener line. The effect of these two parameters can be expressed as an efficiency coefficient given by[8]

$$K_4 = 1 - \frac{\bar{x}}{L} \tag{3-12}$$

where L is the length of the connection (distance from the first fastener to the last one).

The results of more than 1000 tests on tension members are compared in Fig. 3-21 with values predicted by multiplying the net area according to the $s^2/4g$ rule by the tensile strength of the metal. The same tests are compared in Fig. 3-22 with predicted values based on corrections according to Eqs. (3-10) to (3-12) and adjustments for bearing ratio and method of fabrication of holes. Relatively few tests fall outside the 10 percent scatter bands of Fig. 3-22, despite the fact that the

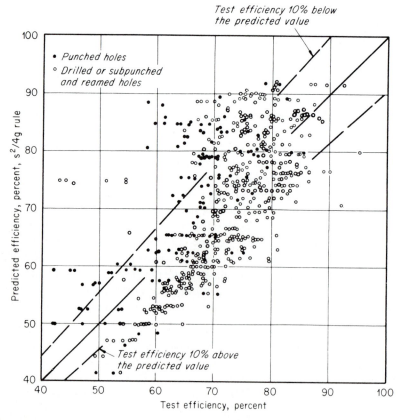

FIGURE 3-21
Comparison of tests with predicted net-section strength. (*From Ref. 8.*)

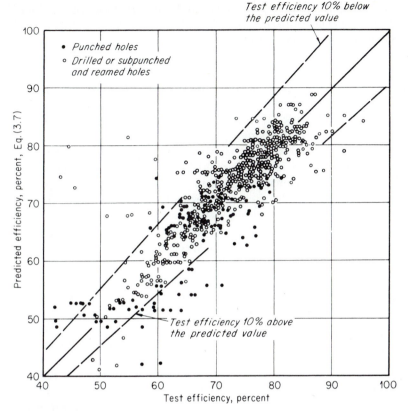

FIGURE 3-22
Comparison of tests with predicted net-section strength. (*From Ref. 8.*)

test data were from a large number of sources and involved various fastener sizes, many different joint configurations (including single angles with and without lug angles), and a variety of materials.

3-9 NET-SECTION DESIGN

It was shown in Art. 3-8 that the strength of a tension member with bolted or riveted connections can be predicted with good accuracy by taking into account the various factors affecting the strength of the net section. This suggests the following procedure for the design of such members. To provide the necessary margin of safety against fracture, the capacity of the member should be determined by multiplying the effective cross-sectional area by an appropriate stress. In the case of allowable stress design this value is obtained by dividing the specified minimum tensile strength F_u by the factor of safety. For AISC load-and-resistance-factor design it is obtained by multiplying the specified minimum tensile strength F_u by a ϕ factor (Art. 3-3).

The effective area A_{eff} is defined by

$$A_{\text{eff}} = K_1 K_2 K_3 K_4 A_n \tag{3-13}$$

where A_n is the net area by the $s^2/4g$ rule and K_1, K_2, K_3, and K_4 are the efficiency coefficients defined in Art. 3-8. Furthermore, to protect the member against unserviceability because of excessive elongation, the allowable load should also be computed by multiplying the gross area by an appropriate stress. For allowable stress design this value is obtained by dividing the specified minimum yield stress F_y by a factor of safety. For load-and-resistance-factor design it is obtained by multiplying the specified minimum yield stress F_y by the ϕ factor. The gross area should be used to investigate elongation, since it is the member itself, rather than the connections, which can be expected to contribute most of the elongation after the yield stress is reached. Furthermore, for reasons discussed in Art. 3-3, the factor of safety with respect to fracture would ordinarily be the larger.

Not all the factors in the procedure suggested above are used in standard specifications. K_1, which is related to material ductility, is taken as 1.0 for the materials approved by the specifications. If other materials are used, the designer should give consideration to this factor. Hole preparation is the basis for the factor K_2. In modern fabrication practice most holes are prepared by means of numerically controlled drilling machines. Improvement in tool steels which permit the use of drills for extended periods without sharpening has reduced dramatically the use of punched holes. Therefore, this factor is taken as 1.0. The efficiency factor K_3 is related to the ratio of A_n to A_g and has been defined in Eq. (3-11). A minimum spacing of $2\frac{2}{3}d$ is usually specified. If the entire cross section of a member were to have fasteners at this spacing, the ratio A_n/A_g would be $(1\frac{2}{3})/(2\frac{2}{3}) = \frac{5}{8} = 0.625$, and the value of K_3 would be 1.16. Designs will generally result in values of A_n/A_g between 0.75 and 0.85, so the range of K_3 will be from 1.07 to 1.0. In view of this relatively small range this factor is taken as 1.0 as a matter of convenience.

The 1978 AISC/ASD specification was the first to require consideration of shear-lag effects, which are accounted for by the factor K_4. Prior to that time only the $s^2/4g$ rule was used to evaluate tension-member capacity. The 1978 and 1989 editions and the 1986 LRFD specification prescribe reduction factors U by which the gross area of members with welded connections and the net area of those with bolted connections are multiplied to obtain an effective area A_e for members with only some of their elements welded or bolted to gusset plates or other connecting elements (Art. 3-4).

The selection of a member's cross section and determination of the number and configuration of the required connectors are a matter of trial and error. Net areas depend upon the fastener distribution, and, in general, are unknown at the beginning of the design process, and various assumptions must be made and verified during the course of the design.

3-10   LOAD TRANSMISSION IN CONNECTIONS AND SPLICES

Calculation of the limiting net-section capacity of a tension member requires that all possible failure paths be considered. Some of these paths may not need to support the full force in the member. This is the case if the failure plane considered is beyond the first fasteners in the member, since they will have transmitted some of the force to an adjacent element. This matter of load transfer is addressed specifically only in the AASHTO specifications, which state:

> When determining the unit stress on any least net width, the amount of stress previously transferred by fasteners adjacent to the section being investigated shall be considered in determining the unit stress on the net section.

The statement in AISC/ASD Sec. B2 which says that "the critical net area A_n of the part is obtained from that chain which gives the least net width" may be misleading because it assumes that all the net areas being compared carry the full load.

Example 3-10-1   (AISC/ASD). Design an A36-steel tension member 16 ft long consisting of two channels, bolted through their webs to a single gusset plate, to transmit 30 kips *DL* and 65 kips *LL* (Fig. 3-23). The connection is bearing type with $\frac{3}{4}$-inch A325 bolts with threads not excluded from the shear planes. Standard holes.

Solution. Allowable stresses are $0.6F_y = 0.6 \times 36 \approx 22$ ksi on the gross area A_g and $0.5F_u = 0.5 \times 58 = 29$ ksi on the effective area A_e.

$$\text{Total load} = 30 + 65 = 95 \text{ kips}$$

$$A_g = \tfrac{95}{22} = 4.32 \text{ in}^2 \text{ req'd} \qquad A_e = \tfrac{95}{29} = 3.28 \text{ in}^2 \text{ req'd}$$

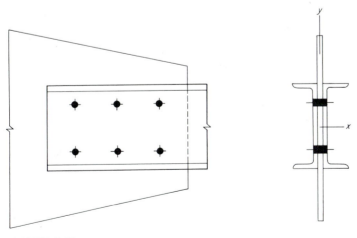

FIGURE 3-23

Assume $U = 0.85$ (Art. 3-3).

$$A_n = \frac{3.28}{0.85} = 3.86 \text{ in}^2 \text{ req'd.}$$

Assuming the ratio A_n/A_g to be about 0.85,

$$A_g = \frac{3.86}{0.85} = 4.54 \text{ in}^2 \text{ req'd}$$

Try two C6 × 8.2:

$$A_g = 4.80 \text{ in}^2$$

Assuming a $\frac{5}{16}$-in gusset plate,

$$I_y = 2(0.693 + 2.40 \times 0.667^2) = 3.52 \text{ in}^4$$

$$r_y = \sqrt{\frac{3.52}{2 \times 2.40}} = 0.86 \text{ in}$$

$$r_x = 2.13 \text{ in} \qquad \text{(from AISC Manual section-properties table)}$$

$$\frac{L}{r_y} = \frac{16 \times 12}{0.86} = 223 < 300 \qquad \text{O.K.}$$

Allowable bolt shearing stress = 21 ksi (Table 2-11). Bolts are in double shear, so allowable shear per bolt = $2 \times 21 \times 0.44 = 18.5$ kips.

Allowable bolt bearing stress = $1.2F_u = 1.2 \times 58 = 69.6$ ksi (Table 2-11). Allowable bearing on two 0.2-in channel webs = $69.6 \times 2 \times 0.2 \times 0.75 = 20.9$ kips ≥ 18.5 kips.

$$\text{Number of bolts} = 95/18.5 = 5.3 \qquad \text{Use 6}$$

The 6-in depth can accommodate only two lines of fasteners. The six bolts will be arranged in two rows of three. Therefore, the assumed value $U = 0.85$ is correct.

$$A_n = 2[2.40 - 2 \times 0.2(\tfrac{3}{4} + \tfrac{1}{8})] = 4.10 \text{ in}^2$$

$$A_e = 0.85 \times 4.10 = 3.49 \text{ in}^2 \geq 3.28 \text{ req'd}$$

$$\text{Gusset-plate thickness } t = \frac{95}{6 \times 69.6 \times 0.75} = 0.30 \qquad \text{Use } \tfrac{5}{16} \text{ in}$$

The gusset plate and the web of the channel must be checked for block shear as in Example 3-4-1. The gusset plate must also be checked for gross area and net area.

Example 3-10-2 (AISD/LRFD). Design an A36-steel tension member 16 ft long consisting of two channels, bolted through their webs to a single gusset plate, to transmit 30 kips *DL* and 65 kips *LL* (Fig. 3-23). The connection is bearing type with $\frac{3}{4}$-inch A325 bolts with threads not excluded from the shear planes. Standard holes.

Solution

Factored load $= 1.2DL + 1.6LL = 1.2 \times 30 + 1.6 \times 65 = 140$ kips

From Eqs. (3-2):

$$0.90 \times 36A_g = 140$$

$$A_g = 4.32 \text{ in}^2 \text{ req'd}$$

$$0.75 \times 58A_e = 140$$

$$A_e = 3.22 \text{ in}^2 \text{ req'd}$$

Assume $U = 0.85$ (Art. 3-3).

$$A_n = \frac{3.22}{0.85} = 4.46 \text{ in}^2 \text{ req'd}$$

Assuming the ratio A_n/A_g to be about 0.85,

$$A_g = \frac{3.79}{0.85} = 4.46 \text{ in}^2 \text{ req'd}$$

Try two C6 × 8.2:

$$A_g = 4.80 \text{ in}^2$$

Assuming a $\frac{5}{16}$-in gusset plate,

$$I_y = 2(0.693 + 2.40 \times 0.667^2) = 3.52 \text{ in}^4$$

$$r_y = \sqrt{\frac{3.52}{2 \times 2.40}} = 0.86 \text{ in}$$

$$r_x = 2.13 \text{ in} \quad \text{(from AISC Manual section-properties table)}$$

$$\frac{L}{r_y} = \frac{16 \times 12}{0.86} = 223 < 300 \quad \text{O.K.}$$

Design double-shear strength (Table 2-13) $= \phi \times 2 \times 48A_b = 0.75 \times 2 \times 48 \times 0.44 = 31.7$ kips per bolt.

Design bearing strength for two 0.2-in channel webs $= \phi \times 2.4dtF_u = 0.75 \times 2.4 \times 0.75 \times 2 \times 0.2 \times 58 = 31.3$ kips per bolt < 31.7.

$$\text{Number of bolts} = 140/31.3 = 4.5 \qquad \text{Use 6}$$

The 6-in depth can accommodate only two lines of fasteners. The six bolts will be arranged in two rows of three. Therefore, the assumed value $U = 0.85$ is correct.

$$A_n = 2[2.40 - 2 \times 0.2(\tfrac{3}{4} + \tfrac{1}{8})] = 4.10 \text{ in}^2$$

$$A_e = 0.85 \times 4.10 = 3.49 \text{ in}^2 \geq 3.22 \text{ req'd}$$

$$\text{Gusset-plate thickness } t = \frac{140}{6 \times 0.75 \times 2.4 \times 0.75 \times 58} = 0.30 \qquad \text{Use } \tfrac{5}{16} \text{ in}$$

(Depending on its configuration, the gusset plate may also need to be checked for net section and block shear as in Example 3-4-2.)

Example 3-10-3   (AISC/ASD). Determine the capacity of the splice shown in Fig. 3-24. All materials are A36 steel. Fasteners are $\frac{7}{8}$-in A325 bolts in a bearing-type connection with threads excluded from the shear planes. Standard holes.

Solution
     Base material
Gross areas:

$$\text{Main plate} \quad 11 \times \tfrac{1}{2} \quad A_g = 5.50 \text{ in}^2$$

$$\text{Splice plates} \quad 2(11 \times \tfrac{5}{16}) \quad A_g = 6.88 \text{ in}^2$$

$$T = F_t A_g = 0.6 F_y A_g = 0.6 \times 36 \times 5.50 = 119 \text{ kips}$$

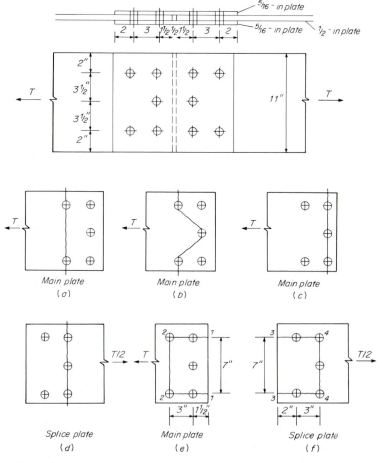

FIGURE 3-24

Net areas:
> Main plate:

Fig. 3-24a:
$$A_g = 5.50$$
$$2(\tfrac{7}{8} + \tfrac{1}{8})\tfrac{1}{2} = -1.00$$
$$A_n = \overline{4.50} \text{ (full load)}$$

Fig. 3-24b:
$$A_g = 5.50$$
$$-3(\tfrac{7}{8} + \tfrac{1}{8})\tfrac{1}{2} = -1.50$$
$$+2\left(\frac{3^2}{4 \times 3\tfrac{1}{2}}\right)\frac{1}{2} = +0.64$$
$$A_n = \overline{4.64} \text{ (full load)}$$

Fig. 3-24c:
$$A_g = 5.50$$
$$-3(\tfrac{7}{8} + \tfrac{1}{8})\tfrac{1}{2} = -1.50$$
$$A_n = \overline{4.00} \text{ (60\% load)}$$

4.0 in^2 for 60 percent load is equivalent to $4.0/0.6 = 6.67$ in^2 for full load.
> Splice plates:

Fig. 3-24d:
$$A_g = 3.44$$
$$-3(\tfrac{7}{8} + \tfrac{1}{8})\tfrac{5}{16} = -0.94$$
$$\overline{2.50} \text{ (full load)}$$

$$2 \text{ plates} \qquad A_n = 2 \times 2.50 = 5.00$$

No other failure paths in the splice plates need be considered because the required capacity is being reduced and the net area of further paths will be greater than the above.

The minimum net area for full load is 4.50 in^2.

$$U = 1.0 \qquad A_e = A_n \qquad \text{(Art. 3-3)}$$
$$T = F_t A_e = 0.5 \times 58 \times 4.5 = 130 \text{ kips}$$

Connector shear. Five connectors in double shear for 10 shear areas.

$$F_v = 30 \text{ ksi} \qquad \text{(Table 2-10)}$$
$$R_v = A_b F_v = 0.6013 \times 30 = 18.04 \text{ kips}$$
$$T = R_v n = 18.04 \times 10 = 180 \text{ kips}$$

Connector bearing. The arrangement of the connectors provides an end spacing greater than $1\tfrac{1}{2}d$ and between-fastener spacing greater than $3d$, so $F_p = 1.2F_u$.

$$R_p = 1.2dtF_u$$

Main plate:
$$R_p = 1.2 \times 0.875 \times 0.5 \times 58 = 30.45 \text{ kips}$$

There are five bearing surfaces in the main plate, so

$$T = 5 \times 30.45 = 152 \text{ kips}$$

Splice plates: $R_p = 1.2 \times 0.875 \times 0.3125 \times 58 = 19.03$ kips

There are 10 bearing surfaces in the splice plates, so

$$T = 10 \times 19.03 = 190 \text{ kips}$$

Block shear (Art. 3-4). Main-plate failure block is 1-2-2-1 (Fig. 3-24e).

Shear path 1-2: $A_g = 4\frac{1}{2} \times \frac{1}{2} = 2.25$ in^2

$A_n = [4\frac{1}{2} - 1\frac{1}{2}(\frac{7}{8} + \frac{1}{8})]\frac{1}{2} = 1.50$ in^2

Tension path 2-2: $A_g = 7 \times \frac{1}{2} = 3.50$ in^2

$A_n = [7 - 2 \times \frac{1}{2}(\frac{7}{8} + \frac{1}{8})]\frac{1}{2} = 3.00$ in^2

The AISC/ASD specification prescribes $0.3F_u$ on the net shear area and $0.5F_u$ on the net tensile area.

$$T = 1.50 \times 0.3 \times 58 + 3.00 \times 0.5 \times 58 = 113 \text{ kips}$$

Splice-plate failure block is 3-4-4-3 (Fig. 3-24f).

Shear path 3-4: $A_g = 2 \times 5 \times \frac{5}{16} = 1.56$ in^2 per plate

$A_n = [5 - 1\frac{1}{2}(\frac{7}{8} + \frac{1}{8})]\frac{5}{16} = 1.09$ in^2 per plate

Tension path 4-4: $A_g = 7 \times \frac{5}{16} = 2.19$ in^2 per plate

$A_n = [7 - 2 \times \frac{1}{2}(\frac{7}{8} + \frac{1}{8})]\frac{5}{16} = 1.88$ in^2 per plate

$T = 1.09 \times 0.3 \times 58 + 1.88 \times 0.5 \times 58 = 73.5$ kips per plate

Allowable load for the two splice plates is $2 \times 73.5 = 147$ kips.

The limiting allowable load is controlled by block shear of the main plate, 113 kips. If the procedure suggested by Hardash and Bjorhovde,[3] in which the net area is used on one path in combination with the gross area on the other path, is applied to this case, the allowable load for block shear is increased to 126 kips. In this case the limiting allowable load would be controlled by gross-area yield of the main plate, 119 kips.

Example 3-10-4   (AISC/LRFD). Determine the capacity of the splice shown in Fig. 3-24. All materials are A36 steel. Fasteners are $\frac{7}{8}$-in A325 bolts in a bearing-type connection with threads excluded from the shear planes. Standard holes.

Solution
   Base material
Gross areas:

Main plate $11 \times \frac{1}{2}$ $A_g = 5.50$ in^2

Splice plates $2(11 \times \frac{5}{16})$ $A_g = 6.88$ in^2

$T = \phi_t P_n = \phi_t F_y A_g = 0.9 \times 36 \times 5.50 = 178$ kips   [Eq. (3-2a)]

Net areas:

Main plate:

Fig. 3-24*a*:

$$A_g \qquad = \quad 5.50$$
$$2(\tfrac{7}{8} + \tfrac{1}{8})\tfrac{1}{2} \qquad = -1.00$$
$$A_n = \quad \overline{4.50} \text{ (full load)}$$

Fig. 3-24*b*:

$$A_g \qquad = \quad 5.50$$
$$-3(\tfrac{7}{8} + \tfrac{1}{8})\tfrac{1}{2} \qquad = -1.50$$
$$+2\left(\frac{3^2}{4 \times 3\tfrac{1}{2}}\right)\frac{1}{2} \quad = +0.64$$
$$A_n = \quad \overline{4.64} \text{ (full load)}$$

Fig. 3-24*c*:

$$A_g \qquad = \quad 5.50$$
$$-3(\tfrac{7}{8} + \tfrac{1}{8})\tfrac{1}{2} \qquad = -1.50$$
$$A_n = \quad \overline{4.00} \text{ (60\% load)}$$

4.0 in^2 for 60 percent load is equivalent to $4.0/0.6 = 6.67$ in^2 for full load.

Splice plates:

Fig. 3-24*d*:

$$A_g \qquad = \quad 3.44$$
$$-3(\tfrac{7}{8} + \tfrac{1}{8})\tfrac{5}{16} \qquad = -0.94$$
$$\overline{2.50} \text{ (full load)}$$

$$2 \text{ plates} \qquad A_n = 2 \times 2.50 = 5.00$$

No other failure paths in the splice plates need be considered because the required capacity is being reduced and the net area of further paths will be greater than the above.

The minimum net area for full load is 4.50 in^2.

$$U = 1.0 \qquad A_e = A_n \qquad \text{(Art. 3-3)}$$
$$T = \phi_t P_n = \phi_t F_u A_e \qquad \text{[Eq. (3-2b)]}$$
$$= 0.75 \times 58 \times 4.5 = 196 \text{ kips}$$

Connector shear. Five connectors in double shear for 10 shear areas.

$$F_v = 60 \text{ ksi} \qquad \phi = 0.75 \qquad \text{(Table 2-13)}$$
$$T = \phi A_b F_v n = 0.75 \times 0.6013 \times 60 \times 10 = 271 \text{ kips}$$

Connector bearing. The arrangement of the connectors provides an end spacing greater than $1\tfrac{1}{2}d$ and between-fastener spacing greater than $3d$, so $F_p = 2.4F_u$.

$$R_n = 2.4dtF_u \qquad \phi = 0.75$$

Main plate: $\quad \phi R_n = 0.75 \times 2.4 \times 0.875 \times 0.5 \times 58 = 45.68$ kips

There are five bearing surfaces in the main plate, so

$$T = 5 \times 45.68 = 228 \text{ kips}$$

Splice plates: $\quad \phi R_n = 0.75 \times 2.4 \times 0.875 \times 0.3125 \times 58 = 28.55$ kips

There are 10 bearing surfaces in the splice plates, so

$$T = 10 \times 28.55 = 285 \text{ kips}$$

Block shear (Art. 3-4). Main-plate failure block is 1-2-2-1 (Fig. 3-24e).

Shear path 1-2: $A_g = 4\frac{1}{2} \times \frac{1}{2} = 2.25 \text{ in}^2$

$A_n = [4\frac{1}{2} - 1\frac{1}{2}(\frac{7}{8} + \frac{1}{8})]\frac{1}{2} = 1.50 \text{ in}^2$

Tension path 2-2: $A_g = 7 \times \frac{1}{2} = 3.50 \text{ in}^2$

$A_n = [7 - 2 \times \frac{1}{2}(\frac{7}{8} + \frac{1}{8})]\frac{1}{2} = 3.00 \text{ in}^2$

The design strength ϕR_n is the larger value from Eqs. (3-3):

$$\phi R_n = 0.75(0.6 \times 36 \times 2 \times 2.25 + 58 \times 3.00) = 203 \text{ kips}$$

$$\phi R_n = 0.75(0.6 \times 58 \times 2 \times 1.50 + 36 \times 3.50) = 173 \text{ kips}$$

Therefore, the design strength is 203 kips.

Splice-plate failure block is 3-4-4-3 (Fig. 3-24f).

Shear path 3-4: $A_g = 2 \times 5 \times \frac{5}{16} = 1.56 \text{ in}^2$ per plate

$A_n = [5 - 1\frac{1}{2}(\frac{7}{8} + \frac{1}{8})]\frac{5}{16} = 1.09 \text{ in}^2$ per plate

Tension path 4-4: $A_g = 7 \times \frac{5}{16} = 2.19 \text{ in}^2$ per plate

$A_n = [7 - 2 \times \frac{1}{2}(\frac{7}{8} + \frac{1}{8})]\frac{5}{16} = 1.88 \text{ in}^2$ per plate

Then, from Eqs. (3-6), the design strength per plate is

$$\phi R_n = 0.75(0.6 \times 36 \times 2 \times 1.56 + 58 \times 1.88) = 132 \text{ kips per plate}$$

$$\phi R_n = 0.75(0.6 \times 58 \times 2 \times 1.09 + 36 \times 2.19) = 116 \text{ kips per plate}$$

Design strength for the two splice plates is $2 \times 132 = 264$ kips.

The limiting design strength is controlled by gross-area yield of the main plate, 178 kips.

3-11   LONG JOINTS

In the design of riveted and bolted joints for tension members, it is generally assumed that the fasteners share the load equally if it is not eccentric. That this assumption may be in error when there are more than two fasteners in the same gage line can be shown by considering the connection shown in Fig. 3-25a. Assuming that each bolt carries a shear $P/3$ and that stress is proportional to strain, the bolts must deform equally and the elongations of the two plate segments between adjacent bolts must be equal. However, if the shear on bolt 1 is $P/3$, the force in the upper plate at section a-a is $2P/3$, while in the lower plate it is $P/3$. Therefore, the upper plate elongates twice as much as the lower, and the shear deformations of bolts 1 and 2 cannot be equal (Fig. 3-25b). Analysis of the joint between bolts 2 and 3 shows that here the lower plate elongates twice as much as the upper one, so the shear deformation of bolt 3 equals that of bolt 1. Thus, the end bolts carry larger shears than the middle bolt. Of course, this

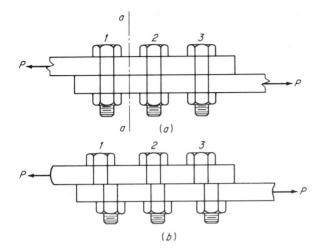

FIGURE 3-25

means that the end bolts reach the proportional limit before the middle bolt does, after which the latter begins to pick up a larger share of the load. Thus, at failure of the joint the bolt forces may be equal, or nearly so. However, the extent to which this redistribution of load can develop depends on the ability of the bolts to tolerate large shear deformations.

Figure 3-26 shows a sawed section of a bolted butt joint with $\frac{7}{8}$-in A325 bolts after it had been tested to its ultimate load in tension.[10] The test was stopped before rupture of the joint, but the large elongation of the holes in the splice plates at the left end shows that the stress on the net section was large, and the large shear deformation of the bolts at the ends suggests that fracture is imminent. The same effect is seen in the riveted joint of Fig. 3-27, in which the end rivets have sheared. Failure of the fasteners in a long joint is usually sequential, beginning with those at the ends and progressing toward the center, and is sometimes called *unbuttoning*. This phenomenon has been known for many years.

FIGURE 3-26
Sawed section of bolted joint after testing. (*Fritz Engineering Laboratory, Lehigh University.*)

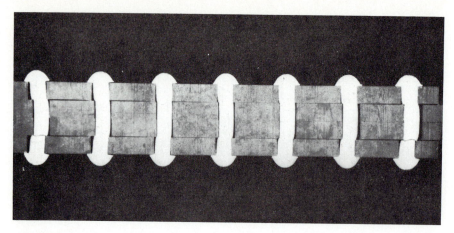

FIGURE 3-27
Sawed section of riveted joint after testing. (*Fritz Engineering Laboratory, Lehigh University.*)

For example, it was observed in a series of tests of large riveted joints in connection with the design of the San Francisco–Oakland Bay Bridge.[11]

The joint of Fig. 3-26 was one of 16 joints that were tested to ultimate load (Fig. 3-28). Each specimen was designed so that the sum of the shear areas of the bolts (two for each bolt) was 10 percent more than the net area of the member; i.e., the tension-shear ratio A_n/A_s was 1/1.10. This was the ratio for a design for which the shear strength of the fasteners equals the tensile strength of the member. The ratio 1/1.10 had been determined in an earlier series of tests.[12] In eight of the specimens the tension-shear ratio was held constant by using a different width of plate for each joint, with the number of bolts in each line ranging from three to ten and the widths of the member from 5.84 to 15.10 in. The grip (sum of the thicknesses of the connected material) was 4 in. Another four specimens had grips of 8 in, with the number of fasteners per line ranging from 10 to 16 and the specimen widths from 8.48 to 12.45 in. The remaining four specimens had widths of 9.88 in, with grips ranging from 4.75 to 6.75 in to maintain the

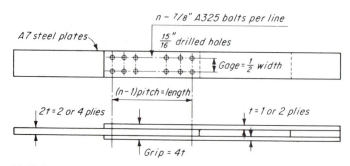

FIGURE 3-28
Test joint reported in Fig. 3-29.

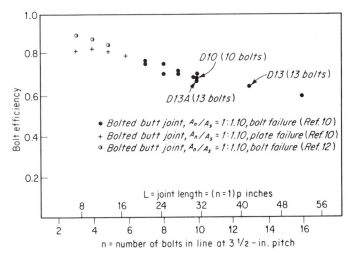

FIGURE 3-29
Efficiency of A325 bolts in A7 butt joints. (*From Ref 10.*)

tension-shear ratio. Figure 3-29 shows the results of the 16 tests. The ordinate in the figure is bolt efficiency, which is the ratio of the average shear per bolt, at ultimate load, to the shear strength of a single bolt of the same grip. It will be noted that four short specimens failed by fracture of the net section, so they are not representative of bolt efficiency. However, failure of the three short specimens from Ref. 12, which are also shown on the figure, was in the bolts.

The pitch of the bolts was $3\frac{1}{2}$ in in all the specimens reported in Fig. 3-29 except one, in which the pitch of $2\frac{5}{8}$ in was used. Specimen D13A had 13 bolts at $2\frac{5}{8}$ in, for which the distance between the end bolts was $31\frac{1}{2}$ in, while specimen D10 had 10 bolts at $3\frac{1}{2}$ in, which gave the same length of connection, $31\frac{1}{2}$ in. The efficiencies of the bolts in these two joints were almost identical (Fig. 3-29). On the other hand, specimen D13 had 13 bolts at $3\frac{1}{2}$ in, which made the connection 42 in long. The bolt efficiency of this connection was 0.65 compared to the 0.70 efficiency for D13A (Fig. 3-29). This suggests that fastener efficiency is a function of joint length rather than of the number of fasteners in line.

It will be noted that bolt efficiency falls to about 60 percent for the longest joint in this series of tests. However, since the differences in the shearing deformations of the fasteners depend on the differential strains in the connected plate, as shown in Fig. 3-25b, the variation of fastener efficiency with joint length depends on the sequence of events in regard to nonproportional behavior of the plate and the fasteners. That this must be the case can be seen by observing that the three bolts in Fig. 3-25b would deform equally if the plates did not deform at all. Therefore, if yielding on the gross areas of the plates can be postponed until after there has been some nonproportional behavior of the fasteners, a better redistribution of the unequal fastener shears will result. On the other hand, of course, early yielding of the plates increases the inequalities in the shearing deformations

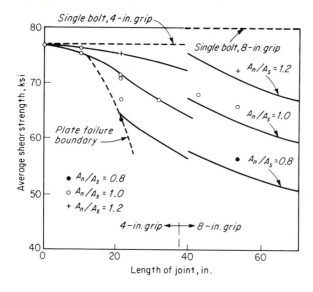

FIGURE 3-30
Efficiency of A325 bolts in A440 butt joints. (*From Ref. 13.*)

of the fasteners and causes premature failure of those at the ends of the joint. For this reason, A325 bolts joining plates of a high-yield steel are more efficient than the A325 bolts joining plates of a low-yield steel. A490 bolts joining A36 steel plates are less efficient than A325 bolts joining A36 steel, given the same geometry. Finally, fastener efficiency for a given combination of materials can be improved by increasing the tension-shear ratio.

Results of tests on A440-steel joints with A325 bolts are compared in Fig. 3-30 with predicted values for tension-shear ratios A_n/A_s of 0.8, 1.0, and 1.2. The predicted behavior is based on a detailed analysis using the measured properties of the plate material and the bolts.[13] The discontinuities in the curves are due in part to the fact that the longer bolts in the joints with 8-in grip were somewhat stronger than the shorter bolts in the specimens with 4-in grip and in part to the changed geometry itself. The plate-failure boundary separates the zone in which net-section failures occur (to the left) and the zone in which bolt failures occur. These results suggest that the allowable shear stress on fasteners in connections of the type discussed in this article should vary with the length of the joint and the tension-shear ratio. Furthermore, since increasing the length of a joint decreases the efficiency of the fasteners but increases the efficiency of the net section of the member where shear lag is involved, there is a trade-off here in the design of a tension member and its connections.

Although connector shear strength is reduced only for joints with three or more connectors in line in the direction of the load and decreases with the length of the joint, the reduction is approximated in the AISC and AASHTO specifications by a two-step function as follows. For joints less than 50 in long the nominal strength is taken to be 0.8 times the ultimate shear strength; for longer joints an additional 20 percent reduction is specified.

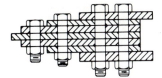

FIGURE 3-31

3-12 LONG-GRIP FASTENERS

The bending of the fasteners in the joints shown in Figs. 3-26 and 3-27 raises a question about the interaction of bending and shear in the case of long fasteners, since there is a possibility that this might further reduce the efficiencies of the fasteners. Some allowance for this has been, and is, customary for long rivets. Both AASHTO and AREA require that the number of rivets in a connection be increased by 1 percent for each additional $\frac{1}{16}$ in of grip in excess of $4\frac{1}{2}$ diameters of the rivet. AISC specifies a like increase if the grip exceeds 5 diameters. However, tests have shown that the shearing strength of high-strength bolts having grips as much as 9 diameters is not less than that of bolts with short grips.[10] Therefore, no penalty attaches to long-grip high-strength bolts.

Sometimes the plates or members forming a structural joint are separated by one or more filler plates, as shown in Fig. 3-31. Usually the plates are extended as shown to improve the transfer of stress through the connection. Specifications require that the filler extension be attached by fasteners sufficient in number to transmit a force equal to the area of the filler times the stress computed by dividing the load on the joint by the combined area of the fillers and the part connected. However, fillers thinner than $\frac{1}{4}$ in need not be extended. Furthermore, fillers in friction-type connections (same as AISC slip-critical connections) with high-strength bolts need not be extended.

3-13 COMPENSATING FOR REDUCTION IN CROSS-SECTIONAL AREA

Ends of tension members may be strengthened to offset reduction in cross-sectional area from threads, fastener holes, etc. Round or square bars threaded on the normal end have a net area equal to the area of the cross section at the root of the thread. To compensate for this loss, the end of the bar may be upset to form an increased cross section into which the threads are cut. Upset bars have an area at the root of the thread at least 15 percent greater than the area of the bar.

Tension members which are field-riveted or bolted to gusset plates may be strengthened at the ends to make up for the loss of section caused by the holes. In the case of H-shaped truss members, either rolled (W shapes) or built-up, this can be done by welding to the flanges thicker plates of the same steel or plates of the same thickness but of higher-strength steel (Fig. 3-32). The ends of certain tension members of the Carquinez Straits bridge in California were increased in area to offset bolt-hole losses by groove welding thicker plates to the ends of the

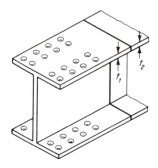

FIGURE 3-32

flange plates. For example, one of the diagonal members in the suspended span consists of 1×18 flange plates and a $\frac{3}{8} \times 20$ web. The cross-sectional area is

Flanges:

$$2 \times 1 \times 18 = 36$$

Web:

$$\frac{3}{8} \times 20 = \underline{7.5}$$
$$43.5 \text{ in}^2$$

The end stubs are made up of $1\frac{3}{8} \times 18$ flanges and a $\frac{3}{8} \times 19\frac{1}{4}$ web, using the same steel. There are four lines of 1-in A325 bolts in each flange. The resulting net area is

Flanges:

$$2 \times 1\frac{3}{8} \times (18 - 4 \times 1\frac{1}{8}) = 37.12$$

Web:

$$\frac{3}{8} \times 19\frac{1}{4} = \underline{7.22}$$
$$44.34 \text{ in}^2$$

It will be noted that stubs and the member are of the same depth, 22 in.

In the Benicia-Martinez bridge, also in California, the end stubs were made of higher-strength steel, so the thicknesses of the flanges and the web were the same in the stubs as in the member. For example, one of the main members which is of A242 steel has A514-steel stubs.

3-14 LUG ANGLES

Example 3-6-2 presented the connection of a channel with connectors only in the web. The same member was used in Example 3-6-3 with angles connected to the flanges and gusset plate. These angles are called *lug angles*. Lug angles are sometimes used to reduce the length of the connection and are commonly used in the end connection of single-angle or double-angle members to a gusset plate (Fig. 3-33). According to Ref. 14, this device reduces shear lag to the extent that the net section of an angle connected in this way is fully effective even though the connection is shorter than it would be without the lug. This is equivalent to saying that the lug angle reduces $\bar{x}$ in Eq. (3-12) to zero. However, the location of the lug angle is of some importance; it should be at the beginning of the joint, as in Fig. 3-33, rather than at the end.

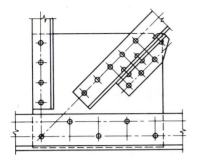

FIGURE 3-33

3-15 TENSION MEMBERS FOR TRUSSES

DP3-15-1 (AISC/ASD) and DP3-15-2 (AISC/LRFD): Tension Members for Welded Truss

The design of the tension members of a welded roof truss for an industrial building is presented in the design sheets. Except where noted, the following discussion applies to both.

There are three trolley beams attached to the bottom chord, one each at L_2 and L'_2 with a reaction of 6.4 kips and one at L_5 with a reaction of 12.3 kips. The snow load is 40 psf, which is the recommended value for the Great Lakes and New England areas (Table 1-3). The wind load is 20 psf on vertical surfaces, which is the average of the BOCA National Building Code requirements for minimum and moderate windstorm areas (Table 1-5). The wind force on the roof is suction and taken at $0.7q$, where q is the velocity pressure, as suggested in Art. 1-8. Since the 20 psf pressure on vertical surfaces is based on a shape factor of 1.3 (Art. 1-8), the velocity pressure (including the gust factor) is $q = 20/1.3 = 15.4$ psf. Therefore, the roof suction is $0.7 \times 15.4 = 10.8$, or 11 psf.

The dead load consists of the weights of covering, purlins, trusses, and bracing. The covering consists of built-up roofing weighing 5.5 psf, which is laid on a steel roof deck welded to the purlins and weighing 2.5 psf. The weight of purlins will vary from about 1.5 to 5 psf and is estimated at 3 psf for this building. The weight of a truss and its bracing seldom exceeds 10 percent of the load supported by the roof, so a slight error in estimating its weight will have a negligible effect. For this building, the weight of the truss and bracing is estimated at 3 psf. Since the wind force on the roof is suction, the trusses are designed for gravity loads alone. The dead load of roofing, decking, purlins, and truss totals 14 psf, and the snow load is 40 psf. The corresponding panel loads are obtained by multiplying these loads by the spacing of the trusses, 20 ft, and the lengths of the contributing areas along the span of the truss. These lengths are $\frac{1}{2} \times 6$ ft 5 in for joint U_0, $\frac{1}{2} \times 6$ ft 5 in $+ \frac{1}{2} \times 6$ ft for joint U_1, and 6 ft for all other panel points.

Chord members for welded trusses are usually tees, W or S shapes, or two angles arranged as in Fig. 3-5b. Angles, channels, or W or S shapes are generally

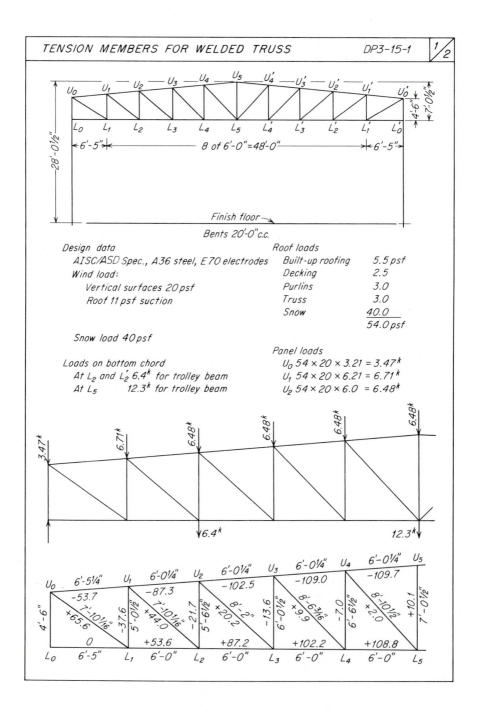

TENSION MEMBERS FOR WELDED TRUSS   DP3-15-1   1/2

Design data
  AISC/ASD Spec., A36 steel, E70 electrodes
Wind load:
    Vertical surfaces 20 psf
    Roof 11 psf suction

Snow load 40 psf

Loads on bottom chord
  At L_2 and L_2' 6.4^k for trolley beam
  At L_5 12.3^k for trolley beam

Roof loads
  Built-up roofing   5.5 psf
  Decking   2.5
  Purlins   3.0
  Truss   3.0
  Snow   40.0
                       54.0 psf

Panel loads
  U_0 54 × 20 × 3.21 = 3.47^k
  U_1 54 × 20 × 6.21 = 6.71^k
  U_2 54 × 20 × 6.0 = 6.48^k

TENSION MEMBERS FOR WELDED TRUSS   DP 3-15-1 $\frac{2}{2}$

From Art. 3-3:
$$P = 0.6 F_y A_g = 0.6 \times 36 A_g = 22 A_g$$
$$P = 0.5 F_u A_e = 0.5 \times 58 \times 0.85 A_g = 24.7 A_g$$

Design of tension members

Member	Force		Reqd. area	Section	Area in.^{2}	L/r	
*$L_0 L_1 L_2$	53.6 @ 22 =	2.44 in.^{2}		WT7×17	5.00	77/1.53 =	51
$L_2 L_3$	87.2 @ 22 =	3.96		do	5.00	72/1.53 =	47
$L_3 L_4$	102.2 @ 22 =	4.65		do	5.00	do	
$L_4 L_5$	108.8 @ 22 =	4.94		do	5.00	do	
$U_0 L_1$	65.6 @ 22 =	2.98		2L 3½×3×¼	3.12	94/1.11 =	85
$U_1 L_2$	44.0 @ 22 =	2.00		2L 2½×2×¼	2.12	94/0.78 =	121
$U_2 L_3$	20.2 @ 22 =	0.92		2L 2×2×³⁄₁₆	1.43	98/0.62 =	158
$U_3 L_4$	9.9 @ 22 =	0.45		do	1.43	102/0.62 =	165
$U_4 L_5$	2.0 @ 22 =	0.09		do	1.43	106/0.62 =	171
$U_5 L_5$	10.1 @ 22 =	0.46		do	1.43	84/0.62 =	135

*This member is checked in DP**4**-15-1 for compression due to wind load.

Joint L_1

Max. fillet weld ³⁄₁₆": shear per in = $0.3 \times 70 \times ³⁄₁₆ \times 0.707 = 2.78^k$

Base metal, angle : shear per in = $0.4F_y \times ¼ = 3.60^k$

Base metal, tee's :   do   = $0.4F_y \times 0.285 = 4.10^k$

Member	$U_1 L_1$	$U_0 L_1$
Reqd. weld per angle	$\dfrac{37.6}{2 \times 2.78} = 6.8$ in	$\dfrac{65.6}{2 \times 2.78} = 11.8$ in
Reqd. weld per angle	$\dfrac{37.6}{4.10} = 9.2$ in	$\dfrac{65.6}{4.10} = 16.0$ in
Toe	$\dfrac{9.2 \times 0.91}{3} = 2.8$ in	$\dfrac{16 \times 1.04}{3.5} = 4.8$ in
Heel	6.4 in	11.2 in

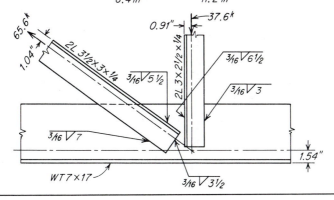

164 DESIGN OF STEEL STRUCTURES

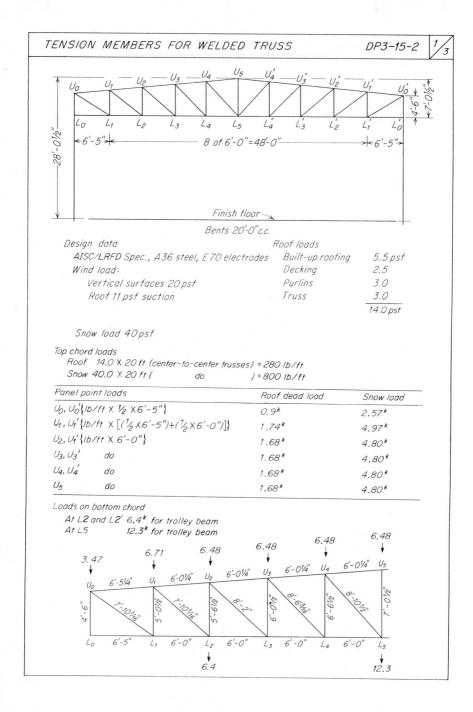

Design data

  AISC/LRFD Spec., A36 steel, E70 electrodes
  Wind load:
     Vertical surfaces 20 psf
     Roof 11 psf suction

Roof loads

Built-up roofing	5.5 psf
Decking	2.5
Purlins	3.0
Truss	3.0
	14.0 psf

  Snow load 40 psf

Top chord loads
  Roof 14.0 × 20 ft (center-to-center trusses) = 280 lb/ft
  Snow 40.0 × 20 ft (do   ) = 800 lb/ft

Panel point loads	Roof dead load	Snow load
U_0, U_0' {lb/ft × ½ × 6'-5"}	0.9^k	2.57^k
U_1, U_1' {lb/ft × [(½ × 6'-5")+(½ × 6'-0")]}	1.74^k	4.97^k
U_2, U_2' {lb/ft × 6'-0"}	1.68^k	4.80^k
U_3, U_3' do	1.68^k	4.80^k
U_4, U_4' do	1.68^k	4.80^k
U_5 do	1.68^k	4.80^k

Loads on bottom chord

  At L2 and L2' 6.4^k for trolley beam
  At L5 12.3^k for trolley beam

| TENSION MEMBERS FOR WELDED TRUSS | | | | | | | DP3-15-2 | $2/3$ |

Design loads

Member	Dead load D	Snow S	Trolley live load L	Case 1	Case 2	Case 3	Design load
$L_0L_1L_2$*	+9.7	+27.9	+16.0	+13.6	+49.3	+64.3	+64.3
L_2L_3	+15.3	+43.7	+28.2	+21.4	+85.3	+102.4	+102.4
L_3L_4	+18.2	+52.0	+32.0	+25.5	+98.8	+121.1	+121.1
L_4L_5	+19.1	+54.7	+35.0	+26.7	+106.3	+128.0	+128.0
U_0L_1	+12.0	+34.1	+19.5	+16.8	+62.7	+78.7	+78.7
U_1L_2	+7.3	+20.8	+15.9	+10.2	+44.6	+50.0	+50.0
U_2L_3	+3.9	+11.2	+5.1	+5.5	+18.4	+25.2	+25.2
U_3L_4	+1.4	+3.9	+4.6	+2.0	+11.0	+10.2	+11.0
U_4L_5	−0.5	−1.6	+4.1	−0.7	+5.2	−1.1	+5.2
U_5L_5	+1.0	+2.8	+6.3	+1.4	+12.7	+8.9	+12.7

*This member is checked in DP4-15-2 for compression due to wind load.

$$\phi_t P_n = \phi_t F_y A_g = 0.9 \times 36 \ A_g = 32.4 \ A_g \qquad (Eq. \ 3-2a)$$
$$\phi_t P_n = \phi_t F_u A_e = 0.9 \times 58 \times 0.85 \ A_g = 44.4 \ A_g \qquad (Eq. \ 3-2b)$$

Design of tension members

Member	Design load	Reqd area	Section	Area	L/r
$L_0L_1L_2$	+64.3	1.98	WT 7×15	4.42	77/1.49 = 52
L_2L_3	+102.4	3.16	do	do	72/1.49 = 48
L_3L_4	+121.1	3.74	do	do	do
L_4L_5	+128.0	3.95	do	do	do
U_0L_1	+78.7	2.43	2L3 × 2½ × ¼	2.63	94/0.75 = 125
U_1L_2	+50.0	1.54	2L2 × 2 × ¼	1.88	94/0.61 = 154
U_2L_3	+25.2	0.78	2L2 × 2 × 3/16	1.43	98/0.62 = 158
U_3L_4	+11.0	0.34	do	do	102/0.62 = 165
U_4L_5	+5.2	0.16	do	do	106/0.62 = 171
U_5L_5	+12.7	0.39	do	do	84/0.62 = 135

Joint L_1

   Max. fillet weld $^3/_{16}$ in

       Shear per inch $= \phi \times F \times 1 \times 0.707 \times S$

                 $= 0.75 \times 0.6\, F_{EXX} \times 1 \times 0.707 \times ^3/_{16}$

                 $= 0.75 \times 0.6 \times 70 \times 1 \times 0.707 \times ^3/_{16}$

                 $= 4.18$ kips/in

   Base metal

       Shear per inch $= \phi \times 0.7 \times A_g \times F_y$

                 $= \phi \times 0.7 \times 1 \times t \times F_y$

           Angle $0.8 \times 0.7 \times 1 \times ^1/_4 \times 36 = 4.85$

           Tee $0.8 \times 0.7 \times 1 \times 0.270 \times 36 = 5.45$

Required weld

U_0L_1 $(T = 78.7)$ U_1L_1 $(C = 45.1)$

$l = \dfrac{78.7}{4.18} = 18.8$ in or $l = \dfrac{45.1}{4.18} = 10.8$ in or

          9.4 in/L 5.4 in/L

$l = \dfrac{78.7}{5.45} = 14.4$ in/L $l = \dfrac{45.1}{5.45} = 8.3$ in/L

   Tee stem controls   Tee stem controls

Toe $\dfrac{14.4 \times 0.91}{3} = 4.4$ Toe $\dfrac{8.3 \times 0.99}{3} = 2.7$

Heel $\dfrac{14.4 \times 2.09}{3} = 10.0$ Heel $\dfrac{8.3 \times 2.01}{3} = 5.6$

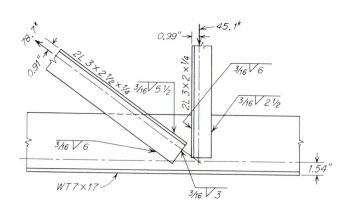

used for web members. A tee section will be used for the lower chord of this truss and double angles for the web members.

DP3-15-1 (ASD). The sum of the dead load D and snow load S is $14 + 40 = 54$ psf. The corresponding panel-point loads and the trolley live loads L are shown on the truss figure on sheet 1. The truss-member forces due to $D + S + L$ are shown in kips on the truss figure on sheet 2. The required member areas are determined by the allowable stresses $F_t = 0.6F_y$ on the gross area A_g and $F_t = 0.5F_u$ on the effective net area A_e. For welded connections of this type $U = 0.85$ and $A_n = A_g$, so $A_e = 0.85A_g$. The two criteria yield $T = 22A_g$ and $T = 29 \times 0.85A_g = 24.65A_g$. The required areas, the section chosen and its area, and the member slenderness ratio are shown in the table on sheet 2.

DP3-15-2 (LRFD). The member design load is the largest of the following combinations (Art. 1-12):

$$1.4D \qquad\qquad \text{(Load case 1)}$$
$$1.2D + 1.6L + 0.5S \qquad \text{(Load case 2)}$$
$$1.2D + 1.6S + 0.5L \qquad \text{(Load case 3)}$$

The tension-member design loads are shown on sheet 2. Required member areas are determined by Eqs. (3-2). The required areas, the section chosen and its area, and the member slenderness ratio are shown in the second table on sheet 2.

The same-size tee is used for the entire lower chord in these examples. A smaller tee could be used for $L_0 L_2$, which would save about 129 lb of steel for the ASD design and 100 lb for the LRFD design, but these savings would probably be canceled by the cost of the two splices.

Some saving would result from the use of single angles for members $U_2 L_3$, $U_3 L_4$, $U_4 L_5$, and $U_5 L_5$. However, this results in an eccentricity which some designers object to. Although angles smaller than $2 \times 2 \times \frac{3}{16}$ would furnish enough area for the lightly loaded members, for example, a pair of $2 \times 2 \times \frac{1}{8}$ angles provides 0.96 in², many designers are reluctant to use material thicknesses smaller than $\frac{3}{16}$ in. In addition, the use of $\frac{1}{8}$-in angles would necessitate a very small weld size which may be difficult to deposit. Angles with legs smaller than 2 in may also be available in some areas and could be used for some of the members provided that the recommended slenderness ratio of 300 for tension members is not exceeded. This maximum slenderness ratio is intended to give the member a stiffness that reduces the chances of noticeable vibration.

Member connection. The joint details of a truss of this kind are usually worked out by the fabricator. However, to review and approve them the engineer must know how to design them. The design of the joint at L_1 is discussed here. Member $U_0 L_1$ is the most highly loaded diagonal and $U_1 L_1$ the most highly loaded vertical. Therefore, these members will require the largest amount of weld metal. (The design of U_1L_1, which is a compression member, is discussed in Chap. 4, DP4-15-1 and DP4-15-2.) Fastening is by fillet welds to the web of the bottom chord. The largest fillet weld that should be used is $\frac{1}{16}$ in less than the thickness of the angle for thicknesses $\frac{1}{4}$ in or more, but may equal the thickness for thicknesses $\frac{3}{16}$ in or smaller. For the angles in this example, a $\frac{3}{16}$-in weld satisfies this limitation.

The shear values of 1-in lengths of $\frac{3}{16}$-in fillet weld and of the $\frac{1}{4}$-in-thick angle and the 0.27-in stem of the tee are calculated, following which the required length of weld is determined by dividing the member load by the smaller of the weld and the base-metal shear values. The distribution of the weld at the toe and the heel is determined as explained in Art. 3-4. There is sufficient room for the required lengths of weld at the toe and the heel of U_1L_1. For U_0L_1, however, there is room for no more than about $5\frac{1}{2}$ in of weld along the heel of the angle. Even with a weld across the end, the weld at the heel would be too long. Therefore, the length of weld at the toe is increased to make up the difference. The resulting eccentricity is small and not in violation of the AISC specification.

It was mentioned in Art. 2-14 that ordinarily the electrode should bisect (approximately) the angle between the legs of a fillet weld. The outstanding legs of U_1L_1 would make this impossible at the corner of U_0L_1 nearest U_1L_1, while the flange of the tee would interfere to some extent at the opposite corner and at the end of U_1L_1. However, this inclination of the electrode is not so important as the inclination in the direction of travel, and, as a general rule, a good operator can produce a sound weld so long as he or she can see the tip of the arcing electrode with his or her hood in place and without using a mirror. Therefore, the disposition of the welds at this joint is not one to be concerned about.

DP3-15-3: Tension Members for Highway-Bridge Truss

Tension-member forces for dead load plus AASHTO HS20-44 live load plus impact plus sidewalk load for one truss of the bridge shown in Fig. 3-34 are given on the design sheet. Members of trusses of this size are usually W's or built-up H shapes, which require two gusset plates at each panel point. Therefore, all the members must be of the same nominal depth in order to avoid excessively thick fill plates at the joints. For tension members with holes allowable stresses are $0.55F_y$ on the gross area and $0.5F_u$ on the net section, which gives 20 and 29 ksi, respectively, for A36 steel. Member selections are given in the table with their gross area A_g, deductions for bolt holes, net areas A_n, and slenderness ratios L/r. The following comments are clarifications of the corresponding lettered computations on the design sheet.

a. Net section of the chord members is based on two holes in the web and two in each side of each flange. These are needed for the splice of L_0L_2 to L_2L_4, whose detail is shown in Fig. 3-35.

TENSION MEMBERS FOR HIGHWAY-BRIDGE TRUSS   DP3-15-3

AASHTO specs
$7/8$ in TA325 bolts

Truss diagram: U_0, U_1 -712 U_2, U_3 -950 U_4 along top; -605, $+446$, -171, -291, $+142$, -171 diagonals; -119, 0, 0; bottom chord L_0, L_1, L_2, L_3, L_4 with $+417$, $+891$. Height $27'-0"$. Span $8 @ 27'-0" = 216'-0"$.

Member	Load	A_n, reqd	Section	A_g	Deduct	A_n	L/r	
$L_0 L_2$	$417 @ 20 = 20.9$		$W14 \times 90$	26.5	$4 \times 1 \times 0.710 = 2.84$	22.8	88	(a)
					$2 \times 1 \times 0.440 = 0.88$			
$L_2 L_4$	$891 @ 20 = 44.6$		$W14 \times 176$	51.7	$4 \times 1 \times 1.313 = 5.25$	44.8	81	
					$2 \times 1 \times 0.820 = 1.64$			
$U_1 L_2$	$446 @ 20 = 22.3$		$W14 \times 90$	26.5	$4 \times 1 \times 0.710 = 2.84$	23.7	124	(b)
$U_3 L_4$	$142 @ 20 = 7.1$		$W14 \times 61$	17.9	$4 \times 1 \times 0.643 = 2.57$	15.3	187	(c)

Splice $L_0 L_2$ to $L_2 L_4$ (d)

$L_0 L_2$: $P/A_n = 417/22 = 19$ ksi $(19 + 20)/2 = 19.5$ design stress for splice (e)

   $7/8$-in. A325 bolts, friction-type connection : $0.6 \times 16 = 9.6^k$ s.s. (f)
                                                                   19.2^k d.s.

   <u>Web</u> $A_g = 0.440 \ (14 - 2 \times 0.710) = 5.5$ (g)
                    2 holes = $2 \times 1 \times 0.440 = \underline{0.9}$
                                         $A_n = 4.6$ in.^{2}

   Use two $3/8 \times 10$ spl. pl. 3 holes out $A_n = 2 \times 7 \times 3/8 = 5.25$ in.^{2}

                              Bolts = $4.5 \times 19.5 / 19.2 = 4.6$, use 6

   <u>Flanges</u> $W14 \times 87$ $A_n = 22.8$
                         Web = $\underline{\ \ 4.6\ \ }$
                    two flgs. = 18.2 in.^{2}
         Use 15" plates : $t = 18.2/(15-4) = 1.65$ (two plates) (h)
         Use two $3/4 \times 15$ spl. pl.

         Bolts = $18.2 \times 19.5 / 9.6 = 36$ (two flanges)

The splice is shown in Fig. 3-35.

FIGURE 3-34
Eldersburg-Louisville Road Bridge. (*J. E. Greiner Company, Inc., Consulting Engineers.*)

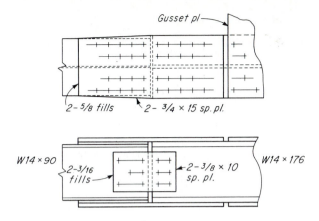

FIGURE 3-35
Splice of $L_0 L_2$ to $L_2 L_4$ of DP3-15-3.

b. Net section of the web members is based on two holes in each side of each flange for connections to the gusset plates.

c. The W14 × 61 selected for $U_3 L_4$ provides almost double the net area required. No smaller W14 can be used without exceeding the specified slenderness limit ($L/r \leq 200$) for main tension members (AASHTO 10.7.5).

d. $L_0 L_2$ is spliced to $L_2 L_4$ just to the left of the gusset plates at panel point 2. Tension chords are usually spliced this way, rather than by the gusset plates, to facilitate erection.

e. AASHTO requires that the splice be designed for not less than the average of the actual stress in the member and the allowable stress.

f. Friction-type connections are mandatory except in compression members and secondary members. Bearing stress is not a factor in friction-type connections.

g. The web is spliced for its portion of the force in the member.

h. There are four bolts at the critical section of the flange splice plates.

Because of the differences in section depth and web thickness, fill plates are needed on $L_0 L_2$. Since this is a friction-type connection, it is not necessary to extend these fill plates beyond the splice plates.

Example 3-15-1 (AISC/ASD). Redesign members $L_0 L_1 L_2$ and $U_0 L_1$ of DP3-15-1 using A36 steel, $\frac{3}{4}$-in-diameter A325 bolts with standard holes in slip-critical connections. Although it is unlikely that a building roof truss would require slip-critical connections, this example is given to demonstrate the application of the requirements and a comparison with the welded truss.

For slip-critical joints the allowable stresses (Table 2-10) are used. In addition, the connections must satisfy all other criteria for strength. These criteria assure that fasteners are sufficient to prevent slip, but if slip should occur, the joint will be capable of supporting the loads as a bearing-type connection. In this example it is assumed that threads are not excluded from the shear planes.

Solution. The ASD criteria for member design are given by

$$T = 0.6F_y A_g = 0.60 \times 36 \times A_g = 22A_g$$

$$T = 0.5F_u A_e = 0.5 \times 58 \times A_e = 29A_e$$

For member selection an estimate of A_g may be obtained by considering estimated values of U and the ratio A_n/A_g.

Member $U_0 L_1$. In the design of this truss for welded construction a tee was selected for the lower chord members. Because of spacing requirements for the bolted connection it will probably be necessary to use pairs of angles for all members, with a single gusset plate.

From DP3-15-1,

$$\text{Design force} = 65.6 \text{ kips}$$

$$A_g \text{ (required)} = \frac{65.6}{22} = 2.98 \text{ in}^2$$

$$A_e \text{ (required)} = \frac{65.6}{29} = 2.26 \text{ in}^2$$

For the slip-critical connection,

$$R = \pi \frac{D^2}{4} F_v = \left[\pi \frac{(\frac{3}{4})^2}{4} \right] \times 17 = 7.51 \text{ kips}$$

$$\text{Shear areas required} = \frac{65.6}{7.51} = 9.2$$

Assume double shear: 5 bolts required.

For a bearing connection,

$$R = \pi \frac{D^2}{4} F_v = \left[\pi \frac{(\frac{3}{4})^2}{4} \right] \times 21 = 9.28 \text{ kips}$$

$$\text{Shear areas required} = \frac{65.6}{9.28} = 7.1$$

Assume double shear: 4 bolts required.

Therefore, 5 bolts will be required in the end connection. If they are placed in a single line, U will be 0.85. The minimum spacing, $2\frac{2}{3}D$, is 2 in. Therefore a 5-bolt connection would require 4 spaces plus the end distance for a total of about $9\frac{1}{2}$ in. Assuming this is satisfactory, assume $U = 0.85$. Then

$$A_n \text{ (required)} = \frac{A_e \text{ (required)}}{U} = \frac{2.26}{0.85} = 2.66 \text{ in}^2$$

With a single line of fasteners the critical-failure path will require the deduction of a single hole from each angle which will remove $2(D + \frac{1}{8})t = 2(\frac{3}{4} + \frac{1}{8})t = 1.75t$ from the pair of angles. For $t = \frac{1}{4}$ in the deduction would be 0.44 in^2, and the required gross area is $2.66 + 0.44 = 3.10$ in^2. It is preferable to use unequal leg angles with the long legs back to back so that the legs which have the greater area will be connected directly to the gusset plate.

Try two $L3\frac{1}{2} \times 3 \times \frac{1}{4}$.

$$A_g = 3.13 \text{ in}^2 > 2.98 \text{ required} \qquad \text{O.K.}$$

$$A_n = 3.13 - 2(\tfrac{3}{4} + \tfrac{1}{8})\tfrac{1}{4} = 2.69 \text{ in}^2$$

$$U = 0.85 \qquad A_e = 2.29 > 2.26 \text{ required} \quad \text{O.K.}$$

$$r_x = 1.11 \qquad r_y \,(\tfrac{3}{8} \text{ gusset}) = 1.33$$

$$\frac{L}{r} = \frac{94}{1.11} = 85 < 300$$

Five $\frac{3}{4}$-in bolts are satisfactory for both slip-critical and bearing-type connection.

End spacing: Use $1\frac{1}{4}$ in.

Use 5 connectors with 2-in spacing plus $1\frac{1}{4}$-in end.

Check bearing strength. Bearing strength is checked for this connection in the event slip occurs. In that case deformation around the hole need not be considered. Therefore, $F_p = 1.5F_u$.

For the angle, $t = \frac{1}{4}$,

$$R_p = \tfrac{3}{4} \times \tfrac{1}{4} \times 1.5 \times 58 = 16.3 \text{ kips}$$

5-bolt areas/angle:

$$\text{Capacity} = 2 \times 5 \times 16.3 = 163 > 65.6$$

For a $\frac{3}{8}$ gusset plate,

$$R_p = \tfrac{3}{4} \times \tfrac{3}{8} \times 1.5 \times 58 = 24.47 \text{ kips}$$

5-bolt areas:

$$\text{Capacity} = 5 \times 24.47 = 122.3 > 65.6$$

Check spacing

End spacing:

$$P \text{ per bolt in angle} = \frac{65.6}{10} = 6.56 \text{ kips}$$

$$\text{Spacing required} = \frac{2 \times 6.56}{58 \times \tfrac{1}{4}} = 0.90 \text{ in}$$

Use $1\frac{1}{4}$ in minimum.

Between fasteners:

$$s = \frac{2 \times 6.56}{58 \times \tfrac{1}{4}} + \frac{\tfrac{3}{4}}{2} = 1.28 \text{ in}$$

Use 2 in minimum.

The length of the connection, $9\frac{1}{4}$ in from the first bolt to the end of the member, will require a gusset plate, and the bottom-chord tension members will be a pair of angles. One pair of angles from L_0 to L_2 and a larger pair from L_2 to L_5 will be used.

Member $L_0 L_2$. For $L_0 L_2$ the required capacity is 53.6 kips.

$$\text{Shear areas} = \frac{53.6}{7.51} = 7.1$$

Use 4 bolts in line.

$$A_g \text{ (required)} = \frac{53.6}{22} = 2.44 \text{ in}^2$$

$$A_e \text{ (required)} = \frac{53.6}{29} = 1.85 \text{ in}^2$$

$$U = 0.85 \qquad A_n \text{ (required)} = 2.18$$

$$1 \text{ hole in each angle} = 2(\tfrac{3}{4} + \tfrac{1}{8})t = 1.75t$$

Try $A_g = 2.18 + 0.44 = 2.62 \text{ in}^2$. Select $2L3 \times 2\tfrac{1}{2} \times \tfrac{1}{4}$.

$$A_g = 2.63$$

Repeat the procedure used for $U_0 L_1$ to verify that these angles with 4 connectors in a line will be satisfactory.

Example 3-15-2 (AISC/LRFD). Redesign members $L_0 L_1 L_2$ and $U_0 L_1$ of DP3-15-2 using A36 steel, $\tfrac{3}{4}$-in-diameter A325 bolts with standard holes in slip-critical connections. Although it is unlikely that a building roof truss would require slip-critical connections, this example is given to demonstrate the application of the requirements and a comparison with the welded truss.

For slip-critical joints the allowable stresses (Table 2-10) must be satisfied for the *service* loads. In addition, *all* connections must have adequate strength for the factored loads. These two criteria assure that fasteners are sufficient to prevent slip at service loads, but if slip should occur, the joint will be capable of supporting the factored loads as a bearing-type connection. In this example it is assumed that threads are not excluded from the shear planes.

Solution. The LRFD criteria for member design are given by Eqs. (3-2):

$$\phi_t P_n = \phi_t F_y A_g = 0.90 \times 36 \times A_g = 32.4 A_g$$

$$\phi_t P_n = \phi_t F_u A_e = 0.75 \times 58 \times A_e = 43.5 A_e$$

For member selection an estimate of A_g may be obtained by considering estimated values of U and the ratio A_n / A_g.

Member $U_0 L_1$. In the design of this truss for welded construction a tee was selected for the lower chord members. Because of spacing requirements for the bolted connection it will probably be necessary to use pairs of angles for all members, with a single gusset plate.

From DP3-15-2,

$$\text{Factored design force} = 78.7 \text{ kips}$$

$$\text{Service force} = 12.0 + 34.1 + 19.5 = 65.6 \text{ kips}$$

$$A_g \text{ (required)} = \frac{78.7}{32.4} = 2.43 \text{ in}^2$$

$$A_e \text{ (required)} = \frac{78.7}{43.5} = 1.81 \text{ in}^2$$

For the slip-critical connection,

$$R = \pi \frac{D^2}{4} F_v = \left[\pi \frac{(\frac{3}{4})^2}{4} \right] \times 17 = 7.51 \text{ kips}$$

$$\text{Shear areas required} = \frac{65.6}{7.51} = 9.2$$

Assume double shear: 5 bolts required.
   For a bearing connection,

$$R = \phi \left(\pi \frac{D^2}{4} \right) F_v = 0.75 \left[\pi \frac{(\frac{3}{4})^2}{4} \right] \times 48 = 15.90 \text{ kips}$$

$$\text{Shear areas required} = \frac{78.7}{15.90} = 4.9$$

Assume double shear: 3 bolts required.
   Therefore, 5 bolts will be required in the end connection. If they are placed in a single line, U will be 0.85. The minimum spacing, $2\frac{2}{3}D$, is 2 in. Therefore a 5-bolt connection would require 4 spaces plus the end distance for a total of about $9\frac{1}{2}$ in. Assuming this is satisfactory, assume $U = 0.85$. Then

$$A_n \text{ (required)} = \frac{A_e \text{ (required)}}{U} = \frac{1.81}{0.85} = 2.13 \text{ in}^2$$

With a single line of fasteners the critical-failure path will require the deduction of a single hole from each angle which will remove $2(D + \frac{1}{8})t = 2(\frac{3}{4} + \frac{1}{8})t = 1.75t$ from the pair of angles. For $t = \frac{1}{4}$ in the deduction would be 0.44 in², and the required gross area is $2.13 + 0.44 = 2.57$ in². It is preferable to use unequal leg angles with the long legs back to back so that the legs which have the greater area will be connected directly to the gusset plate.
   Try two $L3 \times 2\frac{1}{2} \times \frac{1}{4}$.

$$A_g = 2.63 \text{ in}^2 > 2.43 \text{ required} \qquad \text{O.K.}$$

$$A_n = 2.63 - 2(\tfrac{3}{4} + \tfrac{1}{8})\tfrac{1}{4} = 2.19 \text{ in}^2$$

$$U = 0.85 \qquad A_e = 1.86 > 1.81 \text{ required} \qquad \text{O.K.}$$

$$r_x = 0.945 \qquad r_y \, (\tfrac{3}{8} \text{ gusset}) = 1.13$$

$$\frac{L}{r} = \frac{94}{0.945} = 99.5 < 300$$

Five $\frac{3}{4}$-in bolts are satisfactory for both slip-critical and bearing-type connection.
   End spacing: Use $1\frac{1}{4}$ in.
   Use 5 connectors with 2-in spacing plus $1\frac{1}{4}$-in end.
   Check bearing strength. Bearing strength is checked for this connection in the event slip occurs. In that case deformation around the hole need not be considered. Therefore, $F_p = 3.0F_u$.

For the angle, $t = \frac{1}{4}$,

$$R_n = \frac{3}{4} \times \frac{1}{4} \times 3.0 \times 58 = 32.63 \text{ kips}$$

$$\phi R_n = 0.75 \times 32.63 = 24.47 \text{ kips}$$

5-bolt areas/angle:

$$\text{Capacity} = 2 \times 5 \times 24.47 = 244.7 \geq 78.7$$

For a $\frac{3}{8}$ gusset plate,

$$R_n = \frac{3}{4} \times \frac{3}{8} \times 3.0 \times 58 = 48.94 \text{ kips}$$

$$\phi R_n = 0.75 \times 48.94 = 36.70 \text{ kips}$$

5-bolt areas:

$$\text{Capacity} = 5 \times 36.70 = 183.5 \geq 78.7$$

Check spacing
End spacing:

$$P \text{ per bolt in angle} = \frac{78.7}{10} = 7.87 \text{ kips}$$

$$\text{Spacing required} = \frac{78.7}{0.75 \times 58 \times \frac{1}{4}} = 0.72 \text{ in}$$

Use $1\frac{1}{4}$ in minimum.
Between fasteners:

$$s = \frac{7.87}{0.75 \times 58 \times \frac{1}{4}} + \frac{\frac{3}{4} + \frac{1}{8}}{2} = 1.16 \text{ in}$$

Use 2 in minimum.

The length of the connection, $9\frac{1}{4}$ in from the first bolt to the end of the member, will require a gusset plate, and the bottom-chord tension members will be a pair of angles. One pair of angles from L_0 to L_2 and a larger pair from L_2 to L_5 will be used.

Member $L_0 L_2$. For $L_0 L_2$ the factored load is 64.3 kips and the service load is $9.7 + 27.9 + 16 = 53.6$ kips.

$$\text{Shear areas for service load} = \frac{53.6}{7.51} = 7.1$$

$$\text{Shear areas for factored load} = \frac{64.3}{15.90} = 4.0$$

Use 4 bolts in line.

$$A_g \text{ (required)} = \frac{64.3}{32.4} = 1.98 \text{ in}^2$$

$$A_e \text{ (required)} = \frac{64.3}{43.5} = 1.48 \text{ in}^2$$

$$U = 0.85 \qquad A_n \text{ (required)} = 1.74$$

1 hole in each angle $= 2(\frac{3}{4} + \frac{1}{8})t = 1.75t$

Try $A_g = 1.74 + 0.44 = 2.18$ in^2. Select two $L3 \times 2 \times \frac{1}{4}$.

$$A_g = 2.38$$

Repeat the procedure used for $U_0 L_1$ to verify that these angles with 4 connectors in a line will be satisfactory.

3-16   RIVETED ALUMINUM TRUSS

In DP3-16-1 the roof truss of DP3-15-1 is designed for riveted construction in aluminum 6061-T6, using the Specifications for Aluminum Structures of the Aluminum Association.[2] Because of its higher price per pound, the ratio of material cost to fabrication costs is greater for aluminum than it is for steel, so it is more important to design for minimum weight. Nevertheless, availability of shapes must be taken into account, and any saving in material cost must be compared with the cost of splices needed to substitute two members of different size for a single member.

Cold-driven 6061-T6 rivets are usually used with members of alloy 6061-T6 (Table 2-14). Holes may be punched or drilled. Holes for connections in this truss will be drilled, in which case deduction for net section is based on the actual size of the hole (Art. 3-6). The hole for a cold-driven $\frac{3}{4}$-in rivet has a 0.766-in diameter (Table 2-16). The bottom chord is designed in three sections—two members $L_0 L_2$ and one member $L_2 L_2'$. The design loads for $L_2 L_3$, $L_3 L_4$, and $L_4 L_5$ are not significantly different, so any saving in material cost that would result if a lighter member were used for $L_2 L_3$ would almost certainly be less than the cost of the splice.

The $2\frac{1}{2} \times 1\frac{1}{2} \times \frac{3}{16}$ angles furnish more net area than is needed for $U_3 L_4$, $U_4 L_5$, and $U_5 L_5$. However, material thinner than about one-third to one-fourth the diameter of the rivet is considered to be a minimum, and the leg of an angle should not be smaller than about three times the rivet diameter. Therefore, these angles are minimum for $\frac{3}{4}$-in rivets.

Joint L_3. Allowable stresses for 6061-T6 rivets are given in Table 2-14. Since the chord is continuous at L_3, the rivets connecting it to the gusset plate resist only the difference between the tensions in $L_2 L_3$ and $L_3 L_4$. The gusset plate is dimensioned to provide the required distance of two diameters of the rivet from the edge toward which the rivet pressure is directed.

Although this truss weighs only slightly more than half as much as a comparable design for riveted steel construction, it would cost two to three or more times as much. Thus, unless the additional cost were justified by the corrosion hazard, or for some other reason, the aluminum truss could not possibly compete with the steel structure.

3-17   GUSSET PLATES

The riveted joints of the truss considered in DP3-16-1 are simple enough and usually require no more attention than was given to L_3. The lateral dimensions

RIVETED ALUMINUM TRUSS

DP3–16–1

Truss of DP3 - 15 - 1
Material : aluminum 6061 - T6
¾ rivets : aluminum 6061 - T6
Specifications : Aluminum Association (Ref. 2)

Tension members

Member	Force		Reqd. area	Section	Net area	L/r	
$L_0 L_1 L_2$	53.6	@ 19 =	2.82 in.²	2L 3½ × 3½ × ¼	3.00	77/1.07 =	72
$L_2 L_3$	87.2	@ 19 =	4.58	2L 4 × 4 × ⁷⁄₁₆	5.95	72/1.21 =	60
$L_3 L_4$	102.2	@ 19 =	5.38	do	5.95	do	
$L_4 L_5$	108.8	@ 19 =	5.71	do	5.95	do	
$U_0 L_1$	65.6	@ 19 =	3.45	2L 3½ × 3½ × ⁵⁄₁₆	3.70	94/1.06 =	89
$U_1 L_2$	44.0	@ 19 =	2.32	2L 3 × 3 × ¼	2.48	94/0.91 =	103
$U_2 L_3$	20.2	@ 19 =	1.06	2L 2½ × 1½ × ³⁄₁₆	1.15	98/0.63 =	156
$U_3 L_4$	9.9	@ 19 =	0.52	do	1.15	102/0.63 =	162
$U_4 L_5$	2.0	@ 19 =	0.11	do	1.15	106/0.63 =	168
$U_5 L_5$	10.1	@ 19 =	0.53	do	1.15	84/0.63 =	133

Joint L_3 (⁵⁄₁₆" *gusset plate*)

Rivets: shear = 11 × 2 × 0.461 = 10.1ᵏ

brg. = 34 × ⁵⁄₁₆ × 0.766 = 8.14ᵏ

$U_2 L_3$ 20.2/8.14 = 3, $U_3 L_3$ 13.6/8.14 = 2, $L_2 L_3 L_4$ 15/8.14 = 2

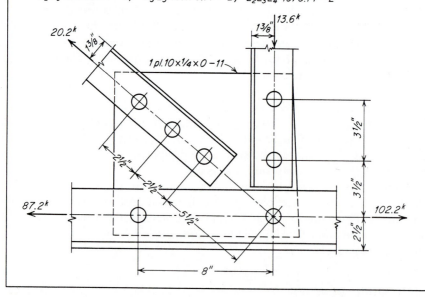

of a gusset plate are determined principally by the fastener requirements of the members, which leaves only the thickness to be based on other considerations. According to the AASHTO specifications, "Gusset plates shall be of ample thickness to resist shear, direct stress, and flexure, acting on the weakest or critical section of maximum stress." This is all very good, but the only practicable method of estimating these stresses is based on the assumption that the elementary formulas for beams apply, and these formulas are valid only for beams whose span is more than twice the depth and at cross sections not closer to concentrated loads than about half the depth. The ordinary gusset plate falls considerably short of these requirements, so the results obtained by the application of beam formulas are of questionable value and may be misleading.

Experimental data from which one can judge the accuracy of the ordinary beam formulas when they are applied to gusset plates are contained in the report of an investigation of stress distributions in the gusset plates of a typical bottom-chord joint of a Warren truss.[15] The tests were made on a model. Strains in the plates were measured at service loads, but the joint was not tested to failure. As might be expected, the tests demonstrated that bending stresses are not distributed linearly and that the neutral axis of a cross section does not coincide with the centroidal axis. The maximum bending stress was found to occur at an interior point rather than on the extreme fiber, and the shearing stresses were not distributed according to the parabolic law which corresponds to a linear distribution of bending stresses.

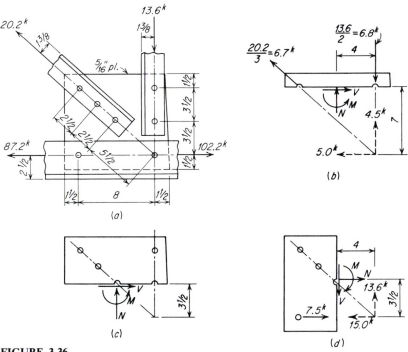

FIGURE 3-36

We will use the joint L_3 of DP3-16-1 to illustrate the conventional analysis of a gusset plate. A plate of this size would not be analyzed in practice, but the investigation is no different in principle for gusset plates of larger trusses. The stresses are determined on sections which, for convenience, are cut parallel to and normal to the chord member. It is impossible to tell by inspection what section will experience the largest stress.

The detail of the joint is shown in Fig. 3-36a. The portion of the gusset plate which lies above a horizontal section through the upper rivets of the gusset plate is shown in Fig. 3-36b. It is assumed that the forces on these rivets act on the part of the plate lying above the section. Therefore, one-half the force in the vertical member and one-third the force in the diagonal member must be resisted by an internal force on the section. The components of this force are the normal force N, the shearing force V, and the couple M. The 6.7-kip force from the diagonal member is resolved into two components at its intersection with the line of action of the vertical force. Then

$$N = 6.8 - 4.5 = 2.3 \text{ kips}$$

$$V = 5.0 \text{ kips}$$

$$M = 5.0 \times 7 + 2.3 \times 4 = 44.2 \text{ in·kips}$$

The corresponding stresses are

$$f_v = \frac{3}{2} \frac{V}{A} = \frac{1.5 \times 5.0}{11 \times 0.31} = 2.2 \text{ ksi}$$

$$f_b = \frac{N}{A} \pm \frac{Mc}{I} = \frac{-2.3}{11 \times 0.31} \pm \frac{44.2 \times 6}{0.31 \times 11^2}$$

$$= -0.7 \pm 7.1 = +6.4 \text{ or } -7.8 \text{ ksi}$$

The portion of the plate above a horizontal section through the lower rivet hole in $U_3 L_3$ is shown in Fig. 3-36c. At this section, the internal force is the resultant of the forces in $L_2 L_3$ and $L_3 L_3$. Therefore, $N = 0$, $V = 15.0$ kips, and $M = 15.0 \times 3.5 = 52.5$ in·kips. Then

$$f_v = \frac{1.5 \times 15.0}{11 \times 0.31} = 6.6 \text{ ksi}$$

$$f_b = \frac{52.5 \times 6}{0.31 \times 11^2} = \pm 8.4 \text{ ksi}$$

A sketch of the part of the plate to the left of a vertical section through the lower rivet of $U_2 L_3$ is shown in Fig. 3-36d. This portion of the plate contains all the rivets in $U_2 L_3$ and one of the two rivets in the chord member. Therefore, the forces acting on it are the two components of the force on $U_2 L_3$, shown at the common intersection of the three members at the joint, and one-half the difference between the forces in $L_2 L_3$ and $L_3 L_4$. The corresponding internal forces on the section are

$$N = 15.0 - 7.5 = 7.5 \text{ kips}$$

$$V = 13.6 \text{ kips}$$

$$M = 13.6 \times 4 - 7.5 \times 3.5 = 28.2 \text{ in·kips}$$

Then

$$f_v = \frac{1.5 \times 13.6}{10 \times 0.31} = 6.6 \text{ ksi}$$

$$f_b = \frac{+7.5}{10 \times 0.31} \pm \frac{28.2 \times 6}{0.31 \times 10^2}$$

$$= +2.4 \pm 5.5 = +7.9 \text{ or } -3.1 \text{ ksi}$$

The calculated stresses all are substantially less than allowable values. It should be reemphasized that no designer would analyze a gusset plate for a truss of this size. The analysis here is intended merely for demonstration. And, in any case, the results are of questionable value, for reasons that were discussed earlier in this article.

Compressive stresses may develop parallel to and at the edge of gusset plates. This is because deflection of a truss tends to change the angles between its members. Thus, the upper part of the gusset plate in Fig. 3-36a will be compressed if the angle between the adjacent members decreases. Therefore, the width of the top edge must not be too large, compared with the thickness, or the plate may buckle. Bending of this kind, which is called *local buckling*, is discussed in Art. 4-12. The AASHTO specifications require than an unsupported edge of a gusset plate be stiffened if it is longer than $11{,}000/\sqrt{F_{y,\text{psi}}}$ times the thickness. This gives, for example, 58 for A36 steel.

3-18 SECONDARY STRESSES IN TRUSS MEMBERS

The principles of design discussed in this chapter are based on the assumption that tension members resist only axial forces. Such a condition is rarely, if ever, realized. If the members of the truss ABC shown in Fig. 3-37a are connected with

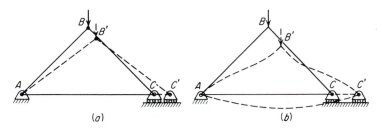

FIGURE 3-37

frictionless pins, the truss will be deformed by the force P to the shape $AB'C'$. If the members are bolted, riveted, or welded at the joints so that the angles formed by the members resist change, the truss must assume the shape $AB'C'$ of Fig. 3-37b. In the first case the tension member AC suffers only elongation. In the second case it undergoes both elongation and bending, and the maximum stress is no longer correctly given by $f = P/A$ but instead by $f = P/A + Mc/I$. The bending stress is called a *secondary stress*.

Joint rigidity may induce one-directional curvature, as in the tension member AC, or reversed curvature, as in the compression member AB. Although values of the corresponding end moments can be determined, secondary stresses are usually neglected in design. This is not to say that they are necessarily small but rather that there is sufficient evidence from both analytical studies and experience to indicate that they can safely be neglected, provided that the engineer is aware of certain precautions which should be observed in order to guard against their becoming excessive. Secondary stresses are inversely proportional to the ratio of the length of the member to its width in the plane of the truss. If this ratio is 10 or more, secondary stresses are not likely to exceed 20 or 30 percent of the primary stresses.

The availability of computer programs to analyze a structure either as a truss or as a plane frame greatly simplifies the evaluation of secondary stresses. Analysis as a plane frame on the assumption of rigid connections provides an upper bound to their magnitude. If the rigidity of the gusset plate can be evaluated, the frame analysis can be made with a reduced stiffness at the ends of the members for a more reasonable evaluation.

3-19 FURTHER DISCUSSION OF RESIDUAL STRESSES

In Art. 3-1 the effect of residual stresses on the behavior of tension members was discussed and the procedure for determining the stress-strain curve for the member was presented for an idealized case. In this article we will discuss the method by which residual stresses are determined in the laboratory and provide more detailed discussion of their effect on member behavior.

The determination of residual stresses requires that a sample cross section be prepared and instrumented at a distance from the ends sufficient for the residual stresses to be developed. For structural applications residual stresses are evaluated over a relatively long gage length, 8 or 10 in, so that average values are obtained. The instrumented section is then separated into small pieces to permit the internal stresses to relax. Care is required during this process so as not to change the residual stresses which are to be measured. When the cross section is separated, a change in the length of the gage of each piece will occur, depending upon the sign and magnitude of the stresses released. Conversion of the change in length to strain in the conventional manner and multiplication by the modulus of elasticity yields the value of the residual stress. Some typical results are presented by Bjorhovde,[16] Nagaraja,[17] and Ingvarsson.[18]

The effect of residual stress on the behavior of a tension member was demonstrated in Art. 3-1 by considering the idealized (webless) H shown in Fig. 3-2b. For the residual-strain distribution shown in Fig. 3-2c the cross section will remain elastic for all strains from zero to 0.0008, and the corresponding stress is $f = E\epsilon$. Between 0.0008 and 0.0016 some parts of the cross section are elastic and some are inelastic, but yielding will be in proportion to strain since the residual-stress distribution is linear. The relation between stress and strain, in this case, is a quadratic equation of the form

$$f = A\epsilon^2 + B\epsilon + C$$

Constants A, B, and C can be evaluated by the following conditions.

$$\epsilon = 0.0008 \qquad f = 24 \text{ ksi}$$

$$\epsilon = 0.0016 \qquad f = 36 \text{ ksi}$$

$$\epsilon = 0.0008 \qquad \frac{df}{d\epsilon} = 30,000 \text{ ksi}$$

The last condition exists because yielding starts gradually at $\epsilon = 0.0008$ so that $df/d\epsilon = E$. Solution of the three simultaneous equations yields

$$f = -18,750,000\epsilon^2 + 60,000\epsilon - 12$$

For residual-stress distributions made up of a series of straight lines, there will be a different equation for each straight-line segment. For distributions of the form shown in Fig. 3-1, it is necessary to calculate the average stress corresponding to a particular value of applied strain for a large number of different values, using the basic procedure described for Fig. 3-2.

Example 3-19-1. Determine the equations for the stress-strain behavior in tension of the 16 × 1 in plate with the residual stresses shown in Fig. 3-38. $F_y = 36$ ksi, $E = 30,000$ ksi.

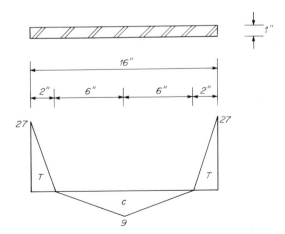

FIGURE 3-38

Solution

$$\text{Maximum residual tensile strain} = +\frac{27}{30,000} = +0.0009 \text{ in/in}$$

$$\text{Maximum residual compressive strain} = -\frac{9}{30,000} = -0.0003 \text{ in/in}$$

$0 \leq \epsilon \leq 0.0003$

$$f = E\epsilon$$

$0.0003 \leq \epsilon \leq 0.0012$. First yield occurs when $\epsilon = 0.0003$ in/in. Yielding proceeds uniformly until $\epsilon = 0.0012$ in/in. With this value $P = 522$ kips and $f = \frac{522}{16} = 32.625$ ksi. Then

$\epsilon = 0.0003$	$f = 9$ ksi	$9 = (0.0003)^2 A + 0.0003B + C$
$\epsilon = 0.0003$	$\dfrac{df}{d\epsilon} = 30,000$	$30,000 = 2(0.0003)A + B$
$\epsilon = 0.0012$	$f = 32.625$ ksi	$32.625 = (0.0012)^2 A + 0.0012B + C$

Solution yields

$$f = -4,166,667\epsilon^2 + 32,500\epsilon - 0.375$$

$0.0012 \leq \epsilon \leq 0.0015$. Complete yield occurs when $\epsilon = 0.0015$ in/in for which

$\epsilon = 0.0012$	$f = 32.625$ ksi	$32.625 = (0.0012)^2 A + 0.0012B + C$
$\epsilon = 0.0015$	$f = 36.0$ ksi	$36.0 = (0.0015)^2 A + 0.0015B + C$
$\epsilon = 0.0015$	$\dfrac{df}{d\epsilon} = 0$	$0 = 2(0.0015)A + B$

Solution yields

$$f = -37,500,000\epsilon^2 + 112,500\epsilon - 48.375$$

This procedure can be applied to a residual-stress distribution with any number of straight-line segments. For segments intermediate between the beginning of yield and full yielding of the cross section, the three conditions must correspond to the average stress for an applied strain.

Typical distributions of residual stresses are irregular. If the actual response to load is desired, the basic procedure can easily be converted into a numerical procedure for computer evaluation. The implementation of the procedure can be accomplished in the following steps:

1. Convert the residual-stress distribution to the residual-strain distribution.

2. Apply a uniform strain to the cross section.

3. Add steps 1 and 2 to obtain the actual strain at every point on the cross section.

4. Convert step 3 to stress using the elastic modulus.

5. Wherever stress by step 4 is greater than the yield point, it should be set equal to the yield point.

6. Perform numerical integration over the cross section to obtain the load corresponding to the applied strain.

7. Calculate the average stress by dividing step 6 by the gross area of the cross section.

8. Plot the average stress from step 7 versus the applied uniform strain from step 2.

PROBLEMS

3-1. Construct the stress-strain curve to the beginning of unrestrained yield for a tension test of the member shown in Fig. P3-1. The residual-stress distribution is given on the figure, with stresses in ksi. The coupon yield point is 40 ksi.

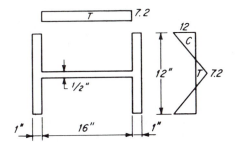

FIGURE P3-1

3-2. Construct the stress-strain curve to the beginning of unrestrained yield for a tension test of the member shown in Fig. P3-2. The residual-stress distribution is given on the figure, with stresses in ksi. The residual-stress distribution is the same for all four plates. The coupon yield point is 36 ksi.

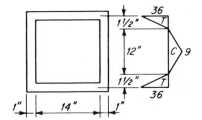

FIGURE P3-2

3-3. The end of a tension member consisting of a $\frac{1}{2} \times 10$ in A36 plate is lap-welded to a member which allows a lap of 8 in. The load is 25 kips *DL* and 75 kips *LL*. Determine the required welds. AISC specification.

3-4. The 6-in leg of an A36 $6 \times 4 \times \frac{1}{2}$ angle is fillet-welded to a $\frac{3}{8}$-in plate. The load is 25 kips *DL* and 75 kips *LL*. Proportion the welds to eliminate eccentricity of the connection in the plane of the welds. The connection cannot be longer than 12 in. AISC specification.

3-5. Design and detail a welded joint at L_3 for the truss of DP3-15-1. Member $U_3 L_3$ consists of two angles $2 \times 1\frac{1}{4} \times \frac{1}{4}$ with the long legs back to back.

3-6. Design and detail a welded joint at L_3 for the truss of DP3-15-2. Member $U_3 L_3$ consists of two angles $2 \times 1\frac{1}{4} \times \frac{1}{4}$ with the long legs back to back.

3-7. Design the bottom-chord and tension web members for the truss of DP3-15-1 using W or S shapes. Position the bottom chord so that its web is in the vertical plane with the web members butting against its top flange. Design and detail the connection at L_1 if member $U_1 L_1$ is an S5 × 10 with its web in the plane of the truss.

3-8. Design the bottom-chord and tension web members for the truss of DP3-15-2 using W or S shapes. Position the bottom chord so that its web is in the vertical plane with the web members butting against its top flange. Design and detail the connection at L_1 if member $U_1 L_1$ is an S5 × 10 with its web in the plane of the truss.

3-9. Design W or S bottom-chord and single-angle web tension members for the truss of DP3-15-1. Design and detail the connection at L_1 if member $U_1 L_1$ is a $3\frac{1}{2} \times 3\frac{1}{2} \times \frac{7}{16}$ angle.

3-10. Design W or S bottom-chord and single-angle web tension members for the truss of DP3-15-2. Design and detail the connection at L_1 if member $U_1 L_1$ is a $3\frac{1}{2} \times 3\frac{1}{2} \times \frac{7}{16}$ angle.

3-11. Suggest several types of web members that would connect satisfactorily if the bottom chord of DP3-15-1 were a W or S with its web in the horizontal plane.

3-12. Suggest several types of web members that would connect satisfactorily if the bottom chord of DP3-15-2 were a W or S with its web in the horizontal plane.

3-13. A balcony in a building is 16 ft wide. It is supported at the outer edge by hangers welded to roof trusses spaced 20 ft on centers. The bottom chord of each truss is a WT7 × 15. Each hanger is welded to the end of a W16 × 40 beam which spans the width of the balcony and is connected at the opposite end to a column at the wall of the building. The live load is 100 psf and the dead load 60 psf. Design the hanger and its connections to the truss and the beam. AISC specification, A36 steel.

3-14. The truss shown in Fig. P3-14 is to be used in a steel-framed building to span a 120-ft column-free space. The truss supports floor loads of 10 kips *DL* and 30 kips *LL* at each upper-chord panel point and additional loads of 40 kips *DL* and 120 kips *LL* at U_2 and U'_2 from columns supporting floors above. Design the tension members for welded construction. AISC specification.

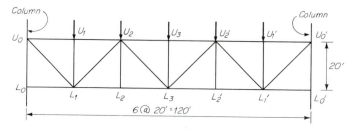

FIGURE P3-14

3-15. A tension member consisting of two $6 \times 3\frac{1}{2} \times \frac{1}{2}$ angles with the long legs back to back (Fig. 3-4a) is connected to a $\frac{3}{8}$-in gusset plate between the legs. There are two rows of bolts in the 6-in legs. A gusset plate for diagonal bracing connects with one row of bolts to each of the $3\frac{1}{2}$-in legs. Determine a bolt pattern that will require deduction for only two holes in each angle, and compute the permissible load. A36 steel, $\frac{3}{4}$-in A325 bolts.

3-16. Design and detail a butt splice to join two tension members, each of which is a $\frac{3}{4} \times 12$ A36 plate. The axial tension is 40 kips *DL* and 125 kips *LL*. AISC specification, $\frac{3}{4}$-in A325 bolts.
(*a*) Slip-critical connection.
(*b*) Bearing-type connection, threads not excluded.
(*c*) Bearing-type connection, threads excluded.

3-17. Design a single-angle tension member and its connection by one leg to a $\frac{5}{16}$-in gusset plate. The axial tension is 20 kips *DL* and 60 kips *LL*. A36 steel, A325 bolts in a bearing-type connection with threads excluded from the shear plane.

3-18. Same as Prob. 3-17 but with AASHTO specifications. AASHTO allows only half the area of the unconnected leg to be counted.

3-19. Compute the factors of safety for the member of Prob. 3-18 with respect to (*a*) gross yielding and (*b*) fracture. Take the various efficiencies in Eq. (3-13) into account. Assume the ductility factor K_1 to be unity and assume punched holes.

3-20. Design a tension member of the type shown in Fig. 3-4*d* and its connection to a $\frac{3}{8}$-in gusset plate with A325 bolts. The connection is to be bearing type with threads included in the shear planes. The tension is 35 kips *DL* and 105 kips *LL*. A36 steel, AISC specification.

3-21. A $\frac{3}{4} \times 9$ in A514 plate carries an axial tension of 75 kips *DL* and 225 kips *LL*. It connects to a $\frac{1}{2}$-in gusset plate with A490 bolts in a bearing-type connection, with no threads in the shear plane. Design the connection. Use a bolt layout which will allow the member to yield on the gross section before breaking on the net section if it is feasible. AISC specification.

3-22. Design double-angle sections for the bottom-chord and tension web members of the truss of DP3-15-1. A36 steel, A307 bolts.

3-23. Design double-angle sections for the bottom-chord and tension web members of the truss of DP3-15-2. A36 steel, A307 bolts.

3-24. Design the hanger for the balcony described in Prob. 3-13, using A325 bolted connections at both the balcony beam and the truss.

3-25. Redesign the members of the truss of DP3-15-3 in A572 Grade 50 steel.

3-26. Design the tension members of the truss of Prob. 3-14 for bolted construction. Design a splice for $L_0 L_2$ to $L_2 L_2$.

3-27. A bridge-truss tension member consists of two $1\frac{1}{4} \times 24$ flange plates and a $\frac{5}{8} \times 20$ web plate welded in the form of an I. The load is 450 kips *DL* and 1350 kips *LL*. The member is designed on the basis of its gross cross-sectional area, so a stub is required at each end for bolted connections (Art. 3-13). Design the stub, using six parallel rows of bolts in each flange (three on each side of the web). The member is of A441 steel, and the bolts are 1-in A325. Use A441 steel for the stub. AASHTO specifications.

3-28. Design stubs for the member of Prob. 3-27 so that the stub flanges and web are the same size as those of the member.

3-29. Design a single-angle tension member 12 ft long and its connection at each end to a $\frac{5}{16}$-in gusset plate. The tension is 20 kips *DL* and 50 kips *LL*. The angle cannot extend more than 15 in on the gusset. AISC specification, A36 steel, $\frac{7}{8}$-in A325 bolts, slip-critical connection.

3-30. Design and detail joint L_1 for the truss of DP3-16-1. Member U_1L_1 consists of two angles $3 \times 2\frac{1}{2} \times \frac{5}{16}$ with long legs back to back.

3-31. Design and detail joint L_2 for the truss of DP3-16-1. Member U_2L_2 consists of two angles $3 \times 2 \times \frac{1}{4}$ with long legs back to back.

REFERENCES

1. Beedle, L. S., and L. Tall: Basic Column Strength, *J. Struct. Div. ASCE*, July 1960.
2. "Specifications for Aluminum Structures," The Aluminum Association, Washington, D.C., April 1982.
3. Hardash, S. G., and R. Bjorhovde: New Design Criteria for Gusset Plates in Tension, *Eng. J., AISC*, 2d quarter, 1985.
4. Cochrane, V. H.: Rules for Rivet Hole Deduction in Tension Members, *Eng. News-Rec.*, Nov. 16, 1922.
5. Brady, W. G., and D. C. Drucker: Investigation and Limit Analysis of Net Area in Tension, *Trans. ASCE*, vol. 120, 1955.
6. Timoshenko, S. P., and J. N. Goodier: "Theory of Elasticity," 3d ed., McGraw-Hill, New York, 1970.
7. Schutz, F. W., and N. M. Newmark: The Efficiency of Riveted Structural Joints, *Univ. Ill. Struct. Res. Ser.* 30, 1952.
8. Munse, W. H., and E. Chesson, Jr.: Riveted and Bolted Joints: Net Section Design, *J. Struct. Div. ASCE*, February 1963.
9. Kuhn, P.: "Stresses in Aircraft and Shell Structures," McGraw-Hill, New York, 1956.
10. Bendigo, R. A., R. M. Hansen, and J. L. Rumpf: Long Bolted Joints, *J. Struct. Div. ASCE*, December 1963.
11. Davis, R. E., G. B. Woodruff, and H. E. Davis: Tension Tests of Large Riveted Joints, *Trans. ASCE*, vol. 105, 1940.
12. Foremen, R. T., and J. L. Rumpf: Static Tests of Compact Bolted Joints, *Trans. ASCE*, vol. 126, 1961, pt. II.
13. Fisher, J. W., and J. L. Rumpf: Analysis of Bolted Butt Joints, *J. Struct. Div. ASCE*, October 1965.
14. Chesson, E., and W. H. Munse: Riveted and Bolted Joints: Truss-Type Tensile Connections, *J. Struct. Div. ASCE*, February 1963.
15. Whitmore, R. E.: Experimental Investigation of Stresses in Gusset Plates, *Univ. Tenn., Eng. Exp. Stn. Bull.* 16, 1952.
16. Bjorhovde, R., J. Brossetti, G. A. Alpsten, and L. Tall: Residual Stresses in Thick Welded Plates, *Weld. J.*, vol. 41, 1972.
17. Nagaraja, N. R., F. R. Estuar, and L. Tall: Residual Stresses In Welded Shapes, *Weld. J.*, vol. 43, 1974.
18. Ingvarsson, Lars: Residual Stresses in Welded Box Columns, *Inst. Byggnadsstatik, Stockholm, Bull.* 119, 1977.

CHAPTER
4

COMPRESSION MEMBERS

4-1 INTRODUCTION

Compression members are usually given names which identify them as particular members in a structure. The vertical compression members in building frames are called *columns* in the United States and *stanchions* in England. Compression members are sometimes called *posts*, and the diagonal members at the end of through-bridge trusses are usually called *end posts*. Other compression members in trusses are known according to their position as chord members or web members. The principal compression member in a crane is called a *boom*. Some types of compression member are called *struts*. Members which connect adjacent frames at the eaves of some types of industrial buildings are called *eave struts*.

4-2 ELASTIC BUCKLING OF COLUMNS

There is a specific magnitude of load at which a straight, homogeneous, centrally loaded column becomes unstable. By this is meant that at this load the column may begin to bend, even though there is no apparent moment to initiate bending. It is instructive to study this phenomenon for the pin-ended member of Fig. 4-1*a*,

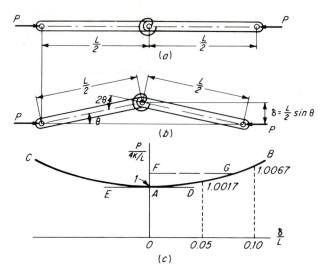

FIGURE 4-1

which consists of two rigid bars connected to one another by a linearly elastic torsion spring and which is loaded with axial compressive forces P. If the member assumes the deflected shape shown in Fig. 4-1b, equilibrium requires that

$$P\delta = P\frac{L}{2}\sin\theta = 2K\theta \tag{a}$$

where δ is the deflection at midlength and K is the spring constant. Equation (a) gives

$$P = \frac{4K}{L}\frac{\theta}{\sin\theta} \tag{b}$$

The curve CAB in Fig. 4-1c is a plot of Eq. (b). If $\delta = 0$, $\theta = 0$ and $P = 4K/L$. For any load less than this, $\delta = 0$ and the column is straight. This condition is represented by a point between O and A on OA in Fig. 4-1c. Thus, if the column is displaced laterally (by an accidental lateral force, say) while it is supporting a load $P \le 4K/L$, it will straighten when the accidental force disappears. This is because the moment in the spring exceeds the moment $P\delta$, so it is a restoring moment. Therefore, any point between O and A represents *stable* equilibrium in the straight configuration of Fig. 4-1a. On the other hand, if the column is straight while it is supporting $P > 4K/L$, which corresponds to a point such as F on OA extended, it is in *unstable* equilibrium, and the slightest disturbance will cause it to deflect the amount δ for which it will be in stable equilibrium (to G on AB). Furthermore, it will not straighten unless P is reduced or it is pushed back.

The value of P at which a straight column becomes unstable is called the *critical load*. When the column bends at the critical load, it is said to have buckled. Therefore, the critical load is also called the *buckling load*. At the critical load the column is extremely sensitive to increase in load, in the sense that a very slight increase is accompanied by a large lateral deflection. Thus, if the critical load $P = 4K/L$ for the column of Fig. 4-1a is increased by only $\frac{2}{3}$ percent, δ is 10 percent of the column length L (Fig. 4-1c).

If we assume that the deflection δ in Fig. 4-1b is small, we can equate it to $\theta L/2$, rather than $(L/2)\sin\theta$, so that

$$P\delta = P\frac{L}{2}\theta = 2K\theta \tag{c}$$

from which

$$P = \frac{4K}{L} \tag{d}$$

Thus, we obtain the critical value of P, but we get no information beyond this; that is, δ is indeterminate if we solve the problem in this fashion. This solution to the stability problem is depicted by OA and EAD in Fig. 4-1c, which show that δ is zero for any P less than the critical load but may have any small value, including zero, at the critical load. In this sense, there are two equilibrium configurations at the critical load, the straight one and one that is slightly bent. Because of this, the critical load is said to correspond to a *bifurcation* of the equilibrium configuration.

Figure 4-2 shows a straight, homogeneous, pin-ended, centrally loaded column which has buckled. At any point of the deflected centerline the bending moment $M = Py$, and equilibrium requires that

$$\frac{EI}{\rho} = Py \tag{e}$$

where ρ is the radius of curvature. Using the known expression for curvature $1/\rho$, we get

$$EI\frac{-d^2y/dx^2}{[1 + (dy/dx)^2]^{3/2}} = Py \tag{f}$$

where the negative sign is needed because d^2y/dx^2 itself is negative.

FIGURE 4-2

Equation (f) is not easy to solve. However, if we make the usual assumption that deflections are small, we can write

$$-EI\frac{d^2y}{dx^2} = Py \tag{g}$$

With the substitution

$$k^2 = \frac{P}{EI} \tag{h}$$

Eq. (g) gives

$$\frac{d^2y}{dx^2} + k^2y = 0 \tag{i}$$

the solution of which is

$$y = A\sin kx + B\cos kx \tag{j}$$

From the boundary condition $y = 0$ at $x = 0$, we find $B = 0$, and

$$y = A\sin kx \tag{k}$$

To satisfy the boundary condition $y = 0$ at $x = L$, we may have either $A = 0$ or $\sin kL = 0$. The first solution gives $y = 0$, in which case the column is straight, while the second gives

$$kL = \pi,\ 2\pi,\ \ldots,\ n\pi \tag{l}$$

From Eqs. (h) and (l)

$$P = \frac{\pi^2EI}{L^2},\ \frac{4\pi^2EI}{L^2},\ \ldots,\ \frac{n^2\pi^2EI}{L^2} \tag{m}$$

If we substitute the several values from Eq. (l) into Eq. (k), we see that the column-deflection curve is a half sine wave for the first value of P, two half waves for the second, and so on. Therefore, since the higher values of P exist only if there are intermediate lateral supports, we take as the fundamental case

$$P_E = \frac{\pi^2EI}{L^2} \tag{4-1}$$

where P_E denotes the Euler load, named for Leonhard Euler, who derived it in 1759. Since the formula is invalid if the stress exceeds the proportional limit, it is more convenient to write it in terms of the Euler (critical) stress F_E:

$$F_E = \frac{P_E}{A} = \frac{\pi^2EI}{AL^2} = \frac{\pi^2E}{(L/r)^2} \tag{4-2}$$

where A is the area and r the radius of gyration of the column cross section. Buckling at stresses exceeding the proportional limit is discussed in Art. 4-4.

Using δ for the deflection A at midlength, Eqs. (k) and (l) give the deflected shape for the Euler load,

$$y = \delta \sin \frac{\pi x}{L} \tag{4-3}$$

The deflection is indeterminate, because we used Eq. (g) as an approximation to Eq. (f). This is analogous to the situation for the two-bar column of Fig. 4-1 when we assume θ to be small, which gives us the critical load [Eq. (d)] but leaves θ undetermined. Thus, OA and EAD in Fig. 4-1c also depict the behavior of the Euler column, provided we change the axis of ordinates to P/P_E.

Exact solutions of Eq. (f) can be obtained in terms of elliptic integrals.[1] An approximate solution for the column with hinged ends is given by[2]

$$\frac{P}{P_E} = 1 + \frac{\pi^2}{8} \frac{\delta^2}{L^2} \tag{4-4}$$

This equation gives values of P accurate to within 1 percent up to $\delta/L = 0.25$. Except for the numerical values of the ordinates, CAB of Fig. 4-1c is a plot of Eq. (4-4), provided the axis of coordinates is labeled P/P_E. The value of P/P_E corresponding to $\delta/L = 0.1$ is 1.0123, which is of the same order of magnitude as that shown (1.0067) for the two-bar column. Thus, a column 10 ft long would be deflected 1 ft by a load only $1\frac{1}{4}$ percent larger than the Euler load, provided it is slender enough to accept such a deflection without being stressed beyond the proportional limit.

To determine the load at which Eq. (4-4) ceases to hold, we compute

$$f = \frac{P}{A} + \frac{Mc}{I} = \frac{P}{A}\left(1 + \frac{\delta c}{r^2}\right) = \frac{P}{A}\left(1 + \frac{\delta}{L} \frac{L}{r} \frac{c}{r}\right) \tag{n}$$

Assume the column to be 10 ft long with a slenderness ratio $L/r = 150$. For the load $P = 1.0001 P_E$, Eq. (4-4) gives $\delta/L = 0.009$, so δ is about 1 in. Also,

$$\frac{P}{A} = \frac{1.0001 P_E}{A} = \frac{1.0001 \pi^2 EI}{AL^2} = \frac{1.0001 \pi^2 E}{(L/r)^2} = \frac{30{,}000\pi^2}{150^2} = 13.2 \text{ ksi}$$

Furthermore, $c \approx 1.25r$ if the cross section is an I. Substituting these values into Eq. (n) gives

$$f = 13.2(1 + 0.009 \times 150 \times 1.25) = 36 \text{ ksi}$$

Thus, if the column is of A36 steel, it reaches yield stress on the extreme fiber at midlength (Fig. 4-3b) when the axial load is only 0.01 percent more than the critical load (point B in Fig. 4-3a). Further increase in load produces strains in

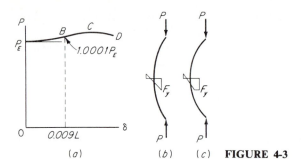

FIGURE 4-3

the region of maximum moment which exceed the yield strain ϵ_y. Therefore, with plane cross sections remaining plane, stress is no longer distributed linearly over a cross section where $\epsilon \geq \epsilon_y$; instead, it varies according to the f-ϵ curve for the material. Thus, for the A36 steel assumed in this example, which has a yield plateau, there will be uniform stress F_y in the yielded zones. For this case, the maximum load P is reached with a distribution of stress at midlength, such as that in Fig. 4-3c.* Equilibrium at still larger deflections is possible only at reduced value of P (CD of Fig. 4-3a). This suggests that the difference between the postbuckling strength (point C) and the buckling strength P_E is so small that the Euler load is a practical measure of the ultimate strength of the perfectly straight axially loaded column, provided it buckles while the stress $f = P/A$ does not exceed the proportional limit.

Since $OP_E BCD$ depicts the behavior of the column, any lateral deflection δ, however small, is necessarily accompanied by some increase in the load P_E which initiates buckling. However, the plot of Eq. (4-4), $P_E B$ of Fig. 4-3a, is tangent to the horizontal at P_E, so this increase in load for a small deflection at the beginning of buckling is a small quantity of the second order. This is why the deflection is indeterminate when we neglect second-order quantities to obtain Eqs. (c) and (g).

4-3   EFFECT OF INITIAL CROOKEDNESS

If the two-bar column of Fig. 4-1a is not initially straight, so that $\theta = \theta_0$ when $P = 0$ (Fig. 4-4a), equilibrium under the load P (Fig. 4-4b) requires that

$$P\delta = P \frac{L}{2} \sin \theta = 2K(\theta - \theta_0) \qquad (a)$$

---

* In some cases there will be penetration of yield stress on the convex side as well as on the concave side when the maximum load is reached.

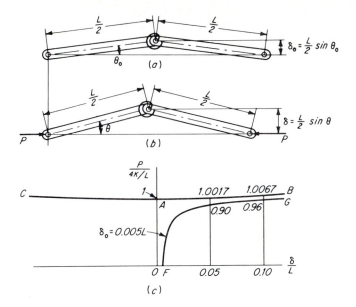

FIGURE 4-4

from which

$$P = \frac{4K}{L} \frac{\theta - \theta_0}{\sin \theta} \tag{b}$$

Curve FG in Fig. 4-4c shows the corresponding variation of P with δ for $\delta_0 = 0.005L$. Curve CAB from Fig. 4-1c for the initially straight column is also shown for comparison. Evidently, FG approaches OAB with diminishing δ_0. However, we see that the behavior represented by OAB cannot be realized in fact, since it requires the member to be absolutely straight in the unloaded condition.

Using the notation P_{cr} for the critical load $4K\theta/(L \sin \theta)$, from Eq. (b) of Art. 4-2, θ in Eq. (b) above is given by

$$\theta = \frac{\theta_0}{1 - P/P_{cr}} \tag{c}$$

This equation shows that θ increases more and more rapidly as P approaches the critical load.

Consider next the column in Fig. 4-5, which has the initial (unloaded) shape

$$y_0 = \delta_0 \sin \frac{\pi x}{L} \tag{d}$$

The equation of equilibrium for this column acted upon by the load P is

$$EI\left(\frac{d^2 y}{dx^2} - \frac{d^2 y_0}{dx^2}\right) = -Py \tag{e}$$

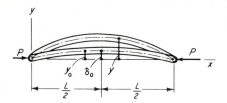

FIGURE 4-5

Substituting y_0 from Eq. (d) into Eq. (e) and using the abbreviation $k^2 = P/EI$ gives

$$\frac{d^2y}{dx^2} + k^2y = -\delta_0 \frac{\pi^2}{L^2} \sin \frac{\pi x}{L} \tag{f}$$

The solution of this equation is

$$y = A \sin kx + B \cos kx + \frac{\delta_0}{1 - k^2L^2/\pi^2} \sin \frac{\pi x}{L} \tag{g}$$

The boundary conditions $y = 0$ at $x = 0$ and $x = L$ give

$$y = \frac{\delta_0}{1 - k^2L^2/\pi^2} \sin \frac{\pi x}{L} = \frac{\delta_0}{1 - P/P_E} \sin \frac{\pi x}{L} \tag{h}$$

The maximum deflection is at $x = L/2$:

$$y_{max} = \frac{\delta_0}{1 - P/P_E} \tag{4-5}$$

Note that this equation is identical in form to Eq. (c) for the two-bar column of Fig. 4-4a.

The maximum stress in the column is

$$f = \frac{P}{A} + \frac{Mc}{I} = \frac{P}{A} + \frac{Py_{max}c}{I} = \frac{P}{A}\left(1 + \frac{\delta_0 c}{r^2} \frac{1}{1 - P/P_E}\right) \tag{4-6}$$

According to ASTM A6 compression members must not deviate from straightness by more than $L/1000$. Substituting this value into Eq. (4-6) gives

$$f = \frac{P}{A}\left(1 + \frac{Lc}{1000r^2} \frac{1}{1 - P/P_E}\right) \tag{4-7}$$

This equation is valid only for stresses below the proportional limit. Assuming that the proportional limit equals the yield stress F_y and taking a rectangular cross section, for which $r = 2c/\sqrt{12}$, we get

$$F_y = f\left(1 + \frac{1.73}{1000} \frac{L}{r} \frac{1}{1 - f/F_E}\right) \tag{4-8}$$

where $f = P/A$ and $F_E = P_E/A$. The graph of this equation for $F_y = 34$ ksi is shown in Fig. 4-6a. The variation of load with lateral deflection δ at midlength

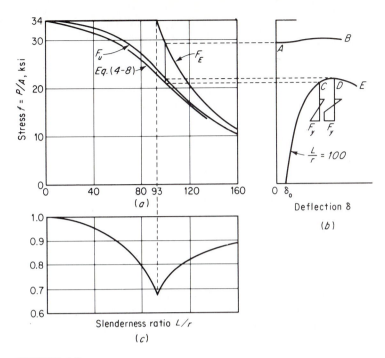

FIGURE 4-6

for a column with $L/r = 100$ is $\delta_0\,CDE$ in Fig. 4-6b. Point C represents the load according to Eq. (4-8). The corresponding distribution of stress at midlength is plotted on the vertical line through C. This is not the ultimate strength. As in the postbuckling behavior of the straight column (Fig. 4-3), the ultimate load, point D, is attained at a stress distribution such as that plotted on the vertical line through D. Beyond this condition the load begins to decrease along the path DE.

The plot of F_u in Fig. 4-6a is based on numerical values from an approximate solution by Jezek for the eccentrically loaded column of rectangular cross section (Ref. 3, p. 40). Also shown is the Euler stress F_E from Eq. (4-2) and, in Fig. 4-6b, the load-deflection curve AB for a straight column with $L/r = 100$. The plot of Euler stress ends at $F_y = 34$ ksi at $L/r = 93$. This means that a perfect column made of steel with a yield plateau at 34 ksi will reach yield stress without buckling if L/r is less than 93. Exceptions to this type of behavior are discussed in Arts. 4-4 and 4-6.

Figure 4-6c shows the variation with L/r of the ratio of the strength F_u of the crooked column to that of the perfect column. It will be noted that the maximum effect of crookedness is in the range $80 < 1/r < 120$, where reductions in strength of as much as 30 percent can be expected.

There is an important difference between the critical load for the perfect column (point A of Fig. 4-6b) and the ultimate load (point D) of the crooked column. When the straight column buckles, it assumes a *stable*, bent equilibrium configuration, but with a slightly larger load. On the other hand, the crooked column does not buckle in this sense at all. Instead, deflection increases from the beginning of loading, and the column is in an *unstable* condition when it reaches its maximum load. This is because deflection increases with decrease in load after the point D is passed. Thus, a distinction is made between the two types of instability, that corresponding to a bifurcation of equilibrium (point A) and that corresponding to a peak load (point D). Of course, $\delta_0 CDE$ represents the behavior of the real (in contrast to perfect) column.

4-4   INELASTIC BUCKLING OF COLUMNS

The preceding discussions have been based on the assumption that the column is made of a metal whose stress-strain curve is linear until a yield plateau is reached. In this article the behavior of columns made of metals which yield gradually after a proportional limit F_p is reached (Fig. 4-7a) will be considered. Assume that such a column is at its critical load at a stress F_{cr} exceeding the proportional limit (point A in the figure), so the stress distribution at a typical cross section is that shown in Fig. 4-7b. Engesser suggested in 1889 that the critical load for this case could be found by replacing Young's modulus E in Eq. (4-2) with the tangent modulus E_t given by the slope of the tangent to the stress-strain curve at A. Thus,

$$F_{cr} = \frac{\pi^2 E_t}{(L/r)^2} \tag{4-9}$$

To determine a point on the tangent-modulus curve for inelastic buckling, a value of F_{cr} and the corresponding value of E_t are substituted into Eq. (4-9) and the value of L/r determined. The curve BD of Fig. 4-8 was obtained in this way.

Later, Engesser's conclusion was challenged on the basis that buckling begins with no increase in load. This argument follows from the results discussed in the previous article where it was demonstrated that buckling occurs without a

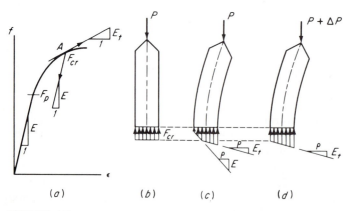

(a)   (b)   (c)   (d)

FIGURE 4-7

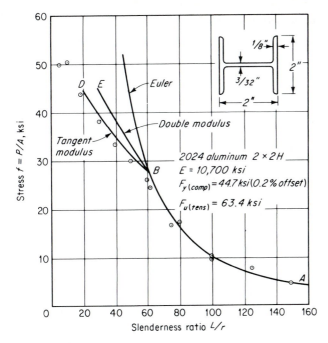

FIGURE 4-8
Column test results. (*From Ref. 4.*)

first-order increase in load. The plot of load vs. deflection has a horizontal tangent at the value of the critical load. If this is true, stress on the convex side decreases at the onset of buckling while that on the concave side increases. But stress decreases at the rate E, that is, parallel to the initial loading path (Fig. 4-7a), while stress increases at the rate E_t. Therefore, the stress distribution for a slightly bent column would be that shown in Fig. 4-7c, in which the slopes of the stress block are E/ρ on the convex side and E_t/ρ on the concave side, where ρ is the radius of curvature at the section. The location of the center of rotation of the cross section is determined by $\int f\, dA = P$. Following this concept, Engesser presented a second solution to the inelastic-buckling problem in 1895, in which the bending stiffness of the cross section is expressed in terms of a double modulus E_r. Evaluation of the reduced modulus requires knowledge of E and E_t and can only be accomplished for a specific cross section. For a simplified H cross section consisting of only the two flanges (Ref. 1, p. 178),

$$E_r = \frac{2EE_t}{E + E_t} \tag{4-10a}$$

For the rectangular cross section,

$$E_r = \frac{4EE_t}{(\sqrt{E} + \sqrt{E_t})^2} \tag{4-10b}$$

The double modulus is also called the *reduced* modulus. The critical stress according to the double modulus is found by replacing E in Eq. (4-2) by E_r:

$$F_{cr} = \frac{\pi^2 E_r}{(L/r)^2} \tag{4-11}$$

To determine a point on the double-modulus curve for inelastic buckling a value of F_{cr} is assumed, which determines E_t, and E_r is computed. Substituting corresponding values of E_r and F_{cr} into Eq. (4-11) gives a corresponding value of L/r. The curve BE of Fig. 4-8 was obtained in this way.

Results of tests on 2×2 in extruded aluminum-alloy H-shaped columns are shown in Fig. 4-8. It will be noted that the tests agree with the tangent-modulus prediction rather than with the double-modulus values. Although this is usually the case, the reason remained unknown for many years. Shanley is credited with having been the first to offer an explanation. He pointed out in 1947 that the tangent-modulus theory is correct if the load increases at the onset of buckling by an amount sufficient to offset strain reversal due to bending.[5] In this case, the stress distribution at midlength could be that shown in Fig. 4-7d, for which $\int f\,dA = P + \Delta P$. The corresponding center of rotation of the cross section is on the convex edge, so the strain there is stationary at the instant bending begins.

Rather than comparing the two theories by postulating on the one hand an increase in load at the onset of buckling (tangent modulus) and no increase on the other (double modulus), it is perhaps easier to understand the difference in terms of the order of magnitude of the increase in load. It was pointed out in Art. 4-2 that the increase in load for a small deflection at the onset of elastic buckling is a small quantity of second order. Stresses due to such an increase in load could not offset those due to a first-order moment $P\,\Delta\delta$. Therefore, if inelastic buckling also begins with a second-order increase in load, there must be strain reversal and the double modulus applies. On the other hand, stresses due to a first-order increase in load could be large enough to offset a first-order reversal. Thus, if inelastic buckling begins with a first-order increase in load ΔP, reversal need not take place and the tangent modulus could apply.

A first-order increase in load as bending begins requires that the postbuckling curve have a positive slope at $\delta = 0$, rather than zero slope as in Figs. 4-1 and 4-4. Therefore, the tangent-modulus postbuckling behavior is represented by curves such as those originating at P_t in Fig. 4-9. However, it has been shown that buckling of a perfect column can begin at any load between P_t and the double-modulus load P_r (Refs. 6 and 7). Thus, there is a family of postbuckling curves originating at points lying between P_t and P_r in Fig. 4-9, each of which is a possible behavior curve for the perfect column. In this sense, then, the tangent-modulus load is a lower bound and the double-modulus load an upper bound on the critical load for a perfect column. However, in order to reach a load higher than P_t, the column must somehow survive the lowest potential instability, namely, P_t.

The load-deflection curve for the crooked column with initial midlength deflection δ_0 is also shown in Fig. 4-9. Conclusive proof that the tangent-

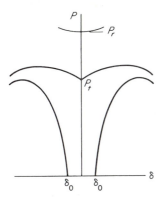

FIGURE 4-9

modulus load is indeed the critical load for inelastic buckling of a real, perfect column (in the sense that the real column can only approach perfection) was given by Duberg and Wilder.[6] Using a webless cross section, as in Fig. 4-13b, to simulate the I, they showed that the tangent-modulus load is the critical load for the perfectly straight column if the straight column is regarded as the limiting case of the crooked column as the initial crookedness vanishes. Furthermore, the peak of the postbuckling curve is only slightly higher than the tangent-modulus load. Therefore, the tangent-modulus load is a good measure of column strength in the inelastic-buckling range and can be considered to be an *upper bound* on the critical load of a *real* column.

Although there is no strain reversal at midlength of the convex side of the column at the beginning of bending at the tangent-modulus load, strain reversal does occur and begins (on the convex side at midlength) immediately after the column starts to bend.[6,7] Reversal then spreads toward each end of the column with increasing load, until the entire convex side is encompassed when the ultimate load (peak of the postbuckling curve) is reached.

Equation (4-9) shows that the shape of the column F_{cr}-L/r curve in the inelastic range depends on the shape of the f-ϵ curve since E_t is determined by the latter. Consider the two steels represented by the f-ϵ curves of Fig. 4-10a. $OABC$ typifies carbon steels and the high-strength low-alloy steels, which have the yield plateau AB, while OAD typifies heat-treated high-strength carbon steels, heat-treated constructional alloy steels, and many of the sheet and strip steels used in cold-formed members. OAD is also typical of the aluminum alloys, except that for them the slope of OA is flatter because of the smaller value of E. For the purposes of this discussion, it is assumed that the proportional limit for the curve OAD is the same as the yield point for $OABC$. The buckling behavior of straight, centrally loaded columns made of these two steels is shown in Fig. 4-10b. Because the modulus of elasticity is the same for all steels, the elastic-buckling curve eaf is the same for all. In the nonproportional range AD of the gradually yielding steel, the slope E_t decreases gradually, so the column curve pulls away from the Euler curve, beginning at a. This gives the inelastic branch ad, corresponding to AD in Fig. 4-10a. On the other hand, the column curve for the steel typified by $OABC$

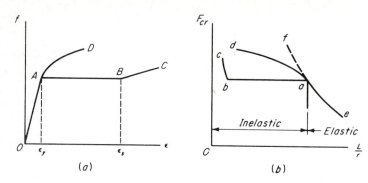

FIGURE 4-10

breaks sharply at a, because the column yields before buckling. This gives the horizontal line ab in Fig. 4-10b. However, if the column is short enough to withstand a strain larger than ϵ_s without buckling, it can strain harden. This results in the branch bc of the inelastic-buckling curve, which corresponds to BC in Fig. 4-10a.

4-5 COLUMNS WITH ENDS ROTATIONALLY RESTRAINED

The pin-ended compression member is rare. Rotation of the ends of the columns in building frames is usually limited by the beams connecting to them, while compression members in trusses may have restricted end rotation because of other members connecting at the joints. Of course, such restraint is never complete in the sense that the column ends are prevented from turning. However, some understanding of the effects of complete restraint is helpful in judging the effects of partial restraint.

Figure 4-11a shows a column supporting an axial load P with both ends rotationally fixed. If P is the critical load, the column buckles as shown, with the

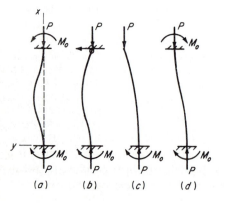

FIGURE 4-11

reactive moments M_0 preventing rotation of the ends. The equation of equilibrium is

$$-EI\frac{d^2y}{dx^2} = Py - M_0 \tag{a}$$

which gives the solution

$$y = A \sin kx + B \cos kx + \frac{M_0}{P} \tag{b}$$

where $k^2 = P/EI$. With the boundary conditions $y = 0$ at $x = 0$ and $x = L$ we get

$$y = \frac{M_0}{P}\left(1 - \cos kx - \frac{1 - \cos kL}{\sin kL}\sin kx\right) \tag{c}$$

Since the ends are prevented from rotating, we have the additional boundary conditions $dy/dx = 0$ at $x = 0$ and $x = L$. Using the first of these, we get

$$\frac{kM_0}{P}\frac{1 - \cos kL}{\sin kL} = 0 \tag{d}$$

The smallest nonzero root of Eq. (d) is $kL = 2\pi$. Thus, since $k^2 = P/EI$, we have

$$P = \frac{4\pi^2 EI}{L^2} = \frac{\pi^2 EI}{(0.5L)^2} \tag{e}$$

Solutions for other cases are obtained similarly. If only one end is fixed against rotation (Fig. 4-11b), we find

$$P = \frac{20.2EI}{L^2} = \frac{2.05\pi^2 EI}{L^2} = \frac{\pi^2 EI}{(0.7L)^2} \tag{f}$$

If one end is fixed and the other completely free (Fig. 4-11c),

$$P = \frac{\pi^2 EI}{4L^2} = \frac{\pi^2 EI}{(2L)^2} \tag{g}$$

Finally, if both ends are rotationally fixed but one end is free to translate relative to the other (Fig. 4-11d),

$$P = \frac{\pi^2 EI}{L^2} \tag{h}$$

which is the same as the critical load for the pin-ended column. It will be noted that the critical loads given by these equations can be expressed in the general form

$$P = \frac{\pi^2 EI}{(KL)^2} \tag{4-12}$$

KL in this equation is called the *effective length* of the column and K the *effective-length factor*. The effective length of columns with limited restraint of end rotation is discussed in Art. 4-11.

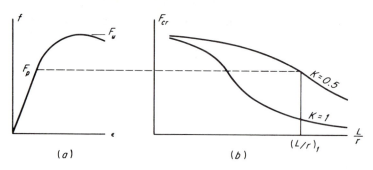

FIGURE 4-12

It should be noted that the reactive moment M_0 in Eq. (d) is indeterminate, so the deflections given by Eq. (c) are also indeterminate. Thus, as was the case for the pin-ended column, we have determined the load at which a perfect column becomes unstable, but the solution tells us nothing about the postbuckling behavior.

According to the tangent-modulus theory, E_t replaces E in Eq. (4-12) if the stress P/A exceeds the proportional limit. Therefore, with the critical load in terms of the stress F_{cr} as in Eq. (4-9), we get

$$F_{cr} = \frac{\pi^2 E_t}{(KL/r)^2} \tag{4-13}$$

In general, the effect of end restraint on the critical stress is less for inelastic buckling than it is for elastic buckling, because the very short column can develop yield stress (and more) whether the ends are pinned or fixed. Thus, column F_{cr}-L/r curves for various values of K converge toward F_u at $L/r = 0$. This is shown in Fig. 4-12b for a pin-ended column and a column with fixed ends, each made of a metal with the f-ϵ variation shown in Fig. 4-12a. $(L/r)_1$ in Fig. 4-12b is the boundary between elastic and inelastic buckling for the case $K = 0.5$. If $L/r \geq (L/r)_1$, a column with fixed ends can support four times as much load as a column with pinned ends. However, this benefit is seen to decrease with decreasing L/r, until F_{cr} finally becomes virtually independent of K.

4-6 EFFECT OF RESIDUAL STRESSES

Residual stresses that are usually present in the steel column may reduce its strength significantly. Sources of residual stress and the ways in which it may be distributed were discussed in Art. 3-1. It will be recalled that residual stresses in tension members cause the section to yield at a stress lower than the yield point of the base material. As a consequence, the elongation for a given load is greater than would be calculated on the basis of the elastic properties of such a member. It was also demonstrated that complete yielding of the cross section did not occur until the applied strain is greater than the yield strain of the base material. Although the deformations and resulting deflections are greater in this case than for elastic behavior, the residual stresses do not affect the load corresponding to full yield of the cross section nor do they affect the behavior of the member for loads greater than the yield load.

The effect of residual stress on column strength is more significant. This effect can be demonstrated by considering the webless H (Fig. 4-13b) that was investigated as a tension member in Art. 3-1. The stress-strain curve for the steel coupon is shown in a and the residual-stress distribution in c. Residual stresses also vary across the thickness (Art. 4-7), so the distribution shown is an average stress. The compressive residual stress, 12 ksi, is the average value found in 21 measurements of residual stresses in wide-flange shapes.[8] The area of the cross section is 24 in². If the column is subjected to a uniform strain of $\epsilon = -0.0008$ in/in and these strains are added to the residual strains corresponding to the stresses in c, the strain distribution will vary from -0.0012 to -0.0004. Converting these strains to stresses produces the stress block shown in Fig. 4-13d. The load is $P = 576$ kips, and the stress $f = P/A = \frac{576}{24} = 24$ ksi. Should the column be of such a length as to become unstable at this load, initiation of buckling induces bending stresses which must be superimposed on those in d. Since it is stressed to yield only at the very edges of the flanges, the entire cross section behaves elastically at the onset of buckling and contributes to the bending resistance. Therefore, the bending stiffness is EI, where I is the moment of inertia of the cross section for the axis about which buckling occurs.

Assume next that the column is short enough to remain stable until the load P is large enough to correspond to a total strain of -0.0008 at the midpoint of each flange. This requires an applied uniform strain of -0.0012, and the resulting strain distribution would vary from -0.0008 at the center of each flange to -0.0016 at the edge of each flange. The resulting stress distribution is shown in Fig. 4-13e, where the flanges are yielded a distance of 3 in from each tip. The load is

$$P = 2(36 \times 6 \times 1 + 30 \times 6 \times 1) = 792 \text{ kips}$$

and the *average* stress on the cross section is $f = \frac{792}{24} = 33$ ksi. Since it is assumed that the column becomes unstable at this load, bending begins. However, the compressive stress cannot increase in the yielded portions of the flanges on the

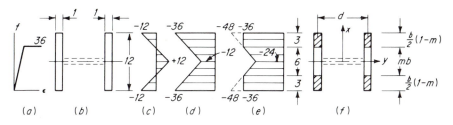

FIGURE 4-13

concave side, and if there is no strain reversal as bending begins (tangent-modulus theory), there can be no stress reversal in the yielded portions on the convex side. Thus, only the unyielded portions can develop a resisting moment, and the bending stiffness of the cross section is reduced. Using I_{eff} to denote the *effective* moment of inertia (the moment of inertia of the unyielded portion of the cross section) the bending stiffness is EI_{eff}. Substituting this into Eq. (4-1) gives

$$P = \frac{\pi^2 E I_{eff}}{L^2} = \frac{\pi^2 EI}{L^2} \frac{I_{eff}}{I}$$

from which

$$F_{cr} = \frac{\pi^2 E}{(L/r)^2} \frac{I_{eff}}{I} \qquad (4\text{-}14)$$

where r is the radius of gyration of the entire cross section for the axis about which buckling occurs.

If the column of Fig. 4-13f buckles about its weak (y) axis, the effective moment of inertia is

$$I_{y,eff} = \frac{2t(mb)^3}{12} = \frac{tm^3 b^3}{6} \qquad (a)$$

so

$$\frac{I_{y,eff}}{I_y} = \frac{tm^3 b^3/6}{2tb^3/12} = m^3 \qquad (b)$$

On the other hand, if the column is supported against weak-axis buckling and buckles about the strong (x) axis,

$$I_{x,eff} = 2mbt\left(\frac{d}{2}\right)^2 = \frac{tmbd^2}{2} \qquad (c)$$

$$\frac{I_{x,eff}}{I_x} = \frac{tmbd^2/2}{2btd^2/4} = m \qquad (d)$$

For the stress distribution of Fig. 4-13e, $P = 792$ kips and $f = 33$ ksi, as determined previously. Also, $m = 0.5$, which determines I_{eff}/I. Substituting the values of I_{eff}/I and f into Eq. (4-14) gives the corresponding value of L/r. Thus

$$33 = \frac{30{,}000\pi^2}{(L/r_x)^2} \times 0.5 \qquad \frac{L}{r_x} = 67$$

$$33 = \frac{30{,}000\pi^2}{(L/r_y)^2} \times 0.5^3 \qquad \frac{L}{r_y} = 34$$

The two curves AB in Fig. 4-14 were obtained by plotting results obtained in this way. Since the strength of the straight, centrally loaded column with no residual stress would be given by $ACBD$, we see that residual stress may reduce the strength considerably. Furthermore, we note that the strength of the H column

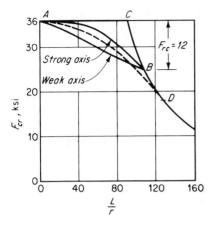

FIGURE 4-14

also depends on the direction of buckling. Finally, we observe that the juncture of the inelastic buckling curves *AB* with the elastic (Euler) buckling curve *CBD* is determined by the magnitude of the compressive residual stress.

Results of tests[8] on W shapes are shown in Fig. 4-15. These are tests on relatively thin cross sections (less than 1 in). The coordinates are non-dimensionalized in terms of F_y. It will be noted that abscissas are directly proportional to L/r. These test results confirm the effect of residual stresses in causing weak-axis buckling at loads smaller than those for strong-axis buckling. Although this suggests two column formulas for the steel W, the Structural Stability Research Council (SSRC) proposed in 1960 that the design procedure be simplified by using a parabola beginning with a vertex at $F_{cr} = F_y$ where $L/r = 0$ and terminating at the point $F_{cr} = F_y/2$ where it intersects and is tangent to the Euler hyperbola. The equation of this parabola is

$$F_{cr} = F_y\left[1 - \frac{F_y}{4\pi^2 E}\left(\frac{KL}{r}\right)^2\right]$$

(4-15)

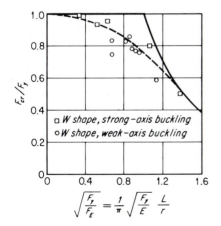

FIGURE 4-15

where K is the effective-length coefficient discussed in Art. 4-5. The equation can also be put in the form

$$F_{cr} = F_y\left[1 - \frac{1}{2}\left(\frac{KL/r}{C_c}\right)^2\right]$$

(4-16)

where $C_c = \pi\sqrt{2E/F_y}$. The dashed curves in Figs. 4-14 and 4-15 are plots of the SSRC formula with $K = 1$.

The inelastic critical stress for a column with residual stress can be determined by using the tangent modulus E_t obtained from the stress-strain curve of a *stub-column* test, which is a compression test of a column short enough not to buckle but long enough to contain the residual-stress distribution. This test has been standardized.[9] (The tensile stress-strain curve for a member with residual stress was discussed in Arts. 3-1 and 3-19.) The procedure outlined in Art. 3-19 by which the stress-strain curve can be described by a quadratic equation if the residual-stress distribution is made up of a series of straight lines can be applied in the same manner for the compressive stress-strain curve. Differentiation of the quadratic equation would permit the tangent modulus to be evaluated analytically.

The stub-column test permits the stress-strain curve to be determined experimentally. The manner in which the tangent modulus defines the critical stress must be determined from an analysis such as the one used to obtain Fig. 4-14. Using the notation $\tau = E_t/E$, the critical stresses for the strong (x) axis and the weak (y) axis of an H shape are given approximately by[10]

$$F_{cr,x} = \frac{\pi^2 E\tau}{(L/r_x)^2} \qquad F_{cr,y} = \frac{\pi^2 E\tau^3}{(L/r_y)^2}$$

(e)

Similarly, for solid round bars with polar symmetric residual stress,[11]

$$F_{cr} = \frac{\pi^2 E\tau^2}{(L/r)^2}$$

(f)

In earlier discussion in this article the effective moment of inertia was used to determine the column curve for a member with residual stresses. It was pointed out that the tangent-modulus concept was employed (no fibers were permitted to undergo reversal of strain) and the effective moment of inertia was evaluated for the portion of the cross section which had not yielded. Although this is indeed the tangent-modulus concept, the resulting column curves are different from the curve which would result by substituting E_t into Eq. (4-13).

It should also be pointed out that the stress-strain curve, whether described analytically by a quadratic equation or by experiment, does not identify the region of the cross section which has yielded. For example, if the residual stresses shown in Fig. 4-13a were reversed, i.e., the tips of the flanges had a residual stress of $+12$ ksi and the centers a residual stress of -12 ksi, the stress-strain curve for the cross section would be the same. However, for this distribution, yielding of the cross section would start at the center of the flange and proceed to the tip and the value of $I_{x,eff}$ would be the same as that for the residual-stress distribution shown in Fig. 4-13c. On the other hand, the value of $I_{y,\text{eff}}$ would be different since initial yielding would now take place at the center of the flange and progress toward the tip, instead of starting at the tip and progressing toward the center.

The procedure described in Art. 3-19 to develop an algebraic equation for the stress-strain curve for members in tension can also be applied to members in compression. As pointed out in Art. 3-19 it is applicable only if the residual-stress distribution is made up of a series of straight lines. In this case it is also possible to establish explicit expressions for I_{eff} for both the x-x and y-y axes. Application of the procedure is demonstrated in the following example.

Example 4-6-1. Determine the equations for the stress-strain curve for the cross section with the residual stresses shown in Fig. 4-16. The residual stresses in the top flange are identical to those in the bottom flange. To simplify the calculations assume that the material is concentrated at midthickness. Draw column curves for the cross section based on E_t, $I_{x,\text{eff}}$, and $I_{y,\text{eff}}$. Use $F_y = 36$ ksi and $E = 30,000$ ksi.

Solution. For the cross section,

$$A = 2(16 \times 1) + 16 \times \tfrac{1}{2} = 40 \text{ in}^2$$

$$I_x = 2(\tfrac{1}{12} \times 16 \times 1^3) + 2[16 \times 1 \times (8\tfrac{1}{2})^2] + (\tfrac{1}{12} \times \tfrac{1}{2} \times 16^3) = 2485 \text{ in}^4$$

$$I_y = 2(\tfrac{1}{12} \times 1 \times 16^3) + [\tfrac{1}{12} \times 16 \times (\tfrac{1}{2})^3] = 683 \text{ in}^4$$

$$0 \le \epsilon \le -0.0006$$

$$\sigma = E\epsilon = 30,000\epsilon$$

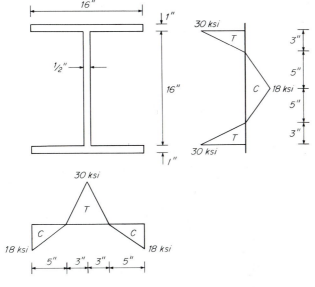

FIGURE 4-16

$-0.0006 \le \epsilon \le -0.0012$. The equations to be solved are

$$18 = a(0.0006)^2 + b(0.0006) + c$$

$$30{,}000 = a(2 \times 0.0006) + b$$

$$30.375 = a(0.0012)^2 + b(0.0012) + c$$

Solution yields

$$\sigma = -15{,}625{,}000\epsilon^2 + 48{,}750\epsilon - 5.625$$

from which

$$E_t = \frac{d\sigma}{d\epsilon} = -31{,}250{,}000\epsilon + 48{,}750$$

In this region

$$I_{x,\text{eff}} = 2\left\{\frac{1}{12}\left[16 - \frac{2 \times 5(\epsilon - 0.0006)}{0.0006}\right] \times 1^3\right\} + 2\left[16 - \frac{2 \times 5(\epsilon - 0.0006)}{0.0006}\right] \times \left(8\tfrac{1}{2}\right)^2$$

$$+ \frac{1}{12} \times \frac{1}{2}\left\{16^3 - \left[\frac{2 \times 5(\epsilon - 0.0006)}{0.0006}\right]^3\right\}$$

$$I_{y,\text{eff}} = 2\left\{\frac{1}{12} \times 1\left[16 - \frac{2 \times 5(\epsilon - 0.0006)}{0.0006}\right]^3\right\} + \frac{1}{12}\left[16 - \frac{2 \times 5(\epsilon - 0.0006)}{0.0006}\right] \times \left(\frac{1}{2}\right)^3$$

$-0.0012 \le \epsilon \le -0.0022$. The equations to be solved are

$$30.375 = A(0.0012)^2 + B(0.0012) + C$$

$$36 = A(0.0022)^2 + B(0.0022) + C$$

$$0 = A(2 \times 0.0022) + B$$

Solution yields

$$\sigma = -5{,}625{,}000\epsilon^2 + 24{,}750\epsilon + 8.775$$

from which

$$E_t = \frac{d\sigma}{d\epsilon} = -11{,}250{,}000\epsilon + 24{,}750$$

In this region

$$I_{x,\text{eff}} = 2\left\{\frac{1}{12}\left[6 - \frac{2 \times 3(\epsilon - 0.0012)}{0.0010}\right] \times 1^3\right\} + 2\left[6 - \frac{2 \times 3(\epsilon - 0.0012)}{0.0010}\right] \times \left(8\tfrac{1}{2}\right)^2$$

$$+ \frac{1}{12} \times \frac{1}{2}\left\{16^3 - \left[10 + \frac{2 \times 3(\epsilon - 0.0012)}{0.0010}\right]^3\right\}$$

$$I_{y,\text{eff}} = 2\left\{\frac{1}{12} \times 1\left[6 - \frac{2 \times 3(\epsilon - 0.0012)}{0.0010}\right]^3\right\}$$

$$+ \frac{1}{12}\left\{16 - \left[10 + \frac{2 \times 3(\epsilon - 0.0012)}{0.0010}\right]\right\} \times \left(\frac{1}{2}\right)^3$$

TABLE 4-1

Stress-strain values for column cross section of Fig. 4-16

ϵ	σ	E_t	$I_{x,\text{eff}}$	$I_{y,\text{eff}}$
0.0000	0.000	30,000	2485	683
0.0002	6.000	30,000	2485	683
0.0004	12.000	30,000	2485	683
0.0006	18.000	30,000	2485	683
0.0008	23.375	23,750	2002	339
0.0010	27.500	17,500	1509	136
0.0012	30.375	11,250	997	36
0.0014	32.400	9,000	807	18.5
0.0016	33.975	6,750	612	7.8
0.0018	35.100	4,500	413	2.5
0.0020	35.775	2,250	209	0.3
0.0022	36.000	0	0	0

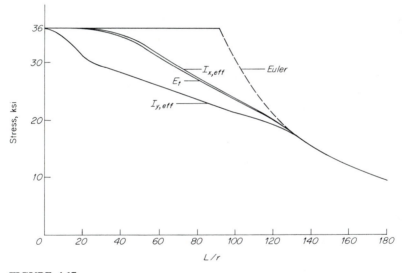

FIGURE 4-17

Values of ϵ, σ, E_t, $I_{x,\text{eff}}$, and $I_{y,\text{eff}}$ for values of strain from 0.0000 to 0.0022 are presented in Table 4-1. Substitution of these values into Eqs. (4-13) and (4-14) permits the value of L/r to be calculated according to E_t, $I_{x,\text{eff}}$, or $I_{y,\text{eff}}$. The results are shown in Fig. 4-17. Note that the curve for the y axis is considerably lower than either the E_t or $I_{x,\text{eff}}$ curve.

4-7 DETERMINANTS OF COLUMN STRENGTH

Because of the variety of imperfections that influence the behavior of a column, it is not easy to predict its strength. Results of tests on a number of steel columns are shown in Fig. 4-18. It is important to note that test results for perfect columns, i.e., those which are absolutely straight, free of residual stress, supported on frictionless hinges, loaded precisely on the centroidal axis, etc., would fall on the Euler curve to its intersection with the line $F_{cr} = F_y$ and thence on the latter line to the axis of ordinates, provided the steel has a yield plateau. Thus, the deviations in this figure are a result of imperfections. However, it is not always easy to identify the imperfection, and in most cases a combination of imperfections is responsible.

The SSRC column curve, Eq. (4-16), is plotted in Fig. 4-18. Except for the welded columns, it appears to be a reasonable, average curve for these tests. Although the test results appear to be more or less randomly scattered, certain patterns emerge when the parameters are studied. The comparison of three welded H's with three identical specimens stress-relieved by annealing (identified by the dashed lines connecting the corresponding points) is convincing evidence of the effect of residual stresses. It is seen that welded columns as a group tend to be weaker than rolled shapes. However, some types of welded columns are stronger than others. Thus, the H fabricated from the flame-cut plates has a more favorable distribution of residual stress (tension at the flange tips) than the H fabricated from universal-mill plates (Fig. 3-1). As a result, the weak-axis strength of the former may be considerably more than that of the latter. This is shown in Fig. 4-19a. However, the strong-axis buckling strengths are more nearly equal. Welded box columns tend to be stronger than the welded H with universal-mill plates (Fig. 4-19b). Of course, this is because the former has a more favorable residual-stress pattern (Fig. 3-1).

Residual stresses in rolled shapes tend to be independent of the yield stress. Thus, reduction in strength tends to be smaller for rolled shapes of higher-

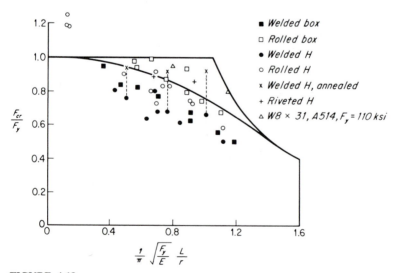

FIGURE 4-18
Column test results. (*From Ref. 12.*)

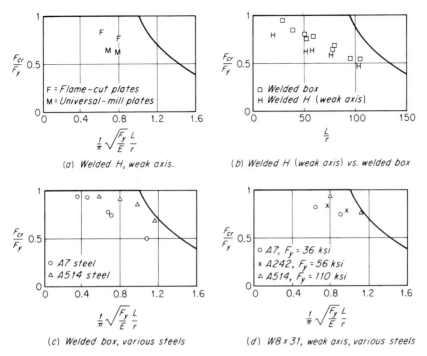

FIGURE 4-19
Effect of residual stress on column strength. (*From Ref. 13.*)

strength steels. Furthermore, the heat treatment used in the production of A514 steel reduces thermal residual stresses even below the level that would normally exist. These effects are shown in Fig. 4-19*d*. The A514 welded box is also relatively stronger than the A7* box (Fig. 4-19*c*).

All the columns for which test results are shown in Figs. 4-18 and 4-19 were composed of relatively thin elements. Residual-stress variation across the thickness of such elements is small. This is not the case for thick parts. Figure 4-20 shows the computed residual-stress distribution in one-half of a $24 \times 3\frac{1}{2}$ in plate and in one-quarter of a W14 × 426 (Ref. 14). The inner surface of the flange of the W shows smaller residual stresses than the outer surface since it is less favorably situated, because of the web, for cooling. It will be noted that the tips of both the flange of the W and the plate have yielded. The yield stress was assumed to be 31 ksi.

Residual stresses tend to increase in magnitude with increase in size of the element. Thus, the *average* residual compression at the ends of $6 \times \frac{1}{2}$, 20×1, and 12×2 plates and the $20 \times 3\frac{1}{2}$ plate of Fig. 4-20*a* was 10, 12, 21, and 31 ksi, respectively. The average tension at the center was 3, 2, 8, and 9 ksi, respectively.

---

* This steel is no longer produced. Its specified yield stress was 33 ksi.

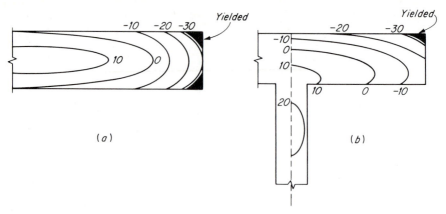

FIGURE 4-20

These residual stresses are likely to constitute the major part of the residual stress in the welded, built-up member composed of thick plates because of the proportionately smaller heat input from welding of such members, for which the welding itself may contribute only 5 to 10 ksi of residual stress.[13] Thus, the weakening effect of residual stress can be expected to be larger for welded columns with thick plates. Of course, this is also true for the W with thick flanges. On the other hand, thick-plated columns are likely to have small slenderness ratios, for which the weakening effect of residual stresses is relatively small. However, this favorable condition may be partially offset by the fact that straightness becomes more important with larger residual compression, because there is earlier yielding in the region of high residual compression, which causes earlier deterioration of bending stiffness.

The fact that columns in the very small L/r range can be stressed well into the strain-hardening region is shown by the three tests in Fig. 4-18 which average about 20 percent higher than the yield stress. This corresponds to the branch bc of the column curve $eabc$ in Fig. 4-10b.

The preceding discussion of column strength as it is affected by differences in cross-sectional shape and in fabrication suggests that a single column-strength curve is inadequate. Of course, questions arise as to practicable groupings and classifications, and compromises are inevitable.

An SSRC task committee has proposed three column curves. The maximum strength of 112 column shapes was computed based on actual residual-stress distributions and an assumed initial crookedness at midheight of the column of $\delta_0 = 0.001L$. The range of the resulting ultimate-strength column curves is shown in Fig. 4-21. Based on detailed study of these results the sections were divided into three groups. The first group included 30 curves, the second group 70, and the third group 12. Curves were developed using the parameter $\lambda = (KL/r\pi)\sqrt{F_y/E}$, called the *column-slenderness parameter*. The value $\lambda = 1$ corresponds to the value of KL/r for which the Euler buckling stress is equal to the yield point. The three curves for these subgroups are:

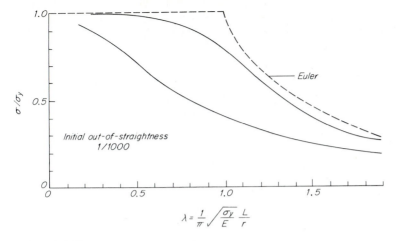

FIGURE 4-21
Range of maximum-strength curves for a number of different column types. (From R. Bjorhovde, Deterministic and Probabilistic Approaches to the Strength of Steel Columns, Ph.D. dissertation, Lehigh University, Bethlehem, PA, 1972)

Curve 1

1. For $0 \leq \lambda \leq 0.15$ $\sigma_u = \sigma_y$

2. For $0.15 \leq \lambda \leq 1.2$ $\sigma_u = \sigma_y(0.990 + 0.122\lambda - 0.367\lambda^2)$

3. For $1.2 \leq \lambda \leq 1.8$ $\sigma_u = \sigma_y(0.051 + 0.801\lambda^{-2})$

4. For $1.8 \leq \lambda \leq 2.8$ $\sigma_u = \sigma_y(0.008 + 0.942\lambda^{-2})$

5. For $\lambda \geq 2.8$ $\sigma_u = \sigma_y\lambda^{-2}$ (= Euler curve)

Curve 2

1. For $0 \leq \lambda \leq 0.15$ $\sigma_u = \sigma_y$

2. For $0.15 \leq \lambda \leq 1.0$ $\sigma_u = \sigma_y(1.035 - 0.202\lambda - 0.222\lambda^2)$

3. For $1.0 \leq \lambda \leq 2.0$ $\sigma_u = \sigma_y(-0.111 + 0.636\lambda^{-1} + 0.087\lambda^{-2})$

4. For $2.0 \leq \lambda \leq 3.6$ $\sigma_u = \sigma_y(0.009 + 0.877\lambda^{-2})$

5. For $\lambda \geq 3.6$ $\sigma_u = \sigma_y\lambda^{-2}$ (= Euler curve)

Curve 3

1. For $0 \leq \lambda \leq 0.15$ $\sigma_u = \sigma_y$

2. For $0.15 \leq \lambda \leq 0.8$ $\sigma_u = \sigma_y(1.093 - 0.622\lambda)$

3. For $0.8 \leq \lambda \leq 2.2$ $\sigma_u = \sigma_y(-0.128 + 0.707\lambda^{-1} - 0.102\lambda^{-2})$

4. For $2.2 \leq \lambda \leq 5.0$ $\sigma_u = \sigma_y(0.0008 + 0.792\lambda^{-2})$

5. For $\lambda \geq 5.0$ $\sigma_u = \sigma_y\lambda^{-2}$ (= Euler curve)

A Committee of the European Convention of Constructional Steelwork has also recommended three formulas. However, the two committees differ in respect to their classification of column types.

Column strengths of aluminum members usually correspond closely to those predicted by the tangent-modulus formula (Fig. 4-8). Furthermore, the plot of the tangent-modulus formula is very nearly a straight line.[15]

Column strength is also dependent on the widths of member elements relative to their thickness, as, for example, the width of the web of a W divided by its thickness or the width of an angle leg divided by its thickness. If these ratios exceed certain limits, the corresponding elements will buckle at a stress lower than that at which overall buckling of the member occurs. This phenomenon, which is called local buckling, is discussed in Arts. 4-12 to 4-14.

Columns may also buckle in a twisting manner, rather than in a bending mode. This is called torsional buckling and is discussed in Art. 4-20.

4-8 ALLOWABLE-STRESS FORMULAS FOR STEEL COLUMNS

It is difficult to establish a simple unique equation for the design of compression members, although it is clear that (among other things) it must allow for imperfections that have been discussed in the preceding articles. Columns in the intermediate range of slenderness (say, $30 \leq L/r \leq 120$) are sensitive to residual stress (Fig. 4-18), crookedness (Fig. 4-6), and eccentricity of load (Art. 6-1), while columns with a small slenderness ratio can be stressed beyond the yield value (Fig. 4-18). This suggests that the margin of safety for columns with a small slenderness ratio should be the same as the margin of safety for tension members but that it should increase in some fashion with L/r, because columns in the range of large L/r are sensitive to errors in estimating their effective lengths, as shown in Art. 4-5.

Some authorities recommend a constant factor of safety, pointing out that the strength of columns in the range of large slenderness is determined by Young's modulus, which varies very little, while the strength of those in the short and intermediate ranges is determined by yield stress, which varies considerably. However, the variation in yield stress is already taken into account for steels bought to ASTM specifications, since the yield stress is guaranteed in the sense that a heat, or lot, of steel may be rejected if the specified yield and tensile strength values are not met.* Therefore, manufacture is so controlled as to give a high probability that the specified properties will be met, so yield strength, ulti-

---

* The specification does allow a retest of one random sample if the results of the original test are within 2000 psi of the specified tensile strength, 1000 psi of the required yield point, or within 2 percentage units of the required elongation.

mate strength, etc., almost always exceed the specified minimums, sometimes by a considerable margin. Therefore, the arguments would seem to favor the varying margin of safety.

Although the considerable variation in column strength in the inelastic range, as it relates to the shape of the cross section, thickness of elements, and the method of manufacture, suggests that a variety of column formulas is needed in this range, it is the practice in standard specifications to use a single formula. Allowable stress for elastic buckling is usually based on the Euler formula.

Allowable-stress formulas from several standard specifications for design will now be discussed. The formulas are not necessarily in the same form as they appear in the specifications but are written so as to facilitate comparison.

The AISC/ASD formulas for allowable stress F_a on axially loaded compression members are

$$F_a = \begin{cases} \dfrac{F_y\left[1 - \dfrac{1}{2}\left(\dfrac{KL/r}{C_c}\right)^2\right]}{\dfrac{5}{3} + \dfrac{3}{8}\dfrac{KL/r}{C_c} - \dfrac{1}{8}\left(\dfrac{KL/r}{C_c}\right)^3} & \dfrac{KL}{r} \leq C_c & (4\text{-}17) \\[4mm] \dfrac{12\pi^2 E}{23(KL/r)^2} = \dfrac{149{,}000}{(KL/r)^2} & \dfrac{KL}{r} \geq C_c & (4\text{-}18) \end{cases}$$

where K is the effective-length coefficient (Art. 4-5) and

$$C_c = \pi\sqrt{\frac{2E}{F_y}}$$

Comparing Eq. (4-17) with Eq. (4-16), we see that the AISC/ASD allowable stress is obtained by dividing the SSRC column-strength equation by a factor of safety which depends on KL/r. This factor of safety varies from 1.67 at $KL/r = 0$ to 1.92 at $KL/r = C_c$. Equation (4-18) is the Euler stress [Eq. (4-2)] with $E = 29{,}000$ ksi, divided by a factor of safety of $\frac{23}{12} = 1.92$.

The AASHTO formulas are

$$F_a = \begin{cases} \dfrac{F_y}{\text{F.S.}}\left[1 - \dfrac{(KL/r)^2 F_y}{4\pi^2 E}\right] & \dfrac{KL}{r} \leq C_c & (4\text{-}19) \\[4mm] \dfrac{\pi^2 E}{\text{F.S.}(KL/r)^2} & \dfrac{KL}{r} \geq C_c & (4\text{-}20) \end{cases}$$

where F.S. = factor of safety. These formulas are also derived from the SSRC formula. The limit C_c is defined as in the AISC/ASD specification. The specification designates a factor of safety of 2.12. The formulas reduce to simple forms for specific yield stresses. Thus, with some roundoff, for $F_y = 36{,}000$ psi,

$$F_a = 16{,}980 - 0.53\left(\frac{KL}{r}\right)^2 \qquad\qquad \frac{KL}{r} \leq 126.1 \qquad (4\text{-}21)$$

AASHTO specifies effective-length coefficients of 0.75 for members with riveted, bolted, or welded end connections and 0.875 for members with pinned ends.

The AREA formulas are

$$
F_a = \begin{cases}
0.55F_y & 0 \le \dfrac{KL}{r} \le \dfrac{3388}{\sqrt{F_y}} & (4\text{-}22) \\[3mm]
0.60F_y - \left(\dfrac{F_y}{1662}\right)^{3/2} \dfrac{KL}{r} & \dfrac{3388}{\sqrt{F_y}} \le \dfrac{KL}{r} \le \dfrac{27{,}111}{\sqrt{F_y}} & (4\text{-}23) \\[3mm]
\dfrac{147{,}000{,}000}{(KL/r)^2} & \dfrac{KL}{r} \ge \dfrac{27{,}111}{\sqrt{F_y}} & (4\text{-}24)
\end{cases}
$$

F_a and F_y in these formulas are in pounds per square inch. It will be noted that two straight-line formulas are used for inelastic buckling, while elastic buckling is based on the Euler stress. The factor of safety is $1/0.55 = 1.82$ for $0 \le KL/r \le 3388/\sqrt{F_y}$, after which it begins to increase until it attains the value 1.95 for elastic buckling, based on $E = 29{,}000{,}000$ psi. The specifications prescribe "under usual conditions" the same values of K as the AASHTO specifications, namely, 0.75 for riveted, bolted, or welded ends and 0.875 for pinned ends. Equations (4-22) and (4-23) reduce to simple form for specific yield stresses. Thus, with some roundoff, for $F_y = 36{,}000$ psi,

$$
F_a = \begin{cases}
20{,}000 & 0 \le \dfrac{KL}{r} \le 15 & (4\text{-}25) \\[3mm]
21{,}500 - 100 \dfrac{KL}{r} & 15 \le \dfrac{KL}{r} \le 143 & (4\text{-}26)
\end{cases}
$$

4-9 AISC/LRFD FORMULAS FOR STEEL COLUMNS

The AISC/LRFD design strength of columns is $\phi_c P_n$, where $\phi_c = 0.85$ and $P_n = A_g F_{cr}$, with F_{cr} given by

$$
F_{cr} = \begin{cases}
0.658^{\lambda_c^2} F_y & 0 \le \lambda_c < 1.5 & (4\text{-}27) \\[3mm]
\dfrac{0.877}{\lambda_c^2} F_y & \lambda_c > 1.5 & (4\text{-}28)
\end{cases}
$$

in which

$$
\lambda_c = \frac{KL}{r\pi} \sqrt{\frac{F_y}{E}}
$$

Equation (4-27) is a lower-bound limit for column strength in the range $0 \le \lambda_c \le 1.5$. The formulas account for an initial crookedness of about $L/1500$. Substitution of λ_c into Eq. (4-28) gives $F_{cr} = 0.877F_E$, where F_E is the Euler stress

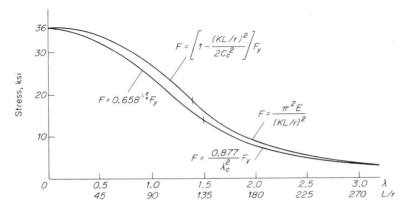

FIGURE 4-22
AISC/ASD and AISC/LRFD column curves, $F_y = 36$ ksi.

$\pi^2 E/(KL/r)^2$. Therefore, the calculated nominal strength of columns for $\lambda_c > 1.5$ is about 88 percent of the column strength on which the AISC/ASD allowable-stress formula, Eq. (4-18), is based.

Equations (4-27) and (4-28) and the formulas on which the ASD allowable stresses are based are compared in Fig. 4-22. A comparison of the two suggests that the LRFD formulas give a more conservative lower bound. A more signifi-cant comparison is obtained by comparing the ASD allowable stresses with equivalent allowables obtained by dividing F_{cr} from Eqs. (4-27) and (4-28) by a factor of safety determined as follows. The ASD factor of safety varies from $\frac{5}{3}$ at $KL/r = 0$ to $\frac{23}{12}$ at $KL/r \geq C_c$. The coefficient 0.877 in Eq. (4-28) is, almost exactly, the ratio of the factors of safety $\frac{23}{12}$ and $\frac{5}{3}$; namely, $\frac{23}{12}/\frac{5}{3} = 0.870$. There-fore, a factor of safety of $\frac{5}{3}$ applied to Eq. (4-28) yields, again almost exactly, the ASD allowable stresses for $\lambda_c > 1.5$. This suggests using the same factor of safety, $\frac{5}{3}$, in Eq. (4-27). The results are shown in Table 4-2, where the ASD allowable stresses are compared with those obtained by dividing F_{cr} by Eqs. (4-27) and (4-28) by a uniform factor of safety of $\frac{5}{3}$. This shows that the differences in results obtained from the two specifications lie in the load factors ϕ, which for ASD are the equivalent of unity while for LRFD they vary with the load combinations

TABLE 4-2
Comparison of allowable stresses

	KL/r						
	0	**30**	**60**	**90**	**120**	**150**	**180**
ASD	21.6	19.9	17.4	14.2	10.3	6.64	4.14
LRFD $\frac{}{5/3}$	21.6	20.6	17.9	14.1	10.1	6.69	4.17

(Art. 1-13). The LRFD formulas were in fact chosen so as to approximate the ASD formulas at $\lambda = 1$ with a live-load to dead-load ratio of 1.1.

4-10 TYPICAL SECTIONS FOR COMPRESSION MEMBERS

A single shape, such as the angle, the W, the tee, the tube, or the pipe, may be used as a compression member. Single angles are used extensively in towers, particularly in transmission towers. They are sometimes used in small roof trusses. The W's are used extensively as columns in buildings and as compression members in large trusses. The tee is a suitable compression-chord member for welded roof trusses; web members may be welded directly to the stem of the tee.

Figure 4-23 shows some of the forms of *built-up* cross sections. The cross section depends to a large extent upon the structure in which the member is to be used, the manner in which the ends are to be connected, and the requirements of other members which connect to it. In this figure, shapes which extend the full length of the member are shown in solid lines. Intermittent connections, such as *lacing* or *tie plates* (Art. 4-17), whose function is to force the several shapes to act as one, are indicated by dashed lines.

The double-angle member in Fig. 4-23*a* is widely used in roof trusses. It may be used for both web and chord members of riveted or bolted trusses, with connections made to gusset plates between the vertical legs. It is suitable for web members of welded trusses in conjunction with the tee chord mentioned previously. In some structures the outstanding legs of the double-angle member may be riveted, bolted, or welded to the connecting member. Two angles are sometimes used, as in Fig. 4-23*b*, with the connection made to two gusset plates, one at each outstanding leg. Again, the gusset plates may usually be omitted in welded construction. Four angles arranged as in Fig. 4-23*c* are used occasionally. Connection is usually through the outstanding legs. Four angles arranged as in Fig. 4-23*d* are common for crane booms. Columns for industrial building are sometimes made as in Fig. 4-23*f*, with one I supporting a crane runway and the other extending past the runway to support the roof.

Occasionally the largest W will have insufficient area, and plates (called *cover* or *flange plates*) may be attached to the flanges as in Fig. 4-23*e*. However, three plates welded to form an I are likely to be a better solution.

Members of the type shown in Fig. 4-23*g* were common in bridge trusses as top-chord members but have been superseded by the W, the welded I, and the

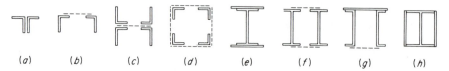

(*a*)   (*b*)   (*c*)   (*d*)   (*e*)   (*f*)   (*g*)   (*h*)

FIGURE 4-23

welded box. The box section is also used for columns in buildings. It is available as a rolled shape, called structural tubing, in square form up to 16×16 in and in rectangular form to 20×12 in. In the form of four plates welded at the corners, its size is virtually unlimited. Box sections are sometimes made as in Fig. 4-23h by welding plates to the W shape.

Approximate radii of gyration of a variety of cross sections are given in the Appendix.

4-11 EFFECTIVE LENGTH OF COLUMNS IN FRAMES

The column rarely occurs as an isolated member, and its end conditions are influenced by the members to which it connects. For example, the frame shown in Fig. 4-24a will take the shape in Fig. 4-24b if it buckles under the vertical loads P, provided the connections at B and C are moment-resistant and stiff enough to allow little change in the 90° angles at B and C. A typical connection that satisfies these requirements is shown in Fig. 4-25a. Such a connection is called a *moment connection*. The connection shown in Fig. 4-25b is called a *framed connection*; it is usually assumed to be moment-free. The essential difference between the framed connection and the moment connection as it affects a supporting column is that the column is usually assumed to be continuous on simple supports ($K = 1$) if the beams are framed but rotationally restrained ($K \neq 1$) if the connections are of the moment type.

Frames whose resistance to lateral displacement depends on the bending resistance of its members and their connections, such as the one in Fig. 4-24a, are called *unbraced frames*, while those whose primary resistance to lateral displacement is provided by some form of bracing, such as that in Fig. 4-24c, are called *braced frames*. Other forms of bracing are shown in Fig. 12-9. Of course, not every bay in a multibay structure need be braced, since the unbraced bays are restrained by those that are braced.

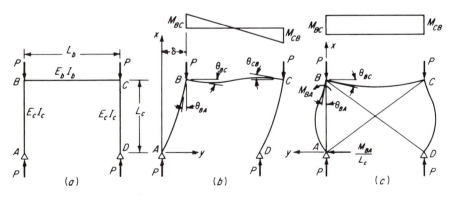

FIGURE 4-24

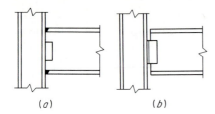

(a)   (b)   **FIGURE 4-25**

The critical load for the frame of Fig. 4-24a with moment connections can be determined as follows. With the coordinate axes shown in b, the equation of equilibrium of column AB is

$$E_c I_c \frac{d^2 y}{dx^2} = -Py \qquad (a)$$

The solution, with $k^2 = P/(E_c I_c)$, is

$$y = A \sin kx + B \cos kx \qquad (b)$$

Since $y = 0$ at $x = 0$,

$$y = A \sin kx \qquad (c)$$

The deflection $y = \delta$ at $x = L_c$ is

$$\delta = A \sin kL_c \qquad (d)$$

so the bending moment M_{BA} in the column is

$$M_{BA} = PA \sin kL_c \qquad (e)$$

The moment M_{BC} for the beam is

$$M_{BC} = \frac{2E_b I_b}{L_b} (2\theta_{BC} + \theta_{CB}) = \frac{6E_b I_b \theta_{BC}}{L_b} \qquad (f)$$

since $\theta_{CB} = \theta_{BC}$. Then, since $M_{BC} = M_{BA}$, Eqs. (e) and (f) give

$$\theta_{BC} = \frac{M_{BA} L_b}{6E_b I_b} = \frac{L_b PA \sin kL_c}{6E_b I_b} \qquad (g)$$

The rotation θ_{BA} of the column is

$$\theta_{BA} = \left(\frac{dy}{dx}\right)_{x=L_c} = Ak \cos kL_c \qquad (h)$$

Equating θ_{BA} and θ_{BC} and simplifying the result gives

$$KL_c \tan kL_c = 6 \frac{(EI/L)_b}{(EI/L)_c} \qquad (i)$$

If the beam is infinitely stiff, Eq. (*i*) gives $\tan kL_c = \infty$, from which $kL_c = \pi/2$ and, since $k^2 = P/(E_c I_c)$,

$$P = \frac{\pi^2 E_c I_c}{4L_c^2} = \frac{\pi^2 E_c I_c}{(2L_c)^2} \tag{j}$$

Therefore, the effective-length coefficient $K = 2$. If beam and column are equally stiff, Eq. (*i*) gives $kL_c \tan kL_c = 6$, from which $kL_c = 1.35$ and

$$P = \frac{1.82 E_c I_c}{L_c^2} = \frac{\pi^2 E_c I_c}{(2.33L_c)^2}$$

so that $K = 2.33$. Thus, the effective length increases with decreasing stiffness of the beam and tends to infinity as the beam stiffness approaches zero.

If the frame of Fig. 4-24*a* is restrained against sidesway, as by diagonal bracing, it buckles as shown in Fig. 4-24*c*. The equation of equilibrium is

$$E_c I_c \frac{d^2 y}{dx^2} = -Py + M_{BA} \frac{x}{L_c} \tag{k}$$

which gives

$$y = A \sin kx + B \cos kx + \frac{M_{BA}}{P} \frac{x}{L_c} \tag{l}$$

Using $y = 0$ at $x = 0$ and at $x = L_c$, we get

$$y = \frac{M_{BA}}{P} \left(\frac{x}{L_c} - \frac{\sin kx}{\sin kL_c} \right) \tag{m}$$

Then, using the boundary conditions $\theta_{BC} = \theta_{BA} = -(dy/dx)_{x=L_c}$, we get

$$1 - kL_c \cot kL_c = -\frac{(kL_c)^2}{2} \frac{(EI/L)_c}{(EI/L)_b} \tag{n}$$

If the beam is infinitely stiff, Eq. (*n*) gives $kL_c = 4.49$, so

$$P = \frac{20.2 E_c I_c}{L_c^2} = \frac{\pi^2 E_c I_c}{(0.7L_c)^2}$$

If the beam and column are equally stiff, Eq. (*n*) gives $kL_c = 3.59$, from which

$$P = \frac{12.9 E_c I_c}{L_c^2} = \frac{\pi^2 E_c I_c}{(0.875L_c)^2}$$

and $K = 0.875$. Thus, the effective-length coefficient increases with decreasing stiffness of the beam and becomes unity with zero stiffness.

These examples show that the critical load for a column depends on its stiffness relative to that of the beams framing into it and on the presence or absence of restraint against lateral displacement of its ends. (Relative lateral joint displacement is usually called *sidesway*.) Critical loads for frames in multibay,

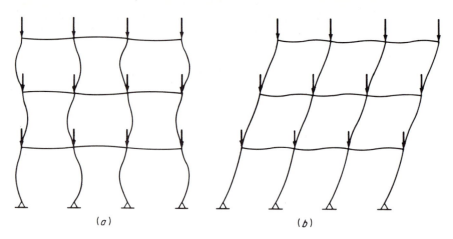

FIGURE 4-26

multistory frames can be determined as in these examples. To simplify the analysis for frames with many members, the following assumptions can be made:

1. The frame is subjected to vertical loads applied only at the joints.
2. All columns in the frame become unstable simultaneously.
3. All joint rotations at a floor are equal. They are alternately clockwise and counterclockwise if there is no sidesway (Fig. 4-26a) and all in the same direction if there is (Fig. 4-26b).
4. The restraining moment exerted by the beams at a joint as the columns begin to buckle is distributed to the columns at the joint in proportion to their stiffnesses EI/L.

    The preceding assumptions enable a single column AB of a frame to be analyzed by using Fig. 4-27a if there is no sidesway and Fig. 4-27b if there is. Using the ordinary slope-deflection equation for beams AC, AE, BD, and BF and the modified (for effect of axial load) slope-deflection equation for column AB, a

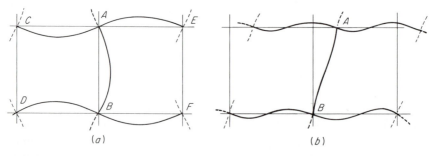

FIGURE 4-27

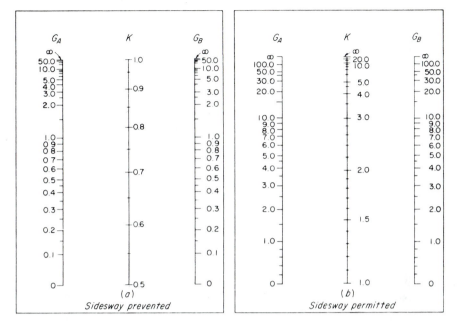

FIGURE 4-28
Nomograph for effective length of columns. (*From Ref. 17.*)

transcendental equation for the effective-length coefficient K can be established[16] for each of the two cases in Fig. 4-27. Solutions of these equations were put in nomographic form in 1959 for use in the Boston Building Code[17] (Fig. 4-28). The symbol G in these diagrams is defined by

$$G = \frac{\sum (EI/L)_c}{\sum (EI/L)_b} \qquad (4\text{-}29)$$

where $\sum (EI/L)_c$ is the sum of stiffnesses of columns entering the joint and $\sum (EI/L)_b$ is the sum of stiffnesses of beams entering the joint. A straight line connecting G_A and G_B intersects the axis of K at the corresponding value of K.

The nomographs can also be used for certain cases where the end rotations of the beams differ from those described in category 3 above. This is done by taking account of the change in beam stiffness. Thus, for the frame of Fig. 4-29a, the moment M_{CB} in the buckled configuration is zero because of the simple support. Using the slope-deflection equations for M_{BC} and M_{CB}, we get $\theta_{BC} = M_{BC} L_b/(3E_b I_b)$. But the nomograph for the case where the frame buckles with sidesway is based on the deflected shape of Fig. 4-24b, for which the joint rotation is given by Eq. (g). Thus, the rotation at B in the frame of Fig. 4-29b is twice that of the frame of Fig. 4-24b, so the beam in Fig. 4-29a is only half as stiff as the beam in Fig. 4-24a. Relative stiffnesses for other cases are determined similarly. The correction factors (by which beam stiffness I/L must be multiplied) for four cases are as shown in Table 4-3.

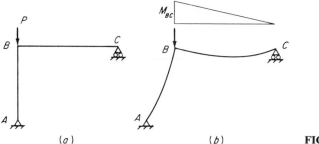

(a)　　　　　　　　　　　　　(b)　　　　　　**FIGURE 4-29**

If a column end is hinged, the value of G at that end is infinite, because the hinge is equivalent to zero stiffness of the connecting beams. On the other hand, if a column end is completely restrained rotationally, G at that end is zero. Intermediate values of $G = 10$ and $G = 1$ have been suggested for the practical case of the simple column base and the fixed column base, respectively.[9]

In the case of a column which buckles upon reaching a stress exceeding the proportional limit, the tangent modulus E_t should be used in evaluating column stiffness in Eq. (4-29). However, because the loads are assumed to act at the joints, the beams are straight at the onset of buckling. Therefore, they are free of stress as bending begins and are governed by Young's modulus. For this case, Eq. (4-29) can be written

$$G = \frac{\sum (\tau EI/L)_c}{\sum (EI/L)_b} \tag{4-30a}$$

where $\tau = E_t/E$. If we assume further that both columns at the joint buckle at the same stress, we have

$$G = \frac{\tau \sum (EI/L)_c}{\sum (EI/L)_b} \tag{4-30b}$$

Equation (4-30b) shows that the correction for inelastic buckling may be made by multiplying the value of G from the alignment chart by $\tau = E_t/E$. But since $F_{cr} = \pi^2 E_t I/(KL)^2 A$ and $F_E = \pi^2 EI/(KL)^2 A$, E_t/E can be written as F_{cr}/F_E so that

$$G_{inel} = \frac{F_{cr}}{F_E} \frac{(I/L)_c}{(I/L)_b} = \frac{F_{cr}}{F_E} G_{el} \tag{4-31}$$

where the subscripts *inel* and *el* denote *inelastic* and *elastic*. The ratio F_{cr}/F_E is called a *stiffness reduction factor*. Except for differences in notation, tables of values of this factor are given for ASD and LRFD in the corresponding AISC

TABLE 4-3

Condition	Sidesway	No sidesway
Far end of beam hinged	$\frac{1}{2}$	$\frac{3}{2}$
Far end of beam fixed	$\frac{2}{3}$	2

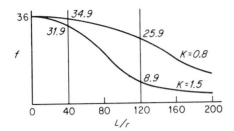

FIGURE 4-30

Manuals. Application of the procedure can be simplified by using P/A instead of F_{cr}, where P is the column force calculated for the structure loading. It is always safe to take $\tau = 1$, which, of course, amounts to using Eq. (4-29). This is because the beams are stiffer, relative to the columns, if the columns buckle inelastically and exert more rotational restraint than they would if the columns buckle elastically. However, G_{inel} can produce substantial reductions in cross-sectional area for columns in unbraced frames.

The effect of end conditions on column strength is influenced to a marked degree by the slenderness of the column. This is demonstrated in Fig. 4-30, where column curves for A36 steel are shown for effective-length coefficients of 0.8 and 1.5, using the SSRC formula for the inelastic range. For a column whose $L/r = 40$, the critical stresses are 34.9 and 31.9 ksi for $K = 0.8$ and 1.5, respectively, while for $L/r = 120$ they are 25.9 and 8.9 ksi. Thus, a reasonably good estimate of end conditions is of primary importance in the design of slender columns.

It is important to remember that the discussion in this article holds only if (1) the beam-to-column connections are moment-resistant and stiff and (2) the loads are concentrated at the joints. Thus, although a connection consisting of two angles connecting the web of the beam to the column (Fig. 4-25b) does develop some moment, it is too flexible to qualify as a stiff or "rigid" connection. The lateral stability of frames in which such connections are used must be assured by walls, partitions, diagonal bracing, shear walls, and the like. Furthermore, the effective-length coefficient of the columns in such a frame is practically unity.

The behavior of frames in which the loads are carried by the beams, rather than by the joints, is considered in Art. 6-4.

Example 4-11-1. Determine the effective-length coefficients for the frame shown in Fig. 4-31. The stiffnesses I/L are as follows (I, in^4, and L, ft):

Member I/L:	AB $\frac{110}{15} = 7.33$	BD $\frac{800}{30} = 26.7$
	CD $\frac{110}{15} = 7.33$	DG $\frac{800}{20} = 40$
	DE $\frac{110}{12} = 9.17$	GJ $\frac{800}{20} = 40$
	FG $\frac{110}{15} = 7.33$	EH $\frac{291}{20} = 14.5$
	GH $\frac{110}{12} = 9.17$	

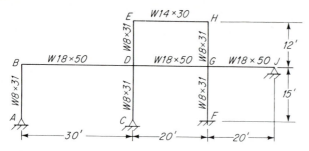

FIGURE 4-31

Solution

Column *AB*:

$$G_A = 10 \qquad G_B = \frac{7.33}{26.7} = 0.274 \qquad K = 0.77 \text{ (Fig. 4-28a)}$$

Column *CD*:

$$G_C = 10 \qquad G_D = \frac{7.33 + 9.17}{26.7 + 40} = 0.247 \quad K = 0.76 \text{ (Fig. 4-28a)}$$

Column *FG*:

$$G_F = 1 \qquad G_G = \frac{7.33 + 9.17}{40 + \frac{3}{2} \times 40} = 0.165 \quad K = 0.67 \text{ (Fig. 4-28a)}$$

Column *DE*:

$$G_D = 0.247 \qquad G_E = \frac{9.17}{14.5} = 0.630 \qquad K = 1.14 \text{ (Fig. 4-28b)}$$

Column *GH*:

$$G_G = \frac{7.33 + 9.17}{40 + \frac{1}{2} \times 40} = 0.275 \quad G_H = \frac{9.17}{14.5} = 0.630 \qquad K = 1.15 \text{ (Fig. 4-28b)}$$

Example 4-11-2. Determine the critical load *P* for the frame of Fig. 4-24a, braced as in Fig. 4-24c, with the following dimensions: $L_b = 40$ ft, $L_c = 20$ ft, $BC = W24 \times 76$, $AB = DC = W12 \times 106$, A36 steel. The columns are placed with their webs in the plane of the frame and are supported against buckling out of the plane. Use the SSRC formula, Eq. (4-16), for buckling in the inelastic range. Use $E = 30,000$ ksi.

Solution

Column: W12 × 106 $I_x = 933$ in^4 $A = 31.2$ in^2 $r_x = 5.47$ in

Beam: W24 × 76 $I_x = 2100$ in^4

$$\text{Column } \frac{I}{L} = \frac{933}{20} = 46.6 \qquad \text{Beam } \frac{I}{L} = \frac{2100}{40} = 52.4$$

$$G_B = \frac{46.6}{52.4} = 0.89 \qquad G_A = 10 \text{ (pinned base)} \qquad K = 0.85 \text{ (Fig. 4-28a)}$$

$$\frac{L}{r_x} = \frac{20 \times 12}{5.47} = 43.9 \qquad \frac{KL}{r_x} = 0.85 \times 43.9 = 37.3$$

$$C_c = \pi \sqrt{\frac{2E}{F_y}} = \pi \sqrt{\frac{60,000}{36}} = 128$$

$$F_{cr} = 36 \left[1 - \frac{1}{2} \left(\frac{37.3}{128} \right)^2 \right] = 34.5 \text{ ksi}$$

$$F_E = \frac{\pi^2}{(KL/r)^2} = \frac{296,000}{37.3^2} = 213 \text{ ksi}$$

$$\tau = \frac{34.5}{213} = 0.162 \qquad G_B = 0.162 \times 0.89 = 0.144 \qquad [\text{Eq. (4-30}b)]$$

$$K = 0.740 \qquad \frac{KL}{r_x} = 0.740 \times 43.9 = 32.5$$

$$F_{cr} = 36 \left[1 - \frac{1}{2} \left(\frac{32.5}{128} \right)^2 \right] = 34.8 \text{ ksi}$$

This value of F_{cr} is only slightly larger than the value for $\tau = 1$. Therefore, no further refinement is necessary, and $P_{cr} = 34.8 \times 31.2 = 1086$ kips. In this case the first evaluation, $F_{cr} = 34.5$ ksi, is close enough for practical purposes.

4-12   LOCAL BUCKLING

The flanges, webs, and other plate elements of structural members may develop wave formations when they are compressed. This is called *local buckling*. Figure 4-32a shows an aluminum H and Fig. 4-32b an aluminum cruciform cross section, each tested in uniform axial compression, which have buckled in this fashion.

The critical stress for rectangular plates with various types of edge support, and with loads in the plane of the plate distributed along the edges in various ways, is given by

$$F_{cr} = \frac{k\pi^2 E}{12(1 - \mu^2)(b/t)^2} \tag{4-32}$$

where $k =$ a constant which depends upon how the edges are supported, upon the ratio of plate length to plate width, and upon the nature of the loading

$\mu =$ Poisson's ratio

$b =$ length of loaded edge of plate (except that it is the smaller lateral dimension when the plate is subjected only to shearing forces)

$t =$ plate thickness

The derivation of this equation for the plate shown in Fig. 4-33a is given in Chap. 10. In this case, the plate is simply supported on all four edges and is uniformly compressed on two opposite edges of width b. Such a plate buckles in

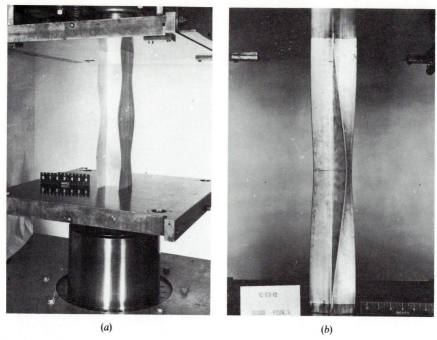

(a)   (b)

FIGURE 4-32
Local buckling of columns: (a) aluminum H, (b) aluminum cruciform. (*National Aeronautics and Space Administration.*)

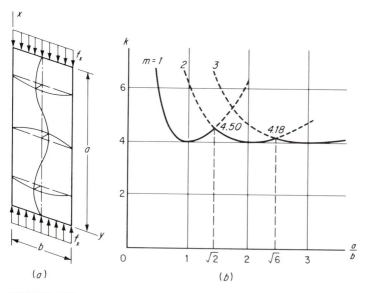

(a)   (b)

FIGURE 4-33

one transverse wave and one or more longitudinal waves. Values of the coefficient k in Eq. (4-32) for this case are given in Fig. 4-33b, where m denotes the number of longitudinal waves. The ratio a/b of plate length to plate width is called the *aspect ratio*. There is one longitudinal wave if $a/b \leq \sqrt{2}$, two if $\sqrt{2} \leq a/b \leq \sqrt{6}$, etc. The coefficient k has a minimum value of 4 for $a/b = 1, 2, 3$, etc. However, except for the unlikely case of the extremely short plate, the error in using $k = 4$ for all cases is at most about 10 percent. The error decreases with increasing a/b, and in the usual case, for which a/b is likely to be of the order of 10 or more, it is extremely small.

Values of k for five cases are given in Fig. 4-34. Case a in this figure is the plate of Fig. 4-33. Behavior of the plates in b, c, and d is similar to that of the plate in a; that is, they buckle in one transverse wave and a number of longitudinal waves. In each of these cases the value of k in the figure is the minimum value. On the other hand, the plate with one unloaded edge free and the other simply supported (case e) buckles in one longitudinal wave regardless of the aspect ratio. The corresponding value of k approaches the limiting value 0.456 with increasing aspect ratio. However, even for a plate as short as $a = 5b$ the value of k (0.496) is only 9 percent larger than the minimum value. Therefore, except for very short plates, the minimum value is a good approximation. Figure 4-32b is an example of this case, except that here the loaded edges are rotationally restrained. Although the member has four plate elements, with one edge each in common, there is no rotational restraint on this edge because all four legs buckle simultaneously since they are identical.

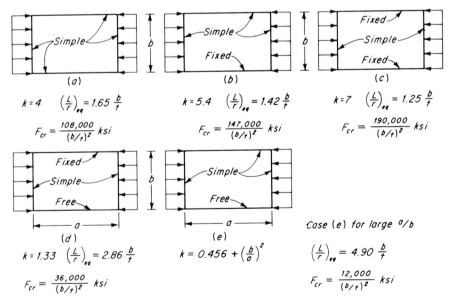

FIGURE 4-34
Plate-buckling coefficients.

The buckling shown in Fig. 4-32a is an example of a case between cases d and e of Fig. 4-34. Each of the four half-flanges is held straight and is rotationally restrained (but not fixed) at the juncture with the web. Of course, the corresponding value of k lies between the values for cases d and e. Values of k for incomplete rotational restraint have been determined for a number of cases (Ref. 3, p. 346).

Comparison of Eq. (4-32) with Eq. (4-2) shows that the ratio b/t of a plate plays the same role in its buckling behavior as the slenderness ratio of a column does. Also, as for the Euler formula, Eq. (4-32) is correct only if the critical stress does not exceed the proportional limit, but it can be extended to the inelastic range by using a reduced modulus of elasticity. However, the reduced modulus is not the tangent modulus, as in the case of the column, because the plate is anisotropic in its resistance to buckling at stresses exceeding the proportional limit. This can be shown by noting that the plate is assumed to be perfectly flat at the onset of buckling. Thus, for the plate loaded as in Fig. 4-33a, stresses at the onset of buckling are f_x (compressive) in the x direction and $f_y = 0$ in the y direction. These are shown in Fig. 4-35, where $f_x > F_p$. Now, if the plate begins to bend in the manner shown in Fig. 4-33a, bending stresses develop in both the x and y directions. The bending stresses in the y direction are governed by E, since they begin with $f_y = 0$ (Fig. 4-35). Thus, the plate stiffness for this direction, per unit of width, is $Et^3/12(1-\mu^2)$. On the other hand, bending stresses in the x direction are superimposed on the uniform compression f_x. According to the double-modulus theory, compressive bending stresses would initiate at the rate E_t, while tensile bending stresses would initiate at the rate E (Fig. 4-34). In this case the plate stiffness per unit of width is $E_r t^3/12(1-\mu^2)$, where E_r is the double modulus (Art. 4-4). According to the tangent-modulus theory, however, there is no reversal of stress at the instant buckling begins (Art. 4-4), in which case the stiffness is $E_t t^3/12(1-\mu^2)$. Either way, the plate is anisotropic, because the stiffness in the y direction is $Et^3/12(1-\mu^2)$. It is shown in Ref. 3, p. 354, that, using the tangent modulus, anisotropy for the cases shown in Fig. 4-35 is accounted for with good, conservative approximation by replacing E with $\sqrt{EE_t} = E\sqrt{\tau}$, where $\tau = E_t/E$.

Critical stresses for plate buckling can be evaluated by determining the *equivalent slenderness ratio* for which a column will buckle at the same stress. The equivalent slenderness ratio is found by replacing E in Eq. (4-32) with $E\sqrt{\tau}$ and

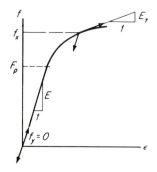

FIGURE 4-35

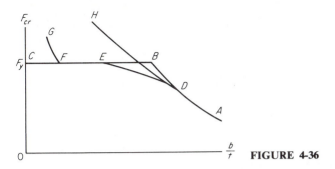

FIGURE 4-36

equating F_{cr} to the value given by Eq. (4-9). The result is

$$\left(\frac{L}{r}\right)_{eq} = \frac{3.3\sqrt[4]{\tau}}{\sqrt{k}}\frac{b}{t} \tag{4-33}$$

The value of τ to be used in this equation depends on the critical stress of the plate, which depends in turn on the value of $(L/r)_{eq}$. Therefore, the inelastic buckling stress should be determined by trial and error. However, it is on the safe side to ignore τ, since this results in a larger value of $(L/r)_{eq}$. The error is not significant, because the error in $(L/r)_{eq}$ is large only for the smaller values of τ, which correspond to stresses close to the yield stress. The critical stress is not very sensitive to L/r in such cases. The resulting equivalent slenderness ratios are given in Fig. 4-34.

Figure 4-36 shows the variation of critical stress with slenderness b/t. For a perfectly flat plate made of steel with a flat-top yield and with no residual stresses and no eccentricities of the edge stresses, the critical stress is given by ABC if strain hardening is neglected and by $ABFG$ if it is not. Of course, as with columns, imperfections reduce the critical stress given by this curve, and the local buckling curve for a real plate is $ADEFG$. On the other hand, DH is typical for inelastic buckling of a plate made of gradually yielding metals, where the ordinate to D is the proportional-limit stress. This curve is determined by Eq. (4-32), using the inelastic modulus $E\sqrt{\tau}$, or by using Eq. (4-2) with the equivalent slenderness ratio from Eq. (4-33).

4-13 LOCAL BUCKLING WITH RESIDUAL STRESSES

The effect of residual stresses on buckling is not the same for local buckling of plates as it is for primary buckling of columns. Thus, in a buckled column, the bending moment at any cross section caused by the residual stress F_r at an adjacent parallel cross section Δx distant is $\Delta\delta \int F_r \, dA$, where $\Delta\delta$ is the increment in deflection in the distance Δx. However, all points of a given cross section deflect equally, so this moment is $\Delta\delta \int F_r \, dA = 0$. Therefore, Eq. ($g$) of Art. 4-2 remains the same in the presence of symmetrical residual-stress patterns, and their only effect is to reduce the bending stiffness of the cross section through premature

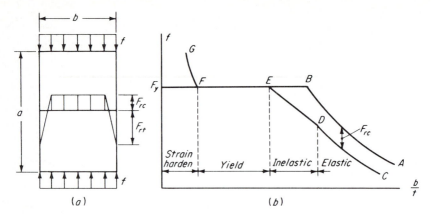

FIGURE 4-37

yielding (Art. 4-6). On the other hand, deflection of the middle surface of a plate varies transversely as well as longitudinally. In this case, the residual-stress bending-moment increment on a transverse section of a buckled plate generally is not zero. This may reduce the local-buckling strength.

In the case of a plate welded along both longitudinal edges, as in the plates of a welded box or the web of a welded I, the large residual tension (usually of yield-stress intensity) induces a fairly uniform residual compression F_{rc} over most of the width of the plate (Fig. 4-37a). When the plate buckles, the contribution of the residual tension to bending at a cross section is small, since the increments of deflection are smaller at the edge of the plate than they are in the interior. The result is a bending moment which is in addition to the moment from the externally applied compressive stress f. This reduces the critical stress. If $F_{rc} \le 0.15F_y$, the reduction is practically equal to F_{rc} if the plate buckles elastically. This is shown in Fig. 4-37b, where CD and AB are the curves for elastic buckling of the plate with and without residual stress, respectively. If $F_{rc} \ge 0.15F_y$, the reduction in critical stress is smaller than F_{rc}. Inelastic buckling is shown by DE. In this case, buckling begins *after* some premature yielding of the cross section because of the residual compression F_{rc}. In this case, the resulting reduction in stiffness of the plate must be taken into account. Thus, the problem is now one of buckling of an anisotropic plate. Methods of solution are discussed in Ref. 18.

4-14   DESIGN PROCEDURES FOR LOCAL BUCKLING OF STEEL COLUMNS

Equation (4-32) is plotted in Fig. 4-38 for four of the cases given in Fig. 4-34. Two levels of yield stress are shown. According to this figure, a perfect plate of A36 steel loaded in compression on two opposite edges and simply supported on the unloaded edges ($k = 4$) can reach yield stress without buckling if $b/t \le 55$. The corresponding value for a yield stress of 50 ksi is 46. However, these values do

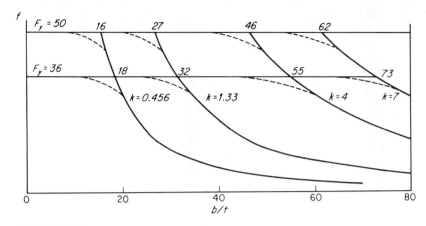

FIGURE 4-38

not account for the various imperfections which lower the proportional limit. Therefore, smaller values, corresponding to point E in Fig. 4-36, must be used. This is indicated by the dashed lines in Fig. 4-38. Of course, these values are not easy to determine because of the considerable variation in out-of-flatness, residual stresses, etc. Therefore, they are largely based on judgment and experience. Where there is likely to be rotational restraint, values are interpolated between simple-edge and clamped-edge values.

Table 4-4 compares typical limiting values of b/t for the AISC, AREA, and AASHTO specifications. The AISC values are used in both the ASD and the LRFD specifications. AISC and AREA values are based on yield stress. In the former F_y is in kips per square inch, in the latter, pounds per square inch. The AASHTO values are based on the calculated ("actual") stress f_a ksi. Each specification defines the various elements in its own way, so there is no uniformity. Therefore, the description of the types of elements in this table is a compromise and may differ from that in the specification. Furthermore, the table is for illustrative purposes and is not complete.

It will be noted that the AISC values suggest precision which is not consistent with the uncertainty in establishing these limits. This is because they were written in round numbers with F_y in pounds per square inch until 1969 and were not rounded when the units were changed. Thus, the limit $253/\sqrt{F_y}$ was $8000/\sqrt{F_y}$ in earlier editions.

The equivalent slenderness ratios of Fig. 4-34 suggest another way in which limiting values of b/t may be determined. Thus, for the plate of Fig. 4-34a, we have

$$\frac{b}{t} = \frac{1}{1.65}\frac{L}{r} = 0.6\frac{L}{r}$$

Primary buckling and local buckling are equally likely at this value of b/t. The German Buckling Specifications[19] DIN 4114 require the following for column

TABLE 4-4
Typical limiting values of b/t for plates in compression

| | Specification | | | Value for $F_y = 36$ ksi | | |
Type of element	AISC F_y, ksi	AREA F_y, psi	AASHTO f_a, psi	AISC	AREA	AASHTO*
Supported on one unloaded edge:						
Single angle	$\dfrac{76}{\sqrt{F_y}}$	...	$\dfrac{1625}{\sqrt{f_a}}$	13	...	12
Projecting element	$\dfrac{95}{\sqrt{F_y}}$	$\dfrac{2300}{\sqrt{F_y}}$	$\dfrac{1625}{\sqrt{f_a}}$	16	12	12
Stem of T	$\dfrac{127}{\sqrt{F_y}}$	$\dfrac{3000}{\sqrt{F_y}}$	...	21	16	
Supported on both unloaded edges:						
Webs	$\dfrac{253}{\sqrt{F_y}}$	$\dfrac{6000}{\sqrt{F_y}}$	$\dfrac{4000}{\sqrt{f_a}}$	42	32	32
Cover plates	$\dfrac{238}{\sqrt{F\dagger}}$	$\dfrac{7500}{\sqrt{F_y}}$	$\dfrac{5000}{\sqrt{f_a}}$	42	40	40
Perforated cover plates	$\dfrac{317}{\sqrt{F\dagger}}$	$\dfrac{7500}{\sqrt{F_y}}$	$\dfrac{6000}{\sqrt{f_a}}$	53	40	48

* Based on f_a = maximum allowable stress.
† ASD: $F = F_y$; LRFD: $F = F_y - F_r$, where $F_r = 10$ ksi for rolled shapes, 16.5 ksi for welded shapes.

web or cover plates supported so as to be essentially hinged on both unloaded edges:

$$\frac{b}{t} \leq \begin{cases} 45 & \text{for } \dfrac{L}{r} \leq 75 \\ 0.6\,\dfrac{L}{r} & \text{for } \dfrac{L}{r} \geq 75 \end{cases}$$

This specification prescribes formulas for various other types of edge support. These take rotational restraint into account, so they are in terms of a parameter which measures the relative stiffnesses of the element and the parts to which it connects.

It should be noted that the critical stress given by Eq. (4-32) is the stress at which local buckling of a perfect plate just begins. Therefore, whether it is a good estimate of the actual strength of a plate can be determined only by investigating the postbuckling behavior, as in the case of the axially loaded column (Fig. 4-3). As it turns out, the strength of the plate under uniform edge compression can be considerably larger than the load at which buckling begins. However, forces in compression members of steel frames in which hot-rolled shapes are used are usually such that economy in weight requires plate elements thick enough to preclude local buckling at stresses less than the yield stress or, as in the German specifications, less than the primary-buckling stress. Thus, limiting values of slenderness such as those in Table 4-4 cover most situations in the design of hot-rolled compression members. However, there are provisions in the AISC and AREA specifications for relaxing these requirements, discussed in Chap. 10. On the other hand, cold-formed construction usually involves elements which are so thin as to require different procedures.

4-15 DESIGN OF COLUMNS

The design of a column is necessarily a trial-and-error procedure since the ASD allowable stress F_a and the LRFD stress $\phi_c F_{cr}$ depend upon the value of KL/r and r is dependent upon the distribution of the cross-sectional area, while the required area depends in turn upon F_a, or $\phi_c F_{cr}$. One may assume a value of F_a, or of $\phi_c F_{cr}$, proportion a section with the corresponding required area, determine the slenderness ratio and the corresponding value of F_a, or $\phi_c F_{cr}$, and, finally, revise the section if these values differ significantly from the assumed ones. The AISC/ASD and AISC/LRFD Manuals contain a number of design aids to assist in the preliminary selection. Computer programs are available to facilitate the selection and checking process.

Columns must also be checked so as to prevent local buckling of one or more of the cross-sectional elements (flange, web, etc.) before overall instability of the column itself, as was explained in Art. 4-14.

Components of built-up cross sections such as those shown in Fig. 4-23b, c, d, and f must be interconnected at intervals to prevent buckling of a segment between the interconnection before overall buckling of the column itself. This is discussed in Arts. 4-17 and 4-18.

The proportioning of built-up sections is somewhat more difficult than the selection of rolled shapes, since there are usually many possible combinations of the components. However, with the help of Appendix Table A-1, one can usually select a trial section which will need only minor revision.

Example 4-15-1 (AISC/ASD). Design a building column of A36 steel, 15 ft long, to support a dead load of 50 kips and a live load of 200 kips. Assume $K = 1$ for both x and y axes.

Solution. Required capacity is $50 + 200 = 250$ kips. Assume $F_a = 15$ ksi.

$$A_{\text{req}} = \tfrac{250}{15} = 16.7 \text{ in}^2$$

Although any rolled shape or built-up section may be used as a column, the shapes most commonly used are the W8's, W10's, W12's, and W14's. A W shape from either the W8's with flange widths of 8 in or the W10's with flange widths of 10 in will have sufficient area. These are commonly called 8×8 and 10×10. Because of its larger radius of gyration, the 10×10 will require less area. Noting that the least radius of gyration for the 10×10 series is 2.54 in, we find

$$\frac{KL}{r} = \frac{15 \times 12}{2.54} = 71 \qquad C_c = \pi \sqrt{\frac{2 \times 29,000}{36}} = 126 \qquad \frac{KL/r}{C_c} = 0.564$$

From Eq. (4-17),

$$F_a = \frac{36(1 - 0.564^2/2)}{\frac{5}{3} + \frac{3}{8} \times 0.564 - \frac{1}{8} \times 0.564^3} = \frac{30.27}{1.86} = 16.3 \text{ ksi}$$

$$A_{req} = \frac{250}{16.3} = 15.3 \text{ in}^2$$

Therefore, the W10 $\times$ 54, which has an area of 15.8 in^2, is adequate.

Example 4-15-2 (AISC/LRFD). Design a building column of A36 steel, 15 ft long, to support a dead load of 50 kips and a live load of 200 kips. Assume $K = 1$ for both x and y axes.

Solution. Required capacity is $1.2 \times 50 + 1.6 \times 200 = 380$ kips. LRFD requires $\phi_c P_n \geq 380$ kips, where $\phi_c = 0.85$, and $P_n = A_g F_{cr}$, in which F_{cr} is determined by λ_c and F_y.

Therefore, $0.85 A_g F_{cr} \geq 380$ kips.

Assuming $F_{cr} = 28$ ksi, $A_{g,req} = 16.0$ in^2.

The shapes most commonly employed as columns are the W8's, W10's, W12's, and W14's, although any rolled shape or built-up section may be used. The W14 $\times$ 61, W12 $\times$ 58, W10 $\times$ 60, and W8 $\times$ 58 may be satisfactory.

Try W8 $\times$ 58, $A = 17.1$ in^2, $r_y = 2.10$ in.

$$\frac{KL}{r} = 15 \times \frac{12}{2.10} = 85.7$$

$$\lambda_c = \frac{KL}{r\pi} \sqrt{\frac{F_y}{E}} = \frac{85.7}{\pi} \sqrt{\frac{36}{29,000}} = 0.961$$

From Eq. (4-27),

$$F_{cr} = 0.658^{\lambda_c^2} F_y = 24.45$$

$$P_n = 17.1 \times 24.45 = 418 \text{ kips}$$

$$\phi_c P_n = 0.85 \times 418 = 355 < 380 \text{ kips} \qquad \text{N.G.}$$

Try W12 $\times$ 58, $A = 17.0$ in^2, $r_y = 2.51$ in. Using these properties and repeating the calculations produces

$$\frac{KL}{r} = 71.7 \qquad \lambda_c = 0.804 \qquad F_{cr} = 27.46 \text{ ksi}$$

$$P_n = 467 \qquad \phi_c P_n = 397 \text{ kips} > 380 \text{ kips} \qquad \text{O.K.}$$

The LRFD Manual contains a variety of design aids which are helpful in making the original trial selection.

Example 4-15-3 (AISC/ASD). Select the lightest W shape of A36 steel to support a dead load of 50 kips and a live load of 150 kips. The column is 32 ft long. Assume that it is pin-supported at the top and bottom in both directions and that an additional support is provided at midlength to prevent buckling about the y axis so that $K_x L_x = 32$ ft and $K_y L_y = 16$ ft.

Solution

$$\text{Design capacity} = 50 + 150 = 200 \text{ kips}$$

Enter the design aid tables in part 3 of the Manual with $KL = 16$ ft and $P = 200$ kips. Some of the possible selections are:

W14 × 53: $P = 202$ $\dfrac{r_x}{r_y} = 3.07$

W12 × 53: $P = 244$ $\dfrac{r_x}{r_y} = 2.11$

W10 × 49: $P = 228$ $\dfrac{r_x}{r_y} = 1.71$

W8 × 58: $P = 240$ $\dfrac{r_x}{r_y} = 1.74$

The ratio of $K_x L_x / K_y L_y = \frac{32}{16} = 2.0$. If r_x/r_y is greater than 2, the weak axis will control and the values tabulated are appropriate. Neither the W10 × 49 nor the W8 × 58 satisfies this requirement. The W10 × 49 is, however, the lightest shape and has a capacity greater than required for the conditions for which the tables apply, so check to see if it is adequate.

The load tables can be used by entering the tables with an adjusted value of KL for the y axis so that $KL/r_y = K_x L_x / r_x$. Therefore, enter with

$$\frac{K_x L_x}{r_x} r_y = \frac{K_x L_x}{r_x/r_y}$$

Try W10 × 49, with $r_x/r_y = 1.71$.

$$KL = \frac{32}{1.71} = 18.7 \text{ ft}$$

The tabulated capacity is 205 kips for $KL = 19$ ft, so this section should be satisfactory.

W10 × 49: $A = 14.4 \text{ in}^2$ $r_x = 4.35 \text{ in}$ $r_y = 2.54 \text{ in}$

$$\frac{K_x L_x}{r_x} = \frac{1 \times 32 \times 12}{4.35} = 88.3$$

$$\frac{K_y L_y}{r_y} = \frac{1 \times 16 \times 12}{2.54} = 75.6$$

For $KL/r = 88.3$ the value of F_a is 14.40 ksi.

$$P_a = 14.40 \times 14.4 = 207 \text{ kips} > 200 \text{ kips} \qquad \text{O.K.}$$

Use <u>W10 $\times$ 49</u>.

Example 4-15-4   (AISC/LRFD). Select the lightest W shape of A36 steel to support a dead load of 50 kips and a live load of 150 kips. The column is 32 ft long. Assume that it is pin-supported at the top and bottom in both directions and that an additional support is provided at midlength to prevent buckling about the y axis so that $K_x L_x = 32$ ft and $K_y L_y = 16$ ft.

Solution

$$\text{Required capacity} = 1.2 \times 50 + 1.6 \times 150 = 300 \text{ kips}$$

Enter the design strength tables in part 2 of the Manual with $KL = 16$ ft and $P = 300$ kips. Some of the possible selections are:

W14 $\times$ 61: $\qquad\qquad$ $P = 396$ $\qquad$ $\dfrac{r_x}{r_y} = 2.44$

W12 $\times$ 53: $\qquad\qquad$ $P = 348$ $\qquad$ $\dfrac{r_x}{r_y} = 2.11$

W10 $\times$ 49: $\qquad\qquad$ $P = 326$ $\qquad$ $\dfrac{r_x}{r_y} = 1.71$

W8 $\times$ 58: $\qquad\qquad$ $P = 337$ $\qquad$ $\dfrac{r_x}{r_y} = 1.74$

The ratio of $K_x L_x / K_y L_y = \frac{32}{16} = 2.0$. If r_x/r_y is greater than 2, the weak axis will control and the values tabulated are appropriate. Neither the W10 $\times$ 49 nor the W8 $\times$ 58 satisfies this requirement. The W10 $\times$ 49 is, however, the lightest shape and has a tabulated capacity greater than 300 kips. The load tables can be used by entering the tables with an adjusted value of KL for the y axis so that $KL/r_y = K_x L_x/r_x$. Therefore, enter the tables with

$$\frac{K_x L_x}{r_x} r_y = \frac{K_x L_x}{r_x/r_y}$$

Try W10 $\times$ 49, for which $r_x/r_y = 1.71$.

$$KL = \frac{32}{1.71} = 18.7 \text{ ft}$$

The tabulated strength for the W10 $\times$ 49 is 301 kips for 18 ft and 288 kips for $KL = 19$ ft. Therefore, it is unlikely that the W10 $\times$ 49 will provide the required capacity with $KL = 18.7$ ft. The next lightest W10 is the W10 $\times$ 54, so the W12 $\times$ 53 would be the lightest shape available.

Try W12 × 53: $A = 15.6 \text{ in}^2$ $r_x = 5.23$ $r_y = 2.48$

$$\frac{K_x L_x}{r_x} = \frac{1 \times 32 \times 12}{5.23} = 73.4$$

$$\frac{K_y L_y}{r_y} = \frac{1 \times 16 \times 12}{2.48} = 77.4$$

For $KL/r = 77.4$,

$$\lambda_c = \frac{KL}{r\pi}\sqrt{\frac{F_y}{E}} = \frac{77.4}{\pi}\sqrt{\frac{36}{29,000}} = 0.868$$

$$F_{cr} = 26.26 \text{ ksi}$$

$$P_n = 15.6 \times 26.26 = 410 \text{ kips}$$

$$\phi_c P_n = 0.85 \times 410 = 348 \text{ kips} > 300 \text{ kips} \qquad \text{O.K.}$$

Use W12 × 53.

Example 4-15-5   (AISC/ASD). Design a minimum-weight welded-I cross section for a pin-ended column which carries a central load of 165 kips. The unsupported length is 18 ft. A36 steel, AISC/ASD specification.

Solution. Assuming $F_a = 16$ ksi,

$$A = \tfrac{165}{16} = 10.32 \text{ in}^2$$

From Table A-1, $r_x = 0.435h$ and $r_y = 0.25b$. For $I_x = I_y$, $h \approx 0.6b$. For a flange width of 12 in, the minimum thickness is $\frac{6}{16} = \frac{3}{8}$ in. The area of the two flanges is 9.00 in^2. A $6\frac{1}{2} \times \frac{3}{16}$ in web, for which $6\frac{1}{2}/\frac{3}{16} = 35 < 42$, gives an additional 1.22 in^2. The proposed section is shown in Fig. 4-39.

Part		Area	I_x	I_y
Flanges	$12 \times \dfrac{3}{8} \times 2$	9.00	$\times 3.44^2 = 106.8$	$\times \dfrac{12^2}{12} = 108$
Web	$6\dfrac{1}{2} \times \dfrac{3}{16}$	1.22	$\times \dfrac{6.5^2}{12} = 4.3$	
		$\overline{10.22}$	$\overline{111.1}$	$\overline{108}$

$$r_y = \sqrt{\frac{108}{10.22}} = 3.24 \text{ in}$$

$$\frac{KL}{r_y} = 1 \times 18 \times \frac{12}{3.24} = 66.8 \qquad F_a = 16.76 \text{ ksi}$$

$$A = \frac{165}{16.76} = 9.86 < 10.22$$

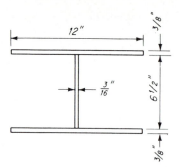

FIGURE 4-39

From column tables of the AISC Manual, the lightest **W** for this member is a W8 × 48. The weight of the built-up section is 3.4 × 10.22 = 32.5 lb. However, it should be noted that a minimum-weight section is not necessarily a minimum-cost section or a "best" design. Architectural considerations, space limitations, costs of fabrication and erection, etc., all enter into the problem.

Example 4-15-6   (AISC/LRFD). Design a minimum-weight welded-I cross section for a pin-ended column which carries a central load of 45 kips *DL* and 120 kips *LL*. The unsupported length is 18 ft. A36 steel, AISC/LRFD specification.

Solution

$$\text{Design load } P = 1.2 \times 45 + 1.6 \times 120 = 246 \text{ kips}$$

$$\phi_c P_n = 0.85 P_n = 246 \text{ kips} \qquad P_n = 289 \text{ kips}$$

Assuming $F_{cr} = 28$ ksi,

$$A = \tfrac{289}{28} = 10.32 \text{ in}^2$$

From Table A-1, $r_x = 0.435h$ and $r_y = 0.25b$. For $I_x = I_y$, $h \approx 0.6b$. For a flange width of 12 in, the minimum thickness is $\tfrac{6}{16} = \tfrac{3}{8}$ in. The area of the two flanges is 9.00 in². A $6\tfrac{1}{2} \times \tfrac{3}{16}$ in web, for which $6\tfrac{1}{2}/\tfrac{3}{16} = 35 < 42$, gives an additional 1.22 in². The proposed section is shown in Fig. 4-39.

Part		Area	I_x	I_y
Flanges	$12 \times \dfrac{3}{8} \times 2$	9.00	$\times 3.44^2 = 106.8$	$\times \dfrac{12^2}{12} = 108$
Web	$6\dfrac{1}{2} \times \dfrac{3}{16}$	1.22	$\times \dfrac{6.5^2}{12} = 4.3$	
		10.22	111.1	108

$$r_y = \sqrt{\frac{108}{10.22}} = 3.24 \text{ in}$$

$$\frac{KL}{r_y} = 1 \times 18 \times \frac{12}{3.24} = 66.8 \qquad \lambda = 0.749 \qquad F_{cr} = 28.5 \text{ ksi}$$

$$P_n = 28.5 \times 10.22 = 291 \text{ kips} > 289 \text{ kips}$$

From column tables of the AISC Manual, the lightest W for this member is a W8 × 48. The weight of the built-up section is 3.4 × 10.22 = 32.5 lb. However, it should be noted that a minimum-weight section is not necessarily a minimum-cost section or a "best" design. Architectural considerations, space limitations, costs of fabrication and erection, etc., all enter into the problem.

DP4-15-1 (AISC/ASD) and DP4-15-2 (AISC/LRFD): Compression Members for Truss of DP3-15-1 and DP3-15-2

In these examples the compression members for the truss of DP3-15-1 and DP3-15-2 are designed. Member forces for DP4-15-1 are shown on sheet 1 of DP3-15-1. The following discussion applies to both examples except where noted otherwise.

In designing the chord, we must decide whether the purlins support the chord against buckling in the plane of the roof. If we decide they do not, the distance between diagonal bracing connections must be taken as the unsupported length for buckling in the plane of the roof and the distance between truss panel points as the unsupported length for buckling in the plane of the truss. In these examples we assume that the purlins do support the chord.

The effective-length coefficients K of compression members in trusses do not exceed unity, because trusses are usually loaded only at the joints so that joint displacement of one end of a member relative to the other end is small. However, K should not be taken less than unity, even in trusses with bolted, riveted, or welded joints, if the truss supports a fixed system of loads and is designed so that all its members fail simultaneously. In this case, there is little, if any, rotational restraint at the joints.

If the compression chord of a truss is of the same cross section for two or more panels, there are rotational restraints if the chord forces are unequal. In this case, the effective lengths are less than unity. If such a chord has the same cross section for the entire length of a truss of approximately constant depth, an effective-length coefficient of 0.9 may be used if the truss supports fixed loads.[3,9]

Simple rules for the effective length of web members which are rotationally restrained by chord members are difficult to formulate. Bleich gives values of K ranging from 0.57 to 1 (Ref. 3, p. 247). If the truss carries moving or movable loads, rotational restraint may be appreciable, because the maximum stress in a web member results from a different position of live load than that which produces maximum stress in the chords. For this case, $K = 0.85$ is suggested as a conservative, approximate rule.[9]

$U_3 U_4$. The section for $U_3 U_4$, which has the largest force, should be used for the entire top chord of the truss, or for at least the portion $U_2 U_5$, since any saving from the use of lighter sections for the less heavily loaded members would be offset by the cost of the additional connections. Therefore, $K = 0.9$. The estimated required area is available in tees ranging in depth from 4 to 8 in. The

---

COMPRESSION MEMBERS FOR TRUSS OF DP3-15-1   DP4-15-1

$\underline{U_4 U_5}$
$P = 109.7^k, L = 6'$
$A = 109.7/19 = 5.77 \, in^2$
Try WT 6x20, $A = 5.89 \, in^2$
$KL/r = 0.9 \times 72/1.57 = 42$
$F_a = 19.0 \, ksi$
$A = 109.7/19.0 = 5.77 < 5.89$
      Use WT 6x20

$\underline{U_1 L_1}$
$P = 37.6^k, L = 5'$
$A = 37.6/19 = 1.98 \, in^2$
Try 2L 3x2
$L/r = 60/0.89 = 67$
$F_a = 16.7 \, ksi$
$A = 37.6/16.7 = 2.25 \, in^2$
      Use 2L 3x2x¼ ⨆ $A = 2.38 \, in^2$

$\underline{U_0 U_1, \ U_1 U_2, \ U_2 U_3, \ U_3 U_4} \ same \ as \ U_4 U_5$

$\underline{U_2 L_2}$
$P = 21.7^k, \ L = 5.5'$
$A = 21.7/12 = 1.81 \, in^2$
Try 2L 2x2
$L/r = 66/0.60 = 110$
$F_a = 11.7 \, ksi$
$A = 21.7/11.7 = 1.86 \, in^2$
      Use 2L 2x2x¼ ⨆ $A = 1.88 \, in^2$

$\underline{U_3 L_3}$
$P = 13.6^k, L = 6'$
$A = 13.6/10 = 1.36 \, in^2$
Try 2L 2x2
$L/r = 72/0.61 = 118$
$F_a = 10.6 \, ksi$
$A = 13.6/10.6 = 1.28 \, in^2$
      Use 2L 2x2 x 3/16 ⨆ $A = 1.43 \, in^2$

$\underline{U_4 L_4}$
$P = 7.0^k, L = 6.5'$
Try 2L 2x2
$L/r = 78/0.61 = 126$
$F_a = 9.41 \, ksi$
$A = 7.0/9.41 = 0.75 \, in^2$
      Use 2L 2x2 x ⅛ $A = 0.96 \, in.^2$

$\underline{L_0 L_1}$ (wind force $p = 10^k$, see DP6-7-1)
*WT 7x17, $A = 5.01, L/r = 77/1.52 = 51$
$F_a = 18.3 \times 1.33 = 24.4 \, ksi$
$P = 24.4 \times 5.00 = 122^k > 10^k$
*See DP3-15-1

COMPRESSION MEMBERS FOR TRUSS OF DP3-15-2   DP4-15-2

Design loads

Member	Dead load	Snow	Trolley LL	Case 1	Case 2	Case 3	Design
U_0U_1	-9.7	-27.8	-16.0	-13.6	-51.2	-64.1	-64.1
U_1U_2	-15.3	-43.8	-28.2	-21.4	-85.4	-102.5	-102.5
U_2U_3	-18.3	-52.3	-32.0	-25.6	-99.3	-121.6	-121.6
U_3U_4	-19.1	-54.7	-35.2	-26.7	-106.6	-128.0	-128.0
U_4U_5	-18.6	-53.1	-38.0	-26.0	-109.7	-126.3	-126.3
U_1L_1	-6.8	-19.6	-11.2	-9.5	-35.9	-45.1	-45.1
U_2L_2	-3.0	-8.5	-10.2	-4.2	-24.2	-22.3	-24.2
U_3L_3	-2.6	-7.5	-3.5	-3.6	-12.5	-16.9	-16.9
U_4L_4	-1.0	-2.8	-3.2	-1.4	-7.7	-7.3	-7.7

U_3U_4

    $P = 128.0^k$, $L = 6'$
    $A = 128.0/25 = 5.12\ in^2$
    Try WT6 x 17.5, $A = 5.17\ in^2$
    $KL/r = 0.9 \times 72/1.54 = 42.1$
    $\lambda = 0.472$ $F_{cr} = 32.8\ ksi$
    $\phi\,P_n = 0.85 \times 32.8 \times 5.17 = 144 > 128$
        Use WT6 x 17.5

U_0U_1, U_1U_2, U_2U_3, U_4U_5 same as U_3U_4

U_2L_2

    $P = 24.2^k$, $L = 5.5'$
    $A = 24.2/17 = 1.42\ in^2$
    Try 2L 2 x 2
    $L/r = 66/0.61 = 108$
    $\lambda = 1.21$ $F_{cr} = 19.44$
    $A = 24.2/(0.85 \times 19.44) = 1.46\ in^2$
        Use 2L 2 x 2 x 1/4 ⅂⌐ $A = 1.88\ in^2$

U_4L_4

    $P = 7.7^k$, $L = 6.5'$
    $A = 7.7/13 = 0.60\ in^2$
    Try 2L 2 x 2
    $L/r = 78/0.61 = 126$
    $\lambda = 1.413$ $F_{cr} = 15.6\ ksi$
    $A = 7.7/(0.85 \times 15.6) = 0.58\ in^2$
        Use 2L 2 x 2 x 1/8 ⅂⌐ $A = 0.96\ in^2$

U_1L_1

    $P = 45.1^k$, $L = 5'$
    $A = 45.1/23 = 1.96\ in^2$
    Try 2L 3 x 2
    $L/r \cong 60/0.89 = 67.4$
    $\lambda = 0.756$ $F_{cr} = 28.3\ ksi$
    $A = 45.1/(0.85 \times 28.3) = 1.87\ in^2$
        Use 2L 3 x 2 x 1/4 ⅂⌐ $A = 2.38\ in^2$

U_3L_3

    $P = 16.9^k$, $L = 6'$
    $A = 16.9/15 = 1.13\ in^2$
    Try 2L 2 x 2
    $L/r = 72/0.61 = 118$
    $\lambda = 1.32$ $F_{cr} = 17.3$
    $A = 16.9/(0.85 \times 17.3) = 1.15\ in^2$
        Use 2L 2 x 2 x 3/16 ⅂⌐ $A = 1.43\ in^2$

L_0L_1 (wind force $P = 10^k$, see DP6-8-1)

    *WT7 x 15, $A = 4.42\ in^2$
    $L/r = 77/1.52 = 50.7$
    $\lambda = 0.569$ $F_{cr} = 31.44\ ksi$
    $\phi\,P_n = 0.85 \times 31.44 \times 4.42 = 118^k$
    $P_{req.} = 1.3 \times 10 = 13^k$

    *See DP3-15-2

smaller size can be ruled out as almost certain to be inadequate for suitable connections of web members. The larger size might be ruled out on the basis of the ratio of length to depth ($\frac{72}{8} = 9$) since it was mentioned in Art. 3-18 that secondary stresses tend to become excessive for trusses with relatively wide members, say, $L/d \leq 10$. Instead of the calculation of load capacity as shown, some designers prefer to compute the "actual" stress and compare it with the allowable stress F_a when using ASD and with $\phi_c F_{cr}$ when using LRFD. A comparison of areas makes it easier to determine whether there is a shape which better meets the requirements of the member.

Web members. Unequal-legged angles with the long legs back to back give more nearly equal radii of gyration for the two principal axes than either angles with equal legs or unequal-legged angles with short legs back to back. The radius of gyration for a specific pair of angles, such as $2\frac{1}{2} \times 2$ or 3×2, is virtually independent of the thickness. Therefore, the allowable stress can be determined without assuming the thickness.

$L_0 L_1$. Although it is nominally a tension member, $L_0 L_1$ may be subjected to compression due to wind. This force, 10 kips, is calculated in DP6-7-1 (AISC/ASD) and DP6-8-1 (AISC/LRFD). There is no dead-load or live-load tension to offset it, and the member is designed as follows:

ASD. In this specification the stress may be increased by one-third when member forces due to wind or combinations of wind and other loads are being investigated. The AASHTO and AREA specifications also allow a one-third increase.

LRFD. In this specification the required design strength is based on the load combination of Eq. (d) of Art. 1-13. Since $D = L = 0$, this gives $1.3 \times 10 = 13$ kips.

Investigation of the wind force in $L_0 L_1$ is not customary. It is given here only as a reminder that there may be situations in which it is not enough to make the usual assumption that the only effect of wind is a pressure on the windward face of a structure.

DP4-15-3 (AISC/ASD) and DP4-15-4 (AISC/LRFD): Interior Column for 26-Story Building

The design of the bottom-tier column B2 of a 26-story building is considered in this example. The floor plan is shown on the design sheet.

The height from the basement to the lobby is 15 ft; other floor heights are 13 ft. The floor system consists of a 3-in cellular steel deck with $2\frac{1}{2}$-in concrete slab supported on steel joists. The joists are 15 ft on center. Live loads are 100 psf on the first, or lobby, floor, 80 psf on the upper floors, and 20 psf on the roof. X bracing in the longitudinal direction and K bracing in the lateral direction of

COLUMN FOR TALL BUILDING   DP4-15-3

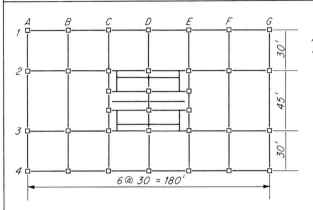

AISC/ASD Specification
A 36 steel

6 @ 30 = 180'

Tributary area = ($\frac{1}{2}$ x 30 + $\frac{1}{2}$ x 45) x 30 = 1125 ft²

LL reduction = 0.08 (1125 −150) = 78%

Max. LL reduction = 23.1 $\frac{D+L}{L}$ = 23.1 x $\frac{58+80}{80}$ = 40%

Roof load (a)		Upper floor load (b)		Lobby floor (b)	
Live	= 20	Live 80 × 0.60	= 48	Live	= 100
Roofing	= 5	Floor	= 42	Floor	= 50
Deck	= 42	Ceiling	= 7	Ceiling	= 7
Ceiling	= 7	Bms & Col.	= 9	Bms & Col	= 13
Beams	= 4		106 psf		170psf
	78 psf				

Bottom tier column B2

Roof	=	78
Upper floors = 106 × 25 =		2650
Lobby	=	170
		2898 × 37.5 × 30 = 3260^k

Assume F_a = 20 ksi   A = 3260 / 20 = 163 in²

Try 16 × 16 × 3$\frac{1}{4}$ box section, A = 166 in²

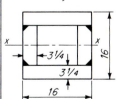

$I_x = I_y = \frac{16^4}{12} - \frac{9.5^4}{12}$ = 4783 in⁴

$r = \sqrt{4783/166}$ = 5.39 in

$KL/r = 1 \times 15 \times 12 / 5.39 = 33.4$ $F_a = 19.7$ ksi

$P = 19.7 \times 166 = 3270^k$ O.K.   (c)

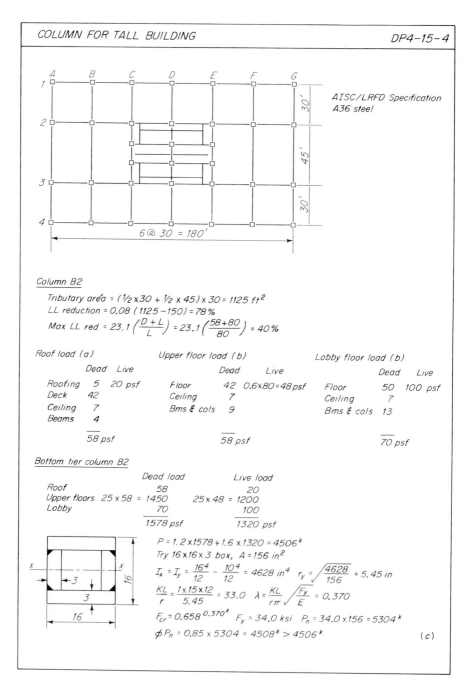

COLUMN FOR TALL BUILDING   DP4-15-4

AISC/LRFD Specification
A36 steel

6 @ 30 = 180'

Column B2

Tributary area = $(1/2 \times 30 + 1/2 \times 45) \times 30 = 1125 \ ft^2$
LL reduction = $0.08 (1125 - 150) = 78\%$
Max LL red. = $23.1 \left(\frac{D+L}{L}\right) = 23.1 \left(\frac{58+80}{80}\right) = 40\%$

Roof load (a)

	Dead	Live
Roofing	5	20 psf
Deck	42	
Ceiling	7	
Beams	4	
	58 psf	

Upper floor load (b)

	Dead	Live
Floor	42	0.6×80 = 48 psf
Ceiling	7	
Bms & cols	9	
	58 psf	

Lobby floor load (b)

	Dead	Live
Floor	50	100 psf
Ceiling	7	
Bms & cols	13	
	70 psf	

Bottom tier column B2

	Dead load	Live load
Roof	58	20
Upper floors 25 × 58 =	1450	25 × 48 = 1200
Lobby	70	100
	1578 psf	1320 psf

$P = 1.2 \times 1578 + 1.6 \times 1320 = 4506^k$
Try 16 × 16 × 3 box, A = 156 in²
$I_x = I_y = \frac{16^4}{12} - \frac{10^4}{12} = 4628 \ in^4 \quad r_y = \sqrt{\frac{4628}{156}} = 5.45 \ in$
$\frac{KL}{r} = \frac{1 \times 15 \times 12}{5.45} = 33.0 \quad \lambda = \frac{KL}{r\pi}\sqrt{\frac{F_y}{E}} = 0.370$
$F_{cr} = 0.658^{0.370^2} \ F_y = 34.0 \ ksi \quad P_n = 34.0 \times 156 = 5304^k$
$\phi P_n = 0.85 \times 5304 = 4508^k > 4506^k$

(c)

the service area are used to resist wind forces. This allows the use of moment-free beam-to-column and beam-to-beam connections throughout. In this case, as mentioned in Art. 4-11, the columns may be considered to be continuous on simple supports. Furthermore, because of the service-area bracing, relative joint translation can be considered to be negligible. Therefore, $K = 1$.

Columns to which beams connect with simple framing connections (Fig. 4-25b) are usually designed as concentrically loaded members. Such a connection is not moment-free, but the moment that can be generated is relatively small compared to that of a typical moment-resistant connection (Fig. 4-25a).

The following comments are intended to clarify computations identified by the corresponding letter on the design sheet.

a. Felt and gravel roofing weighs about 5 psf and the cellular deck and concrete slab 42 psf. Weight of beams and columns depends upon their spacing and spans and the load to be supported.

b. Live-load reduction is discussed in Art. 1-4. The American Standard Building Code reduction is 0.08 percent/ft^2 of supported area in excess of 150 ft^2 but cannot exceed 60 percent or $R = 23.1 (1 + D/L)$ percent. The column weight is averaged for the 26 floors.

c. The W shape is ordinarily used for building columns and will usually be cheaper than the welded box used in this example. According to the AISC/ASD specification a W14 × 605 in A36 steel or a W14 × 426 in A572 Grade 60 can be used instead. According to the AISC/LRFD specification a W14 × 550 in A36 steel or a W14 × 370 in A572 Grade 60 can be used instead. The A36 shapes are approximately 21 in deep with a 17-in flange. The A572 Grade 60 shapes are approximately 18 in deep with a 16.5-in flange. Thus, in some situations the extra cost of the 16 × 16 in box might be justified.

Column loads in a building of this magnitude are ordinarily determined by computer, and in many cases sizing of the members is computerized.

4-16 COLUMN BASES

The base of a column which is supported by a concrete footing must have a bearing plate large enough to distribute the load over an area sufficient to preclude excessive bearing stresses. The base plate may be shop-connected or shipped loose. Except where end moments are involved, the connection need only hold the parts in line if the ends of the column are finished to a plane surface, since the load is transmitted by bearing at the contact surfaces. It may be cheaper to omit planing the ends of lightly loaded columns and to design the connection between base and shaft for the total load.

The distribution of the pressure of the plate on the footing depends upon the relative stiffnesses of the two. Even if the distribution were known, the resulting stresses in the plate could not be determined easily since bending in two directions is involved. The usual analysis is based on two assumptions: (1) the pressure of the footing on the plate is uniformly distributed, and (2) those portions of the plate which project from the column shaft act as cantilever beams. Since the sections of zero shear, and consequently of maximum moment, in the bearing plates are inside the area of contact between the column shaft and plate, the lengths of the cantilevered portions are usually assumed to be longer than the actual projection of the plate. The AISC recommended analysis for H-shaped columns assumes that the maximum moments occur at sections which are $0.95d$ apart in one direction and $0.8b$ apart in the other direction, where d and b are, respectively, the depth and flange width of the shape.

Bases of columns in industrial buildings, and those in tier-building construction designed to resist wind forces, may need to be proportioned to resist end moments resulting from lateral forces. This problem is discussed in Art. 8-31.

Example 4-16-1   (AISC/ASD): Base plate. Design a base plate for the column of DP4-15-3 (AISC/ASD). The columns of this building are supported on reinforced concrete footings for which $f'_c = 3000$ psi.

Solution. The allowable bearing pressure F_p on the concrete (Specification Sec. J9) is

$$F_p = 0.35f'_c \sqrt{\frac{A_2}{A_1}} \leq 0.70f'_c$$

where

$$A_1 = \text{area of base plate}$$

$$A_2 = \text{area of footing}$$

Assume that the area of the base plate for column B2 is one-third the area of the footing.

$$\frac{A_2}{A_1} = 3$$

$$F_p = 0.35 \times 3000\sqrt{3} = 1820 \text{ psi}$$

Therefore, the required area of the base plate is

$$A_1 = \frac{P}{F_p} = \frac{3260}{1.82} = 1800 \text{ in}^2$$

Use a 45×45 in plate, which gives $A = 2025$ in^2. The plate projection for the 16×16 in column is

$$\tfrac{1}{2}(45 - 0.95 \times 16) = 14.9 \text{ in}$$

Therefore,

$$M = F_p \times 14.9 \times \tfrac{1}{2} \times 14.9 = 1.82 \times 111 = 202 \text{ in·kips per 1 in of base-plate width}$$

The allowable bending stress (Specification Sec. F2.1) is $F_b = 0.75F_y = 0.75 \times 36 = 27$ ksi.

$$F_b = \frac{Mc}{I}$$

$$I = \tfrac{1}{12} \times 1 \times t^3 \text{ in}^4$$

$$c = \frac{t}{2}$$

$$\frac{I}{c} = \frac{\tfrac{1}{12} \times 1 \times t^3}{t/2} = \frac{t^2}{6} = \frac{M}{F_b} = \frac{202}{27} = 7.48$$

$$t^2 = 7.48 \times 6$$

$$t = 6.70 \text{ in}$$

Use a 7 × 45 × 45 plate.

Example 4-16-2 (AISC/LRFD): Base Plate. Design a base plate for the column of DP4-15-4 (AISC/LRFD). The columns of this building are supported on reinforced concrete footings for which $f'_c = 3000$ psi.

Solution. The bearing capacity P_p on the concrete (Specification Sec. J9) is

$$P_p = 0.85f'_c A_1 \sqrt{\frac{A_2}{A_1}} \le 1.7f'_c A_1$$

where A_1 is the area of the base plate and A_2 is the area of the footing. Assume that the area of the base plate for column B2 is one-third the area of the footing.

$$P_p = 0.85 \times 3000 A_1 \sqrt{3} = 4417 A_1 \qquad \text{lb}$$

Therefore, the required area of the base plate is

$$\phi_c P_p = 4506 \text{ kips}$$

$$0.6 \times 4.417 A_1 = 4506$$

$$A_1 = 1700 \text{ in}^2$$

Use a 45 × 45 in plate, which gives $A = 2025$ in^2. The plate projection from the 16 × 16 in column is

$$\tfrac{1}{2}(45 - 0.95 \times 16) = 14.9 \text{ in}$$

Therefore,

$$M = 4.417 \times 14.9 \times \tfrac{1}{2} \times 14.9 = 490 \text{ in·kips per 1 in of base-plate width}$$

The limiting moment (Specification appendix F1.7) is

$$\phi_b M_n = \phi_b M_p = \phi_b Z_x F_y$$

where Z_x for a rectangular section of the base plate 1 in wide is $1 \times t^2/4$ and $\phi_b = 0.9$. Therefore,

$$0.9 \times \frac{t^2}{4} \times 36 = 490 \text{ in·kips}$$

$$t = 7.78 \text{ in}$$

Use a $8 \times 45 \times 45$ plate.

4-17 SHEAR IN COLUMNS

The segments of built-up columns with cross sections such as those shown in Fig. 4-23b, c, d, f, and g must be interconnected so that they will act as parts of a whole rather than as individual columns. They may be joined by single lacing (Fig. 4-40a) or by double lacing (Fig. 4-40b). At the ends and at intermediate points where it is necessary to interrupt the lacing (to admit gusset plates, for example), the open sides are connected with *stay plates* (Fig. 4-40d). Stay plates are also called *batten plates* or *tie plates*. Lacing is sometimes omitted, with the segments connected by battens (Fig. 4-40e). Lacing has been largely supplanted by perforated cover plates (Fig. 4-40f) in members of bridge trusses.

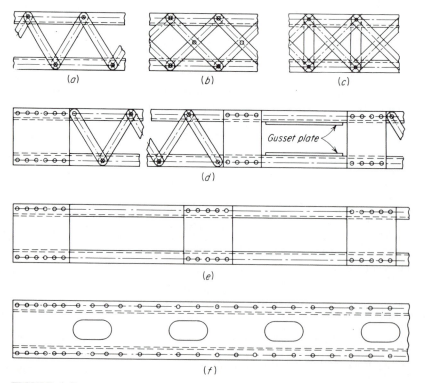

FIGURE 4-40

FIGURE 4-41

The lacing or battens in a column must carry the shear forces which develop when the column bends. The shear V is shown in Fig. 4-41, which pictures a portion of a bent column. Since θ is a small angle, we have

$$V = P \sin \theta = P \tan \theta = P \frac{dy}{dx} \qquad (a)$$

The slope dy/dx for a perfect column is indeterminate, even though the deflected shape is known, because the deflection δ in $y = \delta \sin \pi x/L$ is indeterminate. Therefore, an evaluation of δ must be attempted or else the shear determined for an imperfect column, such as a crooked column or an eccentrically loaded one. Both schemes have been used.

For a column whose load is eccentric equal amounts e at each end, dy/dx is maximum at the end and can be found from Eq. (d) of Art. 6-1. Equating M_2/P and M_1/P in that equation to e, we get

$$y = e\left(\tan \frac{kL}{2} \sin kx + \cos kx - 1 \right) \qquad (b)$$

From Eq. (b), $dy/dx = ek \tan (kL/2)$ at $x = 0$. Substituting this into Eq. (a), we get

$$V = Pek \tan \frac{kL}{2} \qquad (c)$$

Substituting into this equation $k = \sqrt{P/EI}$, we have

$$\frac{V}{P} = \pi \frac{e}{L} \sqrt{\frac{P}{P_E}} \tan \frac{\pi}{2} \sqrt{\frac{P}{P_E}} \qquad (4\text{-}34a)$$

Curves A and B of Fig. 4-42 are plots of Eq. (4-34a) for $F_y = 33$ ksi, $E = 30,000$ ksi, and $e = 0.25r$ and $0.50r$, respectively, where r is the radius of gyration of the

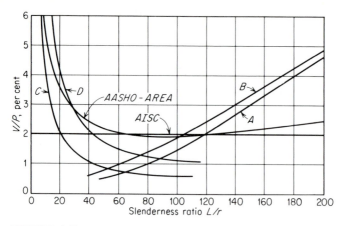

FIGURE 4-42

cross section. Values of V/P were found by substituting in the equation corresponding values of P/A and L/r computed from the secant formula [Eq. (6-2b)] assuming $c = r$. It is seen that V/P increases with L/r. However, since P decreases with increase in L/r, the shear itself does not increase indefinitely but reaches a maximum value at about $L/r = 150$.

If the column load is eccentric equal but opposite amounts e at each end, the maximum value of dy/dx is at midlength. Proceeding as above, the solution is found to be

$$\frac{V}{P} = \pi \frac{e}{L} \sqrt{\frac{P}{P_E}} \csc \frac{\pi}{2} \sqrt{\frac{P}{P_E}} \qquad (4\text{-}34b)$$

Curves C and D of Fig. 4-42 are graphs of this equation for the same values as before, with e/r equal to 0.25 and 0.50, respectively.

Specification requirements are based on empirical formulas which are simpler in form than Eqs. (4-34). AASHTO specifies the shear given by

$$\frac{V}{P} = \frac{1}{100} \left(\frac{100}{L/r + 10} + \frac{L/r}{3,300,000/F_y} \right) \qquad (4\text{-}35)$$

This equation is plotted for $F_y = 33,000$ psi in Fig. 4-42. It will be noted that it gives values which approximate those of Eq. (4-34b) for the e/r values for which it was plotted but falls short of the values according to Eq. (4-34a). AREA uses the same formula, except that the constant in the second term in the parentheses is 3,600,000. On the other hand, the AISC specifications specify a shear which is independent of L/r, namely,

$$V = 0.02P \qquad (4\text{-}36)$$

This formula is also plotted in Fig. 4-42.

The formulas just discussed are intended to predict the shear component of the axial load P which results from curvature of the column. Both AASHTO and

AREA require that the shear force due to any other external force and to the weight of the member be taken into account. The AISC specifications do not.

Specifications for aluminum structures suggest the shear given by[20]

$$V = 0.02F_a A + V_t \tag{4-37}$$

where F_a is the specified allowable stress for short columns and V_t is the shear caused by any transverse load on the column.

The considerable variation in specification requirements for shear for which lacing must be designed reflects the uncertainties in predicting the deflected shape of the column and the differing opinions of specification writers regarding the assumptions that must be made.

Although the shearing force is relatively small, the arrangement of lacing to resist it is of considerable importance. Since the laced column is a trussed framework, secondary stresses in the lacing may result from the axial deformation. These stresses can be quite large in double-lacing systems, particularly in that of Fig. 4-40c (Ref. 3, p. 183). Lacing as in Fig. 4-40b is better in this respect because the accordionlike action permits lateral expansion of the column, which must accompany shortening under load if there is to be no shortening of the lacing bars. The lateral ties in Fig. 4-40c restrain this adjustment.

The spacing of the connections of lacing to the column segments is an important consideration. If this distance is too great, individual segments may buckle alternately in and out between lattice connections. This suggests that the slenderness ratio of a column segment, considered as a column whose length is the spacing of lattice connections, should not be more than that of the column as a whole. This is a requirement of the AISC/LRFD specification. However, the AISC/ASD specification requires that lacing connections be spaced so that the slenderness ratio of the portion of the flange between them be no more than three-fourths the slenderness ratio of the member, while the AASHTO and AREA specifications have the same requirement except that the limit is two-thirds the slenderness ratio of the member, but not to exceed 40.

The lacing bar must be designed to resist either tension or compression. Proportions of perforated cover plates are based on results of analyses and tests. Specification requirements are essentially identical and conform to recommendations in Ref. 21.

4-18 EFFECT OF SHEAR ON CRITICAL LOAD

The shear component of the axial force P, which was discussed in the preceding article, results in shear deformation which is neglected in the derivation of the Euler formula for the critical load. To determine the effect this has on the predicted critical load, the additional curvature of the column due to shear deformation must be considered. The buckled column is shown in Fig. 4-43a, where y_m and y_s are the displacements due to moment and shear, respectively. According to Fig.

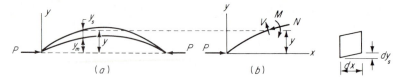

FIGURE 4-43

4-43b, the moment is Py, and the shear is $P\,dy/dx$. Figure 4-43c shows the shear deformation of an element dx long, from which

$$\frac{dy_s}{dx} = \frac{nP}{AG}\frac{dy}{dx} \tag{a}$$

where A = area of cross section
G = modulus of elasticity in shear
n = factor which depends on shape of cross section

The factor n depends on the manner in which the shearing stress is distributed over the cross section. For rectangular cross sections $n = 1.2$, while for an I bent in the plane of the web it is about 2.

The curvature at any point is

$$\frac{d^2 y}{dx^2} = \frac{d^2 y_m}{dx^2} + \frac{d^2 y_s}{dx^2} \tag{b}$$

From Eq. (a)

$$\frac{d^2 y_s}{dx^2} = \frac{d}{dx}\frac{nP}{AG}\frac{dy}{dx} = \frac{nP}{AG}\frac{d^2 y}{dx^2} \tag{c}$$

Furthermore,

$$\frac{d^2 y_m}{dx^2} = \frac{M}{EI} = -\frac{Py}{EI} \tag{d}$$

Substituting these two values into Eq. (b) gives

$$\frac{d^2 y}{dx^2} = -\frac{Py}{EI} + \frac{nP}{AG}\frac{d^2 y}{dx^2} \tag{e}$$

from which

$$\frac{d^2 y}{dx^2} + \frac{Py}{EI(1 - nP/AG)} = 0 \tag{f}$$

Comparing this equation with Eq. (i) of Art. 4-2, we see that they are the same except for the meaning of k^2. Therefore, the solution is obtained from Eq. (l) of Art. 4-2.

$$P = \frac{\pi^2 EI}{L^2}\left(1 - \frac{nP}{AG}\right) \tag{g}$$

Solving this equation for P gives

$$P = \frac{\pi^2 EI}{L^2} \frac{1}{1 + n\pi^2 EI/L^2 AG} \tag{4-38}$$

This equation can be written in terms of an effective-length coefficient. Using the tangent-modulus concept to extend it to the inelastic range and assuming G/E to be constant so that $G = 0.4E$, we get

$$F_{cr} = \frac{\pi^2 E_t}{(K'L/r)^2} \tag{4-39}$$

in which

$$K' = \sqrt{1 + \frac{25n}{(L/r)^2}} \tag{4-40}$$

Values of K' exceed unity only slightly. Using $n = 2$ for the I, $K' = 1.002$ and 1.060 for $L/r = 120$ and 20, respectively. Thus, it is clear that neglecting shear deformation results in a negligible error in the critical load for I columns.

The effect of shear deformation on built-up columns whose segments are connected by lacing, battens, or perforated cover plates is larger than for solid-webbed columns. The strength of a column with single lacing inclined at 60° to the longitudinal axis of the column or with double lacing at 45° can be determined, as for the solid-webbed column, by using the effective-length coefficient given by[9]

$$K' = \begin{cases} 1.1K & \dfrac{KL}{r} \le 40 & (4\text{-}41a) \\[3mm] K\sqrt{1 + \dfrac{300}{(KL/r)^2}} & \dfrac{KL}{r} \ge 40 & (4\text{-}41b) \end{cases}$$

where K is the effective-length coefficient for end restraint. Although the increase in effective-length coefficient is 10 percent for stocky columns, the resulting reduction in strength is small because of the relative insensitivity of short columns to variation in L/r. However, the reduction in strength may be as much as 10 percent for slender columns.

The strength of a battened column (Fig. 4-40e) in buckling about its axis perpendicular to the battens can be determined by using the effective-length coefficient given by[3]

$$K' = \sqrt{1 + \frac{\pi^2}{12}\left(\frac{L_0/r_0}{L/r}\right)^2} \tag{4-42}$$

where $\dfrac{L}{r}$ = slenderness ratio of column for buckling about axis perpendicular to battens

L_0 = center-to-center spacing of battens

r_0 = radius of gyration of one chord for its axis normal to plane of batten

The strength of a steel column with $L/r = 110$ is reduced about 10 percent for $L_0/r_0 = 40$.

DESIGN OF BATTENED COLUMN DP4-18-1

Design data :
  $P = 130^k$
  $L = 20'$ pin-ended, lateral dimensions not restricted
  A36 steel

Try [ ] with 12" channels, $r_x = 0.36 \times 12 = 4.3$ (Table A-1)
  $L/r_x = 240/4.3 = 56$, $F_a = 17.8$ ksi
  $A = \dfrac{130}{17.8} = 7.3$ in^2

Lightest C12 is 6.03 in^2, so try two C10 $\times$ 15.3, $A = 2 \times 4.47 = 8.94$ in^2

C10 $\times$ 15.3 $A = 4.47$ $\bar{x} = 0.64$
             $I_x = 66.9$ $I_y = 2.3$
             $r_x = 3.87$ $r_y = r_0 = 0.72$

  $I_y = 2 \times 2.3 + 2 \times 4.47 \times 3.86^2 = 4.6 + 133 = 138$ in^4
  $r_y = \sqrt{\dfrac{138}{8.94}} = 3.93$ $L/r_y = 240/3.93 = 61$

$L/r_x = 240/3.87 = 62$, $F_a = 17.2$, $P = 17.2 \times 8.94 = 154^k > 130^k$ O.K.

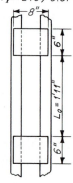

Batten spacing L_0

  $\dfrac{L_0}{r_0} = \dfrac{2}{3} \times \dfrac{L}{r_y} \gtrless \dfrac{2}{3} \times 61 \gtrless 41$
  $L_0 = 41 \times 0.72 = 29.5"$

Try 6" x 8" battens 29" o.c.

  $\dfrac{L_0}{r_0} = \dfrac{29}{0.72} = 40.3$

  $K' = \sqrt{1 + \dfrac{\pi^2}{12} \left(\dfrac{40.3}{61}\right)^2} = 1.17$ [Eq. (4-42)]

  $K'L/r_y = 1.17 \times 61 = 71$, $F_a = 16.3$ ksi

  $P = 16.3 \times 8.94 = 146^k > 130$ O.K.

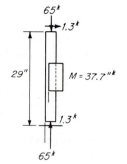

Check batten in bending

  Shear: $V = 0.02 \times 130 = 2.6^k = 1.3^k$ per channel
  $M = 1.3 \times 29/2 = 18.9^{"k}$ per batten
  $\dfrac{M}{S} = f$, $S = \dfrac{t \times 6^2}{6} = 6t$, $\dfrac{18.9}{6t} = 22$, $t = 0.143$

  Use $6 \times 8 \times \tfrac{3}{16}$ battens

DP4-18-1: Design of Battened Column

In this example the channels are spaced 9 in to make the radii of gyration about equal for both axes. The AISC, AASHTO, and AREA specifications do not cover battened columns, as was noted in Art. 4-17. However, the lattice-spacing requirement of the AREA and AASHTO specifications is used to determine the batten spacing. Equation (4-42) is used to determine the effective length. The column shear V, taken to be the AISC value $0.02P$, is divided equally between the two channels. The shear forces in the channel at the point of inflection above the batten and the one below form a couple which is resisted by moments in the battens. The batten moment determines the thickness of the batten.

     Procedures for determining the weldment to connect the batten plate to the channel are discussed in Chap. 8.

4-19 STRUCTURAL MEMBERS IN TORSION

The shearing stresses which result when a circular tube is twisted are shown in Fig. 4-44a. The variation in stress is linear, as shown, if the proportional limit is not exceeded. The angle of twist θ per unit length is

$$\theta = \frac{T}{GI_p} \qquad (a)$$

where T = torsional moment
     G = shearing modulus of elasticity
     I_p = polar moment of inertia

Of course, Eq. (a) also applies to the solid circular cross section.

     If the tube of Fig. 4-44a is cut on a longitudinal section at A, the shearing stresses which result when it is twisted are those shown in Fig. 4-44b. Because the shearing stresses on the longitudinal section of the tube of Fig. 4-44a cannot exist

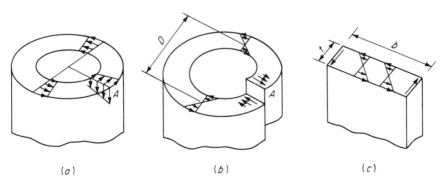

FIGURE 4-44

in the split tube, there is a relative vertical displacement at the split and the distribution of shearing stresses is altogether different. However, the variation in stress is still linear if the proportional limit is not exceeded. The relative stiffnesses of the two tubes can be inferred by noting that the torsional resistance of the closed tube consists of couples with an average moment arm about equal to the diameter of the tube, while in Fig. 4-44b the average moment arm is less than the thickness.

The angle of twist per unit length of a noncircular cross section, solid or tubular, is given by

$$\theta = \frac{T}{GJ} \tag{4-43}$$

where J is the torsion constant of the cross section. Of course, $J = I_p$ if the cross section is circular.

The shearing stresses which result when a solid rectangular cross section is twisted are shown in Fig. 4-44c. The corresponding constant J is given very closely by

$$J = \frac{bt^3}{3}\left(1 - 0.630\,\frac{t}{b}\right) \qquad b > t \tag{b}$$

where b and t are the dimensions shown in the figure. If b/t is large, Eq. (b) may be written

$$J = \frac{bt^3}{3} \tag{4-44}$$

For example, if $b/t = 6$, the error in using Eq. (4-44) is only 10 percent.

The torsion constant of the split tube of Fig. 4-44b is given by Eq. (4-44) with b equal to the circumference. Thus,

$$J = \tfrac{1}{3}\pi D t^3$$

For the tube of Fig. 4-44a

$$I_p = \pi D t \left(\frac{D}{2}\right)^2 = \frac{\pi D^3 t}{4}$$

Then

$$\frac{I_p}{J} = \frac{\pi t D^3/4}{\pi D t^3/3} = \frac{3}{4}\left(\frac{D}{t}\right)^2$$

Thus, a 10-in tube with a 1-in wall is 75 times as stiff as a split tube with the same dimensions.

The torsion constant of any shape composed of rectangular and/or curved elements for which b/t is sufficiently large can be determined by adding the quantities $bt^3/3$ for all the elements, provided no part of the cross section is closed.

Such a section is called an *open section*. Pipes, tubes, box sections, etc., are called *closed sections*. In Fig. 4-23, *a*, *b*, *c*, and *e* are open sections. The section in *h* is closed, and *d*, *f*, and *g* are also if the open sides are adequately laced.

The torsion constant of the single-cell closed section is given by

$$J = \frac{4A^2}{\int ds/t} \tag{4-45}$$

where A = area enclosed by midline of wall
$\quad ds$ = element of circumference of wall
$\quad t$ = thickness of wall

Integration is around the entire periphery. Thus, for a square box section 20 × 20 in outside dimension by $\frac{1}{2}$ in thick,

$$J = \frac{4(19.5 \times 19.5)^2}{4 \times 19.5/0.5} = 3707 \text{ in}^4$$

Values of J for the multicell cross section can be determined by methods given in Ref. 22.

Displacements in the longitudinal direction of the split tube of Fig. 4-44*b* are called *warping displacements*, and the cross section, which does not remain plane, is said to have *warped*. If there is nothing to restrain such warping, it is uniform throughout its length and the stress distributions, such as those in Fig. 4-44*b* and *c*, are also uniform throughout the length. Torsion with uniform warping is usually called *St. Venant torsion*, he having been the first to develop the theory for the general case.

Uniform warping of the I of Fig. 4-45*a* is shown in Fig. 4-45*b*. However, structural members are usually supported in such a manner as to prevent uniform warping. Thus, if the I is rigidly supported at its left end so that warping is prevented there, twisting is accompanied by *nonuniform warping*, as shown in Fig. 4-45*c*. Such nonuniform warping results in additional shearing stresses and an increase in the torsional stiffness. In this case, the oppositely directed bending of the flanges of the I produces the shears V shown in Fig. 4-45*d*, which constitute a couple opposing the applied torque T (Fig. 4-45*e*). Of course, there are also bending stresses; these are shown in the figure. The torsional resistance is evaluated as follows. Since

$$V = \frac{dM}{dz} \qquad M = -EI_f \frac{d^2u}{dz^2} \tag{a}$$

where u is the displacement of one flange (Fig. 4-45*e*) and I_f the moment of inertia of *one* flange about the y axis of the I, we have

$$V = -EI_f \frac{d^3u}{dz^3} \tag{b}$$

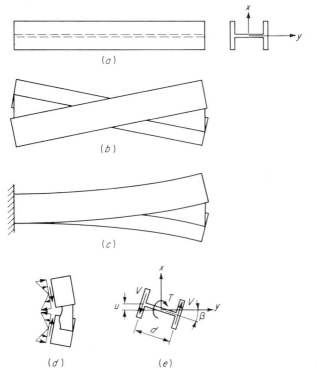

FIGURE 4-45

In Fig. 4-45e, $u = \beta d/2$, where β is the angle of twist and d the distance between centerlines of the flanges. Therefore,

$$V = -EI_f \frac{d}{2} \frac{d^3\beta}{dz^3} \tag{c}$$

The resisting couple is Vd. Therefore

$$T_w = -EI_y \frac{d^2}{4} \frac{d^3\beta}{dz^3} \tag{4-46}$$

where T_w is the torsional resistance due to nonuniform warping and $I_y \, (=2I_f)$ is the moment of inertia of the I.

The St. Venant torsional resistance itself is assumed to be unaffected by nonuniform warping. In other words, the St. Venant resistance is supplemented by the nonuniform-warping resistance T_w. Therefore, using Eq. (4-43) and noting that θ in that equation is the twist per unit of length while β is the angle of twist at any cross section so that $d\beta = \theta \, dz$, we have

$$T = T_v + T_w = GJ \frac{d\beta}{dz} - EI_y \frac{d^2}{4} \frac{d^3\beta}{dz^3} \tag{4-47}$$

Of course, the nonuniform-warping torsional resistance, which for the I is mea-

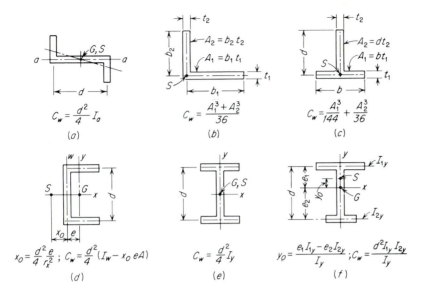

FIGURE 4-46
Values of warping constant C_w. (C_w for the angle and the tee is small enough to be neglected in most applications.)

sured by $d^2 I_y/4$ as determined above, depends upon the shape of the cross section. Therefore, to put Eq. (4-47) in a more general form, we write

$$T = GJ \frac{d\beta}{dz} - EC_w \frac{d^3\beta}{dz^3} \qquad (4\text{-}48)$$

where C_w is the warping constant of the cross section. Values of C_w for various open cross sections are given in Fig. 4-46. Procedures for determining C_w are given in Refs. 3 and 16.

4-20 TORSIONAL BUCKLING OF COMPRESSION MEMBERS

It was shown in Art. 4-19 that the torsional stiffness of open cross sections is quite small. Because of this, open-section columns may buckle in a torsional mode rather than in a bending mode. The column of cruciform cross section shown in Fig. 4-32b is an example, even though this was called a local-buckling failure in Art. 4-12. For this particular cross section, the two modes of collapse are identical. In this article, we consider the failure as a torsional one.

Figure 4-47a shows the cross section and Fig. 4-47b a differential length dz of the member. The element dA in area is acted upon by the force $f\,dA$, where $f = P/A$. At the onset of buckling, this stress is uniform over the cross section and throughout the length because the column is supporting a centrally applied load P. The element, which is located the distance z from the end of the member, is shown in its buckled configuration in Fig. 4-47c. Displacements measured from

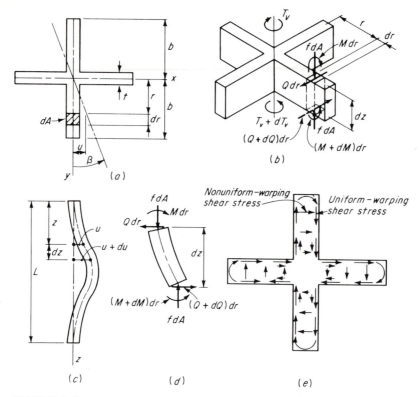

FIGURE 4-47

the unbuckled position are u and $u + du$. From Fig. 4-47a

$$u = r\beta \tag{a}$$

where β is the angle of twist at z and r is the distance from the shear center to dA.

In the buckled state, the element is acted upon by the shears Q and $Q + dQ$ and the bending moments M and $M + dM$ (Fig. 4-47d), where Q is the shear and M is the bending moment, both per unit of length in the direction of r. These are the effects of nonuniform warping. These stresses are accompanied by the stresses associated with uniform warping (St. Venant torsion). Therefore, the shearing stresses acting on the cross section are those shown in Fig. 4-47e. The resultant of the shear stresses due to uniform warping is denoted by T_v (Fig. 4-47b) and is the same as T_v in Eq. (4-47).

Summing moments about the z axis in Fig. 4-47b gives

$$dT_v + \int_A r \, dQ \, dr = 0 \tag{b}$$

Summing moments in Fig. 4-47d gives

$$dM \, dr + Q \, dr \, dz + f \, dA \, du = 0 \tag{c}$$

Solving Eq. (*c*) for $Q\ dr$ and differentiating the result with respect to z gives

$$\frac{dQ}{dz}\ dr = -\frac{d^2M}{dz^2}\ dr - f\ da\ \frac{d^2u}{dz^2} \tag{d}$$

Dividing Eq. (*b*) by dz and substituting for dQ/dz from Eq. (*d*) gives

$$-\frac{dT_v}{dz} + \int_A \frac{d^2M}{dz^2}\ r\ dr + f \int_A \frac{d^2u}{dz^2}\ r\ dA = 0 \tag{e}$$

Since M is the moment per unit of r, the moment on the element $dA = t\ dr$ is $M\ dr$. Therefore,

$$M\ dr = EI\ \frac{d^2u}{dz^2} = E\ \frac{t^3}{12}\ \frac{dr}{}\ \frac{d^2u}{dz^2} \tag{f}$$

where $I = t^3\ dr/12$ is the moment of inertia of the element. Differentiating Eq. (*f*) twice with respect to z and substituting d^2M/dz^2 into Eq. (*e*) gives

$$-\frac{dT_v}{dz} + E\ \frac{t^3}{12} \int_A \frac{d^4u}{dz^4}\ r\ dr + f \int_A \frac{d^2u}{dz^2}\ r\ dA = 0 \tag{g}$$

The St. Venant torsion resultant T_v is found from Eq. (4-43). Since $\theta = d\beta/dz$, we have

$$T_v = GJ\ \frac{d\beta}{dz} \qquad \frac{dT_v}{dz} = GJ\ \frac{d^2\beta}{dz^2} \tag{h}$$

Substituting the values of dT_v/dz from Eq. (*h*) and u from Eq. (*a*) into Eq. (*g*) gives

$$-GJ\beta'' + \frac{Et^3}{12}\ \beta^{\text{iv}} \int_A r^2\ dr + f\beta'' \int_A r^2\ dA = 0 \tag{i}$$

But

$$\int_A r^2\ dr = 4\ \frac{r^3}{3}\ \bigg|_0^b = \frac{4b^3}{3}$$

where b = width of leg (Fig. 4-47a). Furthermore, $\int_A r^2\ dA = I_p$. Therefore,

$$E\ \frac{b^3t^3}{9}\ \beta^{\text{iv}} + (fI_p - GJ)\beta'' = 0 \tag{4-49}$$

The factor $b^3t^3/9$ in Eq. (4-49) is the warping constant C_w, which was discussed in Art. 4-19. The corresponding shear stresses are the nonuniform-warping shear stresses pictured in Fig. 4-47e, which are analogous to the nonuniform-warping shears V in Fig. 4-45d. Thus, the two types of resistance to torsion are represented by $(Eb^3t^3/9)\beta^{\text{iv}}$ and $GJ\beta''$, respectively, in Eq. (4-49).

Using the notation

$$k^2 = \frac{fI_p - GJ}{EC_w} \tag{j}$$

Eq. (4-49) becomes

$$\beta^{iv} + k^2\beta'' = 0 \tag{4-50}$$

The solution of this equation is

$$\beta = A \sin kz + B \cos kz + Cz + D \tag{k}$$

The constants of integration in Eq. (k) will be evaluated for the boundary conditions of the column in Fig. 4-32b. It will be noted in that figure that plane cross sections remain plane at the ends; i.e., there is no warping at the ends. Consequently, $du/dz = 0$ at each end (Fig. 4-47c), which, because of Eq. (a), gives $d\beta/dz = 0$. In addition, $\beta = 0$ at each end. Using these four boundary conditions with Eq. (k) gives

$$B_{z=0} = 0 \qquad 0 = B + D$$

$$B_{z=L} = 0 \qquad 0 = A \sin KL + B \cos kL + CL + D$$

$$\left(\frac{du}{dz}\right)_{z=0} = 0 \qquad 0 = Ak + C$$

$$\left(\frac{du}{dz}\right)_{z=L} = 0 \qquad 0 = AK \cos kL - Bk \sin kL + C$$

Eliminating C and D from these equations gives

$$A(\sin kL - kL) + B(\cos kL - 1) = 0$$

$$A(\cos kL - 1) - B \sin kL = 0$$

These are homogeneous equations in A and B. One solution is $A = B = 0$, in which case $C = D = 0$, and Eq. (k) reduces to $\beta = 0$. Nonzero (indeterminate) values of A and B exist only if the determinant of the coefficients vanishes. This gives

$$\sin \frac{kL}{2} \left(2 \sin \frac{kL}{2} - kL \cos \frac{kL}{2} \right) = 0$$

which is satisfied by $\sin kL/2 = 0$ or $\tan kL/2 = kL/2$. The corresponding smallest roots are $kL/2 = \pi$ and $kL/2 = 4.49$. Substituting the smaller of these roots into Eq. (j) gives the smallest critical stress:

$$F_{cr} = \frac{GJ}{I_p} + \frac{4\pi^2}{L^2} \frac{EC_w}{I_p} \tag{4-51}$$

This equation gives the stress F_{cr} at which torsional buckling begins, provided the column is perfectly straight, free of residual stress, etc. Although it was derived for the cruciform cross section of Fig. 4-32b, it holds for any cross section for which the shear center and the centroid coincide.

If the ends of the column are free to warp, each of the four legs of the cruciform in Fig. 4-32b will bend in single curvature. Since the ends are free to warp only if there is no rotational restraint of the legs, this is equivalent to saying that the moment M in Fig. 4-47d is zero at each end. Thus, $d^2u/dz^2 = 0$ at $z = 0$

and $z = L$. Using these boundary conditions together with $\beta = 0$ at each end gives

$$F_{cr} = \frac{GJ}{I_p} + \frac{\pi^2}{L^2} \frac{EC_w}{I_p} \qquad (4\text{-}52)$$

Comparing Eqs. (4-51) and (4-52), we see that the boundary conditions relating to warping can be expressed in terms of an effective-length coefficient, as in the case of bend buckling. Thus,

$$F_{cr} = \frac{GJ}{I_p} + \frac{\pi^2}{(KL)^2} \frac{EC_w}{I_p} \qquad (4\text{-}53)$$

where $K = 1$ if the end cross sections are free to warp and $K = \frac{1}{2}$ if warping of the end cross section is completely restrained.

Equation (4-53) holds only for buckling which begins when the stress F_{cr} is less than the proportional-limit stress. The following arguments enable us to modify the formula to apply to inelastic buckling as well. The second term on the right is associated with the bending stresses caused by nonuniform warping (Fig. 4-45d). When the column starts to twist, these bending stresses are superimposed on the uniform stress F_{cr} which is above the proportional limit. Therefore, it is reasonable to expect the tangent modulus or double modulus to govern the bending behavior. Furthermore, the same arguments as in Art. 4-4 suggest that the tangent modulus is the correct one. On the other hand, there are no shearing stresses on the cross section at the instant buckling begins, so the elastic modulus G would be expected to hold. Tests on two circular tubes which were twisted after having been compressed to the strain ϵ_s are reported in Ref. 23. The shearing modulus at the beginning of twist was practically equal to the elastic value G. However, it is on the safe side to assume a reduced value of G in the inelastic range, and it is convenient to take the ratio G/E the same for both elastic and inelastic behavior.

The concept of an equivalent radius of gyration, which was used in local buckling of plates, is also useful in torsional buckling. If we replace E and G in Eq. (4-53) with tangent-modulus values and equate the stress F_{cr} to the tangent-modulus bend-buckling stress $\pi^2 E_t/(KL/r_t)^2$, where r_t is the equivalent radius of gyration for torsional buckling, we get

$$r_t^2 = \frac{C_w + 0.04J(KL)^2}{I_{pS}} \qquad (4\text{-}54)$$

The change in notation (I_{pS} in place of I_p, where I_{pS} means the polar moment of inertia with respect to the shear center S) is for the purpose of generalizing the formula for an application to be discussed in Art. 4-21. For the member of this article, the shear center S and centroid G coincide, so that $I_{pS} = I_{pG}$. Equation (4-54) enables the critical load for any column for which the shear center and centroid coincide to be determined. We need only compute r_t and compare it with r_x and r_y. The smallest of the three determines the buckling mode. The critical load is computed by substituting the corresponding KL/r into the appropriate bend-buckling formula, elastic or inelastic.

Example 4-20-1. Compute the critical load for the column with the cruciform cross section shown in Fig. 4-48. The column is A36 steel, 15 ft long, and supported so that warping at the ends is prevented, as in Fig. 4-32*b*. Use the SSRC formula [Eq. (4-16)], for the inelastic range.

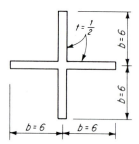

FIGURE 4-48

Solution

$$I_x = I_y = 2\,\frac{tb^3}{3} = \frac{2 \times 0.5 \times 6^3}{3} = 72 \text{ in}^4$$

$$I_{pS} = I_{pG} = I_x + I_y = 144 \text{ in}^4 \qquad J = 4\,\frac{bt^3}{3} = \frac{4 \times 6 \times 0.5^3}{3} = 1 \text{ in}^4$$

$$C_w = \frac{b^3 t^3}{9} = \frac{(6 \times 0.5)^3}{9} = 3 \text{ in}^6 \qquad A = 4 \times 6 \times 0.5 = 12 \text{ in}^2$$

$$r_x = r_y = \sqrt{\tfrac{72}{12}} = 2.45 \text{ in}$$

$$r_t^2 = \frac{3 + 0.04 \times 1(0.5 \times 180)^2}{144} = \frac{3 + 324}{144} = 2.27 \qquad r_t = 1.51$$

Since $r_t < r_x < r_y$, the column fails by twist buckling

$$\frac{KL}{r_t} = \frac{0.5 \times 180}{1.51} = 60 \qquad C_c = \pi\sqrt{\frac{2E}{F_y}} = \pi\sqrt{\frac{30,000}{36}} = 128$$

$$F_{cr} = F_y\left[1 - \frac{1}{2}\left(\frac{KL/r}{C_c}\right)^2\right] = 36\left[1 - \frac{1}{2}\left(\frac{60}{128}\right)^2\right] = 32.0 \text{ ksi}$$

$$P_{cr} = 32.0 \times 12 = 384 \text{ kips}$$

It will be noted that the warping stiffness C_w for the cruciform is so small that its contribution to torsional resistance can be neglected. The warping stiffness of certain other cross sections, such as the angle and the tee, is also small enough to be neglected.[3]

4-21 COLUMNS WITH ONE AXIS OF SYMMETRY

It was shown in Art. 4-20 that columns for which the shear center and the centroid coincide fail in one of three independent buckling modes. This is not the case if the cross section has only one axis of symmetry, as for the channel, the angle, and the tee. In this case, the equations of equilibrium are[3]

$$EI_x v^{iv} + Pv'' = 0 \qquad (4\text{-}55a)$$

$$EI_y u^{iv} + Pu'' + Py_0 \beta'' = 0 \qquad (4\text{-}55b)$$

$$Py_0 u'' + EC_w \beta^{iv} + (fI_{pS} - GJ)\beta'' = 0 \qquad (4\text{-}55c)$$

where y = axis of symmetry

$\quad y_0$ = distance from centroid G of the cross section to its shear center S (Fig. 4-49)

$\quad u, v$ = displacements in direction of x and y, respectively

$\quad I_{pS}$ = polar moment of inertia with respect to shear center S

If G and S coincide, Eq. (4-55c) becomes identical to Eq. (4-49). Also, the three equations are then independent, and the solution of Eqs. (4-55a) and (4-55b) gives the two bend-buckling modes, while Eq. (4-55c) gives the twist-buckling mode.

For the case of one axis of symmetry, which Eqs. (4-55) represent, it is seen that Eq. (4-55a) is independent and can be solved without reference to the other two. On the other hand, Eqs. (4-55b) and (4-55c) are simultaneous equations. This means that the bend-buckling mode corresponding to Eq. (4-55a) is independent, while the other two are coupled. Therefore, the column fails in one of *two* buckling modes, i.e., bend buckling about the x axis or a combination of twisting and bending about the y axis. The bend-buckling mode corresponds to displacements of the cross section in the direction of the axis of symmetry. This is always true because the shear forces which result are symmetrical and produce no torsional moment about the shear center and, consequently, no twist.

The critical load for the coupled buckling mode can be found by determining the equivalent radius of gyration r_{tb} given by

$$\left(1 - \frac{y_0^2}{r_{pS}^2}\right) r_{tb}^4 - (r_y^2 + r_t^2) r_{tb}^2 + r_y^2 r_t^2 = 0 \qquad (4\text{-}56)$$

where r_{pS}, the polar radius of gyration, equals $\sqrt{I_{pS}/A}$ and r_t is the equivalent radius of gyration for torsional buckling, given by Eq. (4-54). The solution of this equation produces two values of r_{tb}, the smaller of which will always be less than r_y.

To determine the critical load for a column whose cross section has one axis of symmetry (y axis), we compute r_{tb} from Eq. (4-56) and compare it with r_x. The smaller of the two identifies the buckling mode and determines the corresponding critical stress. The effective-length coefficient K can be used in evaluating r_t and r_y, provided the boundary conditions for β and u are the same.

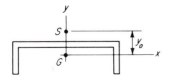

FIGURE 4-49

The solution to these equations can also be presented in terms of F_{ex}, F_{ey}, and F_{ez}, where F_{ex} and F_{ey} are the Euler buckling stresses for the x and y axes, respectively, and F_{ez} is the elastic twist-buckling stress [Eq. (4-53)]. The buckling stress for the coupled-buckling mode, in this form, is presented in the AISC/LRFD specifications in Appendix E as Eq. (A-E3-6). Since this equation gives the elastic-buckling stress, which may be very high, the procedure requires that an equivalent value of λ_c be calculated according to $\lambda_c = \sqrt{F_y/F_E}$, which is then used to evaluate F_{cr}. This procedure is identical to the calculation of r_{tb} according to Eq. (4-56) and using KL/r to determine F_{cr}.

Example 4-21-1. Compute the critical load for the column with the tee cross section shown in Fig. 4-50. The column is of A36 steel, 10 ft long, and supported so that warping, y-axis bending, and x-axis bending are all prevented at each end. Use the SSRC formula [Eq. (4-16)] for the inelastic range.

Solution

$$A = 0.5(8 + 12) = 10 \text{ in}^2$$

$$I_x = 12 \times 0.5 \times 1.6^2 + \frac{0.5 \times 1.6^3}{3} + \frac{0.5 \times 6.4^3}{3} = 59.7 \text{ in}^4$$

$$I_y = \frac{0.5 \times 12^3}{12} = 72 \text{ in}^4 \qquad I_{pS} = 59.7 + 72 + 10 \times 1.6^2 = 157.3 \text{ in}^4$$

$$J = \frac{12 \times 0.5^3}{3} + \frac{8 \times 0.5^3}{3} = 0.833 \text{ in}^4 \qquad C_w \cong 0$$

$$r_x^2 = \frac{59.7}{10} = 5.97 \qquad r_y^2 = \frac{72}{10} = 7.2 \qquad r_{pS}^2 = \frac{157.3}{10} = 15.7$$

$$r_t^2 = \frac{C_w + 0.04J(KL)^2}{I_{pS}} = \frac{0 + 0.04 \times 0.833(0.5 \times 120)^2}{157.3} = 0.763 \text{ in}^2$$

$$\left(1 - \frac{1.6^2}{15.7}\right)r_{tb}^4 - (7.2 + 0.763)r_{tb}^2 + 7.2 \times 0.763 = 0$$

$$0.837r_{tb}^4 - 7.96r_{tb}^2 + 5.49 = 0$$

$$r_{tb}^2 = \frac{7.96 \pm \sqrt{63.3 - 18.4}}{1.674} = 0.751 \text{ in}^2$$

$$r_{tb} = \sqrt{0.751} = 0.87 \text{ in} \qquad r_x = \sqrt{5.97} = 2.44 \text{ in}$$

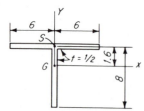

FIGURE 4-50

Since $r_{tb} \leq r_x$, the column fails by twist-bend buckling.

$$\frac{KL}{r_{tb}} = \frac{0.5 \times 120}{0.87} = 69 \qquad C_c = \pi \sqrt{\frac{2E}{F_y}} = \pi \sqrt{\frac{60,000}{36}} = 128$$

$$F_{cr} = F_y \left[1 - \frac{1}{2} \left(\frac{KL/r}{C_c} \right)^2 \right] = 36 \left[1 - \frac{1}{2} \left(\frac{69}{128} \right)^2 \right] = 30.8 \text{ ksi}$$

$$P_{cr} = 30.8 \times 10 = 308 \text{ kips}$$

4-22 COLUMNS WITH NO AXIS OF SYMMETRY

The equations of equilibrium for a column whose cross section has no axis of symmetry are

$$EI_x v^{iv} + Pv'' + Px_0 \beta'' = 0 \qquad (4\text{-}57a)$$

$$EI_y u^{iv} + Pu'' + Py_0 \beta'' = 0 \qquad (4\text{-}57b)$$

$$Py_0 u'' - Px_0 v'' + EC_w \beta^{iv} + (fI_{pS} - GJ)\beta'' = 0 \qquad (4\text{-}57c)$$

where x, y = principal axes of the cross section

x_0, y_0 = coordinates of shear center S with respect to the center of gravity G (Fig. 4-51)

u, v = displacements in direction of x and y, respectively

I_{pS} = polar moment of inertia with respect to shear center S

Since derivatives of the variables u, v, and β appear in all three equations, none of the three can be solved independently. This means that there is only *one* buckling mode, which is a coupling of bending about axes x and y and twisting about the longitudinal axis.

The critical load can be found by determining an equivalent radius of gyration r_e from the following equation, which is a cubic in r_e^2. The smallest of the three roots must be used.

$$(r_{pS}^2 - x_0^2 - y_0^2)r_e^6 - [r_y^2(r_{pS}^2 - x_0^2) + r_x^2(r_{pS}^2 - y_0^2) + r_{pS}^2 r_t^2]r_e^4$$

$$+ r_{pS}^2(r_x^2 r_y^2 + r_x^2 r_t^2 + r_y^2 r_t^2)r_e^2 = 1 \quad (4\text{-}58)$$

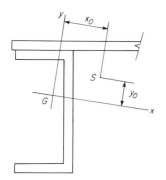

FIGURE 4-51

where r_x, r_y = radii of gyration for x and y axes, respectively

r_{pS} = polar radius of gyration = $\sqrt{I_{pS}/A}$
r_t = equivalent radius of gyration for torsional buckling, given by Eq. (4-54)

The solution of Eqs. (4-57) can also be given in terms of F_{Ex}, F_{Ey}, and F_{Ez}, where F_{Ex} and F_{Ey} are the Euler buckling stresses for the x and y axes, respectively, and F_{Ez} is the elastic twist-buckling stress [Eq. (4-53)]. The buckling stress, in this form, is presented in the AISC/LRFD specifications in Appendix E as Eq. (A-E3-7). Since this equation gives the elastic-buckling stress, which may be very high, the procedure requires that an equivalent value of λ_c be calculated according to $\lambda_c = \sqrt{F_y/F_E}$, which is then used to evaluate F_{cr}.

4-23 ALUMINUM COLUMNS

The tangent-modulus formula (*DB* of Fig. 4-8) may be approximated by a straight line for the aluminum alloys. For alloy 6061-T6 the column strength is given by[24]

$$F_{cr} = 39.4 - 0.246 \frac{KL}{r} \qquad \frac{KL}{r} \le 66 \qquad (4\text{-}59)$$

In the elastic range the Euler equation [Eq. (4-2)] becomes

$$F_{cr} = \frac{\pi^2 E}{(KL/r)^2} = \frac{\pi^2 \times 10{,}100}{(KL/r)^2} = \frac{100{,}000}{(KL/r)^2} \qquad \frac{KL}{r} > 66 \qquad (4\text{-}60)$$

A factor of safety must be applied to the column strength determined from Eqs. (4-59) and (4-60). The ASCE Task Committee on Lightweight Alloys suggests factors of safety of 2.2 for bridges and 1.95 for buildings.[20] The Aluminum Association[25] specifications specify the following allowable stresses for 6061-T6:

$$F_a = \begin{cases} 19 \text{ ksi} & \dfrac{L}{r} \le 9.5 \\[2mm] 20.2 - 0.126 \dfrac{L}{r} & 9.5 \le \dfrac{L}{r} \le 66 \\[2mm] \dfrac{51{,}000}{(L/r)^2} & \dfrac{L}{r} \ge 66 \end{cases}$$

Local-buckling strength of elements of compression members of alloy 6061-T6 can be calculated from the following formulas.

For one unloaded edge free and the other simply supported,

$$F_{cr} = \begin{cases} 45.0 - 1.54 \dfrac{b}{t} & \dfrac{b}{t} \le 12 & (4\text{-}61a) \\[2mm] \left(\dfrac{61.5}{b/t}\right)^2 & \dfrac{b}{t} > 12 & (4\text{-}61b) \end{cases}$$

For both unloaded edges simply supported,

$$F_{cr} = \begin{cases} 45.0 - 0.49\dfrac{b}{t} & \dfrac{b}{t} \leq 37 & (4\text{-}62a) \\[2ex] \left(\dfrac{169}{b/t}\right)^2 & \dfrac{b}{t} > 37 & (4\text{-}62b) \end{cases}$$

The Aluminum Association specifications[25] specify the following allowable stresses for 6061-T6.

For one unloaded edge free and the other simply supported,

$$F_{cr} = \begin{cases} 19\text{ ksi} & \dfrac{b}{t} \leq 5.2 \\[2ex] 23.1 - 0.79\dfrac{b}{t} & 5.2 \leq \dfrac{b}{t} \leq 12 \\[2ex] \dfrac{1970}{(b/t)^2} & \dfrac{b}{t} \geq 12 \end{cases}$$

For both unloaded edges simply supported,

$$F_{cr} = \begin{cases} 19\text{ ksi} & \dfrac{b}{t} \leq 16 \\[2ex] 23.1 - 0.25\dfrac{b}{t} & 16 \leq \dfrac{b}{t} \leq 33 \\[2ex] \dfrac{490}{(b/t)^2} & \dfrac{b}{t} \geq 33 \end{cases}$$

Plates that buckle in the inelastic range [Eqs. (4-61a) and (4-62a)] do not develop appreciable postbuckling strength, so their allowable stresses should be determined by using the same factor of safety as for the allowable primary buckling stresses. On the other hand, plates that buckle in the elastic range [Eqs. (4-61b) and (4-62b)] may have appreciable postbuckling strength. Methods for evaluating this extra load-carrying capacity are discussed in Chap. 10.

Specifications for the design of structures of aluminum alloys 6061-T6, 6062-T6, 6063-T5, and 6063-T6 have been published by the ASCE Task Committee and the Aluminum Association mentioned above. Buckling formulas for columns and plates of typical structural aluminum alloys are given in Ref. 24, p. 10-6.

DP4-23-1: Aluminum-Truss Compression Members

In this example we design the compression members of the roof truss of DP3-15-1 for riveted construction in aluminum 6061-T6, using a factor of safety of 2. Design of the tension members for this truss was presented in DP3-16-1. The comments which follow are identified by corresponding letters on the design sheet.

ALUMINUM TRUSS COMPRESSION MEMBERS DP4-23-1

Same truss as DP3-15-1
Material : aluminum 6061-T6
3/4 rivets : aluminum 6061-T6
5/16-in. gusset plates

$\underline{U_2 U_5}$: $P = 109.7^k$, $L = 6'$
$\qquad A = 109.7/15 = 7.31$
Try 2L $5 \times 3^1/2$, $\top$
$KL/r = 0.9 \times 72/1.47 = 44$
$F_a = {}^1/_2(39.4 - 0.246 \times 44) = 14.3$ (a)
$A = 109.7/14.3 = 7.68$

Try 2L $5 \times 3^1/2 \times {}^1/2$ $A = 8.00$
$\qquad \dfrac{b}{t} = \dfrac{5 - {}^1/2}{{}^1/2} = 9$ (b)
$F = {}^1/2(45.0 - 1.54 \times 9) = 15.57 > 13.67$

$\qquad$ Use 2L $5 \times 3^1/2 \times {}^1/2$ $\top$

$\underline{U_0 U_2}$: $P = 87.3^k$, $L = 6'$
$\qquad A = 87.3/13.5 = 6.48$ (c)
Try 2L $5 \times 3^1/2 \times {}^7/_{16}$ $A = 7.06$
$L/r = 72/1.44 = 50$
$F_a = {}^1/2(39.4 - 0.246 \times 50) = 13.55$
$A = 87.3/13.55 = 6.44$
$\qquad \dfrac{b}{t} = \dfrac{5 - {}^7/_{16}}{{}^7/_{16}} = 10.4$
$F = {}^1/2(45.0 - 1.54 \times 10.4) = 14.5 > 13.55$

$\qquad$ Use 2L $5 \times 3^1/2 \times {}^7/_{16}$ $\top$

$\underline{U_1 L_1}$: $P = 37.6^k$, $L = 5'$
Try 2L $3 \times 2^1/2$ (d)
$L/r = 60/0.94 = 64$
$F_a = {}^1/2(39.4 - 0.246 \times 64) = 11.8$
$A = 37.6/11.8 = 3.18$
Try 2L $3 \times 2^1/2 \times {}^5/_{16}$, $A = 3.24$
$\qquad \dfrac{b}{t} = \dfrac{3 - {}^5/_{16}}{{}^5/_{16}} = 8.6$
$F = {}^1/2(45.0 - 1.54 \times 8.6) = 15.9 > 11.8$

$\qquad$ Use 2L $3 \times 2^1/2 \times {}^5/_{16}$ $\top$

$\underline{U_2 L_2}$: $P = 21.7^k$, $L = 5.5'$
Try 2L 3×2
$L/r = 66/0.86 = 72$
$F_a = {}^1/2 \times 100,000/72^2 = 9.64$ (e)
$A = 21.7/9.64 = 2.25$

Try 2L $3 \times 2 \times {}^1/4$ $A = 2.38$
$\qquad \dfrac{b}{t} = \dfrac{3 - {}^1/4}{{}^1/4} = 11$
$F = {}^1/2(45.0 - 1.54 \times 11) = 14.0 > 9.64$

$\qquad$ Use 2L $3 \times 2 \times {}^1/4$ $\top$

$\underline{U_3 L_3}$: $P = 13.6^k$, $L = 6.04'$
Try 2L $3 \times 2 \times {}^1/4$ $A = 2.38$
$L/r = 72.5/0.86 = 84.3$
$F_a = {}^1/2 \times 100,000/84.3^2 = 7.03 < 14.0$ (f)
$A = 13.6/7.03 = 1.94$

$\qquad$ Use 2L $3 \times 2 \times {}^1/4$ $\top$

$\underline{U_4 L_4}$: $P = 7.0^k$, $L = 6.54'$
Try 2L $2^1/2 \times 2 \times {}^3/_{16}$ $A = 1.62$
$L/r = 78.5/0.76 = 103$
$F_a = {}^1/2 \times 100,000/103^2 = 4.71$
$\qquad \dfrac{b}{t} = \dfrac{2^1/2 - {}^3/_{16}}{{}^3/_{16}} = 12.3$
$F = \dfrac{1}{2}\left(\dfrac{61.5}{12.3}\right)^2 = 12.5 > 4.71$ (g)
$A = 7.0/4.71 = 1.49$

$\qquad$ Use 2L $2^1/2 \times 2 \times {}^3/_{16}$ $\top$

a. The value of the column strength as determined from Eq. (4-59) is multiplied by $\frac{1}{2}$ to provide the factor of safety of 2.

b. Since the two angles are joined by rivets at rather long intervals, with washers as fillers, we assume that the long legs are free to buckle locally.

c. Since these angles are of the same series chosen for members $U_2 U_3$, we use as an initial guess a value approximately equal to the allowable for $U_2 U_5$ but adjusted for $K = 1$.

d. The web members will be small, and so we assume the size of these angles (except for thickness) instead of an allowable stress.

e. For the remaining members $L/r > 66$, and so we use Eq. (4-60).

f. Since the value of $b/t = 11$ is the same as for member $U_2 L_2$, $F = 14.0$.

g. Equation (4-61*b*) applies since $b/t > 12$.

PROBLEMS

4-1. Compare the maximum deflection of a pin-ended column whose unloaded shape is parabolic with that given by Eq. (4-5) for the crooked column of Art. 4-3.

4-2. Derive the formulas for the critical loads of the columns shown in Fig. 4-11*b* to *d*.

Note: To simplify the numerical work in Probs. 4-3 to 4-6, assume the area of each cross-sectional element to be concentrated at midthickness.

4-3. Plot the column curve for the cross section of Fig. P3-1 for both strong-axis and weak-axis buckling using:
(*a*) The tangent modulus of the stress-strain curve
(*b*) The effective moment of inertia about the *x-x* axis
(*c*) The effective moment of inertia about the *y-y* axis

4-4. Plot the column curve for the cross section of Fig. P3-2 using:
(*a*) The tangent modulus of the stress-strain curve
(*b*) The effective moment of inertia about the *x-x* axis
(*c*) The effective moment of inertia about the *y-y* axis

4-5. The cross section is the same as that of Prob. 3-2 except that it consists of four $8 \times 8 \times 1$ angles. The residual-stress distribution is shown in Fig. P4-5. Plot the column curve.

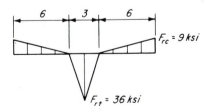

FIGURE P4-5

4-6. Plot the column curve for the cross section of Prob. 3-2 for the residual-stress distribution shown in Fig. P4-6.

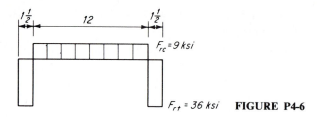

FIGURE P4-6

4-7. Can a buckled form consistent with the buckled forms on which the effective-length nomographs are based be drawn for the frame of Fig. 4-31? Explain.

4-8. Same as Prob. 4-7 except with rollers at J to allow horizontal movement.

4-9. Compute the critical load P for the unbraced frame of Fig. 4-24a, using the same dimensions as in Example 4-11-2.

4-10. Choose a W for the columns of the frame of Fig. 4-24a for the following data: $L_c = 15$ ft, $L_b = 30$ ft, $BC = $ W16 × 36, $P = 40$ kips DL, 120 kips LL. The frame is not braced against sidesway. A36 steel, AISC specification.

4-11. Same as Prob. 4-10 except that the frame is braced against sidesway.

4-12. Design an A36-steel welded-H cross section for a pin-ended column which supports a central load of 125 kips DL and 375 kips LL and has an unsupported length of 24 ft. AISC specification. Compare the weight with that of the lightest W column designed for the same load and conditions.

4-13. Design an A36-steel square box pin-ended column to support a central load of 75 kips DL and 175 kips LL. The unsupported length is 18 ft. For architectural reasons the outside dimension must not exceed 12 in. AISC specification.

4-14. In the article on members consisting of segments connected by lacing bars or by solid cover plates, the AREA specification limits the ratio b/t of the web plate and cover plate to $32\sqrt{p_c/f}$ and $40\sqrt{p_c/f}$ respectively, where p_c is the allowable stress and f the actual stress in the member. What is the logic in support of the factor $\sqrt{p_c/f}$?

4-15. Choose a W shape for an 18-ft building column which supports an axial load of 125 kips DL and 385 kips LL. The column is free to buckle about either axis and has negligible rotational restraints. A36 steel, AISC specification.

4-16. Same as Prob. 4-15 except that the load is 15 kips DL and 50 kips LL.

4-17. Choose a W shape for a 16-ft building column which supports an axial load of 300 kips DL and 900 kips LL. The column is free to buckle about either axis and has negligible rotational restraints. A441 steel, AISC specification.

4-18. Same as Prob. 4-17 except that an attached partition supports the column against weak-axis buckling.

4-19. Choose an A36 W shape for a 12-ft building column which supports an axial load consisting of 310 kips DL and 270 kips LL. The column is free to buckle about either axis and has negligible rotational restraint. Design the section:
(a) Using the SSRC formula with load factors of 1.2 on dead load and 1.6 on live load
(b) Using the AISC/LRFD specifications

4-20. A 14-ft column supports an axial load consisting of 130 kips DL and 95 kips LL. It is free to buckle about either axis and has negligible rotational restraints. Design the column in A36 structural tubing. A36 steel, AISC specification.

4-21. Choose a W shape for a 20-ft column for an elevated highway structure. The load is 210 kips axial. The connections are bolted. A36 steel, AASHTO specifications.

4-22. Same as Prob. 4-21 except that the column is in a railroad structure. AREA specifications.

4-23. The web tension members for the truss of DP4-15-1 were designed in DP3-15-1. Design and detail the joint at U_1.

4-24. The web tension members for the truss of DP4-15-2 were designed in DP3-15-2. Design and detail the joint at U_1.

4-25. Choose a pair of angles for a bolted roof-truss top-chord member 10 ft long whose compressive force is 12 kips *DL* and 36 kips *LL*. The member is supported at each end in both principal planes. AISC specification, A36 steel.

4-26. Design for a welded roof truss a top-chord member whose unsupported length is 8 ft for buckling in either plane. The load is 30 kips *DL* and 82 kips *LL*. AISC specification, A36 steel.

4-27. Same as Prob. 4-26 except that the truss is bolted.

4-28. Same as Prob. 4-26 except that the unsupported length is 8 ft in the plane of the truss and 16 ft in the plane of the roof.

4-29. Design I-shaped top-chord and single-angle web compression members for the welded truss of DP4-15-1. Position the top chord so that its web is in the vertical plane with the web members butting against its bottom flange, and design and detail the connection at U_1 if U_1L_2 is a $3 \times 3 \times \frac{3}{8}$ angle. A36 steel.

4-30. Design I-shaped top-chord and single-angle web-compression members for the welded truss of DP4-15-2. Position the top chord so that its web is in the vertical plane with the web members butting against its bottom flange, and design and detail the connection at U_1 if U_1L_2 is a $3 \times 3 \times \frac{3}{8}$ angle. A36 steel.

4-31. Design two-angle sections for the top-chord and web compression members for bolted construction (A307 bolts) of the truss of DP4-15-1. Choose the gusset-plate thickness, and design the connection of these members and the tension web members you designed in Prob. 3-22. A36 steel.

4-32. Design two-angle sections for the top-chord and web compression members for bolted construction (A307 bolts) of the truss of DP4-15-2. Choose the gusset-plate thickness, and design the connection of these members and the tension web members you designed in Prob. 3-23. AISC specification, A36 steel.

4-33. Design the compression chord and web members for the highway-bridge truss of DP3-15-3.

Note: Since lateral-torsional buckling is not discussed in this chapter, columns of box or tubular cross section should be used in the following problems except where it can be assumed that weak-axis bending is prevented by walls or other construction.

4-34. Columns in tier buildings are usually fabricated in two-story lengths, using the same cross section throughout. Design column B2 for the tenth to twelfth floor of the building of DP4-15-3, using a box section. Investigate the effect of neglecting eccentricity of load. AISC/ASD specification. Use $F_b = 0.66F_y$.

4-35. Columns in tier buildings are usually fabricated in two-story lengths, using the same cross section throughout. Design column B2 for the tenth to twelfth floor of the building of DP4-15-4, using a box section. Investigate the effect of neglecting eccentricity of load. AISC/LRFD specification. Use $M_n = M_p$.

4-36. (*a*) Same as Prob. 4-34 except design the topmost segment (twenty-fifth floor to roof) for column B2. (*b*) Same as Prob. 4-35 except design the topmost segment (twenty-fifth floor to roof) for column B2.

4-37. For the office building of DP4-15-3 design the bottom-tier exterior column A2. Assume the average weight of the exterior wall is 25 psf of surface. Select a box section made of four A36-steel plates. Use $F_b = 0.66F_y$.

4-38. For the office building of DP4-15-4 design the bottom-tier exterior column A2. Assume the average weight of the exterior wall is 25 psf of surface. Select a box section made of four A36-steel plates. Use $M_n = M_p$.

4-39. Same as Prob. 4-37 except design the topmost segment (twenty-fifth floor to roof) for column A1.

4-40. Same as Prob. 4-38 except design the topmost segment (twenty-fifth floor to roof) for column A1.

4-41. Same as Prob. 4-37 except use a built-up section consisting of a W14 and two plates welded to form a closed section.

4-42. Same as Prob. 4-38 except use a built-up section consisting of a W14 and two plates welded to form a closed section.

4-43. Choose an A572 box section for the A36 column of DP4-15-3. If the cost ratios of A572 to A36 are 1.04, 1.08, 1.12, and 1.36 for Grades 42, 45, 50, and 60, respectively, compare the material cost of the two designs. See Table 2-2.

4-44. Choose an A572 box section for the A36 column of DP4-15-4. If the cost ratios of A572 to A36 are 1.04, 1.08, 1.12, and 1.36 for Grades 42, 45, 50, and 60, respectively, compare the material cost of the two designs. See Table 2-2.

4-45. Assume the office building of DP4-15-3 is 18 stories high. Design the exterior column B1 and its base plate. The weight of the exterior wall is 25 psf of surface. Choose a W shape of A36 steel. The wall supports the column in the weak direction.

4-46. Assume the office building of DP4-15-4 is 18 stories high. Design the exterior column B1 and its base plate. The weight of the exterior wall is 25 psf of surface. Choose a W shape of A36 steel. The wall supports the column in the weak direction.

4-47. An 18×22 in box column is made of $1\frac{1}{2}$-in A36-steel plate. The column height is 16 ft. Design an A36 base plate for the maximum concentric load on the column. $f'_c = 3000$ psi.

4-48. The plan of a one-story industrial building is shown in Fig. P4-48. The roof deck is 2-in precast concrete plank, made with slag aggregate, which weighs 14 psf. Roofing

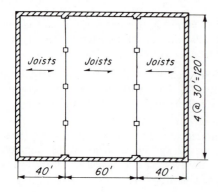

FIGURE P4-48

weighs 6 psf. The deck is supported on standard long-span steel joists spaced 5 ft on centers. The 40-ft joists are 24 in deep and weigh 19 plf. The 60-ft joists are 32 in deep and weigh 28 plf. The beams supporting the joints are A36 W21 × 68.

The building is 16 ft high between the floor and the bottom of the beams. Design columns in A36 steel tubing, and base plates supported on concrete footings with $f'_c = 3000$ psi.

4-49. The reactions on the beams in Fig. P4-49 are beam A, 7 kips DL and 21 kips LL; beam B, 5.3 kips DL and 16.3 kips LL; and beam C, 9 kips DL and 27 kips LL, respectively. In addition to the three beams, the column supports a centroidal axial load of 30 kips DL and 30 kips LL. The beams rest on seats 4 in wide and clear the adjacent surface of the column $\frac{1}{2}$ in. The effective length of the column is 12 ft. What 8 × 8 in standard A36 structural tubing is required? AISC specification.

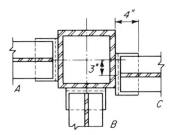

FIGURE P4-49

4-50. Figure P4-50 shows the half elevation of a frame for an industrial building. The frames are 30 ft on centers. The roof dead load is 20 psf, and the live load is 30 psf. The floor dead load is 60 psf and the live load 100 psf. The crane reaction is 38.6 kips. The building is braced at the ends and at several interior bents, so B, C, E, and F can be assumed fixed against translation. Beam-to-column connections are not moment-resistant. Design columns ABC and DEF. AISC specification.

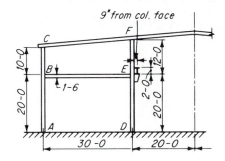

FIGURE P4-50

4-51. Design the column of DP4-18-1 for single lacing instead of batten plates.

4-52. Design the column of DP4-18-1 using four angles with battens. A36 steel.

4-53. Design a pin-ended column, using perforated cover plates on two opposite sides, 24 ft long for an axial load of 75 kips DL and 225 kips LL. AISC specification, A36 steel.

4-54. Compute the angle of twist of an A36 W8 × 31, 10 ft long, subjected to twisting moment $T = 2$ ft·kips at each end.

4-55. Same as Prob. 4-54 except that the member is supported as in Fig. 4-45c.

4-56. Compare the local-buckling stress [Eq. (4-32)] of a long column with equal-legged cruciform cross section with the twist-buckling stress of Eq. (4-52). Use the relation $E = 2G(1 + \mu)$. The value of k in case e of Fig. 4-34 is based on $\mu = 0.25$. The two values of F_{cr} should be the same.

4-57. For what length of pin-ended column of equal-legged cruciform cross section are bend buckling and twist buckling equally likely?

4-58. For what length of pin-ended column whose cross section is a W10 × 49 are bend buckling and twist buckling equally likely?

4-59. Compute the critical load for an A36-steel pin-ended column 12 ft long for the cross section shown in Fig. P4-59. Use the SSRC formula for buckling in the inelastic range.

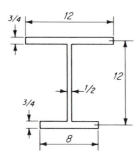

FIGURE P4-59

4-60. The cross section shown in Fig. P4-60 was used for the bottom legs of a 437-ft tower supporting a transmission line crossing the Sacramento River (*Civ. Eng.*, January 1954, p. 41). The unsupported length of the leg is 20 ft and the nominal yield stress of the steel is 33,000 psi. The Bureau of Reclamation specification allowable stress for columns of this steel was $P/A = 22,000 - 98L/r$, in pounds per square inch, assuming failure by bend buckling. If the design load was equal to the allowable value what is the factor of safety? C_w of the cross section is 6300 in⁶.

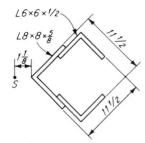

FIGURE P4-60

4-61. Design for aluminum 6061-T6 a two-angle top-chord member for a riveted roof truss. The design load is 40 kips. The unsupported length is 5 ft for buckling in the plane of the truss and 10 ft for buckling in the plane of the roof. Gusset plates are $\frac{1}{4}$ in thick. Use a factor of safety of 2.

4-62. Same as Prob. 4-61 except that the unsupported length is 5 ft for buckling in either direction.

4-63. Design an aluminum 6061-T6 column 20 ft long to support an axial load of 120 kips. The section is to consist of four angles and a plate in the form of an H. Space requirements are such that neither the depth nor the width of the member can exceed 12 in. Assume $K = 1$ and a factor of safety of 2.

4-64. Same as Prob. 4-63 except that the column is 10 ft long.

4-65. Same as Prob. 4-63 except that the column is 30 ft long.

REFERENCES

1. Timoshenko, S., and J. M. Gere: "Theory of Elastic Stability" 3d ed., McGraw-Hill, New York, 1969.
2. Horne, M. R., and W. Merchant: "The Stability of Frames," Pergamon, New York, 1965.
3. Bleich, F.: "Buckling Strength of Metal Structures," McGraw-Hill, New York, 1952.
4. Osgood, W. R., and M. Holt: The Column Strength of Two Extruded Aluminum-Alloy H-sections, *NACA Tech. Rep.* 656, 1939.
5. Shanley, F. R.: Applied Column Theory, *Trans. ASCE*, vol. 115, 1950.
6. Duberg, J. E., and T. W. Wilder: Inelastic Column Behavior, *NACA Tech. Note* 2267, January 1951.
7. Johnston, B. G.: Buckling Behavior above the Tangent Modulus Load, *J. Eng. Mech. Div. ASCE*, December 1961.
8. Beedle, L. S., and L. Tall: Basic Column Strength, *Trans. ASCE*, vol. 127, p. 138, 1962.
9. Structural Stability Research Council, Engineering Foundation: "Guide to Design Criteria for Metal Compression Members," 4th ed., T. V. Galambos (ed.), Wiley, New York, 1988.
10. Huber, A. W., and L. S. Beedle: Residual Stresses and the Compression Strength of Steel, *Weld. J.*, vol. 33, p. 589, December 1954.
11. Nitta, A., and B. Thürlimann: Ultimate Strength of High Yield Strength Constructional-Alloy Circular Columns: Effect of Cold Straightening, *Pub. IABSE*, 1962.
12. Tall, L.: Recent Developments in the Study of Column Behavior, *J. Inst. Eng. Aust.*, vol. 36, no. 12, December 1964.
13. Tall, L.: Welded Built-up Columns, *Lehigh Univ. Fritz Eng. Lab. Rep.* 249.29, 1966.
14. Alpsten, F. A.: Thermal Residual Stresses in Hot-Rolled Steel Members, *Lehigh Univ. Fritz Eng. Lab. Rep.* 337.3, 1968.
15. Clark, J. W., and R. L. Rolf: Buckling of Aluminum Columns, Plates, and Beams, *J. Struct. Div. ASCE*, June 1966.
16. Galambos, T. V.: "Structural Members and Frames," p. 185, Prentice-Hall, Englewood Cliffs, N.J., 1968.
17. Julian, O. G., and L. S. Lawrence: Notes on J and L Nomograms for Determination of Effective Lengths, unpublished, 1959.
18. Ueda, Y., and L. Tall: Inelastic Buckling of Plates with Residual Stresses, *Lehigh Univ. Fritz Eng. Lab. Rep.* 290.2, 1964.
19. German Buckling Specifications, T. V. Galambos and J. Jones (trans.), Column Research Council, June 1957.
20. Suggested Specifications for Structures of Aluminum Alloys 6061-T6 and 6062-T6, Report of Task Committee on Lightweight Alloys, *J. Struct. Div. ASCE*, December 1963.
21. White, M. W., and B. Thürlimann: Study of Columns with Perforated Cover Plates, *AREA Bull.* 531, September–October 1956.
22. McGuire, W.: "Steel Structures," Prentice-Hall, Englewood Cliffs, N.J., 1968.
23. Thürlimann, B.: New Aspects Concerning Elastic Stability of Steel Structures, *Trans. ASCE*, vol. 127, 1962.
24. Clark, J. W.: Aluminum Structures, sec. 11 in E. H. Gaylord and C. N. Gaylord (eds.), "Structural Engineering Handbook," 3d ed., McGraw-Hill, New York, 1990.
25. Specifications for Aluminum Structures, The Aluminum Association, 4th ed., 1982.

CHAPTER
5

BEAMS

5-1 INTRODUCTION

Although there are no hard-and-fast rules, the following names are in common use to describe beams with reference to their function:

Floor beam: In buildings, a major beam usually supporting joists; a transverse beam in bridge floors

Girder: In buildings, the same meaning as (and more commonly used than) floor beam; also any major beam in a structure

Girt: A horizontal member fastened to and spanning the wall columns of industrial buildings, used to support wall covering, such as corrugated metal

Header: A beam framed to two beams at right angles to it, and usually supporting joists on one side of it; used at openings such as stairwells

Joist: A beam supporting floor construction but not major beams

Lintel: A beam spanning door, window, or other wall openings and supporting wall immediately above

Purlin: A roof beam, usually supported by trusses

Rafter: A roof beam, usually supported by purlins

Spandrel beam: A beam at the outside wall of a building, supporting its share of the floor and also the wall up to the floor above

Stringer: In bridge floors, a longitudinal beam supported by floor beams (sometimes called a joist); a beam supporting stair steps

Trimmer: One of the beams or joists supporting a header

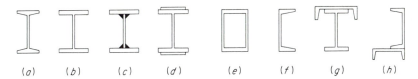

(a)   (b)   (c)   (d)   (e)   (f)   (g)   (h)

FIGURE 5-1

5-2 BEAM CROSS SECTIONS

Typical beam cross sections are shown in Fig. 5-1. Two types of I cross section are rolled in a wide variety of sizes. The American Standard Beam (S), which was the first steel beam section rolled in the United States, ranges in depth from 3 to 24 in (Fig. 5-1a). Increase in section modulus for a given depth is achieved by spreading the rolls to increase the flange width and web thickness while maintaining the same depth. The wide-flange shapes (W) give more section modulus per pound (Fig. 5-1b). They range in depth from 4 to 40 in, but shapes larger than 36 in are not available from U.S. producers. The W shape achieves increase in section modulus by increasing flange and web thicknesses and flange width while maintaining a constant depth *inside* the flanges. Light beams and miscellaneous shapes (M) are of the same shape as the W but of lighter weight (and smaller section modulus) for the same depth. Some producers weld three plates to form standard shapes of the same dimensions as the deeper W's (Fig. 5-1c). The section modulus of the W may be increased by welding plates to the flanges (Fig. 5-1d).

Since the web of an I contributes only a small part of the bending resistance, it is sometimes economical in welded beams of high-strength steel to use a lower-strength steel for the web. Such beams, called *hybrid* beams, are discussed in Chap. 7.

Box sections (Fig. 5-1e) are also efficient beam sections. They are available as rolled shapes, called *structural tubing*, in rectangular form ranging from 3 × 2 to 20 × 12 in. The four-plate welded box is also used extensively.

Channels (Fig. 5-1f) are used occasionally, usually as purlins, girts, eave struts, lintels, and as trimmers and headers for stairwells and other openings. They are sometimes used with the S or W shapes for crane-runway girders, as in Fig. 5-1g. Two channels arranged as in h are commonly used as eave struts in industrial buildings.

5-3 BENDING BEHAVIOR OF BEAMS

Figure 5-2a represents a length of originally straight beam which has been bent to the radius ρ by couples M; that is, the segment is subjected to pure bending. It is assumed that plane cross sections normal to the length of the unbent beam are still plane after the beam is bent. Therefore, considering two cross sections AB

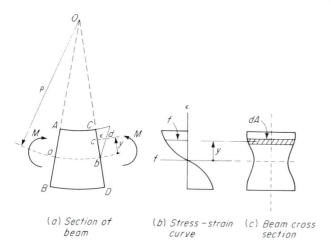

(a) Section of   (b) Stress – strain   (c) Beam cross
    beam   curve   section

FIGURE 5-2
(a) Section of beam; (b) stress-strain curve; (c) beam cross section.

and CD a unit distance apart, similar sectors Oab and bcd give

$$\epsilon = \frac{y}{\rho} \qquad (a)$$

where y is measured from the axis of rotation (neutral axis). Thus, strains are proportional to distance from the neutral axis. The corresponding variation in stress over the cross section is given by the stress-strain diagram of the material, rotated 90° from the conventional orientation, provided the strain axis ϵ is scaled through Eq. (a) with the distance y (Fig. 5-2b). The bending moment M is given by

$$M = \int_A yf \, dA \qquad (b)$$

where dA is an element of area at the distance y (Fig. 5-2c). Thus, the moment M can be determined if the relation between stress and strain shown in Fig. 5-2b is known. If stress is proportional to strain so that $f = E\epsilon$, Eqs. (a) and (b) give

$$M = \frac{E}{\rho} \int_A y^2 \, dA = \frac{EI}{\rho} \qquad (c)$$

or, eliminating ρ through Eq. (a),

$$M = \frac{EI\epsilon}{y} = \frac{fI}{y} \qquad (d)$$

The bending behavior of a beam of rectangular cross section made of a sharply yielding steel (Fig. 5-3) will now be investigated. Equation (d) holds so

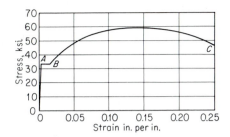

FIGURE 5-3

long as the stress is given by OA of Fig. 5-3, that is, if $f \le F_y$. When the extreme-fiber strain attains the value ϵ_y, the strain distribution and stress distribution are given by Fig. 5-4b and c. The corresponding moment, called the yield moment, is

$$M = \frac{F_y I}{d/2} = \frac{F_y b d^2}{6} \tag{e}$$

where b is the width and d the depth of the cross section (Fig. 5-4a). For $M \le M_y$, moment is proportional to extreme-fiber strain or stress. This is shown by OA in Fig. 5-5, where the ratio M/M_y is plotted against ϵ.

As the load on the beam increases beyond the load corresponding to M_y, strain continues to increase in proportion to distance from the neutral axis, but the stress distribution consists of OA, the elastic region, and a portion of AB, the yield plateau, of Fig. 5-3, provided the extreme-fiber strain is less than ϵ_s, the strain at the beginning of strain hardening. Thus, if the extreme-fiber strain is $2\epsilon_y$, as in Fig. 5-4d, the stress distribution is that shown in Fig. 5-4e. The corresponding resisting moment is

$$M = 2\left[\frac{bdF_y}{4}\left(\frac{d}{4} + \frac{1}{2} \times \frac{d}{4}\right) + \frac{bd}{4}\frac{F_y}{2}\frac{2}{3}\frac{d}{4}\right] = \frac{F_y bd}{4}\frac{3d}{4} + \frac{F_y bd}{8}\frac{d}{3} = \frac{11}{48}F_y bd^2 \tag{f}$$

which gives point B in Fig. 5-5. This moment is only 37.5 percent more than the yield moment M_y even though the extreme-fiber strain is doubled. Still further deformation is shown in Fig. 5-4f, where 90 percent of the cross section has

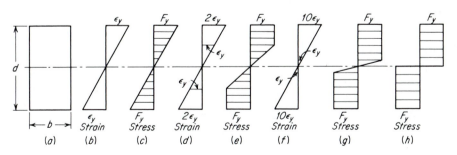

FIGURE 5-4

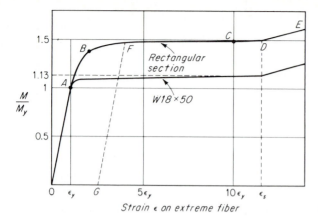

Strain ε on extreme fiber

FIGURE 5-5

yielded. The corresponding moment from Fig. 5-4*g* is $0.249F_y bd^2$, which gives point *C* in Fig. 5-5.

It will be noted in Fig. 5-5 that the rate of increase in moment falls off rapidly soon after M_y is exceeded, so *M* appears to be approaching a limiting value. This limit is determined by the distribution of stress shown in Fig. 5-4*h*, for which

$$M = F_y \frac{bd}{2} \frac{d}{2} = F_y \frac{bd^2}{4} \qquad (g)$$

This is only 0.4 percent larger than the moment for an extreme-fiber strain of $10\epsilon_y$. Thus, although the assumed stress distribution cannot exist, it determines a practical limiting value with negligible error. However, even this limit is exceeded after strain hardening begins, since stresses at and near the extreme fiber now exceed F_y. This is shown by *DE* in Fig. 5-5.

The moment given by Eq. (*g*) is called the *plastic moment* of resistance, denoted by M_p. It is usually taken as the limiting value; i.e., the benefits of strain hardening are neglected. The ratio of the plastic moment to the yield moment for the rectangular cross section is given by

$$\frac{M_p}{M_y} = \frac{F_y bd^2/4}{F_y bd^2/6} = 1.5$$

This ratio is called the *shape factor*.

A beam element that has been strained plastically is left with some permanent deformation after it is unloaded. Thus, if the moment reaches the value at *F* in Fig. 5-5 and the beam is then gradually unloaded, the resisting moment decreases along *FG*. Upon reloading it will increase along *GF* and will continue to behave elastically in subsequent loading and unloading, provided the moment corresponding to *F* is not exceeded. This is the same phenomenon that is observed in the tension test.

For the unequal-flanged I cross section of Fig. 5-6*a*, the stress distribution at the beginning of yield on the extreme fiber is shown in *b*. The moment M_y is given by

$$M = F_y \frac{I}{c} = F_y S$$

where S is the elastic section modulus. To satisfy the condition $\int_A f \, dA = 0$, the neutral axis must pass through the center of gravity of the cross section. The fully plastic stress distribution is shown in *c*. To satisfy the condition $\int_A F_y \, dA = 0$ in this case requires that the neutral axis divide the area A of the cross section into two equal parts, since all fibers are at the stress F_y. The moment M_p is given by

$$M_p = F_y \frac{A}{2} a = F_y Z$$

where a is the distance between the centroids of the two equal areas (Fig. 5-6*d*). Z is called the *plastic section modulus*. In general, the value of M_p can be determined from

$$M_p = F_y \left(\int_0^{c_1} y_1 \, dA + \int_0^{c_2} y_2 \, dA \right) = F_y Z$$

where y_1, y_2, c_1, and c_2 are defined in Fig. 5-6*d*. Values of the section moduli S and Z for the standard shapes commonly used for beams and columns are tabulated in the AISC Manuals.

The variation of moment with extreme-fiber strain for the I or H shape is similar to that of the rectangular cross section. However, the ratio of the plastic moment to the yield moment for bending about the major axis is much smaller. Thus, for the W18 × 50,

$$\frac{M_p}{M_y} = \frac{Z_x}{S_x} = \frac{101}{88.9} = 1.14$$

This is typical of the W shapes, for which the shape factor ranges from 1.10 to 1.18. On the other hand, the ratio M_p/M_y for W shapes bent about the minor

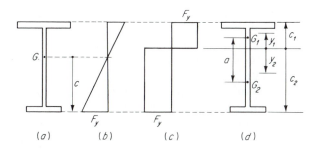

(*a*)   (*b*)   (*c*)   (*d*)   **FIGURE 5-6**

axis is about the same as for the rectangle. Thus, for the W18 × 50, $Z_y/S_y = 16.6/10.7 = 1.55$. The major-axis moment-strain plot for the W18 × 50 is shown in Fig. 5-5. Shape factors for certain other cross sections are the following:

Circular	1.70
Thin-walled circular tube	1.27
Thin-walled rectangular tube	1.12

5-4 LATERAL-TORSIONAL BUCKLING

Shapes that are intended to be used primarily as beams are generally proportioned so that the moment of inertia about the major principal axis is considerably larger than that about the minor principal axis. This is done to produce shapes that make economical beams. As a result, they are relatively weak in resistance to torsion and to bending about the minor axis, and if not held in line by floor construction or by bracing, they may become unstable under load. The instability manifests itself as a sidewise bending accompanied by twist and is called *lateral buckling* or *lateral-torsional buckling*.

It is not always easy to decide whether a beam has adequate support against lateral buckling. Embedment of the top flange in a concrete slab provides support except when the beam is a cantilever so that the compression flange is at the bottom. A completely encased beam is supported no matter which flange is in compression. Wood flooring spiked to nailing strips fastened to the top flange should furnish lateral support. Corrugated sheet-metal roofs are sometimes attached to purlins by metal straps or clips. It is questionable whether such connections provide dependable lateral support.

Lateral bracing must be adequate to hold the braced beam in position. Thus, stiffness as well as strength is required. As a general rule, bracing will be adequate if each lateral brace is designed for 2 percent of the compressive force in the flanges of the beam it braces. This rule of thumb is based on observations from laboratory tests.

Figure 5-7a shows a doubly symmetrical prismatic I beam, both ends of which are simply supported with respect to the x and y axes but held against rotation about the z axis. The beam is subjected to pure bending by moments M_x at each end. In the laterally bent position the center of gravity of the cross section is displaced by the amounts u and v in the direction of x and y, respectively, and there is a rotation β about the z axis. In the projection on the xz plane in Fig. 5-7b, the external moment M_x and the resisting moment at z are shown as vectors. The components of the resisting moment are $M_x \cos \theta$ in the plane of the deflected cross section and $M_x \sin \theta$ in the direction of the normal to it. However, if we restrict ourselves to the determination of the value of the end moments M_x at which a perfect beam just begins to bend out of the plane of these moments, u, v, β, and θ can be considered to be infinitesimal and we may take $\cos \theta = 1$ and $\sin \theta = \tan \theta = du/dz$. This gives M_x and $M_x\, du/dz$ for the components of moment in the deflected position, as shown in Fig. 5-7b. Similarly, in the projec-

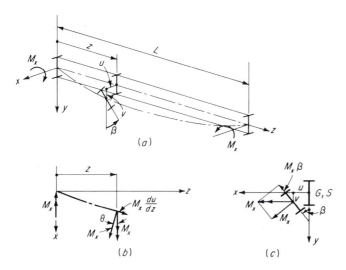

FIGURE 5-7

tion on the xy plane shown in Fig. 5-7c, the components in the directions of the principal axes in the deflected position are $M_x \cos \beta = M_x$ on the strong axis and $M_x \sin \beta = M_x \beta$ on the weak axis.

Equations of equilibrium are formulated by equating the components of M_x to the corresponding resistances. Since the displacements are infinitesimal, curvatures in the principal planes of the deflected cross section may be taken as d^2v/dz^2 and d^2u/dz^2. Therefore, the bending resistances are $EI_x\, d^2v/dz^2$ and $EI_y\, d^2u/dz^2$. The torsional resistance is given by Eq. (4-44). In this way we obtain the following equations

$$-EI_x \frac{d^2v}{dz^2} = M_x \tag{5-1a}$$

$$-EI_y \frac{d^2u}{dz^2} = M_x \beta \tag{5-1b}$$

$$GJ \frac{d\beta}{dz} - EC_w \frac{d^3\beta}{dz^3} = M_x \frac{du}{dz} \tag{5-1c}$$

The negative signs are needed in Eqs. (5-1a) and (5-1b) because the second derivatives are negative. Equation (5-1a) is independent and can be solved directly for the displacement v. However, (5-1b) and (5-1c) are coupled, which means that the displacements u and β cannot exist independently of one another.

Equations (5-1b) and (5-1c) can be reduced by differentiating (5-1c) once with respect to z and eliminating d^2u/dz^2 through (5-1b). This gives

$$EC_w \frac{d^4\beta}{dz^4} - GJ \frac{d^2\beta}{dz^2} - \frac{M_x^2}{EI_y} \beta = 0 \tag{5-2}$$

A solution to this equation can be obtained by taking

$$\beta = \beta_{L/2} \sin \frac{\pi z}{L} \tag{a}$$

where $\beta_{L/2}$ is the angle of twist at midspan. This gives $\beta = 0$ at each end of the beam and, because of Eq. (5-1b), $EI_y \, d^2u/dz^2 = 0$ at each end. Thus, the beam is restrained against twisting at the supports but is free to rotate about the y axis. Furthermore, because $d^2\beta/dz^2$ is also zero at each end, the end cross sections are free to warp (Art. 4-19). Thus, the boundary conditions which were assumed in formulating Eqs. (5-1) are satisfied. Substituting from Eq. (a) into Eq. (5-2) gives

$$\left(\frac{\pi^4}{L^4} EC_w + \frac{\pi^2}{L^2} GJ - \frac{M_x^2}{EI_y} \right) \beta_{L/2} \sin \frac{\pi z}{L} = 0$$

This equation is satisfied by $\beta_{L/2} = 0$, which means that both β and u are everywhere zero, or by

$$M_{x,cr}^2 = \frac{\pi^2}{L^2} EI_y GJ + \frac{\pi^4}{L^4} EI_y EC_w \tag{5-3}$$

This gives the value of M_x at which lateral-torsional buckling begins. It will be noted that, as in the case of the Euler column, the deflection is indeterminate. Thus, Eq. (5-3) identifies the beginning of lateral-torsional buckling but gives no information about the postbuckling behavior.

Since it was derived for pure bending, Eq. (5-3) is limited in scope. It is restricted further by the assumed freedom to warp and to rotate about the y axis at the supports. The first restriction is removed by rewriting Eqs. (5-1) for whatever variation in bending moment is to be considered. Of course, the bending moment is now dependent on z. Solutions of these equations can be obtained by using infinite series.[1] The second restriction is removed by using appropriate boundary conditions. For this case, however, an end-restraint moment M_y (which is an infinitesimal of the same order as β) must be added to the right member of Eq. (5-1b). The resulting critical moments for beams with end moments and beams with transverse loads acting through the shear center can be put in the form of Eq. (5-3) as follows:

$$M_{x,cr}^2 = C_b^2 \left[\frac{\pi^2}{(KL)^2} EI_y GJ + \frac{\pi^4}{(KL)^4} EI_y EC_w \right] \tag{5-4}$$

where C_b is a coefficient which depends on the variation in moment along the span and K is an effective-length coefficient which depends on the conditions of restraint at the supports. Values of C_b and K for a number of cases of practical interest are given in Table 5-1. Values of K in this table are based on identical boundary conditions for both warping and y-axis rotation. In other words, the simple support means one for which both warping and y-axis rotation are permitted at each end, while the fixed support means one for which both are prevented. If boundary conditions are mixed, values of K for y-axis rotation and for

TABLE 5-1
Coefficients in Eq. (5-4)*

Case	Loading	y-axis support at ends	K	C_b†	C_1	C_2
1	$M \longrightarrow M$	Simple Fixed	1 0.5	1 1		1 1
2	(loading diagram)	Simple Fixed	1 0.5	1.77–1.86 1.78–1.85		6.5
3	(loading diagram)	Simple Fixed	1 0.5	2.56–2.74 2.23–2.58		
4	(uniform load)	Simple Fixed	1 0.5	1.13 0.97	0.45 0.29	
5	(uniform load)	Simple Fixed	1 0.5	1.30 0.86	1.55 0.82	
6	(point load)	Simple Fixed	1 0.5	1.35 1.07	0.55 0.42	2.5
7	(point load)	Simple Fixed	1 0.5	1.70 1.04	1.42 0.84	
8	$L/4 \quad L/2 \quad L/4$	Simple	1	1.04	0.42	
9	(uniform load)	Fixed	1	2.05–3.42		
10	(point load)	Fixed	1	1.28–1.71	0.64	

* From Ref. 3.
† Where a range of values is given, the smaller value corresponds to beams with negligible warping resistance.

warping restraint are unequal. Approximate values for such cases are tabulated in Ref. 2. However, mixed boundary conditions are not likely to occur in practice.

Values of C_b for the first three cases in Table 5-1 can be determined from either of the following equations,

$$C_b = 1.75 - 1.05 \frac{M_1}{M_2} + 0.3 \left(\frac{M_1}{M_2} \right)^2 \le 2.3 \tag{5-5a}$$

$$C_b = \frac{1}{0.6 - 0.4 M_1/M_2} \le 2.3 \tag{5-5b}$$

where M_1 is the smaller of the two end moments M_1 and M_2 and where M_1/M_2 is positive for reverse-curvature bending.

The following equation gives more accurate values of C_b if the moment diagram within the unbraced length is not a straight line.[4]

$$C_b = \frac{12.5 M_{max}}{2.5 M_{max} + 3 M_A + 4 M_B + 3 M_C} \tag{5-5c}$$

where M_{max} = absolute value of maximum moment in the unbraced length
$\quad M_A$ = absolute value of moment at the one-quarter point
$\quad M_B$ = absolute value of moment at the midpoint
$\quad M_C$ = absolute value of moment at the three-quarter point

For straight-line moment diagrams in single curvature Eq. (5-5c) reduces to Eq. (5-5b).

Equation (5-5a) was developed by curve fitting to data from numerical analyses of lateral-torsional buckling of a simple beam acted upon only by end moments.[5] Equation (5-5b) gives C_b as the reciprocal of the coefficient C_m given by Eq. (6-7), which was derived from analyses of the in-plane strength of beam columns. It turns out that C_b and C_m are very closely inverse to one another, provided the limiting value $C_b = 2.3$ is observed, even though they were derived for different loading conditions.

Although Eqs. (5-5) are based on values of C_b for single-span beams, they can also be used for beam segments between lateral-brace points, in which case M_1 and M_2 are the moments at the ends of the segment. In effect, this means that cases 1, 2, and 3 of Table 5-1 are treated as laterally braced segments of a beam. This is justified because C_b for these cases is very nearly independent of the y-axis conditions at the ends (simple or fixed), as is shown by the values in Table 5-1.

Lateral braces will usually be spaced uniformly. If a simply supported uniformly loaded beam is braced so that there are an odd number of segments, $C_b = 1$ for the middle segment and is greater than 1 for the adjacent segments. If there are an even number of segments, C_b is the same for each if there are two segments and for each of the two middle ones if there are four. Values of C_b are given in Table 5-2.

Equation (5-3) applies to the symmetrical channel and the point-symmetrical zee as well as to the symmetrical I for which it was derived. Equa-

TABLE 5-2
Values of C_b for middle segments of laterally braced simply supported beams*

Intermediate braces	C_b	
	Eq. (5-5a)	Eq. (5-5c)
None	1.0	1.14
At midspan	1.75	1.30
At third points	1.0	1.0
At quarter points	1.13	1.06
At fifth points	1.0	1.0
At sixth points	1.05	1.03

* Uniformly distributed load.

tion (5-4) can be used as an approximate solution for channels and zees supporting transverse load acting through the shear center.[3] Beams whose loads do not act through the shear center are discussed in the next article.

5-5 INELASTIC LATERAL-TORSIONAL BUCKLING

Equations (5-1) are based on proportionality of stress and strain. Therefore, the value of M_x from Eq. (5-4) must not exceed the moment which gives proportional-limit stress on the extreme fiber of the beam. Thus, in the case of steel with a flat-top yield, a solution $M_x \geq M_y$ is invalid. In this case, behavior of the beam is given by Eq. (5-1a) if there are no residual stresses, which means that the beam develops the yield moment with no lateral-torsional buckling.

   Equation (5-4) can be extended to the inelastic range of buckling of beams made of gradually yielding metals. Figure 5-8a shows the bending stresses at a cross section of a beam bent in the yz plane, with an extreme-fiber stress $f = F_{cr}$ greater than the proportional-limit stress F_p. If the displacement u at the onset of

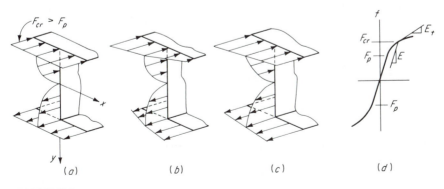

(a)   (b)   (c)   (d)

FIGURE 5-8

buckling is in the positive direction of x, the resulting bending about the y axis puts tension on the $+x$ side of the flanges and compression on the $-x$ side. If the moment increment is of higher order than the corresponding displacement, the stress distribution changes to that shown in Fig. 5-8b, where increase in stress is governed by the tangent modulus E_t and decrease by Young's modulus E (Fig. 5-8d). On the other hand, there need be no stress reversal if the moment increment is a first-order effect (Fig. 5-8c). This is analogous to the inelastic-buckling behavior of columns, which was discussed in Art. 4-4. The stress distribution in Fig. 5-8b changes the bending stiffness EI_y in Eq. (5-4) to $E_r I_y$, where E_r is the double modulus of elasticity, while the distribution in c changes it to $E_t I_y$, where E_t is the tangent modulus.

The torsional displacement β produces shear stresses (St. Venant torsion) and, because of the nonuniform warping, cross bending of the flanges. The stresses due to cross bending are shown in Fig. 4-45d. Since these are also superimposed on the bending stresses of Fig. 5-8a, EC_w in Eq. (5-4) should be replaced by $E_r C_w$ or $E_t C_w$ in accordance with the assumption made for the bending stiffness EI_y. The St. Venant shear stresses are superimposed on any shear stresses which may exist at the onset of buckling. However, shear stresses due to bending are usually relatively small over most of the cross section and are not likely to exceed the proportional limit. Furthermore, the shearing modulus governing twist at the beginning of buckling is practically equal to the elastic value even in the presence of axial stress well beyond the proportional limit (Art. 5-6). Thus, it would appear that the elastic value G should be retained in Eq. (5-4) to the inelastic range. However, it is on the safe side, and results in a simpler equation, if G is replaced by G_t. Thus, Eq. (5-4) becomes

$$M^2_{x,cr} = C_b^2 \tau^2 \left[\frac{\pi^2}{(KL)^2} EI_y\, GJ + \frac{\pi^4}{(KL)^4} EI_y\, EC_w \right] \tag{5-6}$$

where $\tau = E_t/E = G_t/G$. Since τ and M_x are interrelated, this equation must be solved by trial.

The solution of Eq. (5-6) can be simplified by using an equivalent radius of gyration which is obtained by equating the critical bending stress to the tangent-modulus critical stress for a column. Thus,

$$F_{cr}^2 = \frac{M^2_{x,cr}}{S_x^2} = \left[\frac{\pi^2 \tau E}{(KL/r_{eq})^2} \right]^2 \tag{a}$$

Substituting $M^2_{x,cr}$ from Eq. (5-6) into Eq. (a) gives

$$r_{eq}^2 = C_b \frac{\sqrt{I_y}}{S_x} \sqrt{C_w + 0.04 J (KL)^2} \tag{5-7a}$$

Since Eq. (5-4) is based on the assumption that transverse loads act through the shear center of the beam cross section, Eqs. (5-6) and (5-7a), which are derived from it, are equally limited in application. Figure 5-7c shows that a load P applied below the shear center S (at the bottom flange, say) exerts a restoring moment as the beam begins to buckle. Of course, this increases resistance to buckling. On the other hand, a load P applied above S tends to increase the twist once the beam begins to buckle. Procedures for evaluating these effects are discussed in various books.[1] The effect on the equivalent radius of gyration is accounted for in the following equation:[3]

$$r_{eq}^2 = C_b \frac{\sqrt{I_y}}{S_x} [C_1 g \sqrt{I_y} + \sqrt{(C_1 g \sqrt{I_y})^2 + C_w + 0.04J(KL)^2}] \qquad (5\text{-}7b)$$

where g is the distance from the shear center to the point of application of the load, to be taken positive if the load is below the shear center and negative if it is above (Fig. 5-9a). Values of C_1 are given in Table 5-1. This equation reduces to Eq. (5-7a) if $g = 0$.

In I-shaped beams made of steel with a flat-top yield, residual stresses cause premature yielding of portions of the cross section, just as in the case of columns (Art. 4-6). This causes the beam to behave as though it were made of a gradually yielding steel. The corresponding lateral-buckling resistance can be evaluated by using an effective cross section (the unyielded portion) as is done for columns. The effective cross section is not symmetrical, however, because premature yielding begins in the tips of the compression flange, just as it does in the column, while the tension flange yields first at its juncture with the web, where the residual stress is tensile. Thus, the beam is reduced to the equivalent of one with unequal flanges (Art. 5-10). For practical applications, however, a solution based on the properties of the unreduced cross section is to be preferred. Since the proportional limit in compression is the same for lateral buckling of beams as it is for columns, namely, $F_p = F_y - F_{rc}$, the SSRC column formula, with the equivalent radius of gyration from Eqs. (5-7), suggests itself. A comparison of the results of tests on 31 rolled steel beams, reported in Ref. 6, with values computed in this way is shown in Fig. 5-10. The beams were simply supported and ranged in span from 5 to 10 ft for the W10 × 15 and 10 to 50 ft for the W18 × 50. They were tested with concentrated loads acting on the top flange at the quarter points. A lateral-buckling formula for this loading is given in Ref. 6. Since the yield points of the beams ranged from 33.5 to 42.5 ksi, the results are nondimensionalized in Fig. 5-10 by plotting F_{test}/F_y against $F_y/F_{E(equiv)}$, where $F_{E(equiv)}$ denotes the Euler stress for the beam slenderness ratio based on r_{eq} from Eqs. (5-7). The SSRC parabola plots as a straight line in these coordinates, since

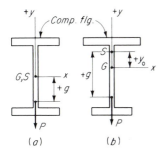

(a)   (b)   **FIGURE 5-9**

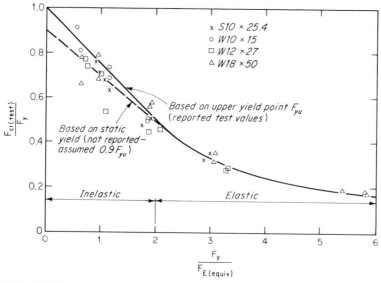

FIGURE 5-10
Comparison of predicted lateral-buckling strengths with test results from Ref. 6.

it reduces to

$$F_{cr} = F_y\left(1 - \frac{1}{4}\frac{F_y}{F_{E(equiv)}}\right) \tag{b}$$

as is seen from Eq. (4-15). The upper yield point for each beam coupon was reported in Ref. 6. The static yield level, which was not reported, may be as much as 10 to 15 percent smaller (Art. 2-4). Two plots of Eq. (b), one based on the reported upper yield point F_{yu} and one on $0.9F_{yu}$, are shown in Fig. 5-10. It will be noted that there is more scatter of test results in the inelastic range, as is to be expected, and that the procedure described above gives a good average prediction of the test results if it is based on the static yield.

Example 5-5-1. Using a factor of safety of 1.75, determine the allowable load for an A36-steel W10 × 22 spanning 10 ft and supporting a concentrated load at midspan. The load is applied at the shear center. The ends are simply supported in the x and y directions, and there is no lateral support at midspan.

Solution. From the AISC Manual, $I_y = 11.4$ in^4, $S_x = 23.2$ in^3, $J = 0.240$ in^4, $C_w = 275$ in^6.

From Table 5-1, $C_b = 1.35$, $K = 1$. Then, from Eq. (5-7a),

$$r_{eq}^2 = 1.35\sqrt{\frac{11.4}{23.2}}\sqrt{275 + 0.04 \times 0.240 \times 120^2} = 3.99$$

$$r_{eq} = 2.00 \qquad \frac{KL}{r_{eq}} = \frac{120}{2.00} = 60$$

Using the SSRC formula [Eq. (4-16)] for the inelastic range,

$$C_c = \pi\sqrt{\frac{2E}{F_y}} = \pi\sqrt{\frac{60,000}{36}} = 128$$

$$F_{cr} = 36\left[1 - \frac{1}{2}\left(\frac{60}{128}\right)^2\right] = 32.0 \text{ ksi}$$

$$M_x = F_{cr}S_x = 32.0 \times \frac{23.2}{12} = 61.9 \text{ ft·kips}$$

$$M_x = \frac{PL}{4} = 2.5P \qquad P = \frac{61.9}{2.5} = 24.8 \text{ kips}$$

$$P_{all} = \frac{24.8}{1.75} = 13.2 \text{ kips}$$

5-6   LOCAL BUCKLING OF BEAM ELEMENTS

If a beam cross section is to develop the yield moment M_y, the compression flange must be able to reach yield stress and the web, or webs, must be able to develop the corresponding bending stresses. Local buckling of the flange and/or web can prevent these limits from being attained. Local buckling of plate elements in uniform compression is discussed in Arts. 4-12 and 4-13 and of beam webs in bending in Art. 5-15. Values of flange slenderness b/t which must not be exceeded if yield stress is to be reached are determined in Art. 4-14, and Table 4-4 gives typical specification values. More restrictive limits must be observed if a beam cross section is to attain the fully plastic moment M_p. This is because the compressive strain in the flange must be several times the yield strain to develop a moment essentially equal to the fully plastic moment (Figs. 5-4 and 5-5). For this case, point F of Fig. 4-36 gives a conservative limiting value since it allows the strain-hardening strain ϵ_s, which may be as much as 12 times ϵ_y, to develop.

Proportions of plates which can be strained beyond the yield value ϵ_y are difficult to determine, partly because of the anisotropic behavior of plates that buckle after yielding has begun and partly because of the discontinuous nature of the yielding process itself. Local buckling of plates in the nonproportional range of stress was discussed in Art. 4-12, where it was shown that, for a gradually yielding material (Fig. 5-11a), the elastic modulus E in Eq. (4-52) should be replaced by $\sqrt{EE_t}$ to extend the formula to the inelastic range. However, in the case of steel with a flat-top yield (Fig. 5-11b), it appears that the modulus changes instantaneously from E to zero at yield. Even in the curved-knee diagram of average stress vs. strain, which results if there are initial residual stresses (Fig. 5-11c), the tangent modulus appears to reach zero at strains much less than the strain-hardening value. Thus, in this situation, it would seem that resistance to local buckling would vanish at strains too small to allow the plastic moment to develop fully. However, plates accept much larger strains than this without buck-

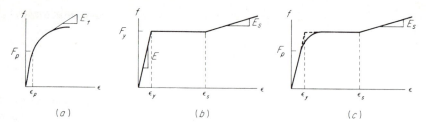

FIGURE 5-11

ling. The reason appears to be that yielding actually develops in small yield planes, or slipbands, in which the strain jumps suddenly from the elastic-limit value to the value ϵ_s at the beginning of strain hardening. This phenomenon was discussed in Art. 2-4. These slipbands form one after another after having initiated at a weak point, such as an inclusion or a point of stress concentration. Thus, there is no material, in the length over which strain is measured, for which $\epsilon_y \le \epsilon \le \epsilon_s$. Instead, some portions are strained to ϵ_y while the remainder is strained to ϵ_s. The *measured* strain averages these values. During this stage, the material is not homogeneous. However, after all the material has been strained to the strain-hardening value, it becomes homogeneous again and the stress begins to increase according to the strain-hardening modulus E_s, in Fig. 5-11b. Nevertheless, the material is anisotropic because of changes caused by slip.

Discontinuous yielding has been taken into account to determine values of b/t corresponding to strains of the order of strain hardening.[7,8] For the uniformly compressed plate simply supported on one unloaded edge and free on the other, the critical stress according to Ref. 7 is

$$F_{cr} = \frac{G_t}{(b/t)^2} + \left[\frac{\pi^2 E}{12(1 - \mu_x \mu_y)}\right]\frac{t^2}{L^2} \qquad (a)$$

where G_t = tangent modulus in shear
μ_x, μ_y = Poisson's ratio in direction of x, y
L = length of plate
b = width of plate
t = thickness of plate

This equation is identical in form to Eq. (4-52) for twist buckling of the cruciform cross section. The identity of twist buckling of the cruciform and local buckling of the plate has already been mentioned (Art. 4-20). Substituting $I_p = 4tb^3/3$, $J = 4bt^3/3$, and $C_w = b^3 t^3/9$ (Art. 4-20) into Eq. (4-52) gives

$$F_{cr} = \frac{G}{(b/t)^2} + \frac{\pi^2 E}{12}\frac{t^2}{L^2} \qquad (b)$$

Thus, the only difference between inelastic buckling and elastic buckling is that $E/(1 - \mu_x \mu_y)$ replaces E and G_t replaces G in the buckling formula. Furthermore, plates used in structural members are long enough to warrant neglecting the second term of Eq. (a), so

$$F_{cr} = \frac{G_t}{(b/t)^2} \tag{5-8}$$

Since the value of b/t which permits a plate to reach the beginning of strain hardening without buckling is needed, G_t in Eq. (5-8) must be evaluated accordingly. Tests on two circular tubes which were compressed to the strain ϵ_s and then twisted are reported in Ref. 9. The shearing modulus at the beginning of twist was practically equal to the elastic value G. However, it dropped rapidly at small values of shear strain. Then, at a value of 2000 or 3000 ksi, it began to decrease more slowly, so a value of this order of magnitude would seem to be reasonable for the buckling problem. Based on torsional-buckling tests on single angles, the value $G_t = 2400$ ksi was suggested.[7] Therefore, from Eq. (5-8),

$$\frac{b}{t} = \frac{\sqrt{2400}}{\sqrt{F_y}} = \frac{49}{\sqrt{F_y}} \tag{5-9}$$

where F_y is in kips per square inch. An analysis of the I flange under compression, taking into account rotational restraint from the web, showed that this value is increased by only 2 or 3 percent by such restraint.[10]

Analysis of the uniformly compressed plate supported on all four edges leads to an equation similar to Eq. (a). If the supports are simple, the plate can reach strain hardening if

$$\frac{b}{t} \le \frac{192}{\sqrt{F_y}} \tag{5-10}$$

For A36 steel, Eqs. (5-9) and (5-10) give $b/t = 8.2$ and 32, respectively.

Summarizing the results of this analysis, we have the following limits of plate slenderness which preclude premature local buckling of compression flanges of beams:

Projecting element:
$$\frac{b}{t} \le \begin{cases} \dfrac{95}{\sqrt{F_y}} & \text{for } M_y \\[2mm] \dfrac{49}{\sqrt{F_y}} & \text{for } M_p \end{cases}$$

Flange of box:
$$\frac{b}{t} \le \begin{cases} \dfrac{253}{\sqrt{F_y}} & \text{for } M_y \\[2mm] \dfrac{192}{\sqrt{F_y}} & \text{for } M_p \end{cases}$$

Since these limits are not well defined, they differ somewhat from one specification to another.

TABLE 5-3
Limiting values of beam flange and web slenderness

Type of element	Ratio	AISC/ASD Compact	AISC/ASD Noncompact	AISC/LRFD Compact	AISC/LRFD Noncompact	AREA	AASHTO
Flange of rolled I or channel	$\dfrac{b}{t}$	$\dfrac{65^a}{\sqrt{F_y}}$	$\dfrac{95^a}{\sqrt{F_y}}$	$\dfrac{65^a}{\sqrt{F_y}}$	$\dfrac{141^{a,b}}{\sqrt{F_{yw}-10}}$	$\dfrac{2300^c}{\sqrt{F_y}}$, psi	$\dfrac{3250^{d,e}}{\sqrt{f}}$, psi
Flange of welded I	$\dfrac{b}{t}$	$\dfrac{65^a}{\sqrt{F_y}}$	$\dfrac{95^a}{\sqrt{F_y/k_c}}$	$\dfrac{65^a}{\sqrt{F_{yf}}}$	$\dfrac{106^a}{\sqrt{F_{yw}-16.5}}$	$\dfrac{2300^c}{\sqrt{F_y}}$, psi	$\dfrac{3250^{d,e}}{\sqrt{f}}$, psi
Flange of box	$\dfrac{b}{t}$	$\dfrac{190}{\sqrt{F_y}}$	$\dfrac{238}{\sqrt{F_y}}$	$\dfrac{190}{\sqrt{F_y}}$	$\dfrac{238}{\sqrt{F_y-F_r}}$	$\dfrac{7500}{\sqrt{F_y}}$, psi	$\dfrac{5000^e}{\sqrt{f}}$, psi
Web[f] of I	$\dfrac{d^g}{t}$	$\dfrac{640}{\sqrt{F_y}}$					
Web[f] of I	$\dfrac{h^{h,i}}{t}$	$\cdots$	$\dfrac{760}{\sqrt{F_b}}$	$\dfrac{640}{\sqrt{F_y}}$	$\dfrac{970}{\sqrt{F_y}}$		

F_y in ksi except where noted.
F_{yf} = yield stress of flange.
F_w = yield stress of web.
F_b = allowable bending stress for beams with no axial force.
F_r = residual stress = 10 ksi for rolled shapes, 16.5 ksi for welded shapes.
$k_c = 4.05/(h/t)^{0.46}$ if $h/t > 70$; otherwise $k_c = 1$. See Art. 5-8.
[a] b = half width of flange.
[b] $106/\sqrt{F_{yw}} - 16.5$ for welded shapes.
[c] b = distance from free edge of flange to fillet.
[d] b = width of flange.
[e] f = service-load stress.
[f] Webs in flexure. See Art. 5-15 for flexure and axial compression.
[g] d = depth of beam.
[h] h = clear distance between flanges of rolled, built-up, or formed sections (AISC/ASD).
[i] h = twice the distance from the neutral axis to the nearest line of fasteners at the compression flange or to the inside face of the compression flange for welded shapes (AISC/LRFD).

Specification values of flange and web slendernesses are given in Table 5-3. The terms *compact* and *noncompact* in the AISC columns of this table refer to the *compact section*, which is one that can develop a fully plastic moment M_p before local buckling of any of its compression elements occurs, and the *noncompact section*, which is one that can develop a moment equal to or greater than M_y, but less than M_p, before local buckling of any of its elements occurs. Elements slenderer than those designated as noncompact are usually called *slender elements*.

All W shapes satisfy the compact-section web requirements for all the steels in which they are available. Furthermore, of all the A36 W's, the flange of only one, the W6 × 15, fails to qualify as compact. Therefore, except for the W6 × 15, web and flange slendernesses need not be checked for A36 W's used as beams. In fact, only 22 of the 295 W's listed in the AISC Manual fail to satisfy the compact-section flange requirement for all the yield points in which they are produced.

The limiting values given in Table 5-3 cover most situations, since it is usually not economical to use thinner elements that require reduction in the allowable stress because of local buckling. Nevertheless, there are provisions in the AISC and AREA specifications, discussed in Chap. 10, for relaxing these requirements.

Rotation capacity. The strain ϵ on the extreme fiber of a beam can be converted to rotation θ of the cross section through the relationship $\theta = 2\epsilon/y_e$, where y_e is the distance from the neutral axis to the extreme fiber. Rotation capacity is important in members of plastically designed structures (Chap. 9) and in structures in earthquake-prone regions. The compact-section limiting slenderness ratios in Table 5-3 provide a rotation capacity of about $3\theta_y$, where θ_y = rotation at initiation of extreme-fiber yield. A greater capacity may be required in regions of high seismicity.

5-7 DESIGN FOR LIMITED DEFLECTION

Although a beam is unsuitable if it cannot support its loads without excessive deflection, it is not easy to set a dividing line between reasonable and unreasonable deflection. Excessive deflection in floor construction is objectionable not only because of the feeling of softness but also because of undesirable vibration characteristics and the possibility of damage to attached construction such as plaster. Excessive deflection in floor construction supporting machinery may result in misalignments as well as dangerous vibration. Excessive deflection in purlins may cause damage to roofing materials and, on flat roofs, accumulation of water during rainstorms which, under certain conditions, can cause collapse. Retention of water due to the deflection of flat-roof framing is called *ponding*.

The maximum deflection Δ of a simply supported beam uniformly loaded in a principal plane is given by

$$\Delta = \frac{5}{384} \frac{WL^3}{EI} \tag{a}$$

where W denotes the total load on the span. But since the maximum bending moment $M = WL/8$, we may eliminate W from Eq. (a) to get

$$\Delta = \frac{5}{48} \frac{ML^2}{EI} \tag{5-11a}$$

Substituting $M/I = f/c = f/(d/2)$ into Eq. (5-11a) gives

$$\Delta = \frac{5}{24} \frac{fL^2}{Ed} \tag{5-11b}$$

Similar equations may be derived for other load distributions. However, Eqs. (5-11) will predict deflection with sufficient accuracy for practically any vertical load. Table 5-4 gives ratios of the true deflection to the value given by Eqs. (5-11) for 13 different load distributions. The first six entries show that the equation is satisfactory for almost any case of distributed load except possibly the first. The next three suggest that the maximum deflection for a single concentrated load is, closely enough, 80 percent of the value given by Eqs. (5-11) unless the load is very near a support. The remaining entries show that the formula can be used without significant error for multiple concentrated loads, with the possible exception of the rather extreme location of loads in case 10.

Permissible deflection of a beam is usually relative to the span, since a deflection of 1 in in a span of 30 ft will not ordinarily be more objectionable than a deflection of $\frac{1}{2}$ in in a span of 15 ft. Occasionally, however, permissible deflection is independent of span. For example, if a lintel is placed to clear a glass-block panel by $\frac{1}{2}$ in, its permissible deflection is somewhat less than $\frac{1}{2}$ in regardless of its span. The most frequently quoted deflection limit prohibits live-load deflections in excess of $\frac{1}{360}$ of the span for beams supporting plastered ceil-

TABLE 5-4
Ratio of true deflection to value given by Eqs. (5-11)

Case	Load	Ratio
1	Uniformly distributed on each end quarter of span	1.15
2	Uniformly distributed on each end third of span	1.11
3	Increases uniformly from zero at one end to maximum at other	0.98
4	Increases uniformly from zero at each end to maximum at center	0.96
5	Uniformly distributed over middle half of span	0.96
6	Uniformly distributed over middle quarter of span	0.89
7	Concentrated at center of span	0.80
8	Concentrated at one of the quarter points	0.75
9	Concentrated at one of the eighth points	0.69
10	Concentrated in two equal parts at $\frac{1}{8}$ span from each support	1.17
11	Concentrated in two equal parts at $\frac{1}{4}$ span from each support	1.10
12	Concentrated in two equal parts at $\frac{1}{3}$ span from each support	1.02
13	Concentrated in three equal parts at equidistant points	0.95

ings. The source of this rule seems to be unknown. Presumably it was given originally as a safe limit with respect to cracking of plastered ceilings. This deflection limit is a requirement of the AISC/ASD specification. AASHTO limits deflection due to live load plus impact to not more than $\frac{1}{800}$ of the span, while AREA limits it to $\frac{1}{640}$.

The ratio L/d of beam span to beam depth which corresponds to a specific ratio Δ/L of deflection to span can be determined from Eq. (5-11b):

$$\frac{L}{d} = \frac{24}{5}\frac{E}{f}\frac{\Delta}{L} \qquad\qquad (b)$$

If we wish to limit deflection to, say, $\frac{1}{300}$ of the span for steel beams designed for $f = 0.6F_y$, we find from Eq. (b) that

$$\frac{L}{d} = \frac{24}{5}\frac{30{,}000}{0.6F_y}\frac{1}{300} = \frac{800}{F_y} \qquad\qquad (5\text{-}12)$$

The commentary to the AISC/ASD specification suggests this value of L/d as a guide to deflection control of beams in floors, with the proviso that larger values may be used if the allowable bending stress is proportionately reduced. For purlins (except those in flat roofs) the value $1000/F_y$ is suggested. It should be noted that these limits are based on deflection due to the total load, rather than live load only, since the allowable stress $0.6F_y$ was used in deriving them.

Equation (b) can be expressed in terms of bending stress by substituting F_b for f. Then for a deflection limit of $\frac{1}{300}$ of the span, and with $E = 30{,}000$ ksi, we get

$$\frac{L}{d} = \frac{480}{F_b} \qquad\qquad (5\text{-}13)$$

This formula is useful in computing the value of L/d for a deflection limit of $L/300$ for live load only by substituting for F_b the live-load bending stress.

The Canadian Standard S16.1-1974 (Ref. 11) suggests maximum values of live-load deflection for a number of types of load on beams.

It should be noted that the deflection limits discussed above are not mandatory. The AISC/ASD Commentary suggests that they be followed "if practicable."

5-8 ALLOWABLE STRESS DESIGN OF BEAMS

Allowable bending stresses for beams not supported laterally at intervals short enough to prevent lateral-torsional buckling are based in part on simplified forms of Eq. (5-4) for elastic buckling, together with various empirical formulas for inelastic buckling.

The simplified forms of Eq. (5-4) are derived as follows. If we neglect the second term in brackets, the critical bending stress is

$$F_{cr} = \frac{M_{x,cr}}{S_x} = C_b \frac{\pi}{KL} \frac{\sqrt{EI_y GJ}}{S_x} \tag{a}$$

Since the webs of I shapes are thin compared to the thickness of their flanges, we can obtain simple and fairly accurate approximations to I_y, J, and S_x of the equal-flanged beam by considering only the flanges. Thus,

$$I_y = \frac{2tb^3}{12} = \frac{tb^3}{6}$$

$$J = \frac{2bt^3}{3}$$

$$S_x = \frac{I_x}{c} = \frac{2bt(d/2)^2}{d/2} = btd$$

where b = flange width
t = flange thickness
d = beam depth

Substituting these values into Eq. (a) and using $E = 2(1 + \mu)G$ with $\mu = 0.25$ gives

$$F_{cr} = \frac{0.21\pi E C_b}{KLd/A_f} \tag{b}$$

where $A_f = bt$ = area of one flange. For steel, Eq. (b) gives

$$F_{cr} = \frac{20,000 C_b}{KLd/A_f} \tag{5-14a}$$

This formula is plotted in Fig. 5-12a. Also shown is an inelastic-buckling curve BD, for which the formula is the same as for elastic buckling, multiplied by the ratio τ of the inelastic modulus E_t to the elastic modulus E (Art. 5-5). (If plastic-

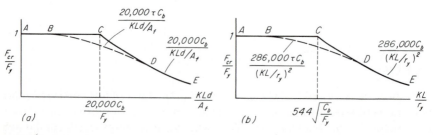

FIGURE 5-12

bending strength is considered, *BD* continues upward to the left of *B* instead of horizontally as shown by *BA*.)

If we neglect the first term in brackets in Eq. (5-4), the critical bending stress is

$$F_{cr} = \frac{M_{x,cr}}{S_x} = C_b \frac{\pi^2}{(KL)^2} \frac{\sqrt{EI_y EC_w}}{S_x} \qquad (c)$$

This equation can be simplified for the equal-flanged I by substituting for C_w its value $d^2 I_y/4$:

$$F_{cr} = C_b \frac{\pi^2 E}{(KL)^2} \frac{I_y d}{2S_x} \qquad (d)$$

Substituting for S_x its value

$$S_x = \frac{I_x}{d/2} = \frac{2A_f(d/2)^2 + t_w d^3/12}{d/2} = d\left(A_f + \frac{A_w}{6}\right) \qquad (e)$$

we get

$$F_{cr} = C_b \frac{\pi^2 E}{(KL)^2} \frac{I_y/2}{A_f + A_w/6} \qquad (f)$$

The last fraction in the equation can be written simply as r_y^2, where r_y is the radius of gyration about the y axis of the T consisting of the compression flange and one-sixth of the web. Therefore,

$$F_{cr} = \frac{\pi^2 E C_b}{(KL/r_y)^2} \qquad (g)$$

For steel, Eq. (*g*) gives

$$F_{cr} = \frac{286,000 C_b}{(KL/r_y)^2} \qquad (5\text{-}14b)$$

This formula is plotted in Fig. 5-12*b*. Also shown is an inelastic-buckling curve, which is obtained in the same manner as for Fig. 5-12*a*. If we use the larger of the values of F_{cr} by Eqs. (5-14) we will underestimate the true critical stress by as much as 29 percent. This is the case if the two are equal, say each equals X, since the correct stress is then $\sqrt{X^2 + X^2} = X\sqrt{2}$ and the error is $(X\sqrt{2} - X)/X\sqrt{2} = 0.29$. Although the equations are derived for equal-flanged beams, they can be used for unequal-flanged beams provided r_y in Eq. (5-14*a*) and A_f in Eq. (5-14*b*) are based on the compression flange. This is equivalent to substituting for the unequal-flanged beam one with equal flanges, each of which is identical to the compression flange of the unequal-flanged beam. It is shown in Art. 5-10 that this procedure gives a good approximation to the critical compressive bending stress.

It was pointed out in Art. 5-4 that Eq. (5-4) applies to any cross section symmetrical about the axis perpendicular to the plane of loading. Thus, it applies to the channel. Equations (5-14) can also be used for the channel, even though they were derived from Eq. (5-4) for the equal-flanged I. The results are conservative.

Since Eq. (5-14a) is derived from the first term in Eq. (5-4) and Eq. (5-14b) from the second, a better value of F_{cr} is given by

$$F_{cr} = \sqrt{F_{cr(1)}^2 + F_{cr(2)}^2} \qquad (5\text{-}15)$$

where $F_{cr(1)}$ and $F_{cr(2)}$ denote the critical stresses by Eqs. (5-14). This formula is used in the Canadian Standard S16.1-1974 (Ref. 11).

Specification Formulas

To facilitate comparison in the discussion to follow, specification formulas are written in forms which are not necessarily the same as in the specifications.

AISC/ASD. The allowable bending stress F_b for channels and I-shaped members of steels with $F_y \leq 65$ ksi, supported against lateral buckling and bent about the major axis, are as follows:

Compact section: $\qquad\qquad\qquad F_b = 0.66F_y \qquad\qquad\qquad (5\text{-}16a)$

Noncompact section: $\qquad\qquad\quad F_b = 0.60F_y \qquad\qquad\qquad (5\text{-}16b)$

If $65/\sqrt{F_y} \leq b_f/2t_f \leq 95/\sqrt{F_y}$:

$$F_b = \begin{cases} F_y\left(0.79 - 0.002\,\dfrac{b_f}{2t_f}\,\sqrt{F_y}\right) & \text{(rolled shapes)} & 5\text{-}16c \\[2ex] F_y\left(0.79 - 0.002\,\dfrac{b_f}{2t_f}\,\sqrt{\dfrac{F_y}{k_c}}\right) & \text{(built-up members)} & (5\text{-}16d) \end{cases}$$

where $\qquad\qquad\qquad k_c = \begin{cases} 1 & \text{if } \dfrac{h}{t} \leq 70 \\[2ex] \dfrac{4.05}{(h/t)^{0.46}} & \text{if } \dfrac{h}{t} > 70 \end{cases}$

Notation in Eqs. (5-16) is as follows:

b_f = flange width
t_f = flange thickness
h = distance between adjacent lines of fasteners, or clear distance between flanges if welds are used
t = web thickness

The ratio 1.1 of the allowable stresses $0.66F_y$ and $0.60F_y$ is approximately equal to the smallest of the shape factors for standard I-shaped members. It should be noted that Eqs. (5-16b), (5-16c), and (5-16d) are not applicable if $b_f/2t_f$ exceeds 95.

Elements as slender as this buckle at stresses less than the yield stress and are treated as described in Chap. 10.

The value of k_c in Eq. (5-16d) is derived from results of tests on built-up members with relatively slender webs and flanges, in which the compression flange was braced against lateral buckling.[12] However, premature buckling in the form of a rotation of the flange and web about their intersection occurred, and Eq. (5-16d) gives the reduced value of F_b to conform to the test results. There is an unexplained discontinuity in the value of k_c at $h/t = 70$. Thus, for $F_y = 36$ ksi and $b/2t_f = 15$, $k_c = 1$ and $F_b = 21.9$ ksi if $h/t = 70$, but for $h/t = 70.1$, $k_c = 0.57$ and $F_b = 19.9$ ksi.

Lateral support may be continuous, as for a beam which is the direct support of a floor, or by bracing members. Lateral-support spacing for beams designed for $F_b = 0.66F_y$ must not exceed the smaller of the values of L_c given by the following:

$$L_c = \frac{76b_f}{\sqrt{F_y}} \tag{5-17a}$$

$$L_c = \frac{20,000}{F_y d/A_f} \tag{5-17b}$$

Equation (5-17a) is equivalent to a limiting value of L/r_y, since, for I-shaped members, $r_y = b/\sqrt{12}$. Thus

$$L_c = \frac{76b_f}{\sqrt{F_y}} = \frac{263r_y}{\sqrt{F_y}}$$

This value of L_c gives a point well to the left of C in Fig. 5-12b. Equation (5-17b) is derived from Eq. (5-14a) with $C_b = K = 1$. Thus, it corresponds to point C in Fig. 5-12a, so the inelastic-buckling curve BD is not taken into account.

Values of L_c from Eqs. (5-17) are tabulated in the AISC/ASD Manual's beam-selection tables for $F_y = 36$ ksi and 50 ksi.

A larger allowable stress, $F_b = 0.75F_y$, is permitted for compact I shapes bent about the minor axis. This is in recognition of the fact that such bending is equivalent to the bending of two rectangles (the flanges) about their major axes, for which the shape factor is 1.5, compared to the 1.10 to 1.15 shape factor for I shapes bent about their major axis. If $65/\sqrt{F_y} \le b_f/2t_f \le 95/\sqrt{F_y}$, the allowable stress is given by

$$F_b = F_y\left(1.075 - 0.005\frac{b_f}{2t_f}\sqrt{F_y}\right) \ge 0.60F_y \tag{5-18}$$

The allowable stress $0.75F_y$ also applies to round and square bars and to solid rectangular bars bent about the minor axis.

Lateral bracing is not required for members bent about the minor axis provided they are loaded through the shear center.

Beams with $L \geq L_c$. Allowable bending stresses for members with laterally unsupported lengths greater than those given by Eqs. (5-17) are based on the bending strengths given by ACE of Fig. 5-12a and $ABDE$ of Fig. 5-13.

In Fig. 5-13b CDE is a plot of Eq. (g) with $K = 1$ and r_y replaced by r_T, where r_T is the radius of gyration of a section consisting of the compression flange and one-third the compression web area. This definition enables the formula to be used for beams with unequal flanges, as explained in Art. 5-10. These are elastic-buckling values. Inelastic buckling is represented by ABD, where BD is a segment of the parabola GBD with vertex at G where $F_{cr} = \frac{10}{9}F_y$. The abscissa $\sqrt{510,000C_b/F_y}$ is found by equating the Euler stress to $\frac{5}{9}F_y$. The abscissa $\sqrt{102,000C_b/F_y}$ is found similarly by equating F_{cr} in the inelastic-buckling formula shown in the figure to F_y. The allowable stress $A'B'D'E'$ is obtained by multiplying the ordinates to $ABDE$ by 0.6 to give a factor of safety of 1.67. The results are

$$
F_b = \begin{cases}
0.6F_y & 0 \leq \dfrac{L}{r_T} \leq \sqrt{\dfrac{102,000C_b}{F_y}} & (5\text{-}19a) \\[3mm]
\left[\dfrac{2}{3} - \dfrac{F_y(L/r_T)^2}{1530 \times 10^3 C_b}\right]F_y & \sqrt{\dfrac{102,000C_b}{F_y}} \leq \dfrac{L}{r_T} \leq \sqrt{\dfrac{510,000C_b}{F_y}} & (5\text{-}19b) \\[3mm]
\dfrac{170,000C_b}{(L/r_T)^2} & \sqrt{\dfrac{510,000C_b}{F_y}} \leq \dfrac{L}{r_T} & (5\text{-}19c)
\end{cases}
$$

These equations are not to be used for channels, because the formula for C_w, which is involved in their derivation, is quite different for channels than for I-shaped members (Fig. 4-46).

Allowable stresses corresponding to ACE of Fig. 5-12a are found by multiplying the ordinates by 0.6 to give a factor of safety of 1.67. This means that

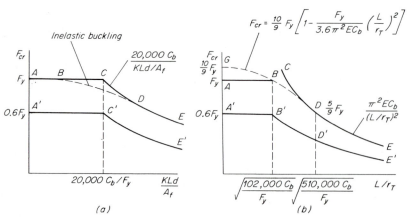

FIGURE 5-13

inelastic buckling is not considered. The results are

$$F_b = \begin{cases} 0.6F_y & 0 \le \dfrac{Ld}{A_f} \le \dfrac{20{,}000C_b}{F_y} & \text{(5-20a)} \\[3mm] \dfrac{12{,}000C_b}{Ld/A_f} & \dfrac{Ld}{A_f} \ge \dfrac{20{,}000C_b}{F_y} & \text{(5-20b)} \end{cases}$$

Equation (5-20b) is to be used only if the compression flange is solid and approximately rectangular in cross section and is not smaller in area than the tension flange. It is applicable for channels in bending about the major axis as well as for I-shaped members.

The larger of the values of F_b given by Eq. (5-20b) and the applicable Eq. (5-19) should be used, as was explained earlier. C_b in these equations is given by Eq. (5-5a). However, the specification requires that C_b be taken as unity if the bending moment at any point within the unbraced length is larger than that at both ends of the unbraced length.

The largest lateral-brace spacing L for which the allowable stress $0.6F_y$ may be used is given by Eqs. (5-19a) and (5-20b):

$$L = r_T\sqrt{\dfrac{102{,}000C_b}{F_y}} \qquad\qquad \text{(5-21a)}$$

$$L = \dfrac{20{,}000C_b}{F_y d/A_f} \qquad\qquad \text{(5-21b)}$$

Since Eqs. (5-19) and (5-20) underestimate the stress that can be allowed, the larger value of L from Eqs. (5-21) should be used. This value is tabulated, for $C_b = 1$, as L_u in the AISC/ASD Manual's beam-selection tables for $F_y = 36$ and 50 ksi.

Since each of Eqs. (5-20) and the applicable Eq. (5-19) is a conservative value of the allowable stress, the specification allows a higher value if it can be "justified on the basis of a more precise analysis," and in the commentary suggests using an equivalent radius of gyration [for example, Eq. (5-7a)] to obtain the higher value. With this procedure the allowable stress may be obtained from Eqs. (5-19), using L/r_{eq} for L/r_T, and Eqs. (5-20) should be ignored.

AASHTO. For beams in bridges designed on the basis of elastic behavior, the allowable tensile bending stress is $0.55F_y$. The allowable compressive bending stress is also $0.55F_y$, provided there is continuous lateral support. This gives a factor of safety of 1.82 with respect to the yield moment M_y. The allowable bending stress for beams not continuously supported laterally is

$$F_b = 0.55F_y\left[1 - \frac{1}{2}\left(\frac{L/r_y}{C_c}\right)^2\right] \qquad\qquad \text{(5-22)}$$

where r_y is the radius of gyration of the compression flange. This is the SSRC formula, Eq. (4-16), with a factor of safety of $1/0.55 = 1.82$. Thus, it corresponds to *ABD* of Fig. 5-12*b*, with a proportional limit of $F_y/2$. These specifications set a limiting length for beams, shown below, such that the elastic-buckling curve *DE* of Fig. 5-12*b* is not needed. Furthermore, there is no formula corresponding to Fig. 5-12*a*, so only Eq. (5-22) is used. Using $r_y^2 = b^2/12$, where *b* is the width of the flange of an I, Eq. (5-22) is put in terms of L/b. For example, for A36 steel,

$$F_b = 20,000 - 7.5\left(\frac{L}{b}\right)^2 \text{ psi} \qquad 0 \le \frac{L}{b} \le 36 \tag{5-23}$$

The upper limit $L/b = 36$ is found by substituting $b = r\sqrt{12}$ into $L/r = C_c$. Thus, $L/r = \pi\sqrt{2E/F_y} = 126$ for $E = 29,000$ ksi, and $L/b = 126/\sqrt{12} = 36$.

AREA. For beams in bridges designed on the basis of elastic behavior, the allowable tensile bending stress is $0.55F_y$. The allowable compressive bending stress is also $0.55F_y$, provided there is continuous lateral support. This gives a factor of safety of 1.82 with respect to the yield moment M_y.

Allowable bending stresses are based on Eq. (*b*) and a parabola representing the inelastic buckling range of Eq. (*d*). With *K* and C_b taken as 1, Eq. (*d*) can be written

$$F_{cr} = \frac{\pi^2 E}{L^2} \frac{I_y d}{2S_x} = \frac{\pi^2 E}{L^2} \frac{d^2 I_y}{4I_x} = \frac{\pi^2 E}{4} \frac{r_y^2}{L^2} \frac{d^2}{r_x^2} \tag{h}$$

The ratio r_x/d is fairly constant for the I and can be taken at 0.4. Thus, Eq. (*h*) becomes

$$F_{cr} = \frac{\pi^2 E}{0.64(L/r_y)^2} \tag{i}$$

The inelastic-buckling parabola is taken tangent to Eq. (*i*) at $F_y/2$ and with its vertex at F_y at $L/r_y = 0$. The abscissa of the point of tangency is found by equating F_{cr} in Eq. (*i*) to $F_y/2$. This gives

$$\frac{L}{r_y} = \pi\sqrt{\frac{2E}{0.64F_y}} = 1.25C_c \tag{j}$$

where $C_c = \pi\sqrt{2E/F_y}$, the abscissa of the corresponding point of the column critical-stress curve. Using a factor of safety of 1.8, the allowable stress F_b becomes

$$F_b = 0.55F_y\left[1 - 0.32\left(\frac{L/r_y}{C_c}\right)^2\right] \tag{5-24a}$$

The specification defines r_y as the radius of gyration of a section comprising the compression flange and the part of the web in compression.

With $E = 29,000$ ksi and *K* and C_b taken as 1 in Eq. (*b*), a factor of safety of 1.8 gives the allowable stress

$$F_b = \frac{10,500}{Ld/A_f} \le 0.55F_y \tag{5-24b}$$

A_f in this formula is defined as the area of the smaller flange. Both Eqs. (5-24a) and (5-24b) can be used for unequal-flanged beams no matter which flange is in compression. As in the AISC/ASD specification, the larger value is used because each is based on an underestimation of the critical stress. Since AREA limits L/r_y to not more than the value by Eq. (j), an allowable-stress formula corresponding to Eq. (i) is not needed. Thus, the specification is based on ACE of Fig. 5-12a [Eq. (5-24b)] and ABD of Fig. 5-12b [Eq. (5-24a)].

Aluminum. Because of the nonlinear stress-strain curve for aluminum, the bending stress computed by $f = M/S$ can exceed the yield strength (0.2 percent offset) appreciably before the beam yields significantly. This can be taken into account in computing the yield moment M_y by using a shape factor. Thus, the shape factor for the I bent about the major axis is 1.07, while that for bending about the minor axis is 1.30. Shape factors for other cross sections are given in Ref. 13. It should be noted that these are yield-moment shape factors rather than plastic-moment shape factors. However, aluminum beams also develop the plastic moment, provided they are proportioned to preclude local buckling and lateral buckling. Shape factors for plastic moment are the same as those discussed in Art. 5-2. Allowable bending stresses to be used in evaluating the moment capacity are suggested in Ref. 14. These allowable stresses take the plastic-moment shape factor into account.

Lateral-buckling strength can be determined from column-buckling formulas by using the equivalent radius of gyration r_{eq}, Eq. (5-7a). Thus, the lateral-buckling strength of 6061-T6 beams is found by substituting the equivalent slenderness ratio into Eqs. (4-59) and (4-60) of Art. 4-23.

A good approximation to r_{eq} for the I and the channel is given by[13]

$$\frac{KL}{r_{eq}} = \frac{L}{1.2r_y} \tag{5-25}$$

where r_y is the radius of gyration of the cross section about the y axis. This approximation becomes quite conservative for KL/r_{eq} greater than about 50, so Eqs. (5-7) should be used for such cases.

The Aluminum Association uses factors of safety of 2.2 for bridges and 1.95 for buildings.[14]

Box sections. Because of the superior torsional stiffness of the box, lateral-torsional buckling of box-section beams is not usually a problem. Since the effect of nonuniform warping is small, the warping constant C_w may be neglected in computing the equivalent radius of gyration [Eqs. (5-7)]. The value of J is given by Eq. (4-45) as

$$J = \frac{4A^2}{\int ds/t}$$

The AREA specification gives for the box an equivalent slenderness ratio L/r which is based on Eq. (5-7a). The AISC/ASD specification does not require lateral-torsional buckling to be investigated for box sections with depth less than six times the width. In order to attain the fully plastic moment, for box sections with depth less than six times the width and with flange thickness less than two times the web thickness the limiting spacing of the braces is

$$L_b \leq \left(1950 + 1200\, \frac{M_1}{M_2}\right) \frac{b}{F_y}$$

but need not be less than $1200b/F_y$.

> **Example 5-8-1 (AISC/ASD).** Select the lightest W section to carry a uniformly distributed live load of 1.5 kips/ft and a dead load (not including the weight of the beam) of 0.50 kips/ft on a 30-ft simply supported span. The beam does not have continuous lateral support and so must be braced. Assuming that it will be braced to satisfy compact-section requirements, design the beam using (a) $F_y = 36$ ksi and (b) $F_y = 65$ ksi.

Solution

(a) Assume beam weight 60 lb/ft.

$$\text{Design load} = 1.5 + 0.50 + 0.06 = 2.06 \text{ kips/ft}$$

$$M = \tfrac{1}{8}wL^2 = \tfrac{1}{8} \times 2.06 \times 30^2 = 231.8 \text{ ft·kips}$$

$$F_b = 0.66 \times 36 = 24 \text{ ksi} \qquad \text{(The rounded value is customary)}$$

$$S_x = \frac{231.8 \times 12}{24} = 115.9 \text{ in}^3$$

From the AISC Manual's beam-selection table, the lightest W shape for this section modulus is the W21 × 62 ($S_x = 127$ in^3). This is obviously more than adequate to compensate for the 2 lb/ft difference between the beam weight and its assumed value, 60 lb/ft.

Deflection. The ratio L/d for the W21 is $\frac{360}{21} = 17.1$, which is less than the deflection-control value $\frac{480}{24} = 20$ given by Eq. (5-13). Therefore, deflection is less than the allowable value.

Lateral support. The spacing of the bracing must not exceed the smaller of the values by Eqs. (5-17):

$$L_c = \frac{76b_f}{\sqrt{F_y}} = \frac{76 \times 8.24}{\sqrt{36}} = 104 \text{ in} = 8.7 \text{ ft}$$

$$L_c = \frac{20{,}000}{36 \times 4.14} = 134 \text{ in} = 11.2 \text{ ft}$$

Values of L_c are listed in the Manual's beam-selection table.

Use W21 × 62 with three braces spaced at 7.5 ft.

(*b*) Assume beam weight 40 lb/ft.

$$\text{Design load} = 1.5 + 0.50 + 0.04 = 2.04 \text{ kips/ft}$$

$$M = \tfrac{1}{8}wL^2 = \tfrac{1}{8} \times 2.04 \times 30^2 = 229.5 \text{ ft·kips}$$

$$F_b = 0.66 \times 65 = 42.9 \text{ ksi}$$

$$S_x = \frac{229.5 \times 12}{42.9} = 64.2 \text{ in}^3$$

The lightest W shape for this section modulus is the W16 × 40 ($S_x = 64.7$ in^3).

Deflection. The ratio L/d for the W16 is $30 \times \frac{12}{16} = 22.5$. If only the live-load deflection is of concern, Eq. (5-13) should be checked for a stress F_b times the ratio of live load to live load plus dead load, that is, $42.9 \times 1.5/2.04 = 31.5$ ksi. Therefore, from Eq. (5-13), $L/d = 480/31.5 = 15.2$. For the W16, $L/d = 30 \times \frac{12}{16} = 22.5$. Since this exceeds the control value 15.2, a larger section is needed. The next larger, the W18 × 40, turns out to be inadequate. For the next larger, the W21 × 44, we have

$$S_x = 81.6 \text{ in}^3 \qquad f_b = \frac{229.5 \times 12}{81.6} \times \frac{1.5}{2.04} = 24.8 \text{ ksi}$$

$$\frac{L}{d} = \frac{480}{24.8} = 19.4 \text{ allowed} \qquad \frac{L}{d} = \frac{30 \times 12}{21} = 17.1 \text{ actual}$$

Therefore, use W21 × 44.

Lateral support. The total-load bending stress for the W21 × 44 is $f_b = 229.5 \times 12/81.6 = 33.8$ ksi. Since this is less than the maximum allowable, $0.6 \times 65 = 39$ ksi, for noncompact sections, lateral bracing need be spaced only to obtain the necessary allowable stress by Eqs. (5-19) and (5-20).

Try three braces spaced 7.5 ft. Then $C_b = 1.13$ (Table 5-2), and the limiting values of L/r_T for Eqs. (5-19) are the following:

$$\sqrt{\frac{102{,}000 \times 1.13}{65}} = 42.1 \qquad \sqrt{\frac{510{,}000 \times 1.13}{65}} = 94.2$$

For the W21 × 44, $r_T = 1.57$, so $L/r_T = 90/1.57 = 57.3$. Therefore, Eq. (5-19*b*) applies, and

$$F_b = \left(\frac{2}{3} - \frac{65 \times 57.3^2}{1530 \times 10^3 \times 1.13} \right) 65 = 35.3 \text{ ksi}$$

Since this value of F_b exceeds f_b, F_b by Eqs. (5-20) need not be calculated. This is because the *larger* value controls, and since F_b by Eq. (5-19*b*) is larger than f_b, its value by Eqs. (5-20) is immaterial.

Braces need not be equally spaced unless equal spacing is desirable or necessary for other than bracing purposes. For example, try two braces 7 ft apart, equidistant from the beam midspan, which gives end spans of $(30 - 7)/2 = 11.5$ ft. The end moments for the center (7-ft) segment are

$$M = \frac{w}{2}x(L - x) = \frac{2.04}{2} \times 11.5(30 - 11.5) = 217.0 \text{ ft·kips}$$

$$f_b = \frac{217.0 \times 12}{81.6} = 31.9 \text{ ksi}$$

$$\frac{L}{r_T} = \frac{7 \times 12}{1.57} = 53.5 \qquad C_b = 1 \text{ (Table 5-2)}$$

$$\sqrt{\frac{102,000 \times 1}{65}} = 39.6 \qquad \sqrt{\frac{510,000 \times 1}{65}} = 88.6$$

Therefore, Eq. (5-19b) applies, and

$$F_b = \left(\frac{2}{3} - \frac{65 \times 53.5^2}{1530 \times 10^3}\right)65 = 35.4 \text{ ksi} > 33.8$$

Equations (5-20) need not be checked.

For the 11.5-ft end segments, $M_1 = 0$ and $M_2 = 217.0$ ft·kips in Eq. (5-5a), from which $C_b = 1.75$:

$$\frac{L}{r_T} = \frac{11.5 \times 12}{1.57} = 87.9$$

$$\sqrt{\frac{102,000 \times 1.75}{65}} = 52.4 \qquad \sqrt{\frac{510,000 \times 1.75}{65}} = 117$$

$$F_b = \left(\frac{2}{3} - \frac{65 \times 87.9^2}{1530 \times 10^3 \times 1.75}\right)65 = 31.2 \text{ ksi} \approx 31.9$$

Equations (5-20) need not be checked. The beam is adequate with only two lateral braces spaced 7 ft apart equidistant from the center.

Example 5-8-2 (AISC/ASD). Determine the lightest W section to support concentrated loads of 1.4 kips dead load and 4.0 kips live load at each quarter point of a 60-ft simple span. The beam is laterally supported at the ends and at the points of load application. Live-load deflection is limited to $\frac{1}{300}$ of the span. $F_y = 36$ ksi.

Solution. The moment of inertia required to satisfy the deflection limit can be calculated from Eq. (5-11a). However, the value of Δ by this equation should be multiplied by 0.95 for the case of three concentrated loads (Table 5-4). The maximum moment due to the concentrated loads of $1.4 + 4.0 = 5.4$ kips is

$$M = 1\tfrac{1}{2} \times 5.4 \times 30 - 5.4 \times 15 = 162 \text{ ft·kips}$$

and Eq. (5-11a) yields

$$I = 0.95 \times \frac{5}{48}\frac{ML^2}{E\Delta} = 0.95 \times \frac{5}{48} \times \frac{162 \times 12(60 \times 12)^2}{29,000(60 \times 12/300)} = 1433 \text{ in}^4$$

From the Manual's moment-of-inertia selection tables we find the lightest section to be the W24 × 62, for which $I = 1550$ in^4.

From Eq. (5-17a)

$$L_c = \frac{76b_f}{\sqrt{F_y}} = \frac{76 \times 7.04}{\sqrt{36}} = 89 \text{ in}$$

Since this is less than the 15-ft spacing of the lateral supports, Eqs. (5-19) and (5-20) apply. Equation (5-17b) need not be checked since the smaller of the values by Eq. (5-17) applies. To determine which of Eqs. (5-19) should be used, we compute, using $C_b = 1.13$ from Table 5-2,

$$\sqrt{\frac{102,000 \times 1.13}{36}} = 57 \qquad \sqrt{\frac{510,000 \times 1.13}{36}} = 127$$

Therefore, since $L/r_T = 180/1.71 = 105$, Eq. (5-19b) applies:

$$F_b = \left(\frac{2}{3} - \frac{36 \times 105^2}{1530 \times 10^3 \times 1.13}\right)36 = 15.7 \text{ ksi}$$

From Eq. (5-20b) with $Ld/A_f = 180 \times 5.72 = 1030$,

$$F_b = \frac{12,000 \times 1.13}{1030} = 13.2 \text{ ksi}$$

The beam-weight moment is

$$M = \tfrac{1}{8}wL^2 = \tfrac{1}{8} \times 0.062 \times 60^2 = 27.9 \text{ ft·kips}$$

Therefore $M = 162 + 28 = 190$ ft·kips and

$$f_b = \frac{M}{S_x} = \frac{190 \times 12}{131} = 17.4 \text{ ksi}$$

This exceeds the allowable stress, which is the larger of the two values of F_b calculated above.

The next larger section shown in the moment-of-inertia table, the W24 × 68, for which the calculations will not be shown, is adequate.

If a deflection check is not needed, an initial sizing of the beam can be based on M_p. The initial selection is then checked as above and revised if it proves to be inadequate. Also, the Manual contains design-moment charts from which the lightest section to satisfy a specific moment requirement can be determined. However, since the charts are based on $C_b = 1$, if $C_b > 1$ the section so indicated may be larger than necessary and it, or, say, the next lighter section shown in the chart should be checked until a suitable one is found.

Example 5-8-3. Using a factor of safety of 1.6, determine the allowable moment for an A36 12 × 6 × $\tfrac{1}{4}$ structural tube spanning 24 ft and supporting a concentrated load P at midspan. The ends are simply supported in the x and y directions, and there is lateral support at midspan.

Solution. From the AISC/ASD Manual, $I_y = 55.2$ in⁴ and $S_x = 26.9$ in³. From Eq. (4-45) the torsional stiffness is

$$J = \frac{4 \times 11.75^2 \times 5.75^2}{2(11.75/0.25 + 5.75/0.25)} = 130 \text{ in}^4$$

Since there is lateral support at midspan, each half of the beam corresponds to case 2 of Table 5-1, with $K = 1$. Thus, $1.77 \leq C_b \leq 1.86$. [Using $M_1/M_2 = 0$ in Eq. (5-5a), we get $C_b = 1.75$.] Then from Eq. (5-7a), with $C_w = 0$,

$$r_{eq}^2 = 1.75 \frac{\sqrt{55.2 \times 0.04 \times 130 \times 144^2}}{26.9}$$

$$r_{eq} = 12.6 \text{ in} \qquad \frac{KL}{r_{eq}} = 11.4$$

This is so small that no reduction in stress for lateral buckling need be made. Therefore,

$$M_{all} = \frac{F_y S_x}{1.6} = 36 \times \frac{26.9}{1.6} = 605 \text{ in·kips}$$

5-9   LOAD AND RESISTANCE FACTOR DESIGN OF BEAMS

The AISC/LRFD specification design strength of beams is $\phi_b M_n$, where $\phi_b = 0.90$ and M_n = nominal moment as defined in the following formulas. Either elastic analysis or plastic analysis may be used to determine the moments which must be provided for, but allowable unbraced lengths are more restricted for plastic analysis. Unbraced-length formulas in this article are for beams whose moments have been determined by elastic analysis. Unbraced lengths for plastic analysis are discussed in Art. 9-12.

Compact sections. Figure 5-14 shows the variation in the nominal moment of compact sections (defined in Table 5-3) with the laterally unbraced length L_b. L_p in this figure is the largest unbraced length that enables the plastic moment M_p to be developed when $C_b = 1$, while L_r is the unbraced length, for $C_b = 1$, at which the elastic lateral-torsional buckling regime begins. The coefficient C_b is given by Eq. (5-5c).

The moment M_n for $L_p \leq L_b \leq L_r$ is assumed to vary linearly with L_b according to the formula

$$M_n = C_b \left[M_p - (M_p - M_r) \frac{L_b - L_p}{L_r - L_p} \right] \leq M_p \qquad (5\text{-}26)$$

The limiting elastic-buckling moment M_r is given by

$$M_r = S_x(F_y - F_r) \qquad (5\text{-}27)$$

where S_x = elastic section modulus
$\quad F_r$ = residual stress in compression flange
$\qquad$ = 10 ksi for rolled shapes and 16.5 ksi for welded shapes

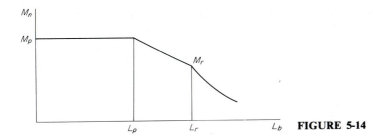

FIGURE 5-14

The length L_p for I-shaped members and channels bent about the major axis is given by

$$L_p = \frac{300 r_y}{\sqrt{F_{yf}}} \tag{5-28}$$

where F_{yf} = flange yield stress.

Solution of Eq. (5-3) for the spacing L_r corresponding to $M_{x,cr} = M_r = S_x(F_y - F_r)$ yields

$$L_r = \frac{r_y \pi}{S_x(F_y - F_r)} \sqrt{\frac{EGJA}{2}} \left[1 + \sqrt{1 + \frac{4C_w}{I_y}\left(\frac{S_x}{GJ}\right)^2 (F_y - F_r)^2} \right]^{1/2} \tag{5-29a}$$

In the specification this equation is given in the form

$$L_r = \frac{r_y X_1}{F_{yw} - F_r} \sqrt{1 + \sqrt{1 + X_2(F_{yw} - F_r)^2}} \tag{5-29b}$$

where $X_1 = \dfrac{\pi}{S_x} \sqrt{\dfrac{EGJA}{2}}$

$$X_2 = 4\frac{C_w}{I_y}\left(\frac{S_x}{GJ}\right)^2$$

Values of X_1 and X_2 for all W shapes are tabulated in part 1 of the LRFD Manual and of L_p and L_r for W shapes with $F_y = 36$ ksi and 50 ksi commonly used as beams in part 3.

M_n for members of compact section with $L_b > L_r$ is given for I-shaped members, including singly symmetric ones with the compression flange larger than the tension flange, and for channels loaded in the plane of the web by Eq. (5-4), which is written in the form

$$M_n = M_{cr} = \frac{C_b S_x X_1 \sqrt{2}}{L_b/r_y} \sqrt{1 + \frac{X_1^2 X_2}{2(L_b/r_y)^2}} \le C_b M_r \le M_p \tag{5-30}$$

where X_1 and X_2 are the same as for Eq. (5-29b).

Plots of Eqs. (5-26) and (5-30) for a W18 × 50 of A36 steel are shown in Fig. 5-15. The upper limit of M_n is M_p as is indicated by the formulas, in this case 303 ft·kips. It will be noted that, for the larger values of C_b, the inelastic-buckling regime, given by Eq. (5-26), disappears.

The limiting length L_p of Eq. (5-28) that enables the plastic moment to be developed for the uniform-moment case, and the corresponding length $L_c = 76b_f/\sqrt{F_y}$ of the AISC/ASD specification [Eq. (5-17a)] are about the same, which can be shown as follows. The value of r_y for I shapes varies from about $0.21b_f$ to $0.25b_f$ (Table A-1). Substituting the average of these values into Eq. (5-28) yields $L_p = 69b_f/\sqrt{F_{yf}}$, which is roughly the same as the ASD value. Of course, this is to be expected. However, there is a significant difference in the way these two limits are applied. The capacity of beams, or of beam segments between points of lateral braces, to develop the plastic moment for other than the uniform-moment case is accounted for in the LRFD specification by multiplying the uniform-moment value by C_b [Eq. (5-26)]. The ASD specification does not contain such a provision; instead, the moment M_p is permitted only for spacing of lateral braces of $76b_f/\sqrt{F_y}$ no matter what the shape of the moment diagram. This inconsistency gives an LRFD-based design for nonuniform moments a considerable advantage over an ASD-based design for cases where $C_b > 1$, as is evident from Fig. 5-15.

The laterally unbraced length L_b which enables the nominal moment M_n to be developed can be determined as a function of C_b by solving Eq. (5-26) for L_b. The result is

$$L_b = L_p + \frac{(L_r - L_p)(C_b M_p - M_n)}{C_b(M_p - M_r)} \tag{5-31}$$

This equation can be used to determine the required spacing of lateral-bracing members.

Box sections. For compact-section box beams loaded in the plane of symmetry and bent about the major axis, the limiting lengths L_p and L_r and the moment M_r

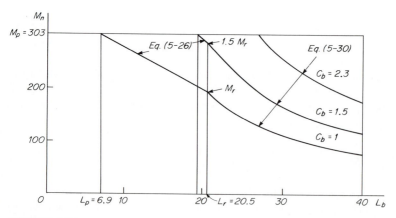

FIGURE 5-15

to be used in Eq. (5-26) are given by

$$L_p = \frac{3750r_y}{M_p} \sqrt{JA}$$

$$L_r = \frac{57,000r_y}{M_r} \sqrt{JA}$$

$$M_r = (F_{yw} - F_r)S_x$$

where J = torsion constant
 A = cross-sectional area
 S_x = major-axis section modulus

For symmetric box sections with $L_b > L_r$ the critical moment is given by

$$M_{cr} = \frac{57,000C_b}{L_b/r_y} \sqrt{JA}$$

Noncompact sections. Beams with noncompact elements must be checked for lateral-torsional buckling, as explained above, if they do not have continuous lateral support, and, in addition, whether or not they have such support, for local buckling of the elements. The local-buckling nominal strength is given by

$$M_n = M_p - (M_p - M_r) \frac{\lambda - \lambda_p}{\lambda_r - \lambda_p} \tag{5-32}$$

where λ, λ_r, and λ_p are defined as follows for I-shaped members and channels loaded in the plane of the web:

For flange local buckling: $\quad \lambda = \dfrac{b_f}{2t_f}$

$$\lambda_p = \frac{65}{\sqrt{F_{yf}}}$$

$$\lambda_r = \begin{cases} \dfrac{141}{\sqrt{F_{yw} - 10}} & \text{for rolled beams} \\[4mm] \dfrac{106}{\sqrt{F_{yw} - 16.5}} & \text{for welded shapes} \end{cases}$$

For web local buckling: $\quad \lambda = \dfrac{h_c}{t_w}$

$$\lambda_p = \begin{cases} \dfrac{640}{\sqrt{F_{yf}}} \\[4mm] \dfrac{970}{\sqrt{F_{yf}}} \end{cases}$$

F_{yf} and F_{yw} in these formulas are the flange yield stress and web yield stress, respectively. Of course, the smallest of M_n as determined by lateral buckling or local buckling applies.

For beams with standard W sections, web local buckling never determines M_n and flange local buckling determines it for only a few shapes, as was pointed out in Art. 5-7.

Slender elements. In the design of beams with element slendernesses exceeding the values for noncompact elements, given in Table 5-3, the postbuckling strength of such elements is taken into account. Design procedures are discussed in Chap. 10.

Example 5-9-1 (AISC/LRFD). Select the lightest W section to carry a uniformly distributed live load of 1.5 kips/ft and a dead load (not including the weight of the beam) of 0.50 kips/ft on a 30-ft simply supported span. The beam does not have continuous lateral support and so must be braced. Design the beam using (a) $F_y = 36$ ksi and (b) $F_y = 65$ ksi.

Solution
(a) Assume beam weight 60 lb/ft.

$$\text{Dead load} = 0.50 + 0.06 = 0.56 \text{ kips/ft, load factor } 1.2$$

$$M_D = 1.2 \times 0.56 \times \frac{30^2}{8} = 75.6 \text{ ft·kips}$$

$$\text{Live load} = 1.5 \text{ kips/ft, load factor } 1.6$$

$$M_L = 1.6 \times 1.5 \times \frac{30^2}{8} = 270 \text{ ft·kips}$$

$$M_D + M_L = 346 \text{ ft·kips} = \phi_b M_p = 0.9 M_p$$

$$M_p = 384 \text{ ft·kips}$$

$$Z_x = \frac{384 \times 12}{36} = 128 \text{ in}^3$$

From the AISC Manual's beam-selection table, the lightest W shape for this plastic section modulus is the W24 × 55 ($Z_x = 134 \text{ in}^3$).

Lateral support. The spacing of the braces is given by Eq. (5-28).

$$L_p = \frac{300 r_y}{\sqrt{F_{yf}}} = \frac{300 \times 1.34}{\sqrt{36}} = 67.0 \text{ in} = 5.58 \text{ ft}$$

This value of L_p would require braces at 5-ft intervals. However, the section modulus of the W24 × 55 (134 in³) exceeds the required value 128 in³, so M_n from Eq. (5-26) may be sufficient with a larger bracing interval. Values of ϕM_r and L_r (also of ϕM_p and L_p) are given in the AISC Manual's table of uniform-load constants for beams:

$$\phi M_p = 362 \text{ ft·kips} \qquad M_p = \frac{362}{0.9} = 402 \text{ ft·kips}$$

$$\phi M_r = 222 \text{ ft·kips} \qquad M_r = \frac{222}{0.9} = 247 \text{ ft·kips}$$

$$L_p = 5.6 \text{ ft} \qquad L_r = 16.6 \text{ ft}$$

Try braces at 7.5 ft, for which $C_b = 1.06$ (Table 5-2). Then from Eq. (5-26)

$$M_n = 1.06\left(402 - 155 \frac{7.5 - 5.6}{16.6 - 5.6}\right) = 398 \text{ ft·kips}$$

Therefore, $M_n = 398$ ft·kips, which exceeds the required value, 384 ft·kips. Use the W24 × 55 with braces spaced 7.5 ft.

Deflection. The LRFD specification does not prescribe or suggest limiting values of deflection. Instead, it is left to the designer to decide, in the absence of any required specification or code limit, what deflection is acceptable. Assume in this example that the acceptable live-load deflection is $L/300$. This is the Canadian Code[11] suggested live-load deflection limit for simple-span members supporting floors and gives the same results as Eq. (5-13) if F_b is taken as the live-load stress.

$$\Delta = \frac{5}{384} \frac{WL^3}{EI} = \frac{5}{384} \times \frac{1.5 \times 30 \times 360^3}{29,000 \times 1350} = 0.70 \text{ in}$$

$$\frac{\Delta}{L} = \frac{0.70}{360} = \frac{1}{515} < \frac{1}{300} \qquad \text{O.K.}$$

(b) Assume beam weight 40 lb/ft.

Dead load $= 0.50 + 0.04 = 0.54$ kips/ft, load factor 1.2

$$M_D = 1.2 \times 0.54 \times \frac{30^2}{8} = 72.9 \text{ ft·kips}$$

Live load $= 1.5$ kips/ft, load factor 1.6

$$M_L = 1.6 \times 1.5 \times \frac{30^2}{8} = 270 \text{ ft·kips}$$

$$M_D + M_L = 343 \text{ ft·kips} = \phi_b M_p = 0.9 M_p$$

$$M_p = 381 \text{ ft·kips}$$

$$Z_x = \frac{381 \times 12}{65} = 70.4 \text{ in}^3$$

From the AISC Manual's beam-selection table, the lightest W shape for this plastic section modulus is the W16 × 40 ($Z_x = 72.9 \text{ in}^3$).

Deflection. I_x for the W16 × 40 is 518 in⁴. Then

$$\Delta = \frac{5}{384} \frac{WL^3}{EI} = \frac{5}{384} \times \frac{1.5 \times 30 \times 360^3}{29,000 \times 518} = 1.82 \text{ in}$$

$$\frac{\Delta}{L} = \frac{1.82}{360} = \frac{1}{198} > \frac{1}{300} \qquad \text{N.G.}$$

The required moment of inertia for $\Delta/L = \frac{1}{300}$ is $518 \times \frac{300}{198} = 785$ in⁴. The lightest W for this moment of inertia is the W21 × 44.

Lateral support. Since the beam cross section was determined by deflection rather than strength, the allowable unbraced length is given by Eq. (5-31). Values of L_p and L_r are not tabulated for $F_y = 65$ ksi in the AISC Manual, so they must be calculated from Eqs. (5-28) and (5-29b). The following properties of the W21 × 44 are from the AISC Manual:

$$S_x = 81.6 \text{ in}^3 \qquad r_y = 1.26 \text{ in}$$

$$Z_x = 95.4 \text{ in}^3 \qquad X_1 = 1550 \text{ ksi}$$

$$I_y = 20.7 \text{ in}^4 \qquad X_2 = 0.0366 \text{ (ksi)}^{-2}$$

Then

$$M_p = 95.4 \times 65 = 6201 \text{ in·kips}$$

$$M_r = 81.6(65 - 10) = 4488 \text{ in·kips} \qquad [\text{Eq. (5-27)}]$$

$$L_p = \frac{300 \times 1.26}{\sqrt{65}} = 46.9 \text{ in} \qquad [\text{Eq. (5-28)}]$$

$$L_r = \frac{1.26 \times 1550}{65 - 10} \sqrt{1 + \sqrt{1 + 0.0366(65 - 10)^2}} = 120.8 \text{ in} \qquad [\text{Eq. (5-29b)}]$$

The required nominal moment M_n is given by

$$M_n = \frac{M_D + M_L}{0.9} = \frac{72.9 + 270}{0.9} = 381 \text{ ft·kips} = 4572 \text{ in·kips}$$

Then from Eq. (5-31), with $C_b = 1$,

$$L_b = 46.9 + \frac{(120.8 - 46.9)(6201 - 4572)}{6201 - 4488} = 117 \text{ in} = 9.8 \text{ ft}$$

If they need not be spaced uniformly, lateral braces at 10.5 ft from each end give a central unbraced length of 9 ft. This gives three panels, 10.5, 9.0, and 10.5 ft, so $C_b = 1$ for the central panel, as was assumed. The 10.5-ft end segments will be more than adequate, since for them Eq. (5-5c) gives $C_b = 1.45$.

Example 5-9-2 (AISC/LRFD). Determine the lightest W section to support concentrated loads of 1.4 kips dead load and 4.0 kips live load at each quarter point of a 60-ft simple span. The beam is laterally supported at the ends and at the points of load application. Deflection due to the service live load is limited to $\frac{1}{300}$ of the span. $F_y = 36$ ksi.

Solution. The moment of inertia required to satisfy the deflection limit can be calculated from Eq. (5-11a). However, the value of Δ by this equation should be multiplied by 0.95 for the case of three concentrated loads (Table 5-4). The maximum moment due to the concentrated loads of $1.4 + 4.0 = 5.4$ kips is

$$M = 1\tfrac{1}{2} \times 5.4 \times 30 - 5.4 \times 15 = 162 \text{ ft·kips}$$

and Eq. (5-11a) yields

$$I = 0.95 \times \frac{5}{48} \frac{ML^2}{E\Delta} = 0.95 \times \frac{4}{48} \times \frac{162 \times 12(60 \times 12)^2}{29,000(60 \times \frac{12}{300})} = 1433 \text{ in}^4$$

From the Manual's moment-of-inertia selection tables we find the lightest section to be the W24 × 62, for which $I = 1550 \text{ in}^4$.

The factored design load at each of the three load points is $1.2(1.4 + 0.062 \times 15) + 1.6 \times 5.4 = 11.4$ kips, so

$$M = 1\tfrac{1}{2} \times 11.4 \times 30 - 11.4 \times 15 = 342 \text{ ft·kips}$$

From Eq. (5-28)

$$L_p = \frac{300 r_y}{\sqrt{F_{yf}}} = \frac{300 \times 1.38}{\sqrt{36}} = 69 \text{ in}$$

Since this is less than the 15-ft spacing of the lateral supports, Eq. (5-26) applies. The following properties of the W24 × 62 are from the Manual's load-factor design selection table:

$$L_p = 5.8 \text{ ft} \qquad\qquad L_r = 17.2 \text{ ft}$$
$$\phi M_p = 413 \text{ ft·kips} \qquad \phi M_r = 255 \text{ ft·kips}$$

Since $\phi = 0.90$,

$$M_p = \frac{413}{0.9} = 459 \text{ ft·kips}$$

$$M_r = \frac{255}{0.9} = 283 \text{ ft·kips}$$

From Eq. (5-5c), $C_b = 1.11$. Then from Eq. (5-26)

$$M_n = 1.11\left(459 - 176 \frac{15 - 5.8}{17.2 - 5.8}\right) = 352 \text{ ft·kips} < M_p = 459$$

The design strength is $\phi M_n = 0.9 \times 352 = 316$ ft·kips. Since this is less than the required value of 342 ft·kips, the W24 × 62 is inadequate.

The next lightest shape with $I > 1433$ is the W21 × 68. The following properties of the W21 × 68 are from the Manual's load-factor design selection table:

$$L_p = 7.5 \text{ ft} \qquad\qquad L_r = 22.8 \text{ ft}$$
$$\phi M_p = 432 \text{ ft·kips} \qquad \phi M_r = 273 \text{ ft·kips}$$

Since $\phi = 0.90$,

$$M_p = \frac{432}{0.9} = 480 \text{ ft·kips}$$

$$M_r = \frac{273}{0.9} = 303 \text{ ft·kips}$$

From Eq. (5-5c), $C_b = 1.11$. Then from Eq. (5-26)

$$M_n = 1.11\left(480 - 177\,\frac{15 - 7.5}{22.8 - 7.5}\right) = 436 \text{ ft·kips} < M_p = 480$$

The design strength is $\phi M_n = 0.9 \times 436 = 393$ ft·kips. Since this exceeds the required value of 342 ft·kips, the W21 × 68 is adequate.

If a deflection check is not needed, an initial sizing of the beam can be based on M_p. The initial selection is then checked as above and revised if it proves to be inadequate. Also, the Manual contains design-moment charts, based on $C_b = 1$, which may be used. If C_b is greater than unity, the charts must be entered with a moment equal to the required value divided by C_b. For this example $C_b = 1.11$, and entering the chart with $\phi M_n = 342/1.11 = 308$ ft·kips and an unbraced length of 15 ft, we find the lightest section to be the W21 × 62.

DP5-9-1 (AISC/ASD) and DP5-9-2 (AISC/LRFD): Floor Framing for Tall Building

Beams for a typical floor of the building of DP4-15-3 (AISC/ASD) and DP4-15-4 (AISC/LRFD) are designed in these examples. A complete floor plan and a general description of the framing are given in DP4-15-3 (AISC/ASD) and DP4-15-4 (AISC/LRFD). The floor, which is a cellular steel deck weighing 42 psf, spans the 15 ft between joists. The live load is 80 psf. The frame is designed for simple-beam framing connections; wind bracing is provided in the walls around the service area. Lateral support of the beams is provided by the floor system. The following comments are intended to clarify computations identified by the corresponding letters on the design sheets and apply to both examples except where noted otherwise.

a. Live-load reduction is discussed in Art. 1-4. The American Standard Building Code reduction is 0.08 percent/ft² of supported area in excess of 150 ft², but not to exceed $R = 23.1(1 + D/L)$ percent.

b. Girder G1 carries a concentrated load at midspan, which is the sum of the two 30-ft joist reactions. Therefore, $M = PL/4$.

c. Girder G2 supports the end reactions of two 30-ft joists at the one-third points on the 45-ft span. Therefore, each girder reaction is equal to one of the loads. The moment is equal to the reaction times 15 ft.

d. **ASD.** Although a W33 × 118 is the lightest W section that will provide the required capacity, a W24 × 146 is chosen in order to keep the same depth for the girders.

   LRFD. Although a W30 × 116 is the lightest W section that will provide the required capacity, a W24 × 131 is chosen in order to keep the same depth for the girders.

e. Spandrel S1 supports one story of wall, which weighs 25 psf, in addition to its share of floor. The floor height is 13 ft, and the wall is assumed to weigh 25 psf.

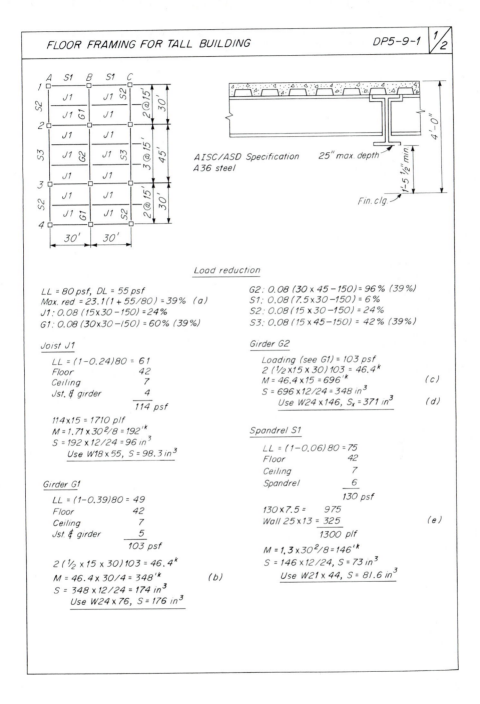

FLOOR FRAMING FOR TALL BUILDING   DP5-9-1 $\frac{1}{2}$

AISC/ASD Specification   25" max. depth
A36 steel

Load reduction

LL = 80 psf, DL = 55 psf
Max. red = 23.1(1 + 55/80) = 39% (a)
J1: 0.08 (15×30 −150) = 24%
G1: 0.08 (30×30 −150) = 60% (39%)

G2: 0.08 (30 × 45 −150) = 96% (39%)
S1: 0.08 (7.5×30 −150) = 6%
S2: 0.08 (15 × 30 −150) = 24%
S3: 0.08 (15 × 45 −150) = 42% (39%)

Joist J1

   LL = (1−0.24)80 = 61
   Floor   42
   Ceiling   7
   Jst. & girder   4
                    114 psf

114×15 = 1710 plf
M = 1.71 × 30²/8 = 192$^{\prime k}$
S = 192 × 12/24 = 96 in³
   Use W18×55, S = 98.3 in³

Girder G1

   LL = (1−0.39)80 = 49
   Floor   42
   Ceiling   7
   Jst. & girder   5
                    103 psf

2 (½ × 15 × 30) 103 = 46.4^k
M = 46.4 × 30/4 = 348$^{\prime k}$ (b)
S = 348 × 12/24 = 174 in³
   Use W24×76, S = 176 in³

Girder G2

   Loading (see G1) = 103 psf
   2 (½×15 × 30) 103 = 46.4^k
   M = 46.4 ×15 = 696$^{\prime k}$ (c)
   S = 696 ×12/24 = 348 in³
     Use W24×146, S_x = 371 in³   (d)

Spandrel S1

   LL = (1−0.06)80 = 75
   Floor   42
   Ceiling   7
   Spandrel   6
                   130 psf

130 ×7.5 =   975
Wall 25 ×13 = 325   (e)
              1300 plf

M = 1.3 ×30²/8 = 146$^{\prime k}$
S = 146 ×12/24, S = 73 in³
     Use W21×44, S = 81.6 in³

Fin. clg.

FLOOR FRAMING FOR TALL BUILDING — DP5-9-1 — 2/2

Spandrel S2

LL = (1−0.24)80 =	61
Floor	42
Ceiling	7
Spandrel	4
	114 psf

Joist reaction = $\frac{1}{2} \times 114 \times 15 \times 30 = 25.7^k$

$M = 25.7 \times 30/4 = 193'^k$ (f)

Wall 325 plf (see S1)

$M = 0.325 \times 30^2/8 = 37'^k$

$M_{total} = 193 + 37 = 230'^k$

$S = 230 \times 12/24 = 115$ in^3

Use W24×55, $S = 114$ in^3 (g)

Spandrel S3

Loading (see G1) = 102 psf

Joist reaction = $\frac{1}{2} \times 102 \times 15 \times 30 = 23.0^k$

$M = 23.0 \times 15 = 345'^k$ (h)

Wall = 325 plf (see S1)

$M = 0.325 \times 45^2/8 = 82'^k$

$M_{total} = 345 + 82 = 427'^k$

$S = 427 \times 12/24 = 214$ in^3

Use W24×94, $S = 222$ in^3

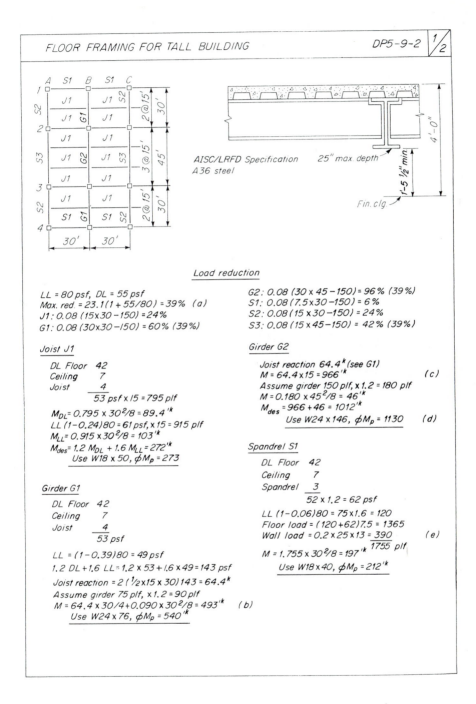

AISC/LRFD Specification   25" max. depth
A36 steel

Load reduction

$LL = 80\ psf,\ DL = 55\ psf$
$Max.\ red. = 23.1(1 + 55/80) = 39\%$ (a)
$J1: 0.08\ (15 \times 30 - 150) = 24\%$
$G1: 0.08\ (30 \times 30 - 150) = 60\%\ (39\%)$

$G2: 0.08\ (30 \times 45 - 150) = 96\%\ (39\%)$
$S1: 0.08\ (7.5 \times 30 - 150) = 6\%$
$S2: 0.08\ (15 \times 30 - 150) = 24\%$
$S3: 0.08\ (15 \times 45 - 150) = 42\%\ (39\%)$

Joist J1

DL Floor	42
Ceiling	7
Joist	4
	53 psf x 15 = 795 plf

$M_{DL} = 0.795 \times 30^2/8 = 89.4\ ^{'k}$
$LL\ (1 - 0.24)80 = 61\ psf,\ x\ 15 = 915\ plf$
$M_{LL} = 0.915 \times 30^2/8 = 103\ ^{'k}$
$M_{des} = 1.2\ M_{DL} + 1.6\ M_{LL} = 272\ ^{'k}$
    Use W18 x 50, $\phi M_p = 273$

Girder G1

DL Floor	42
Ceiling	7
Joist	4
	53 psf

$LL = (1 - 0.39)80 = 49\ psf$
$1.2\ DL + 1.6\ LL = 1.2 \times 53 + 1.6 \times 49 = 143\ psf$
Joist reaction = $2\ (^1/2 \times 15 \times 30)\ 143 = 64.4^k$
Assume girder 75 plf, x 1.2 = 90 plf
$M = 64.4 \times 30/4 + 0.090 \times 30^2/8 = 493\ ^{'k}$ (b)
    Use W24 x 76, $\phi M_p = 540\ ^{'k}$

Girder G2

Joist reaction 64.4^k *(see G1)*
$M = 64.4 \times 15 = 966\ ^{'k}$
Assume girder 150 plf, x 1.2 = 180 plf
$M = 0.180 \times 45^2/8 = 46\ ^{'k}$
$M_{des} = 966 + 46 = 1012\ ^{'k}$
    Use W24 x 146, $\phi M_p = 1130$ (d)

Spandrel S1

DL Floor	42
Ceiling	7
Spandrel	3
	52 x 1.2 = 62 psf

$LL\ (1 - 0.06)80 = 75 \times 1.6 = 120$
Floor load = $(120 + 62)7.5 = 1365$
Wall load = $0.2 \times 25 \times 13 = 390$ (e)
    1755 plf
$M = 1.755 \times 30^2/8 = 197\ ^{'k}$
    Use W18 x 40, $\phi M_p = 212\ ^{'k}$

FLOOR FRAMING FOR TALL BUILDING | *DP5-9-2* | 2/2

Spandrel S2

DL Floor 42
Ceiling $\underline{7}$
$\qquad \overline{49} \times 1.2 = 59\,psf$

LL = $(1-0.24)80 = 61$, $\times 1.6 = 98\,psf$
Joist reaction = $(59+98)\,15 \times 30/2 = 35.3^k$
$M = 35.3 \times 30/4 = 265^{'k}$
Wall (see S1) 390
Spandrel: $1.2 \times 50 = \underline{60}$
$\qquad\qquad\quad \overline{450}\,plf$
$M = 0.450 \times 30^2/8 = 51^{'k}$
$M_{des} = 265 \times 51 = 316^{'k}$
$\qquad$ Use W24×55, $\phi M_p = 362^{'k}$

                                                  (f)

Spandrel S3

DL Floor 42
Ceiling 7
Joist $\underline{2}$
$\qquad \overline{51} \times 1.2 = 61\,psf$

LL $(1-0.39)80 = 49$, $\times 1.6 = 78\,psf$
Joist reaction = $(78 \times 61)\,15 \times 30/2 = 31.3^k$
$M = 31.3 \times 15 = 470^{'k}$
Wall (see S1) 390
Spandrel $1.2 \times 84 = \underline{101}$
$\qquad\qquad\qquad \overline{491}\,plf$
$M = 0.491 \times 45^2/8 = 124^{'k}$
$M_{des} = 470 + 124 = 594^{'k}$
$\qquad$ Use W24×84, $\phi M_p = 605^{'k}$

                                                  (h)

f. Spandrel S2 carries the end reaction of one joist plus one story of wall. The joist reaction produces the moment $PL/4$, while the wall is a uniform loading.

g. **ASD.** Although $S_x = 114$ for the W24 × 55, which is less than the 115 required, a recalculation of the moment taking into account the actual weight of the spandrel beam results in a total moment of 228 ft·kips for which the W24 × 55 is adequate.

h. Spandrel S3 carries the reactions of two joists plus one story of wall. The joists are at the one-third points of the span, so the moment is the end reaction times 15 ft.

DP5-9-3 (AISC/ASD) and DP5-9-4 (AISC/LRFD): Crane for Shop Building

In these examples the bridge and the runway girder for a pendant-operated traveling crane are designed. The hoist shown in the figure is supported by a trolley riding the bridge, which is supported on trucks that can be moved along the girder. The lifting capacity is 5000 lb. The following comments are intended to clarify the correspondingly lettered computations in the examples and apply to both except where noted otherwise.

a. Impact for crane bridges is not specified by AISC. Some manufacturers use 15 percent.

b. The estimated weight of the bridge beam is 40 plf.

c. Because the bridge beam is not supported against lateral buckling, an ASD allowable stress or an LRFD design moment cannot be determined directly. The ASD allowable-moment charts and the LRFD design-moment charts can be used for this situation. The charts do not include the S shape, so the specification lateral-buckling provisions, ASD Eqs. (5-19) and (5-20) and LRFD Eq. (5-30) must be used.

The S shape is chosen, rather than a W, because standard trolley wheels are made to fit the 1:6 slope of the inside face of the flange of the S. W's have slopes ranging from 0 to 1:20, depending on the manufacturer.

d. Equation (5-11a) is used to calculate the deflection/span ratio Δ/L. Deflection due only to live load, excluding impact, needs to be considered. The factor 0.8 corrects the formula to account for the fact that the load is concentrated at the center instead of being uniformly distributed (Table 5-4). The AISC specifications do not prescribe deflection limits for crane bridges and girders. The Canadian standard[11] suggests a limit of $\frac{1}{600}$ for runway girders for cranes with a capacity less than 25 tons but makes no recommendation for deflection limits of crane bridges.

e. The loads are positioned for maximum moment at midspan. The absolute maximum moment occurs when the two wheels are positioned so that the resultant of the two, and one of the two, are equidistant from midspan. The difference between the two maximums is negligible in this case.

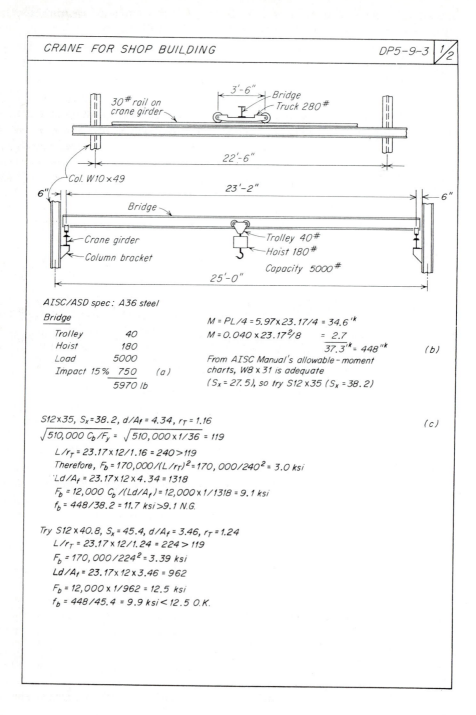

CRANE FOR SHOP BUILDING DP5-9-3 1/2

30$^{\#}$ rail on crane girder

3'-6"

Bridge Truck 280$^{\#}$

22'-6"

Col. W10×49

23'-2"

6"

Bridge

Crane girder

Column bracket

Trolley 40$^{\#}$

Hoist 180$^{\#}$

Capacity 5000$^{\#}$

25'-0"

AISC/ASD spec: A36 steel

Bridge

Trolley	40
Hoist	180
Load	5000
Impact 15%	750	(a)
	5970 lb

$M = PL/4 = 5.97 \times 23.17/4 = 34.6^{\prime k}$

$M = 0.040 \times 23.17^2/8 \quad = 2.7$

$\overline{37.3^{\prime k}} = 448^{\prime\prime k}$ (b)

From AISC Manual's allowable-moment charts, W8×31 is adequate $(S_x = 27.5)$, so try S12×35 $(S_x = 38.2)$

S12×35, $S_x = 38.2$, $d/A_f = 4.34$, $r_T = 1.16$ (c)

$\sqrt{510,000\,C_b/F_y} = \sqrt{510,000 \times 1/36} = 119$

  $L/r_T = 23.17 \times 12/1.16 = 240 > 119$

  Therefore, $F_b = 170,000/(L/r_T)^2 = 170,000/240^2 = 3.0$ ksi

  $Ld/A_f = 23.17 \times 12 \times 4.34 = 1318$

  $F_b = 12,000\,C_b/(Ld/A_f) = 12,000 \times 1/1318 = 9.1$ ksi

  $f_b = 448/38.2 = 11.7$ ksi > 9.1 N.G.

Try S12×40.8, $S_x = 45.4$, $d/A_f = 3.46$, $r_T = 1.24$

  $L/r_T = 23.17 \times 12/1.24 = 224 > 119$

  $F_b = 170,000/224^2 = 3.39$ ksi

  $Ld/A_f = 23.17 \times 12 \times 3.46 = 962$

  $F_b = 12,000 \times 1/962 = 12.5$ ksi

  $f_b = 448/45.4 = 9.9$ ksi < 12.5 O.K.

| CRANE FOR SHOP BUILDING | DP5-9-3 | 2/2 |

Bridge (continued)

Deflection:

$M = 5 \times 23.17 \times 12/4 = 348^{"k}$

$$\frac{\Delta}{L} = 0.8 \frac{5}{48} \frac{ML}{EI} = 0.8 \times \frac{5}{48} \frac{348 \times 23.17 \times 12}{29,000 \times 272} = \frac{1}{979} \qquad (d)$$

Runway girder

Hoist, etc.	$(5970 - 750) \times 22.17/23.17$	$= 4994$	(e)
Truck		$= 280$	
Bridge	40.8×12	$= 490$	
Impact	$(4994 + 280 + 490)0.10$	$= \underline{576}$	(f)
		6340 lb	

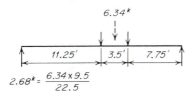

6.34^{k}

$\overbrace{\qquad 11.25' \qquad}\ \ \overbrace{3.5'}\ \ \overbrace{\quad 7.75' \quad}$

$2.68^{k} = \dfrac{6.34 \times 9.5}{22.5}$

$M = 2.68 \times 11.25 \qquad = 30.2$

$M = 0.040 \times 22.5^{2}/8 = \underline{2.5}$

$\qquad\qquad\qquad\qquad 32.7^{'k} = 392^{"k} \qquad (g)$

From AISC Manual's allowable-moment charts, W8 × 28 is adequate.
But L/d = 22.5 × 12/8 = 34 for this section, so deflection may be excessive.

Try W12 × 30, S_x = 38.6, d/A_f = 4.30, r_T = 1.73

$L/r_T = 22.5 \times 12/1.73 = 156 > 119$

$F_b = 170,000/156^2 = 6.99$ ksi

$Ld/A_f = 22.5 \times 12 \times 4.30 = 1161$

$F_b = 12,000/1161 = 10.3$ ksi

$f = 392/38.6 = 10.2$ ksi < 10.3 O.K. $\qquad (h)$

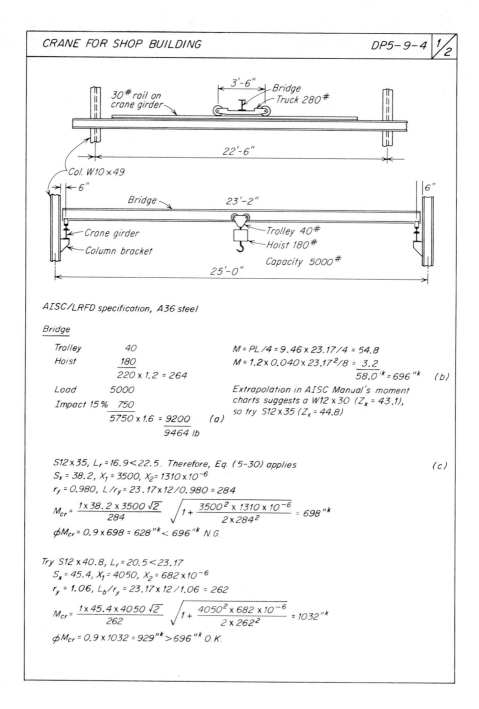

CRANE FOR SHOP BUILDING — DP5-9-4 1/2

30# rail on crane girder

3'-6" Bridge Truck 280#

22'-6"

Col. W10×49

6"

Bridge — 23'-2"

6"

Crane girder — Trolley 40#

Column bracket — Hoist 180#

Capacity 5000#

25'-0"

AISC/LRFD specification, A36 steel

Bridge

Trolley	40	$M = PL/4 = 9.46 \times 23.17/4 = 54.8$
Hoist	180	$M = 1.2 \times 0.040 \times 23.17^2/8 = \underline{3.2}$
	$220 \times 1.2 = 264$	$58.0^{'k} = 696^{''k}$ (b)
Load	5000	Extrapolation in AISC Manual's moment
Impact 15%	750	charts suggests a W12×30 ($Z_x = 43.1$),
	$5750 \times 1.6 = \underline{9200}$ (a)	so try S12×35 ($Z_x = 44.8$)
	9464 lb	

S12×35, $L_r = 16.9 < 22.5$. Therefore, Eq. (5-30) applies.   (c)

$S_x = 38.2$, $X_1 = 3500$, $X_2 = 1310 \times 10^{-6}$

$r_y = 0.980$, $L/r_y = 23.17 \times 12/0.980 = 284$

$$M_{cr} = \frac{1 \times 38.2 \times 3500 \sqrt{2}}{284} \sqrt{1 + \frac{3500^2 \times 1310 \times 10^{-6}}{2 \times 284^2}} = 698^{''k}$$

$\phi M_{cr} = 0.9 \times 698 = 628^{''k} < 696^{''k}$ N.G.

Try S12×40.8, $L_r = 20.5 < 23.17$

$S_x = 45.4$, $X_1 = 4050$, $X_2 = 682 \times 10^{-6}$

$r_y = 1.06$, $L_b/r_y = 23.17 \times 12/1.06 = 262$

$$M_{cr} = \frac{1 \times 45.4 \times 4050 \sqrt{2}}{262} \sqrt{1 + \frac{4050^2 \times 682 \times 10^{-6}}{2 \times 262^2}} = 1032^{''k}$$

$\phi M_{cr} = 0.9 \times 1032 = 929^{''k} > 696^{''k}$ O.K.

Bridge (continued)

Deflection:

$M = 5 \times 23.17 \times 12/4 = 348''^k$

$$\frac{\Delta}{L} = 0.8 \times \frac{5}{48} \frac{ML}{EI} = 0.8 \times \frac{5}{48} \times \frac{348 \times 23.17 \times 12}{29,000 \times 272} = \frac{1}{979}$$

(d)

Runway girder

Factored bridge reaction on girder

Hoist, etc. 1.6 (220 + 5000) 22.17/23.17 = 7992   (e)

Bridge $1.6 \times 40 \times 23.17/2 = \underline{741}$

                          8733

               Impact 10% $\underline{873}$ (f)

                       9606 lb

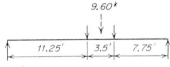

9.60ᵏ

| 11.25' | 3.5' | 7.75' |

$4.05^k = 9.60 \times 9.5/22.5$

$M = 4.05 \times 11.25 \quad\quad = 45.6$

$M = 1.2 \times 0.04 \times 22.5^2/8 = \underline{3.0}$

                    $48.6'^k = 583''^k$ (g)

Extrapolation in moment charts suggests a W12 x 30

W12 x 30: $L_r = 19.1 < L_b = 22.5$. Use Eq. (5-30)

$S_x = 38.6$, $X_1 = 2090$, $X_2 = 7950 \times 10^{-6}$

$r_y = 1.52$, $L/r_y = 22.5 \times 12/1.52 = 178$

$$M_{cr} = \frac{1 \times 38.6 \times 2090\sqrt{2}}{178} \sqrt{1 + \frac{2090^2 \times 7950 \times 10^{-6}}{2 \times 178^2}} = 797''^k$$

$\phi M_{cr} = 0.9 \times 797 = 717''^k > 583$ O.K.   (h)

f. AISC prescribes 10 percent impact for runway girders of pendant-operated cranes.

g. Since the trolley is not motor-driven, no lateral forces on the runway due to acceleration and deceleration of the load on the bridge are assumed. Examples where such forces are considered are given in DP5-19-1 and DP5-19-2.

h. The deflection/span ratio of the bridge beam is well within acceptable limits, and since the runway-girder moment and span are of the same order of magnitude as those of the bridge beam, deflection of the runway girder need not be checked.

5-10 LATERAL BUCKLING OF UNEQUAL-FLANGED BEAMS

Built-up beams are sometimes made with unequal flanges. The compression flange is usually larger. The critical bending stress for lateral-torsional buckling of unequal-flanged beams can be determined by analysis similar to that of Art. 5-4. The results can be put in terms of the equivalent radius of gyration given by Eq. (5-33), provided the cross section is symmetrical about the axis of the web (y axis)[3]

$$r_{eq}^2 = C_b \frac{\sqrt{I_y}}{S_{xc}} \left[C_2 k\sqrt{I_y} + \sqrt{(C_2 k\sqrt{I_y})^2 + C_w + 0.04J(KL)^2} \right] \qquad (5\text{-}33)$$

in which

$$k = y_0 - \frac{1}{2I_x} \int_A (x^2 + y^2)y \, dA \qquad (5\text{-}34)$$

where y_0 = distance from centroid to shear center, positive when shear center lies between centroid and compression flange (Fig. 5-9b)

$\quad\ \ y$ = ordinate with origin at center of gravity, positive when directed toward compression flange

$\quad S_{xc}$ = section modulus for compression flange

For pure bending $C_2 = 1$. Values for two other cases are given in Table 5-1. The critical stress is determined by using KL/r_{eq} in the column formula, as with Eq. (5-7a).

Except for pure bending, Eq. (5-33) applies only if the transverse loads act through the shear center. When this is not the case, the equivalent radius of gyration can be determined by replacing $C_2 k\sqrt{I_y}$ where it occurs by $C_1 g + C_2 k\sqrt{I_y}$, where $C_1 g$ is the same as in Eq. (5-7b).

An approximate solution for the case of pure bending ($C_b = 1$) with $K = 1$ was developed in Ref. 15. It is equivalent to using for k in Eq. (5-33) the distance from the shear center to the middepth as an approximation to the value from Eq. (5-34). Expressed as an equivalent radius of gyration, the result is

$$r_{eq}^2 = \frac{\sqrt{I_y}\sqrt{C_w' + 0.04JL^2} + (I_c - I_t)d/2}{S_{xc}} \qquad (5\text{-}35)$$

where $I_c = y$-axis moment of inertia of compression flange
$I_t = y$-axis moment of inertia of tension flange
$C'_w = (d^2/4)(I_c + I_t)$
$d = $ center-to-center distance of flanges

The warping constant is denoted by C'_w, rather than C_w, because it differs from the theoretically correct value for a beam with unequal flanges (Fig. 4-46). This formula tends to overestimate the buckling stress if $I_c \geq I_t$. Of course, it reduces to Eq. (5-7a) if $I_c = I_t$.

Another approximate solution[16] consists in equating the integral in Eq. (5-34) to zero so that $k = y_0$. This solution tends to underestimate the buckling stress if $I_c \geq I_t$. Still another approximate solution, which gives good results, is obtained by assuming the tension flange to be identical with the compression flange so that the critical stress is based on r_{eq} from Eq. (5-7a).

Example 5-10-1. Compute the critical pure-bending moment for a simply supported A36 WT9 × 35.5 spanning 15 ft. The moment is in the plane of the web, with the flange in compression. Compare the results according to Eq. (5-33) and the approximate solutions by Eqs. (5-35) and (5-7a). Assume the proportional limit to be $F_y/2$, and use the SSRC formula [Eq. (4-16)] for inelastic buckling.

The cross section is shown in Fig. 5-16a. The following properties are from the AISC/ASD Manual:

$$I_x = 78.2 \text{ in}^4 \qquad S_{xt} = 11.2 \text{ in}^3$$

$$I_y = 30.1 \text{ in}^4 \qquad S_{xc} = \frac{78.2}{2.26} = 34.6 \text{ in}^3$$

$$\bar{y} = 2.26 \text{ in}$$

The shear center S is at the intersection of the flange and web centerlines.

Solution according to Eq. (5-33). $K = 1$ for simple y-axis support and $C_b = C_2 = 1$ for pure bending (Table 5-1). The warping stiffness C_w for the tee is small enough to be neglected (Fig. 4-46). The value of J is one-half the value for the W18 × 71 from which the tee is cut. Therefore, $J = 3.48/2 = 1.74 \text{ in}^4$. To evaluate k in Eq. (5-34), we

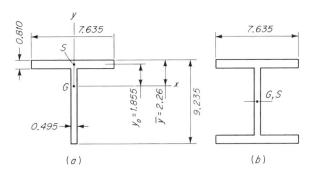

(a)　　　　(b)　　　　**FIGURE 5-16**

need $\int x^2 y \, dA + \int y^3 \, dA$:

Flange: $\displaystyle\int x^2 y \, dA = y_0 \int x^2 \, dA = y_0 I_y = 1.85 \times 30.1$ $\qquad = \quad 57$

Flange: $\displaystyle\int y^3 \, dA = y_0^3 \int dA = 1.85^3 \times 7.635 \times 0.810$ $\qquad = \quad 39$

Web: $\displaystyle\int x^2 y \, dA = \text{negligible}$

Web: $\displaystyle\int y^3 \, dA = t \int y^3 \, dy = t \left.\frac{y^4}{4}\right]_{-6.98}^{1.45} = \frac{0.495}{4}(4 - 2374) = -293$

$$\text{Total} = -197$$

$$k = 1.85 - \frac{-197}{2 \times 78.2} = 1.85 + 1.26 = 3.11$$

$$k\sqrt{I_y} = 3.11\sqrt{30.1} = 17.1$$

$$r_{eq}^2 = \frac{\sqrt{30.1}}{34.6}[17.1 + \sqrt{17.1^2 + 0 + 0.04 \times 1.74 \times 180^2}] = 10.71$$

$$r_{eq} = 3.27$$

$$\frac{KL}{r_{eq}} = \frac{180}{3.27} = 55$$

$$C_c = \pi\sqrt{\frac{2E}{F_y}} = \pi\sqrt{\frac{60,000}{36}} = 128$$

$$F_{cr} = 36\left[1 - \frac{1}{2}\left(\frac{55}{128}\right)^2\right] = 32.7 \text{ ksi}$$

$$M_{cr} = 32.7 S_{xc} = 32.7 \times 34.6 = 1130 \text{ in·kips}$$

$$M = 36 S_{xt} = 36 \times 11.2 = 403 \text{ in·kips}$$

The stress on the tension flange governs.

Approximate solution by Eq. (5-35)

$$C_w' = \frac{8.83^2}{4} \times 30.1 = 587 \text{ in}^6$$

$$r_{eq}^2 = \frac{\sqrt{30.1}\sqrt{587 + 0.04 \times 1.74 \times 180^2 + 30.1 \times 8.83/2}}{34.6} = 12.3$$

$$r_{eq} = 3.51$$

$$\frac{KL}{r_{eq}} = \frac{180}{3.51} = 51.3$$

$$F_{cr} = 36\left[1 - \frac{1}{2}\left(\frac{51.3}{128}\right)^2\right] = 33.1 \text{ ksi}$$

$$M_{cr} = 33.1 S_{xc} = 33.1 \times 34.6 = 1145 \text{ in·kips}$$

Approximate solution by Eq. (5-7a). Here we compute r_{eq} for the symmetrical shape of Fig. 5-16b. The following properties of the cross section are needed:

$$I_x = 2 \times 763.5 \times 0.810 \times 4.21^2 + 0.495 \times \frac{7.62^3}{12} = 219 + 18.3 = 237 \text{ in}^4$$

$$I_y = 2 \times 30.1 = 60.2 \text{ in}^4$$

$$J = 2 \times \tfrac{1}{3} \times 763.5 \times 0.81^3 + \tfrac{1}{3} \times 7.62 \times 0.495^3 = 2.705 + 0.308 = 3.01 \text{ in}^4$$

$$C_w = \frac{8.425^2}{4} \times 60.2 = 1068 \text{ in}^6$$

$$S_x = \frac{237}{4.5} = 51.3 \text{ in}^3$$

$$r_{eq}^2 = \frac{\sqrt{60.2}}{51.3} \sqrt{1068 + 0.04 \times 3.01 \times 180^2} = 10.66$$

$$r_{eq} = 3.27$$

$$\frac{KL}{r_{eq}} = \frac{180}{3.27} = 55$$

$$F_{cr} = 36\left[1 - \frac{1}{2}\left(\frac{55}{128}\right)^2\right] = 32.7 \text{ ksi}$$

$$M_{cr} = 32.7 S_{xc} = 32.7 \times 34.6 = 1130 \text{ in·kips}$$

It should be noted that once the critical stress is found by using the value of r_{eq} for the cross section with equal flanges, the critical moment is found by multiplying this critical stress by the section modulus for the given shape. A disadvantage of this approximate procedure is that the compression-flange section modulus must be computed for both the given shape and its equal-flanged counterpart. However, this is simpler than calculating k.

5-11 CONTINUOUS BEAMS

An important difference between the behavior of statically determinate beams and statically indeterminate beams is discussed in this article. Bending behavior of beam cross sections was discussed in Art. 5-3, where it was shown that, except for strain hardening, the plastic moment is the bending strength of the section. The variation of moment with strain on the extreme fiber is shown in Fig. 5-5. Figure 5-17a shows this variation for the I cross section for both positive and negative bending. For the S or W of the proportions used for beams, the plastic moment M_p averages about 12 percent larger than the moment M_y at the beginning of yield on the extreme fiber. Although residual stresses and other imperfections of the beam lower the proportional limit, so nonlinear behavior begins at a moment less than M_y, $B'C'OCB$ is a good approximation to the bending behavior.

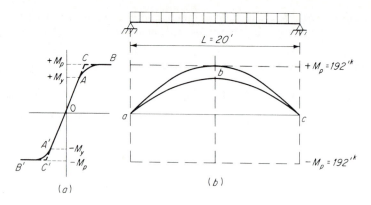

FIGURE 5-17

Figure 5-17b shows a simply supported, uniformly loaded A36-steel beam spanning 20 ft. The cross section is a W16 × 36. The beam is supported against lateral buckling. It is clear that, under gradually increasing load, the parabolic moment diagram abc increases in amplitude until the moment at midspan reaches the value of M_p. The corresponding load W is given by

$$M_p = ZF_y = 64.0 \times \tfrac{36}{12} = 192 \text{ ft·kips}$$

$$W = 8 \times \tfrac{192}{20} = 76.8 \text{ kips}$$

Any attempt to increase the load beyond this value fails because, except for strain hardening, the moment cannot exceed M_p. Thus, if deformation of the beam increases, rotation at midspan continues with no increase in moment, along CB in Fig. 5-17a, and the beam is said to have developed a *plastic hinge*. The plastic hinge differs from a real hinge in that the latter allows free rotation at no load, whereas the former allows free rotation only after the plastic moment has been attained. When the beam develops the plastic hinge at midspan, it is unstable. In this form, it behaves like a linkage, and because of this analogy it is called a *mechanism*.

The midspan deflection of the beam at the instant the mechanism develops is given by

$$\Delta = \frac{5}{384} \frac{WL^3}{EI} = \frac{5 \times 76.8 \times 240^3}{384 \times 30,000 \times 447} = 1.03$$

OAB in Fig. 5-18a shows the assumed variation of load with deflection. In the actual beam, nonlinear behavior begins at the yield moment, which, for the W16 × 36, is $M_y = SF_y = 56.5 \times \tfrac{36}{12} = 169$ ft·kips. The corresponding load W is $76.8 \times \tfrac{169}{192} = 67.6$ kips, for which $\Delta = 0.91$ in.

Figure 5-19a shows the beam of Fig. 5-17a with both ends fixed. As long as stress is proportional to strain, the bending moments at the ends are double the moment at midspan. Thus, under uniformly increasing load the moment diagram

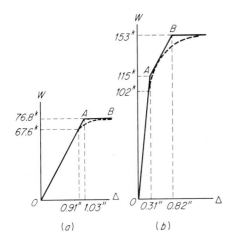

FIGURE 5-18

abc of Fig. 5-19*b* will eventually be reached, where the end moments are represented by point 1 in Fig. 5-19*c* and the midspan moment by point 2. At this stage the beam has a plastic hinge at each support (Fig. 5-19*d*) and corresponds to a simply supported beam carrying the uniformly distributed load and moment M_p at each end. Further increase in load causes the moment at midspan to increase while the end moments hold at M_p. Thus, the vertex of the parabolic moment diagram in Fig. 5-19*b* continues to rise until the midspan moment attains the value M_p. At this stage, the midspan moment is represented by point 2′ and the end moments by 1′ in Fig. 5-19*c*. It is obvious that these moments can increase no further. Therefore, the beam now has three plastic hinges (Fig. 5-19*e*) and is a mechanism, so it has reached its load capacity. This peak load is called the *limit load* or *collapse load*. The collapse-load moment diagram in Fig. 5-19*b* is said to result from a redistribution of the moments *abc* corresponding to elastic behavior.

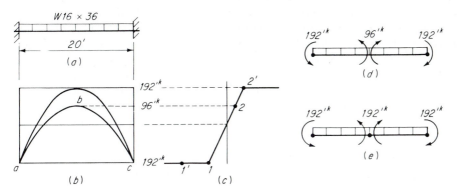

FIGURE 5-19

The load W_1 at which plastic hinges form at the supports is given by

$$W_1 = \frac{12 \times 192}{20} = 115 \text{ kips}$$

The corresponding deflection is

$$\Delta_1 = \frac{W_1 L^3}{384EI} = \frac{115 \times 240^3}{384 \times 30,000 \times 447} = 0.31 \text{ in}$$

The additional positive moment, 96 ft·kips, which produces the third plastic hinge, corresponds to the additional load W_2 on a simply supported beam:

$$W_2 = \frac{8 \times 96}{20} = 38 \text{ kips}$$

The corresponding increment of deflection is

$$\Delta_2 = \frac{5}{384} \frac{W_2 L^3}{EI} = \frac{5 \times 38 \times 240^3}{384 \times 30,000 \times 447} = 0.51 \text{ in}$$

The load-deflection diagram is shown in Fig. 5-18b. As is the case for the simply supported beam, nonlinear behavior begins at the yield moment M_y rather than at the development of the first plastic hinge. Therefore, the load-deflection plot begins to curve at the load 102 kips, as shown in the figure.

It will be noted that the load which initiates yielding of the fixed-end beam is 50 percent larger than that for the simply supported beam. On the other hand, the collapse load of the fixed-end beam is twice that of the simple beam.

Since the W16 × 36 is a compact section in A36 steel, the AISC/ASD allowable bending stress is $0.66F_y$. As pointed out in Art. 5-9, this is 10 percent larger than the allowable stress $0.60F_y$ for noncompact sections and is an allowance for the difference between the yield moment and the plastic moment. In the case of the simple beam of Fig. 5-17, it accounts for the fact that the collapse load is larger than the yield load in the ratio M_p/M_y. In the case of the fixed-end beam, Fig. 5-19a, the ratio of the collapse load to the yield load is $153/102 = 1.50$, part of which is due to the difference between the plastic moment and yield moment and part to the redistribution of moment. To provide for the redistribution of moment, both the AISC/ASD and AISC/LRFD specifications allow compact continuous beams and compact beams rigidly framed to columns to be designed for 90 percent of the negative moments at points of support if these moments are calculated by elastic analysis, provided the maximum positive moment in the span is increased by 10 percent of the average of the negative moments at the ends of the span. While this reduction in moment is not sufficient to account fully for the 33 percent redistribution of the fixed-end beam of Fig. 5-19, the reduction must be small enough to allow for the fact that the effect of redistribution is smaller in many cases. For example, there is no redistribution of moment in the fixed-end beam with a concentrated load at midspan, since the midspan moment and the two end moments are equal $(WL/8)$ from the beginning of loading. Plastic design, which takes rational account of redistribution of moment, is discussed in Chap. 9.

Example 5-11-1 (AISC/ASD). Determine the A36 W shape required for the continuous beam shown in Fig. 5-20. The beam is supported against lateral buckling. The loading consists of a uniform load of 0.4 kips/ft dead load and 1.4 kips/ft live load.

Solution

$$w_{des} = 0.4 + 1.4 = 1.8 \text{ kips/ft}$$

$$-M = \frac{WL^2}{8} = \frac{1.8 \times 20^2}{8} = 90 \text{ ft·kips}$$

$$+M = \frac{9}{128} WL^2 = \frac{9 \times 1.8 \times 20^2}{128} = 50.6 \text{ ft·kips}$$

The beam may be designed for $0.9 \times 90 = 81$ ft·kips negative moment and $50.6 + 0.1(90 + 0)/2 = 55.1$ ft·kips positive moment.

$$F_b = 0.66F_y = 0.66 \times 36 = 24 \text{ ksi}$$

$$S = \frac{81 \times 12}{24} = 40.5 \text{ in}^3$$

Use a W14 × 30.

Example 5-11-2 (AISC/LRFD). Determine the A36 W shape required for the continuous beam shown in Fig. 5-20. The beam is supported against lateral buckling. The loading consists of a uniform load of 0.4 kips/ft dead load and 1.4 kips/ft live load.

Solution

$$w_{des} = 1.2 \times 0.4 + 1.6 \times 1.4 = 2.72 \text{ kips/ft}$$

$$-M = \frac{WL^2}{8} = \frac{2.72 \times 20^2}{8} = 136 \text{ ft·kips}$$

$$+M = \frac{9}{128} WL^2 = \frac{9 \times 2.72 \times 20^2}{128} = 76.5 \text{ ft·kips}$$

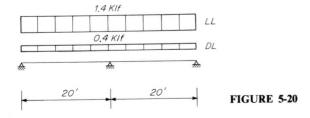

FIGURE 5-20

The beam may be designed for $0.9 \times 136 = 122.4$ ft·kips negative moment and $76.5 + 0.1(136 + 0)/2 = 83.3$ ft·kips positive moment.

$$\phi_b M_n = 122.4 \text{ ft·kips}$$

$$M_n = \frac{122.4}{0.9} = 136 \text{ ft·kips}$$

$$Z = 136 \times \tfrac{12}{36} = 45.3$$

Use a W14 $\times$ 30.

5-12 HOLES IN BEAM FLANGES

Sometimes there must be open holes in beams for piping, conduit, reinforcing steel, etc., or to receive brick and stone anchors and bolts for wood nailing strips. Holes for rivets or bolts to attach reinforcing plates to the flanges, or stiffener angles to the webs, are required occasionally. The effect of such holes on the strength of a beam is not easy to evaluate.

The question of location of the neutral axis for beams with holes in only one flange has been widely discussed. Some writers argue that its position is the same as it would be if there were no holes, while others contend that the beam-flexure formula requires that it lie at the center of gravity of the net section. The latter argument is questionable, since it is the linear distribution of stress assumed by the flexure formula that places the neutral axis at the center of gravity. Stress concentrations at the edges of holes, which were discussed in Art. 3-5, alter the linear distribution of stress and therefore also invalidate the statement $\int y \, da = 0$.

If the neutral axis of a beam does not shift at a cross section containing one or more holes, it is a simple matter to compute either the moment of inertia or the section modulus. From the gross moment of inertia we need only subtract $\sum Ay^2$, where A is the area to be deducted for each hole and y the distance from the neutral axis to the hole. If the holes are only in the flanges, the deduction in section modulus is $\sum Ay^2/c$, but since y is in this case practically the equal of c, we take the deduction as $\sum Ac$. Some designers consider both flanges to have holes even though there may be holes in only one.

The effect of a hole in the tension flange of a beam cannot be deduced from the behavior of tension members. The strength of a steel beam is usually determined by the strength of the compression flange. Thus, it is possible that an open hole in the compression flange affects the strength of a steel beam more than one in the tension flange does. On the other hand, if a hole in the compression flange contains a rivet or bolt, the weakening effect is probably reduced, since the fastener can transmit compression through the hole. Therefore it would seem reasonable up to a point to neglect holes in steel beams, provided there is no question of fatigue. The AISC and AASHTO specifications allow the designer to neglect reduction in area of beam and girder flanges up to 15 percent of the gross area of the flange, provided the holes are for rivets or bolts. If the reduction in area exceeds 15 percent of the gross area of the element, only the excess need be considered. On the other hand, AREA requires full deduction for holes for the computation of the tensile stress. The compressive stress may be calculated based on the moment of inertia of the entire gross section.

Holes in beam webs are discussed in the next article.

5-13 SHEAR IN BEAMS

Shearing stress is seldom a factor in the design of a steel beam, and it is usually calculated, if at all, only as a check after the beam has been designed for bending. Shear may determine the design of beams which support heavy concentrated loads near the reaction points and of very short (small values of L/d) beams uniformly loaded.

Figure 5-21a shows a differential length dz of a beam which is symmetrical about the y axis. Figure 5-21b shows a portion of this element obtained by separation on the plane $abcd$. The resultant forces on the vertical faces of this portion are T and $T + dT$. An equilibrating shear force dT acts in the plane of separation. Division of dT by dz gives the shear q per lineal inch (also called the *shear flow*): $q = dT/dz$. But

$$T = \int_{ab}^{e} f \, dA = \int_{ab}^{e} \frac{M_x y}{I_x} \, dA = \frac{M_x Q_x}{I_x}$$

where $Q_x = \int_{ab}^{e} y \, dA$, so

$$q = \frac{dT}{dz} = \frac{dM_x}{dz} \frac{Q_x}{I_x} = \frac{V_y Q_x}{I_x} \tag{5-36a}$$

Note that the section $abcd$ may be passed through the beam in any direction so long as it is parallel to the z axis and that it may be a zigzag or curved

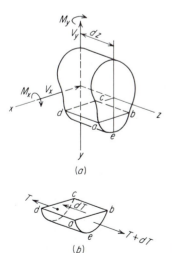

(a)

(b)   **FIGURE 5-21**

section. The shearing stress at any point on *abcd* cannot be determined from this analysis. However, if we assume the shear force dT to be uniformly distributed along the width *ab*, the shear stress f_v is found by dividing q by *ab*. Thus, denoting the width *ab* by t, we get

$$q = f_v t = \frac{V_y Q_x}{I_x} \tag{5-36b}$$

so

$$f_v = \frac{V_y Q_x}{I_x t} \tag{5-36c}$$

By virtue of the equality of horizontal and vertical stresses at a point, Eqs. (5-36) also determine the shearing stresses in the surface *abe* along the line *ab*.

The distribution of shear stresses in the web of a W18 × 50 due to a shear of 50 kips acting in the plane of the web is shown in Fig. 5-22. To calculate the maximum stress, which is at the neutral axis, we use the following value of Q_x in Eq. (5-36c):

$$Q_x = 7.33 \times (8.995 - 2.12) = 50.4 \text{ in}^3$$

This value is determined from the AISC Manual's table of properties of the WT9 × 25, which is one-half of a W18 × 50. The result is

$$f_v = \frac{50 \times 50.4}{800 \times 0.355} = 8.9 \text{ ksi}$$

The shearing stress at the juncture of the flange and web, neglecting the fillet, is obtained by using

$$Q_x = A_f\left(\frac{d}{2} - \frac{t_f}{2}\right)$$

$$= b_f t_f\left(\frac{d}{2} - \frac{t_f}{2}\right)$$

$$= 7.495 \times 0.57\left(8.995 - \frac{0.570}{2}\right)$$

$$= 37.2 \text{ in}^3$$

The result is

$$f_v = \frac{50 \times 37.2}{800 \times 0.355} = 6.55 \text{ ksi}$$

The total shearing force is found by integrating f_v over the area of the web to be 48.5 kips, which is 97 percent of the shearing force.

The shearing stress in W beams loaded in the plane of the web can be approximated satisfactorily by assuming the shear to be distributed uniformly over an area equal to the product of the depth of the beam and the thickness of the web. Thus, in the example above, we get $f_v = 50/(17.99 \times 0.355) = 7.83$ ksi.

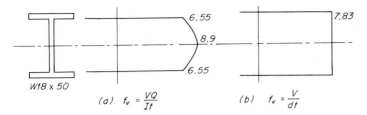

FIGURE 5-22
Shear-stress distribution, W18 × 50, $V = 50$ kips.

This is 12 percent less than the true maximum value. Design-specification stresses are based on the assumption that the shearing stress will be computed in this way.

Holes are often needed in webs of beams in buildings to accommodate ducts, conduits, and other services. In some cases the beam must be reinforced in the vicinity of the hole by welding doubler plates or stiffening angles to the web or by welding flats or bars to the periphery of the hole, while in other cases no reinforcement is required. Procedures have been developed for both elastic and plastic design of beams with unreinforced holes with depths not exceeding six-tenths the depth of the beam.[17] Procedures for the design of reinforcements have also been published.[18] Fatigue tests of beams with rectangular holes in the web have also been made.[19]

Since the web of an I beam is a flat plate, it may buckle at shearing stresses less than the shearing yield strength of the metal. This must be considered in establishing allowable shear stresses. Shear buckling of webs is discussed in the next article.

5-14 SHEAR BUCKLING OF BEAM WEBS

Figure 5-23 shows a flat plate acted upon by shear stresses distributed uniformly along the four boundaries. Because this is a state of pure shear, the shear stresses are equivalent to principal stresses of the same magnitude, one tension and one compression, acting at 45° to the shear stresses. These are shown on an interior element of the web in the figure. Thus, it can be seen that buckling in the form of

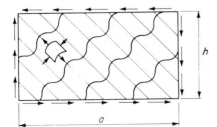

FIGURE 5-23

waves or wrinkles inclined at about 45° may develop. Such shear buckling of the web of an aluminum beam is shown in Fig. 5-24.

The shear stress $F_{v,cr}$ at which buckling of a perfect plate begins is given by

$$F_{v,cr} = \frac{k\pi^2 E}{12(1 - \mu^2)(h/t)^2} \tag{5-37}$$

This is the same as Eq. (4-32), which is derived in Art. 10-1, except that h is used, instead of b, to denote the depth of the web. Values of k are defined by a system of intersecting curves similar to those of Fig. 4-33b. However, the common tangent to these curves is itself a curve, rather than a straight line as in Fig. 4-33b. This tangent curve for a plate with all four edges simply supported is given to good approximation by[1]

$$k = \begin{cases} 4 + \dfrac{5.34}{(a/h)^2} & \dfrac{a}{h} \leq 1 & (5\text{-}38a) \\[3mm] 5.34 + \dfrac{4}{(a/h)^2} & \dfrac{a}{h} \geq 1 & (5\text{-}38b) \end{cases}$$

where a/h is the aspect ratio of the plate (Fig. 5-23). A single formula, valid for all a/h, also gives good results:[20]

$$k = 5 + \frac{5}{(a/h)^2} = 5\left[1 + \left(\frac{h}{a}\right)^2\right] \tag{5-39}$$

Equations (5-38) and (5-39) are compared in Fig. 5-25. Both formulations are

FIGURE 5-24
Shear postbuckling of aluminum-beam web. (*National Aeronautics and Space Administration.*)

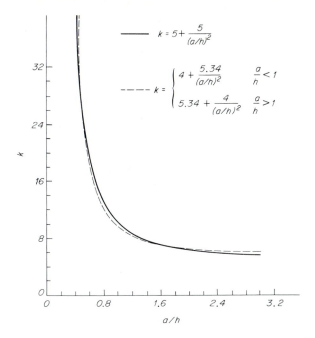

$$k = 5 + \frac{5}{(a/h)^2}$$

$$k = \begin{cases} 4 + \dfrac{5.34}{(a/h)^2} & \dfrac{a}{h} < 1 \\ 5.34 + \dfrac{4}{(a/h)^2} & \dfrac{a}{h} > 1 \end{cases}$$

FIGURE 5-25

used in the several specifications. The AISC/ASD specification uses Eqs. (5-38), while the AISC/LRFD and the AASHTO specifications use Eq. (5-39).

If the four edges are clamped,

$$k = \begin{cases} 5.60 + \dfrac{8.98}{(a/h)^2} & \dfrac{a}{h} \le 1 \qquad\qquad (5\text{-}40a) \\ 8.98 + \dfrac{5.60}{(a/h)^2} & \dfrac{a}{h} \ge 0 \qquad\qquad (5\text{-}40b) \end{cases}$$

We note from Eq. (5-38b) that k is only slightly larger than 5.34 for a hinged-edge plate with large aspect ratio. Thus, if $a/h = 5$, $k = 5.50$. Therefore, the shear-buckling behavior of the webs of rolled beams can be conservatively evaluated by using $k = 5.34$ from Eq. (5-38) or $k = 5$ from Eq. (5-39). In any case, some approximation is involved in using Eq. (5-37), since bending stresses will always be present. However, at the ends of simply supported beams these stresses are small enough to be neglected in investigating shear stresses. Substituting $k = 5.34$, $E = 29{,}000$ ksi, and $\mu = 0.30$ into Eq. (5-37) gives

$$F_{v,cr} = \frac{139{,}000}{(h/t)^2} \text{ ksi} \qquad\qquad (5\text{-}41)$$

ABC of Fig. 5-26 is a graph of Eq. (5-41). When $h/t = 82$, $F_{v,cr} = 21$ ksi, the shearing yield stress of A36 steel. *ABD* shows the behavior of a perfect web. Of course, imperfections lower the proportional limit to a point such as E. Moreover, for small h/t, beam webs can strain harden, as is shown by the test results plotted in the figure.[21] These tests were on welded beams with web slenderness

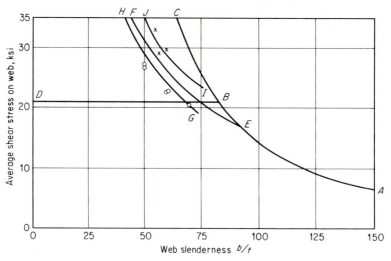

FIGURE 5-26

h/t ranging from 50 to 70. One group consisted of five beams made of steel for which $29.7 \le F_y \le 33.7$ ksi. For the second group (three beams) $43.3 \le F_y \le 49.6$ ksi. Assuming the proportional limit stress F_{vp} to be $0.8F_{vy}$, where F_{vy} is the yield stress in shear, the critical shear stress $F_{v(cr)i}$ in the inelastic and strain-hardening ranges can be expressed by[22]

$$F_{v(cr)i} = \sqrt{0.8 F_{vy} F_{v,cr}} \qquad (5\text{-}42)$$

Line EF in Fig. 5-26 is the plot of Eq. (5-42) for $F_y = 36$ ksi. GH is a plot for $F_y = 32$ ksi, which is the average yield stress for the group of five test specimens mentioned above, while IJ is a plot for $F_y = 47$ ksi, the average yield stress for the group of three.

The shear stresses F_v represented by $DIEA$ in Fig. 5-26 are given by the following equations:

$$F_v = \begin{cases} F_{vy} & 0 < \dfrac{h}{t} < 144\sqrt{\dfrac{k}{F_{vy}}} & (5\text{-}43a) \\[3ex] \dfrac{144}{h/t}\sqrt{kF_{vy}} & 144\sqrt{\dfrac{k}{F_{vy}}} < \dfrac{h}{t} < 181\sqrt{\dfrac{k}{F_{vy}}} & (5\text{-}43b) \\[3ex] \dfrac{26{,}000k}{(h/t)^2} & \dfrac{h}{t} > 181\sqrt{\dfrac{k}{F_{vy}}} & (5\text{-}43c) \end{cases}$$

Specification provisions are derived from these equations.

AISC/ASD. With $F_{vy} = F_y/\sqrt{3}$ and with factors of safety of 1.45 for Eq. (5-43a) and 1.67 for Eqs. (5-43b) and (5-43c), we get

$$
F_v = \begin{cases} 0.4F_y & 0 < \dfrac{h}{t} < 165\sqrt{\dfrac{k}{F_y}} & (5\text{-}44a) \\[3mm] \dfrac{66}{h/t}\sqrt{kF_y} & 165\sqrt{\dfrac{k}{F_y}} < \dfrac{h}{t} < 238\sqrt{\dfrac{k}{F_y}} & (5\text{-}44b) \\[3mm] \dfrac{15{,}570k}{(h/t)^2} & \dfrac{h}{t} > 238\sqrt{\dfrac{k}{F_y}} & (5\text{-}44c) \end{cases}
$$

The smaller factor of safety (1.45) for Eq. (5-43a) is justified by the test results in Fig. 5-26 that lie above the line DB. Equations (5-44) are given in the following form in the specification:

$$
F_v = \begin{cases} 0.4F_y & \dfrac{h}{t} \le \dfrac{380}{\sqrt{F_y}} & (5\text{-}45a) \\[3mm] \dfrac{C_v F_y}{2.89} \le 0.4F & \dfrac{h}{t} > \dfrac{380}{\sqrt{F_y}} & (5\text{-}45b) \end{cases}
$$

$$
\text{where } C_v = \begin{cases} \dfrac{45{,}000k}{F_y(h/t)^2} & \text{if } C_v < 0.8 \\[3mm] \dfrac{190}{h/t}\sqrt{\dfrac{k}{F_y}} & \text{if } C_v > 0.8 \end{cases}
$$

The stress F_v is defined as the stress on the area equal to the overall depth of the beam times the web thickness, and the depth h as the clear depth between flanges. The coefficient k is determined by Eqs. (5-38).

The coefficient C_v in Eq. (5-45b) is the ratio of the shear critical stress to the shear yield stress, that is, $C_v = F_{v,cr}/F_{vy}$. Thus, from Eq. (5-43c) we get

$$
\frac{F_{v,cr}}{F_{vy}} = \frac{F_{v,cr}}{F_y/\sqrt{3}} = \frac{26{,}000k}{(h/t)^2 F_y/\sqrt{3}} = \frac{45{,}000k}{F_y(h/t)^2}
$$

The formula for C_v for $C_v > 0.8$ is derived in the same way from Eq. (5-43b). The factor 0.8 which separates the two formulas results from the assumption that the shear proportional limit F_{vy} is $0.8F_{vy}$.

AISC/LRFD. Nominal shears $V_n = F_{v,cr}A_w$ are obtained from $V_n = F_v A_w$, where F_v is the stress from Eqs. (5-43), expressed in terms of F_y instead of F_{vy}, and A_w is defined as the overall depth times the web thickness:

$$
V_n = \begin{cases} 0.6F_y A_w & 0 < \dfrac{h}{t} < 187\sqrt{\dfrac{k}{F_y}} & (5\text{-}46a) \\[3mm] 0.6F_y A_w \dfrac{187\sqrt{k/F_y}}{h/t} & 187\sqrt{\dfrac{k}{F_y}} < \dfrac{h}{t} < 234\sqrt{\dfrac{k}{F_y}} & (5\text{-}46b) \\[3mm] \dfrac{26{,}400k}{(h/t)^2}A_w & \dfrac{h}{t} > 234\sqrt{\dfrac{k}{F_y}} & (5\text{-}46c) \end{cases}
$$

The depth h for rolled sections is defined as the clear distance between flanges minus the fillet or corner radii, and for built-up sections as the distance between lines of fasteners or the clear distance between flanges if welds are used.

It will be noted that the shear stress $0.6F_y$ in Eq. (5-46a) is somewhat larger than the shear-yield value $F_y/\sqrt{3}$. This is consistent with the smaller factor of safety involved in Eq. (5-44a) compared to that in Eqs. (5-44b) and (5-44c). The specification prescribes k according to Eq. (5-39) except that it is to be taken as 5 if a/h exceeds 3 or $[260/(h/t)]^2$. Design strengths are obtained by multiplying the nominal strengths by the resistance factor $\phi = 0.9$.

AASHTO. This specification does not recognize the inelastic behavior represented by Eq. (5-43b). Instead, allowable stresses are based on the values given by *DBEA* in Fig. 5-26. Since the ratio a/h is large for beams we may use $k = 5$ from Eq. (5-39). Then with $F_{vy} = F_y/\sqrt{3}$ and a factor of safety of 1.75, we get from Eqs. (5-43a) and (5-43c)

$$F_v = \frac{F_y}{3} \qquad (5\text{-}47a)$$

$$F_v = \frac{7.33 \times 10^7}{(h/t)^2} \text{ psi} \qquad \frac{h}{t} > \frac{14{,}830}{\sqrt{F_{y,\text{psi}}}} \qquad (5\text{-}47b)$$

AREA. Allowable stresses in this specification are based on values by only *DB* in Fig. 5-26, that is, the shear yield stress is considered to be the maximum that can be obtained without some stiffening of the web. (Stiffening means are discussed in Chap. 7). The allowable stress is given by

$$F_v = 0.35F_y \qquad \frac{h}{t} \leq \frac{11{,}400}{\sqrt{F_{y,\text{psi}}}} \qquad (5\text{-}48)$$

The upper limit of h/t is 60 for A36 steel. The line *DB* in Fig. 5-26 is plotted at the yield stress for A36 steel ($F_v = 36/\sqrt{3} = 20.8$ ksi). It will be noted that $h/t = 60$ falls well to the left of point I, so the limiting value of h/t is perhaps overly conservative.

The webs of all rolled I-shaped sections are of such thickness that they can usually be counted on to develop much larger shear strengths than are required. However, the slenderness of plate-girder webs is generally much larger than that of rolled beams, which requires that they be proportioned for shear buckling and, usually, that web stiffeners be used to reduce a/h. This is discussed in Chap. 7.

It was noted in Art. 5-13 that shear is usually not a significant design consideration unless the beam supports heavy concentrated loads near the reaction points. To evaluate this situation we consider the case where a concentrated load acts at a point such that the shear strength and the moment strength are reached at the same time. Let a be the distance from such a point to the end of the beam.

Then, with AISC/ASD, we have for the reaction R, which equals the shear,

$$R = 0.4F_y \, dt_w$$

and for the moment at the point of application of the load

$$M = Ra = 0.6F_y S_x$$

Substitution yields

$$a = 1.5 \frac{S_x}{dt_w} \tag{a}$$

The corresponding values of R and M with AISC/LRFD are

$$R = 0.9 \times 0.6F_y \, dt_w$$
$$M = 0.9F_y Z_x$$

from which

$$a = 1.67 \frac{Z_x}{dt_w} \tag{b}$$

For the W shapes most commonly used as beams the value of a by Eqs. (a) and (b) varies from $1.25d$ to $2d$. A concentrated load must therefore be located within approximately $2d$ from the support in order for shear to be of consequence.

The shear-buckling strength of aluminum beams is given by Eq. (5-37) in the elastic range and by the tangent-modulus equivalent of that equation for the inelastic range. For alloy 6061-T6, the values are[13]

$$F_{v(cr)i} = 25.8 - 0.164 \frac{b}{t} \qquad \frac{b}{t} \le 65 \tag{5-49a}$$

$$F_{v,cr} = \frac{63{,}100}{(b/t)^2} \qquad \frac{b}{t} \ge 65 \tag{5-49b}$$

These stresses are based on edge conditions about halfway between hinged and fixed. The Aluminum Association[14] recommends factors of safety of 2.2 and 1.95 for bridge structures and building structures, respectively.

Example 5-14-1 (AISC/ASD). Evaluate the actual and allowable shears for the beams designed in Example 5-8-1 (AISC/ASD). The beams were designed for a uniform load of 2 kips/ft on a span of 30 ft, so the reaction is 30 kips, not including the weight of the beam. Allowable shear stresses are given by Eqs. (5-44) or (5-45).

Solution

(a) A36 steel, W21 × 62:

$$d = 20.99 \text{ in} \qquad t_w = 0.400 \text{ in} \qquad A_w = 20.99 \times 0.400 = 8.40 \text{ in}^2$$

$$V = 30 + 0.062 \times 15 = 30.9 \text{ kips}$$

Using Eqs. (5-44),

$$\frac{h}{t} = \frac{20.99 - 2 \times 0.615}{0.40} = 49.4 \qquad 165\sqrt{\frac{k}{F_y}} = 165\sqrt{\frac{5.34}{36}} = 63.5 > 49.4$$

$$F_v = 0.4F_y = 0.4 \times 36 = 14.4 \text{ ksi} \qquad V_{\text{all}} = 14.4 \times 8.40 = 121 \text{ kips} > 30.9$$

Alternatively, using Eqs. (5-45),

$$\frac{h}{t} = \frac{20.99 - 2 \times 0.615}{0.40} = 49.4 \qquad \frac{380}{\sqrt{F_y}} = \frac{380}{\sqrt{36}} = 63.3 > 49.4$$

$$F_v = 0.4F_y = 0.4 \times 36 = 14.4 \text{ ksi} \qquad V_{\text{all}} = 14.4 \times 8.40 = 121 \text{ kips} > 30.9$$

(b) A572 Grade 65 steel, W21 × 44:

$$d = 20.66 \text{ in} \qquad t_w = 0.350 \text{ in} \qquad A_w = 20.66 \times 0.350 = 7.23 \text{ in}^2$$

$$V = 30 + 0.44 \times 15 = 30.7 \text{ kips}$$

Using Eqs. (5-44),

$$\frac{h}{t} = \frac{20.66 - 2 \times 0.45}{0.35} = 56.5$$

$$165\sqrt{\frac{k}{F}} = 165\sqrt{\frac{5.34}{65}} = 47 < 56.5 \qquad 238\sqrt{\frac{k}{F}} = 238\sqrt{\frac{5.34}{65}} = 68 > 56.5$$

$$F_v = \frac{66}{56.5}\sqrt{5.34 \times 65} = 21.7 \text{ ksi} \qquad V_{\text{all}} = 21.7 \times 7.23 = 157 \text{ kips} > 30.7$$

Alternatively, using Eqs. (5-45),

$$\frac{h}{t} = \frac{20.66 - 2 \times 0.45}{0.35} = 56.5 \qquad \frac{380}{\sqrt{F_y}} = \frac{380}{\sqrt{65}} = 47.1 < 56.5$$

$$C_v = \frac{45{,}000 \times 5.34}{65 \times 56.5^2} = 2.09 > 0.8 \quad \text{N.G.} \qquad C_v = \frac{190}{56.5}\sqrt{\frac{5.34}{65}} = 0.96 > 0.80 \quad \text{O.K.}$$

$$F_v = \frac{0.96 \times 65}{2.89} = 21.7 \text{ ksi} \qquad V_{\text{all}} = 21.7 \times 7.23 = 157 \text{ kips} > 30.7$$

Example 5-14-2 (AISC/LRFD). Evaluate the actual and design-strength shears for the beams designed in Example 5-9-1 (AISC/LRFD). The beams were designed for a uniform live load of 1.5 kips/ft and a uniform dead load, not including the weight of the beam, of 0.5 kips/ft on a span of 30 ft. The factored reaction, not including the weight of the beam, is $15(1.6 \times 1.5 + 1.2 \times 0.5) = 36.9$ kips. Nominal shears are given by Eqs. (5-46).

Solution

(*a*) A36 steel, W24 × 55:

$$d = 23.57 \text{ in} \qquad t_w = 0.395 \text{ in} \qquad A_w = 23.57 \times 0.395 = 9.31 \text{ in}^2$$

$$V = 36.9 + 1.2 \times 0.055 \times 15 = 37.9 \text{ kips}$$

$$\frac{h}{t} = \frac{23.57 - 2 \times 0.505}{0.395} = 55.5 \qquad 187\sqrt{\frac{k}{F_y}} = 187\sqrt{\frac{5}{36}} = 69.7 > 55.5$$

$$V_n = 0.6 \times 36 \times 9.31 = 201 \text{ kips}$$

$$\phi V_n = 0.9 \times 201 = 181 \text{ kips} > 37.9$$

(*b*) A572 Grade 65 steel, W21 × 44:

$$d = 20.66 \text{ in} \qquad t_w = 0.350 \text{ in} \qquad A_w = 20.66 \times 0.350 = 7.23 \text{ in}^2$$

$$V = 36.9 + 1.2 \times 0.044 \times 15 = 37.7 \text{ kips}$$

$$\frac{h}{t} = \frac{20.66 - 2 \times 0.45 - 2 \times 1\frac{3}{16}}{0.350} = 49.7 \qquad 187\sqrt{\frac{k}{F_y}} = 187\sqrt{\frac{5}{65}} = 51.9 > 49.7$$

$$V_n = 0.6 \times 65 \times 7.23 = 282 \text{ kips}$$

$$\phi V_n = 0.9 \times 282 = 254 \text{ kips} > 37.7$$

5-15   BEND BUCKLING OF BEAM WEBS

Since bending stresses are compressive over part of the depth of the beam, they may cause local buckling of the web. Figure 5-27 shows a flat plate, simply supported on all four edges, which has buckled due to the bending stresses shown. As in the case of plates under uniform edge compression, beam webs bend buckle in a single transverse wave and multiple lengthwise waves. Figure 5-28 shows

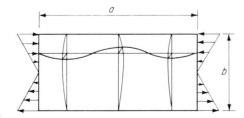

FIGURE 5-27

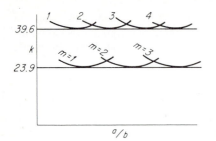

FIGURE 5-28

values of k in Eq. (5-37) for a plate with the four edges simply supported and the unloaded edges clamped.[1] The number of longitudinal waves is shown by $m = 1$, etc. It will be noted that the minimum values of k, 23.9 for simply supported edges and 39.6 for the unloaded edges clamped, are the same for all values of m. The corresponding critical stresses for $E = 30,000$ ksi and $\mu = 0.3$ are

$$F_{b,cr} = \frac{650,000}{(b/t)^2} \quad \text{ksi} \tag{5-50a}$$

$$F_{b,cr} = \frac{1,080,000}{(b/t)^2} \quad \text{ksi} \tag{5-50b}$$

Tests show that beam webs are partially restrained against rotation by the flanges to the extent that the critical stress is likely to be at least 30 percent higher than that given by Eq. (5-50a). Thus, we may use

$$F_{b,cr} = \frac{850,000}{(b/t)^2} \quad \text{ksi} \tag{5-50c}$$

Figure 5-28 shows that the critical stress is independent of a/b except for very short plates (a/b less than about 0.5). From Eq. (5-50c) we find that the critical stress for bend buckling equals the yield stress for A36 steel at $b/t = 154$. For $F_y = 100$ ksi, the corresponding value is 92. Thus, even with some allowance for a lower proportional limit because of imperfections, there is no likelihood of bend buckling of the webs of rolled-steel W shapes since, as mentioned in Art. 5-14, their webs are such that $b/t < 70$. However, plate girders usually have webs much thinner than those of rolled sections, so bend buckling may have to be considered. This is discussed in Chap. 7.

Bend-buckling critical stresses can be calculated by using an equivalent slenderness ratio in column-buckling formulas, as in the case of the flat plate under uniform edge compression (Art. 4-12). Thus, from Eq. (4-33), with $\tau = 1$, and using $k = 23.9$ for simply supported edges, we get

$$\left(\frac{L}{r}\right)_{eq} = \frac{3.3}{\sqrt{23.9}} \frac{b}{t} = 0.67 \frac{b}{t} \tag{5-51a}$$

Similarly, with $k = 39.6$ for unloaded edges clamped we have

$$\left(\frac{L}{r}\right)_{eq} = 0.52 \frac{b}{t} \tag{5-51b}$$

The equivalent slenderness for the partially restrained plate corresponding to Eq. (5-50c) is

$$\left(\frac{L}{r}\right)_{eq} = 0.59 \frac{b}{t} \tag{5-51c}$$

The value of $(L/r)_{eq} = 0.60b/t$ has been recommended for calculating the bend-buckling stress for webs of aluminum beams. Because of the considerable postbuckling strength, factors of safety of 1.2 for buildings and 1.35 for bridges are suggested.[14]

Bend buckling of the webs of beams proportioned to develop the plastic moment must also be considered. It is clear that the bending-stress distribution of the web of Fig. 5-29a involves an extreme-fiber strain which is several times the yield strain. In this case, the web is anisotropic in its resistance to buckling; i.e., its properties are direction-dependent. This is because the longitudinal bending stresses resulting from buckling begin in a direction in which the web is already strained inelastically while the transverse bending stresses begin in a direction in which it is unstressed. This phenomenon is discussed in Art. 4-21. Such bend buckling is analyzed in Ref. 8, assuming that the extreme fiber of the web is strained inelastically ($\epsilon > \epsilon_y$) in the longitudinal direction at the onset of buckling and that there is no strain reversal as buckling begins. It was found that b/t for a web of A36 steel must not exceed about 60 if the web is to develop an extreme-fiber strain $\epsilon = 4\epsilon_y$ in pure bending. However, research in plastic design demonstrated that this limit is conservative. The AISC/ASD and AISC/LRFD specifications use the limit $b/t \leq 640/\sqrt{F_y}$ for compact sections.

The preceding discussion of bend buckling of beam webs is limited to pure bending. The plate-buckling coefficient k for a beam-column web hinged on its four edges will lie between the value $k = 23.9$ for pure bending and $k = 4$ for uniform compression. Values for various combinations of moment and axial force have been determined.[1] For example, $k = 7.8$ for a plate with the distribution of stress shown in Fig. 5-29b. For such a web in A36 steel, a consistent slenderness limit would be $b/t = 42/\sqrt{(7.8/4)} = 59$, where 42 is the AISC pre-

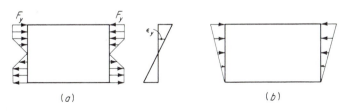

(a) (b)

FIGURE 5-29

scribed value for uniformly compressed plates (Table 4-4). Such limits are not ordinarily used in allowable-stress design. However, they are essential in plastic design and as compact-section limitations in allowable-stress design.

The following AISC/ASD formulas, which are based on the research noted above (Ref. 8), are requirements for compact sections:

$$\frac{b}{t} \leq \begin{cases} \dfrac{640}{\sqrt{F_y}}\left(1 - 3.74\,\dfrac{f_a}{F_y}\right) & \dfrac{f_a}{F_y} \leq 0.16 & (5\text{-}52a) \\[3mm] \dfrac{257}{\sqrt{F_y}} & \dfrac{f_a}{F_y} > 0.16 & (5\text{-}52b) \end{cases}$$

In these formulas $f_a = P/A$ is the service-load axial compression. The value $640/\sqrt{F_y}$ is the beam-web limit mentioned earlier in this article. Thus, the limiting values for A36-steel webs range from $b/t = 640/\sqrt{36} = 107$ for bending alone to $b/t = 257/\sqrt{36} = 43$ for axial compression alone.

The AISC/LRFD formulas are

$$\lambda_p = \frac{h_c}{t_w} = \frac{640}{\sqrt{F_y}}\left(1 - \frac{2.75P_u}{\phi_b P_y}\right) \qquad \text{for } \frac{P_u}{\phi_b P_y} \leq 0.125 \qquad (5\text{-}53a)$$

$$\frac{h_c}{t_w} = \frac{191}{\sqrt{F_y}}\left(2.33 - \frac{P_u}{\phi_b P_y}\right) \geq \frac{253}{\sqrt{F_y}} \qquad \text{for } \frac{P_u}{\phi_b P_y} > 0.125 \qquad (5\text{-}53b)$$

where h_c = twice the distance from the neutral axis to inside face of compression flange minus fillet or corner radius for rolled shapes
   h_c = twice the distance from the neutral axis to nearest line of fasteners at compression flange, or to inside face when welds are used, for built-up sections
   t_w = thickness of web
   P_u = required axial strength
   P_y = yield strength
   ϕ_b = resistance factor for bending

Since Eq. (5-53b) requires that $h_c/t_w \geq 253/\sqrt{F_y}$, the limits for A36-steel webs are identical to AISC/ASD values. As in the case of flange local buckling these criteria provide an inelastic rotation capacity of about 3. For structures in seismic areas a greater rotation capacity may be advisable. The AISC/LRFD specification contains recommendations for this case in the commentary on Chap. B. The recommended value is approximately 0.80 times the value of λ_p according to Eqs. (5-53).

5-16   COMBINED SHEAR AND BENDING OF WEBS

Shear buckling and bend buckling of webs were discussed in preceding articles as independent buckling modes. While bend buckling can occur alone (where pure bending is involved), shear cannot exist without some bending. Furthermore, webs at the interior supports of continuous beams are subjected concurrently to large bending moments and shears. Therefore, the effect of these combinations of stress must be considered.

Figure 5-30 shows a flat plate with hinged edges subjected to bending stresses and to shear stresses distributed along the edges.[1] The curve in the figure gives, for a square plate, the relation between the ratios $F'_{b,cr}/F_{b,cr}$ and $F'_{v,cr}/F_{v,cr}$, where $F_{b,cr}$ is the critical stress on the extreme fiber for pure bending, $F_{v,cr}$ is the critical stress for pure shear, and $F'_{b,cr}$ and $F'_{v,cr}$ are the bending and shearing stresses which, acting simultaneously, cause buckling. It is seen that the effect of shearing stress on the critical bending stress is small if $F'_{v,cr}/F_{v,cr}$ is small. Thus if $F'_{v,cr}/F_{v,cr} = 0.4$, a bending stress of almost $0.9 F_{b,cr}$ can be resisted. Similarly, the effect of bending stress on the critical shear stress is small if $F'_{b,cr}/F_{b,cr}$ is small.

The interaction curve of Fig. 5-30 is very nearly circular. Furthermore, curves for other aspect ratios a/b differ from it only slightly. Therefore, the interaction of shear stress and bending stress can be written in the form

$$\left(\frac{F'_{v,cr}}{F_{v,cr}}\right)^2 + \left(\frac{F'_{b,cr}}{F_{b,cr}}\right)^2 = 1 \tag{5-54}$$

This equation is based on critical stresses. It can be expressed in terms of actual stresses and allowable stresses by dividing the numerator and denominator of each term by the factor of safety. Thus

$$\left(\frac{f_v}{F_v}\right)^2 + \left(\frac{f_b}{F_b}\right)^2 = 1 \tag{5-55}$$

where f_v, f_b = concurrent actual shearing and bending stresses
F_v = allowable shear stress in absence of bending
F_b = allowable bending stress in absence of shear

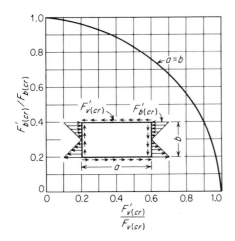

FIGURE 5-30

Equation (5-55) is recommended for webs of aluminum beams.[13] The AISC specifications make no provision for combined shear and bending except where the postbuckling shear strength of thin webs is taken into account. Since webs of standard rolled shapes are thick enough not to buckle, except possibly for the thinner webs in the highest-strength steels, this means that interaction need be considered in the AISC specifications only for plate girders. This is discussed in Chap. 7.

The AASHTO and AREA specifications make no provision for interaction of shear and bend buckling of beam webs. However, at sections where maximum shear and bending occur simultaneously, AREA specifies $0.55F_y$ as the allowable diagonal tension in the web. This principal stress f_t is determined from

$$f_t = \frac{f_b}{2} + \sqrt{\left(\frac{f_b}{2}\right)^2 + f_v^2}$$

where $f_b = M/S$ and $f_v = V/A_w$.

5-17 CRIPPLING AND VERTICAL BUCKLING OF WEBS

In addition to shearing and bending stresses in the web of a beam, there are compressive stresses in the vertical direction because of bearing of the loads on the flanges. In the beam shown in Fig. 5-31, we see that there must be vertical compression immediately above the bearing plate at the support. Furthermore, since there is no load on the top flange above the support, the vertical compression must diminish at successively higher horizontal sections until it becomes zero at the top flange. To estimate this stress, we isolate a portion of the beam below the section 1-1 at the edge of the fillet of the beam cross section and to the left of section 1-2. The inclination of section 1-2 is arbitrary; it is intended to account for the dispersion of the compressive stresses. Similar compression exists on section 3-3 below the top flange at the supported column. The failure that

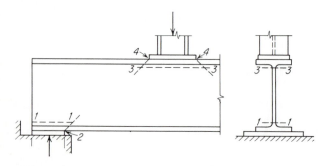

FIGURE 5-31

may result as a result of such localized compression is called by various names, such as direct compression, web crippling, and local yielding.

In the AISC specifications web local compression at concentrated loads is computed on sections obtained by taking the slopes of lines 1-2 and 3-4 in Fig. 5-31 at $2\frac{1}{2}$ horizontal to 1 vertical. This is in agreement with the assumed dispersion in column webs of localized compressive forces that may cause web crippling in welded beam-to-column connections, which is based on test results (Art. 8-21). The resulting criteria are the following.

ASD. For interior loads,

$$R = 0.66F_y t_w(N + 5k) \qquad (5\text{-}56a)$$

For end reactions,

$$R = 0.66F_y t_w(N + 2.5k) \qquad (5\text{-}56b)$$

LRFD. $R = \phi R_n$, with $\phi = 1$ and R_n as follows: For interior loads,

$$R_n = F_y t_w(N + 5k) \qquad (5\text{-}57a)$$

For end reactions,

$$R_n = F_y t_w(N + 2.5k) \qquad (5\text{-}57b)$$

Notation in Eqs. (5-56) and (5-57) is as follows:

R = concentrated load or reaction

R_n = nominal resistance

N = length of bearing

t_w = web thickness

k = distance from extreme fiber to toe of fillet

Roberts investigated web crippling by considering a mechanism involving the flange and web.[23] (The mechanism concept is discussed in Art. 5-11.) Roberts' mechanism involves a bulging of the web along lines of yielding and the development of four plastic hinges in the flange (Fig. 5-32). The resultant load P is given by

$$P = 0.5t_w^2 \left(EF_{yw} \frac{t_f}{t_w} \right)^{0.5} \left[1 + \frac{3c}{d} \left(\frac{t_w}{t_f} \right)^{1.5} \right] \qquad (5\text{-}58)$$

where c = length of bearing contact of P
d = depth of beam
t_f = thickness of flange
t_w = thickness of web

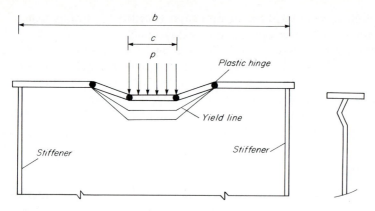

FIGURE 5-32
Roberts' mechanism for web buckling.

The loads predicted by this equation were compared with data from 114 tests. The ranges of the variables in the tests were as follows:

$$b = \text{width of panel (Fig. 5-32)} = 12 \text{ to } 98 \text{ in}$$

$$c = 0 \text{ to } 8 \text{ in}$$

$$d = 10 \text{ to } 40 \text{ in}$$

$$t_f = 0.12 \text{ to } 1.2 \text{ in}$$

$$t_w = 0.04 \text{ to } 0.12 \text{ in}$$

$$F_{yw} = 26 \text{ to } 47 \text{ ksi}$$

The panel aspect ratio b/d ranged from 1 to 14 and the web slenderness ratio d/t_w from 75 to 400. The ratio of the experimental value of P to the value predicted by Eq. (5-58) ranged from 1.03 to 2.16, with a coefficient of variation of 15.3 percent.

According to Roberts it is unrealistic to assume that the flange remains straight between the two inner plastic hinges, as is assumed in the mechanism geometry, if c/d is large. Therefore, he recommends that c/d be taken not larger than 0.2.

The following AISC provisions for web crippling are based on Roberts' work.

ASD. Concentrated load at a distance $d/2$ or more from end of member:

$$R = 67.5t_w^2\left[1 + 3\left(\frac{N}{d}\right)\left(\frac{t_w}{t_f}\right)^{1.5}\right]\sqrt{\frac{F_{yw}t_f}{t_w}} \qquad (5\text{-}59a)$$

Concentrated load at a distance less than $d/2$ from end of member:

$$R = 34t_w^2\left[1 + 3\left(\frac{N}{d}\right)\left(\frac{t_w}{t_f}\right)^{1.5}\right]\sqrt{\frac{F_{yw}t_f}{t_w}} \qquad (5\text{-}59b)$$

LRFD. $R = \phi R_n$, with $\phi = 0.75$ and R_n as follows. Concentrated load at a distance $d/2$ or more from end of member:

$$R_n = 135t_w^2 \left[1 + 3\left(\frac{N}{d}\right)\left(\frac{t_w}{t_f}\right)^{1.5} \right] \sqrt{\frac{F_{yw}t_f}{t_w}} \qquad (5\text{-}60a)$$

Concentrated load at a distance less than $d/2$ from end of member:

$$R_n = 68t_w^2 \left[1 + 3\left(\frac{N}{d}\right)\left(\frac{t_w}{t_f}\right)^{1.5} \right] \sqrt{\frac{F_{yw}t_f}{t_w}} \qquad (5\text{-}60b)$$

Vertical buckling. Vertical compression in beam webs may also result in an overall-buckling failure (Fig. 5-33). An exact solution of this problem requires a stability analysis of the entire web with unlike load systems on two opposite edges. However, a good approximation can be developed for the beam supporting a uniformly distributed load on its top flange. In this case, the vertical compression stress in the web varies from zero at the bottom edge to w at the top edge. It is shown in Ref. 24 that a pin-ended column can support twice as much load if the reactive forces are distributed uniformly along its length as it can if the load is concentrated at the ends. The same conclusion can be shown to hold for a plate loaded in the same manner. Thus, the critical vertical compressive stress for the web of a beam supporting a uniformly distributed load is twice the critical stress for a plate uniformly compressed on two opposite edges. This buckling problem is discussed in Art. 10-1, where it is shown that the critical stress for a plate with all four edges simply supported is given by Eq. (10-8), provided the plate buckles in a single wave in the direction of the compression. This requires that the aspect ratio a/b be less than $\sqrt{2}$ (Fig. 4-33). For the case of the beam web, a in Eq. (10-8) is the depth of the beam and b its length, so a/b is very small

FIGURE 5-33
Buckling failure of web of rolled I. (*University of Illinois Experiment Station.*)

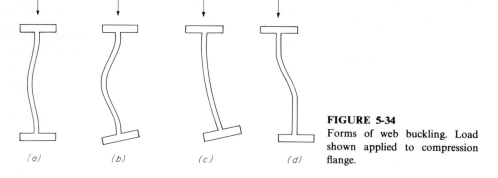

FIGURE 5-34
Forms of web buckling. Load shown applied to compression flange.

(*a*)   (*b*)   (*c*)   (*d*)

(*b* will rarely be less than 10*a*). Therefore, Eq. (10-8) applies. Furthermore, *a/b* can be dropped because it is small, which reduces the formula to the simpler form of Eq. (10-4). Thus, the vertical buckling stress for the web of a beam loaded uniformly on its top flange is twice the value from Eq. (10-4). Therefore,

$$F_{cr} = \frac{2\pi^2 E}{12(1 - \mu^2)(b/t)^2} \tag{5-61}$$

where *b* is the depth of web and *t* the thickness of web.

The critical stress of Eq. (5-61) is increased if the web is rotationally restrained by the flanges, just as is the column with rotationally restrained ends. Several possible buckling modes other than the one corresponding to this equation (no rotational restraint at either longitudinal edge) are shown in Fig. 5-34.

Web buckling due to concentrated loads is harder to evaluate. Figure 5-35 shows the vertical stresses on three horizontal sections of a beam of rectangular cross section of unit thickness and depth *d* supporting a concentrated load *P*. It will be noted that, at all three levels, the stress is compressive over a length about equal to *d*. The stress at middepth varies from zero at each end of the length *d* to $0.91P/d$ at the center.[25] The average stress on the area is about $0.5P/d$. Thus, in terms of average stress, the decrease in compression with depth is the same as that for a uniformly distributed load. There is no simple way to evaluate web

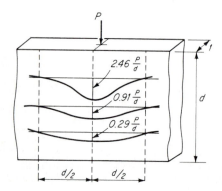

FIGURE 5-35

stability under these conditions. Various approximations have been developed by analyzing the buckling of a full-depth segment of the web acted upon by the concentrated load distributed over the length of the segment.

Concentrated-load web buckling of the type shown in Fig. 5-34c is influenced by the lateral bending stiffness of the beam flange. Buckling of this type was observed in tests at Lehigh University and the University of Texas-Austin. Beams in the Texas tests were braced against lateral movement at the point of loading (on the compression flange). Formulas derived from an analysis of the buckling of a segment of the web in which the lateral displacement of the unloaded edge depends on the lateral stiffness of the beam flange were in good agreement with the test results.[26] In the AISC specifications this type of buckling is called *sidesway* web buckling, for which the following formulas, based on Ref. 26, are prescribed.

ASD. Loaded flange restrained against rotation and $(d_c/t_w)/(l/b_f) < 2.3$:

$$R_n = \frac{6800t_w^3}{h}\left[1 + 0.4\left(\frac{d_c/t_w}{l/b_f}\right)^3\right] \qquad (5\text{-}62a)$$

Loaded flange not restrained against rotation and $(d_c/t_w)/(l/b_f) < 1.7$:

$$R_n = \frac{6800t_w^3}{h}\left[0.4\left(\frac{d_c/t_w}{l/b_f}\right)^3\right] \qquad (5\text{-}62b)$$

LRFD. Loaded flange restrained against rotation and $(d_c/t_w)/(l/b_f) < 2.3$:

$$R_n = \frac{12{,}000t_w^3}{h}\left[1 + 0.4\left(\frac{d_c/t_w}{l/b_f}\right)^3\right] \qquad (5\text{-}63a)$$

Loaded flange not restrained against rotation and $(d_c/t_w)/(l/b_f) < 1.7$:

$$R_n = \frac{12{,}000t_w^3}{h}\left[0.4\left(\frac{d_c/t_w}{l/b_f}\right)^3\right] \qquad (5\text{-}63b)$$

The resistance factor $\phi = 0.85$ for Eqs. (5-63). The notation in these equations is as follows:

R_n = nominal resistance

d_c = web depth clear of fillets

t_w = web thickness

l = largest unbraced length along either flange

b_f = flange width

According to the definitions in the specifications, h is the same as d_c.

Stiffeners. If the value of R in the applicable Eqs. (5-56), (5-57), (5-59), (5-60), (5-62), and (5-63) is less than the load to be supported and cannot be increased

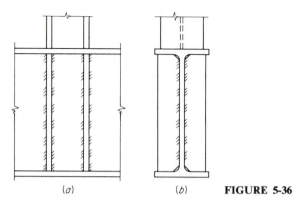

(a) (b) **FIGURE 5-36**

by changing one or more of the dimensions involved, web stiffeners must be provided. Stiffeners supporting a concentrated load on the top flange of a beam are shown in Fig. 5-36. Such stiffeners are designed as columns (see Art. 7-12).

DP5-17-1 (AISC/ASD) and DP5-17-2 (AISC/LRFD): Column Underpinning

An existing column in a building is to be underpinned temporarily during alteration of the building. It is to be supported on two parallel beams which will be supported in turn on temporary concrete pedestals or timber mats. The base plate is 16 × 20 in. The column will be supported by jacks bearing on temporary brackets while the beams are being placed. The specification formulas for the web forces are discussed in Art. 5-17.

It will be noted that the section chosen for the beam is the S, rather than the W, although the W is tried first since it will usually be the least-weight shape. Webs of S shapes are usually thicker than those of comparable W's, which is likely to make the S better suited for beams with relatively large shear and vertical compressive stresses. Such beams are usually characterized by a small span/depth ratio, in these examples $6/2 = 3$.

5-18 BEAM BEARING PLATES

A beam supported on masonry or concrete must usually be provided with bearing plates which, in addition to having enough length along the beam to control vertical compression in the web, have bearing area sufficient to give adequate safety with respect to crushing of the supporting material. Since they can be placed in advance of the beams and grouted level at the required elevation, bearing plates also facilitate erection. For this reason they are sometimes advisable even if the beam itself has contact area sufficient to distribute its reaction.

Although the bearing plate is a simple enough structural element, it is virtually impossible to determine the distribution of the forces acting on it. As a result of deflection of the beam, bearing pressures are larger at the edge of the

UNDERPINNING FOR COLUMN   DP5-17-1

2 pipe separators
at each end

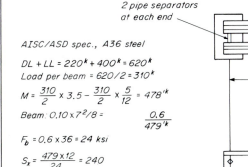

AISC/ASD spec., A36 steel

$DL + LL = 220^k + 400^k = 620^k$
Load per beam $= 620/2 = 310^k$

$M = \dfrac{310}{2} \times 3.5 - \dfrac{310}{2} \times \dfrac{5}{12} = 478^{'k}$

Beam: $0.10 \times 7^2/8 = \dfrac{0.6}{479^{'k}}$

$F_b = 0.6 \times 36 = 24 \ ksi$

$S_x = \dfrac{479 \times 12}{24} = 240$

3'6"   **3'6"**

$220^k \ DL + 400^k \ LL$

1'8"

Try W27x94, $S_x = 243$, $b_f = 9.99$, $d/A_f = 3.62$
  $L_c = 76 \times 9.99/\sqrt{36} = 126"$ $L_c = 20,000/(36 \times 3.62) = 153"$
  Since $L = 7'$ is less than the smaller L_c, $F_b = 0.66 \ F_y$ as assumed

Web local yield: $k = 1 \ ^{7}/_{16}$, $t_w = 0.49$

$f = \dfrac{R}{t \ (N+5k)} = \dfrac{310}{0.49 \ (20 + 5 \times 1.44)} = 23.2 \ ksi < 0.66 \times 36 \ O.K.$

Web crippling: $t_f = 0.745$, $t_w = 0.49$, $d = 26.9$

$R = 67.5 \times 0.49^2 \left[1 + 3 \ \dfrac{20}{26.9} \left(\dfrac{0.49}{0.745} \right)^{1.5} \right] \sqrt{36 \ \dfrac{0.745}{0.49}} = 262^k < 310 \ N.G.$

Try S24x106, $S_x = 240$, $t_f = 1.09$, $t_w = 0.620$, $d = 24.5$
  $L_c = 36 \times 7.87/\sqrt{36} = 100"$ $L_c = 20,000/(36 \times 2.86) = 194"$

Web local yield: O.K.

Web crippling:

$R = 67.5 \times 0.620^2 \left[1 + 3 \ \dfrac{20}{24.5} \left(\dfrac{0.620}{1.09} \right)^{1.5} \right] \sqrt{36 \ \dfrac{1.09}{0.620}} = 423^k > 310 \ O.K.$

Web sidesway buckling: $k = 2.0$, $b_f = 7.87$, $l = 6' = 72"$

$d_c = 24.5 - 2 \times 2 = 20.5$ $\dfrac{d_c/t_w}{l/b_f} = \dfrac{20.5/0.620}{72/7.87} = 3.6 > 2.3 \ O.K.$

Shear: $\dfrac{310/2 + 0.106 \times 3.5}{24.5 \times 0.62} = 10.2 \ ksi < 0.4 \times 36 \ O.K.$

UNDERPINNING FOR COLUMN — *DP5-17-2*

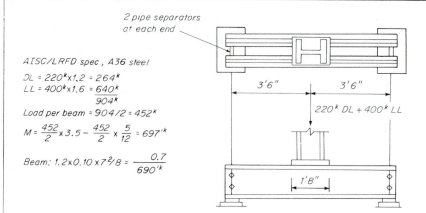

2 pipe separators at each end

AISC/LRFD spec., A36 steel

$DL = 220^k \times 1.2 = 264^k$
$LL = 400^k \times 1.6 = \underline{640^k}$
904^k

Load per beam $= 904/2 = 452^k$

$M = \dfrac{452}{2} \times 3.5 - \dfrac{452}{2} \times \dfrac{5}{12} = 697^{'k}$

Beam: $1.2 \times 0.10 \times 7^2/8 = \dfrac{0.7}{690^{'k}}$

$3'6''$ $3'6''$

$220^k \, DL + 400^k \, LL$

$1'8''$

$W27 \times 94$: $\phi M_p = 751$. $L_p = 8.8 > L_b = 7'$ O.K.

<u>Web local yield</u>: $k = 1\tfrac{7}{16}$, $t_w = 0.490$

$R = \phi R_n = \phi(N + 5k)F_y t_w = 1(20 + 5 \times 1\tfrac{7}{16})36 \times 0.490 = 480^k > 452$ O.K.

<u>Web crippling</u>: $t_f = 0.745$, $t_w = 0.490$, $d = 26.9$

$R = \phi R_n = 0.75 \times 135 \times 0.49^2 \left[1 + 3 \dfrac{20}{26.9}\left(\dfrac{0.490}{0.745}\right)^{1.5}\right]\sqrt{36 \dfrac{0.745}{0.490}} = 388^k < 452$ N.G.

<u>Try S24 x106</u>: $\phi M_p = 753$, $L_p = 6.5 < L_b = 7$, $L_r = 24.2$, $\phi M_r = 468$

$\phi M_n = \phi M_p - (\phi M_p - \phi M_r)\dfrac{L_b - L_p}{L_r - L_p}$

$= 753 - (753 - 468)\dfrac{7 - 6.5}{24.2 - 6.5} = 745^{'k} > 690$ O.K.

<u>Web local yield</u>: O.K.

<u>Web crippling</u>: $t_f = 1.09$, $t_w = 0.620$, $d = 24.5$

$R = 0.75 \times 135 \times 0.620^2 \left[1 + 3 \dfrac{20}{24.5}\left(\dfrac{0.620}{1.09}\right)^{1.5}\right]\sqrt{36 \dfrac{1.09}{0.620}} = 635^k > 452$ O.K.

<u>Web sidesway buckling</u>: $k = 2$, $b_f = 7.87$, $l = 7' = 84''$

$c_c = 24.5 - 2 \times 2 = 20.5$ $\dfrac{d_c/t_w}{l/b_f} = \dfrac{20.5/0.620}{84/7.87} = 3.10 > 2.3$ O.K.

<u>Shear</u>: $\phi V_n = 0.9 \times 0.6 \, F_y A_w = 0.54 \times 36 \times 24.5 \times 0.620 = 295^k > 452/2$ O.K.

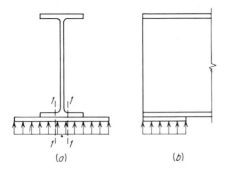

(a)   (b)   **FIGURE 5-37**

plate nearest the center of the beam than they are at the end. Pressures at the outer two edges are relieved by bending of the plate in the direction normal to the beam, and as a consequence the distribution of pressure in this direction also is not uniform.

   Various assumptions as to the distribution of the bearing stresses might be made, but it is customary to consider them to be uniform, which amounts to saying that the plate is designed for an average bearing stress. With this assumption, the design procedure resolves itself into one of choosing a plate which has (1) sufficient dimension lengthwise of the beam to satisfy local web yielding and web crippling requirements [Eqs. (5-56b) and (5-59b) for ASD, Eqs. (5-57b) and (5-60b) for LRFD], (2) sufficient area to satisfy requirements for bearing on the concrete, and (3) sufficient thickness to satisfy requirements for bending normal to the beam. With respect to the last of these requirements, there is the question of the location of the section of maximum bending moment. There is little to say except that it lies somewhere between the centerline of the plate and the edge of the beam flange. If the beam flange has no stiffness, the maximum moment in the plate is at its centerline, but if the flange is infinitely stiff, it is at the edge of the flange. Since in order for it to perform its function of distributing load the plate requires stiffness as well as strength, it is advisable to take the section of maximum moment somewhere near the center of the plate and to neglect the pressures exerted on it by the flange. The AISC specifications recommend that the design be based on the moment at the section 1-1 at the edge of the flange fillet (Fig. 5-37a).

5-19   BIAXIAL BENDING

The design of beams which have cross sections with at least one axis of symmetry and which are loaded through the shear center parallel to one of the two principal axes has been considered in preceding articles. If the load on the beam is not parallel to a principal axis, it can be resolved into components in the directions of the principal axes. The resulting shears and moments are shown in Fig.

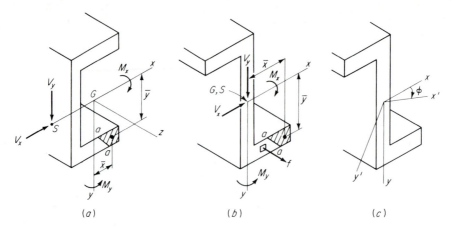

FIGURE 5-38

5-38a. The bending stress f_b is given by

$$f_b = \frac{M_x y}{I_x} + \frac{M_y x}{I_y} \tag{5-64}$$

The shear flow q in kips per lineal inch on a plane through a-a parallel to the axis is

$$q = \frac{V_y A\bar{y}}{I_x} + \frac{V_x A\bar{x}}{I_y} \tag{5-65}$$

where A is the shaded area in Fig. 5-38a and $\bar{x}$, $\bar{y}$ are the coordinates of its center of gravity. If x, y are not principal axes, as in the case of the zee shown in Fig. 5-38b, f_b and q are given by

$$f_b = \frac{M_x I_y - M_y I_{xy}}{I_x I_y - I_{xy}^2} y + \frac{M_y I_x - M_x I_{xy}}{I_x I_y - I_{xy}^2} x \tag{5-66}$$

$$q = \frac{V_y I_y - V_x I_{xy}}{I_x I_y - I_{xy}^2} A\bar{y} + \frac{V_x I_x - V_y I_{xy}}{I_x I_y - I_{xy}^2} A\bar{x} \tag{5-67}$$

where I_{xy} is the product of inertia $\int xy\, dA$. Taking tensile stress positive, the moments M_x and M_y in Eq. (5-66) are positive when they produce tension in the first quadrant (Fig. 5-38b). If x, y are principal axes, $I_{xy} = 0$ and Eqs. (5-66) and (5-67) reduce to Eqs. (5-64) and (5-65). If the beam cross section has an axis of symmetry, that axis is a principal axis. If there is no axis of symmetry, the direction of the principal axes x', y' is given by

$$\tan 2\phi = \frac{2 I_{xy}}{I_y - I_x} \tag{5-68}$$

where x, y are orthogonal axes originating at the centroid of the cross section

(Fig. 5-38c) and a positive value of ϕ indicates a clockwise rotation of the axes. The moments of inertia about the principal axes are

$$I_{x'} = I_x \cos^2 \phi + I_y \sin^2 \phi - I_{xy} \sin 2\phi \qquad (5\text{-}69a)$$

$$I_{y'} = I_x \sin^2 \phi + I_y \cos^2 \phi + I_{xy} \sin 2\phi \qquad (5\text{-}69b)$$

The calculations required to compute the principal moments of inertia offset most if not all of the advantage of Eq. (5-64) over Eq. (5-66). This is readily apparent since, in addition to evaluating ϕ and the moments of inertia about the principal axes, it is also necessary to determine the coordinates x and y for any point to be investigated with respect to the new coordinate-axis system.

Bending-stress calculation according to Eq. (5-66) is illustrated in Example 5-19-1.

The strength of beams subjected to bending moments in both principal planes depends upon their lateral-buckling characteristics. If, in Fig. 5-7a, in addition to the couples M_x at each end there are couples M_y producing single curvature in the xz plane, each of Eqs. (5-1) takes on an additional term involving M_y (Ref. 1). The solution to these equations is

$$\frac{M_x^2}{EI_y} + \frac{M_y^2}{EI_x} = \frac{\pi^2}{L^2} GJ + \frac{\pi^4}{L^4} EC_w \qquad (a)$$

This equation reduces to Eq. (5-3) if $M_y = 0$. It holds only if the bending stress does not exceed the proportional limit. Therefore, M_x and M_y must also satisfy

$$\frac{M_x}{S_x} + \frac{M_y}{S_y} \leq F_p \qquad (b)$$

It is instructive to interpret Eqs. (a) and (b) graphically. Graphs of Eq. (a) for a steel W12 × 40 on spans of 20, 25, and 30 ft, with $E = 30,000$ ksi and $G = 12,000$ ksi, are shown in Fig. 5-39. Assuming $F_p = F_y = 36$ ksi, Eq. (b) gives the line AB in the figure. The intersection C of AB and the ellipse for the 30-ft span gives simultaneous values of M_x and M_y for which the combined bending stress is 36 ksi. No point higher than C on the graph for the 30-ft span is significant because it represents values of M_x and M_y that do not satisfy Eq. (b). No point on AB to the right of C is valid because it represents values of M_x and M_y that do not satisfy Eq. (a). Similarly, combinations for a 25-ft span lie on the line AEF, while only points on the line AB are valid for the 20-ft span.

Points D and F in Fig. 5-39 represent the critical values of M_x, denoted by $M_{x(cr)}$, for pure bending about the x axis, while point A represents the yield moment for pure bending about the y axis, denoted by $M_{y(yield)}$. Therefore, a conservative evaluation of biaxial bending can be obtained by using a straight line from A to D which, in terms of moments, gives

$$\frac{M_x}{M_{x(cr)}} + \frac{M_y}{M_{y(yield)}} = 1 \qquad (5\text{-}70a)$$

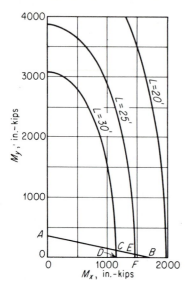

FIGURE 5-39

This equation can also be written in terms of stress by dividing the moments by the section moduli which gives

$$\frac{f_{bx}}{F_{bx(cr)}} + \frac{f_{by}}{F_y} = 1 \tag{5-70b}$$

Equation (5-70b) can also be written in terms of allowable stresses.

Specifications do not cover biaxial bending except as it may be considered to be a special case of the beam column, for which the AISC formulas, Eqs. (6-23b) and (6-26b) apply. Thus, for LRFD, Eq. (6-26b) yields, with $P = 0$,

$$\frac{M_{ux}}{\phi M_{nx}} + \frac{M_{uy}}{\phi M_{ny}} \leq 1 \tag{5-71}$$

while for ASD, Eq. (6-23b) gives, with $f_a = 0$,

$$\frac{f_{bx}}{F_{bx}} + \frac{f_{by}}{F_{by}} \leq 1 \tag{5-72}$$

Beams subjected to biaxial bending can be designed only by trial and error. If an approximate range of the ratio S_x/S_y for a particular shape or combination of shapes is known, a fairly close design can often be obtained on an allowable-stress basis from the following rearrangement of Eq. (5-64):

$$S_x = \frac{M_x}{f_b} + \frac{S_x}{S_y} \frac{M_y}{f_b} \tag{5-73}$$

Approximate values of S_x/S_y are given in Table 5-5 for W, S, and C shapes. The smaller numbers in each group of W's are for those shapes with relatively wide flanges, i.e., those which are more nearly square. Values for the S and C are

TABLE 5-5
Approximate values of S_x/S_y

Shape	Depth d, in	S_x/S_y
W	8–16	3–8
W	16–24	5–10
W	24–36	7–12
S	6–8	d
S	10–18	$0.75d$
S	20 and 24	$0.6d$
C	7 and under	$1.5d$
C	8–10	$1.25d$
C	12 and 15	d

related roughly to the depth. For an S12, for example, S_x/S_y is about $0.75 \times 12 = 9$.

A variation of Eq. (5-73) which is convenient for the W may be obtained by using approximate values of moment of inertia. If we neglect the web, the section moduli are given by

$$S_x = \frac{2bt(d/2)^2}{d/2} = btd$$

$$S_y = \frac{2tb^3/12}{b/2} = \frac{tb^2}{3}$$

from which $S_x/S_y = 3d/b$. The error in this approximation due to the omission of the moment of inertia of the web is offset closely by increasing the coefficient of d/b from 3 to 3.5. Substituting this value into Eq. (5-73), we get

$$S_x = \frac{M_x}{f_b} + 3.5\frac{d}{b}\frac{M_y}{f_b} \tag{5-74a}$$

Values of d/b for W's range about as follows:

Shapes 8 to 16 in deep, 1 to 2
Shapes 16 to 24 in deep, 1.5 to 2.5
Shapes 24 to 36 in deep, 2 to 3

Equation (5-74a) is based on yield moments. For LRFD or other specifications which are based on the plastic moment, the following modification may be used:

$$Z_x = \frac{M_x}{F_y} + 2.5\frac{d}{b}\frac{M_y}{F_y} \tag{5-74b}$$

Since Eqs. (5-74) make no allowance for lateral buckling, several trials may be necessary.

It will be recalled that lateral buckling is aggravated if vertical load acts on the top flange of a beam but relieved if it acts on the bottom flange (Art. 5-5). If lateral load acts on either flange, there is a twisting moment which is not accounted for in Eqs. (*a*) and (*b*). This twisting moment is likely to be adequately compensated for by the greater resistance to lateral buckling resulting from vertical load acting on the bottom flange, but if lateral load acts on either flange in combination with vertical load on the top flange, the effect is cumulative. Therefore, some provision must be made for the latter combination. It is quite common to make an allowance for the twisting moment by assuming that the lateral load is resisted only by the flange on which it acts. For symmetrical cross sections this is equivalent to taking the section modulus for the minor axis of the I at one-half its actual value or to doubling the bending moment due to the lateral loads.

An illustration of design for biaxial bending is given in the following example.

DP5-19-1 (AISC/ASD) and DP5-19-2 (AISC/LRFD): Crane-Runway Girder

In these examples the crane-runway girder for a crane which operates on a 42-ft bridge is designed. The lifting capacity is 15 tons and the weight of the trolley is 8 kips. The end-truck wheels are 9 ft 6 in on centers and run on 60-lb rails (rail weights are expressed in pounds per yard). The maximum wheel load from the weights of the lifted load, the trolley, and the weight of the bridge and cab is 26.8 kips. The following comments are intended to clarify the correspondingly lettered computations in the examples and apply to both except where noted otherwise.

a. The AISC-specified impact is 25 percent of the live load for runway girders of cab-operated traveling cranes.

b. The estimated weight of the girder includes 20 plf for the weight of the rail.

c. The lateral forces due to accelerations of the trolley and load are resisted by contact of the truck wheels with the rails, so the position of the wheels for maximum lateral moment is the same as that for maximum moment in the vertical plane. The specified lateral force is a minimum of 20 percent of the sum of the weights of the lifted load and the crane trolley. According to the specifications, this force may be assumed to be divided equally between the two girders of the runway, which explains the factor 0.10 in this calculation. The lateral force gives rise to twisting moments on the crane girder, as well as bending moments in the horizontal plane, and since the vertical loads act on the top flange, some provision must be made for the twisting moment. In this example we use the approximation mentioned in Art. 5-19, namely, that only the top flange of the girder resists the lateral force.

d. A crane girder 40 ft long is certain to be more than 2 ft deep. Therefore, in Eq. (5-74) we take the most favorable value of d/b for W shapes in the 24- to 36-in range, which is 2. Furthermore, we double the moment due to the lateral force, which is equivalent to the assumption that it is resisted only by the top flange.

e. **ASD.** The W30 × 173 is the lightest shape for which d/b is about 2 and whose section modulus S_x is close to the estimated required value. Values of S_x, S_y, d/A_f, and r_T are from the AISC Manual.

CRANE RUNWAY GIRDER   DP5–19–1

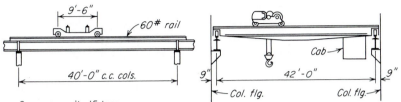

Crane capacity 15 tons
Max. end-truck wheel load 26.8^k
Weight of trolley 8.0^k
AISC/ASD spec. A36 steel

Crane girder

$$M = \frac{53.6 \times 17.62 \times 17.62}{40} = 416^{'k}$$
$$M = \frac{53.6 \times 15.25 \times 20}{40} = 409^{'k}$$

Impact 25% $104^{'k}$ (a)
Girder $0.275 \times 40^2/8$ $\underline{55^{'k}}$ (b)
                              $575^{'k} = 6900^{''k}$

Moment from lateral force $= 0.10 \times \dfrac{30+8}{53.6} \times 416^{'k} = 29.5^{'k} = 354^{''k}$ (c)

$S_x = \dfrac{6900}{24} + 3.5 \times 2 \times \dfrac{2 \times 354}{24} = 287 + 206 = 493$ (d)

Try $W30 \times 173$, $S_x = 539$, $S_y = 79.8$, $d/A_f = 1.91$, $r_T = 3.94$ (e)

$\dfrac{Ld}{A_f} = 480 \times 1.91 = 917$, $F_{bx} = \dfrac{12,000}{917} = 13.1$ ksi

$\dfrac{L}{r_T} = \dfrac{480}{3.94} = 122$; $\sqrt{\dfrac{510,000}{36}} = 119$; $F_{bx} = \dfrac{170,000}{122^2} = 11.4$ ksi

$\dfrac{f_{bx}}{F_{bx}} + \dfrac{f_{by}}{F_{by}} = \dfrac{6900/539}{13.1} + \dfrac{2 \times 354/79.8}{0.75 \times 36} = 1.30 > 1$ N.G.   (f)

Try $W30 \times 211$, $S_x = 663$, $S_y = 100$, $d/A_f = 1.56$, $r_T = 3.99$

$\dfrac{Ld}{A_f} = \dfrac{480}{1.56} = 749$, $F_{bx} = \dfrac{12,000}{749} = 16.0$ ksi

$\dfrac{L}{r_T} = \dfrac{480}{3.99} = 120$, $F_{bx} = \dfrac{170,000}{120^2} = 11.8$ ksi

$\dfrac{f_{bx}}{F_{bx}} + \dfrac{f_{by}}{F_{by}} = \dfrac{6900/63}{16.0} + \dfrac{2 \times 354/100}{0.75 \times 36} = 0.91 < 1$ O.K.

Deflection: $\dfrac{\Delta}{L} = \dfrac{5}{48} \dfrac{ML}{EI} = \dfrac{5}{48} \times \dfrac{416 \times 12 \times 40 \times 12}{29,000 \times 10,300} = \dfrac{1}{1197}$ (g)

CRANE RUNWAY GIRDER   DP5-19-2

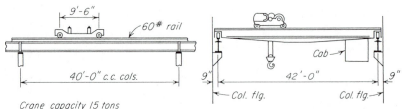

Crane capacity 15 tons
Max. end-truck wheel load 26.8^k
Weight of trolley 8.0^k
AISC/LRFD spec. A36 steel

Factored wheel load = 1.6 x 26.8 = 42.9^k
Factored estimated weight of girder = 1.2 x 0.275 = 0.330 kips/ft   (a)

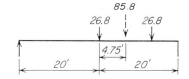

$M_x = 85.8 \times 17.62 \times 17.62/40 = 666^{'k}$

Impact 25%	167	(a)
Girder 0.33 x 40²/8	66	(b)
	899$^{'k}$= 10,790 $^{"k}$	

Fractored lateral-force moment = $0.10 \dfrac{1.6\,(30+8)}{85.8} \times 666 = 47^{'k} = 564^{"k}$ (c)

$$Z_x = \frac{10,790}{0.9 \times 36} + 2.5 \times 2\,\frac{2 \times 564}{0.9 \times 36} = 507$$ (d)

Try W27 x 161, $Z_x = 512$, $Z_y = 109$, $\phi M_{px} = 1380^{'k}$, $\phi M_r = 887^{'k}$, $L_p = 13.5^{'k}$, $L_r = 42.8'$ (e)

$$\phi M_{nx} = \phi M_{px} - (\phi M_{px} - \phi M_{pr})\,\frac{L_b - L_p}{L_r - L_p}$$

$$1380 - (1380 - 887)\frac{40 - 13.5}{42.8 - 13.5} = 934^{'k} < 1380$$

$\phi M_{ny} = 0.9 \times 109 \times 36/12 = 294^{'k}$

$$\frac{M_{ux}}{\phi M_{nx}} + \frac{M_{uy}}{\phi M_{ny}} = \frac{10,790}{934 \times 12} - \frac{2 \times 564}{294 \times 12} = 1.12 > 1$$ (f)

Try W30 x 191, $Z_y = 138$, $\phi M_{px} = 1820^{'k}$, $\phi M_{ux} = 1170^{'k}$, $L_p = 14.4'$, $L_r = 45.4'$

$$\phi M_{nx} = 1820 - (1820 - 1170)\frac{40 - 14.4}{45.4 - 14.1} = 1283^{'k} < 1820$$

$\phi M_{ny} = 0.9 \times 138 \times 36/12 = 373^{'k}$

$$\frac{10,790}{1283 \times 2} + \frac{2 \times 564}{373 \times 12} = 0.95 < 1 \ \ O.K.$$

Deflection:

$$M = 666/1.6 = 416^{'k} \quad \frac{\Delta}{L} = \frac{5}{48}\frac{ML}{EI} = \frac{5}{48} \times \frac{416 \times 12 \times 40 \times 12}{29,000 \times 9170} = \frac{1}{1065}$$ (g)

LRFD. The W27 × 161 is the lightest shape for which d/b is about 2 and whose plastic section modulus is close to the estimated required value. Values of Z_x, S_x, Z_y, L_p, and r_T are from the AISC Manual.

f. The specification interaction formula for members subject to bending and axial force is used here, with $P = 0$.

g. Equation (5-11a) is used to calculate Δ/L. Deflection due only to live load, excluding impact, need be considered. According to Table 5-4, Δ would be multiplied by 1.02 if the two wheels were at the third points of the girder. However, the wheels are only 9 ft 6 in apart, so the correction factor would be somewhat smaller. The AISC specifications do not prescribe deflection limits for crane-runway girders. The Canadian standard[11] recommendation for simple-span runway girders for cranes with a capacity less than 25 tons is 1/600.

It will be noted that the LRFD design is a W30 × 191, while for ASD it is a W30 × 211. This is largely because the ASD allowable stresses in the denominators of the moment terms in the interaction formula are conservative. The lateral-buckling allowable stress in the first moment term is conservative because it is taken as the larger of the two values obtained by omitting, in turn, one of the two terms on the right side of Eq. (5-4), as was explained in Art. 5-8. But both terms are used in the LRFD formula, Eq. (5-30). Thus, the first term in the interaction formula will always be larger in ASD, Eq. (5-72), than in LRFD, Eq. (5-71). This difference could be reduced to a negligible value if the AISC/ASD specification were to adopt a formula of the type used in the Canadian Standard[11] [Eq. (5-15)]. The second term in Eq. (5-72) yields $M/0.75F_y S_y$, while the second term in Eq. (5-71) gives $1.6M/0.9F_y Z_y$, where 1.6 is the live-load load factor and 0.9 is the resistance factor. The ratio of the ASD value to the LRFD value is $0.75Z_y/S_y$, and since Z_y/S_y is about 1.5 for weak-axis bending of W shapes (Art. 5-2), this gives 1.12. Thus, the W in biaxial bending will, in general, be heavier in ASD design than in LRFD design.

If the design procedure illustrated in Fig. 5-39 and described in Art. 5-19 is used in the ASD design of the crane girder, a W30 × 173, rather than the W30 × 211, turns out to be adequate. The analysis is expressed in the form

$$f_{bx} \le F_{bx(cr)}$$

$$f_{bx} + f_{by} \le F_{bx}$$

where $F_{bx(cr)}$ is the allowable lateral-buckling stress and F_{bx} is the allowable stress without regard to lateral buckling. Substituting the requisite values from the design sheet into these equations yields

$$f_{bx} = \frac{6900}{539} = 12.8 \text{ ksi} < 13.1 \qquad \text{O.K.}$$

$$f_{by} = 2 \times \frac{354}{79.8} = 8.9 \text{ ksi}$$

$$\overline{21.7 \text{ ksi} < 24} \qquad \text{O.K.}$$

Cranes of the type considered in these examples also exert longitudinal forces on their runways. The AISC specifications prescribe a longitudinal force equal to 10 percent of the maximum wheel loads, acting at the top of the rail. This force is $0.10 \times 53.6 = 5.36$ kips for the crane of these examples. The cross-sectional area of the W30 × 191 is 56.1 in², so the axial-force stress is only 5360/56.1 = 95 psi.

Example 5-19-1. Compute the bending stresses in a simply supported beam 20 ft long with a cross section made of two channels, a C12 × 20.7 and a C7 × 9.8 (Fig. 5-40). The load including the self-weight of the beam is 400 lb/ft. Assume that the load acts through the shear center (Art. 5-21), so there is no twisting moment.

Solution. The moments of inertia I_x and I_y and the product of inertia I_{xy} are computed in the table in Fig. 5-40. A multiplication sign preceding a number in the table indicates that the area (column 2) is being multiplied by that number to get the

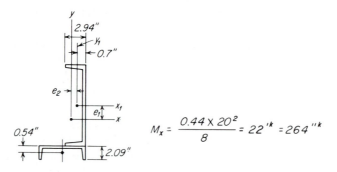

$$M_x = \frac{0.44 \times 20^2}{8} = 22^{\,\prime k} = 264^{\,\prime\prime k}$$

Shape	Area	Mom. abt. x_1	Mom. abt. y_1	I_x	I_y	I_{xy}
C12 × 20.7	6.09	—	—	×2.1²= 26.6	×0.9²= 4.9	×0.9 × 2.1 = 11.4
C7 × 9.8	2.87	×6.54= 18.7	× 2.8 = 8	×4.45²= 56.4	× 1.9²=10.3	×(-1.9) (-4.45)=24.1
	8.96	$\underline{18.7}$	$\underline{8}$	128.1	3.9	—
		$e_1 = 2.1''$	$e_2 = 0.9''$	$\underline{1.0}$	$\underline{21.1}$	—
				212.1	40.2	35.5

Since $M_y = 0$, Eq. (5-66) gives $f_b = \dfrac{M_x(I_y y - I_{xy} x)}{I_x I_y - I_{xy}^2}$

$I_x I_y - I_{xy}^2 = 212.1 \times 40.2 - 35.5^2 = 8530 - 1260 = 7270, \quad M_x = -264^{\,\prime\prime k}$

$\therefore f_b = \dfrac{-264(40.2y - 35.5x)}{7270} = -1.463y + 1.290x$

At neutral axis $f_b = 0 = -1.463y + 1.290x; \quad y = 0.881x$

Point 1: $x = -(2.94 - e_2 - 0.7) = -1.34''$

$\qquad y = 6 + e_1 = 8.1''$

$\qquad f_b = -1.463 \times 8.1 + 1.290(-1.34) = -11.8 - 1.7 = -13.5\ ksi$

Point 2: $x = e_2 + 0.7 = 1.6''$

$\qquad y = -(6 + 2.09 - e_2) = -6.0''$

$\qquad f_b = -1.463(-6.0) + 1.290 \times 1.6 = 8.8 + 2.1 = +10.9\ ksi$

FIGURE 5-40
Example 5-19-1.

product which follows the equal sign. The center of gravity is computed by taking moments of area about the axes $x_1 y_1$ of the 12-in channel. The moments of inertia I_x and I_y are determined next. The third and fourth entries in each column are the moments of inertia for the 12-in and the 7-in channels, respectively. In computing the product of inertia, I_{xy}, we note that the product of inertia for each channel about its own principal axes is zero, so only the term Axy in the transfer theorem contributes to I_{xy}.

According to the sign convention established in Art. 5-19 for bending (positive moment produces tension on an element of area in the first quadrant), M_x is negative. Equation (5-66) reduces to a simple form. The neutral axis is located in order to determine the points of maximum stress, following which the bending stresses are easily computed.

If it is assumed that there is no sidewise bending, the stresses reduce to those resulting from bending in the vertical plane, i.e.,

$$f_{b1} = \frac{-264 \times 8.1}{212} = -10.1 \text{ ksi} \qquad f_{b2} = \frac{-264 \, (-6.0)}{212} = 7.5 \text{ ksi}$$

These values are, respectively, 25 and 31 percent less than those previously computed. Whether lateral bending actually exists in any situation depends upon the nature of any attached construction and the manner in which it is fastened to the beam. In any case, it is always conservative to assume no restraint.

5-20 BUILT-UP BEAMS

Built-up sections are often required for special-purpose beams such as crane bridge beams and runway girders, spandrel beams, eave struts, and lintels. Sometimes it is a question of reinforcing a shape, as in Fig. 5-41a, to increase its capacity to support vertical loads. Crane runway girders are sometimes made as in Fig. 5-41b and c. The reinforcement of the top flange is intended to increase resistance to lateral forces. A top flange plate may be required as in Fig. 5-41b to serve as a shelf, rather than reinforcement, when the section is used as a lintel. In the case of lintels and eave struts it is usually a question of devising a section to suit the requirements of supported construction, as in Fig. 5-41d to f.

Assumptions are sometimes made to simplify the design of these sections. For example, an eave strut such as that of Fig. 5-41d may be designed as two independent members, the vertical channel to support gravity loads and the horizontal channel to support lateral loads. Similarly, when Fig. 5-41e and f are used as lintels, the shelf angle may be ignored and the channel designed to support the entire load. A crane runway built as in Fig. 5-41c may be designed on the

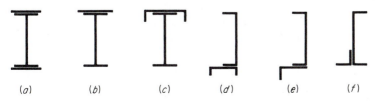

(a) $\qquad$ (b) $\qquad$ (c) $\qquad$ (d) $\qquad$ (e) $\qquad$ (f)

FIGURE 5-41

assumption that the I supports the vertical load while the channel resists the lateral force.

The required size of reinforcing plates of equal area on both flanges as in Fig. 5-41a can be determined very closely by noting that the moment of inertia of the compound beam is

$$I = I_i + 2A_f\left(\frac{d}{2}\right)^2 \tag{a}$$

where I_i = moment of inertia of primary shape (the I)
   A_f = area of one flange plate
   d = distance between centers of gravity of flange plates

Since the distances from the neutral axis to the outside flange surface and to the center of gravity and outside surface of the flange plate are very nearly the same, we may set them all equal to $d/2$. With this assumption, division of each term of Eq. (a) by $d/2$ gives

$$S = S_i + A_f d \tag{5-75}$$

where S and S_i are the section moduli of the compound section and the primary shape, respectively.

Although the design of unsymmetrical built-up beams is necessarily a trial-and-error procedure, it is possible to derive useful and fairly simple formulas to obtain close approximations for sections of the type shown in Fig. 5-41b and c. In Fig. 5-42, let A_i be the area of the primary shape and A_f the area of the flange plate. The eccentricity e is found by taking moments around the x axis of the primary shape

$$A_f c = (A_f + A_i)e$$

from which

$$e = \frac{pc}{1 + p} \tag{b}$$

where $p = A_f/A_i$. Then

$$c_1 = c - e = \frac{c}{1 + p} \tag{c}$$

$$c_2 = c + e = \frac{c(1 + 2p)}{1 + p} \tag{d}$$

The moment of inertia of the compound section is

$$I = I_i + A_i e^2 + pA_i c_1^2 \tag{e}$$

Substituting into this equation the values of e and c_1 from Eqs. (b) and (c) and simplifying, we find

$$I = I_i + A_i \frac{pc^2}{1 + p} \tag{f}$$

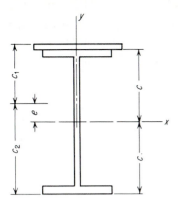

FIGURE 5-42

The section moduli $S_1 = I/c_1$ and $S_2 = I/c_2$ are found from Eqs. (c), (d), and (f) to be

$$S_1 = S_i(1 + p) + A_i pc \tag{g}$$

$$S_2 = \frac{1}{1 + 2p}[S_i(1 + p) + A_i pc] = \frac{S_1}{1 + 2p} \tag{h}$$

If the primary shape is an S or W, Eq. (g) can be put into a more convenient form. Substituting for S_i in Eq. (g) the value

$$\frac{I_i}{c} = \frac{A_i r_i^2}{c}$$

we get

$$S_1 = S_i + A_i p\left(\frac{r_i^2}{c} + c\right)$$

But, for I sections, $r^2 = 2c^2/3$ very nearly, so finally

$$S_1 = S_i + \tfrac{5}{3}A_f c \tag{5-76}$$

$$S_2 = \frac{S_1}{1 + 2p} \tag{5-77}$$

These equations will give close approximations for sections of the type shown in Fig. 5-41b and c. For design purposes, Eqs. (5-76) and (5-77) may be written

$$A_f = 0.6\frac{S_1 - S_i}{c} \tag{5-78a}$$

$$A_f = 0.6\frac{S_2 - S_i}{c - 1.2S_2/A_i} \tag{5-78b}$$

It is important to remember that c in this equation refers to the primary shape and not to the compound section (Fig. 5-42).

The expressions derived above are useful in allowable-stress design but not in plastic design or in LRFD design of compact sections, which are based on the plastic moment M_p. In Art. 5-3 it was pointed out that for the stress distribution corresponding to the fully plastic condition the location of the neutral axis requires equal areas above and below the axis. If a symmetrical W or S shape is reinforced with equal plates on the top and the bottom so as to retain its symmetry,

$$Z = Z_i + 2A_p\left(\frac{d}{2} + \frac{t}{2}\right) = Z_i + A_p(d + t) \tag{i}$$

If the shape is made unsymmetrical by adding a plate to only one flange, it is necessary to determine the location of the neutral axis and then evaluate Z. The location of the neutral axis can be determined from

$$A_p + b_f t_f + t_w d_1 = b_f t_f + t_w d_2 \tag{j}$$

where A_p = area of reinforcing plate
  b_f = width of flange of primary shape
  t_f = thickness of flange of primary shape
  t_w = thickness of web of primary shape
  d_1 = vertical dimension of web which acts with reinforcing plate and flange to which it is attached
  d_2 = vertical dimension of the web which acts with the other flange of the primary shape

Substituting $d_2 = d - d_1 - 2t_f$ into Eq. (j), we find

$$d_1 = \frac{d}{2} - t_f - \frac{1}{2}\frac{A_p}{t_w} \tag{5-79a}$$

where d = depth of primary shape. The value of Z can then be written as

$$Z = A_p\left(d_1 + t_f + \frac{t_p}{2}\right) + b_f t_f(d_1 + d_2 + t_f) + \frac{t_w}{2}(d_1^2 + d_2^2) \tag{5-79b}$$

Although this is an accurate expression for Z, it is of little assistance in determining the required area of the plate. Therefore, either Eqs. (5-78) must be employed as a guide or a trial-and-error procedure must be used.

Example 5-20-1 (AISC/ASD and AISC/LRFD). A number of beams in an existing building must be strengthened because of remodeling. The beams are A36 W24 × 55, supported laterally. The increased load produces moments of 65 ft·kips DL and 205 ft·kips LL. The construction is such that reinforcement is limited to a plate welded to the bottom flange. What A36 plate can be used?

Solution

ASD. The W24 × 55 is compact in A36 steel. Therefore, $F_b = 0.66 \times 36 = 24$ ksi, and with $M = 65 + 205 = 270$ ft·kips we get

$$S_x = \frac{270 \times 12}{24} = 135 \text{ in}^3$$

The section modulus of the W24 × 55 is 114 in³. The required size of the plate can be approximated by Eq. (5-78b):

$$A_f = 0.6 \, \frac{135 - 114}{23.55/2 - 1.2 \times 135/16.2} = \frac{0.6 \times 21}{11.78 - 10.00} = 7.1 \text{ in}^2$$

The flange of the W24 is 7 in wide. A 9-in plate can be welded to it downhand. Therefore, try a $9 \times \frac{13}{16}$ plate, for which $A = 7.32$ in². The eccentricity e (Fig. 5-42) is

$$e = \frac{7.32 \times 12.19}{7.32 + 16.2} = 3.80 \text{ in}$$

The moment of inertia of the reinforced section is

$$I_x = 1340 + 16.2 \times 3.80^2 + 7.32 \times 8.39^2 = 2090 \text{ in}^4$$

$$\frac{I_x}{c} = \frac{2090}{15.58} = 134 \text{ in}^3 \qquad M = \frac{134 \times 24}{12} = 268 \text{ ft·kips}$$

This moment is about 0.7 percent less than the required value, 270 ft·kips. If a $9 \times \frac{7}{8}$ plate is used instead of the $9 \times \frac{13}{16}$ plate, the moment is 272 ft·kips.

LRFD. The required capacity is

$$M = 1.2 \times 65 + 1.6 \times 205 = 406 \text{ ft·kips}$$

For the W24 × 55, $d = 23.57$ in, $b_f = 7.005$ in, $t_f = 0.505$ in, $t_w = 0.395$ in. Try a $9 \times \frac{1}{2}$ plate, for which $A = 4.50$ in².
From Eq. (5-79a)

$$d_1 = \frac{23.57}{2} - 0.505 - \frac{1}{2} \times \frac{4.50}{0.395} = 5.58 \text{ in}$$

$$d_2 = d - 2t_f - d_1 = 23.57 - 2 \times 0.505 - 5.58 = 16.98 \text{ in}$$

Substituting these values and the other dimensions of the section into Eq. (5-79b) gives $Z = 173.2$ in³. Then

$$M_p = 173.2 \times 36 = 6235 \text{ in·kips} = 520 \text{ ft·kips}$$

$$\phi M_p = 0.9 \times 520 = 468 \text{ ft·kips} > 406$$

5-21 THE SHEAR CENTER

If the load on a beam is in a plane parallel to a principal plane (the yz plane, say) and passes through the shear center, the beam bends, without twisting, about the x axis. The stresses are given by $f = M_x y/I_x$ and $q = V_y A\bar{y}/I_x$. For any other condition of loading there are additional stresses because of twisting. Such twisting is not a primary consideration so long as the load passes through the shear center even if it is not in a principal plane. This is because the twisting moments in this case result from eccentricities of the end reactions due to the component of deflection normal to the plane of loading. If the load does not pass through the shear center, the resulting twisting moments are more significant. However, in many cases attached construction forces the beam to bend in the plane of the loads even when that plane does not intersect the shear center. Shearing stresses resulting from twist and the bending stresses caused by nonuniform warping can be determined by methods discussed in Art. 4-19.

The shear center can be located by considering the z-axis moment of the shear stresses caused by bending. In Fig. 5-43a are shown four elements cut from the channel in Fig. 5-43b, which supports a load P, parallel to the web, acting through the shear center S. The bending stresses increase in the direction of the positive z axis. The difference between the tensile forces acting on the element *abcd* must be balanced by a shearing force on the vertical face *cd*, since there is no force on the external vertical face *ab*. This shearing force and the resultant of the tensile forces form a couple which is balanced by a couple consisting of shearing forces on the vertical surfaces *ad* and *bc*. The same reasoning proves the existence of the shearing forces shown on the other three elements. The resultant internal shearing forces are shown in Fig. 5-43b. Since the horizontal shearing forces H form a couple, equilibrium exists only if the load P and the vertical shearing force $V = P$ constitute an equal and opposite couple.

The shearing forces on several types of cross section are shown in Fig. 5-44. In all but Fig. 5-44e bending is assumed to be in the vertical plane. The horizontal shears for the symmetrical I in Fig. 5-44a form self-equilibrating couples, so the shear center S coincides with the center of gravity G. If the bottom flange is smaller than the top flange, S lies above G at the distance given in Fig. 4-46f. In the limiting case where the section becomes a tee, the shear center falls at the intersection of the flange and web centerlines (Fig. 4-46c).

The shear center of the equal-legged zee in Fig. 5-44b is at the centroid, since the resultant of the equal horizontal shears intersects the vertical shear at that point. The inclination θ_x of the resultant R of these shear forces can be found from Eq. (5-66) as follows. Since the cross section is bent around the x axis, the second term on the right in that equation must vanish. Thus, $M_x/M_y = I_x/I_{xy}$.

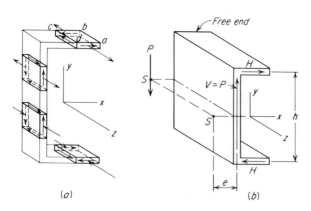

(a)   (b)   **FIGURE 5-43**

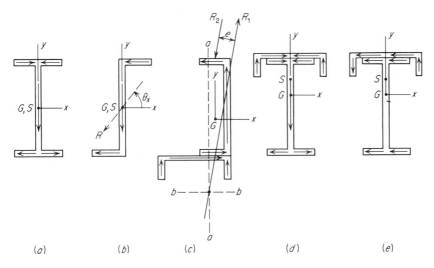

FIGURE 5-44

But the resultant R must lie in the plane of the loading, so

$$\tan \theta_x = \frac{M_x}{M_y} = \frac{I_x}{I_{xy}} \qquad (a)$$

The shearing forces for a section consisting of an I and a channel are shown in Fig. 5-44d for bending in the vertical plane and in Fig. 5-44e for bending in the horizontal plane. The resultant of the forces in Fig. 5-44d is evidently a vertical force at the centerline of the web. The resultant in Fig. 5-44e is horizontal, but it lies nearer the top flange than the bottom. The intersection of this resultant with that of Fig. 5-44d is the shear center. For a section with this kind of symmetry, the position of the horizontal resultant can be determined by observing that if the member bends sidewise without twisting, the two flanges have equal radii of curvature at the neutral (y) axis. Then since $M = EI/\rho$, the lateral moment must be resisted by the flanges in proportion to their moments of inertia. Since the shearing forces on the two flanges are in the same ratio as the moments and since their sum is the resultant horizontal shear, a simple equation of moments locates the resultant. The position of the shear center shown in Fig. 4-46f can be verified in this way. The higher shear center of the cross section in Fig. 5-44d as compared with that in Fig. 5-44a demonstrates the effectiveness of the reinforced compression flange in reducing the twisting moments from lateral forces on crane girders.

The cross section shown in Fig. 5-44c is often used as an eave strut. The shearing forces shown result if the strut is constrained to bend in the vertical plane. The resultant of the vertical shearing forces lies on a line aa, while that of the horizontal shearing forces is on bb. The resultant shearing force R_1 acts at the intersection of aa and bb and makes with the horizontal the angle θ_x given by Eq. (a). If the strut supports a gravity load on its top flange, the resultant R_2 of this

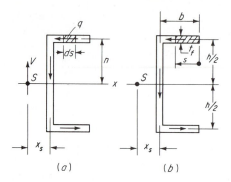

(a) (b) **FIGURE 5-45**

load and of a lateral restraining force supplied by roof construction attached to the top flange acts on the flange. The corresponding eccentricity e is shown in the figure. The shear center for this cross section is not at the intersection of aa and bb. Its position can be determined by locating the resultant shearing force for bending in the horizontal plane and finding the intersection of this resultant with R_1.

If the cross section has an axis of symmetry, the shear center S lies on that axis, as in the channel of Fig. 5-45. If x is the axis of symmetry, the location of S is given by

$$Vx_s = \int qr \, ds \tag{5-80}$$

where x_s = distance of S from center of moments
q = shear-flow intensity
r = moment arm of q with respect to the center of moments
ds = element of length

The center of moments is arbitrary and is shown here at the web centerline to eliminate the web shear in the equation of moments.

To evaluate x_s for the channel, we compute q at the distance s from the flange tip (Fig. 5-45b),

$$q = \frac{Va\bar{y}}{I_x} = \frac{V}{I_x} t_f s \frac{h}{2}$$

The moment arm r of q is $h/2$. Substituting these values into Eq. (5-80) and multiplying by 2 to account for the moment of the shear force in the opposite flange, we get

$$Vx_s = 2 \int_0^b \frac{V}{I_x} t_f s \frac{h}{2} \frac{h}{2} \, ds = 2 \frac{V}{I_x} \frac{t_f h^2}{4} \frac{b^2}{2}$$

$$x_s = \frac{t_f b^2 h^2}{4 I_x}$$

If the cross section has no axis of symmetry, the shear center is located by evaluating Eq. (5-80) twice, once for a shear V_y and once for a shear V_x. If x, y are principal axes, the shear intensity q for V_y is given by the first term on the right in Eq. (5-65), while that for V_x is given by the second term. If x, y are not principal axes, Eq. (5-67) must be used.

5-22 COMPOSITE BEAMS

Floor construction in buildings and bridges often consists of a reinforced-concrete slab supported on steel beams. In the preceding discussions in this chapter, it has been assumed that the beams act independently of the floor slab, because a natural bond cannot be depended upon to develop the shear VQ/I on the interface between the slab and the beam. If the beam is completely encased in concrete, however, as in Fig. 5-46, the two will act as a unit, provided certain conditions (to be discussed later) are satisfied. Alternatively, a mechanical bond can be established by means of *shear connectors*, which force the slab to act as an integral part of the beam. Such beams are called *composite beams*. They offer advantages in the form of possible reductions in depth, reduction of 20 to 30 percent in the weight of the steel beam, and increased stiffness of the floor system. (In the elastic range, composite beams are two to three times as stiff as noncomposite beams.)

Two types of construction are used. Commonly, formwork for the concrete slab is supported on the steel beams so that the weight of the concrete is carried by the steel beam alone. However, if the steel beam is supported by shores that are not removed until the concrete has attained sufficient strength, both dead load and live load are resisted by composite action.

It is common practice to use light-gage stay-in-place formed steel deck which serves as a form for the concrete and acts with it to resist floor loads. Such decking is available in a variety of configurations. Metal decking is generally placed so that the ribs or corrugations are perpendicular to the supporting beams, although they may also be placed so that the ribs are parallel to the beam axis.

A composite floor is assumed to act as a series of T beams. The beams are analyzed by transforming the effective cross-sectional area of the concrete slab into an equivalent area of steel. For normal concrete ACI 318-89 permits the modular ratio $n = E_s/E_c$ to be based on $E_c = 57,000\sqrt{f'_c}$, where E_c and f'_c are in pounds per square inch. This gives $n = (29 \times 10^6)/(57,000\sqrt{f'_c}) = 500/\sqrt{f'_c}$. The AISC/LRFD specification suggests $E_c = w^{1.5}\sqrt{f'_c}$, where $w =$ unit weight of

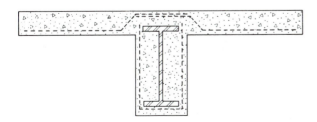

FIGURE 5-46

concrete, lb/ft^3, and f'_c is in kips per square inch. This formula gives E_c in kips per square inch.

The effective flange width of the slab varies with the specification. The AASHTO specification considers the effective width of the slab to be the smaller of:

1. One-fourth of the beam span
2. The distance center to center of girders
3. Twelve times the thickness of the slab

and for girders having a flange on one side only:

1. One-twelfth of the span
2. One-half the distance center to center of the next girder
3. Six times the thickness of the slab

According to the AISC ASD and LRFD specifications the effective widths on each side of the beam center-line must not exceed:

1. One-eighth of the beam span, center-to-center of supports
2. One-half the distance to the centerline of the adjacent beam, or, for edge beams, the distance to the edge of the slab

It will be noted that AISC specifies effective widths on each side of the beam, while AASHTO specifies the sum of the two, that is, the full width of the flange. Also, in the AISC definition there is no limit to the effective width in terms of the slab thickness, as in the AASHTO specification. Previous editions of the AISC/ASD specification limited the effective projection beyond the edge of the beam to eight times the slab thickness. According to specification commentaries on composite beams, dropping this requirement is in accord with both theoretical and experimental studies, as well as composite-beam codes in other countries.

5-23 DESIGN OF COMPOSITE BEAMS

Encased beams. Steel sections totally encased in concrete (Fig. 5-46) which depend on natural bond for interaction must have adequate cover. Requirements of the AISC specifications are the following:

1. Concrete cover over the beam sides and soffit must be at least 2 in
2. Cover must be at least $1\frac{1}{2}$ in at the top of the beam and 2 in at the bottom

3. The concrete encasement must contain adequate mesh or other reinforcement throughout the depth and across the soffit to prevent spalling of the concrete.

Since there can be no local or lateral buckling of an encased beam, it can be treated as a compact section. In the AISC specifications two alternative methods of design are allowed.

1. The beam may be sized assuming the steel section to carry all loads applied prior to hardening of the concrete, unless such loads are supported by shoring, and the composite section to carry all dead and live load acting after the concrete has hardened. If shoring is used, all loads may be assumed to be resisted by the composite section.
2. The steel section alone may be proportioned to resist the positive moment due to all loads. If this method is used, shoring is not required.

ASD. The allowable stress is $0.66F_y$ for method 1 described above and $0.76F_y$ for method 2. It will be noted that these allowable values are based on the yield moment and the plastic moment, respectively, since the second is about 15 percent larger than the first. Section properties to compute these stresses are based on the elastic theory.

LRFD. For method 1 described above the nominal moment M_n is based on the superposition of elastic stresses, while in method 2 it is the plastic moment. In both cases the resistance factor $\phi_b = 0.90$. Permanent loads are multiplied by the dead-load factor and live loads by the live-load factor.

Beams with shear connectors. Most composite beams are built with shear connectors. The stress distribution at the ultimate bending strength of such a beam is shown in Fig. 5-47. The neutral axis may be in the slab, as in b, or in the steel beam, as in c. In either case, the moment is easily determined. Thus, for the case

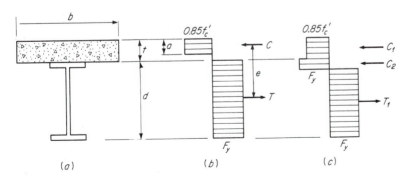

FIGURE 5-47

shown in b,

$$C = 0.85f_c'\,ba \qquad T = F_y A_s \qquad\qquad (5\text{-}81)$$

where a and b are defined in the figure and A_s is the area of the steel section. Since $C = T$ and f_c', b, F_y, and A_s are known, a can be computed to determine the moment arm of the couple. For the case shown in c,

$$C_1 = 0.85f_c'\,bt \qquad T = F_y A_s - C_2 \qquad T = C_1 + C_2 \qquad\qquad (5\text{-}82)$$

Eliminating T from the second and third of Eqs. (5-82) and substituting into the result the value of C_1 from the first gives

$$2C_2 = A_s F_y - 0.85f_c'\,bt \qquad\qquad (5\text{-}83)$$

Since everything on the right is known, C_2 can be computed, after which T and C_1 and the resulting moment are easily determined. Thus, whether the neutral axis is in the slab or in the steel beam, the adequacy of a given composite section is readily determined.

A good estimate of the AISC/LRFD required area A_s of the steel section, based on the ultimate moment M_u, is given by

$$A_s = \frac{M_u}{(0.5d + 0.8t)F_y} \qquad\qquad (5\text{-}84)$$

Design by the AISC/ASD specification gives a factor of safety of about 2.2 on ultimate strength. Therefore, an estimate of A_s in terms of the service-load moment M_s can be determined from

$$A_s = \frac{2.2M_s}{(0.5d + 0.8t)F_y} \qquad\qquad (5\text{-}85)$$

AISC/ASD. Design is based on elastic analysis, using the transformed section. The allowable stress in the steel section is $0.66F_y$. Lateral-torsional buckling need not be considered for the completed structure, but it must be guarded against during construction. The allowable stress in the concrete is $0.45f_c'$. However, the neutral axis is close to the top of the section, so the stress in the steel is usually the determining factor. Because of this, a lighter (but not necessarily cheaper) design can be achieved by using a cover plate on the bottom flange.

Reinforcement in the concrete slab parallel to the beam within the effective width of the slab may be included in computing the properties of composite sections. Such reinforcement must be anchored in compliance with the provisions of the applicable building code, and adequate shear connectors must be provided to develop the necessary shear force.

Section properties for unshored construction are computed by the elastic theory. The bending stress in the steel beam is taken to be the sum of (1) the stress based on the assumption that the steel section alone resists all loads applied before the concrete has reached 75 percent of its specified strength and (2) the stress based on the assumption that subsequent loads are resisted by the composite section. The allowable stress is $0.90F_y$. This requirement yields the equation

$$f = \frac{M_D}{S_{ts}} + \frac{M_L}{S_{tc}} \leq 0.90F_y \qquad (5\text{-}86)$$

where S_{ts} = section modulus of steel section and S_{tc} = section modulus of composite section. If this equation is satisfied, the stress on the steel section will not exceed 1.36 times the allowable stress for the steel section alone ($0.90F_y/0.66F_y = 1.36$).

The compressive stress in the concrete is calculated for the composite section, based on the load acting after the concrete has reached 75 percent of its specified compressive strength. The allowable stress is $0.45f'_c$.

AISC/LRFD. For positive moment the nominal value M_n is computed for the plastic distribution of stress on the composite section (Fig. 5-47) if $h_c/t_w \leq 640/\sqrt{F_{yf}}$ for the steel section, where h_c is defined in Table 5-3 and t_w is the web thickness. The resistance factor is $\phi_b = 0.85$. If $h_c/t_w > 640/\sqrt{F_{yf}}$, M_n is based on superposition of elastic stresses. The resistance factor is 0.90.

For negative moment M_n is based on the steel section alone. The resistance factor is 0.90. Alternatively M_n may be determined from the plastic stress distribution on the composite section, provided certain conditions are satisfied. For this procedure $\phi_b = 0.85$.

The steel section for unshored construction must be designed to support all loads applied before the concrete attains 75 percent of the specified value of f'_c, using the LRFD steel-beam procedures.

Shear and deflection. Shear in composite beams is assumed to be resisted by the steel beam alone. Deflection is computed by the usual formulas. Because of creep of the concrete, however, the deflection due to loads of long duration, such as dead loads, will be larger than the predicted value based on the properties of the transformed section used to evaluate stresses. A good estimate of long-term deflection can be made by using a transformed section based on double the value of n used to compute stresses. Deflection due to live loads of short duration should be based on the standard value of n.

Partially composite beams. It may be impossible to attain full composite action because enough shear connectors cannot be provided in the space available. Also, in cases where standard sizes result in a larger cross section than is needed, some economy may be achieved by using fewer connectors than the number required for full composite action. Such beams are called partially composite beams. Design is discussed in Art. 5-24.

Beams with stay-in-place decking. Examples of composite beams with stay-in-place corrugated metal decking are shown in Fig. 5-48. In order for the beams

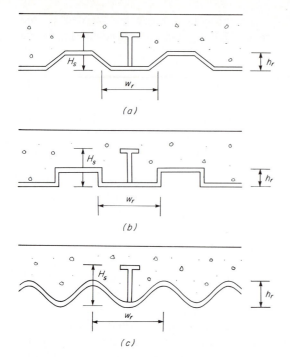

(a)

(b)

(c)

FIGURE 5-48
Composite beams with stay-in-place metal decking.

supporting this type of decking to be designed as composite beams the nominal rib height of the corrugations must not exceed 3 in. In addition, the average width of the concrete rib, w_r, should not be less than 2 in. The slab thickness above the steel deck must be at least 2 in and the stud shear connectors shown in the figure must be $\frac{3}{4}$ in in diameter or less and must extend at least $1\frac{1}{2}$ in above the top of the steel deck.

If the ribs are perpendicular to the steel beam, the concrete below the top of the steel deck is neglected in the determination of section properties, but for ribs parallel to the steel beam, the concrete below the top may be included. If the depth of the steel deck is equal to or greater than $1\frac{1}{2}$ in, the average width of the rib must not be less than 2 in if a single stud is placed at any transverse section along the beam. If more than one stud is to be placed at any transverse section along the beam, the width of the rib must be 2 in plus 4 stud diameters for each stud after the first one.

The limiting dimensions noted above were established to hold the dimensions of formed-deck composite beams within those of the specimens used in 75 tests.

Example 5-23-1 (AISC/ASD). The layout of beams and girders for a typical warehouse floor is shown in Fig. 5-49. The live load is 200 psf. The slab thickness is 4 in, concrete strength f'_c is 3000 psi, and steel is A36. Determine the beam required. Assume it to be simply supported. Construction is to be without shores.

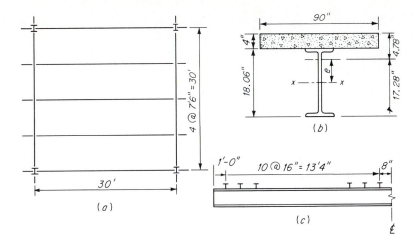

FIGURE 5-49

Solution. The allowable stresses and the modular ratio are $F_b = 24$ ksi (assuming the section will be compact), $f_c = 0.45f'_c = 1.35$ ksi, $n = 500/\sqrt{3000} = 9$. The dead-load and live-load moments are:

Load		Weight, klf	Moment
Dead:	Slab $= 7.5 \times \frac{4}{12} \times 150 = 0.375$		
	Beam (estimated) $= 0.050$		
	$\overline{0.425} \times 30^2 \times \frac{12}{8} =$		575
Live:	7.5×200	$= 1.500 \times 30^2 \times \frac{12}{8} = 2025$	
		$\overline{1.925}$ klf	$\overline{2600}$ in·kips

The dead load calculated above is based on each beam supporting the slab from centerline to centerline of beams, a dimension of 7.5 ft. The weight of the concrete is taken at 150 lb/ft³, so the weight of the slab is $\frac{4}{12} \times 150$. Each beam is assumed to support live load from centerline to centerline of beams.

From Eq. (5-85), assuming a 16-in beam,

$$A_s = \frac{2.2 \times 2600}{(0.5 \times 16 + 0.8 \times 4)(36)} = 14.2 \text{ in}^2$$

A W16 × 50 gives 14.7 in². Assuming an 18-in beam,

$$A_s = \frac{2.2 \times 2600}{(0.5 \times 18 + 0.8 \times 4)(36)} = 13.1 \text{ in}^2$$

A W18 × 46 gives 13.5 in². The lightest 21-in W weighs 44 plf. This would give a slightly lighter beam but at a cost of 3 in of headroom. Therefore, the W18 × 46 appears to be a good choice. It is a compact section, as was assumed.

The effective flange width on each side of the steel section is the smaller of (a) $L/8 = \frac{30}{8} = 3.75$ ft and (b) half the spacing of beams = 3.75 ft (Art. 5-22). The transformed effective flange width is $b/n = 2 \times 3.75 \times \frac{12}{9} = 10.0$ in. The properties of the transformed section, Fig. 5-49b, are:

Section	Area	Moment about x		I_x
W18 × 46 = 13.5			× 8.25^2 =	919
			I_0 =	712
4 × 10.0 =	40.0	× 11.03 = +441	40.0 × 2.78^2 =	309
	53.5	+441	10.0 × $4^3/12$ =	53
		$e = +8.25$ in		1993 in⁴

The tension-flange moduli are $S_s = 78.8$ in³ for the W18 × 46 and $S_{tc} = 1993/(8.25 + 9.03) = 115$ in³ for the transformed composite section. Since construction is to be without shores, Eq. (5-86) must be satisfied. This gives

$$f = \frac{575}{78.8} + \frac{2025}{115} = 7.30 + 18.08 = 25.4 \text{ ksi} < 0.9F_y$$

The concrete compressive stress is determined for the composite section based on the load applied after the concrete has attained 75 percent of its required strength (Art. 5-23). Therefore, $M = 2025$ in·kips and

$$f_c = \frac{Mc}{nI} = \frac{2025 \times 4.78}{9 \times 1993} = 0.54 < 1.35 \text{ ksi}$$

The deflections are given by Eq. (5-11a). Using the dead-load moment of 575 in·kips with the moment of inertia of the W18 × 46,

$$\Delta = \frac{5 \times 575 \times 360^2}{48 \times 29,000 \times 712} = 0.376 \text{ in}$$

For the live-load moment of 2025 in·kips we use the moment of inertia of the composite section:

$$\Delta = \frac{5 \times 2025 \times 360^2}{29,000 \times 1993} = 0.473 \text{ in}$$

The ratio of live-load deflection to span is 0.473/360 = 1/761. There is no allowance for creep in this calculation, however, and if the live load is likely to be sustained for long periods of time, as in a warehouse, $n = 2 \times 9 = 18$ should be used to compute the moment of inertia.

The ultimate resisting moment of the beam will now be determined. This is for illustrative purposes, since it is not required by the AISC/ASD specification.

Assuming the neutral axis to be in the slab, Eq. (5-81) gives

$$C = T = F_y A_s = 36 \times 13.5 = 486 \text{ kips}$$

$$a = \frac{C_c}{0.85f_c' b} = \frac{486}{0.85 \times 3 \times 90} = 2.12 \text{ in}$$

Since $a < t$, the neutral axis is in the slab, as was assumed. The moment arm of the resisting couple is

$$\frac{d}{2} + t - \frac{a}{2} = \frac{18.06}{2} + 4 - \frac{2.12}{2} = 11.97 \text{ in}$$

Therefore, $M = 486 \times 11.97 = 5820$ in·kips. Since the maximum service-load moment is 2600 in·kips, the factor of safety is $5820/2600 = 2.24$.

Example 5-23-2 (AISC/LRFD). The layout of beams and girders for a typical warehouse floor is shown in Fig. 5-50. The live load is 200 psf. The slab thickness is 4 in, concrete strength f'_c is 3000 psi, and steel is A36. Determine the beam required. Assume it to be simply supported. Construction is to be without shores.

Solution. The modular ratio is $n = 500/\sqrt{3000} = 9$. The dead-load and live-load moments are:

Load		Weight, klf	Moment
Dead:	Slab $= 7.5 \times \frac{4}{12} \times 150 = 0.375$		
	Beam (estimated) $= 0.050$		
	$\overline{0.425} \times 30^2 \times \frac{12}{8} = 575$		
Live:	7.5×200	$= 1.500 \times 30^2 \times \frac{12}{8} = 2025$	

The dead load calculated above is based on each beam supporting the slab from centerline to centerline of beams, a dimension of 7.5 ft. The weight of the concrete is taken at 150 lb/ft³, so the weight of the slab weight is $\frac{4}{12} \times 150$. Each beam is assumed to support live load from centerline to centerline of beams.

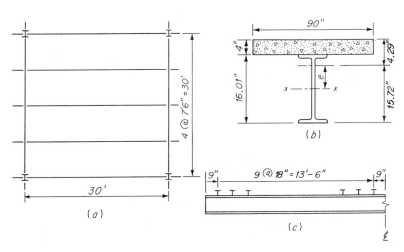

FIGURE 5-50

The design moment is

$$M = 1.2M_{DL} + 1.6M_{LL} = 1.2 \times 575 + 1.6 \times 2025 = 3930 \text{ in·kips}$$

Since $\phi_b = 0.85$ the required ultimate capacity is $3930/0.85 = 4625$ in·kips. Then from Eq. (5-84), assuming a 16-in beam,

$$A_s = \frac{4625}{(0.5 \times 16 + 0.8 \times 4)(36)} = 11.5 \text{ in}^2$$

A W16 × 40 gives 11.8 in². Assuming an 18-in beam,

$$A_s = \frac{4625}{(0.5 \times 18 + 0.8 \times 4)(36)} = 10.5 \text{ in}^2$$

A W18 × 40 gives 11.8 in². The lightest 21-in W weighs 44 plf. Therefore, either the W18 × 40 or the W16 × 40 may be satisfactory. The W16 × 40 provides additional headroom, so we will try it as the first choice.

The effective flange width on each side of the steel section is the smaller of (a) $L/8 = \frac{30}{8} = 3.75$ ft and (b) half the spacing of the beams = 3.75 ft (Art. 5-22). The transformed effective flange width is $b/n = 2 \times 3.75 \times \frac{12}{9} = 10.0$ in. From Fig. 5-47b

$$T = A_s F_y = 11.8 \times 36 = 425 \text{ kips}$$

$$C = 0.85 f'_c a \times 90 = 425 \text{ kips}$$

With $f'_c = 3$ ksi, $a = 1.85$ in. Then with $d = 18.16$ in,

$$e = \tfrac{1}{2} \times 16.01 + 4 - \tfrac{1}{2} \times 1.85 = 11.08 \text{ in}$$

$$M_n = 11.08 \times 425 = 4709 \text{ in·kips}$$

$$\phi_b M_n = 0.85 \times 4709 = 4000 \text{ in·kips} > 3930 \qquad \text{O.K.}$$

Deflections must be checked for the service loads. The properties of the transformed section, Fig. (5-50b), are:

Section	Area	Moment about x	I_x	
W16 × 40 = 11.8			× 7.72² =	703
			I_0 =	518
4 × 10.0 =	40.0	× 10.0 = +400	40.0 × 2.29² =	210
	51.8	+400	10.0 × 4³/12 =	53
		$e = +7.72$ in		1484 in⁴

The deflections are given by Eq. (5-11a). Using the dead-load moment of 575 in·kips with the moment of inertia of the W16 × 40,

$$\Delta = \frac{5 \times 575 \times 360^2}{48 \times 29,000 \times 518} = 0.517 \text{ in}$$

For the live-load moment of 2025 in·kips on the composite section,

$$\Delta = \frac{5 \times 2025 \times 360^2}{48 \times 29{,}000 \times 1484} = 0.635 \text{ in}$$

The ratio of live-load deflection to span is $0.635/360 = 1/567$. There is no allowance for creep in this calculation, however, and if the live load is likely to be sustained for long periods of time, as in a warehouse, $n = 2 \times 9 = 18$ should be used to compute the moment of inertia.

Since construction is to be without shores, the W16 × 40 must be able to support the dead-load moment of 575 ft·kips on its laterally unsupported length of 30 ft, according to the procedure discussed in Art. 5-9. From the LRFD Manual's table of uniform-load constants, $L_r = 14.7$ ft. Therefore, the capacity must be checked by Eq. (5-30). Then from the Manual's table of shape dimensions, we have $X_1 = 1890$ ksi, $X_2 = 0.0129$ ksi^{-2}, $S_x = 64.7$ in^3, $r_y = 1.57$ in. With $L_b = 360$ in, $L/r_y = 360/1.57 = 229$, and with $C_b = 1$, Eq. (5-30) gives

$$M_{cr} = \frac{1 \times 64.7 \times 1890\sqrt{2}}{229}\sqrt{1 + \frac{1890^2 \times 0.0129}{2 \times 229^2}} = 963 \text{ in·kips}$$

Since this is less than $C_b M_r = C_b S_x(F_y - 10) = 1 \times 64.7 \times 26 = 1682$ in·kips, the nominal moment M_n is $0.9 \times 963 = 867$ in·kips. The factored dead-load moment is $1.2 \times 575 = 690$ in·kips. Therefore, the W16 × 40 is adequate during construction.

5-24 SHEAR CONNECTORS

The stud shear connector is a short length of round steel bar with a round head to provide anchorage. The diameter of the head is $\frac{1}{2}$ in larger than that of the stud. The other end of the stud is welded to the beam flange. The usual diameters are $\frac{1}{2}$, $\frac{5}{8}$, $\frac{3}{4}$, and $\frac{7}{8}$ in, and the most commonly used lengths are 3 and 4 in. Longer studs are needed if the slab is haunched over the beam, however, since connectors should penetrate not less than $1\frac{1}{2}$ in into the slab. Furthermore, the concrete cover on connectors should be at least 1 in in any direction.

The channel shear connector is a short length of rolled channel with one flange welded to the beam and the other providing an anchorage for the slab. Channels 3 in at 4.1 lb and 4 in at 5.4 lb are most commonly used. These are usually welded with continuous fillet welds in front and back of the channel.

The function of the shear connector is to transfer the horizontal shear at the slab-beam interface, so the required spacing of connectors at any cross section is determined by dividing the shear VQ/I at that section by the resistance of one connector (two if they are in pairs, etc.). This suggests that the spacing should vary along the span continuously with V. For practical purposes, however, it is changed at larger intervals and held constant within the interval. Where fatigue must be considered, as in bridges, connector spacing must be based on the appropriate fatigue strength of the connector and the expected range of the shear V.

The static strength Q_u of a stud shear connector is given by[27]

$$Q_u = 930 d_s^2 \sqrt{f'_{c,\text{psi}}} \tag{5-87a}$$

where d_s is the diameter of the stud. For a channel connector

$$Q_u = 550(t_f + 0.5t_w)L_c\sqrt{f'_{c,\text{psi}}} \qquad (5\text{-}87b)$$

where t_f = average thickness of flange of channel
t_w = web thickness of channel
L_c = length of channel

These formulas are based on results of tests. Equation (5-87a) should not be used for studs shorter than $4d_s$.

It is common practice to use lightweight concrete in the floor systems of multistory buildings to reduce the dead load. The formulas for stud and channel shear connectors must be revised to reflect the weight and the strength of the concrete. The static strength of a stud shear connector is given by[27]

$$Q_u = 0.5A_{sc}\sqrt{f'_c E_c} \le A_{sc}F_u \qquad (5\text{-}88a)$$

where A_{sc} = cross-sectional area of connector, in^2
F_u = specified tensile strength of connector, ksi (stud shear connectors are made using ASTM-A108, AISI Grades C1010, C1015, C1017, or C1020 cold-drawn steel with a minimum tensile strength of 60 ksi)

For channel shear connectors,

$$Q_u = 0.3(t_f + 0.5t_w)L_c\sqrt{f'_c E_c} \qquad (5\text{-}88b)$$

For normal-weight concrete Eqs. (5-87) and (5-88) give comparable results. In the AISC/ASD specification the capacity of stud and channel shear connectors for normal-weight concrete are provided as standard values (Table 5-6). A reduction factor is applied to the standard value if lightweight concrete is used (Table 5-7). In the AISC/LRFD specification Eqs. (5-88) are used.

Tests have shown that the ultimate strength of a composite beam under static load is largely independent of the spacing of the shear connectors. The strength of beams in which the connectors were spaced uniformly between the

TABLE 5-6
AISC/ASD allowable loads for shear connectors

	Allowable load q, kips		
Type and size of connectors*	$f'_c = 3$ ksi	$f'_c = 3.5$ ksi	$f'_c = 4$ ksi
$\frac{1}{2}$-in stud × 2 in	5.1	5.5	5.9
$\frac{5}{8}$-in stud × 2.5 in	7.9	8.6	9.2
$\frac{3}{4}$-in stud × 3 in	11.5	12.5	13.3
$\frac{7}{8}$-in stud × 3.5 in	15.6	16.8	18.0
3-in channel 4.1 lb	4.3w	4.7w	5.0w
4-in channel 5.4 lb	4.6w	5.0w	5.3w
5-in channel 6.7 lb	4.9w	5.3w	5.6w

* Studs longer than those shown have the same allowable loads.

TABLE 5-7
Reduction coefficients for Table 5-6 for lightweight concrete

Specified compressive strength of concrete, f'_c	Air dry unit of weight of concrete, pcf						
	90	**95**	**100**	**105**	**110**	**115**	**120**
≤ 4.0 ksi	0.73	0.76	0.78	0.81	0.83	0.86	0.88
≥ 5.0 ksi	0.82	0.85	0.87	0.91	0.93	0.96	0.99

points of maximum moment and zero moment was the same as for beams with the same number of connectors spaced according to the intensity of the shear.[28] This is because deformation of the concrete and the more heavily stressed shear connectors redistributed the horizontal shear among the less heavily stressed connectors. This action is analogous to that which takes place in connections having a number of fasteners in line (Art. 3-11).

The number of connectors required between the point of maximum moment and the point of zero moment is determined by dividing the compression-flange force at the point of maximum moment by the connector strength. If the neutral axis is in the slab (Fig. 5-47b), the flange compression C is found by determining the equal force $T = A_s F_y$. If the neutral axis is in the steel beam (Fig. 5-47c), the flange compression is $C_1 = 0.85f'_c bt$. This procedure is prescribed by the AISC/LRFD specification. Therefore,

$$V_h = \begin{cases} A_s F_y & \text{neutral axis in slab} & (5\text{-}89a) \\ 0.85f'_c bt & \text{neutral axis in beam} & (5\text{-}89b) \end{cases}$$

Identical expressions are used in the AISC/ASD specification, except that the flange compression is reduced to a service-load value by dividing by a factor of safety of 2, so the horizontal shear is given by

$$V_h = \begin{cases} \dfrac{A_s F_y}{2} & \text{neutral axis in slab} & (5\text{-}90a) \\[2ex] \dfrac{0.85f'_c bt}{2} & \text{neutral axis in beam} & (5\text{-}90b) \end{cases}$$

The corresponding allowable shear Q per connector according to the AISC/ASD specification is given in Table 5-6. These values are based on Eqs. (5-87) using a factor of safety of 2.5.

If a composite section is proportioned on the basis of its bending strength as in the AISC/LRFD specification, the location of the neutral axis is known, so the applicable Eq. (5-89) is also known. But if proportioning is on an allowable-stress basis, as in the AISC/ASD specification, the location of the neutral axis at ultimate load is not known. However, instead of determining its position, it is simpler to compute the connector requirement for both of Eqs. (5-90), since it turns out that the smaller value is the correct one. This can be proved by noting in Fig. 5-47 that T is less than C_1 (because $C < C_1$), while C_1 is less than T_1

which itself is less than T. Therefore, the correct number of connectors is always given by the smaller value of V_h by Eqs. (5-90).

Properties of partially composite beams. Tests have shown that the bending strength in the case of partially developed composite action can be determined by a parabolic interpolation between the case of no composite action (the steel beam alone) and the case of complete composite action.[29] Therefore, denoting the required transformed section modulus by S_{eff}, the corresponding horizontal shear is given by

$$\sqrt{\frac{V'_h}{V_h}} = \frac{S_{\text{eff}} - S_s}{S_{tr} - S_s} \tag{5-91}$$

where V'_h = horizontal shear for partially composite beam
V_h = horizontal shear for fully composite beam
S_s = tension-flange section modulus of steel beam
S_{tr} = section modulus of fully composite transformed section referred to steel-section tension flange

This equation is based on elastic behavior of the composite beam. Solving it for S_{eff} yields

$$S_{\text{eff}} = S_s + \sqrt{\frac{V'_h}{V_h}} (S_{tr} - S_s) \tag{5-92}$$

Using the relationship $S = I/c$, Eq. (5-92) can be put in the form

$$I_{\text{eff}} = I_s + \sqrt{\frac{V'_h}{V}} (I_{tr} - I_s) \tag{5-93}$$

Equation (5-93) can be used to compute deflections. Both these equations are in the AISC/ASD specification. They are also referred to in the commentary on the LRFD specification except that V'_h/V_h is replaced with $\sum Q_n/C_f$, where $\sum Q_n =$ strength of shear connectors between points of maximum and zero moment and $C_f =$ compression force in concrete slab of fully composite beam, i.e., the smaller of the values of V_h by Eqs. (5-89).

Example 5-24-1 (AISC/ASD). Determine the shear-connector requirement for the beam of Example 5-23-1.

Solution. From Eqs. (5-90),

$$V_h = \frac{13.5 \times 36}{2} = 243 \text{ kips} \qquad V_h = \frac{0.85 \times 3 \times 90 \times 4}{2} = 459 \text{ kips}$$

Therefore, connectors must be provided to develop 243 kips. Using $\frac{3}{4}$-in studs, the allowable shear per connector is 11.5 kips (Table 5-6). Therefore, $n = 243/11.5 = 22$ for each half of the beam. Using two studs at 16-in intervals uniformly along the beam gives 22 for each half (Fig. 5-49c).

Since the beam has some excess bending capacity, Eq. (5-91) will be used to see what saving in connectors is possible. The required section modulus S_{eff} is $M/F_b = 2600/24 = 108$ in^3. The modulus S_{tr} furnished is 115 in^3. Then from Eq. (5-91)

$$\sqrt{\frac{V_h'}{238}} = \frac{108 - 78.8}{115 - 78.8} \qquad V_h' = 155 \text{ kips}$$

The corresponding connector requirement is $n = 155/11.5 = 14$. These can be furnished by connectors in pairs at equal 24-in spaces along the beam.

Example 5-24-2 (AISC/LRFD). Determine the shear-connector requirement for the beam of Example 5-23-2.

Solution. From Eqs. (5-89)

$$V_h = 11.8 \times 36 = 425 \text{ kips} \qquad V_h = 0.85 \times 3 \times 90 \times 4 = 918 \text{ kips}$$

Therefore, connectors must be provided to develop 425 kips. Using $\frac{3}{4}$-in studs, the allowable shear per connector according to Eq. (5-88a) is 21.6 kips. Therefore, $n = 425/21.6 = 20$ for each half of the beam. Using two studs at 18-in intervals uniformly along the beam gives 20 for each half (see Fig. 5-50c).

Concentrated loads. The abrupt changes in shear in beams with concentrated loads suggest a modification of the uniform connector spacing discussed above. This is because the moment at concentrated loads near midspan may be almost as large as the midspan moment, so the difference in flange compression at these cross sections may be small. Thus, relatively few of the required connectors are needed in this portion of the span. Since the distribution of the connectors is proportional to the horizontal shears, it can be determined by Eq. (5-91).

Example 5-24-3 (AISC/ASD). The cross section of the beam in Fig. 5-51 is the same as that of the beam in Fig. 5-49. Determine the connector requirements.

Solution. The bending moment and the required section modulus at midspan are

$$M = 8 \times 10 + \frac{1.2 \times 30^2}{8} = 215 \text{ ft·kips} \qquad S = \frac{215 \times 12}{24} = 107.5 \text{ in}^3$$

The moment and required section modulus at the 8-kip load are

$$M = 8 \times 10 + \frac{1.2 \times 10 \times 20}{2} = 200 \text{ ft·kips} \qquad S = \frac{200 \times 12}{24} = 100 \text{ in}^3$$

From Example 5-23-1, $S_{tc} = 115$ in^3 and $S_s = 78.8$ in^3. The number of $\frac{3}{4}$-in connectors for full composite action is $n = 21$. This number can be reduced because

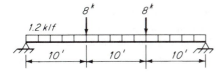

FIGURE 5-51

the full bending capacity of the beam is not needed. From Eq. (5-91)

$$\sqrt{\frac{n}{21}} = \sqrt{\frac{V_h'}{V_h}} = \frac{107.5 - 78.8}{115 - 78.8} = \frac{28.7}{36.2} \qquad n = 13$$

Thus, with the connectors furnished in pairs a total of 14 studs will be provided. To determine the number of these which should be put in the outer 10-ft segment of the beam, Eq. (5-91) is used again, this time with the required section moduli at midspan and at the concentrated load:

$$\sqrt{\frac{n}{18}} = \frac{100 - 78.8}{107.5 - 78.8} = \frac{21.2}{28.7} \qquad n = 10$$

Therefore, 10 of the 14 connectors should be located between the end of the beam and the 8-kip load, with the remaining four between the 8-kip load and midspan.

The extension of this procedure to the case of additional concentrated loads involves similar successive applications of Eq. (5-91).

Both AISC/ASD and AISC/LRFD require that a reduced value of the shear-connector capacity be used when cold-formed metal deck is used in the floor construction. When the deck ribs are oriented perpendicular to the axis of the steel supporting member, the basic value must be multiplied by the reduction factor:

$$\frac{0.85}{\sqrt{N_r}} \frac{w_r}{h_r} \left(\frac{H_s}{h_r} - 1.0 \right) \le 1.0 \qquad (5\text{-}94)$$

where N_r = number of stud connectors on a beam in one rib, not to exceed 3 in the computation, although more than 3 studs may be installed
w_r = average width of concrete rib, in (Fig. 5-48)
h_r = nominal rib height, in (Fig. 5-48)
H_s = length of stud connector after welding, in, not to exceed the value $h_r + 3$ in computations, although the actual length may be greater

For deck ribs oriented parallel to the steel supporting member the following reduction factor is applicable when the ratio w_r/h_r is less than 1.5:

$$0.6 \left(\frac{w_r}{h_r} \right) \left(\frac{H_s}{h_r} - 1.0 \right) \le 1.0 \qquad (5\text{-}95)$$

5-25 CONTINUOUS COMPOSITE BEAMS

The composite beams of the floor in Examples 5-23-1 and 5-23-2 were designed as simply supported beams. If the slab is cast continuously over the girders to which the beams connect, deflection of the beams will cause cracking of the concrete over the girder unless reinforcement or an expansion joint is used. This suggests that it may pay to make the composite beam continuous at the supports. Tests show that negative reinforcement in the slab acts compositely with the steel beam if shear connectors are used. The composite behavior results from the bond of the reinforcing bars to the slab and thence through the connectors to the steel beam. All the reinforcement within the effective width can be considered effective, provided it is anchored beyond the points of inflection as is required for reinforced-concrete beams.

Since the shear connectors are the link between the reinforcing bars and the steel beam, they must be capable of developing a shear equal to the tensile force in the bars within the effective width. Therefore, the number of connectors is obtained by dividing $F_y A_r$, where A_r is the total area of reinforcing, by the strength Q_u of one connector. In the AISC/ASD specification, this is put on a service-load basis by dividing $F_y A_r/2$ by the allowable shear capacity from Table 5-6.

PROBLEMS

5-1. Prove that the shape factor for the circular cross section is 1.70.

5-2. Compute the shape factor for the cross section consisting of two equal isosceles triangles whose common base constitutes the neutral axis.

5-3. Compute the shape factor for the tee of Fig. 4-50.

5-4. A simply supported beam spanning 15 ft carries a uniformly distributed load of 0.75 klf *DL* and 2.25 klf *LL*, not including the weight of the beam. Floor construction restrains it against lateral buckling. What size beam of A36 steel is required?

5-5. Purlins 20 ft long and spaced 6 ft on centers support a roof which is on a slope of 1 in 12. The roof is decked with 2-in-thick precast slabs made of lightweight concrete weighing 65 pcf and securely fastened to the purlins. The built-up roofing weighs 6 psf. For the snow load recommended in Table 1-3, what size A36 joist is required if the building is located in (*a*) Alabama, (*b*) Wisconsin?

5-6. A simply supported beam spanning 30 ft carries uniformly distributed loads of 1.2 klf *DL* and 1.6 klf *LL* and a concentrated live load of 8 kips 12 ft from one end. Headroom limits the depth to not more than 22 in. Determine the laterally supported A36-steel beam required.

5-7. The beam shown in Fig. P5-7 has continuous lateral support. The 16-kip concentrated loads are made up of 12 kips *DL* and 4 kips *LL*. What size A36-steel beam is required?

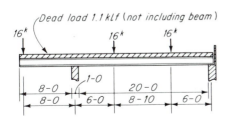

FIGURE P5-7

5-8. Same as Prob. 5-7 except that, instead of the fixed concentrated loads shown, the beam supports a moving live load consisting of two wheel loads of 10 kips each spaced at 6 ft on centers.

5-9. Design the joists and girders for the floor of the building shown in Fig. P5-9. The live load is 80 psf uniform. The floor is a 4-in concrete slab. A36 steel, AISC specification.

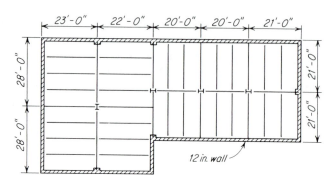

FIGURE P5-9

5-10. A cross section of the roadway of a highway beam bridge is shown in Fig. P5-10. The span is 40 ft. The bridge is to be designed to the AASHTO HS20-44 loading (Fig. 1-2). Since a beam cannot deflect unless there is a transverse bending of the roadway slab, the result is that part of the wheel directly over a beam may be supported by adjacent beams. Therefore the load on any one beam may be more or less than the load on a wheel directly over it, depending upon the stiffness of the floor and the spacing of the beams. According to the AASHTO specifications, for concrete floor slabs the fraction of a wheel load supported by an interior beam directly underneath it is $S/5.5$, where S is the spacing of the beams in feet, while the load on an outside beam is computed on the assumption that the flooring acts as a simple beam.

    Design the beams in A36 steel. The clearance diagram for the truck loading is shown in Fig. 1-2, and the impact requirement is given by Eq. (1-4).

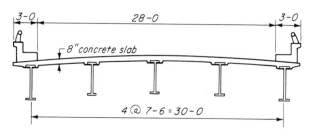

FIGURE P5-10

5-11. The framing plan for an office building is shown in Fig. P5-11. Design the beams in A36 steel. Given:

> *Floor:* $2\frac{1}{2}$-in concrete on cellular steel, 40 psf
> *Ceiling:* Acoustical plaster and hung ceiling, 10 psf
> *Exterior walls:* Aluminum window wall 10 ft high at 20 psf
> *Live load:* Office area 70 psf (includes 20 psf for movable partitions)

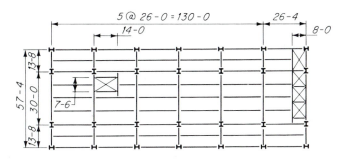

FIGURE P5-11

5-12. Determine the allowable load for the beam of Example 5-5-1 if the concentrated load acts (*a*) on the top flange, (*b*) on the bottom flange.

5-13. Determine the allowable load for the beam of Example 5-5-1 if there is lateral support at midspan.

5-14. A cantilever beam 10 ft long with no lateral support carries a concentrated live load of 10 kips acting on the top flange at the free end. Determine the A36-steel beam required.

5-15. A simply supported beam spanning 24 ft supports a concentrated live load of 20 kips acting on the top flange at midspan. Determine the A441-steel beam required. The beam has no lateral support except at the ends.

5-16. Same as Prob. 5-15 except that the beam is also supported laterally at midspan by a beam framing at right angles.

5-17. A simply supported W24 × 68 beam of A572 Grade 45 steel spans 36 ft. It supports a concentrated load P 10 ft from the left end and another concentrated load of 1.5P 20 ft from the left end. The beam is supported laterally at each end as well as at the load points, where beams frame in at right angles. Determine the value of P at which lateral-torsional buckling can be predicted.

5-18. Same as Prob. 5-17 except that there is no lateral support at the points of load. The loads act on the top flange.

5-19. Compute the critical pure-bending moment for the tee of Example 5-10-1 with the flange in tension.

5-20. The A36 steel beam shown in Fig. P5-20 is supported laterally at the ends and also at midspan where the beam which delivers the load P is attached. Determine the critical value of P.

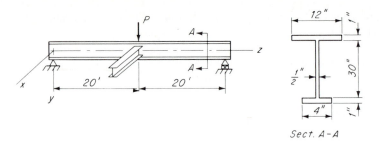

FIGURE P5-20

5-21. A monorail hoist weighing 850 lb has a lifting capacity of 5 tons. The trolley weighs 120 lb and is designed to run on the bottom flange of a standard S shape. The trolley beams run lengthwise of the building and are attached through their top flanges to the bottom chords of a series of roof trusses spaced 20 ft on centers. Design the beam. A36 steel.

5-22. A beam in a power plant spans 40 ft. It supports only a column, which stands at the center of the beam and carries a load of 60 kips *DL* and 60 kips *LL*. There is no lateral support in the 40-ft length. What size A36 beam is required?

5-23. The mezzanine walkway shown in Fig. P5-23 is to be installed along a row of columns spaced 22 ft on centers in an existing building. The floor is to be steel grating spanning 4 ft and weighing 10 psf. The design live loads are 80 psf for the floor and 50 plf laterally at the top of the railing. Design the railing, the supporting structure for the floor, and the hanger to the beam overhead. Design welded connections for the hanger. Design a welded connection of the beam to the column. A36 steel.

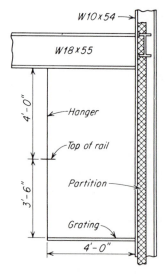

FIGURE P5-23

5-24. Figure P5-24 shows a part transverse section of a one-story shop building which is 96 ft long inside its 8-in end walls. The purlins are wall-bearing at the ends of the building. The local building code specifies a roof live load of 30 psf. Each monorail is equipped with a hoist of 2000 lb capacity weighing 125 lb, suspended from a 50-lb trolley designed to run on the bottom flange of a standard S shape. Choose a spacing for the roof beams, and design the monorail, purlins, and beams. A36 steel.

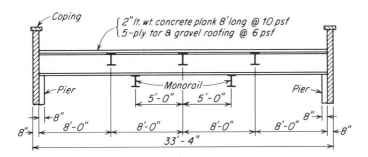

FIGURE P5-24

5-25. Compute the factor of safety for the bridge beam and the crane girder of DP5-9-3 taking into account the position of the load relative to the shear center.

5-26. Choose a pair of equal-legged angles, separated $\frac{3}{8}$ in for gusset plates, for a member 8 ft long supporting an axial tension of 10 kips dead load and 30 kips live load and two transverse loads of 2 kips live load each located 2.5 ft from either end. There are no holes at the points of attachment of the transverse loads, but there is a single line of $\frac{3}{4}$-in bolts connecting the member at its ends. Assume simply supported ends. A36 steel.

5-27. A fixture to support a shaft bearing is to be welded to the bottom chord of the truss of DP3-15-1, midway between L_2 and L_3. The shaft load is 600 lb live load. What change is required in the member? Assume simply supported ends.

Can you suggest a more rigid support for this bearing (other than a larger shape for the bottom chord) that might be desirable if alignment of the shaft is critical and if vibration is an important consideration?

5-28. A fixture to support a shaft bearing is to be welded to the bottom chord of the truss of DP3-15-2, midway between L_2 and L_3. The shaft load is 600 lb live load. What change is required in the member? Assume simply supported ends.

Can you suggest a more rigid support for this bearing (other than a larger shape for the bottom chord) that might be desirable if alignment of the shaft is critical and if vibration is an important consideration?

5-29. A laterally supported beam built in at one end and simply supported at the other spans 20 ft and carries a concentrated load at midspan. The cross section is an A36 W12 × 30. Determine its collapse load, and plot the load-deflection curve.

5-30. A laterally supported two-span continuous beam carries a concentrated load at the middle of each 20-ft span. The cross section is an A572 Grade 50 W16 × 45. Determine the collapse load and plot a load-deflection curve.

5-31. The end spans of a three-span continuous beam are each 30 ft long, and the central span is 40 ft long. There is continuous lateral support. The design load is 0.6 klf *DL* and 1.9 klf *LL* not including the weight of the beam itself. What W shape of A36 steel is required?

5-32. One of the end spans of a three-span continuous beam is 16 ft long; the other is 20 ft. The central span is 24 ft long. There is a concentrated load of 5 kips *DL* and 15 kips *LL* at the center of each span. The beam is supported laterally at the supports and at the points of load. What W shape of A441 steel is required?

5-33. An existing column in a building is to be underpinned temporarily during alteration of the building. It is to be supported on one or more parallel beams, which will be supported in turn on temporary concrete pedestals. Each pedestal furnishes a 12-in bearing length whose center is 3 ft from the column. The base plate of the column is 20 × 24 in, the 20-in dimension being parallel to the underpinning beam. The load on the column is 80 kips *DL* and 230 kips *LL*. Design the supporting beam (or beams). A36 steel.

5-34. The four lines of columns in an existing building are 24 ft on centers, as shown in Fig. P5-34. The columns are 18 ft on centers in each line. Floors are concrete slabs 4 in thick, and the design live load is 80 psf. An alteration requires that the width of a part of the central aisle at the lowest level be increased to 28 ft. New columns will support a girder 28 ft long, which because of headroom limitations cannot be more than 25 in deep. In addition to the existing upper-floor columns, the new girder will support the existing W12 × 26 joists, which are 8 ft on centers. Each column load, not including the joists framing at that point, is 60 kips *DL* and 150 kips *LL*. The girder will be supported against lateral buckling only at the points where the four lines of joists connect to it. Design the girder. A36 steel.

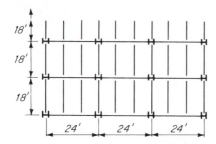

FIGURE P5-34

5-35. A beam 20 ft between supports overhangs 2 ft on one end. Between the supports is a uniformly distributed load of 2 klf. A W8 column stands on the overhang, its center-line 6 in from the tip. The column load is 240 kips. Therefore, excluding the negligible weight of the beam itself, the maximum moment is 360 ft·kips and the maximum shear 240 kips. Since the beam is supported laterally, the designer plans to use a W24 × 94, which is adequate for moment but not for shear. The idea is to reinforce the overhang by welding to the beam two plates 20 × $\frac{1}{4}$, one on each side of the web. The designer says the web area will be $24 \times 0.515 + 2 \times 20 \times \frac{1}{4} = 22.4$ in² and the shearing stress $240/22.4 = 10.7$ ksi as compared with $240/12.4 = 19.4$ ksi without the plates.

Why is the designer's analysis wrong? What is the magnitude of the largest shearing stress on the vertical section at the support? Suggest a way out of the difficulty other than using a larger beam or thicker reinforcing plates.

5-36. Design a bearing plate for a laterally supported A36 W24 × 76 which spans 15 ft and carries its permissible uniformly distributed load. The bearing plates rest on concrete piers for which $f'_c = 3000$ psi.

5-37. Design bearing plates for a laterally supported A36 W18 × 35 which spans 15 ft and carries its permissible concentrated load at 3 ft from the center of one support. The bearing plates rest on concrete piers for which $f'_c = 3000$ psi.

5-38. A simply supported, laterally restrained beam for a machine-shop floor spans 24 ft. It supports a distributed load of 200 plf *DL* and 400 plf *LL* and a concentrated load of 1 kip *DL* and 2 kips *LL* located 6 ft from one end. Impact for the concentrated live load is 30 percent. Clearance requirements limit the depth of the beam to 12 in. What A36 W shape is required?

5-39. Choose a shape for the runway girder of a 25-ton crane which operates on a 40-ft bridge. The trolley weighs 10 kips. The end-truck wheels are 11 ft on centers and run on 60-lb rails. The maximum wheel load is 24 kips *LL* plus 13 kips *DL*. Columns are 25 ft on centers. A36 steel.

5-40. Choose a shape for the runway girder of a 40-ft 20-ton crane with a 5-ton auxiliary hoist. The trolley weighs 14 kips. The end-truck wheels are 10 ft 6 in on centers and run on 60-lb rails. The maximum wheel load is 18 kips *LL* plus 18 kips *DL*. Columns are 40 ft on centers. A36 steel.

5-41. A strut lying in a plane normal to the longitudinal axis of a 20-ft simply supported beam intersects the centroid of the cross section at an angle of 60° with the horizontal. The force in the strut is 3 kips *DL* and 7 kips *LL*, and there are no other loads. Design the beam, assuming no lateral support except at the ends. A36 steel.

5-42. A W21 × 93 simply supported on a span of 16 ft supports at its midpoint a vertical concentrated load of 8 kips *DL* and 24 kips *LL*. The web of the beam is on a slope of 6 vertical in 1 horizontal. Compute the maximum bending stresses if the beam is free to bend in any direction.

5-43. A simply supported beam with a cross section consisting of a C12 × 20.7 and a $6 \times 3\frac{1}{2} \times \frac{1}{4}$ angle with its long leg attached to the bottom flange and the outside face of its short leg 6 in from the back of the channel (Fig. 5-41*e*) is simply supported on a span of 20 ft. Compute the bending stresses due to a moment of 264 in·kips acting as in Fig. 5-40 if the beam is (*a*) free to bend in any direction, (*b*) free to bend only in the vertical plane.

5-44. An $8 \times 6 \times \frac{1}{2}$ angle positioned with the long leg pointing vertically downward is used as a beam on a span of 12 ft. If it supports a uniform load of 400 plf and is free to bend in any direction, what is the maximum bending stress? Compare this value with the maximum stress if the angle can bend only in the vertical plane.

5-45. Design a symmetrical cross section with welded cover plates for a laterally supported beam whose maximum bending moment is 150 ft·kips *DL* and 450 ft·kips *LL*. Because of requirements for clearance, the depth of the beam cannot exceed 26 in, and its width is limited to 10 in. A36 steel.

5-46. Design for the crane runway of DP5-19-1 a girder of the type shown in Fig. 5-41*c*.

5-47. Design for the crane runway of DP5-19-2 a girder of the type shown in Fig. 5-41*c*.

5-48. Design a 25-ft crane-runway girder of the type shown in Fig. 5-41*c* for a 30-ton crane operating on a 40-ft bridge. The truck wheels are 12 ft on center and run on 80-lb (per yard) rails. The maximum wheel load is 30 kips *LL* plus 16 kips *DL*. Compare the section with the required W shape without a reinforced flange. A36 steel.

5-49. An old building in a town which has no building code is being remodeled. A 20-ft clear opening is required in an exterior 13-in brick wall. It is 2 ft from the top of the opening to the bottom of 3 × 14 wood joists which support a 1-in pine subfloor with a $\frac{7}{8}$-in hardwood finish. There are no openings above the floor. Design a lintel with a welded bottom reinforcing plate which will also serve as a shelf to support a 4-in brick veneer.

Because of the arching action of masonry over openings, lintels need support only the masonry beneath the "arch." It is usual to assume that the lintel supports a section of wall in the shape of a triangle whose altitude is half the span of the beam. However, if the bottom of the next higher opening falls within the triangle, it is better to assume that the lintel supports all the masonry between the two openings. Furthermore, if the wall is load-bearing and a floor falls within the triangle, it is safer to design the lintel to support the floor load and the masonry between it and the lintel in addition to the triangular section of masonry above the floor.

5-50. Locate the shear centers for the cross sections of Fig. P5-50.

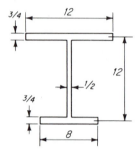
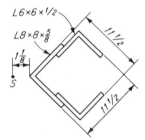

FIGURE P5-50

5-51. A C15 × 33.9 spans 20 ft and supports a uniformly distributed load of 1.4 klf. The line of action of the load is centered on the top flange. If the vertical reactions are centered on the web, compute the twisting moment exerted by the channel on its supports.

5-52. Design the composite beam of Example 5-23-1 using a steel beam with $F_y = 50$ ksi.

5-53. Design the composite beam of Example 5-23-2 using a steel beam with $F_y = 50$ ksi.

5-54. Design the composite beam of Example 5-23-1 for continuous construction, with $F_y = 36$ ksi, $f'_c = 3000$ psi, and $F_{yr} = 40$ ksi.

5-55. Design the composite beam of Example 5-23-2 for continuous construction, with $F_y = 36$ ksi, $f'_c = 3000$ psi, and $F_{yr} = 40$ ksi.

5-56. A floor system with steel beams 8 ft on centers spans 40 ft, simply supported. The 4-in reinforced-concrete slab is made of 4000-psi concrete. The live load is 125 psf. Design a composite beam in A36 steel for a load factor of 2 on ultimate strength.

REFERENCES

1. Timoshenko, S., and J. M. Gere: "Theory of Elastic Stability," 3d ed., McGraw-Hill, New York, 1969.
2. Galambos, T. V.: "Structural Members and Frames," Prentice-Hall, Englewood Cliffs, N.J., 1968.
3. Clark, J. W., and H. N. Hill: Lateral Buckling of Beams, *J. Struct. Div. ASCE*, July 1960.
4. Kirby, P. A., and D. A. Nethercot: "Design for Structural Stability," Wiley, New York, 1979.
5. Salvadori, M.: Lateral Buckling of Eccentrically Loaded I Columns, *Trans. ASCE*, vol. 121, p. 1163, 1956.

6. Hechtman, R. A., J. S. Hattrup, E. F. Styer, and J. L. Tiedemann: Lateral Buckling of Rolled Steel Beams, *Proc. ASCE*, vol. 81, pap. 797, 1955.
7. Haaijer, G.: Plate Buckling in the Strain-Hardening Range, *Trans. ASCE*, vol. 124, 1959.
8. Haaijer, G., and B. Thürlimann: Inelastic Buckling in Steel, *Trans. ASCE*, vol. 125, 1960.
9. Thürlimann, B.: New Aspects Concerning Elastic Instability of Steel Structures, *Trans. ASCE*, vol. 127, 1962.
10. Lay, M.: Flange Local Buckling in Wide-Flange Shapes, *J. Struct. Div. ASCE*, December 1965.
11. Canadian Standards Association: Steel Structures for Buildings—Limit States Design, CSA Standard S16.1-1974, Ontario, Canada.
12. Johnson, D. L.: An Investigation into the Interaction of Flanges and Webs in Wide-Flange Shapes, 1985 Proceedings SSRC Annual Technical Session, 1985.
13. Clark, J. W.: Aluminum Structure, sec. 11 in E. H. Gaylord and C. N. Gaylord (eds.), "Structural Engineering Handbook," 3d ed., McGraw-Hill, New York, 1990.
14. Specifications for Aluminum Structures, The Aluminum Association, 2d ed., November 1971.
15. Winter, G.: Lateral Stability of Unsymmetrical I-Beams and Trusses in Bending, *Trans. ASCE*, vol. 108, p. 247, 1943.
16. Hill, H. N.: Lateral Stability of Unsymmetrical I-Beams, *J. Aeronaut. Sci.*, vol. 9, no. 5, March 1942.
17. Bower, J. E.: Design of Beams with Web Openings, *J. Struct. Div. ASCE*, March 1968.
18. Segner, E. P., Jr.: Reinforcement Requirements for Girder Web Openings, *J. Struct. Div. ASCE*, June 1964.
19. Frost, R. W., and R. E. Leffler: Fatigue Tests of Beams with Rectangular Web Holes, *J. Struct. Div. ASCE*, February 1971.
20. Vincent, G. S.: Tentative Criteria for Load Factor Design of Steel Highway Bridges, *AISI Bull.* 15, March 1969.
21. Lyse, I., and H. J. Godfrey: Investigation of Web Buckling in Steel Beams, *Trans. ASCE*, vol. 100, 1935.
22. Basler, K.: Strength of Plate Girders in Shear, *Trans. ASCE*, vol. 128, pt. II, 1963.
23. Roberts, T. M.: Slender Plate Girders Subjected to Edge Loading, *Proc. Inst. Civ. Eng.*, pt. 2, vol. 71, September 1981.
24. Vol'mir, A. S.: Stability of Elastic Systems, translated from the Russian, Defense Documentation Center, Defense Supply Agency, November 1965.
25. Timoshenko, S. P., and J. N. Goodier: "Theory of Elasticity," 3d ed., p. 119, McGraw-Hill, New York, 1970.
26. Yura, J. A.: The Behavior of Beams Subjected to Concentrated Loads, PMFSEL Report No. 82-5, University of Texas at Austin, August 1982.
27. Slutter, R. G., and G. C. Driscoll: Flexural Strength of Steel-Concrete Composite Beams, *J. Struct. Div. ASCE*, April 1965.
28. Ollgaard, J. G., R. G. Slutter, and J. W. Fisher: Shear Strength of Stud Connectors in Light Weight and Normal Weight Concrete, *AISC Eng. J.*, April 1971.
29. Grant, J. A., J. W. Fisher, and R. G. Slutter: Composite Beams with Formed Steel Deck, *AISC Eng. J.*, vol. 14, no. 1, 1st Quarter, 1977.

CHAPTER

6

BEAM-COLUMNS

6-1 BEAM-COLUMNS

Members subjected to both axial compressive force and moment are called *beam-columns*. An initially straight pin-ended column subjected to axial forces P and end moments M_1 and M_2, with $M_1 \le M_2$, is shown in Fig. 6-1. Equating bending moment to bending resistance, we get

$$-EI \frac{d^2y}{dx^2} = Py + M_1 + (M_2 - M_1) \frac{x}{L} \qquad (a)$$

Using the notation $k^2 = P/EI$, Eq. (a) becomes

$$\frac{d^2y}{dx^2} + k^2y = \frac{k^2}{P}(M_1 - M_2)\frac{x}{L} - \frac{k^2}{P}M_1 \qquad (b)$$

The solution of this equation is

$$y = A \sin kx + B \cos kx + \frac{M_1 - M_2}{P}\frac{x}{L} - \frac{M_1}{P} \qquad (c)$$

With the boundary conditions $y = 0$ at $x = 0$ and $x = L$, Eq. (c) becomes

$$y = \left(\frac{M_2}{P} - \frac{M_1}{P} \cos kL\right)\frac{\sin kx}{\sin kL} + \frac{M_1}{P}(\cos kx - 1) + (M_1 - M_2)\frac{x}{PL} \qquad (d)$$

410

FIGURE 6-1

The bending moment at any point is determined from $M = -EI \, d^2y/dx^2$. The maximum value is found to be

$$M_{max} = M_2 \csc kL \sqrt{\left(\frac{M_1}{M_2}\right)^2 - 2\frac{M_1}{M_2}\cos kL + 1} \qquad (e)$$

Equation (e) is valid so long as Hooke's law holds. Assuming the proportional-limit stress to be equal to the yield stress F_y, values of P and M_2 (M_1/M_2 is assumed known) at which yielding begins are found by using $F_y = P/A + M_{max}c/I$. The result, with P/EI substituted for k^2, is

$$F_y = \frac{P}{A} + \frac{M_2 c}{I} \sqrt{\left(\frac{M_1}{M_2}\right)^2 - 2\frac{M_1}{M_2}\cos \pi\sqrt{\frac{P}{P_E}} + 1} \ \csc \pi\sqrt{\frac{P}{P_E}} \qquad (6\text{-}1)$$

For the case $M_1 = M_2 = M$, Eq. (6-1) reduces to

$$F_y = \frac{P}{A} + \frac{Mc}{I}\sec\frac{\pi}{2}\sqrt{\frac{P}{P_E}} \qquad (6\text{-}2a)$$

or

$$F_y = \frac{P}{A}\left(1 + \frac{ec}{r^2}\sec\frac{\pi}{2}\sqrt{\frac{P}{P_E}}\right) \qquad (6\text{-}2b)$$

where $e = M/P$. Equation (6-2) is called the *secant formula*. In the form of Eq. (6-2b) it resembles Eq. (4-6) for the crooked column. This and the correspondence (Fig. 6-2) of $\sec[(\pi/2)\sqrt{P/P_E}]$ and $1/(1 - P/P_E)$ show that equal end eccentricities e of the load P for the straight column have much the same effect as crookedness of amplitude $\delta_0 = e$. Thus, Eqs. (6-2) can be put in the simpler, approximate form

$$F_y = \frac{P}{A} + \frac{Mc}{I}\left(\frac{1}{1 - P/P_E}\right) = \frac{P}{A}\left(1 + \frac{ec}{r^2}\frac{1}{1 - P/P_E}\right) \qquad (6\text{-}3)$$

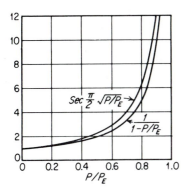

FIGURE 6-2

Equation (6-3) is usually put in different form by dividing through by F_y. The result is

$$\frac{P}{P_y} + \frac{M}{M_y} \frac{1}{1 - P/P_E} = 1 \qquad (6\text{-}4)$$

where $P_y = F_y A$ and $M_y = F_y I/c$. The equation in this form is called an *interaction formula*. The factor $1/(1 - P/P_E)$ is sometimes called an *amplification factor* since it is the factor by which the end moment M is multiplied to approximate the moment $M + Py$.

It is instructive to determine the extreme values of P and M in Eq. (6-4). To do this, we write the equation in the form

$$\frac{M}{M_y} = \left(1 - \frac{P}{P_y}\right)\left(1 - \frac{P}{P_E}\right) \qquad (f)$$

Obviously, $M = M_y$ when $P = 0$. However, there are two extreme values of P. Thus, when $M = 0$, $P = P_y$ or $P = P_E$. These are the values for the perfect column; that is, P is the smaller of P_y and P_E. Therefore, Eq. (6-4) does not allow for the effect of imperfections such as residual stress or crookedness on the strength of a column made of flat-yielding steel or for the increase of P beyond P_y for a gradually yielding material. Since the formula gives the correct extreme value of P for elastic buckling, namely, P_E, we change the inelastic extreme P_y by substituting P_{cr} for P_y, where by P_{cr} we mean the strength of the imperfect column of flat-yielding steel or the tangent-modulus load for a column of gradually yielding metal. Thus, Eq. (6-4) becomes

$$\frac{P}{P_{cr}} + \frac{M}{M_y} \frac{1}{1 - P/P_E} = 1 \qquad (6\text{-}5)$$

This equation gives correct extreme values of P. It is used to predict the concurrent values of P and M which produce yield stress on the extreme fiber of that cross section between the ends of a beam-column at which the moment is a maximum. Therefore, it underestimates the strength of the member. This is because the extreme value $M = M_y$ is not correct for $P = 0$, since bending strength is not fully developed when the extreme fiber begins to yield. Instead, beams can tolerate considerable penetration of yield stress into the cross section. Thus, Fig. 6-3a shows the strain over a cross section where the extreme-fiber strain is several times larger than ϵ_y. The resulting stress distribution is shown in *b*. For large values of extreme-fiber strain the stress distribution can be approx-

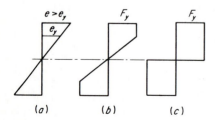

(a) (b) (c) **FIGURE 6-3**

imated closely by two rectangles, as shown in c. The corresponding moment is the plastic moment M_p which is discussed in Art. 5-3. (Plastic bending is discussed further in Art. 5-3.) A formula giving correct extreme values of both M and P is obtained by substituting M_p for M_y in Eq. (6-5). This gives

$$\frac{P}{P_{cr}} + \frac{M}{M_p} \frac{1}{1 - P/P_E} = 1 \tag{6-6}$$

Of course, such an extension of a formula based on proportionality of stress and strain to a form intended to predict strength (which may involve a considerable amount of nonproportional behavior) may not give very good results. Therefore, Eq. (6-6) must be checked by comparing it with results of analysis based on inelastic behavior and of tests. This is discussed in Art. 6-2.

It remains to extend Eqs. (6-5) and (6-6) to the case of unequal end moments. This could be done by using Eq. (6-1). However, a much simpler procedure, based on a formula which approximates data from a numerical analysis, consists in replacing M by $C_m M$, where C_m is given by

$$C_m = 0.6 - 0.4 \frac{M_1}{M_2} \tag{6-7}$$

M_1 in this equation is the smaller of the end moments M_1 and M_2, and M_1/M_2 is positive if the member bends in reverse curvature. This formula is used in the AISC specifications, which, in earlier editions, set a limit $C_m \geq 0.4$ on the result. This limit was dropped in the 1986 LRFD specification and the 1990 ASD specification because it turned out to have resulted from a misinterpretation of Ref. 1. It is important to note that Eq. (6-7) applies only if there are no transverse loads and no displacement, in the plane of the moments, of one end of the member with respect to the other. These cases are discussed in Art. 6-2. Finally, then, we have

$$\frac{P}{P_{cr}} + \frac{C_m M}{M_y} \frac{1}{1 - P/P_E} = 1 \tag{6-8}$$

$$\frac{P}{P_{cr}} + \frac{C_m M}{M_p} \frac{1}{1 - P/P_E} = 1 \tag{6-9}$$

where M is understood to be the larger of the two end moments.

Equation (6-8) gives values of P and M at yielding of the extreme fiber, while Eq. (6-9) gives ultimate values of P and M. Equation (6-9) is compared in Art. 6-2 with the results of a detailed analysis of the beam-column of I cross section and with results of tests.

6-2   COLUMNS WITH MAXIMUM MOMENT AT ONE END

The moment $C_m M/(1 - P/P_E)$ in Eqs. (6-8) and (6-9) is the maximum moment at an interior cross section of the beam-column. This is shown for the member in Fig. 6-4a in the moment diagram in b. In some cases, however, this maximum

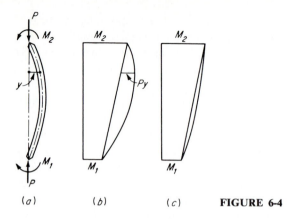

(a)   (b)   (c)   **FIGURE 6-4**

moment does not exist. Instead, the largest moment is M_2 itself, as shown in the moment diagram of Fig. 6-4c. For this case, beginning of yield on the extreme fiber is given by

$$F_y = \frac{P}{A} + \frac{M_2 c}{I} \qquad (a)$$

which gives the interaction formula

$$\frac{P}{P_y} + \frac{M}{M_y} = 1 \qquad (6\text{-}10)$$

This is the same as Eq. (6-4) with an amplification factor of unity, which is as it should be because the moment Py is zero at the end. The extreme values are correct; that is, $M = M_y$ if $P = 0$ and $P = P_y$ if $M = 0$. The latter is correct because there is no question of stability.

Equation (6-10) does not give the maximum values of P and M which the cross section can support. To determine this we must consider the postyielding behavior. Since there is no question of buckling, extreme-fiber strains can increase well beyond the strain ϵ_y at the beginning of yield, as shown in Fig. 6-5b. The corresponding stress distribution for a flat-yielding steel is shown in Fig. 6-5c. The interaction formula for this stress distribution acting on the rectangular cross section of Fig. 6-5a is easily determined. The stress distribution can be

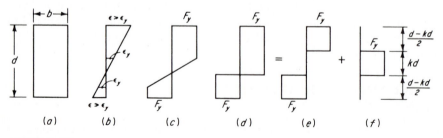

(a)   (b)   (c)   (d)   (e)   (f)

FIGURE 6-5

approximated very closely by two rectangular stress blocks (Fig. 6-5d), which can then be decomposed into the two distributions shown in e and f. From e we get

$$M = F_y \frac{b(d - kd)}{2} \frac{d + kd}{2} = F_y \frac{bd^2}{4} (1 - k^2) \tag{b}$$

while that in f gives

$$P = F_y bkd \tag{c}$$

If $k = 0$, $P = 0$ and $M = F_y bd^2/4$, which is the plastic resisting moment M_p of the cross section. Similarly, if $k = 1$, $M = 0$ and $P = F_y bd$, which is the axial load capacity P_y. Therefore, Eqs. (b) and (c) can be written

$$\frac{M}{M_p} = 1 - k^2 \qquad \frac{P}{P_y} = k \tag{d}$$

which, upon eliminating k, give

$$\left(\frac{P}{P_y}\right)^2 + \frac{M}{M_p} = 1 \tag{e}$$

This equation is plotted in Fig. 6-6.

Analysis of the I leads to similar curves, which, for cross sections of practical proportions, are bounded by the two curves shown in Fig. 6-6. These curves are approximated closely by

$$\frac{P}{P_y} + 0.85 \frac{M}{M_p} = 1 \qquad \frac{P}{P_y} \geq 0.15 \tag{6-11a}$$

$$M = M_p \qquad \frac{P}{P_y} \leq 0.15 \tag{6-11b}$$

These formulas are also plotted in Fig. 6-6.

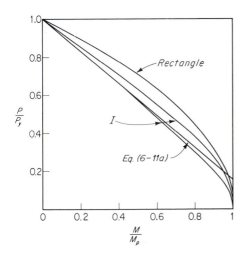

FIGURE 6-6

Both Eq. (6-9) and Eqs. (6-11) must be used to evaluate the strength of the beam-column of I shape. As has already been noted, this is because Eq. (6-9) is based on the existence of a maximum moment between the ends (Fig. 6-5b), while with Eqs. (6-11) it is assumed that the largest moment is at an end (Fig. 6-5c). These equations are compared in Fig. 6-7a, b, and c with a detailed investigation of a W8 × 31 steel beam-column.[2] Thermal residual stresses were taken into account in this analysis. Deflected shapes were established by an iterative procedure in which elements of the member are fitted together, the curvature of each element being found from predetermined variations of moment with strain for various values of P. (Figure 5-5 shows a typical plot, in this case for P = 0.) The

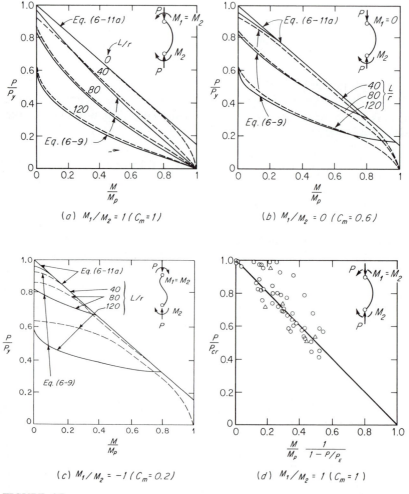

(a) $M_1/M_2 = 1$ ($C_m = 1$)

(b) $M_1/M_2 = 0$ ($C_m = 0.6$)

(c) $M_1/M_2 = -1$ ($C_m = 0.2$)

(d) $M_1/M_2 = 1$ ($C_m = 1$)

FIGURE 6-7

procedure involves assuming a deflected shape, computing the corresponding moments in the elements into which the member is divided, determining the curvatures, and fitting the elements together to see whether the resulting deflected shape agrees with the assumed one. The process is repeated until the differences between the assumed deflections and the calculated deflections are negligible.

Results from Ref. 2 are shown in the dashed lines in Fig. 6-7; Eqs. (6-9) and (6-11) are shown in solid lines. The case $M_1 = M_2$ ($C_m = 1$) is shown in Fig. 6-7a. Agreement is seen to be very good. Values for $L/r = 0$ agree with Eqs. (6-11), while those for $L/r = 40$, 80, and 120 agree with Eq. (6-9). The case $M_1 = 0$ ($C_m = 0.6$) is shown in Fig. 6-7b, where the correspondence is again very good except for columns with $L/r = 120$ and whose M is larger than $0.8M_p$. It will be noted that Eq. (6-9) holds for $L/r = 40$ if M/M_p is smaller than about 0.25, while Eqs. (6-11) apply for larger values. The case $M_1 = -M_2$ ($C_m = 0.2$) is shown in Fig. 6-7c. Here the agreement of Eq. (6-9) with the results of Ref. 2 is not very good for $L/r = 80$ and 120. However, results from the equation are on the safe side. Finally, then, since it is shown in Ref. 2 that the predicted strengths are in good agreement with the results of a number of tests on steel beam-columns, we can conclude that Eq. (6-9) and Eqs. (6-11) also give good predictions of beam-column strength except for slender members subjected to reversed-curvature bending, for which they underestimate the strength.

Equation (6-9) is compared in Fig. 6-7d with the results of tests of 53 aluminum beam-columns[3] whose slenderness ratios ranged from 20 to 150. Since the eccentricity was the same at both ends, $C_m = 1$. Only five of the specimens were I's, the remainder being rectangular bars, rectangular tubes, and round tubes. Test results for the five I's are shown by the triangular symbol. It should be noted that the coordinates in Fig. 6-7d differ from those in the other plots in the figure, so Eq. (6-9) plots as a straight line. The test strengths ranged from 11 percent more to 9 percent less than those predicted by Eq. (6-9).

It should be remembered that Eqs. (6-8) and (6-9) are based on the assumption that the beam-column bends in the plane of the end moments. Cross sections which are much stiffer in bending about one axis than about the other, as the I is, may bend in the weak direction, even if they are loaded so as to bend in the strong direction, unless weak-axis bending is prevented by some kind of support. This is called lateral-torsional buckling (Art. 5-4).

6-3 BEAM-COLUMNS: GENERAL CASE

In the derivation of Eqs. (6-8) and (6-9) we assumed that the column is acted upon only by end moments, in addition to P, and that there is no lateral displacement of one end relative to the other. In this article, we consider the effects of transverse load and of lateral displacement.

For a simply supported member with transverse loads in addition to P, the moment at any point is given by

$$M = M_0 + Py \qquad (a)$$

where M_0 is the moment due to the transverse loads alone. The deflection y can be found by integrating $EI\, d^2y/dx^2 = M$. However, it is given to good approximation by

$$y = \frac{y_0}{1 - P/P_E} \qquad (b)$$

where y_0 is the deflection due to the transverse loads alone. This equation is identical in form to Eq. (4-5) for the column with initial crookedness of amplitude δ_0. Substituting from Eq. (b) into Eq. (a) gives

$$M = M_0 + \frac{Py_0}{1 - P/P_E} = M_0 \frac{1 + (P_E y_0/M_0 - 1)(P/P_E)}{1 - P/P_E} \qquad (c)$$

which can be written

$$M = M_0 \frac{1 + \Psi P/P_E}{1 - P/P_E} = \frac{C_m M_0}{1 - P/P_E} \qquad (6\text{-}12a)$$

where

$$C_m = 1 + \Psi \frac{P}{P_E} \qquad \Psi = \frac{P_E y_0}{M_0} - 1 \qquad (6\text{-}12b)$$

The beam-column with transverse load can now be evaluated by using Eq. (6-8) or (6-9), provided M is taken to be the maximum value of M_0 and C_m is determined by Eq. (6-12b).

If the member and its loads are symmetrical, both M_0 and y_0 are maximum at midlength. Thus, for the pin-ended beam-column of length L with a transverse load W at midlength,

$$M_0 = \frac{WL}{4} \qquad y_0 = \frac{WL^3}{48EI} \qquad P_E = \frac{\pi^2 EI}{L^2}$$

from which

$$\Psi = \frac{\pi^2 EI}{L^2} \frac{WL^3}{48EI} \frac{4}{WL} - 1 = 0.822 - 1 = -0.178 \qquad (d)$$

$$C_m = 1 - 0.178 \frac{P}{P_E} \qquad (e)$$

Similarly, for a pin-ended beam-column of length L with a uniformly distributed load W,

$$M_0 = \frac{WL}{8} \qquad y_0 = \frac{5WL^3}{384EI} \qquad P_E = \frac{\pi^2 EI}{L^2}$$

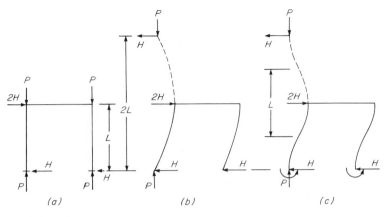

FIGURE 6-8

$$\Psi = \frac{\pi^2 EI}{L^2} \frac{5WL^3}{384EI} \frac{8}{WL} - 1 = 1.028 - 1 = 0.028 \tag{f}$$

$$C_m = 1 + 0.028 \frac{P}{P_E} \tag{g}$$

Values of C_m for the beam-column with lateral displacement of one end are more difficult to determine. An approximate value can be found for the case where there are no transverse loads between supports by considering the frame with an infinitely stiff beam (Fig. 6-8a). Each column can be considered to be a simply supported beam of span $2L$ supporting a load $2H$ at midspan if the bases are hinged (Fig. 6-8b) or, if the bases are fixed, as a beam of span L supporting a load $2H$ at midspan (Fig. 6-8c). In either case, C_m is given by Eq. (e). However, a constant value of $C_m = 0.85$ gives a good approximation to the multiplier $C_m/(1 - P/P_E)$ of M_0 in Eq. (6-12a), as is shown in Table 6-1. For this reason, the AISC/ASD specification prescribes $C_m = 0.85$ for all compression members in frames subject to joint translation. The AISC/LRFD multiplier, which is denoted by CB_2, is discussed in Art. 6-8.

An approximate value of C_m for the beam-column with transverse loads between the ends can be determined in the same way as for the frame of Fig. 6-8a. Thus, if there is a uniformly distributed load on the column, the two cases

TABLE 6-1

$\dfrac{P}{P_E}$	$\dfrac{1 - 0.18P/P_E}{1 - P/P_E}$	$\dfrac{0.85}{1 - P/P_E}$
0	1	0.85
0.2	1.20	1.06
0.4	1.55	1.42
0.6	2.23	2.13
0.8	4.28	4.25

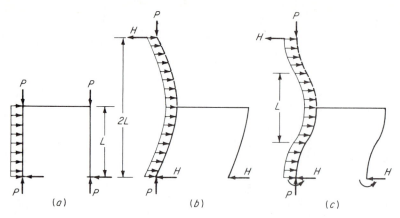

FIGURE 6-9

shown in Fig. 6-9*b* and *c* show that the equivalent uniformly loaded beam is of span 2*L* for hinged bases and *L* for fixed bases. In either case, C_m is given by Eq. (*g*). A constant value $C_m = 1$ gives a good approximation to $C_m/(1 - P/P_E)$, as is shown in Table 6-2. The AISC specifications prescribe $C_m = 0.85$ for this case.

6-4 BUCKLING OF FRAMES WITH LOADED BEAMS

The behavior of the braced frame shown in Fig. 6-10*a* and *b*, in which symmetrically placed loads *P* are carried by the beam, is quite different from that of the same frame in Fig. 6-10*c* and *d*, where the loads act at the joints. Thus, lateral deflection of a point on the column (at midheight, say) of the frame in *a* begins at $P = 0$ and increases until a maximum value of *P* is reached (*OAB* in Fig. 6-10*e*). On the other hand, there is no lateral deflection of a point on the column of the frame in Fig. 6-10*c* until the critical load is reached, at which buckling begins (*C* in Fig. 6-10*e*). Furthermore, the points of inflection are in the beams in the one case and in the columns in the other (Fig. 6-10*b* and *d*). Since the columns in the frame with the loaded beam are beam-columns, the peak load can be determined by Eqs. (6-9) and (6-11), provided the frame moments are determined by plastic

TABLE 6-2

$\dfrac{P}{P_E}$	$\dfrac{1 + 0.028P/P_E}{1 - P/P_E}$	$\dfrac{1}{1 - P/P_E}$
0	1	1
0.2	1.26	1.25
0.4	1.69	1.67
0.6	2.54	2.50
0.8	5.11	5.00

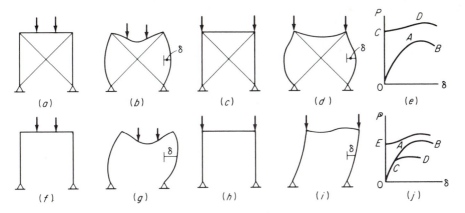

FIGURE 6-10

rather than elastic analysis. The critical load corresponding to point C is determined by the procedures described in Examples 4-11-1 and 4-11-2.

If the frame with the loaded beam is not braced (Fig. 6-10f), it will follow, at least for a time, the same load-deflection path as the braced frame (OAB in Fig. 6-10j). However, before point A is reached, it may become unstable in the symmetrical configuration and shift to the asymmetrical one shown in Fig. 6-10g. The subsequent load-deflection curve is CD in Fig. 6-10j. This behavior is the same as that of the frame in Fig. 6-10h and i, which buckles at a load corresponding to point E in Fig. 6-10j; that is, there is a bifurcation of the equilibrium configuration. The critical load corresponding to point E is determined in the same way as the critical load corresponding to point C in Fig. 6-10e; the only difference in the solution is in the effective-length coefficient K to be used in the column-buckling formula. The problem, then, is to determine the load at which the unbraced frame with loaded beams becomes unstable in respect to lateral movement. As it turns out, this critical load is relatively insensitive to the location of the loads P. In other words, the critical values of P for the frame of Fig. 6-10f and h are practically equal. This was shown first by Chwalla, who investigated the sidesway stability of the one-bay one-story frame which buckles elastically (Ref. 4, p. 227).

The frame shown in Fig. 6-11a has been used to investigate the sidesway stability of multistory frames which buckle elastically.[5] The load $(n-1)wL_b/2$ at each column top represents the load from the upper stories of an n-story frame. Of course, the simulation is approximate because continuity with the second-story column is neglected. The calculated loads at bifurcation of equilibrium are shown in Fig. 6-11b, together with the corresponding values of the effective-length coefficients K. Results of the analysis were in excellent agreement with tests on two small-scale frames; the ratio of test load to predicted load was 0.98 in one case and 0.96 in the other. OCD shows the variation of P with the horizontal reaction H for a simulated three-story frame. Bifurcation occurs at point C. Thus, OCD corresponds to OCD in Fig. 6-10j. The effective-length coefficient for

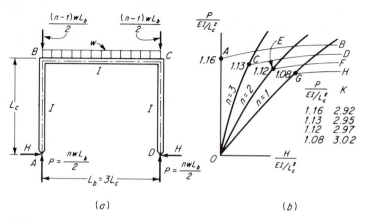

FIGURE 6-11

this case is $K = 2.95$. OAB shows the variation of P with H for the frame loaded only at the column tops. The value $K = 2.92$ for this case is given by the nomograph, Fig. 4-28b. It is clear that the difference between the extreme case where only the beam is loaded ($K = 3.02$) and the other extreme case where only the column tops are loaded is of no consequence. This is an important conclusion because, to the extent that we can expect the behavior shown in Fig. 6-11 to be typical, it means that the nomograph in Fig. 4-28b can be used to determine the critical load for the unbraced frame with loaded beams, provided buckling occurs before the beams become inelastic. The case where the beam yields before the frame becomes unstable is discussed in Art. 9-19.

A braced frame loaded to simulate a multistory frame is shown in Fig. 6-12. The columns are W8 × 31, 20 ft long, and the beam a W18 × 50, 30 ft long, all A36 steel. The load nP which produces first yielding is determined by Eqs. (6-8) and (6-10) for the columns, using the SSRC formula to compute P_{cr} in the inelastic range, and by $F_y = Mc/I$ for the beam. The results, $nP = 32, 128,$ and 184 kips

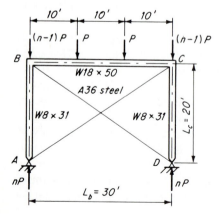

FIGURE 6-12

for $n = 1$, 4, and 8, respectively, are shown on the $nP\text{-}\delta$ plots OB, OC, and OD of Fig. 6-13a. The peaks of these load-deflection curves, $nP = 39$, 143, and 250 kips, are determined by Eqs. (6-9) and (6-11), using frame moments determined by plastic analysis. Also shown is the critical load $nP = 280$ kips for the frame with all the load acting at the column tops. This load is given by the SSRC formula, using the effective-length coefficient K from Fig. 4-28a. It is seen that this critical load can be orders of magnitude larger than the load that can be supported when part of it acts on the beam.

The critical load $nP = 134$ kips for the unbraced frame with the loads nP at the column tops is also shown in Fig. 6-13a. This load is also easily determined, this time with K from Fig. 4-28b. Thus,

$$G_B = \frac{(I/L)_c}{(I/L)_b} = \frac{110/20}{802/30} = 0.205$$

$$G_A = \infty \qquad \text{for hinged base}$$

$$K = 2.05 \qquad \frac{KL}{r} = \frac{2.05 \times 20 \times 12}{3.47} = 142$$

$$F_E = \frac{\pi^2 E}{(KL/r)^2} = \frac{296,000}{142^2} = 14.7 \text{ ksi}$$

$$P_{cr} = F_E A = 14.7 \times 9.12 = 134 \text{ kips}$$

This critical load, as has already been shown (Fig. 6-11), is not sensitive to the position of the loads. Therefore, it is also a close estimate of the critical load for sidesway stability of unbraced frames loaded as in Fig. 6-12. From this we can

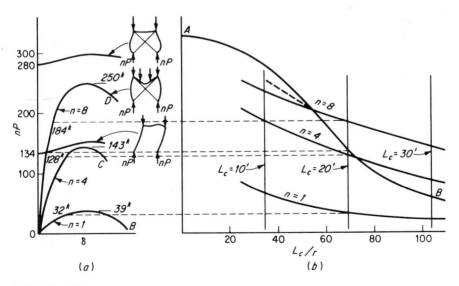

(a)

(b)

FIGURE 6-13

conclude that the one-story frame can attain the peak load 39 kips with or without bracing against lateral displacement. Also, the four-story frame should be able to reach the beginning-of-yield load, 128 kips, without bracing but would be unlikely to reach its peak load, 143 kips, in the unbraced condition. Finally, if $n = 8$, the frame can be expected to buckle laterally at about 134 kips if it is not braced, so it cannot attain even its yield load unless it is braced.

Figure 6-13b shows the variation in first-yield loads with column slenderness. The curves for $n = 1$, 4, and 8 were plotted by computing additional first-yield loads for the frame of Fig. 6-12 with $L_c = 10$ and 30 ft and corresponding beam length $L_b = 15$ and 45 ft, so the ratio of column stiffness to beam stiffness is constant. Also shown is the variation in critical load for the unbraced frame (curve AB). According to this figure, the one-story frame would be stable to its first-yield load even if the W8 × 31 columns were longer than 30 ft. Similarly, for $n = 8$, the frame should be stable to its first-yield load for columns shorter than about 15 ft.

Sidesway stability of unbraced frames at loads exceeding first-yield values are not as readily determined, because penetration of yield stress into those cross sections of a beam where the bending moment exceeds M_y reduces the beam stiffness. This reduces the rotational restraint of the columns, which increases their effective lengths. Therefore, AB in Fig. 6-13b is lowered to the left of its intersection with each n curve, as is shown by the dashed line at the intersection with the curve for $n = 8$. This problem is discussed further in Art. 9-19.

An extensive theoretical study of the strength of beam-columns in frames has been reported by Kanchanalai.[6] Parameters taken into account include the slenderness ratio, relative column-to-beam stiffness, bending axis, residual stress, and the effect of axial load on any pinned-end columns in the frame. Experimental studies of several unbraced frames, as well as tests of full-size biaxially loaded restrained beam-columns under loading and support conditions simulating the actual condition in unbraced frames, are also reported.

6-5 LATERAL-TORSIONAL BUCKLING OF BEAM-COLUMNS

In Art. 5-4 we discussed the three differential equations of equilibrium for lateral-torsional buckling of beams [Eqs. (5-1)]. These equations can be extended to include the effect of a centrally applied compression force P by adding to the components of the end moments M_x the moments due to P. Figure 6-14 shows that the load P produces a moment Pv about the beam's x axis and a moment Pu about its y axis. These must be added to the right sides of Eqs. (5-1a) and (5-1b), respectively. Thus,

$$-EI_x \frac{d^2v}{dz^2} = M_x + Pv \tag{6-13a}$$

$$-EI_y \frac{d^2u}{dz^2} = M_x\beta + Pu \tag{6-13b}$$

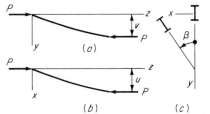

(b)　　　　　　(c)　　　**FIGURE 6-14**

Because the resultant internal force P is not perpendicular to the cross section in Fig. 6-14, it also produces a twisting moment. It was shown in Art. 4-20 that the rate of change of this moment with respect to z is given by $fI_p\, d^2\beta/dz^2$, where $f = P/A$ [see Eq. (4-49) and Eq. (h) of Art. 4-20]. Therefore, the moment itself at any cross section is $fI_p\, d\beta/dz$. This must be added to the right side of Eq. (5-1c), which gives

$$-EC_w \frac{d^3\beta}{dz^3} + GJ \frac{d\beta}{dz} = M_x \frac{du}{dz} + \frac{P}{A} I_p \frac{d\beta}{dz} \tag{6-13c}$$

Equation (6-13a) is independent and, when integrated, gives the deflected shape in the yz plane in which the moment $M_x + Pv$ acts. On the other hand, the lateral displacement u and the twist β are not independent and must be found by solving Eqs. (6-13b) and (6-13c) simultaneously. The boundary conditions for a beam which is supported at each end ($u = 0$ and $\beta = 0$ at each end) and which also has no y-axis rotational restraint and is free to warp at each end ($d^2u/dz^2 = 0$ and $d^2\beta/dz^2 = 0$ at each end) are satisfied by

$$u = A \sin \frac{\pi z}{L} \qquad \beta = B \sin \frac{\pi z}{L}$$

If these displacement functions are solutions to the problem, they must satisfy Eqs. (6-13b) and (6-13c). Substituting into the equations gives

$$M_x^2 = \frac{I_p}{A} (P_{Ey} - P)(P_T - P) \tag{a}$$

where I_p = polar moment of inertia
P_{Ey} = Euler load for y-axis buckling
P_T = twist-buckling load determined by Eq. (4-51)

Equation (a) can also be expressed in terms of the critical moment for pure bending given by Eq. (5-3). Thus,

$$M_{x,cr}^2 = \frac{\pi^2}{L^2} EI_y\, GJ + \frac{\pi^4}{L^4} EI_y\, EC_w = \frac{\pi^2}{L^2} EI_y\left(GJ + \frac{\pi^2}{L^2} EC_w\right) = \frac{I_p}{A} P_{Ey} P_T \tag{b}$$

Dividing Eq. (a) by Eq. (b) gives

$$\left(\frac{M_x}{M_{x,cr}}\right)^2 = \left(1 - \frac{P}{P_{Ey}}\right)\left(1 - \frac{P}{P_T}\right) \tag{6-14}$$

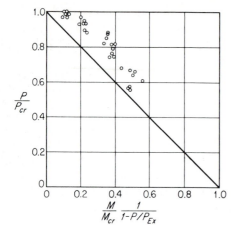

FIGURE 6-15

Comparison of Eq. (6-15) with tests on laterally unsupported aluminum beam-columns reported in Ref. 3.

Equation (6-14) is not used in design specifications. Instead, the interaction formulas derived for the beam which does not buckle laterally are used. These interaction formulas are based on Eq. (6-5), which is derived from the secant formula. The secant formula is the solution to Eq. (6-13a). Equation (6-5) is arbitrarily extended to cover lateral-torsional buckling by redefining P_{cr} as the smaller of $P_{cr,x}$ and $P_{cr,y}$ and M_y as the critical moment for lateral-torsional buckling. Thus, Eq. (6-5) becomes

$$\frac{P}{P_{cr(x \text{ or } y)}} + \frac{M}{M_{cr}} \frac{C_m}{1 - P/P_{Ex}} = 1 \tag{6-15}$$

The interaction formula Eq. (6-6) can be extended similarly. In this case, however, M_{cr} must approach M_p, rather than M_y, as a limiting value. The following formula is based on tests:

$$\frac{M_{cr}}{M_p} = 1.07 - \frac{\sqrt{F_y}}{3160} \frac{L}{r_y} \le 1 \tag{6-16}$$

This formula is used for plastic design in the AISC/ASD specification, except that M_{cr} is denoted by M_m.

A comparison of Eq. (6-15) with tests of 36 aluminum beam-columns that failed by lateral-torsional buckling is shown in Fig. 6-15. These tests were of the same type as those described in Art. 6-2, Fig. 6-7d, except that all the cross sections were of I shape.[3] The actual strengths ranged from 4 to 22 percent more than the predicted values.

6-6   FORMULAS FOR DESIGN OF BEAM-COLUMNS

The preceding discussions suggest two possible criteria for determining the limiting load on a beam-column:

1. First yielding (on the extreme fiber) or

2. Attainment of the peak load (topmost point on the P-δ curve)

For convenience in the discussion to follow, the corresponding formulas from Arts. 6-1 and 6-2 are repeated here. For first yielding of the extreme fiber,

$$\frac{P}{P_{cr}} + \frac{C_m M}{M_y} \frac{1}{1 - P/P_E} = 1 \tag{6-17}$$

$$\frac{P}{P_y} + \frac{M}{M_y} = 1 \tag{6-18}$$

For attainment of peak load,

$$\frac{P}{P_{cr}} + \frac{C_m M}{M_p} \frac{1}{1 - P/P_E} = 1 \tag{6-19}$$

$$\frac{P}{P_y} + 0.85 \frac{M}{M_p} = 1 \qquad \frac{P}{P_y} \geq 0.15 \tag{6-20a}$$

$$M = M_p \qquad \frac{P}{P_y} \leq 0.15 \tag{6-20b}$$

Equations (6-17) and (6-19) check the member for the case where the moment is maximum at a point between the ends, while Eqs. (6-18) and (6-20) check it for the case where the moment is maximum at one end. Both checks must be made because it is not known in advance which one governs.

There are several ways in which these formulas can be used to evaluate the strength of members in frames with moment-resistant beam-to-column connections:

1. Analyze the frame by a method based on elastic behavior, e.g., slope-deflection equations, and then evaluate the members by Eqs. (6-17) and (6-18). In this case, the evaluation of the frame moments and evaluation of member strengths are consistent in that both are based on elastic behavior.
2. Analyze the frame as in procedure 1 but evaluate the members by Eqs. (6-19) and (6-20). This corresponds to the ultimate-strength design procedure used for reinforced-concrete frames. Of course, it gives larger values of frame capacity than procedure 1. Since we assume elastic behavior to determine frame moments and inelastic behavior to determine member strength, the assumptions in procedure 2 are inconsistent.
3. Analyze the frame by theories of plastic behavior (these take into account certain redistributions of moment which develop with increased loading of a frame after first yielding) and evaluate the members by Eqs. (6-19) and (6-20). Here the assumptions are consistent in that frame moments and assessment of member strength are both based on inelastic behavior. This procedure is called *plastic design* when applied to steel frames and *limit design* when applied to reinforced-concrete frames. In general, this procedure gives larger values of frame capacity than procedure 2. Plastic design is discussed in Chap. 9.

6-7 ALLOWABLE-STRESS FORMULAS FOR BEAM-COLUMNS

The AISC/ASD specification uses Eqs. (6-19) and (6-20) for the beam-column in plastically designed frames. Equations (6-17) and (6-18) are used for structures designed on a first-yield basis, except that they are written in terms of allowable stress. Thus, if P and M are defined as service-load (working-load) values and n is the factor of safety, nP and nM should be substituted for P and M in Eq. (6-17). This gives

$$\frac{nP}{P_{cr}} + \frac{nM}{M_y} \frac{C_m}{1 - nP/P_E} = 1 \tag{a}$$

Dividing P and P_{cr} in the first term by the cross-sectional area A and, in the second term, dividing M and M_y by the section modulus S and P and P_E by the area A, we can write Eq. (a) in the form

$$\frac{f_a}{F_{cr}/n} + \frac{f_b}{F_y/n} \frac{C_m}{1 - f_a/(F_E/n)} = 1 \tag{b}$$

where f_a and f_b are service-load stresses. The stresses which are divided by the factor of safety are now allowable stresses, so

$$\frac{f_a}{F_a} + \frac{f_b}{F_b} \frac{C_m}{1 - f_a/F'_E} = 1 \tag{6-21}$$

where F_a = axial compressive stress that would be allowed if there were only the axial force P

F_b = bending compressive stress that would be allowed if there were only the moment M

F'_E = allowable Euler stress

F_a is given by Eqs. (4-17) and (4-18). Allowable bending stresses F_b are discussed in Chap. 5. F'_E is given by Eq. (4-18) for all values of KL/r, so the factor of safety n for F_E in Eq. (b) is the same as it is for columns which buckle elastically. C_m is given by Eq. (6-7); that is, $C_m = 0.6 - 0.4M_1/M_2$ if there are no transverse loads on the member and there is no translation of one end relative to the other, as was assumed in the derivation. If there are transverse loads, AISC/ASD specifies $C_m = 0.85$ if the member ends are rotationally restrained and $C_m = 1$ if they are not. If there is relative joint translation, $C_m = 0.85$.

Equation (6-18) is transformed similarly, the result being

$$\frac{f_a}{0.6F_y} + \frac{f_b}{F_b} = 1 \tag{6-22}$$

Of course, both equations must be checked, since one corresponds to the case where the moment is a maximum at a section between the ends while the other corresponds to the case where it is a maximum at one end.

Equations (6-21) and (6-22) are written in more general form in the AISC/ASD specification so as to include the case of biaxially eccentric load, i.e., a load

P together with x-axis end moments M_{1x} and M_{2x} and y-axis end moments M_{1y} and M_{2y}. This is done by adding a bending term, so

$$\frac{f_a}{F_a} + \frac{f_{bx}}{F_{bx}} \frac{C_{mx}}{1 - f_a/F'_{Ex}} + \frac{f_{by}}{F_{by}} \frac{C_{my}}{1 - f_a/F'_{Ey}} = 1 \qquad (6\text{-}23a)$$

$$\frac{f_a}{0.6F_y} + \frac{f_{bx}}{F_{bx}} + \frac{f_{by}}{F_{by}} = 1 \qquad (6\text{-}23b)$$

The accounting in Eq. (6-23a) for the effect of the moments M_y is approximate because it neglects the effect of the twisting which accompanies biaxial bending.[7] Nevertheless, the formula is generally conservative, because it is based on first yield, rather than attainment of peak load, and this turns out to be more than enough to offset the neglect of twist.[8] Equations (6-23) are also used in the AREA and AASHTO specifications, except that they are based on a larger factor of safety.

If $f_a/F_y < 0.15$, the AISC/ASD specification allows the following simpler formula to be used in lieu of Eqs. (6-23a) and (6-23b):

$$\frac{f_a}{F_a} + \frac{f_{bx}}{F_{bx}} + \frac{f_{by}}{F_{by}} = 1 \qquad (6\text{-}23c)$$

The proportioning of beam-columns is a trial-and-error procedure. A formula for obtaining a trial section can be obtained by omitting the terms involving C_{mx} and C_{my} in Eq. (6-23a), substituting P/A for f_a, M_x/S_x for f_{bx}, M_y/S_y for f_{by}, and solving for A. The result is

$$A = \frac{P}{F_a} + \frac{M_x}{F_{bx}} \frac{A}{S_x} + \frac{M_y}{F_{by}} \frac{A}{S_y} \qquad (c)$$

The AISC/ASD Manual lists values of A/S_x and A/S_y as B_x and B_y, respectively, so Eq. (c) can be written

$$A = \frac{P}{F_a} + B_x \frac{M_x}{F_{bx}} + B_y \frac{M_y}{F_{by}} \qquad (6\text{-}24a)$$

A similar transformation of Eq. (6-23b) gives

$$A = \frac{P}{0.6F_y} + B_x \frac{M_x}{F_{bx}} + B_y \frac{M_y}{F_{by}} \qquad (6\text{-}24b)$$

An equivalent axial force P^* can be obtained from Eq. (6-24a) by multiplying through by F_a, which, with $F_a A = P^*$, gives

$$P^* = P + B_x M_x \frac{F_a}{F_{bx}} + B_y M_y \frac{F_a}{F_{by}} \qquad (6\text{-}24c)$$

With the value of P^* one may choose a trial section from the Manual's tables of allowable axial load. It should be noted that the allowable axial loads are tabulated for an effective length KL based on the least radius of gyration (r_y). Therefore, if the column is supported against lateral buckling or bending about the y

axis, the table should be entered with an effective length based on r_x. This effective length can be obtained by dividing the unsupported length of the column by the ratio r_x/r_y. Values of r_x/r_y are given in the table. They are about 2.1 for "square" columns ($b = d$) and 1.7 for columns with $b \approx 0.8d$. An example is given in DP6-7-1.

Instead of the approximation involved in omitting the C_m terms in Eq. (6-23a), one can retain them as follows:

$$\frac{C_m}{1 - f_a/F'_E} = C_m \frac{F'_E}{F'_E - f_a} = C_m \frac{(KL)^2 F'_E}{(KL)^2(F'_E - f_a)} = C_m \frac{0.149 \times 10^6 r^2}{0.149 \times 10^6 r^2 - (P/A)(KL)^2}$$

Denoting $0.149 \times 10^6 r^2$ by a and substituting the resulting values of $C_m/(1 - f_a/F'_E)$ into Eq. (6-23a) yields

$$P^* = P + B_x M_x C_{mx} \frac{F_a}{F_{bx}} \frac{a_x}{a_x - P(KL)^2} + B_y M_y C_{my} \frac{F_a}{F_{by}} \frac{a_y}{a_y - P(KL)^2} \quad (6\text{-}25a)$$

Equation (6-23b) can be transformed similarly to obtain

$$P^* = P \frac{F_a}{0.6F_y} + B_x M_x \frac{F_a}{F_{bx}} + B_y M_y \frac{F_a}{F_{by}} \quad (6\text{-}25b)$$

The use of Eqs. (6-25) is facilitated by tabular values of a_x, a_y, B_x, and B_y in the Manual.

Equation (6-30) can also be used to obtain a preliminary selection.

Example 6-7-1. Design the columns of the frame shown in Fig. 6-16, using W shapes with the y axis in the plane of the frame. The 8-kip horizontal force is a wind load. The wind load would normally be distributed along the column by girts or siding but is assumed concentrated at B to simplify the problem. A frame with wind load distributed along the column is presented in DP6-7-1. Assume the moment of inertia of member BC is twice that of the columns. The columns are braced at top and bottom against y-axis displacement and at midheight against y-axis buckling. A36 steel, AISC/ASD specification.

Solution. Since $K = 1$ for y-axis buckling, $(KL)_y = 10$ ft. But K may be nearly 2 for x-axis buckling, so $(KL)_x \approx 2 \times 20 = 40$ ft and will control. Use Eq. (6-30) to make a preliminary selection, based on the no-wind case.

$$P = 10 + 30 + (1 + 0.5)25 = 77.5 \text{ kips}$$

$$M_x = 136(1 + 0.5) = 204 \text{ ft·kips}$$

$$P^* = P + \frac{2M_x}{d}$$

$$P^* = 77.5 + \frac{2 \times 204 \times 12}{d} = 77.5 + \frac{4806}{d}$$

$$= \begin{cases} 486 \text{ kips} & \text{for } d = 12 \\ 427 \text{ kips} & \text{for } d = 14 \end{cases}$$

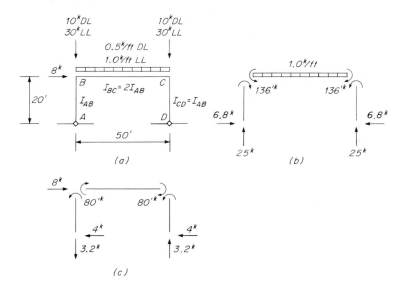

FIGURE 6-16

For x-axis buckling

$$G_{\text{top}} = \frac{1/20}{2/50} = 1.25 \qquad G_{\text{bot}} = 10 \quad \text{(Art. 4-11)}$$

for which Fig. 4-28 yields $K = 1.9$. Therefore, $KL = 1.9 \times 20 = 38$ ft.

For $b/d = 0.8$, $r_x/r_y \approx 2.1$, so the Manual's column-strength tables should be entered with $KL = 38/2.1 = 18$ ft. There is no W12 for which $r_x/r_y \approx 2.1$ and $P = 486$ kips for $KL = 18$ ft.

For $b/d = 1$, $r_x/r_y \approx 1.7$, for which the column-strength tables should be entered with $KL = 38/1.7 = 22$ ft. For a W14 $\times$ 90, $P = 432$ kips (>427 kips).

Try W14 $\times$ 90: $A = 26.5$ in^2, $r_x = 6.14$ in, $r_y = 3.70$ in, $S_x = 143$ in^3. The Manual's table of beam constants shows the maximum unbraced length to allow $F_b = 0.66F_y$ is 15.3 ft. The unbraced length is only 10 ft, so $F_b = 0.66 \times 36 = 24$ ksi.

$$\frac{KL}{r_y} = \frac{10 \times 12}{3.70} = 32.4 \qquad \frac{KL}{r_x} = \frac{1.9 \times 20 \times 12}{6.14} = 74.3$$

From Manual tables, $F_a = 16.2$ ksi and $F'_{Ex} = 27.0$ ksi

$$f_a = \frac{77.5}{26.5} = 2.92 \text{ ksi} \qquad f_b = \frac{204 \times 12}{143} = 17.1 \text{ ksi}$$

Then, since $C_m = 0.85$ for compression members in frames subject to joint translation, Eq. (6-23a) gives

$$\frac{2.92}{16.2} + \frac{17.1}{24} \frac{0.85}{1 - 2.92/27.0} = 0.850 < 1$$

Equation (6-23b) yields

$$\frac{2.92}{22} + \frac{17.1}{24} = 0.845 < 1$$

Check for loads including wind.

$$P = 10 + 30(1 + 0.5) + 3.2 = 80.7$$

$$M_x = 136(1 + 0.5) + 80 = 284 \text{ ft·kips}$$

$$f_a = \frac{80.7}{26.5} = 3.04 \text{ ksi} \qquad f_b = \frac{284 \times 12}{143} = 23.8 \text{ ksi}$$

The specification permits allowable stresses to be increased by one-third for wind load and load combinations that include wind. Therefore, Eq. (6-23a) gives

$$\frac{3.04}{16.2 \times \frac{4}{3}} + \frac{23.8}{24 \times \frac{4}{3}} \frac{0.85}{1 - 3.04/27.0} = 0.853 < 1$$

Equation (6-23b) yields

$$\frac{3.04}{22 \times \frac{4}{3}} + \frac{23.8}{24 \times \frac{4}{3}} = 0.848 < 1$$

Since the interaction formulas show the sum of the stress ratios to be only about 0.85, a lighter section may be adequate. The next lighter W is the W14 × 82. However, for this section Eq. (6-23a) yields 1.04 > 1.

DP6-7-1 (AISC/ASD): Column for Building of DP3-15-1

Discussion of this example and explanatory comments identified by letters alongside the computations are given in Art. 6-9, p. 443.

6-8 AISC/LRFD FORMULAS FOR BEAM-COLUMNS

The AISC/LRFD beam-column interaction formulas are the following:

$$\frac{P_u}{\phi_c P_n} \geq 0.2 \qquad \frac{P_u}{\phi_c P_n} + \frac{8}{9}\left(\frac{M_{ux}}{\phi_b M_{nx}} + \frac{M_{uy}}{\phi_b M_{ny}}\right) \leq 1 \qquad (6\text{-}26a)$$

$$\frac{P_u}{\phi_c P_n} < 0.2 \qquad \frac{P_u}{2\phi_c P_n} + \frac{M_{ux}}{\phi_b M_{nx}} + \frac{M_{uy}}{\phi_b M_{ny}} \leq 1 \qquad (6\text{-}26b)$$

where P_u = required compressive strength

P_n = nominal compressive strength determined in accordance with procedures discussed in Art. 4-9

M_u = required flexural strength determined in accordance with procedures discussed in the following text

M_n = nominal flexural strength determined in accordance with procedures discussed in Art. 5-9

COLUMN FOR BUILDING OF *DP3-15-1* and *DP4-15-1*   *DP6-7-1*

Building of *DP3-15-1*
  AISC/ASD specs.
  Bents 20' c.c. ⎤
  Wind   20 psf ⎥
  DL   14 psf ⎬ See *DP3-15-1*
  Snow   40 psf ⎦

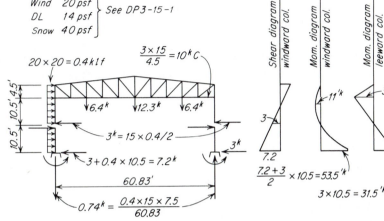

$20 \times 20 = 0.4\,klf$

$\dfrac{3 \times 15}{4.5} = 10^k\,C$

$3^k = 15 \times 0.4/2$

$3 + 0.4 \times 10.5 = 7.2^k$

3^k

$60.83'$

$0.74^k = \dfrac{0.4 \times 15 \times 7.5}{60.83}$

Shear diagram windward col.

Mom. diagram windward col.

Mom. diagram leeward col.

$11^{'k}$

$31.5^{'k}$

3

7.2

$\dfrac{7.2 + 3}{2} \times 10.5 = 53.5^{'k}$

$3 \times 10.5 = 31.5^{'k}$

Column load : $34 \times 20 \times 60.83/2 = 20.7^k\,DL + Snow$ (a)
                3.4 siding
                12.5 conc. loads from trolley beams
                $36.6^k - 0.7^k = 35.9^k$ (windward col.)
                      $+ 0.7^k = 37.3^k$ (leeward col.)

Design loads with wind : Windward col.   Leeward col.
                $35.9 \times \tfrac{3}{4} = 26.9^k$ $37.3 \times \tfrac{3}{4} = 28.0^k$ (b)
                $53.5 \times 12 \times \tfrac{3}{4} = 480^{''k}$ $31.5 \times 12 \times \tfrac{3}{4} = 283^{''k}$

Windward column

$$A = \frac{P}{0.6F_y} + B_x\,\frac{M_x}{F_{bx}} = \frac{26.9}{22} + \frac{480}{24}\,B_x = 1.22 + 20\,B_x \qquad (c)$$

Try W8: $B_x \approx 0.33$ for W8s, so $A = 1.22 + 20 \times 0.33 = 7.82\,in^2$
Try W8 × 28: $A = 8.25\,in^2$, $S_x = 24.3\,in^3$, $F_b = 0.66 \times 36 = 24\,ksi$
$f_a = 26.9/8.25 = 3.26\,ksi$, $f_b = 480/24.3 = 19.8\,ksi$

$$\frac{f_a}{0.6F_y} + \frac{f_b}{F_{bx}} = \frac{3.26}{22} + \frac{19.8}{24} = 0.148 + 0.825 = 0.973 < 1 \;\; O.K. \qquad (d)$$

Leeward column W8 × 28 O.K.

ϕ_c = resistance factor for compression = 0.85
ϕ_b = resistance for flexure = 0.90

Equations (6-26) are plotted in Fig. 6-17 for the case of uniaxial bending. Also shown in the figure are the plots in Fig. 6-6 of the I cross section.

The specification provides for three methods of analysis by which the required flexural capacity M_u may be evaluated:

1. M_u may be determined from a plastic analysis.
2. M_u may be determined from a second-order analysis, using the factored loads (second-order analysis is discussed in Art. 6-10).
3. In lieu of a second-order analysis, M_u may be taken as the sum of the moments M_{nt} and M_{lt} determined from a first-order analysis, each multiplied by a factor to take account of the effects of deflection, according to the formula

$$M_u = B_1 M_{nt} + B_2 M_{lt} \qquad (6\text{-}27)$$

where M_{nt} = moment assuming no lateral translation of the frame
$\quad\;\; M_{lt}$ = moment due to a lateral translation of the frame
$\quad B_1, B_2$ = amplification factors

The amplification factors are given by Eqs. (6-28) and (6-29):

$$B_1 = \frac{C_m}{1 - P_u/P_E} \geq 1 \qquad (6\text{-}28)$$

where P_u = required compressive strength
$\quad\;\; P_E = \pi^2 E A_g/(KL/r)^2$ = Euler load for buckling in plane of frame, with $K = 1$ unless analysis, e.g., by the alignment chart (Fig. 4-28), shows that a smaller value may be used

C_m in Eq. (6-28) is defined as follows.

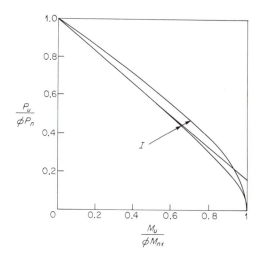

FIGURE 6-17

For rotationally restrained members with no transverse loads between supports,

$$C_m = 0.6 - 0.4 \frac{M_1}{M_2} \qquad [\text{Eq. (6-7)}]$$

where M_1 is the smaller of the end moments M_1 and M_2 and M_1/M_2 is positive if the member bends in reverse curvature.

For members with transverse loads between supports,

$$C_m = \begin{cases} 0.85 & \text{if member ends are rotationally restrained} \\ 1 & \text{if member ends are not rotationally restrained} \end{cases}$$

$$B_2 = \frac{1}{1 - \sum P_u(\Delta_{oh}/L \sum H)} \qquad (6\text{-}29a)$$

or

$$B_2 = \frac{1}{1 - \sum P_u/\sum P_E} \qquad (6\text{-}29b)$$

where $\sum P_u$ = required axial strength of all columns in a story
Δ_{oh} = translation deflection of the story, in
$\sum H$ = sum of all story horizontal forces producing Δ_{oh}
L = story height, in
$P_E = \pi^2 E A_g/(KL/r)^2$ = Euler load for buckling in plane of frame with $K \geq 1$, as determined by analysis, e.g., by the alignment chart (Fig. 4-28)

The moments M_{nt} and M_{lt} can be evaluated by either of two procedures. In the first procedure the structure is analyzed for the prescribed loads for two cases: (a) as a braced structure in which no joint translations are permitted and (b) as an unbraced structure in which joint translations are permitted. Solution (a) produces the values of M_{nt}, and the moments M_{lt} are determined by subtracting the results of (a) from the results of (b). The second procedure requires a solution as a braced structure as discussed in (a) above, except that in this case the holding forces required to prevent the lateral translation are calculated. The M_{lt} moments can then be determined by analyzing the structure as an unbraced frame subject to the holding forces calculated from solution (a). This procedure requires some care in the selection of the location of the holding forces, since computer programs generally take account of the axial deformations in all the members in the determination of the member forces. Some members may experience either compressive forces and the resulting shortening, or tensile forces and the resulting lengthening. For example, consider a structure subject to forces which would produce a translation to the right. If the holding forces are established at the right hand of the structure, the horizontal members will be subjected to axial compression, but if they are established at the left hand, the horizontal members will be subjected to axial tension. The differences in the results will be small for structures in which the lateral translation is small but may be significant for a flexible structure in which the lateral translation is significant. This difficulty is avoided if the first procedure is used.

The proportioning of beam columns is a trial-and-error procedure. A trial section can be obtained from the formula[9]

$$P^* = P + \frac{2M_x}{d} + \frac{7.5M_y}{b} \tag{6-30}$$

where P^* = equivalent axial force
d = depth of section
b = width of flange

To use Eq. (6-30) one assumes values of d and b and selects a trial section from the Manual's tables of column axial strength. It should be noted that axial strengths in these tables are for effective length KL based on the least radius of gyration (r_y). Therefore, if the column is supported against lateral buckling or bending about the y axis, the table should be entered with an effective length based on r_x. This effective length can be obtained by dividing the column length by the ratio r_x/r_y. Values of r_x/r_y are given in the table. They are about 2.1 for "square" columns $(b = d)$ and about 1.7 for columns with $b \approx 0.8d$. An example is given in DP6-8-1.

In developing Eqs. (6-26) a number of alternative formulations were compared to the inelastic solutions of 82 cases involving sidesway. The formulas are essentially alternative forms, with some modification, of the AISC/ASD formulas, Eqs. (6-23). Thus, for the case $M_{uy} = 0$, substitution of M_u from Eq. (6-27), B_1 from Eq. (6-28), and B_2 from Eq. (6-29b) into Eq. (6-26a) yields

$$\frac{P_u}{\phi P_n} + \frac{8}{9}\left(\frac{M_{nt(x)}}{\phi M_{nx}}\frac{C_{mx}}{1 - P_u/P_E} + \frac{M_{lt(x)}}{\phi M_{nx}}\frac{1}{1 - \sum P_u/P_{E}}\right) \le 1 \tag{6-31}$$

In Eq. (6-23a), $f_{bx} = M_x/S_x$, where M_x is the sum of the moments M_{ntx} assuming no lateral translation and M_{ltx} due to a lateral translation, that is, $f_{bx} = f_{bx(nt)} + f_{bx(lt)}$. Substituting this value of f_{bx} into Eq. (6-23a) gives

$$\frac{f_a}{F_a} + \frac{f_{bx(nt)}}{F_{bx}}\frac{C_{mx}}{1 - f_a/F'_{Ex}} + \frac{f_{bx(lt)}}{F_{bx}}\frac{C_{mx}}{1 - f_a/F'_{Ex}} \le 1 \tag{6-32}$$

Equation (6-31) can be put into the form of Eq. (6-32) by dividing values of P by the cross-sectional area A and values of M by the section modulus S. When this is done, it will be noted that the differences between the two formulas are the factor $\frac{8}{9}$, the absence of C_{mx} in the third term of Eq. (6-31), and the difference in the denominators of the third term. But if all the columns in a story are the same and P is the same for all, $\sum f_a/\sum F'_{Ex} = f_a/F'_{Ex}$. Thus, in general, the difference between the third terms of the equations will be small.

The LRFD formulas also differ from the ASD formulas in that both of the latter must be checked, while only one of the LRFD formulas need be used. The value of the first term in the LRFD equations determines which of the two is to be used.

Example 6-8-1. Design the columns of the frame shown in Fig. 6-18, using W shapes with the y axis in the plane of the frame. The 8-kip horizontal force is a wind load. The wind load would normally be distributed along the column by girts or siding but is assumed concentrated at B to simplify the problem. A frame with wind load distributed along the column is presented in DP6-8-1. Assume the moment of inertia of member BC to be twice that of the columns. The columns are braced at top and bottom against y-axis displacement and at midheight against y-axis buckling. A36 steel, AISC/LRFD specification.

Solution. The load combinations of Art. 1-13 are

$$1.4D \qquad (a)$$

$$1.2D + 1.6L \qquad (b)$$

$$1.2D + 0.8W \qquad (c)$$

$$1.2D + 1.3W + 0.5L \qquad (d)$$

Figure 6-18b shows the forces resulting from a load of 1 kip/ft on member BC and Fig. 6-18c those from the 8-kip horizontal load. The forces in the leeward column for each of the combinations are:

(a) $P = 1.4(10 + 0.5 \times 25) = 31.5$ kips
     $M = 1.4(0.5 \times 136) = 95.2$ ft·kips
(b) $P = 1.2(10 + 0.5 \times 25) + 1.6(30 + 25) = 115$ kips
     $M = 1.2(0.5 \times 136) + 1.6 \times 136 = 299.2$ ft·kips

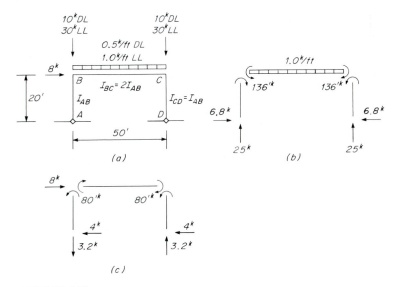

(a)

(b)

(c)

FIGURE 6-18

(c) $P = 1.2(10 + 0.5 \times 25) + 0.8 \times 3.2 = 29.6$ kips
$M = 1.2(0.5 \times 136) + 0.8 \times 80 = 145.6$ ft·kips

(d) $P = 1.2(10 + 0.5 \times 25) + 1.3 \times 3.2 + 0.5(30 + 25) = 58.7$ kips
$M = 1.2(0.5 \times 136) + 1.3 \times 80 + 0.5 \times 136 = 253.6$ ft·kips

The largest design forces occur for loading case (b). However, this loading produces no lateral translation, so $M_u = B_1 M_{nt}$ in Eq. (6-27), while loading case (d) produces lateral translation, so both terms of Eq. (6-27) must be evaluated. Therefore, both loading conditions must be checked. Use load combination (b) and Eq. (6-30) to make a preliminary selection.

Since $K = 1$ for y-axis buckling, $(KL)_y = 10$ ft. But K may be nearly 2 for x-axis buckling, so $(KL)_x \approx 2 \times 20 = 40$ ft and will control.

$$P^* = 115 + \frac{2 \times 299 \times 12}{d} = 115 + \frac{7176}{d}$$

$$= 115 + \frac{7176}{12} = 713 \text{ kips} \qquad \text{for a 12-in section}$$

$$= 115 + \frac{7176}{14} = 628 \text{ kips} \qquad \text{for a 14-in section}$$

For x-axis buckling

$$G_{\text{top}} = \frac{1/20}{2/50} = 1.25 \qquad G_{\text{bot}} = 10 \quad \text{(Art. 4-11)}$$

for which Fig. 4-28 yields $K = 1.9$.

For $b/d = 0.8$, $r_x/r_y \approx 2.1$, so the Manual's column-strength tables should be entered with $KL = 1.9 \times 20/2.1 = 18$ ft. The tables show no W12 with this value of r_x/r_y that can carry 713 kips at $KL = 18$ ft. For $b/d = 1$, $r_x/r_y \approx 1.7$ and $KL = 1.9 \times 20/1.7 = 22$ ft. The tables show that a W14 × 90 can carry 620 kips at 22 ft.

Try W14 × 90: $A = 26.5$ in^2, $I_x = 999$ in^4, $Z_x = 157$ in^3, $r_x = 6.14$ in, $r_y = 3.70$ in. Check load combination (b).

P_n:

$$\frac{KL}{r_y} = \frac{10 \times 12}{3.70} = 32.4$$

$$\frac{KL}{r_x} = \frac{1.9 \times 20 \times 12}{6.14} = 74.3$$

From Manual's table 3-36, $\phi F_{cr} = 22.9$ ksi.

$$\phi P_n = \phi F_{cr} A = 22.9 \times 26.5 = 606 \text{ kips}$$

M_{ux}: With $G_{\text{top}} = 1.25$ and $G_{\text{bot}} = 10$, Fig. 4-28 gives $K = 0.87$.

$$\frac{KL}{r} = \frac{0.87 \times 20 \times 12}{6.14} = 34.0$$

From Manual table 9, $P_E/A = 248$ ksi, so $P_E = 248 \times 26.5 = 6572$ kips. From Eq. (6-28),

$$B_1 = \frac{C_m}{1 - P_u/P_E} = \frac{0.85}{1 - 115/6572} = 0.865 < 1 \qquad \text{Use 1}$$

From the Manual's table of beam constants, $L_p = 15.4$ ft. Therefore, since the laterally unsupported length L_b is 10 ft, $\phi M_n = \phi M_p = 424$ ft·kips, also taken from the table of beam constants.

$$\frac{P_u}{\phi P_n} = \frac{115}{606} = 0.190 < 0.2 \qquad \text{Use Eq. (6-26}b)$$

$$\frac{P_u}{2\phi P_n} + \frac{M_{ux}}{\phi M_n} = 0.095 + \frac{299}{424} = 0.80 < 1 \qquad \text{O.K.}$$

Check load combination (d).

$$P = 58.7 \text{ kips}$$

$$M_{nt} = 1.2 \times 0.5 \times 136 + 0.5 \times 136 = 149.6 \text{ ft·kips}$$

$$M_{lt} = 1.3 \times 80 = 104 \text{ ft·kips}$$

For $(KL/r)_x = 74.3$, $P_E/A = 52.1$ ksi, $P_E = 52.1 \times 26.5 = 1381$ kips. From Eq. (6-29b)

$$B_2 = \frac{1}{1 - \sum P_u/\sum P_E} = \frac{1}{1 - 2 \times 58.7/2 \times 1381} = 1.04$$

Then $M_{ux} = 1 \times 149.6 + 1.04 \times 104 = 258$ ft·kips.

$$\frac{P_u}{\phi P_n} = \frac{58.7}{606} = 0.097 < 0.2 \qquad \text{Use Eq. (6-26}b)$$

$$\frac{P_u}{2\phi P_n} + \frac{M_{ux}}{\phi M_n} = 0.048 + \frac{258}{424} = 0.66 < 1 \qquad \text{O.K.}$$

DP6-8-1 (AISC/LRFD): Column for Building of DP3-15-2

Discussion of this example and the comments identified by letters alongside the computations are given in Art. 6-9.

6-9 DISCUSSION OF DP6-7-1 (AISC/ASD) AND DP6-8-1 (AISC/LRFD)

We assume that the wind force acts entirely on the windward side of the building. Since there are three reaction components at the base of each column, the bent is statically indeterminate to the third degree. If the horizontal member were a beam, the indeterminate quantities could be readily computed, but taking account of 41 truss members in a statically indeterminate analysis is a tedious

COLUMN FOR BUILDING OF DP3-15-2 and DP4-15-2   DP6-8-1 1/2

Building of DP3-15-2
 AISC/LRFD specs.
 Bents   20 ft c.c.
 Wind   20 psf
 DL   14 psf   } See DP3-15-2
 Snow   40 psf

$20 \times 20 = 0.4 \, klf$

$\dfrac{3 \times 15}{4.5} = 10^k C$

6.4^k 12.3^k 6.4^k

$3^k = 15 \times 0.4/2$

3^k

$3 + 0.4 \times 10.5 = 7.2^k$

$60.83'$

$0.74^k = \dfrac{0.4 \times 15 \times 7.5}{60.83}$

Shear diagram windward col.

3

7.2

$\dfrac{7.2 + 3}{2} \times 10.5 = 53.5^{'k}$

Mom. diagram windward col.

11^k

$3 \times 10.5 = 31.5^{'k}$

Mom. diagram leeward col.

$31.5^{'k}$

Column dead load:
   Roof truss $14 \times 20 \times 60.83/2 = 8.5$
   Siding $\underline{3.4}$
                                   11.9^k

Column live load:
   Crane $\frac{1}{2} \times 25.1$ 12.5^k
   Snow $40 \times 20 \times 60.83/2 = 24.4^k$
Column wind load: windward column -0.7^k, leeward column $+0.7^k$

Design loads: $1.2 D + 1.3 W + 0.5 L + 0.5 S$ (a)
   Windward column:

   $P = 1.2 \times 11.9 - 1.3 \times 0.7 + 0.5 \times 12.5 + 0.5 \times 24.4 = 31.8^k$
   $M_{bot} = 1.3 \times 53.5 = 69.6^{'k}$
   $M_{top} = 1.3 \times 11.0 = 14.3^{'k}$

   Leeward column:

   $P = 1.2 \times 11.9 + 1.3 \times 0.7 + 0.5 \times 12.5 + 0.5 \times 24.4 = 33.6^k$
   $M_{bot} = 1.3 \times 31.5 = 41.0^{'k}$
   $M_{top} = 1.3 \times 31.5 = 41.0^{'k}$

COLUMN FOR BUILDING OF DP3–15–2 and DP4–15–2   DP6–8–1   2/2

$$P^* = P + \frac{2M_x}{d} = 31.8 + \frac{2 \times 69.6 \times 12}{d} = 31.8 + \frac{1670}{d} \tag{b}$$

$$= 31.8 + \frac{1670}{10} = 199^k \text{ for } 10'' \text{ section}$$

$$= 31.8 + \frac{1670}{8} = 241^k \text{ for } 8'' \text{ section}$$

For $b/d \approx 0.8$, $r_x/r_y = 2.1$ $KL = 1.2 \times 21/2.1 = 12.0'$ (c)
   W10 × 33: $P = 222^k > 199^k$

For $b/d \approx 1$, $r_x/r_y = 1.7$ $KL = 1.2 \times 21/1.7 = 14.8'$
   W8 × 40: $P = 238^k \approx 241^k$

Try W10 × 33: $A = 9.71 \text{ in}^2$ $I_x = 170 \text{ in}^4$ $r_x = 4.19 \text{ in}$ $Z_x = 38.8 \text{ in}^3$

   P_n : $KL/r_x = 1.5 \times 21 \times 12/4.19 = 90.2$

        $\phi F_{cr} = 19.94^k$

        $\phi P_n = \phi F_{cr} A = 19.94 \times 9.71 = 193.6^k$

   M_{ux} : $P_E/A = 35.2$ $P_E = 35.2 \times 9.71 = 341.6^k$

        $B_2 = \dfrac{1}{1 - \Sigma P_u / \Sigma P_E} = \dfrac{1}{1 - (31.8 + 33.6)/(2 \times 341.6)} = 1.11$

          $M_{ux} = 1.11 \times 69.6 = 77.0^{'k}$ windward column   (d)

          $M_{ux} = 1.11 \times 33.6 = 45.5^k$ leeward column

   M_n: $\phi M_n = \phi Z_x F_y = 0.9 \times 38.8 \times 36/12 = 104.8^{'k}$ (e)

Windward column:

   $\dfrac{P_u}{\phi P_n} = \dfrac{31.8}{193.6} = 0.164 < .2.$ Use Eq. (6–26b)

   $\dfrac{1}{2} \times \dfrac{P_u}{\phi P_n} + \dfrac{M_{ux}}{\phi M_n} = \dfrac{1}{2} \times 0.164 + \dfrac{77.0}{104.8} = 0.82 < 1$ O.K.

Leeward column: O.K.

and time-consuming problem. One way to simplify the analysis is to assume the location of the point of inflection in each column and the share of the wind load taken by each. This is equivalent to assuming the values of the two reactive moments and one of the two horizontal reaction components. This procedure is used here. Another way to simplify the analysis is to replace the truss with a beam having a uniform moment of inertia equal to the average moment of inertia of the truss. This procedure is discussed later in this article.

The points of inflection of the columns are taken midway between the column base and the bottom of the truss, as in DP4-15-1 and DP4-15-2. This is equivalent to the assumption that the column bends as shown by the solid line in Fig. 6-19. This condition exists if the column remains straight between A and B and if the base does not rotate. Of course, rotation of the base is a function of the base detail. For example, if the anchor bolts are placed on the centerline of the column which is normal to the web, resistance to rotation around this axis may be relatively small unless the axial load is large. With a moment-resistant base, some designers would take the point of inflection below the midpoint, on the reasonable assumption that the column base is not likely to furnish complete restraint. This condition is shown by the dashed line to the right in Fig. 6-19. On the other hand, the column will rotate at B, accompanied by bending of the bottom chord connecting at B, unless the chord is infinitely stiff and rigidly connected. This rotation tends to pull the point of inflection upward, as indicated by the dashed line at the left in the figure. Since the two rotations offset each other, the point of inflection may actually lie either above or below the midpoint, depending upon the relative rotations at B and C. For this reason, the point of inflection might just as well be assumed at midheight. The wind pressure on the part of the building above the points of inflection is assumed to be divided equally between the columns.

Although it is nominally a tension member, $L_0 L_1$ may be subjected to compression due to wind pressure. The compressive force is found by taking

FIGURE 6-19

moments about U'_0, as shown on the figure. The member is checked for this force in DP4-15-2.

The moments shown in the moment diagrams on the design sheet are those due only to wind load. The roof gravity loads also produce moments in the columns, but except for an outright estimate they can be determined only by a statically indeterminate analysis. They are ignored here but are discussed further later in this article.

The following comments are identified by letters corresponding to those alongside the computations on the design sheets.

DP6-7-1 (AISC/ASD)

a. Although the basic snow load is 40 psf, it is assumed here that a snow load of 20 psf is ample in combination with wind load. This, together with dead load, gives 34 psf. [Note that AISC/LRFD specifies $0.5S$ in combination with $1.2D$ plus $1.6L$ (Eq. (b) of Art. 1-13).]

b. For load due to wind alone or the combinations of wind and other forces, the basic allowable stresses may be increased by one-third. This is equivalent to designing for three-quarters of the expected load, using the basic allowable stress.

c. Maximum moment is at the base, so Eq. (6-24b) is used to obtain a trial section. Also, since the exterior wall supports the column against bending about the minor axis, lateral-torsional buckling is prevented and $F_{bx} = 0.66F_y = 24$ ksi.

d. Equation (6-23a) would be used to check the stress at the interior point of maximum moment. However, this maximum is only 11 ft·kips (see moment diagram), and it is evident that it would not be increased sufficiently by the moment Py to require a check.

The columns have now been checked for gravity load plus wind load at the permitted increased allowable stress for this loading condition. They must also be checked for gravity load alone at the normal allowable stress. Since we reduced the live load from 40 to 20 psf in combination with wind, the 20.7-kip load computed in a must be corrected to $P = 54 \times 20 \times 60.83/2 = 32.9$ kips. Adding the siding and concentrated loads to this gives 48.8 kips, for which $f_a = 48.8/8.23 = 5.9$ ksi. Since the gravity-load moments are not evaluated in this analysis, we can compute only the direct stress f_a, which is obviously well below the allowable value.

DP6-8-1 (AISC/LRFD)

a. This is the LRFD specified combination of loads (see Art. 1-14).

b. Equation (6-30) is used to obtain a trial section.

c. Values of r_x/r_y and P are from the LRFD Manual's table of column design strengths. Since the column is fixed at the base and very nearly fixed at the top, the theoretical value of K is about 1. The SSRC recommends $K = 1.2$ for columns which are theoretically rotationally fixed at both ends and with one end free to translate. The column is supported by wall construction against y-axis buckling, so its strength is determined by the x-axis slenderness ratio. But column strengths in the Manual's table are tabulated for KL based on y-axis buckling. To obtain the x-axis strength we enter the table with the value $KL/(r_x/r_y)$ (see Art. 6-8).

d. Only the moment due to lateral displacement contributes to M_{ux} because the gravity loads have been assumed to produce only axial forces in the columns, so $M_{nt} = 0$ in Eq. (6-27). Gravity-load moments are discussed below.

e. Since the attached wall prevents lateral-torsional buckling, the moment capacity is $M_p = Z_x F_y$.

Statically indeterminate analysis. The moment of inertia of the WT6 × 20 top chord and the WT7 × 17 bottom chord of the truss, with respect to the center-of-gravity axis between them, is approximately 7000 in⁴ at $L_0 U_0$ and 17,000 in⁴ at $U_5 L_5$. An approximate equivalent frame is obtained by replacing the truss with a girder of uniform depth having a moment of inertia of $(7,000 + 17,000)/2 = 12,000$ in⁴. The girder centerline is assumed to be at the column tops, so the equivalent frame is 21 ft high from column base to middepth of the girder and spans 60.82 ft. The equivalent frame under full gravity load (dead load plus trolley-beam loads plus snow load) is shown in Fig. 6-20 and under dead load plus trolley-beam loads plus half snow load plus wind load in Fig. 6-21. The 1.8-kip concentrated load at the top of the windward column in Fig. 6-21 is the wind load on the 4.5 ft of wall above, and the moment $M = 4.05$ ft·kips is its moment at the column top. These frames can be analyzed by the slope-deflection equations, moment distribution, or other methods for statically indeterminate structures. For this example, however, the indeterminate quantities were evaluated by formulas from Ref. 10, which has 62 pages of formulas for two-legged

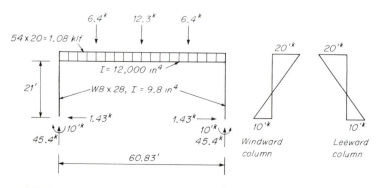

FIGURE 6-20

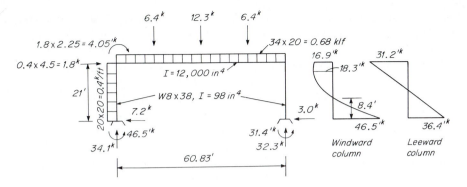

FIGURE 6-21

bents, three-legged bents, and rectangular frames under a variety of combinations of horizontal loads and vertical loads.

Moment diagrams for the two columns are shown in Figs. 6-20 and 6-21. A comparison of the diagrams of Fig. 6-21 with those of the design sheets is of interest where it will be noted that the maximum moments due to wind and gravity loads do not differ significantly. It should also be noted that the maximum moment, 10 ft·kips, is not large enough, compared to the 46.5-ft·kip moment with wind, to make any combination of loads that excludes wind a determining factor in sizing the column.

6-10 FIRST- AND SECOND-ORDER ANALYSES OF FRAMES

Symmetrical braced frames supporting symmetrically located gravity loads experience no lateral translation except for minor amounts resulting from inaccuracies in the frame geometry due to differences between the design lengths and fabricated lengths of its members and from specification-permitted deviations from member straightness. Furthermore, deformation of the braces due to unsymmetrical or lateral loads are generally small and are not normally taken into account. Consequently, moments in the columns are amplified only by the moment produced by the axial force acting through the deflections along the member. These moments are called $P\delta$ moments, where P is the column axial load and δ is the lateral deflection of the member with respect to the chord connecting its end points. The factor $1/(1 - P/P_E)$ in formulas such as Eq. (6-4) of Art. 6-1 accounts for the $P\delta$ moment.

Unbraced frames subjected to unsymmetrical loads and/or lateral forces undergo lateral displacements. As a result of these displacements, columns in the frame are subjected to additional moments $P\Delta$, where Δ is the lateral displacement of one end of a column with respect to the other end. These moments are not accounted for in formulas such as Eq. (6-4). In multistory structures the $P\Delta$

moment for the columns in any one story is $(\sum P)\Delta$, where $\sum P$ is the total vertical load on the story and Δ is the lateral deflection of the story with respect to the one below.

Analyses based on the dimensions of an undeformed frame are called *first-order* analyses, while those based on the deformed frame, taking into account both the $P\delta$ and the $P\Delta$ effects, are called *second-order* analyses. Second-order analyses require the use of computer programs, which are readily available, but not all programs that are advertised as programs for second-order analysis consider the $P\delta$ moments. Therefore, if the designer wants to take account of both the $P\delta$ and the $P\Delta$ moments, he or she should make certain that these moments are included in the program. Computer programs are discussed in Refs. 11 to 15 and many other publications.

It was pointed out in Art. 6-8 that the AISC/LRFD specification permits first-order analyses of the moment M_{nt} produced with the frame assumed not to translate laterally and of the moment M_{lt} resulting from a lateral translation. It also permits, as an alternative, a second-order analysis, provided it includes the effects of both the $P\delta$ and the $P\Delta$ moments. In this article we present two examples of the two procedures. In Example 6-10-1 a symmetrical frame subjected to an unsymmetrical load is analyzed. In Example 6-10-2 a symmetrical frame is subjected to a symmetrical gravity loading which, if acting alone, would produce no lateral translation, plus a horizontal load.

Example 6-10-1. The single-bay frame shown in Fig. 6-22a is considered in this example. All members are W14 × 74 of A36 steel, with the weak (y) axis in the plane of the frame. The frame is braced in the direction perpendicular to its plane at the top of the column, so $(KL)_y = 18$ ft.

Results of the first- and second-order analyses are shown in the figure.

Solution

   Pδ effect

Beam: $\dfrac{I}{L} = \dfrac{796}{40 \times 12} = 1.66$ Column: $\dfrac{I}{L} = \dfrac{796}{18 \times 12} = 3.68$

$G_{\text{top}} = \dfrac{3.68}{1.66} = 2.2$ $G_{\text{bot}} = 10$ for pinned-end   (Art. 4-11)

From Fig. 4-28, $K = 0.91$,

$$P_E = \frac{\pi^2 \times 29{,}000 \times 796}{(0.91 \times 18 \times 12)^2} = 5897 \text{ kips}$$

From Eq. (6-7)

$$C_m = 0.6 - 0.4 \frac{M_1}{M_2} = 0.6$$

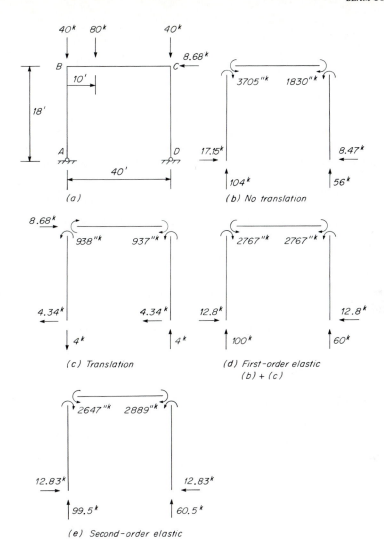

FIGURE 6-22

From Eq. (6-28)

Column AB: $\quad B_1 = \dfrac{0.6}{1 - 104/5897} = 0.61 < 1 \quad$ Use 1

Column CD: $\quad B_1 = \dfrac{0.6}{1 - 56/5897} = 0.61 < 1 \quad$ Use 1

$P\Delta$ **effect.** From Fig. 4-28, $K = 2.2$

$$P_E = \frac{\pi^2 \times 29{,}000 \times 796}{(2.2 \times 18 \times 12)^2} = 1009 \text{ kips}$$

From Eq. (6-29b)

$$B_2 = \frac{1}{1 - \sum P_u/\sum P_E} = \frac{1}{1 - (104 + 56)/(2 \times 1009)} = 1.086$$

Moments. With $B_1 = 1$ and $B_2 = 1.086$,

$$M_u = \begin{cases} 1 \times 3705 - 1.086 \times 938 = 2686 \text{ in·kips} & \text{for column } AB \\ 1 \times 1830 + 1.086 \times 937 = 2848 \text{ in·kips} & \text{for column } CD \end{cases}$$

These moments are almost exactly equal to those from the second-order analysis shown in Fig. 6-22e.

The moments at the column tops for the case of lateral translation (Fig. 6-22c) would be equal in a solution by the slope-deflection equations. The difference results from the fact that the computer program takes account of the axial deformations of the members, which are not accounted for in a slope-deflection solution.

$\phi Pn.$ $(KL)_x = 2.2 \times 18 = 39.6$ ft $(KL)_y = 1 \times 18 = 18$ ft

Then, from LRFD Manual's column tables, $\phi P_n = 447$ kips.

$\phi M_n.$ From Manual's beam tables, $L_p = 10.3$ ft, $L_r = 40.0$ ft.

$$\phi_b M_p = 340 \text{ ft·kips} \qquad M_p = \frac{340}{0.9} = 378 \text{ ft·kips}$$

$$\phi_b M_r = 218 \text{ ft·kips} \qquad M_r = \frac{218}{0.9} = 242 \text{ ft·kips}$$

From Eq. (5-5c), $C_b = 1.67$ since $M_1 = 0$. Then from Eq. (5-26),

$$M_n = 1.67\left[378 - (378 - 242)\frac{18 - 10.3}{40 - 10.3} \right] = 570 \text{ ft·kips} > M_p$$

Therefore, $\phi M_n = \phi M_p = 340$ ft·kips = 4082 in·kips.

Column AB. $P_u = 100$ kips, $\phi P_n = 447$ kips, $P_u/\phi P_n = 100/447 = 0.224 > 0.2.$ Use Eq. (6-26a):

$$\frac{P_u}{\phi_c P_n} + \frac{8}{9}\frac{M_u}{\phi_b M_n} = \frac{100}{447} + \frac{8}{9}\frac{2686}{4082} = 0.808 < 1 \qquad \text{O.K.}$$

Column CD. $P_u = 60$ kips, $\phi P_n = 447$ kips, $P_u/\phi P_n = 60/447 = 0.134 < 0.2.$ Use Eq. (6-26b):

$$\frac{P_u}{2\phi_c P_n} + \frac{M_u}{\phi_b M_n} = \frac{60}{2 \times 447} + \frac{2848}{4082} = 0.765 < 1 \qquad \text{O.K.}$$

The alternative value of B_2 [Eq. (6-29a)] involves the sum of the horizontal forces H and the resulting story lateral displacement Δ_{oh}. For this example these values were obtained in the slope-deflection solution. The horizontal force is shown in Fig. 6-22c. Δ_{oh}, also from the slope-deflection solution, is 1.33 in. These values yield

$$B_2 = \frac{1}{1 - 1.33(104 + 56)/(8.68 \times 216)} = 1.128$$

The value by Eq. (6-29b) was 1.086. It is obvious that the differences between the results using these two values is of no consequence.

Example 6-10-2. In this example we consider the frame shown in Fig. 6-23a. Members *AB* and *CD* are W14 × 53 and member *BC* is a W18 × 46. All members are A36 steel, with the weak (*y*) axis in the plane of the frame. The frame is braced in the direction perpendicular to its plane at the top of the columns, so $(KL)_y = 20$ ft. The results of the first- and second-order analyses are presented in Fig. 6-23. As in Example 6-10-1 the differences in the column-top moments in Fig. 6-23c result from the consideration of axial deformations of the members in the computer program.

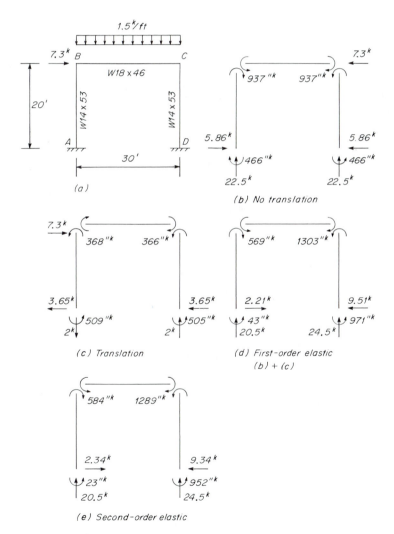

FIGURE 6-23

Solution. Because of its much larger moments compared to column AB, column CD will be critical.

$$G_{top} = \frac{541/20}{712/30} = 1.14$$

$$G_{bot} = 1 \text{ for fixed end} \qquad (\text{Art. 4-11})$$

$P\delta$ effect. From Fig. 4-28, $K = 0.78$,

$$P_E = \frac{\pi^2 \times 29{,}000 \times 541}{(0.78 \times 20 \times 12)^2} = 4419 \text{ kips}$$

From Eq. (6-7)

$$C_m = 0.6 - 0.4 \frac{466}{937} = 0.4$$

$$B_1 = \frac{0.40}{1 - 24.5/4419} = 0.40 < 1 \qquad \text{Use 1}$$

$P\Delta$ effect. From Fig. 4-28, $K = 1.35$,

$$P_E = \frac{\pi^2 \times 29{,}000 \times 541}{(1.35 \times 18 \times 12)^2} = 1475 \text{ kips}$$

$$B_2 = \frac{1}{1 - \sum P_u/\sum P_E} = \frac{1}{1 - (2 \times 22.5)/(2 \times 1475)} = 1.016$$

M_u. With $B_1 = 1$ and $B_2 = 1.016$,

$$M_{u,top} = 1 \times 937 + 1.016 \times 366 = 1309 \text{ in·kips}$$

$$M_{u,bot} = 1 \times 466 + 1.016 \times 505 = 979 \text{ in·kips}$$

These moments differ only slightly from the moments by the second-order analysis (Fig. 6-23e).

ϕPn. $(KL)_x = 1.35 \times 20 = 27 \text{ ft}$ $(KL)_y = 1 \times 20 = 20 \text{ ft}$

Then, from LRFD Manual's column tables, $\phi P_n = 210$ kips.

$$\frac{P_u}{\phi_c P_n} = \frac{22.5}{210} = 0.10 < 0.2 \qquad \text{Use Eq. (6-26b)}$$

ϕM_n. From Manual's beam tables, $L_p = 8.0$ ft, $L_r = 28.0$ ft.

$$\phi_b M_p = 235 \text{ ft·kips} \qquad M_p = \frac{235}{0.9} = 261 \text{ ft·kips}$$

$$\phi_b M_r = 152 \text{ ft·kips} \qquad M_r = \frac{152}{0.9} = 169 \text{ ft·kips}$$

From Eq. (5-5c), $C_b = 2.2$.

$$M_n = 2.2\left[261 - (261 - 169)\frac{20 - 8}{28 - 8}\right] = 452 \text{ ft·kips} > M_p$$

Therefore, $\phi M_n = \phi M_p = 235$ ft·kips $= 2820$ in·kips. From Eq. (6-26b)

$$\frac{P_u}{2\phi_c P_n} + \frac{M_u}{\phi_b M_n} = \frac{22.5}{2 \times 210} + \frac{1309}{2820} = 0.52 < 1 \qquad \text{O.K.}$$

PROBLEMS

6-1. Determine the permissible load P for the frame of Fig. 6-12 with $n = 1$. The frame is supported against out-of-plane buckling.

6-2. Same as Prob. 6-1 except that the frame is unbraced.

6-3. Given a braced frame of the type shown in Fig. 6-12 with $L_b = 40$ ft and $L_c = 16$ ft. The frame is to be designed for a uniform load of 1600 plf, of which 1000 plf is dead load. Determine member sizes in A36 steel. The frame is supported against out-of-plane buckling.

6-4. Check the adequacy of the frame of Fig. 6-12, without bracing but supported against out-of-plane buckling, for a uniform load of 0.8 klf dead load and 1.0 klf live load together with a wind force of 6 kips at B. A36 steel.

6-5. Check the adequacy of the A36 frame shown in Fig. P6-5. The frame is to be considered braced and supported against out-of-plane buckling.

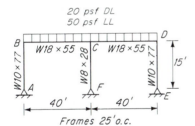

FIGURE P6-5

6-6. Check the adequacy of the A36-steel frame shown in Fig. P6-6. The frame is unbraced but is supported against out-of-plane buckling.

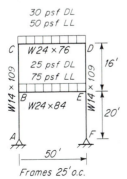

FIGURE P6-6

6-7. Same as Prob. 6-6 except that there is a wind load of 20 psf in addition to the specified gravity loads. Assume the wind load to be concentrated at B and C.

6-8. Check the adequacy of the A36-steel frame shown in Fig. P6-8. The frame is to be considered braced and supported against out-of-plane buckling.

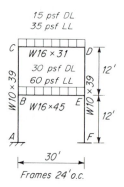

Frames 24′o.c.   **FIGURE P6-8**

6-9. Use the procedure discussed in Art. 6-4 to determine whether the frame of Fig. P6-8 can support the loads without in-plane bracing.

6-10. Choose a tee for a member 9 ft long supporting an axial compression of 15 kips dead load and 35 kips live load and a uniformly distributed transverse dead load of 500 plf. The uniform load is delivered through attached construction which supports the member against lateral buckling. Assume simple supports. A36 steel.

6-11. Choose a W shape for the member of Prob. 6-10.

6-12. Same as Prob. 6-10 except that the member is not supported against lateral buckling.

6-13. Choose a pair of aluminum 6061-T6 angles separated by $\frac{3}{8}$ in for gusset plates for the member of Prob. 6-10.

6-14. Same as Prob. 6-13 except that the member is not supported against lateral buckling.

6-15. The horizontal top chord of a welded roof truss is to be a W shape with the web members butted against its bottom flange and welded to it. The chord is continuous over panel points. Panel lengths are 16 ft and the purlin spacing 8 ft. The purlin reaction at each truss is 4.2 kips dead load and 4 kips live load, and the axial compression in the chord is 40 kips dead load and 38 kips live load. Dependable lateral support exists only at the panel points. Design the chord. A36 steel.

6-16. The jib crane shown in Fig. P6-16 is to be installed in an existing building. The mast is to be supported on a new concrete footing and is to be welded at its top to the existing roof truss, whose bottom chord consists of two angles $5 \times 3\frac{1}{2} \times \frac{1}{2}$ with their long legs vertical. The lifting capacity of the hoist is 3000 lb. The trolley weighs 500 lb, and its wheels are designed to run on the flange of a standard S-shape beam. The boom must be free to rotate about the mast, approximately 90° in either direction from its midposition. A36 steel.
 (a) Design the boom, the mast, and the tie.
 (b) Design the welded connection of the mast to the truss.
 (c) Design the connection of the tie.
 (d) Design the connection of the boom to the mast.

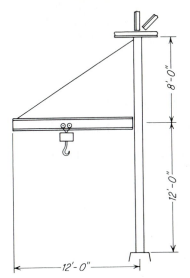

FIGURE P6-16

6-17. Same as Prob. 6-15 except use A501 structural tubing.

6-18. The frame shown in Fig. P6-18 is unbraced. The design load is 0.5 klf *DL* and 1.3 klf *LL*. Design the frame in A36 steel.

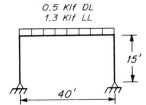

FIGURE P6-18

6-19. The frame shown in Fig. P6-19 is unbraced. The design load is 0.5 klf *DL* and 1.5 klf *LL*. Design the frame in A36 steel.

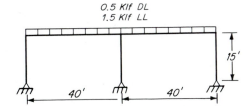

FIGURE P6-19

REFERENCES

1. Austin, W. J.: Strength and Design of Metal Beam-Columns, *J. Struct. Div. ASCE*, April 1961.
2. Ketter, R. L.: Further Studies of the Strength of Beam-Columns, *J. Struct. Div. ASCE*, August 1961.
3. Hill, H. N., E. C. Hartmann, and J. Clark: Design of Aluminum Alloy Beam-Columns, *Trans. ASCE*, vol. 121, p. 1, 1956.

4. Bleich, F.: "Buckling Strength of Metal Structures," McGraw-Hill, New York, 1952.
5. Lu, Le-Wu: Stability of Frames under Primary Bending Moments, *J. Struct. Div. ASCE*, June 1963.
6. Kanchanalai, T.: Design and Behavior of Beam-Columns in Unbraced Steel Frames, Department of Civil Engineering, Structural Research Laboratory, *Univ. Tex. Austin, CESRL Rep.* 77-2, October 1977.
7. Galambos, T. V.: "Structural Members and Frames," Prentice-Hall, Englewood Cliffs, N.J., 1968, p. 185.
8. Sharma, S. S., and E. H. Gaylord: Strength of Steel Columns with Biaxially Eccentric Load, *J. Struct. Div. ASCE*, December 1969.
9. Yura, J. A.: "Combined Bending and Axial Load," notes distributed by AISC at 1988 National Steel Construction Conference, Miami Beach.
10. Hool, G. A., and W. S. Kinne (eds.): "Stresses in Framed Structures," 2d ed., McGraw-Hill, New York, 1942.
11. Goto, Y., and W. F. Chen, Second-Order Elastic Analysis for Frame Design, *J. Struct. Div. ASCE*, pp. 1501–1519, July 1987.
12. Chen, W. F., and Lui, E. M.: "Structural Stability: Theory and Implementation," Elsevier, New York, 1987.
13. Nixon, D., D. Beaulieu, and P. F. Adams: Simplified Second-Order Frame Analysis, *Can. J. Civ. Eng.*, vol. 2, no. 4, 1975.
14. Le Messurier, W. J.: A Practical Method of Second-Order Analysis, parts I and II, *Eng. J. Am. Inst. Steel Constr.*, no. 4, pp. 89–96, 1976, and no. 2, pp. 49–67, 1977.
15. White, D. W., and W. McGuire: "Method of Analysis in LRFD," preprint of Structural Engineering Congress 1985, Chicago, Structural Division, ASCE, 1985.

CHAPTER 7

PLATE
GIRDERS

7-1 INTRODUCTION

A *girder* is a flexural member which is required to carry heavy loads on relatively long spans. In building construction, flexural members that support beams which frame into them are sometimes called girders regardless of the magnitude of the loads. Such members may be W cross sections or built-up sections, depending on the magnitude of the loads and the span length. More commonly the term girder is used to describe a flexural cross section made up of a number of elements. They are generally considerably deeper than the deepest rolled sections and usually have webs which are relatively thinner than rolled sections.

In its simplest form the plate girder is a built-up beam consisting of two flange plates welded to a web plate to form an I (Fig. 7-1a). Box girders (Fig. 7-1b) are also used. Prior to the development of welding, plate girders usually consisted of four angles riveted to the web, as in Fig. 7-1c. Plates, called cover plates, were riveted to the angles to increase the flange area (Fig. 7-1d).

Plate girders (or trusses) are used in buildings where long spans are needed over large assembly areas such as auditoriums. They are also used extensively in bridges for spans ranging from 60 to 1000 ft. The principal differences between the design of a rolled beam and the design of a plate girder are that the designer has greater freedom in proportioning the cross section of a plate girder and that the larger depth of the plate girder often results in relatively thin webs which make web-buckling problems more important.

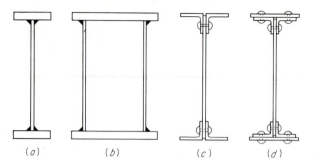

FIGURE 7-1

Rolled beams are generally proportioned with relatively compact webs and flanges, so local buckling and shear buckling are not probable limit states. In plate girders the sizes of the flange and web are at the discretion of the designer, so buckling must be considered in establishing their dimensions.

Girder flanges are usually proportioned with width-thickness ratios small enough to preclude local buckling prior to attainment of the yield moment of the cross section. But an efficient section may require a web with a depth-thickness ratio large enough to cause buckling by bending or shear, or both, before the bending moment is large enough to produce yield stress in the flanges.

Web buckling does not determine the ultimate strength of a plate girder. Subsequent to elastic buckling, postbuckling strength develops and may be taken into account in determining the ultimate strength.

The criteria for design of plate girders may be based on the following conditions:

Elastic bend-buckling strength
Elastic shear-buckling strength
Post-bend-buckling strength
Post-shear-buckling (tension-field) strength

Some specifications are based on the limits corresponding to the elastic buckling strengths, while others permit the postbuckling strengths to be taken into account. In specifications which permit the postbuckling strengths in both bending and shear to be taken into account, the designer has the choice of four combinations for the limits of behavior:

1. Elastic bend buckling in combination with elastic shear buckling. This is sometimes referred to as *conventional flexural behavior*.
2. Elastic bend buckling in combination with post-shear-buckling (tension-field) strength.
3. Post-bend-buckling strength in combination with elastic shear buckling.
4. Post-bend-buckling strength in combination with post-shear-buckling (tension-field) strength.

7-2 BEND BUCKLING OF PLATE-GIRDER WEBS

Bend buckling of webs is discussed in Art. 5-15. The extreme-fiber bending stress at which a perfectly flat web buckles is given by Eq. (5-50a) for webs not rotationally restrained by the flanges and by Eq. (5-50b) for webs that are completely restrained. It was shown that webs of standard rolled beams reach yield stress on the extreme fiber without buckling. This is not usually the case for plate girders, and if bend buckling is to be avoided, upper limits of web slenderness must be determined. Such limits can be established from Eqs. (5-50). Thus, assuming the edges of a web of depth h and thickness t to be hinged at the junctures with the flanges and using a factor of safety of 1.25 with respect to the service-load bending stress f_b, Eq. (5-50a) gives

$$1.25 f_b = \frac{650 \times 10^6}{(h/t)^2} \qquad \text{psi}$$

from which

$$\frac{h}{t} = \frac{23,000}{\sqrt{f_{b,\text{psi}}}} \tag{7-1}$$

This is the AASHTO specifications' slenderness limit for plate-girder webs without longitudinal stiffeners. According to the AREA specifications, $h/t = 32,500/\sqrt{F_y}$. Using the AASHTO allowable stress $f_b = 0.55F_y$, Eq. (7-1) gives $h/t = 165$ for A36 steel. The corresponding AREA limit is 170.

Except for the relatively small factor of safety, slenderness limits derived as above make no allowance for the fact that thin-webbed beams and plate girders can develop a considerable additional bending resistance beyond that at which bend buckling of the web occurs. This postbuckling behavior is discussed in Art. 7-3. The bend-buckling resistance of beam webs can be increased considerably by longitudinal stiffeners. Since this means that webs much thinner than those given by Eq. (7-1) can be used, longitudinal stiffeners may be economical for deep girders.

Thin webs also require transverse stiffeners to increase their resistance to shear (Fig. 7-2a). Stiffeners usually consist of rectangular bars welded to the web. Transverse stiffeners may be in pairs, one each side of the web, or they may be placed on one side of the web. Longitudinal stiffeners are usually placed on one side. The effect of a longitudinal stiffener on bend buckling of a web plate is shown in Fig. 7-2b. It increases resistance to bend buckling by enforcing a longitudinal node in the buckled configuration. The figure suggests that the efficiency of the stiffener is a function of its location in the compression zone. A stiffener midway between the neutral axis and the compressive edge of the web increases the value of k in the plate-buckling formula [Eq. (4-32)] to 101 for hinged edges, as compared with 23.9 for unstiffened webs. The optimum location for a longitudinal stiffener has been determined to be at the distance $h/5$ from the compressive edge of the web, in which case $k = 129$ (Ref. 1). The corresponding allowable web

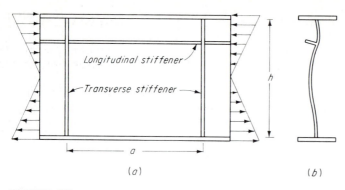

(a)

(b)

FIGURE 7-2

slenderness (for the same factor of safety) is found by multiplying the slenderness limit for webs with no longitudinal stiffeners by $\sqrt{129/23.9} = 2.32$. Thus, the slenderness limit 165, given by Eq. (7-1) for the unstiffened web in A36 steel, becomes 380. However, according to the AASHTO specifications this limit is 330, and, in general

$$\frac{h}{t} = \frac{46,000}{\sqrt{f_{b,\text{psi}}}} \le 340 \tag{7-2}$$

The longitudinal stiffener must be stiff enough to produce the higher buckling mode shown in Fig. 7-2b. In doing so, it acts as a beam supported at the ends where the vertical stiffeners hold the web in line. It must also resist axial compression because of its location in the compressive zone of the web. Thus, it is a beam-column and must be proportioned in terms of both cross-sectional area and moment of inertia. Furthermore, as a beam-column, its strength is influenced by the distance a between the vertical stiffeners (Fig. 7-2a). Consequently, the buckling coefficient $k = 129$ is attained only with certain combinations of these factors. The AASHTO requirement for longitudinal stiffeners, which is independent of the ratio of the area A_s of the stiffener to web area ht, gives an acceptable upper bound to the required moment of inertia of the stiffener given in Ref. 1. The AASHTO formula is

$$I_s = ht^3 \left[2.4\left(\frac{a}{h}\right)^2 - 0.13 \right] \tag{7-3}$$

According to Massonnet,[2] results of tests suggest that the theoretical values of I_s on which Eq. (7-3) is based should be multiplied by about 7 to obtain a stiffener which will remain practically straight up to collapse of the web. He also notes that a longitudinal strip of the web acts as a part of the stiffener and suggests that the width of the strip be taken equal to $20t$. However, according to the AASHTO specifications, I_s is the moment of inertia of the stiffener alone, taken at the edge in contact with the web.

The numerical data from the analysis on which Eq. (7-3) is based covered values of the ratio A_s/ht of stiffener area to web area ranging from 0 to 0.1 and panel aspect ratio a/h from 0.5 to 1.5. The equation should not be used for values outside this range. This requirement is met in the AASHTO specifications, since they limit a/h to not more than 1.5.

The stiffener must also be proportioned to resist local buckling, according to procedures discussed in Art. 4-12. For plates supported on only one longitudinal edge, AASHTO requires $b/t \leq 1625/\sqrt{f_{a,\text{psi}}}$ (Table 4-4), where f_a is the service-load stress. For a stiffener at $h/5$, $f_a = 0.6f_b$, where f_b is the bending on the compression flange. Substituting this into the equation above gives $b/t \leq 2100/\sqrt{f_{b,\text{psi}}}$; AASHTO uses $2250/\sqrt{f_{b,\text{psi}}}$.

A single longitudinal stiffener is not likely to be sufficient to produce economical webs for the large depths required for long-span bridges, where haunch depths as much as 40 ft have been used. Thus, for a 30-ft web with $F_y = 60$ ksi, the AASHTO requirement is $h/t = 46,000/\sqrt{0.55 \times 60,000} = 253$ [Eq. (7-2)], so $t = \frac{360}{253} = 1.42$ in. Multiple longitudinal stiffeners are used in such cases.

According to tests reported in Ref. 3, the linear distribution of stress corresponding to beam theory is preserved in longitudinally stiffened webs with slenderness ratios even greater than those discussed above. However, for this to be assured, a longitudinal stiffener at $h/5$ must satisfy an additional requirement, namely, that its critical stress as a column of length equal to the transverse-stiffener spacing be not less than 0.6 times the critical stress for the flange. However, it is pointed out that one or more additional longitudinal stiffeners may be needed for webs with $h/t \geq 450$.

Longitudinal stiffeners are not covered by the AISC specifications because they attain large web slenderness by accepting bend buckling of the web and taking the postbuckling strength into account. This is discussed in Art. 7-3.

7-3 POSTBUCKLING BENDING STRENGTH OF PLATE-GIRDER WEBS

Figure 7-3a shows a beam-web panel for which the critical bending stress F_{cr} is less than the yield stress F_y. If the bending strain increases after F_{cr} is reached, the upper edge of the panel shortens and the bottom edge lengthens. Provided no lateral-torsional buckling of the girder occurs, the edges remain straight and the extreme-fiber stresses continue to increase. If the web were to remain flat, proportionate increases in stress would develop in the remainder of the web. Because the web has buckled, however, the increase in stress will be nonlinear in the compression zone, as shown in the figure, because some of the shortening in the length AB will be taken up by an increase in the amplitude of the buckle. During the increase in moment beyond that corresponding to F_{cr}, the neutral axis moves down. The maximum moment for a symmetrical cross section is reached at an extreme-fiber stress F_y in the compression flange if strain hardening is neglected.

The bending behavior discussed above is an idealization of the actual behavior. Since beam webs are not perfect, there will be some waviness even in

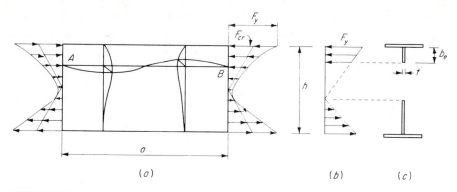

FIGURE 7-3

the unloaded beam. Therefore, lateral deflection of the web begins at the beginning of loading. However, the rate of increase of these deflections increases rapidly when F_{cr} is reached. Thus, the behavior is analogous to that of the axially loaded column.

Since the variation in stress in the postbuckled state is unknown, simplifying assumptions must be made to determine the maximum moment. The one shown in Fig. 7-3b was proposed in Ref. 4. Here the nonlinear compression of Fig. 7-3a is replaced with a linear distribution according to elastic-behavior beam theory, acting on an effective depth of web b_e (Fig. 7-3c). This enables the moment to be calculated, provided b_e is known. In Ref. 4 it was assumed that $b_e = 30t$ for girders with $h/t = 360$. Using this value and $F_y = 36$ ksi, values of M are computed for $A_f/ht = 0$, 0.5, and 2 and plotted in the nondimensional form M/M_y in Fig. 7-4. Also shown is the point $M_{cr}/M_y = 0.18$, where M_{cr} is the moment based on the critical bending stress for the web given by Eq. (5-50c). We

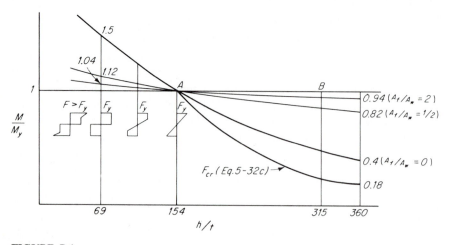

FIGURE 7-4

can also use Eq. (5-50c) to determine the web slenderness h/t that enables a girder to reach its full yield moment $M_y = F_y I/c$. The result is

$$\frac{h}{t} = \sqrt{\frac{850,000}{F_y}} = \frac{925}{\sqrt{36}} = 154$$

which gives point A in Fig. 7-4. Also shown are the ratios 1.5, 1.12, and 1.04, of the plastic moment M_p to M_y, for $A_f/A_w = 0$, 0.5, and 2, respectively. In order for these moments to be developed, web slenderness must not exceed $640/\sqrt{F_y}$ (Art. 5-15). For A36 steel, this gives $h/t = 107$.

If the girder has a longitudinal stiffener at $h/5$ from the compression flange, $k = 129$ in the plate-buckling formula, so

$$F_{cr} = \frac{3,510,000}{(h/t)^2}$$

With $F_{cr} = F_y = 36$ this yields

$$\frac{h}{t} = \sqrt{\frac{3,510,000}{36}} = 315$$

which gives point B in Fig. 7-4. This shows the effectiveness of longitudinal stiffeners in increasing the bending strength of thin-webbed girders.

The variation of M/M_y in the regions between $h/t = 0$, 69, 107, 154, and 360 in Fig. 7-4 is not determined by the analysis above, so the curves shown in the figure are approximate. The variation where web efficiency is reduced by buckling was assumed in Ref. 4 to be linear. Furthermore, the slenderness at which reduction in web effectiveness was assumed to begin was taken to be $980/\sqrt{F_y}$ rather than the value corresponding to point A of Fig. 7-4. This was because the AISC specification used 170 as the upper limit of slenderness of girders of A7 steel ($F_y = 33$ ksi) prior to the revision in which postbuckling strength was taken into account. The resulting equation connecting the revised point A with the points corresponding to $h/t = 360$ in Fig. 7-4 is

$$\frac{M}{M_y} = 1 - 0.0005 \frac{A_w}{A_f}\left(\frac{h}{t} - \frac{980}{\sqrt{F_y}}\right) \tag{7-4}$$

Equation (7-4) is compared in Ref. 4 with results of nine tests. The ratio of test moment to computed moment ranged from 0.96 to 1.11.

AISC/ASD. Equation (7-4) can be expressed in terms of an equivalent stress $f_{eq} = Mc/I$, where I is the moment of inertia of the gross cross section. Thus, dividing M and M_y by I/c, we get

$$\frac{f_{eq}}{F_y} = 1 - 0.0005 \frac{A_w}{A_f}\left(\frac{h}{t} - \frac{980}{\sqrt{F_y}}\right) \tag{7-5}$$

Using a factor of safety of 1.65, the allowable bending stress $F'_b = f_{eq}/1.65$ is

$$F'_b = 0.6F_y \left[1 - 0.0005 \frac{A_w}{A_f} \left(\frac{h}{t} - \frac{980}{\sqrt{F_y}} \right) \right] \tag{7-6}$$

But $0.6F_y$ is the maximum allowable bending stress F_b for a plate girder with a fully effective web. Therefore, substituting $F_y = 1.65F_b$, we get

$$F'_b = F_b \left[1 - 0.0005 \frac{A_w}{A_f} \left(\frac{h}{t} - \frac{760}{\sqrt{F_b}} \right) \right] \tag{7-7}$$

The web depth h in this equation is defined as the clear distance between flanges. To extend the formula to cover hybrid girders (Art. 7-13) it is given in the form

$$F'_b = F_b R_{PG} R_e \tag{7-8}$$

where $R_{PG} = 1 - 0.0005 \dfrac{A_w}{A_f} \left(\dfrac{h}{t} - \dfrac{760}{\sqrt{F_y}} \right)$

$\qquad R_e$ = reduction factor given by Eq. (7-37a)

For nonhybrid girders $R_e = 1$. For the tension flange $F_b = 0.6F_y$. To cover failure by lateral-torsional buckling, F_b for the compression flange is defined as the allowable bending stress according to Eqs. (5-19). The formula also applies to singly symmetric girders, provided the compression flange is larger than the tension flange (Art. 5-10).

AISC/LRFD. The nominal moment M_n based on tension-flange yield is

$$M_n = S_{xt} R_{PG} R_e F_{yf} \tag{7-9a}$$

and on compression-flange buckling,

$$M_n = S_{xc} R_{PG} R_e F_{cr} \tag{7-9b}$$

where S_{xt} = tension-flange section modulus
$\qquad S_{xc}$ = compression-flange section modulus
$\qquad R_e$ = reduction factor for hybrid girders [Eq. (7-37b)]
$\qquad R_e$ = 1 for nonhybrid girders
$\qquad F_{yf}$ = yield strength of flange
$\qquad F_{cr}$ = smaller of critical stresses for lateral-torsional buckling and flange local buckling

The factor R_{PG} is given by

$$R_{PG} = 1 - 0.0005 \frac{A_w}{A_f} \left(\frac{h_c}{t_w} - \frac{970}{\sqrt{F_{cr}}} \right) \tag{7-10}$$

where h_c = twice the distance from the neutral axis to the inside face of the compression flange less the fillet or corner radius
$\qquad t_w$ = web thickness

It will be noted that R_{PG} is from Eq. (7-4) except that the limiting web slenderness is $970/\sqrt{F_{cr}}$.

Figure 7-4 shows that a girder with a large h/t and no longitudinal stiffener can develop almost as much moment as the same girder with a longitudinal stiffener. Thus, the stiffener appears to offer little advantage. However, tests show that the fatigue life of the unstiffened girder with large h/t is less than that of the stiffened girder.[5-7] Several girders with $h/t \geq 200$ failed at fewer than 2 million cycles of load because of excessive lateral deflection of the web. This is not a significant consideration for girders in buildings, so no provision is made for it in either of the AISC specifications. However, in the AASHTO specification for load-factor design of steel highway bridges, web slenderness for girders without longitudinal stiffeners is limited by

$$\frac{h}{t} \leq \frac{36,500}{\sqrt{F_{y,\text{psi}}}} \tag{7-11}$$

For A36 steel, this gives $h/t \leq 192$. This is somewhat larger than the limit $23,000/\sqrt{f_b}$ discussed in Art. 7-2, which gives $h/t \leq 165$ for A36 steel.

7-4 VERTICAL BUCKLING OF THE COMPRESSION FLANGE

If a plate-girder web is too slender, the compression flange may buckle in the vertical plane at a stress less than yield stress. This failure mode is shown in Fig. 7-5. A study of this photograph shows that the compression flange is a beam-column, continuous over the vertical stiffeners as supports, whose stability depends on the stiffener spacing and the relative stiffnesses of the flange and the web. The difficulty in analyzing this phenomenon is compounded by the bending stresses in the web. The following analysis of the problem was presented in Ref. 4.

Figure 7-6 shows a vertical element, of unit width, of a girder which is stressed to its yield moment. The extreme-fiber strains ϵ produce a relative rotation $\epsilon/(h/2)$ of the vertical edges of the element. Equilibrium of the flange forces $F_y A_f$ requires a vertical compression $F_y A_f \epsilon/(h/2)$ in the element, which the web must be able to support without buckling. The stability of webs in vertical compression was discussed in Art. 5-17. The critical stress for a web without transverse stiffeners is given by Eq. (10-4):

$$F_{cr} = \frac{\pi^2 E}{12(1 - \mu^2)(h/t)^2} \tag{a}$$

For equilibrium of the element in Fig. 7-6a, we have

$$F_{cr} \times 1 \times t = \frac{F_y A_f \epsilon}{h/2} \tag{b}$$

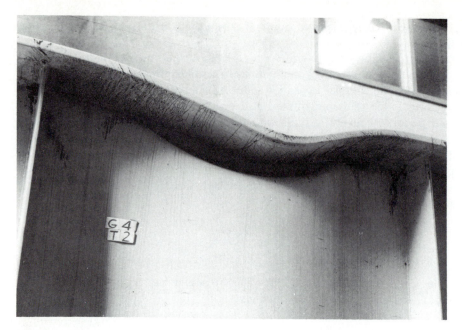

FIGURE 7-5
Vertical buckling of plate-girder flange. (*Fritz Engineering Laboratory, Lehigh University.*)

Equations (*a*) and (*b*) give

$$\left(\frac{h}{t}\right)^2 = \frac{\pi^2 E}{24(1 - \mu^2)} \frac{A_w}{A_f} \frac{1}{\epsilon F_y} \qquad (c)$$

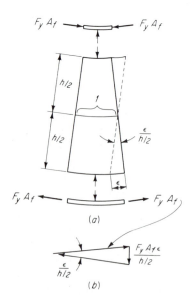

FIGURE 7-6

Because of residual stresses in the flanges, the extreme-fiber strain ϵ must exceed ϵ_y by an amount sufficient to offset the residual strain of opposite sign in order to obtain uniform yielding of the flanges. Therefore, $\epsilon = \epsilon_y + \epsilon_r = (F_y + F_r)/E$, which, upon substitution in Eq. (c), yields

$$\left(\frac{h}{t}\right)^2 = \frac{\pi^2 E^2}{24(1 - \mu)^2} \frac{A_w}{A_f} \frac{1}{F_y(F_y + F_r)} \tag{7-12}$$

Since Eq. (7-12) is based on the vertical-buckling strength of a web with no transverse stiffeners, it will give conservative results for a web with closely spaced stiffeners. According to tests reported in Ref. 8, the slenderness of webs with vertical stiffeners can be taken conservatively at

$$\frac{h}{t} \leq \begin{cases} \dfrac{2500}{\sqrt{F_y}} & \text{for } \dfrac{a}{h} \leq 1 \qquad\qquad (d) \\[2mm] \dfrac{2000}{\sqrt{F_y}} & \text{for } \dfrac{a}{h} \leq 1.5 \qquad\quad (e) \end{cases}$$

AISC ASD and LRFD. The h/t limits in these specifications are based on Eqs. (7-12) and (e). The ratio A_w/A_f in Eq. (7-12) is taken at 0.5, which is a lower limit for girders of practical proportions, and the residual stress F_r at 16.5 ksi. The result is

$$\frac{h}{t} \leq \frac{14{,}000}{\sqrt{F_y(F_y + 16.5)}} \tag{7-13}$$

except that h/t need not be less than $2000/\sqrt{F_y}$ for $a/h \leq 1.5$.

Although Eq. (7-12) involves the ratio of the areas of the flange and the web, it contains no parameter involving their stiffnesses. Therefore, it gives conservative results for flanges with large bending stiffnesses.

7-5 PROPORTIONING OF PLATE GIRDERS

The depth of a plate girder is influenced by many factors, and it is impossible to lay down workable rules to which no exception will occur. In many cases the determining factor is headroom, or in the case of deck bridges, clearance for high water or for traffic passing beneath. Even when no such limitations exist, the range of depths for economical results is considerable. Although the depth of the average girder is one-tenth to one-twelfth of its span, depths of as much as one-eighth to one-sixth of the span may occasionally be necessary, particularly if there are heavy concentrated loads such as occur for girders supporting columns in buildings. On the other hand, lighter loads may be accommodated economically with depths as small as one-fourteenth or one-fifteenth of the span.

In proportioning the cross section, one determines a web which has the necessary capacity in shear, and flanges which, together with the web, have the required section modulus. Since it is more convenient to proportion by area than by moment of inertia, a procedure that enables a tentative determination of the flange is desirable.

Let A_f be the area of one flange, h_g the distance between the centers of gravity of the two flanges, h_w and t the height and thickness, respectively, of the web plate, and h_0 the overall depth. Except for the small moment of inertia of each flange about its own gravity axis, the moment of inertia of the cross section is

$$I = 2A_f\left(\frac{h_g}{2}\right)^2 + \frac{th_w^3}{12}$$

But h_w and h_g are approximately equal, and $th_w = A_w$, the area of the web. Therefore,

$$I = \frac{h_g^2}{2}\left(A_f + \frac{A_w}{6}\right) \tag{7-14}$$

Substituting this value of I into the equation $I/c = M/f$ with $c = h_0/2$, we get

$$A_f = \frac{Mh_0}{fh_g^2} - \frac{A_w}{6}$$

But fh_g/h_0 is the bending stress at the center of gravity of the flange, which we denote by f_g. Therefore,

$$A_f = \frac{M}{h_g f_g} - \frac{A_w}{6} \tag{7-15}$$

In this equation f_g is based on the allowable bending stress for allowable-stress design and on F_y for AISC/LRFD, unless the compression-flange lateral support requires a reduction. Therefore, an estimate of f_g must be used to determine a first-trial value of A_f. The moment M is the service-load moment for ASD and the nominal moment M_n for LRFD.

Although plate-girder components are usually welded, bolted field splices are sometimes used. Opinion differs as to the effect of bolt holes on the bending strength. This question was discussed in Art. 5-12. Both AASHTO and AREA specifications require that the tensile bending stress be based on the moment of inertia of the net section, i.e., holes on both sides of the neutral axis are deducted, while the compressive bending stress is based on the moment of inertia of the gross cross section. The AISC specification requires a reduction in area of the flange of only the area lost in excess of 15 percent of the gross area of the flange.

DP7-5-1 (AISC/ASD) and DP7-5-2 (AISC/LRFD): Transfer Girder

The girder to be designed is one of a series over an assembly hall in a tier building. In addition to its share of the twelfth floor, each girder supports two columns

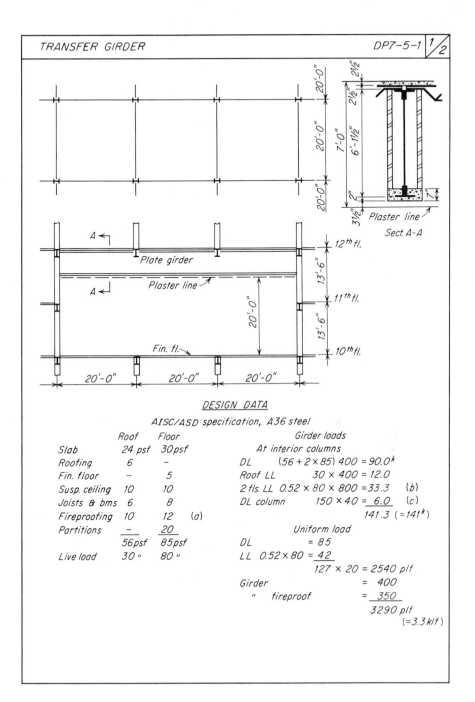

TRANSFER GIRDER   DP7-5-1 | 1/2

Sect. A-A

DESIGN DATA

AISC/ASD specification, A36 steel

	Roof	Floor
Slab	24 psf	30 psf
Roofing	6	–
Fin. floor	–	5
Susp. ceiling	10	10
Joists & bms	6	8
Fireproofing	10	12 (a)
Partitions	–	20
	56 psf	85 psf
Live load	30 "	80 "

Girder loads

At interior columns

$$DL \quad (56 + 2 \times 85)\,400 = 90.0^k$$
$$Roof\ LL \quad 30 \times 400 = 12.0$$
$$2\ fls.\ LL \quad 0.52 \times 80 \times 800 = 33.3 \quad (b)$$
$$DL\ column \quad 150 \times 40 = \underline{6.0} \quad (c)$$
$$141.3 \ (=141^k)$$

Uniform load

$$DL \qquad\qquad = 85$$
$$LL \quad 0.52 \times 80 = \underline{42}$$
$$127 \times 20 = 2540\ plf$$
$$Girder \qquad\qquad = 400$$
$$"\quad fireproof \qquad = \underline{350}$$
$$3290\ plf$$
$$(=3.3\,klf)$$

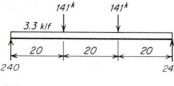

$V = 3.3 \times 30 + 141 = 240^k$

$M = 3.3 \times 60^2/8 + 141 \times 20$

$\quad = 1485 + 2820 = 4300^k$

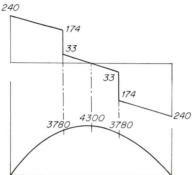

WEB

Max. depth girder 6-1½ (Sect. AA)

Try 68 × ³⁄₈ web   (d)

$A = 68 \times \frac{3}{8} = 25.5 \text{ in.}^2$

$\frac{h}{t} = \frac{68}{3/8} = 181$

$\frac{h}{t} = \frac{14,000}{\sqrt{36(36 + 16.5)}} = 322$ (e)

$\leq \frac{2,000}{\sqrt{36}} = 333 \text{ if } a/h \leq 1.5$ (e)

FLANGE

$A = \frac{4300 \times 12}{70 \times 21.4} = 34.5$ (f)

$A_w/6 = 25.5/6 = \quad \underline{4.2}$

$ 30.3 \text{ in.}^2$

1 ℞ 14 × 2¼ = 31.5 in.²

Moment of Inertia

		Weight
Web 3/8 × 68³/12	9830	87
Flg. 2 × 31.5 × 35.12² =	77750	214
	87,580	301

$f = \frac{4300 \times 12 \times 36.25}{87,580} = 21.4 \text{ ksi}$

$760/\sqrt{F_b} = 760/\sqrt{22} = 162$

$F_b' = 22\left[1 - 0.0005 \frac{25.5}{31.5}(181 - 162)\right]$ Eq. (7-7)

$\quad = 21.7 > 21.4 \text{ ksi O.K.}$

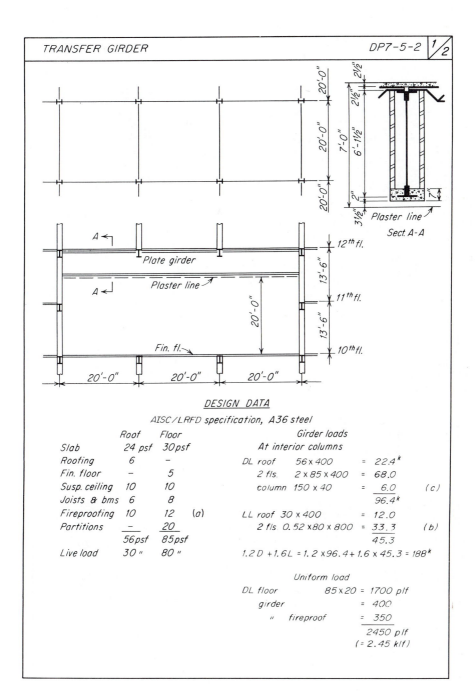

TRANSFER GIRDER DP7-5-2 | 1/2

20'-0"
20'-0"
20'-0"

2½"
2½"
2½"
7'-0"
6'-1½"
2"
3½"
7"

Plaster line
Sect. A-A

A ←
Plate girder
12ᵗʰ fl.
13'-6"
Plaster line
A ←
11ᵗʰ fl.
20'-0"
13'-6"
Fin. fl.
10ᵗʰ fl.

20'-0"   20'-0"   20'-0"

DESIGN DATA

AISC/LRFD specification, A36 steel

	Roof	Floor		Girder loads
				At interior columns
Slab	24 psf	30 psf		
Roofing	6	–		DL roof 56×400 $= 22.4^k$
Fin. floor	–	5		2 fls. $2 \times 85 \times 400$ $= 68.0$
Susp. ceiling	10	10		column 150×40 $= \underline{6.0}$ (c)
Joists & bms	6	8		96.4^k
Fireproofing	10	12	(a)	LL roof 30×400 $= 12.0$
Partitions	–	20		2 fls. 0.52 $\times 80 \times 800$ $= \underline{33.3}$ (b)
	56 psf	85 psf		45.3
Live load	30 "	80 "		$1.2D + 1.6L = 1.2 \times 96.4 + 1.6 \times 45.3 = 188^k$

Uniform load

DL floor $\qquad 85 \times 20 = 1700$ plf

girder $\qquad\qquad = 400$

" fireproof $\qquad = \underline{350}$

2450 plf

$(= 2.45$ klf$)$

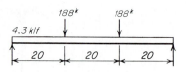

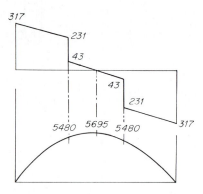

$$LL\ 0.52 \times 80 = 42\ psf$$
$$42 \times 20 = 840\ plf$$

$$1.2D + 1.6L = 1.2 \times 2450 + 1.6 \times 840$$
$$= 4284\ plf = 4.3\ klf$$

$$V = 4.3 \times 30 + 188 = 317^k$$
$$M = 4.3 \times 60^2/8 + 188 \times 20 = 5695^{'k}$$

WEB

Max. depth girder 6-1½ (Sect. A A)
Try 68 × 3/8 web, A = 68 × 3/8 = 25.5 in² (d)

$$\frac{h}{t} = \frac{68}{3/8} = 181 > \frac{970}{\sqrt{F_y}} = 161$$

∴ use spec. appendix G

$$\frac{h}{t} = \frac{14,000}{\sqrt{36(36 + 16.5)}} = 322 \qquad (e)$$

$$\leq \frac{2,000}{\sqrt{36}} = 333\ if\ a/h \leq 1.5 \qquad (e)$$

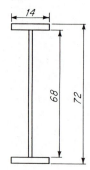

FLANGE

$$\phi M_n = 5695^{'k}$$
$$M_n = 5695/0.9 = 6328^{'k}$$

$$A = \frac{6328 \times 12}{70 \times 35} = 31.0 \qquad (f)$$

$$A_w/6 = 25.5/6 = \underline{4.2}$$
$$26.8\ in^2$$

1 ℞ 14 × 2 = 28 in²

Moment of inertia   Weight
Web 3/8 × 68³/12   9830   87
Flg. 2 × 28 × 35²   = 68,600   190
                         78,430   277 plf

$$S_x = 78430/36 = 2179\ in^3$$

$$R_{PG} = 1 - 0.0005\frac{A_w}{A_f}\left(\frac{h_c}{t_w} - \frac{970}{\sqrt{F_{cr}}}\right) \leq 1\ Eq.\ (7\text{-}10)$$

$$= 1 - 0.0005(25.5/28)(181 - 162) = 0.991$$
$$M_n = 2179 \times 0.991 \times 36/12 = 6478^{'k} > 6328\ O.K.$$

which carry the thirteenth and fourteenth floors and the roof. The design live loads are 30 psf for the roof and, except for the assembly room, 80 psf for the floors. The concrete slab for the roof is 2 in thick, while that for the floors is $2\frac{1}{2}$ in thick. Both are supported on 12-in truss joists spaced 2 ft on centers. The girder is fireproofed, as shown in section A-A of the figure, with $1\frac{3}{4}$ in of gypsum plaster on metal lath. The comments which follow are intended to clarify the correspondingly lettered computations on the design sheets.

a. This item of dead load is the weight of fireproofing for the beams. The suspended ceiling fireproofs the joists.

b. Since the girder supports a floor area in excess of 150 ft², the basic live load may be reduced in accordance with the BOCA National Building Code (Art. 1-4). The allowable reduction is 8 percent/100 ft² of supported area in excess of 150 ft² but not to exceed 60 percent or the value given by Eq. (1-3), namely, $R = 23.1(1 + D/L)$. In our case Eq. (1-3) controls, since $D = 85$ psf, $L = 80$ psf, and $R = 23.1(1 + \frac{85}{80}) = 48$ percent, while the supported area is 20×60 at the twelfth floor and 20×20 at each column for each of the two floors above, or 2800 ft² altogether.

c. Each column together with its fireproofing weighs 150 plf.

d. The 68-in web allows flanges $2\frac{1}{2}$ in thick within the 73-in allowable overall depth. The $\frac{3}{8}$-in thickness is a preliminary judgment which will be checked in the investigation for shear.

e. These are the maximum allowable values of web slenderness, which were discussed in Art. 7-4.

f. The joists, which are attached to the top flange of the girder, provide adequate support against lateral-torsional buckling. Therefore, $F_b = 0.6 \times 36 = 22$ ksi for ASD and 36 ksi for LRFD. Assuming 2-in flange plates, $h_g = 70$ in and $h_0 = 72$ in. Therefore, in Eq. (7-15) $f_g = 22 \times \frac{70}{72} = 21.4$ ksi for ASD and $36 \times \frac{70}{72} = 35$ ksi for LRFD.

7-6 LENGTH OF FLANGE PLATES

Some economy may be achieved by varying the area of the flange plate to suit the variation in moment. This can be done for welded girders by flanking the flange plate required for maximum moment by one or more successively thinner plates butt-welded end to end. The theoretical cutoff point of a plate is found by calculating the moment capacity of the reduced cross section and locating the corresponding point on the moment diagram. In the case of simple load systems, cutoff points can be determined by formula. Thus, since the moment diagram for a uniformly loaded, simply supported beam is a parabola,

$$\frac{L_1}{L} = \sqrt{\frac{M_1 - M_2}{M_1}} = \sqrt{\frac{A_1 - A_2}{A_1 + A_w/6}} \qquad (7\text{-}16)$$

where A_1 = area of center plate
   M_1 = corresponding moment
   A_2 = area of adjacent plate
   M_2 = corresponding moment
   L_1 = length of center plate
   L = span of girder

Substitution of the areas A for the corresponding moments M in Eq. (7-16) is approximate. It is based on the assumption that $h_g f_g$ in Eq. (7-15) does not change with the change in cross section of the girder. In any case, a strict interpretation of standard specifications requires that the cross section at the cutoff be checked for moment capacity. Equation (7-16) can be extended to a third pair of plates by substituting L_2, M_3, and A_3 for L_1, M_2, and A_2.

If the plate girder supports moving loads, as in the case of highway and railway bridges, the envelope of maximum moments is needed. Since the maximum moment at each point results from a different position of the moving live load, the envelope is not the same thing as a moment diagram. However, a satisfactory approximate method which avoids the construction of the envelope has been developed.[9] It is based on the assumption that the envelope is a straight line through the point of maximum moment, extending $0.05L$ on either side of the center point of the span, flanked by parabolas tangent at its ends and passing through the ends of the span. Since each parabolic segment has a base $0.45L$ in length, cover-plate lengths can be determined by adding $0.1L$ to the value of L_1 from Eq. (7-16), provided L in that equation is replaced with $0.9L$.

In some cases (and in particular in the case of continuous spans) plotting the various resisting moments on a plot of the maximum-moment envelope helps to determine cutoff points.[10]

Cover plates used to vary flange area, as in the case of the cover plate added to the flange of a rolled shape to increase its moment capacity, must extend beyond the theoretical cutoff a distance sufficient to develop the capacity of the plate; i.e., the fastener strength beyond the cutoff must equal the axial force in the plate.

It is highly unlikely that the saving in the cost of the steel would offset the additional cost of fabrication if a reduction in flange-plate area is made in the girders of DP7-5-1 and DP7-5-2. However, to illustrate the procedure, the point at which a $1\frac{1}{2}$-in flange plate is adequate for the girder in DP7-5-1 will be determined. Since Eq. (7-16) cannot be used in this case because of the concentrated loads, we proceed as follows:

$$I = \tfrac{1}{12}(\tfrac{3}{8})(68)^3 + [2 \times 14 \times 1.5 \times 34.75^2] = 9,830 + 50,000 = 60,530 \text{ in}^4$$

$$M = \frac{22 \times 60,530}{35.5 \times 12} = 3120 \text{ ft·kips}$$

From the data in DP7-5-1

$$M = 240x - \frac{3.3x^2}{2}$$

where x is the distance from either end to the point where the $1\frac{1}{2}$-in plate is adequate. Equating the two moments and solving the equation, we get $x = 14.4$ ft.

7-7 SHEAR BUCKLING OF PLATE-GIRDER WEBS

Shear buckling of beam webs was discussed in Art. 5-14, where it was shown that shear is seldom a determining factor in the design of rolled-section beams. However, plate-girder web slenderness h/t is usually much larger than that of rolled beams, so transverse stiffeners as shown in Fig. 7-2 must be used to increase the shear-buckling strength. Such stiffeners increase the buckling strength by increasing the factor k in Eqs. (5-43) to (5-46) through a reduction in the aspect ratio a/h [Eqs. (5-38) and (5-39)]. Transverse-stiffener spacing can be determined from the following formulas.

ASD. From Eq. (5-44c) with k from Eq. (5-39) we get

$$F_v = \frac{15,570}{(h/t)^2} \times 5\left(1 + \frac{h^2}{a^2}\right)$$

With $F_v = f_v$, where f_v is the shear stress V/A_w, this equation yields

$$a = \frac{280t}{\sqrt{f_v - \left(\dfrac{280}{h/t}\right)^2}} \qquad \text{for } \frac{h}{t}\sqrt{\frac{F_y}{1 + (h/a)^2}} > 537 \qquad (7\text{-}17a)$$

From Eqs. (5-44b) and (5-39) we get

$$a = \frac{148t}{\sqrt{\dfrac{f_v^2}{F_y} - \left(\dfrac{148}{h/t}\right)^2}} \qquad \text{for } 369 < \frac{h}{t}\sqrt{\frac{F_y}{1 + (h/a)^2}} < 537 \qquad (7\text{-}17b)$$

Values of a by these equations may differ slightly from the specification theoretical values because they are based on k from Eq. (5-39) instead of Eqs. (5-38). Therefore, the designer may wish to validate the spacing by comparing the shear stresses f_v with the allowable values F_v by Eqs. (5-44), using k from Eqs. (5-38).

LRFD. From Eq. (5-46c) with k from Eq. (5-39) we get

$$V_n = \frac{26,400}{(h/t)^2} \times 5\left(1 + \frac{h^2}{a^2}\right)A_w$$

With $\phi V_n = V_f$, where ϕ is the resistance factor and V_f the factored-load shear, this equation gives

$$a = \frac{363t}{\sqrt{\dfrac{V_f}{\phi A_w} - \left(\dfrac{363}{h/t}\right)^2}} \qquad \text{for } \frac{h}{t}\sqrt{\frac{F_y}{1 + (h/a)^2}} > 523 \qquad (7\text{-}18a)$$

From Eqs. (5-46b) and (5-39) we get

$$a = \frac{251t}{\sqrt{\dfrac{1}{F_y}\left(\dfrac{V_f}{\phi A_w}\right)^2 - \left(\dfrac{251}{h/t}\right)^2}} \qquad \text{for } 418 < \frac{h}{t}\sqrt{\frac{F_y}{1 + (h/a)^2}} < 523 \quad (7\text{-}18b)$$

AASHTO. This specification does not consider the increase in shear-buckling strength obtained by using transverse stiffeners. Instead, transverse-stiffener requirements are based on postbuckling shear strength (Art. 7-8). Otherwise, webs are treated as unstiffened, for which the allowable stress is given by Eq. (5-47b).

AREA. Transverse-stiffener spacing is given by

$$a = \frac{10{,}500t}{\sqrt{f_{v,\text{psi}}}} \le 72 \text{ in} \qquad (7\text{-}19)$$

This formula may be considered to be a simplified form of Eq. (7-17a), the numerator of which would be $280\sqrt{1000} = 8850$ if f_v is expressed in pounds per square inch.

Since transverse stiffeners support the boundaries of a panel by keeping them straight, they must be stiff enough to prevent them from buckling with the web. Several investigators have developed theoretical solutions of this problem. Stein and Fralich devised a solution for the infinitely long, simply supported plate reinforced with equally spaced stiffeners, which shows fair agreement with laboratory tests on 20 specimens with various sizes of stiffeners.[11] They give numerical results for three different values of a/h, namely, 0.2, 0.5, and 1. Bleich developed from these data a formula for the required moment of inertia I_s of the transverse stiffener,[12] which can be put in the form

$$I_s = 2.5ht^3\left(\frac{h}{a} - 0.7\frac{a}{h}\right) \qquad a \le h \qquad (7\text{-}20)$$

If the web is stiffened on only one side, I_s is to be computed at the face of the stiffener which is in contact with the web.

The AISC/LRFD specification and the AASHTO specification require a moment of inertia of the stiffener according to the formula

$$I_s = at_w^3 J \qquad (7\text{-}21a)$$

in which

$$J = 2.5\left(\frac{h}{a}\right)^2 - 2 \geq 0.5 \qquad (7\text{-}21b)$$

where a is the spacing of the stiffeners. Substitution of Eq. (7-21b) into (7-21a) yields

$$I_s = 2.5ht_w^3\left(\frac{h}{a} - 0.8\,\frac{a}{h}\right) \geq 0.5at_w^3 \qquad (7\text{-}21c)$$

The moment of inertia is calculated about the web center for each stiffener of a pair or about the face in contact with the web for a single stiffener. In addition, the width of the stiffener b must be not less than 2 in plus one-thirtieth the depth of the girder and preferably not less than one-fourth the full width of the girder flange. The stiffener thickness t must also satisfy the requirement $b/t \leq 16$.

The AISC/ASD provision is $I_s = (h/50)^4$, which gives values of I_s that are the same for all webs of a given depth, regardless of their thickness. Since Eq. (7-20) shows that the required moment of inertia is proportional to the cube of the web thickness for given values of a and h, it is clear that this formula is deficient.

AREA specifies the same dimensions b and t of the stiffener as AASHTO but makes no provision for moment of inertia except to say that stiffeners on one side of a web must have the same moment of inertia as that of the minimum allowable pair.

The procedure for determination of stiffener spacing is illustrated in Examples 7-10-1 (AISC/ASD) and 7-10-2 (AISC/LRFD).

7-8 POSTBUCKLING SHEAR STRENGTH OF PLATE-GIRDER WEBS

Figure 7-7a shows a panel of a plate girder acted upon by shear forces V. Bending stresses are assumed to be small enough to be neglected. The resulting shearing stresses f_v on an element of the web are equivalent to principal stresses f_v, one tensile and one compressive, at 45° to the shear stresses. Values of f_v at which

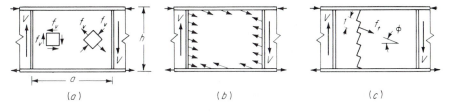

(a)   (b)   (c)

FIGURE 7-7

FIGURE 7-8
Shear buckling of plate-girder web. (*Fritz Engineering Laboratory, Lehigh University.*)

buckling occurs were discussed in Art. 7-7. The direction of the principal compression indicates that these buckles will be in the form of waves or wrinkles running in the direction of the principal tension. Shear buckling in an aluminum girder is shown in Fig. 5-24; shear buckling of a steel girder with longitudinal stiffeners is shown in Fig. 7-8.

After the web buckles in the manner just described, the compressive principal stress can increase very little. On the other hand, the tensile principal stress continues to increase with increase in strain in the diagonal direction. This suggests that such a panel may have a considerable postbuckling strength, since the increase in tension is limited only by the yield stress, provided the flanges and stiffeners framing the panel are stiff enough.

Figure 7-7b shows the action of the incremental tension on the boundary members and suggests that the tension will be uniform if they are infinitely stiff. The shearing resistance that can be developed by a uniform tension field, inclined at ϕ with the horizontal, can be determined by considering the equilibrium of the stresses on the serrated cross section of Fig. 7-7c. Summation of vertical forces gives

$$V_t = f_t ht \cos \phi \sin \phi = \tfrac{1}{2} f_t ht \sin 2\phi \qquad (7\text{-}22)$$

If the tension field develops at the optimum angle $\phi = 45°$,

$$V_t = \tfrac{1}{2} f_t ht$$

When f_t reaches F_y, $V_{ty} = \frac{1}{2}F_y ht$. Comparing this with the shear capacity of a web which is thick enough to develop the shearing yield stress F_{vy}, for which $V_y = F_{vy}ht$, we get

$$\frac{V_{ty}}{V_y} = \frac{\frac{1}{2}F_y ht}{F_{vy}ht} = \frac{F_y}{2F_{vy}}$$

Therefore,

$$V_{ty} = \frac{\sqrt{3}}{2} V_y = 0.87 V_y$$

Thus, a panel which resists shear entirely by tension-field action may be nearly as strong as one which resists it entirely by shear-field action.

The shear strength V_u of a panel whose web buckles before reaching shear yield is the sum of the shear resistance V_{cr} at buckling and the shear component V_t of the tension field (Fig. 7-9a):

$$V_u = V_{cr} + V_t = F_{v,cr} ht + V_t$$

Assuming that the panel develops a uniform tension field, V_t is given by Eq. (7-22) and substitution yields

$$V_u = F_{v,cr} ht + \frac{1}{2}f_t ht \sin 2\phi$$

from which

$$F_{vu} = \frac{V_u}{ht} = F_{v,cr} + \frac{1}{2}f_t \sin 2\phi \tag{7-23}$$

According to Basler,[13] the tension field in a welded girder with plate flanges will be incomplete because the bending strength of the flanges is insufficient to develop the necessary anchorage (Fig. 7-7b). He assumes instead the partial field of width b_e shown in Fig. 7-9b. Here the flanges are free and the tension field in the panel is reacted by the fields in the adjacent panels. From the geometry of the

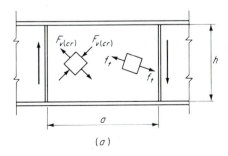

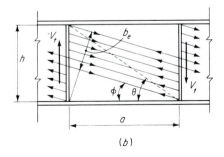

(a)   (b)

FIGURE 7-9

panel

$$b_e = h \cos \phi - a \sin \phi$$

The shear component V_t of the tension field is

$$V_t = f_t b_e t \sin \phi = f_t t(h \cos \phi - a \sin \phi) \sin \phi$$

$$= f_t t \left[\frac{h}{2} \sin 2\phi - \frac{a}{2} (1 - \cos 2\phi) \right]$$

Assuming that the tension develops at the angle ϕ which maximizes V_t,

$$\frac{dV_t}{d\phi} = f_t t(h \cos 2\phi - a \sin 2\phi) = 0$$

so

$$\tan 2\phi = \frac{h}{a}$$

But $h/a = \tan \theta$, where θ is the angle of the panel diagonal with the horizontal (Fig. 7-9b). Therefore, $2\phi = \theta$. Substituting this into Eq. (7-23) gives

$$F_{vu} = F_{v,cr} + \tfrac{1}{2} f_t \sin \theta \tag{7-24}$$

There is an obvious inconsistency in determining ϕ for the partial tension field of Fig. 7-9b and assuming that the complete tension field of Eq. (7-23) forms at the same angle. However, with f_t determined as explained in the next paragraph, Eq. (7-24) (which was developed differently in Ref. 13) is in satisfactory agreement with results of tests.

The ultimate shear is assumed to be reached when the two stress fields in Fig. 7-9a produce general yielding of the panel. The Mises yield criterion, which was used in Ref. 13, is given by

$$f_1^2 - f_1 f_2 + f_2^2 = F_y^2 \tag{a}$$

where f_1 and f_2 are principal stresses. The ellipse in Fig. 7-10 is the plot of this equation. The directions of the principal stresses represented by points A, B, C, and D are as shown. The coordinates of E on a line OE at 45° are $f_1 = F_y/\sqrt{3}$ and $f_2 = -F_y/\sqrt{3}$. This is a condition of pure shear. Therefore, the combination of the stress fields in Fig. 7-9a is represented by a point on EA. To simplify the result, Basler took instead the chord EA, whose equation is

$$f_1 = F_y + (\sqrt{3} - 1)f_2 \tag{b}$$

Furthermore, instead of using Mohr's circle to get the true principal stresses, he assumed that the difference in direction of the principal tensions $F_{v,cr}$ and f_t could be neglected. Therefore,

$$f_1 = F_{v,cr} + f_t \qquad f_2 = -F_{v,cr}$$

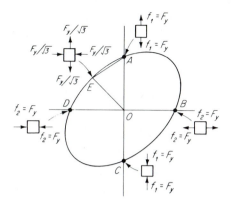

FIGURE 7-10

Substituting these values into Eq. (b), we get

$$F_{v,cr} + f_t = F_y + (\sqrt{3} - 1)(-F_{v,cr})$$

from which

$$f_t = F_y - \sqrt{3}\,F_{v,cr} \qquad (c)$$

Substituting f_t from Eq. (c) into Eq. (7-24) gives

$$F_{vu} = F_{v,cr} + \tfrac{1}{2}(F_y - \sqrt{3}\,F_{v,cr})\sin\theta \qquad (7\text{-}25)$$

where

$$\sin\theta = \frac{h}{\sqrt{a^2 + h^2}} = \frac{1}{\sqrt{1 + (a/h)^2}}$$

The effect of the simplifying assumptions used in deriving Eq. (7-25) was investigated in Ref. 13 by using Mohr circle stresses in Eq. (a). The results differed by less than 10 percent.

The critical stress to be used in Eq. (7-25) is given by Eq. (5-37) provided the value of $F_{v,cr}$ so determined does not exceed F_{vy} or, if the proportional limit is taken into account, provided it does not exceed F_{vp}. The inelastic and strain-hardening ranges of shear behavior were discussed in Art. 5-14, where it was shown that the nonproportional range of stress can be determined by Eq. (5-42). Thus

$$F_{v(cr)i} = \sqrt{0.8 F_{vy} F_{v,cr}} = \sqrt{F_{vp} F_{v,cr}} \qquad (7\text{-}26)$$

where $0.8F_{vy}$ is the proportional limit F_{vp} and $F_{v,cr}$ is given by Eq. (5-37). For this case, Eq. (7-25) becomes

$$F_{vui} = F_{v(cr)i} + \tfrac{1}{2}(F_y - \sqrt{3}\,F_{v(cr)i})\sin\theta \qquad (7\text{-}27a)$$

It will be noted that the factor in parentheses in this equation vanishes if $F_{v(cr)i} = F_{vy} = F_y/\sqrt{3}$. This means that the panel yields as a shear field, so no tension field

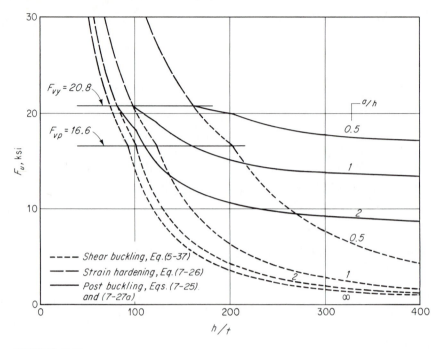

FIGURE 7-11

can develop and

$$F_{vui} = F_{v(cr)i} \tag{7-27b}$$

Figure 7-11 shows plots of the shear-buckling stress, the strain-hardening stress, and the postbuckling stress of webs of A36 steel for four values of a/h. With no transverse stiffeners a/h is infinite, in which case Eqs. (7-25) and (7-26) reduce to $F_{vu} = F_{v,cr}$ and $F_{vui} = F_{v(cr)i}$, and there is no postbuckling strength. It will be noted that the postbuckling strength of slender webs is considerable. Thus, with $h/t = 300$ and $a/h = 1$, the shear-buckling stress is 2.8 ksi while the postbuckling strength is 13.8 ksi.

Equations (7-25) and (7-27a) are compared in Ref. 13 with results of tests on girders with 50-in webs whose slenderness h/t ranged from 131 to 382. The ratio of the test shears to the predicted values ranged from 0.88 to 1.12. A comparison of the strain-hardening shear strength with results of tests on beams without transverse stiffeners, whose web slenderness ranged from 50 to 70, is shown in Fig. 5-26.

Example 7-8-1. Compute V_u for an A36-steel plate-girder panel, for which $a = 84$ in and $h = 60$ in, for the following web thicknesses: (a) $t = \frac{1}{4}$ in, (b) $t = \frac{5}{8}$ in, (c) $t = 1$ in.

Solution. Common data:

$$\frac{a}{h} = \frac{84}{60} = 1.4 \qquad k = 5.34 + \frac{4}{1.4^2} = 7.38$$

$$\sin \theta = \frac{1}{\sqrt{1 + 1.4^2}} = 0.577 \qquad F_{vy} = \frac{36}{\sqrt{3}} = 21 \text{ ksi}$$

$$F_{vp} = 0.8 \times 21 = 16.8 \text{ ksi}$$

$$F_{v,cr} = \frac{k\pi^2 E}{12(1 - \mu^2)(h/t)^2} = \frac{27,000k}{(h/t)^2} = \frac{196,000}{(h/t)^2}$$

(a)

$$\frac{h}{t} = \frac{60}{0.25} = 240 \qquad F_{v,cr} = \frac{196,000}{240^2} = 3.42 \text{ ksi}$$

From Eq. (7-25)

$$F_{vu} = 3.42 + \tfrac{1}{2}(36 - 3.42\sqrt{3})0.577 = 3.42 + 8.66 = 12.08 \text{ ksi} < F_{vp}$$

$$V_u = F_{vu} ht = 12.08 \times 60 \times 0.25 = 181 \text{ kips}$$

(b)

$$\frac{h}{t} = \frac{60}{0.625} = 96 \qquad F_{v,cr} = \frac{196,000}{96} = 18.1 \text{ ksi} > F_{vp}$$

From Eq. (7-26)

$$F_{v(cr)i} = \sqrt{0.8F_{vy} F_{v,cr}} = \sqrt{16.8 \times 18.1} = 17.5 \text{ ksi} < F_{vy}$$

From Eq. (7-27a)

$$F_{vui} = 17.5 + \tfrac{1}{2}(36 - 17.5\sqrt{3})0.577 = 17.5 + 1.7 = 19.2 \text{ ksi}$$

$$V_u = 19.2 \times 60 \times 0.625 = 720 \text{ kips}$$

(c)

$$\frac{h}{t} = 60 \qquad F_{v,cr} = \frac{196,000}{60^2} = 54.5 \text{ ksi} > F_{vp}$$

From Eq. (7-26)

$$F_{v(cr)i} = \sqrt{0.8F_{vy} F_{vcr}} = \sqrt{16.8 \times 54.5} = 30.4 \text{ ksi} > F_y$$

From Eq. (7-27b)

$$F_{vui} = F_{v(cr)i} = 30.4 \text{ ksi}$$

$$V_u = 30.4 \times 60 \times 1 = 1820 \text{ kips}$$

Figure 7-7b shows that the transverse stiffeners of a tension-field plate girder serve as supports for the flanges, which are subjected to transverse loading. In the case of the partial tension fields shown in Fig. 7-9b, the stiffeners can be thought of as the vertical compression members of a truss in which the web panels act as diagonal tension members and the flanges as chords. In either case,

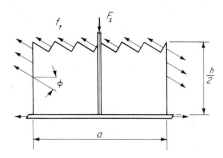

FIGURE 7-12

the stiffener forces F_s can be determined by summing vertical components in Fig. 7-12. Thus,

$$F_s = f_t at \sin \phi \cos \phi = f_t \frac{at}{2} (1 - \cos 2\phi) = \tfrac{1}{2} f_t at(1 - \cos \theta)$$

which gives, using Eq. (c),

$$F_s = \tfrac{1}{2} at(F_y - \sqrt{3} F_{v,cr})(1 - \cos \theta) \tag{7-28}$$

For panel a of the example above

$$\cos \theta = \frac{a}{\sqrt{a^2 + h^2}} = \frac{a/h}{\sqrt{1 + (a/h)^2}} = \frac{1.4}{\sqrt{1 + 1.4^2}} = 0.813$$

$$F_s = \tfrac{1}{2} \times 84 \times 0.25(36 - 3.42\sqrt{2})(1 - 0.813) = 59 \text{ kips}$$

As has been mentioned, the tension-field formulas in this article are based on the assumption that the flanges are flexible. According to Rockey,[14] the collapse mechanism of a shear panel is that shown in Fig. 7-13, where plastic hinges develop in the flanges. With increasing flexibility of the flanges each hinge moves toward the near stiffener, so the limiting case for flanges with no stiffness is as shown in Fig. 7-9b. In tests on two longitudinally stiffened girders with webs 50 in deep and 0.0666 in thick ($h/t = 750$), one with flanges whose moment of inertia was $7.35 \times 10^{-6} a^3 t$ and the other with flanges whose moment of inertia was $2.54 \times 10^{-4} a^3 t$, he found that the shear capacity of the panel with the stiffer flanges was 75 percent greater than that of the one with the more flexible flanges. Equation (7-25) would predict the same shear capacity for both.

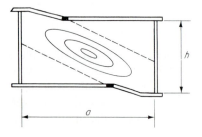

FIGURE 7-13
Shear buckling of plate-girder panel. (*From Ref. 14.*)

7-9 SPECIFICATION PROVISIONS FOR TENSION-FIELD SHEAR

The AISC provisions for shear on plate-girder webs in which the tension-field contribution to the shear resistance is taken into account are based on Eqs. (7-25), (7-26), and (7-27a). Equation (7-25) can be written in the form

$$F_{vu} = F_{vy}\left[\frac{F_{v,cr}}{F_{vy}} + \frac{1}{2}\left(\frac{F_y}{F_{vy}} - \sqrt{3}\,\frac{F_{v,cr}}{F_{vy}}\right)\frac{1}{\sqrt{1 + (a/h)^2}}\right]$$

Substituting $F_{vy} = F_y/\sqrt{3}$ and using the notation $C_v = F_{v,cr}/F_{vy}$ of Eq. (5-45b) we get

$$F_{vu} = \frac{F_y}{\sqrt{3}}\left[C_v + \frac{\sqrt{3}}{2}\,\frac{1 - C_v}{\sqrt{1 + (a/h)^2}}\right] \tag{7-29}$$

AISC/ASD. Applying a factor of safety of 1.65 to Eq. (7-29) gives the allowable shear stress F_v as

$$F_v = \frac{F_{vu}}{1.65} = \frac{F_y}{2.89}\left[C_v + \frac{1 - C_v}{1.15\sqrt{1 + (a/h)^2}}\right] \tag{7-30}$$

where

$$C_v = \begin{cases} \dfrac{45{,}000k}{F_y(h/t)^2} & \text{if } C_v < 0.8 \\[2ex] \dfrac{190}{h/t}\sqrt{\dfrac{k}{F_y}} & \text{if } C_v > 0.8 \end{cases}$$

The coefficient k is determined by Eqs. (5-38):

$$k = \begin{cases} 4 + \dfrac{5.34}{(a/h)^2} & \dfrac{a}{h} \le 1 \\[2ex] 5.34 + \dfrac{4}{(a/h)^2} & \dfrac{a}{h} \ge 1 \end{cases}$$

The specification also allows the design of plate-girder webs to be based on the limit of elastic shear buckling. For this case, only Eqs. (5-45), or the alternative form Eqs. (5-44), are needed. Furthermore, Eq. (7-30) should not be used for hybrid girders (Art. 7-13) because test data indicate that, under some conditions, such girders may have very little postbuckling shear strength.

AISC/LRFD. The design shear strength is given by ϕV_n, where $\phi = 0.9$ and $V_n = F_v A_w$. For webs which can develop shear yields, $V_n = A_w F_{vy} = A_w F_y/\sqrt{3} = 0.577 A_w F_y$. The coefficient 0.577 is increased to 0.6 to take some advantage of strain-hardening shear, as was discussed in Art. 5-14. The result is

$$V_n = 0.6 A_w F_{yw} \qquad \frac{h}{t} \le 187\sqrt{\frac{k}{F_{yw}}} \tag{7-31a}$$

The h/t limit for this formula is the limiting value that enables shear yield to be attained and is, of course, the same as the limit in Eq. (5-46a). For girders with webs that cannot develop shear yield, F_v is derived from Eq. (7-29), where $F_y/\sqrt{3}$ is again replaced with $0.6F_y$. The result is

$$V_n = 0.6A_w F_{yw}\left[C_v + \frac{1 - C_v}{1.15\sqrt{1 + (a/h)^2}}\right] \tag{7-31b}$$

where
$$C_v = \begin{cases} \dfrac{187}{h/t}\sqrt{\dfrac{k}{F_{yw}}} & \text{for } 187\sqrt{\dfrac{k}{F_{yw}}} \le \dfrac{h}{t} \le 234\sqrt{\dfrac{k}{F_{yw}}} \\[4mm] \dfrac{44{,}000k}{F_{yw}(h/t)^2} & \dfrac{h}{t} > 234\sqrt{\dfrac{k}{F_{yw}}} \end{cases}$$

The value of k is from Eq. (5-39):

$$k = 5 + \frac{5}{(a/h)^2}$$

The specification also allows the design of plate-girder webs to be based on the limit of elastic shear buckling. For this case, only Eqs. (5-46) are needed. Furthermore, Eqs. (7-31) should not be used for hybrid girders (Art. 7-14) because test data indicate that, under some conditions, such girders may have very little postbuckling shear strength.

AASHTO. Applying a factor of safety of 1.75 to Eq. (7-29) gives the following allowable shear stress F_v:

$$F_v = \frac{F_y}{3}\left[C_v + \frac{0.87(1 - C_v)}{\sqrt{1 + (a/h)^2}}\right] \tag{7-32}$$

where
$$C_v = \begin{cases} \dfrac{6000\sqrt{k}}{(h/t)\sqrt{F_{y,\text{psi}}}} & \dfrac{6000\sqrt{k}}{\sqrt{F_{y,\text{psi}}}} \le \dfrac{h}{t} \le \dfrac{7500\sqrt{k}}{\sqrt{F_{y,\text{psi}}}} \\[4mm] \dfrac{4.5 \times 10^7 k}{F_{y,\text{psi}}(h/t)^2} & \dfrac{h}{t} > \dfrac{7500\sqrt{k}}{\sqrt{F_{y,\text{psi}}}} \end{cases}$$

The value of k is from Eq. (5-39). Note that stress in this specification is expressed in pounds per square inch rather than kips per square inch. Otherwise Eq. (7-32) and the range of values of C_v for which it is applicable are identical with Eq. (7-30) and the corresponding values of C_v.

AASHTO notation has been changed in these equations to conform with that used in the other formulas in this article in order to facilitate comparisons.

AREA. This specification does not permit plate-girder design based on tension-field webs.

The AISC/ASD formula for the transverse-stiffener area A_{st} is derived by dividing the stiffener force F_s of Eq. (7-28) by the yield stress of the stiffener. The result is

$$A_{st} = \frac{1 - C_v}{2} \left[\frac{a}{h} - \frac{(a/h)^2}{\sqrt{1 + (a/h)^2}} \right] Y Dht \qquad (7\text{-}33a)$$

where Y is the ratio of F_y for the web steel to F_y for the stiffener steel. In addition, the stiffener is required to have a moment of inertia not less than $(h/50)^4$, the value for transverse stiffeners in shear-field webs, which was discussed in Art. 7-7.

The AISC/LRFD formula for the transverse-stiffener area is derived similarly except that a portion of the web, $18t_w^2$, is assumed to act with the stiffener:

$$A_{st} = \frac{F_{yw}}{F_{yst}} \left[0.15Dht_w(1 - C_v) \frac{V_u}{\phi V_n} - 18t_w^2 \right] \qquad (7\text{-}33b)$$

The factor D in Eqs. (7-33) accounts for the eccentricity of the diagonal tension in the web relative to the centroid of the stiffeners. Thus $D = 1$ for a pair of stiffeners, 1.8 for a single-angle stiffener, and 2.4 for a single-plate stiffener.

If a web panel which has developed a tension field adjoins panels with similar fields, as in Fig. 7-9b, it is assumed that the stiffeners need furnish only the axial force according to Eqs. (7-33). This is only approximately true, since it is clear from the figure that there will be some bending of the stiffener if it alone equilibrates the adjacent tension fields. However, the stiffener at an end of a girder resists diagonal tension on only one side, and if it is not designed accordingly, the tension field may not develop fully because of premature bending failure of the stiffener. Instead of prescribing a design procedure for this situation, the AISC and AASHTO specifications require that end panels and panels adjacent to panels containing large holes be designed as shear panels in which buckling does not occur. This enables them to anchor tension fields in the adjacent panels. The length of the end panel must be such as to satisfy the following equations:

AISC/ASD: $\qquad\qquad f_v = \dfrac{F_y}{2.89} C_v \le 0.4 F_y$

AISC/LRFD: $\qquad\qquad V_n \le 0.6 A_w F_y C_v$

AASHTO: $\qquad\qquad f_v \le \dfrac{F_y}{3} C_v \le \dfrac{F_y}{3}$

7-10 COMBINED SHEAR AND BENDING IN WEBS

An interaction formula based on elastic behavior of beam webs under combined shear and bending was discussed in Art. 5-16. In this article, an interaction formula for beams with tension-field webs is discussed. It is based on the following reasoning. If the web of a beam or plate girder is completely yielded in shear, any accompanying moment must be resisted entirely by the flanges. The largest moment that can be developed in this case is $M = F_y A_f h$, where h is the distance between the flange centroids. This situation is represented by

$$V_y = F_{vy} A_w$$

$$0 \le M_f \le F_y A_f h$$

These equations can be written

$$\frac{V_y}{F_{vy} A_w} = 1$$

$$0 \le \frac{M}{M_y} \le \frac{F_y A_f h}{F_y(A_f + A_w/6)h} = \frac{A_f}{A_f + A_w/6} = \frac{1}{1 + A_w/6A_f}$$

A plot of these equations is shown in Fig. 7-14. AB represents the case $A_w/A_f = 2$, for which the abscissa of point B is

$$\frac{M}{M_y} = \frac{1}{1 + \frac{2}{6}} = 0.75$$

Similarly, AC represents $A_w/A_f = 1$, for which the abscissa of point C is $M/M_y = 0.83$.

If M/M_y exceeds 0.75 for a girder with $A_w/A_f = 2$, the web must contribute part of the bending resistance. In this case, the shear V must be less than V_y. A curve such as BEF represents this situation. If the girder proportions allow the fully plastic moment M_p to develop, the abscissa of point F is given by

$$\frac{M_p}{M_y} = \frac{F_y(A_f + A_w/4)h}{F_y(A_f + A_w/6)h} = \frac{1 + A_w/4A_f}{1 + A_w/6A_f} = \frac{1 + \frac{1}{2}}{1 + \frac{1}{3}} = 1.12$$

Similarly, the abscissa of point G on the curve CEG for a girder with $A_w/A_f = 1$ is found to be 1.07. In Ref. 15 these curves are assumed to be parabolas with vertices on the M/M_y axis. They have a common intersection E at $V/F_{vy} A_w = 1/\sqrt{3}$. However, since beams with thin webs can develop little or no moment in excess of M_y, $ABEH$ is taken as the interaction curve, instead of $ABEG$, etc.

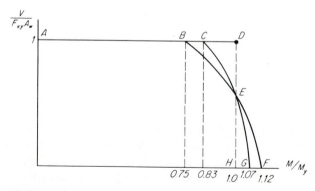

FIGURE 7-14

Results of tests on 11 girders show good agreement with the interaction envelope.[15]

Provisions of the AISC specifications are based on a straight line connecting B and E. The equation of the line is

$$\frac{M}{M_y} = 1.375 - 0.625 \, \frac{V}{F_{vy} A_w} \qquad (7\text{-}34)$$

ASD. In terms of allowable stresses $F_b = 0.6F_y$ and $F_v \,(=0.4F_y)$, Eq. (7-34) yields

$$\frac{f_b}{0.6F_y} \, 1.375 - 0.625 \, \frac{f_v}{F_v}$$

from which

$$f_b = \left(0.825 - 0.375 \, \frac{f_v}{F_v} \right) F_y \le 0.6F_y \qquad (7\text{-}35)$$

This is the AISC/ASD interaction formula.

LRFD. With $M = M_u$, $V = V_u$, $M_y = \phi M_n$, and $F_{vy} A_w = \phi V_n$, Eq. (7-34) yields

$$\frac{M_u}{M_n} + 0.625 \, \frac{V_u}{V_n} \le 1.375\phi \qquad (7\text{-}36)$$

This is the LRFD interaction formula.

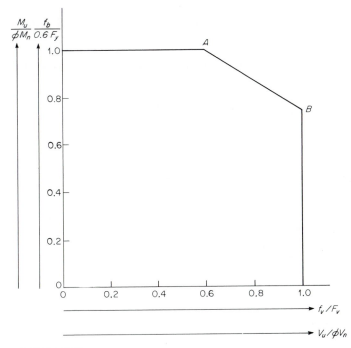

FIGURE 7-15

Line *AB* in Fig. 7-15 is a plot of Eqs. (7-35) and (7-36) within the limiting values of the variables for which they are applicable.

Example 7-10-1 (AISC/ASD). Determine the spacing of intermediate stiffeners for the girder of DP7-5-1. Bearing stiffeners will be provided at the supports and at the location of the column loads. Their design is presented in Example 7-11-1 (AISC/ASD).

Solution. From the data of DP7-5-1 we have

$$h = 68 \text{ in} \qquad t = 0.375 \text{ in} \qquad \frac{h}{t} = \frac{68}{0.375} = 181$$

$$A_w = 25.5 \text{ in}^2 \qquad V = 240 \text{ kips}$$

$$f_v = \frac{240}{25.5} = 9.41 \text{ ksi}$$

The stiffener spacing at the end of the girder must be proportioned on the basis of shear buckling. Try Eq. (7-17a).

$$a = \frac{280 \times \frac{3}{8}}{\sqrt{9.41 - (\frac{280}{181})^2}} = 39.6$$

$$\frac{h}{a} = \frac{68}{39.6} = 1.71 \qquad \frac{h}{t}\sqrt{\frac{F_y}{1 + (h/a)^2}} = 181\sqrt{\frac{36}{1 + 1.71^2}} = 548 > 537 \qquad \text{O.K.}$$

Use $a = 36$ in. This is the distance from the end bearing stiffener to the first transverse stiffener (Fig. 7-16a). If tension-field action is considered in determining the spacing of the remaining stiffeners, Eq. (7-30) must be used. Tables of the allowable shear F_v according to this equation are given in part 2 of the AISC Manual. The shear at the end of the first panel is

$$V = 240 - 3.3 \times \tfrac{36}{12} = 230 \text{ kips}$$

$$f_v = \frac{230}{25.5} = 9.02 \text{ ksi}$$

With $f_v = 9.02$ ksi and $h/t = 181$, table 2-36 of the Manual gives $a/h \approx 1.1$, or $a = 74$ in. The decrease in shear in the 17-ft distance to the bearing stiffener at the interior

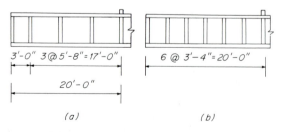

3'-0" 3@5'-8"=17'-0"

20'-0"

6 @ 3'-4"=20'-0"

(a)   (b)

FIGURE 7-16

column is not large enough to save a stiffener by increasing the spacing as the shear decreases. Therefore, the layout shown in Fig. 7-16a satisfies the stiffener-spacing requirement.

Check the center 20-ft panel

$$V = 33 \text{ kips} \qquad f_v = \frac{33}{25.5} = 1.29 \text{ ksi}$$

This shear stress is so small that it will probably be unnecessary to take advantage of tension-field action. Therefore, we check it as a shear-buckling panel. Since $a/h = \frac{20}{6} = 3.3$, the minimum value of k, 5.34, from Eq. (5-38) must be used.

$$C_v = \frac{45{,}000 \times 5.34}{36 \times 181^2} = 0.204$$

$$F_v = \frac{F_y}{2.89} C_v = \frac{36}{2.89} \times 0.204 = 2.54 \text{ ksi} > 1.29 \qquad \text{O.K.}$$

The stiffener locations shown in Fig. 7-16a are based on tension-field action, and, therefore, the required area of the stiffener must be determined according to Eq. (7-33a). Try

$$C_v = \frac{45{,}000k}{F_y(h/t)^2} \le 0.8$$

For $a/h = \frac{68}{68} = 1.0$, $k = 4 + 5.34/1^2 = 9.34$. Thus

$$C_v = \frac{45{,}000 \times 9.34}{36 \times 181^2} = 0.356 < 0.8$$

Equation (7-33a) yields, assuming a single-plate stiffener ($D = 2.4$),

$$A_{st} = \frac{1 - 0.356}{2} \left(1 - \frac{1^2}{\sqrt{1 + 1^2}} \right) \times 1 \times 2.4 \times 68 \times 0.375 = 5.77 \text{ in}^2$$

The required moment of inertia I_s and slenderness b/t are

$$I_s = \left(\frac{h}{50} \right)^4 = \left(\frac{68}{50} \right)^4 = 3.18 \text{ in}^4$$

$$\frac{b}{t} = \frac{95}{\sqrt{F_y}} = 16$$

A stiffener 1×6 in gives $A = 6 \text{ in}^2$ and $I_s = 1 \times 6^3/3 = 72 \text{ in}^4$.

Since the stiffener-spacing requirements have been based on shear alone, the combined effect of shear and bending must be checked in the panel adjacent to the interior column. With $h/t = 181$ and $a/h = 1$, AISC Manual table 2-36 yields $F_v = 9.4$ ksi. Then with $f_v = 174/25.5 = 6.83$ ksi, we get from Eq. (7-35)

$$f_b = \left(0.825 - 0.375 \times \frac{6.83}{9.4} \right) F_y = 0.552 F_y = 19.9 \text{ ksi}$$

From DP7-5-1 the moment in the girder at the concentrated column load is 3780 ft·kips and $I = 87,580$ in^4, from which

$$f_b = 3780 \times 12 \times \frac{36.25}{87,580} = 18.8 \text{ ksi} < 19.9$$

Therefore, the 68-in panel length is satisfactory.

If the AISC option of neglecting tension-field action is taken, the stiffeners must be spaced according to Eqs. (5-45). Assuming that $C_v \le 0.8$,

$$F_v = \frac{F_y}{2.89} C_v = \frac{F_y}{2.89} \frac{45,000k}{F_y(h/t_w)^2} = \frac{45,000k}{2.89 \times 181^2} = 0.474k$$

For $f_v = 9.06$ ksi the value of k required is $9.06/0.474 = 19.1$. Assuming $a/h \le 1$

$$4 + \frac{5.34}{(a/h)^2} = 19.1 \qquad \frac{a}{h} = 0.596$$

$$a = 0.596 \times 68 = 40 \text{ in}$$

The layout shown in Fig. 7-16b satisfies this requirement. (The decrease in shear in the 20-ft distance to the concentrated load is not large enough to save a stiffener by increasing the spacing as the shear decreases.) The only requirements for the stiffener are the values of I_s and b/t calculated above. A stiffener $\frac{1}{4}$ in $\times$ 4 in gives $I_s = 0.25 \times 4^3/3 = 5.3$ in^4 and $b/t = 16$.

Since the girder according to this design would have 10 intermediate stiffeners, it would require $10 \times 6 = 60$ ft of steel with a cross section of $4 \times \frac{1}{4} = 1$ in^2 (3.4 lb/ft), a total of $60 \times 3.4 = 204$ lb, for its stiffeners. The tension-field design requires 6 intermediate stiffeners, each $1 \times 6 = 6$ in^2 (20.4 lb/ft) in cross section, for a total of $6 \times 6 \times 20.4 = 734$ lb. Although the difference appears to be substantial, the extra cost of fabrication of the 10-stiffener design might well make the 6-stiffener tension-field design cheaper.

Example 7-10-2 (AISC/LRFD). Determine the spacing of intermediate stiffeners for the girder of DP7-5-2. Bearing stiffeners will be provided at the supports and at the location of the column loads. Their design is presented in Example 7-11-2 (AISC/LRFD).

Solution. From the data of DP7-5-2,

$$h = 68 \text{ in} \qquad t = 0.375 \text{ in} \qquad \frac{h}{t} = \frac{58}{0.375} = 181$$

$$A_w = 25.5 \text{ in}^2 \qquad V = 319 \text{ kips}$$

The Manual contains tabulated values of $\phi V_n/A_w$ for a range of values of a/h and

h/t. The stiffener spacing at the end of the girder must be proportioned on the basis of shear buckling.

$$\frac{\phi V_n}{A_w} = \frac{319}{25.5} = 12.5 \text{ ksi}$$

$$a/h \approx 0.65$$

$$a = 0.65 \times 68 = 44 \text{ in}$$

Try $a = 42$ in. Then $a/h = 0.618$ and

$$k = 5 + \frac{5}{(a/h)^2} = 5 + \frac{5}{0.618^2} = 18.09$$

The appropriate equation from Eqs. (5-46) can be determined by examining the limits

$$234\sqrt{\frac{k}{F_{yw}}} = 234\sqrt{\frac{18.09}{36}} = 166$$

$$\frac{h}{t} = 181 \geq 166$$

Use Eq. (5-46c),

$$V_n = A_w \frac{26,400k}{(h/t_w)^2}$$

$$= 25.5 \times \frac{26,400 \times 18.09}{(181)^2} = 372 \text{ kips}$$

$$\phi = 0.90 \qquad \phi V_n = 335 \text{ kips} \geq 319$$

At 42 in

$$V = 319 - 4.3 \times \tfrac{42}{12} = 304 \text{ kips}$$

$$f_v = \frac{304}{25.5} = 11.9 \text{ ksi}$$

The distance from the first intermediate stiffener to the concentrated load is $240 - 42 = 198$ in. If this distance is divided into two panels,

$$\frac{a}{h} = \frac{99}{68} = 1.46$$

$$k = 5 + \frac{5}{(1.46)^2} = 7.34$$

From Eq. (7-31b) with

$$C_v = \frac{44,000k}{(h/t_w)^2 F_y} = \frac{44,000 \times 7.34}{181^2 \times 36} = 0.274$$

$$V_n = 0.6 A_w F_{yw}\left[C_v + \frac{1 - C_v}{1.15\sqrt{1 + (a/h)^2}}\right]$$

Substitution yields

$$V_n = 348 \text{ kips}$$

$$\phi V_n = 0.9 \times 348 = 313 \text{ kips} \geq 304$$

The layout shown in Fig. 7-17a satisfies the stiffener-spacing requirement.

Check the center 20-ft panel

$$V_n = 43 \text{ kips}$$

The specifications limit the value of a/h to the smaller of $[260/(h/t)]^2$ or 3.0 when tension-field action is used in the design. Therefore,

$$(\tfrac{260}{181})^2 = 2.06$$

$$a = 2.06 \times 68 = 140 \text{ in} = 11.7 \text{ ft}$$

This is less than 20 ft. However, a spacing of 20 ft may be permitted if the girder is capable of resisting the shear without tension-field action taken into account. For this case,

$$\frac{a}{h} = 20 \times \tfrac{12}{68} = 3.53$$

For $a/h > 3.0$ the panel must be checked with $k = 5$.

$$234\sqrt{\frac{k}{F_{yw}}} = 87 \leq 181 \qquad \text{Use Eq. (5-46c)}$$

$$V_n = \frac{26{,}400k}{(h_c/t_w)^2} A_w = \frac{26{,}400 \times 5}{181^2} \times 25.5 = 103 \text{ kips}$$

$$\phi V_n = 0.9 \times 103 = 92.5 \text{ kips} \geq 43 \qquad \text{No stiffeners needed in center panel.}$$

The stiffener locations shown in Fig. 7-17a are based on tension-field action, and therefore, the required area of the stiffener must be determined from Eq. (7-33b).

$$A_{st} \geq \frac{F_{yw}}{F_{yst}} \left[0.15Dht_w(1 - C_v)\frac{V_u}{\phi V_n} - 18t_w^2 \right]$$

where $F_{yw} = 36$ ksi

$F_{yst} = 36$ ksi

$D = 2.4$, single-plate stiffener

$C_v = 0.274$, from the calculations above

$V_u = 304$ kips, from the calculations above

$\phi V_n = 313$ kips, from the calculations above

$A_{st} = [0.15 \times 2.4 \times 68 \times 0.375(1 - 0.27)\tfrac{304}{313} - 18(0.375)^2]$

$\quad = 3.94 \text{ in}^2$

The required moment of inertia I_s and slenderness b/t are

$$I_s = at_w^3 J$$

where, from Eq. (7-21b),

$$J = \frac{2.5}{(a/h)^2} - 2 \geq 0.5$$

$$\frac{b}{t} = \frac{95}{\sqrt{F_y}} = 16$$

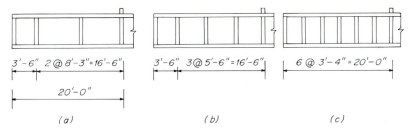

FIGURE 7-17

Therefore,

$$J = \frac{2.5}{\left(\frac{99}{68}\right)^2} - 2 = -0.821 \qquad \text{Use } J = 0.5$$

from which

$$I_s = 99 \times 0.375^3 \times 0.5 = 2.62 \text{ in}^4$$

A stiffener $\frac{3}{4} \times 4$ in gives $A = 3$ in^2 and $I_s = \frac{1}{3} \times \frac{3}{4} \times 4^3 = 16$ in^4.

Since the stiffener-spacing requirements have been based on shear alone, the combined effect of shear and bending must be checked if $V_u > 0.6V_n$ and $M_u > 0.75\,M_n$.

For the 99-in panel adjacent to the concentrated load,

$$V_u = 233 \text{ kips}$$

$$V_n = 348 \text{ kips}$$

$$M_u = 5520 \text{ ft·kips}$$

$$M_n = 6478 \text{ ft·kips}$$

$$\frac{V_u}{V_n} = \frac{233}{348} = 0.670 > 0.6$$

$$\frac{M_u}{M_n} = \frac{5520}{6475} = 0.852 > 0.75$$

Therefore, check Eq. (7-36):

$$\frac{M_u}{M_n} + 0.625\,\frac{V_u}{V_n} \le 1.375\phi$$

$$\frac{5520}{6478} + 0.625\,\frac{233}{348} \le 1.375 \times 0.9$$

$$0.852 + 0.418 \le 1.238$$

$$1.270 \ge 1.238 \qquad \text{N.G.}$$

Therefore, the spacing shown in Fig. 7-17a does not satisfy the requirements for shear and moment interaction. The requirement can be satisfied by increasing either V_n or M_n. V_n can be increased by using three spacings of 66 in, as shown in Fig. 7-17b. This would also require that the stiffener size be reinvestigated. M_n is easily increased by increasing the thickness of the flange plate. Space is available to increase the flange plate to $2\frac{1}{4}$ in which should be more than adequate to satisfy the requirement for interaction.

If the AISC option of neglecting tension-field action is chosen, the stiffeners must be spaced to satisfy Eqs. (5-46a), (5-46b), and (5-46c). At 42 in from the support the shear is 304 kips. Assuming that Eq. (5-46c) will apply, we have

$$\phi V_n = \phi A_w \frac{26{,}400k}{(h/t)^2} = 0.9 \times 25.5 \times \frac{26{,}400k}{181^2} = 304$$

$$k = 16.44$$

$$\frac{h}{t} = 234 \sqrt{\frac{k}{F_y}} = 234 \sqrt{\frac{16.44}{36}} = 158$$

Since $h/t = 181 > 158$, Eq. (5-46c) is applicable as assumed.

$$5 + \frac{5}{(a/h)^2} = 16.44 \qquad \frac{a}{h} = 0.661$$

$$a = 0.661 \times 68 = 45 \text{ in}$$

A detailed check using the procedure for subsequent panels reveals that the distance from the first intermediate stiffener to the concentrated load, 198 in, cannot be accommodated with only four additional panels and that five panels will be required. For this case each panel would then be 39.6 in, which is shorter than the first panel. In order to facilitate fabrication the layout shown in Fig. 7-17c would be preferable.

The only requirements for the stiffener for this case are the values of I_s and b/t calculated above. A stiffener $\frac{1}{4}$ in × 4 in gives $I_s = 0.25 \times 4^3/3 = 5.3$ in^4 and $b/t = 16$.

7-11   BEARING STIFFENERS

Bearing stiffeners are required whenever concentrated loads which could cause vertical buckling of the web of the girder are applied to either flange. Such situations occur on the bottom flange at the reactions and on the top flange at the point of concentrated loads. Figure 7-18 shows bearing stiffeners consisting of plates welded to the web. They must fit tightly against the loaded flange. There must be sufficient area of contact between the stiffeners and the flange to deliver the load without exceeding the permissible bearing on either the flange material

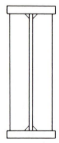

FIGURE 7-18

or the stiffener material, the stiffeners must be adequate against buckling, and the connection to the web must be sufficient to transmit the load.

The bearing stress on the contact area between stiffener and flange is analogous to the compressive stress at the junction of web and flange of rolled beams subjected to concentrated loads. Because it is a bearing stress, permissible values can be relatively large. The AISC/LRFD nominal strength R_n is given by $R_n = 2F_y A$, where A is the bearing area. The AISC/ASD allowable stress is $0.90F_y$. Both the AASHTO and AREA require milled or ground contact surfaces or a full-penetration groove-weld connection, for which the allowable bearing stresses are $0.80F_y$ and $0.83F_y$, respectively.

Since buckling of bearing stiffeners is analogous to buckling of webs at points of concentrated load, the required moment of inertia of the stiffener is not easy to evaluate. The buckled stiffener may take any of the forms pictured for beam webs in Fig. 5-34, depending on the manner in which the flanges are restrained. In most cases, the compression flange of the girder will be supported laterally at points of concentrated load by bracing or by beams framing into it, so buckling will approximate the form of an end-fixed column. Even if the flanges are free to rotate, the stiffeners need not be considered as end-hinged columns because the load concentrated on one end of the stiffener is resisted by forces distributed along its connection to the web instead of by a force concentrated at the opposite end, as in columns.

Both AISC/ASD and AISC/LRFD specifications stipulate that the effective length of a pair of stiffeners be taken at three-fourths the depth of the girder. A strip of web of width not more than $25t$, where t is the thickness of the web, is considered to be a part of the cross section if the stiffeners are at an interior point of the girder. For stiffeners at the end of the girder, the strip is taken to be $12t$ in width. AASHTO also requires that bearing stiffeners be designed as columns but does not specify the effective length. The effective strip of web is $18t$. AREA specifies a maximum allowable compression of $0.55F_y$.

Slenderness limits for bearing stiffeners are $b/t \leq 95/\sqrt{F_{y,\text{ksi}}}$ for AISC, $2300/\sqrt{F_{y,\text{psi}}}$ for AREA, and $12\sqrt{33,000/F_{y,\text{psi}}}$ for AASHTO.

The connection to the web is merely a matter of providing sufficient welding to transmit the calculated load on the stiffener.

Example 7-11-1 (AISC/ASD). Design bearing stiffeners for the girder of DP7-5-1 for the end reaction and for the column load. Use A36 steel.

Solution

    Bearing stiffeners at the supports. The allowable bearing stress on the stiffeners is $F_p = 0.90 \times 36 = 32.4$ ksi. Therefore, $A = 240/32.4 = 7.41$ in^2. Try two $7 \times \frac{3}{4}$ in stiffeners: $b/t = 9.3 < 95/\sqrt{F_y} = 15.8$. The area in bearing is $A = 2 \times 6.5 \times 0.75 = 9.75$ in$^2 > 7.41$ in^2 ($\frac{1}{2}$ in is deducted from the 7-in width to allow for the fillet weld connecting the flange and web).

    The two stiffeners together with a strip $12t$ of the web are checked as a column of effective length $L = 0.75 \times 68 = 51$ in. Although the moment of inertia should be calculated about an axis in the centerline of the web, it is conservatively approximated by the moment of inertia of the stiffener alone about an axis at the junction with the web.

$$I \approx 2 \times \tfrac{1}{3} \times 0.75 \times 7^3 = 172 \text{ in}^4$$

$$12t = 12 \times 0.375 = 4.50 \text{ in}$$

$$A = 2 \times 7 \times 0.75 + 4.50 \times 0.375 = 12.2 \text{ in}^2$$

$$r = \sqrt{\frac{172}{12.2}} = 3.75 \qquad \frac{L}{r} = \frac{51}{3.75} = 13.6$$

$$F_a = 21.0 \text{ ksi} \qquad P = 12.2 \times 21.0 = 256 \text{ kips} \geq 240$$

Use two plates $7 \times \tfrac{3}{4}$ in.

Bearing stiffeners at interior column. The required area is $A = 141/32.4 = 4.35 \text{ in}^2$. Try two $5 \times \tfrac{1}{2}$ in stiffeners: $b/t = 10$, $A = 2 \times 4.5 \times 0.5 = 4.5 \text{ in}^2$ ($\tfrac{1}{2}$ in is deducted from the 5-in width to allow for the fillet weld connecting flange and web).

The two stiffeners together with a strip $25t$ of the web are checked as a column of effective length $L = 0.75 \times 68 = 51$ in.

$$25t = 25 \times 0.375 = 9.4 \text{ in}$$

$$A = 2 \times 5 \times 0.5 + 9.4 \times 0.375 = 8.5 \text{ in}^2$$

$$I = 2 \times \tfrac{1}{3} \times 0.5 \times 5^3 = 42 \text{ in}^4$$

$$r = \sqrt{\frac{42}{8.5}} = 2.22 \qquad \frac{L}{r} = \frac{51}{2.22} = 23$$

$$F_a = 20.4 \text{ ksi} \qquad P = 20.4 \times 8.5 = 173 \text{ kips} \geq 141$$

Use two plates $5 \times \tfrac{1}{2}$ in.

Example 7-11-2 (AISC/LRFD). Design bearing stiffeners for the girder of DP7-5-2 for the end reactions and for the concentrated column load. A36 steel.

Solution

Bearing stiffeners at the supports. The two stiffeners together with a strip $12t$ of the web must be designed as a column of effective length $L = 0.75 \times 68 = 51$ in. This will be a very stocky column. Therefore, assume $F_{cr} \approx 35$ ksi.

$$\phi P_n = 0.85 A_g F_{cr} = 0.85 \times 35 A_g = 319 \text{ kips}$$

$$A_g = 10.7 \text{ in}^2$$

$$12t_w = 12 \times 0.375 = 4.50 \text{ in} \qquad 4.50 \times 0.375 = 1.7 \text{ in}^2$$

Required stiffener area $= 10.7 - 1.7 = 9.0 \text{ in}^2$

Try two plates $6 \times \tfrac{3}{4}$: $b/t = 8 < 95/\sqrt{F_y}$. Check bearing:

$$R_n = 2 \times 36 \times 2 \times 5\tfrac{1}{2} \times 0.75 = 594 \text{ kips} \geq 319$$

($\tfrac{1}{2}$ in is deducted from the 6-in width to allow for the fillet weld connecting flange and web.)

Although the moment of inertia is to be calculated about an axis in the plane of the centerline of the web, it is closely approximated by taking the moment of inertia of the stiffener about the plane of contact of the stiffener and the web. Therefore,

$$I \approx 2 \times \tfrac{1}{3} \times \tfrac{3}{4} \times 6^3 = 108 \text{ in}^4$$

$$A = 2 \times 6 \times \tfrac{3}{4} + 4.50 \times 0.375 = 10.7 \text{ in}^2$$

$$r = \sqrt{\frac{108}{10.7}} = 3.2$$

$$KL = 0.75 \times 68 = 51 \text{ in} \qquad \frac{KL}{r} = \frac{51}{3.2} = 15.9$$

$$\lambda = 0.179 \qquad F_{cr} = 35.5 \text{ ksi} \qquad P_n = 35.5 \times 10.7 = 380 \text{ kips}$$

$$\phi P_n = 0.85 \times 380 = 323 \text{ kips} \geq 319 \qquad \text{O.K.}$$

Use 2 plates $6 \times \tfrac{3}{4}$.

Bearing stiffeners at interior column

$$R_n = 233 \text{ kips}$$

$$= 2F_y A_{pb} = 2 \times 36 A_{pb} = 233 \text{ kips} \qquad A_{pb} = 3.24 \text{ in}^2$$

Assume $F_{cr} \approx 35$ ksi.

$$\phi P_n = 0.85 P_n = 0.85 A_g F_r = 0.85 A_g \times 35 = 233 \text{ kips}$$

$$A_g = 7.83 \text{ in}^2$$

The two stiffeners together with a strip $25t$ of the web are checked as a column of effective length $L = 0.75 \times 68 = 51$ in.

$$25 t_w = 25 \times 0.375 = 9.4 \text{ in} \qquad 9.4 \times 0.375 = 3.5 \text{ in}^2$$

Stiffener area required $= 7.83 - 3.5 = 4.33 \text{ in}^2$
Try two plates $5 \times \tfrac{1}{2}$: $b/t = 10 < 95/\sqrt{F_y}$. Check bearing:

$$R_n = 2 \times 36 \times 2 \times 4\tfrac{1}{2} \times \tfrac{1}{2} = 324 \text{ kips} > 233 \qquad \text{O.K.}$$

$$I \approx 2 \times \tfrac{1}{3} \times \tfrac{1}{2} \times 5^3 = 42 \text{ in}^4$$

$$A = 2 \times 5 \times \tfrac{1}{2} + 9.4 \times 0.375 = 8.5 \text{ in}^2$$

$$r = \sqrt{\frac{42}{8.5}} = 2.22 \text{ in} \qquad \frac{KL}{r} = \frac{51}{2.22} = 23$$

$$\lambda = 0.258 \qquad F_{cr} = 35.0 \text{ ksi}$$

$$P_n = 35.0 \times 8.5 = 298 \text{ kips}$$

$$\phi P_n = 0.9 \times 298 = 253 \text{ kips} > 233 \qquad \text{O.K.}$$

Use two plates $5 \times \tfrac{1}{2}$ in.

7-12 HYBRID PLATE GIRDERS

Since the web of a beam or plate girder contributes only a small part of the bending resistance and since its strength in shear depends on its slenderness h/t, it may be economical to make the web of a lower-strength steel than the flange. Studies have shown that this is often the case.[16] Thus, with the price of A514 steel ($F_y = 100$ ksi) about twice that of A36 steel, a $\frac{1}{2}$-in A36 web costs no more than a $\frac{1}{4}$-in A514 web. Furthermore, for a given depth, the web slenderness of the $\frac{1}{2}$-in A36 web would be only one-half that of the A514 web. Therefore the A36 shear-field web may be able to carry a larger shear than the A514 shear-field web. On the other hand, the tension-field strength of a $\frac{1}{4}$-in A514 web may be more than that of the $\frac{1}{2}$-in A36 web.

Beams with stronger steel in the flanges than in the web are called *hybrid beams*. The bending-stress distributions of a hybrid beam at various stages of loading are shown in Fig. 7-19. Beginning of yield in the web is shown in *b* and *c*. If the load is increased beyond that at this stage to the beginning of yield of the flange, the strain distribution shown in Fig. 7-19*d* is reached. The corresponding distribution of stress is shown in *e*. Continued increase in strain leads eventually to the plastic-moment distribution shown in Fig. 7-19*f*.

Variation in moment with strain on the extreme fiber for the cross section of Fig. 7-19*a* is shown in Fig. 7-20*b*. Although the variation is linear only to the stage where the edge of the web yields (point *A*), the curvature of the segment *AB* is so small that *OAB* is practically straight. After yielding of the flange the rate of increase of moment falls off rapidly. Thus, the bending behavior of the hybrid beam is virtually the same as that of the homogeneous beam.

The ratio of test moment to the predicted moment at beginning of yield of the flange in a series of tests on eight hybrid girders with A514 flanges and A36 webs ranged from 0.88 to 1.01. Web slenderness h/t ranged from 95 to 298. The slenderness b/t of the flange projection was about 7.6. Three girders (with $h/t = 298$) failed by vertical buckling of the compression flange, four by local buckling of the flange, and one by lateral-torsional buckling.[17] Failure in the latter case was caused by failure of the lateral supports.

Both AISC specifications employ two reduction factors in the formulas for the determination of moment capacity of hybrid girders. The first is required to

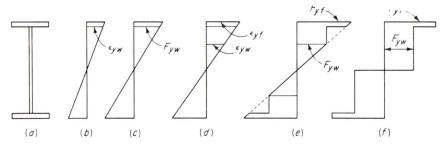

FIGURE 7-19

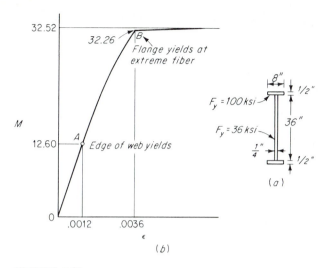

FIGURE 7-20

account for the reduction in capacity as a result of the redistribution of bending stresses which occurs if the web is subject to bend buckling. This topic was discussed in Art. 7-2. AISC/ASD uses the reduction factor R_{PG} of Eq. (7-8), while AISC/LRFD uses that of Eq. (7-10).

The second reduction factor accounts for the distribution of stresses shown in Fig. 7-19e and f. An approximate equivalent extreme-fiber stress was developed[8] which, when applied to a homogeneous girder of the same steel as the flange, gives the allowable moment for the hybrid girder. The reduction factors in the AISC specifications are as follows:

ASD

$$R_e = \frac{12 + (3\alpha - \alpha^3)A_w/A_f}{12 + 2A_w/A_f} \tag{7-37a}$$

where $\alpha = 0.6F_{yw}/F_b$.

LRFD

$$R_e = \frac{12 + (3m - m^3)A_w/A_f}{12 + 2A_w/A_f} \tag{7-37b}$$

where $m = F_{yw}/F_{cr}$.

Local buckling of the compression flange and lateral-torsional buckling of the member must be checked to determine the limiting stress in the compression flange.

AASHTO. This specification uses a somewhat more complex expression for the reduction factor; however, for comparable situations it produces results which are very close to those of Eqs. (7-37).

Example 7-12-1 (AISC/ASD). Design a hybrid cross section for the girder of DP7-5-1 (AISC/ASD), using an A514 flange and an A36 web.

Solution. Since the flange will need roughly only $\frac{36}{100}$ times the flange area for the A36 girder, a flange about 1 in thick should be sufficient. Therefore, the web can be made 70 in deep without exceeding the allotted depth of girder of 73 in.

Assuming the web to be about half as effective as for a homogeneous girder, the required flange area is given by

$$A_f = \frac{M}{F_b h} - \frac{A_w}{12}$$

The increased allowable bending stress $0.66F_y$ for compact sections cannot be used for hybrid girders even if the flange and web b/t ratios satisfy the requirements for compact sections. This 10 percent increase is permitted because the ratio of the plastic moment to the yield moment of a homogeneous girder is about 1.10. This ratio will be smaller for a hybrid girder. Therefore, $F_b = 0.6 \times 100 = 60$ ksi, and with a web $\frac{3}{8} \times 70 = 26.25$ in^2 we get

$$A_f = \frac{4300 \times 12}{60 \times 71} - \frac{26.25}{12} = 12.1 - 2.2 = 9.9 \text{ in}^2$$

Before proceeding, a check of the reduction factors, Eqs. (7-8) and (7-37a), should be carried out.

$$\frac{h}{t} = \frac{70}{0.375} = 187 \qquad \frac{760}{\sqrt{F_b}} = \frac{760}{\sqrt{60}} = 98$$

Assuming a 1×10 flange plate

$$\frac{A_w}{A_f} = \frac{26.25}{10} = 2.625 \qquad \alpha = \frac{0.6 \times 36}{60} = 0.36$$

The reduction factor for web postbuckling is

$$R_{PG} = 1 - 0.0005 \times 2.625(187 - 98) = 0.883$$

The reduction factor for hybrid-girder cross section is

$$R_e = \frac{12 + (3 \times 0.36 - 0.36^3)2.625}{12 + 5.25} = 0.853$$

A revised calculation for the required flange area yields

$$A_f = \frac{4300 \times 12}{0.883 \times 0.853 \times 60 \times 71} - \frac{26.25}{12} = 13.9 \text{ in}^2$$

An increase in the flange area will cause a corresponding increase in the two reduction factors, so a smaller flange may be adequate. The limit for $b_f/2t_f$ is

$$\frac{b_f}{2t_f} \le \frac{95}{\sqrt{F_y/k}}$$

where
$$k = \frac{4.05}{(h/t)^{0.46}} \quad \text{if } \frac{h}{t} \geq 70 \quad \text{(Art. 5-8)}$$

For this girder $h/t = 187$, so $k = 0.365$. Therefore, the limit of $b_f/2t_f$ is 5.74. A flange $1\frac{1}{8} \times 12$ with $b_f/2t_f = 5.33$ is satisfactory. The revised reduction factors are

$$R_{PG} = 1 - 0.0005 \times 1.944(187 - 98) = 0.913$$

$$R_e = \frac{12 + (3 \times 0.36 - 0.36^3)1.944}{12 + 3.888} = 0.882$$

The allowable stress is

$$F'_b = 0.913 \times 0.882 \times 60 = 48.3 \text{ ksi}$$

The moment of inertia is

$$I = 2 \times 13.5\left(\frac{71.125}{2}\right)^2 + \frac{3}{8}\frac{70^3}{12} = 34,147 + 10,720 = 44,867 \text{ in}^4$$

This gives

$$M = \frac{48.3 \times 44,867}{36.125 \times 12} = 5000 \text{ ft·kips}$$

Therefore, the allowable moment is 5000 ft·kips; the required value is 4300 ft·kips. Since the required value is only 86 percent of the allowable, a flange of smaller area may be adequate.

Try a $1\frac{1}{4} \times 10$ flange plate.

$$\frac{b_f}{2t_f} = \frac{10}{2 \times 1.25} = 4 < 5.74 \qquad \frac{A_w}{A_f} = \frac{26.25}{12.5} = 2.10$$

$$R_{PG} = 1 - 0.0005 \times 2.10(187 - 98) = 0.907$$

$$R_e = \frac{12 + (3 \times 0.36 - 0.36^3) \times 2.10}{12 + 2 \times 2.10} = 0.875$$

Allowable stress $F'_b = 0.907 \times 0.875 \times 60 = 47.6$ ksi

$$I = 2 \times 12.5\left(\frac{71.25}{2}\right)^2 + \frac{3}{8} \times \frac{70^3}{12} = 42,447 \text{ in}^4$$

$$M = \frac{47.6 \times 42,447}{36.25 \times 12} = 4644 \text{ ft·kips} > 4300$$

Example 7-12-2 (AISC/LRFD). Design a hybrid cross section for the girder of DP7-5-2, using an A514 flange and an A36 web.

Solution. The maximum moment from DP7-5-2 (AISC/LRFD) is 5735 ft·kips. Applying $\phi = 0.90$, the required capacity is $5735/0.9 = 6375$ ft·kips. Since the flange will need roughly only $\frac{36}{100}$ times the flange area for the A36 girder, a flange about 1 in thick should be sufficient. Therefore, the web can be made 70 in deep without exceeding the allotted depth of girder of 73 in.

Assuming the web to be about half as effective as for a homogeneous girder, the required flange area is given by

$$A_f = \frac{M}{F_y h} - \frac{A_w}{12}$$

Using a web $\frac{3}{8} \times 70 = 26.25$ in^2,

$$A_f = \frac{6375 \times 12}{100 \times 71} - \frac{26.25}{12} = 10.8 - 2.2 = 8.6 \text{ in}^2$$

Before proceeding, a check of the reduction factors, Eqs. (7-10) and (7-37b) should be carried out.

$$\frac{h}{t} = \frac{70}{0.375} = 187 \qquad \frac{970}{\sqrt{F_y}} = \frac{970}{\sqrt{100}} = 97$$

Assuming a 1×9 flange plate,

$$\frac{A_w}{A_f} = \frac{26.25}{9} = 2.917 \qquad m = \frac{36}{100} = 0.36$$

The reduction factor for web postbuckling is

$$R_{PG} = 1 - 0.0005 \times 2.917(187 - 97) = 0.869$$

The reduction factor for hybrid-girder cross section is

$$R_e = \frac{12 + (3 \times 0.36 - 0.36^3)2.917}{12 + 2 \times 2.917} = 0.842$$

A revised calculation for the required flange area yields

$$A_f = \frac{6375 \times 12}{0.869 \times 0.842 \times 100 \times 71} - \frac{26.25}{12} = 12.5 \text{ in}^2$$

The limit of $b_f/2t_f$ for $F_{cr} = F_{yf}$ is

$$\frac{b_f}{2t_f} \leq \frac{65}{\sqrt{F_{yf}}}$$

For $F_{yf} = 100$ ksi the limit is 6.5. A flange plate 1×12 satisfies this criterion. An increase in the flange area will cause a corresponding increase in the two reduction factors, so a smaller flange may be adequate. Using a 1×12 flange plate the revised reduction factors are

$$R_{PG} = 1 - 0.0005 \times 2.1875(187 - 97) = 0.902$$

$$R_e = \frac{12 + (3 \times 0.36 - 0.36^3)2.1875}{12 + 2 \times 2.1875} = 0.871$$

The moment capacity is determined with the stress

$$F = 0.902 \times 0.871 \times 100 = 78.6 \text{ ksi}$$

The moment of inertia is

$$I = 2 \times 12 \times 35.5^2 + \frac{3}{8}\frac{70^3}{12} = 30{,}246 + 10{,}720 = 40{,}966 \text{ in}^4$$

This gives

$$M_n = \frac{78.6 \times 40{,}966}{36 \times 12} = 7440 \text{ ft·kips}$$

Therefore, the moment ϕM_n is 6700 ft·kips, which exceeds the required value of 5735 ft·kips. Since the required value is only 86 percent of the design strength, a flange of smaller area may be adequate.

Try a 1×11 flange plate.

$$\frac{b_f}{2t_f} = \frac{11}{2 \times 1} = 5.5 < 6.5 \qquad \frac{A_w}{A_f} = \frac{26.25}{11} = 2.386$$

$$R_{PG} = 1 - 0.0005 \times 2.386(187 - 97) = 0.893$$

$$R_e = \frac{12 + (3 \times 0.36 - 0.36^3) \times 2.386}{12 + 2 \times 2.386} = 0.862$$

Maximum stress $F = 0.893 \times 0.862 \times 100 = 76.98$ ksi

$$I = 2 \times 11\left(\frac{71}{2}\right)^2 + \frac{3}{8} \times \frac{70^3}{12} = 38{,}444 \text{ in}^4$$

$$M_n = \frac{76.98 \times 38{,}444}{36 \times 12} = 6850 \text{ ft·kips}$$

Therefore, $\phi M_n = 0.9 \times 6850 = 6165$ ft·kips > 5735.

7-13 WEBS OF HYBRID GIRDERS

Shear tests on two hybrid girders with $h/t = 191$ and one combined shear and bending test on a girder with $h/t = 147$ are described in Ref. 17. The experimental values for the two shear tests were 86 and 92 percent of the value predicted by Eq. (7-25), upon which the AISC/ASD formula [Eq. (7-30)] and the AISC/LRFD formula [Eq. (7-31b)] are based. On the other hand, in six tests in combined shear and bending reported in Ref. 8, the shear strength in some cases was significantly less than that predicted by Eq. (7-25), and in two cases it was less than the critical stress computed by Eqs. (5-37) and (5-42). For this reason, it has been recommended that webs of hybrid beams be designed as shear fields and that stiffener spacing be determined accordingly.[8] Hence, with the AISC/ASD specification Eqs. (5-45) and with the AISC/LRFD specification Eqs. (5-46) would be used, while for the AASHTO specifications Eqs. (5-47) are applicable. Accordingly, the stiffener requirements for the hybrid girder designed in the preceding article would be the same as for the A36 girder of Example 7-10-1 (AISC/ASD) and Example 7-10-2 (AISC/LRFD). These requirements were determined in Art. 7-10, where it was found that a stiffener spacing of 40 in was needed.

The zone of yielding in the compression portion of the web of hybrid girders raises a question about web crippling under transverse loads not carried by bearing stiffeners. Tests performed to answer this question showed that crippling loads equal to or greater than the value obtained by multiplying the effective bearing area shown in Fig. 5-31 by the yield stress of the web can be supported.[18] These tests also showed that the bending strength of the girder is slightly reduced by the transverse load but that the reduction is negligible.

7-14   FLANGE BUCKLING IN HYBRID GIRDERS

Tests have shown that the yielding in the compression zone of hybrid girders does not significantly affect the ability of the web to support the compression flange against vertical buckling[8] (Fig. 7-5). The tests also show that the prescribed slenderness limits b/t according to AISC and AASHTO are adequate to control local buckling of the compression flange. Thus, according to AISC, $b/t \leq 95/\sqrt{F_y/k}$ for ASD and $65/\sqrt{F_y}$ for LRFD. AASHTO uses the limit $b/t \leq 1625/\sqrt{F_{a,\text{psi}}}$ (Table 4-4).

Regarding lateral-torsional buckling in hybrid girders, it will be recalled that the torsional resistance of the girder as well as its lateral bending resistance are involved in this phenomenon (Art. 5-4) and that the torsional resistance consists of two parts, the St. Venant torsion and the additional contribution of nonuniform warping. The latter, which is given by $EC_w \, d^3\beta/dz^3$, is contributed almost entirely by the flanges. Furthermore, since $J = bt^3/3$, most of the St. Venant resistance is also contributed by the flanges. Thus, it would appear that lateral-torsional buckling should be affected only slightly by yielding of the compression zone of the web. However, it is suggested in Ref. 8 that only the nonuniform-warping torsion be considered. This would mean, for example, that J would be taken zero in Eq. (5-7a) in using the equivalent radius of gyration procedure for evaluating lateral-torsional buckling.

7-15   WELDING OF GIRDER COMPONENTS

Fillet welds connecting the flange to the web may be as small as the specifications permit for the thickness of the flange, provided the allowable stresses or nominal strengths are not exceeded. The effect of flange thickness on the size of the weld should be kept in mind in proportioning the girder, since the minimum permissible size of weld increases with thickness of the flange (Table 2-17). A $\frac{5}{16}$-in fillet is usually the largest that can be placed in one pass without special equipment.

Although modern shop practice makes continuous welds very desirable, intermittent welds may be economical. For example, using $\frac{1}{4}$-in continuous fillet welds made by automatic welding equipment, instead of, say, $\frac{3}{8}$-in intermittent fillet welds, would probably result in a considerable saving in cost. However, it is questionable whether any savings would ensue from substituting a $\frac{1}{4}$-in continuous weld made with automatic equipment for $\frac{1}{4}$-in intermittent fillet welds.

Transverse stiffeners may be stopped short of the tension flange but should have a tight fit at the compression flange. If the stiffeners are on one side of the web, they should be welded to the compression flange. Bearing stiffeners must have a tight fit against the flange through which they receive their load and, according to AASHTO, must have a milled or ground surface or be attached to the flange by full-penetration groove welds. Because of the difficulty of starting and stopping automatic welding machines, fabricators often prefer the continuous weld.

Example 7-15-1 (AISC/ASD). The minimum size fillet weld for the $2\frac{1}{4}$-in flange of the girder of DP7-5-1 (AISC/ASD) is $\frac{5}{16}$ in (Table 2-17). The allowable shear per inch for two $\frac{5}{16}$-in E60 fillet welds is

$$q = 2 \times 0.3 \times 60 \times 0.707 \times 0.3125 = 8.0 \text{ kli}$$

Although the two fillet welds can transmit 8.0 kli, the ability of the web to transfer this force must be checked. The allowable stress in shear on the base metal is $0.4F_y$. Therefore, 1 in of the web can transmit $0.4 \times 36 \times 0.375 = 5.40$ kli.

The actual shear is

$$q = \frac{VQ}{I} = \frac{240 \times 31.5 \times 35.12}{87,580} = 3.0 \text{ kli}$$

The yield strength of the weld metal need not equal the yield strength of the flange. The yield strength of the weld metal was less than that of the flange in most of the hybrid beams tested in Ref. 8, and no problems were encountered even in the beams which were loaded to their shear strength.

If intermittent welds are used, their longitudinal clear spacing connecting the tension flange must not exceed 24 times the thickness of the thinner plate or 12 in. For the compression flange the clear spacing must not exceed $127/\sqrt{F_y}$ times the thickness of the thinner plate or 12 in. The length of the intermittent welds should be at least four times their nominal size and not less than 1.5 in.

For 4-in $\frac{5}{16}$-in E60 fillet welds the spacing is

$$s = 4 \times \frac{5.4}{3.0} = 7.2 \text{ in}$$

If 4-in welds are used at a spacing of 7 in, the clear spacing is 3 in, which satisfies the above requirements. The limiting clear spacing from $(127/\sqrt{F_y})t_{min}$ is 7.94 in. Therefore, 10-in welds at a spacing of 18 in would also be satisfactory.

Example 7-15-2 (AISC/LRFD). The minimum size fillet weld for the 2-in flange of the girder of DP7-5-2 (AISC/LRFD) is $\frac{5}{16}$ in (Table 2-17). The shear capacity per inch for two $\frac{5}{16}$-in E60 fillet welds is

$$q = 2 \times 0.6 \times 60 \times 0.707 \times 0.3125 = 15.9 \text{ kli}$$

With $\phi = 0.75$,

$$q = 0.75 \times 15.9 = 11.93 \text{ kli}$$

Although the two fillet welds can transmit 11.93 kli, the ability of the web to transfer this force must be checked. The allowable capacity in shear on the base metal is $0.6F_y$. Therefore, 1 in of the web can transmit $\phi \times 0.6 \times 36 \times 0.375 = 0.75 \times 0.6 \times 36 \times 0.375 = 6.08$ kli.

The actual shear is

$$q = \frac{VQ}{I} = \frac{319 \times 28 \times 35}{78{,}430} = 4.0 \text{ kli}$$

The yield strength of the weld metal need not equal the yield strength of the flange. The yield strength of the weld metal was less than that of the flange in most of the hybrid beams tested in Ref. 8, and no problems were encountered even in the beams which were loaded to their shear strength.

If intermittent welds are used, their longitudinal clear spacing connecting the tension flange must not exceed 24 times the thickness of the thinner plate or 12 in. For the compression flange the clear spacing must not exceed $127/\sqrt{F_y}$ times the thickness of the thinner plate or 12 in. The length of the intermittent welds should be at least four times their nominal size and not less than 1.5 in.

For 4-in $\frac{5}{16}$-in E60 fillet welds the spacing is

$$s = 4 \times \frac{6.08}{4.0} = 6.1 \text{ in}$$

If 4-in welds are used at a spacing of 6 in, the clear spacing is 2 in, which satisfies the above requirements. The limiting clear spacing from $(127/\sqrt{F_y})t_{min}$ is 7.94 in. Therefore, 12-in welds at a spacing of 18 in would also be satisfactory.

7-16   SHOP AND FIELD SPLICES

The locations of web shop splices generally depend upon available lengths of plates and are often left to the fabricator. Since they are usually connected by full-penetration groove welds, no computations are needed to verify the adequacy of the splice.

The splice of abutting flange plates of different thicknesses must be sloped to avoid an abrupt change in cross section. According to the AWS specifications, this slope must not exceed 1 vertical in $2\frac{1}{2}$ horizontal. The transition may be provided by chamfering the thicker plate, by sloping the weld itself, or by a combination of chamfering and weld sloping (Fig. 7-21).

Field splices are required in continuous spans and in single spans too long to ship in one piece. Field splices in bridge girders may be bolted because of the difficulty of welding large girders in the field. In some cases, the flange may be groove-welded and the web bolted. Flanges which must be welded from both sides present a problem on the inner face because it is difficult to get a sound weld at the juncture of the flange and the web. Coping the web facilitates complete welding of the flange and gives access for cleaning, chipping, or gouging (Fig. 7-21). However, the resulting stress concentration decreases the fatigue life

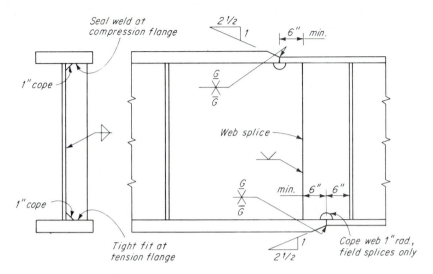

FIGURE 7-21

of the girder.[19] The coped area may be filled with weld metal after the flange has been welded.

A bolted web splice is made with two splice plates (Fig. 7-22*b*). To determine the bolt pattern, we consider a strip of web plate *p* in high, where *p* is the distance between adjacent horizontal rows of bolts (Fig. 7-23). This portion of the web is acted upon by the bending stresses and the shearing forces shown. Figure 7-23*b* shows half the corresponding portion of the splice plates, the right edges of which are assumed to be subjected to the forces that would exist in the web plate were it continuous at the splice. The upper edges and the left edges are free of forces, but there may be a shearing force at the lower edges. If we neglect the latter force, the two bolts shown must furnish horizontal forces sufficient to balance the resultant of the bending stresses and, in addition, vertical forces sufficient to balance the vertical shearing force. Let f_b be the average bending stress, f_v

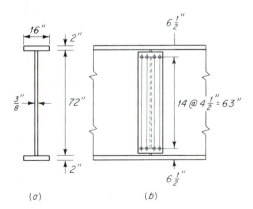

(*a*)   (*b*)   **FIGURE 7-22**

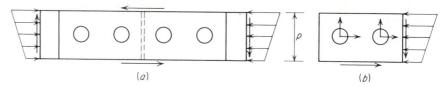

(a) (b)

FIGURE 7-23

the average shearing stress, and t the thickness of the web plate. Then, if R is the allowable force on one bolt and if the load is shared equally by n bolts, we have

$$\left(\frac{f_b pt}{n}\right)^2 + \left(\frac{f_v pt}{n}\right)^2 = R^2$$

whence

$$p = \frac{Rn}{t\sqrt{f_b^2 + f_v^2}} \tag{7-38}$$

The shearing stress at any section is practically constant throughout the depth of the web. Therefore, since the bending stress depends upon the distance from the neutral axis, Eq. (7-38) would seem to indicate that the pitch p may increase as we approach the neutral axis or that the number of bolts in each row may decrease if p is held constant. This would be true if R were the same for all rows. But the resisting force that can be developed by any bolt depends upon the amount of its deformation. This deformation must depend on the distance from the neutral axis and must in fact vanish at the neutral axis since deformations in the horizontal direction are reversed on the tension side of the girder. Therefore, if we assume behavior of the bolts consistent with the behavior of the girder itself, the bending stress f_b and the horizontal component of the bolt obey the same law. Therefore, the horizontal rows in the splice plates should be equidistant, or nearly so.

Opinions differ as to the shear and moment for which a bolted web splice should be designed. Splices are often located at points where the web has excess strength, in which case it would seem reasonable to design the splice for the most unfavorable combination of shear and moment at the point of the splice. This is required by the AISC specification. However, the AASHTO specifications require that the splice be designed to resist a shear and moment each equal to the average of the calculated service-load value and the allowable value but not less than 75 percent of the latter. The AREA specifications require design for the allowable shear on the gross cross section of the web and for the combined effect of the allowable moment on the net section and the maximum service-load shear at the point of the splice.

Example 7-16-1. Design a slip-critical splice with A325 bolts for the web of the A36 girder shown in Fig. 7-22a. The concurrent values of the shear and moment on the girder at the section to be spliced are 210 kips and 320 ft·kips. The moment of inertia of the cross section is 99,260 in⁴. Allowable stresses for slip-critical connections are identical in both AISC specifications and must be checked for the service loads. Consequently, the following ASD solution is applicable for both specifications.

Solution. Assuming the first row of bolts to be 4 in from the inside face of the flange, the bending stress at the outer row of bolts in the splice is

$$f_b = \frac{320 \times 12 \times 32}{99,260} = 12.4 \text{ ksi}$$

The shearing stress on the web is

$$f_v = \frac{210}{72 \times 0.375} = 7.8 \text{ ksi}$$

With $\frac{3}{4}$-in A325 bolts, the allowable double shear per bolt is $2 \times 17 \times 0.44 = 15.0$ kips. For one vertical row of bolts on each side of the splice, Eq. (7-38) gives

$$p = \frac{15.0 \times 1}{0.375\sqrt{12.4^2 + 7.8^2}} = 2.7 \text{ in}$$

Use two rows with $p = 4\frac{1}{2}$ in. This gives 15 bolts per vertical row (Fig. 7-22b). The splice is checked by computing the resultant of the horizontal and vertical components of the shear on the extreme bolt. The horizontal component is given by

$$R_x = \frac{Mc}{I} A = \frac{McA}{\sum y^2 A} = \frac{Mc}{\sum y^2}$$

From Eq. (b) of Art. 8-7,

$$\sum y^2 = \frac{np^2(n^2 - 1)}{12} \text{ per row}$$

$$= \frac{15 \times 4.5^2(15^2 - 1)}{12} = 5670$$

Therefore

$$R_x = \frac{320 \times 12 \times 7 \times 4.5}{2 \times 5670} = 10.7 \text{ kips}$$

The vertical component is given by the shear divided by the number of connectors:

$$R_y = \frac{210}{2 \times 15} = 7.0 \text{ kips}$$

$$R = \sqrt{10.7^2 + 7.0^2} = 12.8 \text{ kips}$$

Since the allowable shear per bolt is 15.0 kips, the bolt layout is satisfactory. Since the splice is often located at points where the cross section has excess strength, as mentioned above, the thickness of each splice plate may sometimes be less than half the thickness of the web.

For the AISC/LRFD specification, it would also be necessary to check the splice for strength based on the factored loads. This check would be based on a bearing-type connection according to procedures discussed in Chap. 3.

PROBLEMS

7-1. Given an A36-steel girder with a $75 \times \frac{1}{4}$ in web and with each flange consisting of a $12 \times 1\frac{1}{2}$ in plate. Compute the ultimate resisting moment.

7-2. Same as Prob. 7-1 but with a longitudinal stiffener 15 in from the compression flange. Compute the ultimate resisting moment and determine the stiffener cross section.

7-3. Redesign the girder of DP7-5-1 using a $\frac{1}{4}$-in web. Compare the weights per foot of cross section.

7-4. Redesign the girder of DP7-5-2 using a $\frac{1}{4}$-in web. Compare the weights per foot of cross section.

7-5. A simply supported plate girder spanning 70 ft supports a uniformly distributed load, not including its own weight, of 0.5 klf *DL* and 3.5 klf *LL*. There is no fire-proofing, and the girder is supported against lateral buckling. Design a cross section. AISC specification, A36 steel.

7-6. A simply supported plate girder spans 90 ft and supports a uniformly distributed load, not including its own weight, of 1 klf *DL* and 7 klf *LL*. There are lateral supports at intervals of 18 ft. The depth of the girder cannot exceed 7 ft. Design a cross section. AISC specification, A36 steel.

7-7. Columns in a 14-story building similar to that of DP7-5-1 and 7-5-2 are 22 ft on centers in each direction. The floor-to-floor height is 13 ft. In one area of the building a row of columns between the tenth and twelfth floors is to be omitted in an assembly room, with the columns that support the twelfth, thirteenth, and fourteenth floors to be carried on a 44-ft plate girder. The design live load and the weights of slab, roofing, etc., are the same as for DP7-5-1 and 7-5-2. Design a plate girder to allow a 20-ft ceiling in the assembly room. AISC specification, A36 steel.

7-8. Given a simply supported welded plate girder whose flange consists of one central flange plate flanked by two thinner plates butt welded to it. If the girder supports a load concentrated at midspan and the weight of the girder itself is negligible, prove that the weight of the flange plates is a minimum if the length of the central plate is half the span of the girder. Assume that the girder is supported against lateral buckling.

7-9. Determine the cutoff for the flange plate of the girder of DP7-5-1 or 7-5-2 if the abutting flange plates are to be $1\frac{1}{4}$ in thick.

7-10. Check the stiffener requirements and the combined bending and shear for the girder of Prob. 7-3.

7-11. Check the stiffener requirements and the combined bending and shear for the girder of Prob. 7-4.

7-12. Check the stiffener requirements and the combined bending and shear for the girder of Prob. 7-7.

7-13. An A572 Grade 42 plate girder consists of a $\frac{7}{16} \times 84$ in web with 2×16 in flange plates. The girder is simply supported on a 72-ft span and has continuous support against lateral buckling. It carries a concentrated load of 110 kips *DL* and 110 kips

LL at midspan and a load of 1 klf *DL* and 3 klf *LL* distributed over the full span. Check the stiffener requirements and the combined bending and shear. AISC specification.

7-14. A simply supported plate girder spans 120 ft. There are concentrated loads at midspan and at each quarter point; each is 120 kips dead and 80 kips live. The uniformly distributed load is 1.8 klf dead and 1.2 klf live. There is continuous lateral support. Design the girder and its stiffeners. AISC specification.

7-15. A railroad plate-girder deck bridge spans 100 ft center to center of bearings. The dead load of track, etc., including an allowance for the weight of the girder is 2.1 klf. There are no conditions at the site that restrict the depth. Live load is Cooper E80 (Fig. 1-3). Design the girder and its stiffeners. AREA specification.

7-16. A simply supported plate girder spans 98 ft and supports a uniform live load of 6 klf and a uniform dead load of 2 klf, not including its own weight. It has continuous lateral support. The depth of the girder cannot exceed 7 ft. Design a cross section with A514 flanges and A36 web, and determine the transverse-stiffener requirements. AISC specification.

7-17. A simply supported plate girder spans 72 ft and supports a uniform live load of 3.2 klf and a uniform dead load of 1.0 klf, not including its own weight. There are lateral supports at intervals of 18 ft. Design a cross section with A572 flanges and A36 web, and determine the transverse-stiffener requirements. AISC specification.

7-18. Same as Prob. 7-14 except design a cross section with A514 flanges and A36 web.

7-19. Design a bolted web splice for an A36 plate girder with a $\frac{1}{2} \times 100$ in web and 3×18 in flanges. The values of the concurrent shear and moment at the point of splice are 100 kips dead, 310 kips live and 1800 ft·kips dead and 5400 ft·kips live. A325 bolts, AISC specification.

7-20. Design a bolted web splice for a hybrid plate girder with $\frac{1}{2} \times 100$ in A36 web and 3×18 in A514 flanges. The values of the concurrent shear and moment at the point of splice are 130 kips dead, 390 kips live and 5300 ft·kips dead and 15,900 ft·kips live. A325 bolts, AISC specification.

7-21. Design a bolted flange splice for the girder of Prob. 7-19 to be located at the same cross section as the web splice.

7-22. Design a bolted flange splice for the girder of Prob. 7-20 to be located at the same cross section as the web splice.

REFERENCES

1. Dubas, C.: A Contribution to the Buckling of Stiffened Plates, *Prelim. Rep. 3d Congr. IABSE Liege*, 1948.
2. Massonnet, C. E. L.: Stability Considerations in the Design of Steel Plate Girders, *Trans. ASCE*, vol. 127, 1962.
3. Cooper, P. B.: Strength of Longitudinally Stiffened Plate Girders, *J. Struct. Div. ASCE*, April 1967.
4. Basler, K., and B. Thurlimann: Strength of Plate Girders in Bending, *Trans. ASCE*, vol. 128, pt. II, p. 655, 1963.
5. Yen, B. T., and J. A. Mueller: Fatigue Tests of Large-Size Welded Plate Girders, *WRC Bull.* 118, November 1966.
6. Lew, H. S., and A. A. Toprac: Fatigue Strength of Hybrid Plate Girders under Constant Moment, *HRB Proc. 40th Annu. Meet.*, 1967.

7. Mueller, J. A., and B. T. Yen: Girder Web Boundary Stresses and Fatigue, *WRC Bull.* 127, January 1968.
8. Report of Subcommittee 1, Joint ASCE-AASHTO Committee on Flexural Members, Design of Hybrid Steel Beams, *J. Struct. Div. ASCE*, June 1968.
9. Kuntz, F. C.: "Design of Steel Bridges," p. 156, McGraw-Hill, New York, 1915.
10. Elliott, A. L.: Bridges, sec. 18 in E. H. Gaylord and C. N. Gaylord (eds.), "Structural Engineering Handbook," 3d ed., McGraw-Hill, New York, 1990.
11. Stein, M., and R. W. Fralich: Critical Shear Stress of Infinitely Long, Simply Supported Plate with Transverse Stiffeners, *NACA Tech. Note* 1851, 1949.
12. Bleich, F.: "Buckling Strength of Metal Structures," McGraw-Hill, New York, 1952.
13. Basler, K.: Strength of Plate Girders in Shear, *Trans. ASCE*, vol. 128, pt. II, 1963.
14. Rockey, K. C.: Factors Influencing Ultimate Behaviour of Plate Girders, *Br. Constr. Steelwork Assoc. Conf. Steel Bridges, Inst. Civ. Eng., London*, June 1968, sess. 1., pap. 3.
15. Basler, K.: Strength of Plate Girders under Combined Bending and Shear, *Trans. ASCE*, vol. 128, pt. II, 1963.
16. Haaijer, G.: Economy of High-Strength Steel Structural Members, *J. Struct. Div. ASCE*, December 1961.
17. Lew, H. S., M. Natarajan, and A. A. Toprac: Static Tests of Hybrid Girders, *Weld. J.*, vol. 48, no. 2, February 1969.
18. Schilling, C. G.: Web Crippling Tests on Hybrid Beams, *J. Struct. Div. ASCE*, February 1967.
19. Stallmeyer, J. E., W. H. Munse, and B. J. Goodal: Behavior of Welded Built-Up Beams under Repeated Loads, *Weld. J.*, January 1957.

CHAPTER

8

CONNECTIONS

8-1 INTRODUCTION

The design of the structural members discussed in the preceding chapters is based on theories which usually can be depended upon to produce satisfactory results. On the other hand, the behavior of connections is so complex that, in many cases, it is impossible to describe in terms of simple formulas, or for that matter any formula. For this reason, formulas which are derived analytically often require modification to bring them into agreement with test results. Design of connections is sometimes left to the fabricator, and designers do not always give them the attention they deserve. Investigations of structural failures often show connections or other details, rather than the members, to be the origin of failure.

Connections may be subjected to direct shear; eccentric shear, which produces a combination of direct shear and a twisting moment; direct tension, which produces tension in the connectors; moment, which produces tension on some connectors and compression on the opposite side of the connection; and combinations of these. Because of the wide variety of loading conditions to which a connection may be subjected and the range of details which may be employed, it is essential that the designer have a considerable knowledge of behavior. Connections for tension members were discussed in Chaps. 2 and 3. In this chapter beam connections, column splices, and moment-resistant column bases will be discussed.

Beam connections are classified as (1) *simple*, meaning that only a negligible resisting moment can be developed, (2) *rigid*, meaning that relative rotation of the interconnecting members is prevented, and (3) *semirigid*, meaning, of course, that they are neither moment-free nor rigid. This topic is discussed further in Art. 8-15.

It should be noted that all the specifications referred to throughout this text prescribe the allowable capacities of fasteners for particular conditions of stress, but none prescribe the method of analysis to be employed to investigate the connections in which they are used. Design aids are available from a variety of sources; however, the designer should evaluate the method of analysis used in the development of such aids and determine the extent to which any assumptions may or may not be applicable to the particular situation.

8-2 BOLTED AND RIVETED CONNECTIONS FOR BEAMS

A bolted or riveted connection between two beams framing at right angles is usually made with two angles placed as shown in Fig. 8-1a to form a *framed* beam connection. If the flanges of the two beams are at the same elevation, the connecting beam is cut to clear (Fig. 8-1b). This detail of the top flange of the connecting beam is called a *cope*. The same connection without the flange cope is suitable for beam-to-column connections (Fig. 8-1c). If the single row of fasteners connecting the angles to the web in Fig. 8-1c is insufficient, angles with legs wide enough for two rows can be used. The outstanding legs of the connecting angles can also be made wide enough to accommodate two rows each. The connections in Fig. 8-1a and b can of course be similarly modified.

The *seated* beam connection shown in Fig. 8-1d is often used when the beam connects to the web of a column. It may also be used to connect the beam to a column flange. In its simplest form the seat consists of a single angle (Fig. 8-1e). When the number of fasteners that can be placed in the leg connected to the column is not enough to support the load, the angle stiffener shown in Fig. 8-1d can be added. A second stiffener may be placed alongside the single one shown. The top angle is an essential part of the connection, since it holds the top flange in position and therefore contributes significantly to the resistance of the web to vertical buckling. If the beam rests on a seat connected to the web of another beam, as in Fig. 8-1e, the side angle shown should be used if clearance does not permit a top angle.

The connection shown in Fig. 8-1f is called a *tee-framed* shear connection. It is made with a tee whose web is connected to one side of the web of the beam, instead of the two angles as in Fig. 8-1a, b, and c. The rotational capacity of this connection will depend on the thickness of the flange of the tee and the spacing of the fasteners which connect the flange. Figure 8-1g shows a framed connection made with a plate which is shop-welded to the column and field-bolted to the web of the beam. This is called a *single-plate* shear connection. The connection to the column may be made with a full-penetration single-vee weld or by fillet welds on both sides of the plate.

Conventional design procedure for the framed and seated connections of Fig. 8-1 assumes that they offer no resistance to rotation of the end of the beam in the vertical plane, so the beam reaction is the only force to be considered.

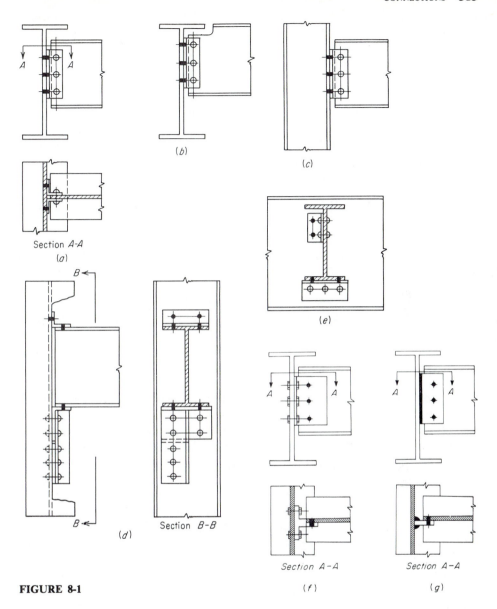

FIGURE 8-1

Thus, they are considered to be simple connections, as defined in Art. 8-1. It is evident that rotation of the end of the beam exerts some moment on the connection. The rotation is accommodated in part by an elongation of the upper fasteners of framed connections and in part by a distortion of the upper portion of the framing angles somewhat as pictured in Fig. 8-2. This suggests that framing angles should be relatively thin and that the gage g should be reasonably large in order to relieve the top fasteners of the framing angles. For the same reason, the top angle of the seat connection should be relatively flexible. Ordinarily, framing

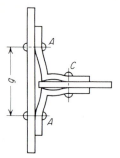

FIGURE 8-2

angles need be only thick enough to develop in bearing the shear value of the fastener.

Framed connections and seated connections are used so extensively that standard types have been developed. The AISC Manuals give data for a variety of such connections, which are adequate for all but exceptional cases of span and loading.

In Fig. 8-1, the parts of the connections which are shown to be shop-connected (denoted by the open circles) are more likely to be welded. Comparable welded connections are discussed in Art. 8-16.

8-3   UNSTIFFENED BEAM SEATS

The action which takes place when an unstiffened seat angle supports a beam may be inferred from a study of the photographs of Fig. 8-3. It will be noted that the angle acts approximately as a cantilever beam and that the thicker seat in Fig. 8-3a tends to concentrate the reaction at the toe of the outstanding leg, while the thinner seat in Fig. 8-3b tends to distribute it somewhat more. On the other hand, the web thickness of the beam and the stiffness of its flange both influence the distribution of the reaction. It is virtually impossible to take all these variables into account in an analysis. It is common practice to assume the reaction to be uniformly distributed over a length, measured from the end of the beam, sufficient to satisfy the web-crippling and web-yielding requirements of the beam. This is obviously a compromise which makes some allowance for the effect of web thickness but none for the relative stiffnesses of the beam and seat. Since this assumption is the same as is used in evaluating web stresses at beam bearing plates (Fig. 5-31), Eqs. (5-56b) and (5-57b) apply. For beams with small reactions these equations may be satisfied with a value of N less than k, but the AISC specifications require that N be taken at not less than k.

If the beam were not connected to the seat, the critical section for bending of the seat would be at the top row of fasteners in the vertical leg. However, as the bottom of the beam elongates under load, the angle is forced against the column so that the moment in the vertical leg is relieved. Furthermore, the outstanding leg cannot bend as a cantilever because of the restraining action of the beam flange to which it is attached. Consequently, it is not easy to determine

FIGURE 8-3
Failure of riveted beam-to-column connections. (*Final Rep. Steel Struct. Res. Comm., Dept. Sci. Ind. Res., H. M. Stationery Office, London, 1936.*)

where the maximum bending occurs. It is usually assumed to be at the toe of the fillet in the horizontal leg.

Example 8-3-1 (AISC/ASD). A bolted beam seat to connect a W16 × 40 beam to the web of a W8 × 35 column (A36 steel and A325 bolts) is designed in this example. The beam reaction is 17.3 kips. The allowable compression F_c is $0.66F_y = 24$ ksi.

Solution. For the W16 × 40, $k = 1\frac{3}{16}$ in (1.19 in), and Eq. (5-56b) gives

$$N = \frac{17.3}{24 \times 0.305} - 2.5 \times 1.19 = -0.61$$

Therefore, use $N = k = 1.19$ in.

The value of k for angles $\frac{1}{2}$ to $\frac{5}{8}$ in thick ranges from about $\frac{7}{8}$ to $1\frac{1}{4}$ in, depending on the size of the angle. Using $k = 1$ in, the critical section for bending is 1 in from the face of the column (Fig. 8-4). Beams are usually detailed to clear the column by $\frac{1}{2}$ in. This dimension is called the *setback*. To allow for underrun in the length of the beam the clearance will be taken as $\frac{3}{4}$ in. Therefore the moment at the critical section is

$$M = 17.3\left(\frac{1.19}{2} + 0.75 - 1\right) = 5.97 \text{ in·kips} \tag{a}$$

A 6-in length of seat is the largest that can fit the web of the column. The allowable bending stress is $F_b = 0.66F_y = 24$ ksi. Then, with $F_b = M/S = 6M/bt^2$, we get

$$t = \sqrt{\frac{6 \times 5.97}{6 \times 24}} = 0.499 \text{ in} \tag{b}$$

Web crippling of the beam must also be checked according to Eq. (5-59b) of Art. 5-17. With $N = 1.19$, $d = 16.01$, $t_f = 0.505$, $t_w = 0.305$, and $F_{yw} = 36$, this equation yields $R = 27.0$ kips > 17.3.

Assuming a bearing connection with threads excluded from the shear plane, the allowable shear stress is $F_v = 30$ ksi. For $\frac{3}{4}$-in bolts,

$$R = 30 \times 0.44 = 13.2 \text{ kips} \qquad n = \frac{17.3}{13.2} = 2$$

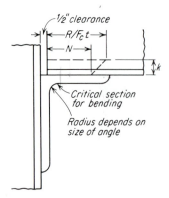

FIGURE 8-4

A $4 \times 4 \times \frac{1}{2}$ angle would accommodate these bolts and has the thickness calculated in Eq. (*b*). However, $k = \frac{7}{8}$ in for this angle, while the moment in Eq. (*a*) was computed for $k = 1$ in. Since a smaller k increases M (and t), the next thicker angle, $4 \times 4 \times \frac{5}{8}$, is chosen. For this angle, $k = 1$. A check of the required bolt length shows that threads will be excluded from the shear plane for the thicknesses to be joined. Therefore, the $4 \times 4 \times \frac{5}{8}$ angle, 6 in long, satisfies the requirements.

Example 8-3-2 (AISC/LRFD). A bolted beam seat to connect a W16 × 40 beam to the web of a W8 × 35 column (A36 steel and A325 bolts) is designed in this example. The beam reaction is 17.3 kips, of which 3.3 kips is dead load and 14.0 kips live load.

Solution. The required capacity is $1.2 \times 3.3 + 1.6 \times 14.0 = 26.4$ kips. For the W16 × 40, $k = 1\frac{3}{16}$ in (1.19 in), and Eq. (5-57b) gives

$$26.4 = [2.5 \times 1.19 + N]36 \times 0.305$$

from which $N = -0.57$. Therefore, use $N = k = 1.19$ in.

The value of k for angles $\frac{1}{2}$ to $\frac{5}{8}$ in thick ranges from about $\frac{7}{8}$ to $1\frac{1}{4}$ in, depending on the size of the angle. Using $k = 1$ in, the critical section is 1 in from the face of the column (Fig. 8-4). Beams are usually detailed to clear the column by $\frac{1}{2}$ in. This dimension is called the *setback*. To allow for underrun in the length of the beam the clearance will be taken as $\frac{3}{4}$ in. Therefore the moment at the critical section is

$$M = 26.4\left(\frac{1.19}{2} + 0.75 - 1\right) = 9.1 \text{ in·kips} \qquad (c)$$

A 6-in length of seat is the largest that can fit the web of the column. The moment capacity is ϕM_n, where $\phi = 0.9$ and $M_n = M_p = F_y(bt^2/4)$. The required value of M_p is $9.1/0.9 = 10.1$ in·kips. Therefore,

$$t = \sqrt{\frac{4 \times 10.1}{6 \times 36}} = 0.433 \text{ in} \qquad (d)$$

Web crippling of the beam must also be checked according to Eq. (5-60b) of Art. 5-17. With $N = 1.19$, $d = 16.01$, $t_f = 0.505$, $t_w = 0.305$, and $F_{yw} = 36$, this equation yields $R = 53.9$ kips > 26.4.

Assuming a bearing connection with threads excluded from the shear plane, the capacity of one shear surface is $\phi(\pi d^2/4)F_u$, where $\phi = 0.75$ and $F_u = 60$. For $\frac{3}{4}$-in bolts,

$$R = 0.75 \times 60 \times 0.44 = 19.9 \text{ kips} \qquad n = \frac{26.4}{19.9} = 2$$

A $4 \times 4 \times \frac{7}{16}$ angle would accommodate these bolts and has the thickness calculated in Eq. (*d*). However, $k = \frac{13}{16}$ in for this angle, while the moment in Eq. (*c*) was computed for $k = 1$ in. Recalculation with $k = \frac{13}{16}$ in requires that M_n be 14.1 in·kips so that the required $t = 0.54$ in. Therefore the next thicker angle, $4 \times 4 \times \frac{1}{2}$, is chosen. For this angle, $k = \frac{7}{8}$, M_n is 12.4 in·kips and the required thickness is 0.505. The $4 \times 4 \times \frac{1}{2}$ angle is satisfactory. A check of the required bolt length shows that threads will be excluded from the shear plane for the thicknesses to be joined. Therefore, the $4 \times 4 \times \frac{1}{2}$ angle, 6 in long, satisfies the requirements.

Discussion of Examples 8-3-1 and 8-3-2. The procedure just described is extremely sensitive to small changes in the clearance at the end of the beam, the beam-web thickness, and the values of k for the beam and the seat angle. For example, if the beam clearance or the value of k for the angle is changed by only $\frac{1}{16}$ in, the moments computed in Eqs. (a) and (c) are changed by 18 percent. This sensitivity can lead to inconsistent results which raise some doubts about the validity of the analysis.

8-4   STIFFENED BEAM SEATS

The capacity of an unstiffened seat angle is limited by the number of fasteners (usually four) that can be accommodated by the leg which connects to the column. Larger reactions require one or two stiffeners which fit tightly against the underside of the seat angle (Fig. 8-1d). The width, parallel to the beam, of the horizontal leg of the seat angle will be determined by web-crippling requirements of the beam unless the web of the beam is provided with stiffeners. Since the seat stiffeners relieve the seat of the bending which was discussed in Art. 8-3, it is good practice to have them extend as near to the edge of the seat as practicable. Their outstanding legs must have sufficient area in contact with the seat to support the load at a safe bearing stress. Because it is impracticable to cut the stiffener to fit tightly against the fillet of the seat angle, the effective width of the outstanding leg in bearing against the seat is less than its actual width by at least the radius of the fillet of the seat. This radius varies from $\frac{3}{8}$ to $\frac{5}{8}$ in for angles ordinarily used as seats, but it is customary for design purposes to use $\frac{1}{2}$ in.

Since the outstanding leg of the stiffener is in compression, it may fail by local buckling. Except for the fact that the beam reaction which is applied at the upper end is resisted along the supported edge instead of at the edge opposite the load, the stiffener leg is a compressed element free on one unloaded edge. Therefore it should be on the safe side to use the same limiting thickness as for outstanding elements of compression members, as discussed in Art. 4-14. For example, this would require the b/t ratio for steel stiffeners designed according to either AISC/ASD or AISC/LRFD specifications to be not more than $95/\sqrt{F_y}$.

The design of stiffened seats is illustrated in the following two examples.

Example 8-4-1 (AISC/ASD). Design a seat to connect a W18 × 65 beam to the web of a W8 × 40 column. The beam reaction is 72 kips which results from 18 kips DL and 54 kips LL. The A325 bolts are $\frac{3}{4}$ in in a bearing-type connection with threads excluded from the shear planes; steel is A36.

Solution. Properties of the W18 × 65 are

$$d = 18.35 \text{ in} \qquad t_f = 0.750 \text{ in} \qquad t_w = 0.450 \text{ in} \qquad k = 1\frac{7}{16} = 1.44 \text{ in}$$

To prevent yielding of the beam web, the necessary length of bearing is given by Eq. (5-56b):

$$N = \frac{72}{24 \times 0.450} - 2.5 \times 1.44 = 3.1 \text{ in}$$

Check Eq. (5-59b) for web crippling:

$$R = 34t_w^2\left[1 + 3\,\frac{N}{d}\left(\frac{t_w}{t_f}\right)^{1.5}\right]\sqrt{\frac{F_{yw}t_f}{t_w}}$$

With $R = 72$ kips and properties of the W18 × 65 we find $N = 4.6$ in.

Allowing $\frac{3}{4}$ in from the face of the column to the end of the beam, a 6-in seat is required. The allowable bearing stress is $0.90 \times 36 = 32.4$ ksi, so the required bearing area is $72/32.4 = 2.22$ in². The stiffening angles must be clipped to provide clearance for the fillet of the seat angle. An allowance of $\frac{1}{2}$ in is sufficient. For two stiffeners with 5-in outstanding legs, $t = 2.22/(2 \times 4.5) = 0.25$ in. But since the ratio b/t for a $\frac{1}{4}$-in thickness exceeds $95/\sqrt{36} = 15.8$, two angles 5 × 3 × $\frac{5}{16}$ are chosen. The width of the connected leg (3 in) is determined by the width between fillets of the column ($6\frac{3}{8}$ in). Since the beam flange is too wide to clear the column flanges, it must be cut to fit.

The allowable load for each bolt of the group which connects the stiffeners to the web of the column is $R = 30 \times 0.44 = 13.25$ kips and $R = 1.2 \times 58 \times 0.75 \times 0.312 = 16.3$ kips in bearing on the leg of the stiffener. The required number of bolts is therefore $n = 72/13.25 = 5.4$, or three in each stiffener. However, since these bolts pass through a loose filler (Fig. 8-1d) and as a consequence tend to bend, one should consider the advisability of increasing their number. This question is discussed following Example 8-4-2.

Since the beam reaction acts on the outstanding leg of the stiffener, it is eccentric with respect to the bolts connecting the stiffener to the column. This condition is shown in Fig. 8-5. If the gage on the 3-in connected leg is the standard $1\frac{3}{4}$ in, the bolt group is subjected to a moment

$$M_{xy} = 36 \times 1\tfrac{3}{4} = 63.0 \text{ in·kips}$$

and an additional moment

$$\dot{M}_{yz} = 36 \times 3 = 108 \text{ in·kips}$$

With the required three bolts per stiffener spaced 3 in,

$$\sum y^2 = 4 \times 3^2 = 36$$

so the shear on the extreme bolt resulting from M_{xy} is $R = 63 \times \frac{3}{36} = 5.25$ kips.

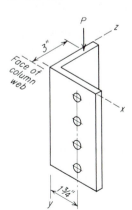

FIGURE 8-5

Combining this with the shear in the direction of the y axis, $R = \frac{36}{3} = 12$ kips, the resultant is $\sqrt{(12.0)^2 + (5.25)^2} = 13.1$ kips. The effect of this eccentricity is usually ignored. Of course, if the outstanding legs of the stiffeners are fastened together, the bolts are relieved of the additional shear just computed. Usually, this is not done.

Example 8-4-2 (AISC/LRFD). Design a seat to connect a W18 × 65 beam to the web of a W8 × 40 column. The beam reaction is 72 kips which results from 18 kips DL and 54 kips LL. The A325 bolts are $\frac{3}{4}$ in in a bearing-type connection with threads excluded from the shear planes; steel is A36.

Solution. Properties of the W18 × 65 are

$$d = 18.35 \text{ in} \qquad t_f = 0.750 \text{ in} \qquad t_w = 0.450 \text{ in} \qquad k = 1\tfrac{7}{16} = 1.44 \text{ in}$$

The design load is

$$R = 1.2 \, DL + 1.6 \, LL = 1.2 \times 18 + 1.6 \times 54 = 108 \text{ kips}$$

To prevent yielding of the web, the necessary length of bearing is given by ϕR_n, where $\phi = 1$ and R_n is from Eq. (5-57b):

$$N = \frac{108}{1 \times 36 \times 0.450} - 2.5 \times 1.44 = 3.1 \text{ in}$$

Check Eq. (5-60b) for web crippling:

$$R = 0.75 \times 68 t_w^2 \left[1 + 3 \frac{N}{d} \left(\frac{t_w}{t_f} \right)^{1.5} \right] \sqrt{\frac{F_{yw} t_f}{t_w}}$$

With $R = 108$ kips and properties of the W18 × 65 we find $N = 4.6$ in.

Allowing $\frac{3}{4}$ in from the face of the column to the end of the beam, a 6-in seat is required. The bearing capacity is

$$R = \phi R_p = 0.75 \times 2.0 F_y A_{pb}$$

where A_{pb} is the projected bearing area. Therefore,

$$108 = 0.75 \times 2.0 \times 36 A_{pb}$$

from which $A_{pb} = 2.00$ in^2.

The stiffening angles must be clipped to provide clearance for the fillet of the seat angle. An allowance of $\frac{1}{2}$ in is sufficient. For two stiffeners with 5-in outstanding legs, $t = 2.00/(2 \times 4.5) = 0.22$ in. But since the ratio b/t for a $\frac{1}{4}$-in thickness exceeds $95/\sqrt{36} = 15.8$, two angles 5 × 3 × $\frac{5}{16}$ are chosen. The width of the connected leg (3 in) is determined by the width between fillets of the column ($6\frac{3}{8}$ in). Since the beam flange is too wide to clear the column flanges, it must be cut to fit.

The capacity for each bolt of the group which connects the stiffeners to the web of the column is $R = \phi \times 60 \times 0.44 = 0.75 \times 60 \times 0.44 = 19.9$ kips in single shear and $R = \phi R_p = \phi(2.4 dt F_u) = 0.75(2.4 \times 0.75 \times 0.312 \times 58) = 24.4$ kips in bearing on the leg of the stiffener. The required number of bolts is therefore $n = 108/19.9 = 5.4$, or three in each stiffener. However, since these bolts pass through a loose filler (Fig. 8-1d) and as a consequence tend to bend, one should consider the advisability of increasing their number. This question is discussed following the example.

Since the beam reaction acts on the outstanding leg of the stiffener, it is eccentric with respect to the bolts connecting the stiffener to the column. This condition is shown in Fig. 8-5. If the gage on the 3-in connected leg is the standard $1\frac{3}{4}$ in, the bolt group is subjected to a moment

$$M_{xy} = 54 \times 1\tfrac{3}{4} = 94.5 \text{ in·kips}$$

and an additional moment

$$M_{yz} = 54 \times 3 = 162 \text{ in·kips}$$

With the required three bolts per stiffener spaced 3 in,

$$\sum y^2 = 4 \times 3^2 = 36$$

so the shear on the extreme bolt resulting from M_{xy} is $R = 94.5 \times \frac{3}{36} = 7.88$ kips. Combining this with the shear in the direction of the y axis, $R = \frac{54}{3} = 18$ kips, the resultant is $\sqrt{(18)^2 + (7.88)^2} = 19.65$ kips. The effect of this eccentricity is usually ignored. Of course, if the outstanding legs of the stiffeners are fastened together, the bolts are relieved of the additional shear just computed. Usually, this is not done.

Discussion of Examples 8-4-1 and 8-4-2. The AISC specifications require that:

> When bolts or rivets carrying computed stress pass through fillers thicker than $\frac{1}{4}$ inch, except in slip-critical connections, the fillers shall be extended beyond the splice material and the filler extension secured by enough bolts or rivets to distribute the total stress in the member uniformly over the combined sections of the member and the filler.

In these examples, one might extend the filler beyond the lower end of the stiffener a distance sufficient to receive one additional bolt in each line. It should be mentioned, however, that this is not always done in the case of stiffened beam seats, and in fact the specification is ignored in determining the allowable loads on certain standard seats listed in the AISC Manual.

The moment M_{yz} tends to rotate the seat in the yz plane. Resistance to this moment must therefore come from tensile forces in the upper bolts of the connection together with bearing pressures between the web of the column and the lower end of the stiffener. This question is discussed in Art. 8-6.

8-5 BOLTED OR RIVETED FRAMED CONNECTIONS

Framed connections of the type shown in Fig. 8-1a, b, and c are widely used. The number of fasteners required is determined by their shear and bearing capacities, which are dependent upon the thickness of the web of the beam and the thickness of the angles. In addition, the shear capacity of the framing angles should be checked for rupture through the net area and for yield on the gross area. In the calculation for net area in shear the deduction for the hole is taken as the actual hole dimension. The minimum spacing of the fastener at the end of the beam is determined by procedures discussed in Chap. 3, in which the force in the connector should be taken as the end reaction divided by the number of connectors.

For connections of the type shown in Fig. 8-1b, where the flange of the beam is coped, it is necessary to check the beam for failure by shear rupture

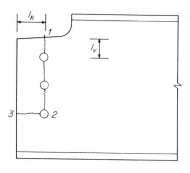

FIGURE 8-6

along a vertical plane from the cope through the bolt holes to the bottom hole in combination with tensile failure along a horizontal plane from the bottom hole to the end of the beam. This failure plane is shown in Fig. 8-6. It is an example of the block-shear failures shown in Fig. 3-5 and discussed in Art. 3-4. The AISC/ASD allowable stresses are given by Eqs. (3-3) and the LRFD design strengths by Eqs. (3-6).

Based on a study of experimental data on single-plate shear connections (Fig. 8-1g), Astaneh[1] recommends that the bolts used to attach the beam to the plate be analyzed for a combination of direct shear and a torsional moment and that the weldment connecting the plate to the adjacent member be checked for direct shear and an accompanying bending moment. In the analysis of the weld the eccentricity of the weld line may be taken as n, where n is the number of bolts. In the analysis of the bolts the eccentricity e_b of the bolt line may be assumed to be 3 in, which is the usual distance from the bolt line to the weld line. This will generally be conservative if the plate is welded to a rigid support. The following equations may be used to calculate e_b.

Plate welded to a rotationally rigid support:

$$e_b = (n - 1) - a \tag{8-1}$$

Plate welded to a rotationally flexible support, the larger of Eq. (8-1) and

$$e_b = a \tag{8-2}$$

where a = distance from bolt line to weld line, in.

Rotational capacity may need to be considered. Such capacity is reduced as the number of fasteners is increased. In experiments by Astaneh beam end rotation was approximately 0.06 rads for a three-bolt connection, 0.05 for a five-bolt connection, and 0.025 for a seven-bolt connection. Thus, single-plate shear connections may have inadequate rotational capacity for large span-to-depth ratios and for high-strength steels.

Tee-framed connections of the type shown in Fig. 8-1f may be welded or bolted to the support. In either case the connection should be checked for direct shear plus a bending moment equal to the reaction multiplied by the distance from the bolt line to the face of the supporting member. For bolted connections the effect of prying action (Art. 8-10) should be taken into account.

Erection of bolted connections may be facilitated by using short slotted holes.

Example 8-5-1 (AISC/ASD). Framed connections for the beams shown in Fig. 8-7 are designed in this example. The beams are of A36 steel, and the connections are made with $\frac{3}{4}$-in A307 bolts. The beam reactions are 22 kips on the W12 × 26 and 35 kips on the W16 × 40. Edge distances and fastener spacing are to be provided for the allowable bearing stress of $1.2F_u = 1.2 \times 58 = 69.6$ ksi, so the bearing values on the beam webs are

$$69.6 \times 0.75 \times 0.230 = 12.0 \text{ kips} \qquad \text{W12}$$
$$69.6 \times 0.75 \times 0.305 = 15.9 \text{ kips} \qquad \text{W16}$$

The allowable shear is 10 ksi, and the double-shear value per bolt is $2 \times 10 \times 0.44 = 8.8$ kips. The number of bolts required to connect the framing angles to the webs of the W12 and W16 is

$$n = \frac{22}{8.8} = 2.5 \qquad \text{use 3 (W12 × 26)}$$

$$n = \frac{35}{8.8} = 4.0 \qquad \text{use 4 (W16 × 40)}$$

The bolts in the W21 × 73 beam must be sufficient to transmit the reactions of the two beams, or 22 + 35 kips = 57 kips. The allowable bearing on the web is $69.6 \times 0.75 \times 0.455 = 23.8$ kips, so shear controls. The required number of bolt-shear areas is 57/4.4 = 13. With the arrangement shown in the figure there are six bolts in double shear and two in single shear, which gives 14 shear areas.

If the cope is 2 in, the W12 × 26 can accept a framing angle 9 in long and the W16 × 40 can accept one $12\frac{1}{2}$ in long. The arrangement shown in the figure is satisfactory. The end spacing of $1\frac{1}{4}$ in is greater than $1\frac{1}{2}d$ and the between-fastener spacing of 3 in is greater than $3d$, so the requirements for $F_p = 1.2F_u$ are satisfied. Framing angles $3\frac{1}{2} \times 3\frac{1}{2} \times \frac{3}{8}$ will be used. The standard gage of $3\frac{1}{2}$-in angles is 2 in which, with a $\frac{1}{2}$-in setback, provides an end distance of $1\frac{1}{2}$ in in the beam web, which is satisfactory.

For the angles connecting the W12 × 26,

$$A_{vg} = 2 \times 9 \times 0.375 = 6.75 \text{ in}^2$$
$$R = 6.75 \times 0.4 \times 36 = 97.0 \text{ kips} > 22$$
$$A_{vn} = 2 \times [9 - 3(\tfrac{3}{4} + \tfrac{1}{16})] \times 0.375 = 4.92 \text{ in}^2$$
$$R = 4.92 \times 0.3 \times 58 = 85.6 \text{ kips} > 22$$

Therefore, $R = 85.6$ kips.

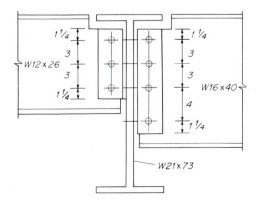

FIGURE 8-7

Repeating these calculations for the angles connecting the W16 × 40, we have

$$A_{vg} = 9.38 \text{ in}^2 \qquad R = 135 \text{ kips} > 35$$
$$A_{vn} = 6.94 \text{ in}^2 \qquad R = 121 \text{ kips} > 35$$

Therefore, $R = 121$ kips.

Check the beam for web tear-out [Eqs. (3-3)].

W12 × 26: $A_{vn} = [7.25 - (2\frac{1}{2})(\frac{13}{16})] \times 0.230 = 1.20 \text{ in}^2$

$A_{nt} = [1.50 - (\frac{1}{2})(\frac{13}{16})] \times 0.230 = 0.25 \text{ in}^2$

$R = 1.20 \times 0.3 \times 58 + 0.25 \times 0.5 \times 58 = 26.3 \text{ kips} > 22$

W16 × 40: $A_{vn} = [11.25 - (3\frac{1}{2})(\frac{13}{16})] \times 0.305 = 2.56 \text{ in}^2$

$A_{nt} = [1.50 - (\frac{1}{2})(\frac{13}{16})] \times 0.305 = 0.33 \text{ in}^2$

$R = 2.56 \times 0.3 \times 58 + 0.33 \times 0.5 \times 58 = 54.1 \text{ kips} > 35$

The $3\frac{1}{2} \times 3\frac{1}{2} \times \frac{3}{8}$ angles are large enough to accommodate the bolts with the necessary clearances for tightening. Angles $\frac{1}{4}$ in thick would also be satisfactory.

Example 8-5-2 (AISC/LRFD). Framed connections for the beams shown in Fig. 8-7 are designed in this example. The beams are of A36 steel, and the connections are made with $\frac{3}{4}$-in A307 bolts. The factored beam reactions are 33 kips on the W12 × 26 and 53 kips on the W16 × 40. Edge distances and fastener spacing are to be provided for a bearing stress of $2.4F_u = 2.4 \times 58 = 139.2$ ksi, so the bearing values on the beam webs are

$$139.2 \times 0.75 \times 0.230 = 24.0 \text{ kips} \qquad \text{W12}$$
$$139.2 \times 0.75 \times 0.305 = 31.8 \text{ kips} \qquad \text{W16}$$

The shear strength of A307 bolts is $\phi F_{vu} = 0.75 \times 24 = 18.0$ ksi, and the double-shear value per bolt is $2 \times 18.0 \times 0.44 = 15.8$ kips. The number of bolts required to connect the framing angles to the webs of the W12 and W16 is

$$n = \frac{33}{15.8} = 2.1 \qquad \text{use 3 (W12 × 26)}$$

$$n = \frac{53}{15.8} = 3.4 \qquad \text{use 4 (W16 × 40)}$$

The bolts in the W21 × 73 beam must be sufficient to transmit the reactions of the two beams, or 33 + 53 kips = 86 kips. The allowable bearing on the web is $139.2 \times 0.75 \times 0.455 = 47.5$ kips, so shear controls. The required number of bolt-shear areas is 86/7.9 = 11. With the arrangement shown in the figure there are six bolts in double shear and two in single shear, which gives 14 shear areas.

If the cope is 2 in, the W12 × 26 can accept a framing angle 9 in long and the W16 × 40 can accept an angle $12\frac{1}{2}$ in long. The arrangement shown in the figure is satisfactory. The end spacing of $1\frac{1}{4}$ in is greater than $1\frac{1}{2}d$ and the between-fastener spacing of 3 in is greater than $3d$, so the requirements for $F_p = 2.4F_u$ are satisfied. Framing angles $3\frac{1}{2} \times 3\frac{1}{2} \times \frac{3}{8}$ will be used. The standard gage of $3\frac{1}{2}$-in angles is 2 in which, with a $\frac{1}{2}$-in setback, provides an end distance of $1\frac{1}{2}$ in in the beam web, which is adequate.

For the angles connecting the W12 × 26,

$$A_{vg} = 2 \times 9 \times 0.375 = 6.75 \text{ in}^2$$

$$R = A_{vg} \times \phi \times 0.6F_y = 6.75 \times 0.9 \times 0.6 \times 36 = 131 \text{ kips} > 33$$

$$A_{vn} = 2 \times [9 - 3(\tfrac{3}{4} + \tfrac{1}{16})] \times 0.375 = 4.92 \text{ in}^2$$

$$R = A_{vn} \times \phi \times 0.6F_u = 4.92 \times 0.75 \times 0.6 \times 58 = 128 \text{ kips} > 33$$

Therefore, $R = 128$ kips.

Repeating these calculations for the angles connecting the W16 × 40, we get

$$A_{vg} = 9.38 \text{ in}^2 \qquad R = 182 \text{ kips} > 53$$

$$A_{vn} = 6.94 \text{ in}^2 \qquad R = 181 \text{ kips} > 53$$

Therefore, $R = 181$ kips.

Check the beam for web tear-out [Eqs. (3-6)].

W12 × 26:
$$A_{vg} = 7.25 \times 0.230 = 1.67 \text{ in}^2$$

$$A_{vn} = [7.25 - (2\tfrac{1}{2})(\tfrac{13}{16})] \times 0.230 = 1.20 \text{ in}^2$$

$$A_{gt} = 1.50 \times 0.230 = 0.35 \text{ in}^2$$

$$A_{nt} = [1.50 - (\tfrac{1}{2})(\tfrac{13}{16})] \times 0.230 = 0.25 \text{ in}^2$$

$$R = \phi(A_{vn} F_{vu} + A_{gt} F_y)$$

$$= 0.75(1.20 \times 0.6 \times 58 + 0.35 \times 36) = 40.8 \text{ kips}$$

or

$$R = \phi(A_{vg} F_{vy} + A_{nt} F_u)$$

$$= 0.75(1.67 \times 0.6 \times 36 + 0.25 \times 58) = 37.9 \text{ kips}$$

W16 × 40:
$$A_{vg} = 11.25 \times 0.305 = 3.43 \text{ in}^2$$

$$A_{vn} = [11.25 - (3\tfrac{1}{2})(\tfrac{13}{16})] \times 0.305 = 2.56 \text{ in}^2$$

$$A_{gt} = 1.50 \times 0.305 = 0.46 \text{ in}^2$$

$$A_{nt} = [1.50 - (\tfrac{1}{2})(\tfrac{13}{16})] \times 0.305 = 0.33 \text{ in}^2$$

$$R = 0.75(2.56 \times 0.6 \times 58 + 0.46 \times 36) = 79.2 \text{ kips}$$

$$R = 0.75(3.43 \times 0.6 \times 36 + 0.33 \times 58) = 69.9 \text{ kips}$$

The larger of the two values of R for the two beams is the correct one. Therefore, $R = 40.8$ kips for the W12 × 26 and 79.2 kips for the W16 × 40.

The $3\tfrac{1}{2} \times 3\tfrac{1}{2} \times \tfrac{3}{8}$ angles are large enough to accommodate the bolts with the necessary clearances for tightening. Angles $\tfrac{1}{4}$ in thick would also be satisfactory.

8-6 FASTENERS IN TENSION

The behavior of a connection that is loaded in such a way as to produce tension on the fasteners must be studied in terms of the tension which exists in the fasteners in the unloaded state. Since hot-driven rivets are not free to contract during cooling, they attain large tensile forces upon reaching normal temperatures. Tests indicate that an initial tensile stress of the order of 24 ksi may be expected. The initial tension in high-strength bolts is much greater (Art. 2-8). The initial tension in the fasteners of a connection produces a compressive force between the faying surfaces. If an external moment tends to rotate the connection, as in the stiffener angle shown in Fig. 8-5, the initial tension in the fasteners will increase on one side of the neutral axis while the initial compression will decrease. Similarly, on the opposite side of the neutral axis, the initial tension in the fastener decreases while the initial compression increases.

Two parts connected by a single fastener are shown in the unloaded state in Fig. 8-8a. A free-body sketch of one of the parts is shown in Fig. 8-8b. T_0 is the initial tension in the fastener, and C_0 is the resultant of the initial compressive stresses. The distribution of the latter is unknown but is assumed to be uniform. Then for equilibrium,

$$T_0 = C_0 \tag{a}$$

If a pull P is applied to the parts, as shown in Fig. 8-8c, the tension in the fastener and the resultant of the compressive stresses become T and C, respectively, as shown in Fig. 8-8d. Then

$$P + C = T \tag{b}$$

If the increase in the length of the fastener due to the increment of tension equals the increase in the thickness of the plates due to the decrease in compression,

$$\frac{T - T_0}{A_f E_f} = \frac{C_0 - C}{A_p E_p} \tag{c}$$

where the subscripts f and p refer to the fastener and the plate, respectively. Substituting the values of C_0 from Eq. (a) and C from Eq. (b), we get

$$(T - T_0)\frac{A_p E_p}{A_f E_f} = T_0 - (T - P) \tag{d}$$

From this equation we find, for T,

$$T = T_0 + \frac{P}{1 + A_p E_p/A_f E_f} \tag{e}$$

Equation (e) is valid only if the faying surfaces remain in contact. This condition obtains until $C = 0$, after which the connection opens up and $P = T$.

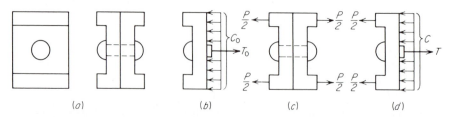

(a)   (b)   (c)   (d)

FIGURE 8-8

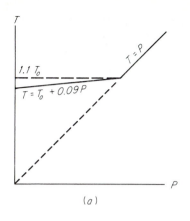

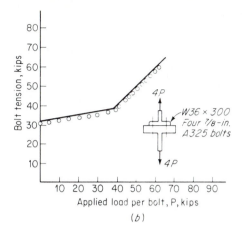

FIGURE 8-9

To find the value of P at which contact is lost, we put $C = 0$ in Eq. (*c*). Since $C_0 = T_0$, this gives

$$T = T_0\left(1 + \frac{A_f E_f}{A_p E_p}\right) \qquad (f)$$

If the lateral dimensions of the connected part are as small as specifications permit for the size of the fastener (usually three diameters), then $A_p = (3d)^2 - \pi d^2/4 = 8.2d^2$ and $A_f = \pi d^2/4$. Then, if the fastener and connected part are of the same material so that $E_p = E_f$, Eq. (*e*) gives

$$T = T_0 + \frac{P}{1 + 8.2/0.79} \approx T_0 + 0.09P \qquad (g)$$

while Eq. (*f*) gives

$$T \approx 1.1T_0 \qquad (h)$$

These results are shown in Fig. 8-9*a*. This behavior is confirmed in Fig. 8-9*b*, which shows results of a test on a connection consisting of a tee cut from a W36 × 300 connected by four $\frac{7}{8}$-in A325 bolts to a heavy plate assembly.[2]

According to Eq. (*g*) the increase in tensile force in the fastener is 9 percent of the load P. This increment is reduced if we increase the contact area of the connected parts. However, it is obvious that the distribution of the compressive stresses tends to become less and less uniform as the contact area increases. However, Eqs. (*c*) and (*f*) are still applicable, provided a reduced, or effective, area is used in place of the actual contact area.

8-7 CONNECTIONS WITH FASTENERS IN TENSION

Let Fig. 8-10*a* represent an unloaded tee, with two rows of fasteners (one on each side of the stem) connecting it to a stiff member. In Fig. 8-10*b* a couple M acts on

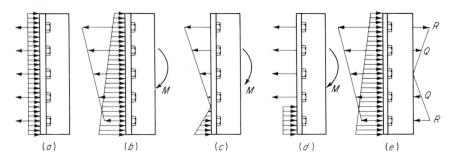

FIGURE 8-10

the tee. If the tee is also stiff, the distribution of the altered tensile forces and compressive stresses will be linear as shown, so long as the connection does not open up at the top. If M in Fig. 8-10b is large enough to release the compression on the upper portion of the faying surfaces, the forces acting on the connection may be assumed to be distributed as shown in Fig. 8-10c if the extreme fastener has not yielded. With progressive yielding of the fasteners the distribution of the forces approaches that shown in Fig. 8-10d.

The distributions of forces in Fig. 8-10b and c are both consistent with the fundamental assumptions of elastic analysis, while that in Fig. 8-10d is consistent with plastic analysis. If the analysis is based on the distribution of Fig. 8-10b, the couple M can be shown in the equivalent form of two pairs of forces, R and Q, each acting on a length of tee equal to the pitch of the fasteners (Fig. 8-10e). The topmost section is analogous to the connection of Fig. 8-8, as is the section immediately below. We have already shown that T is not significantly greater than T_0. Therefore we may design the connection on the basis of a prescribed allowable tensile stress on the fastener as though the maximum tension in the fastener were equal to R.

For the distribution of forces in Fig. 8-10e we have for the moment M of a connection with m lines of fasteners

$$M = m \sum Qy = m \sum \frac{yR}{d/2} y = \frac{2mR}{d} \sum y^2 \tag{8-3}$$

where y = distance from neutral axis to any fastener in the line
d = length of fastener line

A formula for the required number of fasteners can be developed as follows. For an odd number of fasteners (Fig. 8-11a)

$$\sum y^2 = 2[p^2 + (2p)^2 + (3p)^2 + \cdots + (kp)^2]$$

$$= 2p^2(1^2 + 2^2 + 3^2 + \cdots + k^2) \tag{a}$$

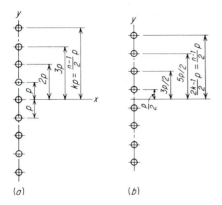

(a)   (b)   **FIGURE 8-11**

The sum of the k terms in parentheses is $(k/6)(k + 1)(2k + 1)$. From the figure, $k = (n - 1)/2$, and therefore

$$\Sigma y^2 = 2p^2 \frac{n-1}{2 \times 6}\left(\frac{n-1}{2} + 1\right)(n - 1 + 1) = \frac{np^2(n^2 - 1)}{12} \qquad (b)$$

Similarly, for an even number of fasteners (Fig. 8-11b),

$$\Sigma y^2 = 2\left[\left(\frac{p}{2}\right)^2 + \left(\frac{3p}{2}\right)^2 + \left(\frac{5p}{2}\right)^2 + \cdots + \left(\frac{2k-1}{2}p\right)^2\right]$$

$$= \frac{p^2}{2}\left[1^2 + 3^2 + 5^2 + \cdots + (2k - 1)^2\right] \qquad (c)$$

The sum of the terms in the bracketed series is $(k/3)(2k + 1)(2k - 1)$. In this case $k = n/2$, and therefore

$$\Sigma y^2 = \frac{p^2}{2}\frac{n}{6}(n + 1)(n - 1) = \frac{np^2(n^2 - 1)}{12} \qquad (d)$$

Since it is identical with Eq. (b), Eq. (d) may be used for either an odd number of fasteners or an even number. In each case the distance $d/2$ from the centroid to the extreme fastener is $p(n - 1)/2$. Substituting this value and the value of Σy^2 into Eq. (8-3) and solving for R, we get

$$R = \frac{Mp(n - 1)/2}{mnp^2(n^2 - 1)/12} = \frac{6M}{mnp(n + 1)} \qquad (8\text{-}4)$$

Solving Eq. (8-4) for n, we get

$$n = \sqrt{\frac{6M}{mpR} + \frac{1}{4}} - \frac{1}{2} \qquad (8\text{-}5)$$

The neutral axis for the force distribution shown in Fig. 8-10c lies at the center of gravity of a cross section consisting of the fastener areas on one side of the neutral axis and the bearing area of the tee on the other. The distance y from the bottom of the connection to its neutral axis will be one-sixth to one-seventh the length of the connection. Its value may either be assumed and checked or solved directly by equating moments of the areas. The tensile force can then be determined from the flexure formula. A formula has been derived from which one can determine the number of fasteners required to resist a given moment.[3] This number is about 80 percent of the number given by Eq. (8-5). Therefore, the number of fasteners for a trial design can be obtained as 0.8 times the value of n from Eq. (8-5).

A conservative estimate of the ultimate moment capacity of a connection using high-strength bolts can be determined by assuming (1) the bolt tensions in Fig. 8-10d to be equal to the minimum required tension at installation, which is 70 percent of the specified minimum tensile strength of the bolt, and (2) the area in bearing to be stressed to the yield point of the connected material. This procedure was suggested for the design of bolted connections for plastically designed rigid frames.[4] Since the compressive force equals the sum of the tensions in the bolts on the tension side of the neutral axis, the bearing area and the location of the neutral axis are easily determined. Of course, the moment is the moment of the couple consisting of the compressive force and the sum of the tensile forces.

Cold-driven rivets are sometimes used in structural work. The absence of initial tension invalidates the distribution of forces of Fig. 8-10b, so the distribution of Fig. 8-10c or d should be used.

Example 8-7-1. The bracket shown in Fig. 8-12 will be used to illustrate the methods of analysis discussed in this article. The AISC/ASD allowable tension in a $\frac{3}{4}$-in A325 bolt is $R = 0.442 \times 44 = 19.45$ kips. For the distribution of forces of Fig.

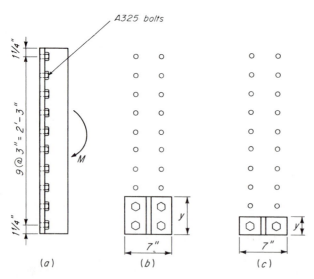

FIGURE 8-12

8-10*e*, Eq. (8-4) gives

$$M = \frac{Rmnp(n + 1)}{6} = \frac{19.45 \times 2 \times 10 \times 3 \times 11}{6} = 2140 \text{ in·kips}$$

For the distribution of forces of Fig. 8-10*c*, knowing that y is one-sixth to one-seventh the length of the connection, the cross section will be as shown in Fig. 8-12*b*. Equating the moment of the contact area below the neutral axis to the moment of the bolt areas above the neutral axis, we have

$$\frac{7y^2}{2} = 16 \times 0.442(17.75 - y)$$

$$y = 5.06 \text{ in}$$

The moment of inertia is

$$I = 2 \times 0.442(2.19^2 + 5.19^2 + 8.19^2 + 11.19^2 + 14.19^2 + 17.19^2 + 20.19^2 + 23.19^2)$$

$$+ 7 \times \frac{5.06^3}{3}$$

$$= 1774 \text{ in}^4$$

The distance to the top bolt from the neutral axis is $27 + 1.25 - 5.06 = 23.19$ in. The allowable moment is

$$M = \frac{44 \times 1774}{23.19} = 3366 \text{ in·kips}$$

For the distribution of forces shown in Fig. 8-10*d*, assuming the neutral axis to be located between the bottom two rows, we have the cross section shown in Fig. 8-12*c*. The specified minimum installation tension of the $\frac{3}{4}$-in bolt is 28 kips (Table 2-7). Equating the compressive force on the contact area below the neutral axis to the tension in the bolts above the neutral axis, we have, for A36 steel,

$$36 \times 7y = 18 \times 28$$

$$y = 2.0 \text{ in}$$

The ultimate moment is

$$M_u = 18 \times 28 \times 15.25 = 7680 \text{ in·kips}$$

Allowable-stress design. The ratios of the ultimate moment M_u to the two allowable moments calculated above are

$$\frac{7680}{2140} = 3.59 \quad \text{and} \quad \frac{7680}{3366} = 2.28$$

In the absence of a specification provision regarding the assumptions to be used in the analysis of connections of this type, the authors suggest design according to Fig. 8-10*c*, since it gives the smaller of the two ratios of M_u to M. The smaller ratio should be acceptable, since even it is larger than the usual factors of safety for allowable-stress design. Furthermore, a case can be made for using the analysis according to Fig. 8-10*d*, with a factor of safety of, say, 1.7 for AISC/ASD and 1.9 for AASHTO and AREA specifications. This would be analogous to allowable-stress design procedures for taking advantage of plastic or partially plastic moments by specifying increased allowable stresses for resisting moments based on elastic stress distributions.

LRFD design. Analysis according to Fig. 8-10*d* is consistent with LRFD design. The LRFD nominal tensile stress for A325 bolts is 90 ksi. With the specified resistance factor $\phi = 0.75$, this gives a design force of $0.75 \times 90 \times 0.442 = 29.8$ kips for $\frac{3}{4}$-in bolts. The moment M_u calculated above was based on the installation tension of 28 kips.

8-8 COMBINED TENSION AND SHEAR

Many connections support loads which produce both tension and shear on the fasteners. Tests indicate that the shearing strength of hot-driven rivets is 0.75 times their tensile strength.[5] The tests show that the ultimate strength under combined tension and shear is given closely by

$$\left(\frac{f_v}{0.75F_u}\right)^2 + \left(\frac{f_t}{F_u}\right)^2 = 1 \tag{8-6a}$$

Tests on high-strength bolts subjected to shear and tension show that their ultimate strength may also be approximated by ellipses.[6] For A325 bolts with a single shear plane through the shank, the equation is

$$\left(\frac{f_v}{0.83F_u}\right)^2 + \left(\frac{f_t}{F_u}\right)^2 = 1 \tag{8-6b}$$

For A325 bolts with shear planes through the threads, the equation is

$$\left(\frac{f_v}{0.64F_u}\right)^2 + \left(\frac{f_t}{F_u}\right)^2 = 1 \tag{8-6c}$$

where f_v, f_t are, respectively, simultaneous shearing stress and tensile stress at failure, based on nominal area, and F_u is the tensile strength of fastener subjected only to tension, based on nominal area.

Equations (8-6) can be written in the form

$$f_t = (F_u^2 - Cf_v^2)^{0.5}$$

The Research Council on Structural Connections recommends equations of this type for A325 and A490 bolts, as follows.

Load factor design ($\phi = 0.75$)
A325 bolts:

Threads excluded $\qquad\qquad f_t = (90^2 - 2.25f_v^2)^{0.5}$
Threads not excluded $\qquad f_t = (90^2 - 3.52f_v^2)^{0.5}$

A490 bolts:

Threads excluded $\qquad\qquad f_t = (113^2 - 2.27f_v^2)^{0.5}$
Threads not excluded $\qquad f_t = (113^2 - 3.54f_v^2)^{0.5}$

Allowable-stress design
A325 bolts:

Threads excluded $\qquad\qquad f_t = (44^2 - 2.15f_v^2)^{0.5}$
Threads not excluded $\qquad f_t = (44^2 - 4.39f_v^2)^{0.5}$

A490 bolts:

Threads excluded $\qquad\qquad f_t = (54^2 - 1.82f_v^2)^{0.5}$
Threads not excluded $\qquad f_t = (54^2 - 3.72f_v^2)^{0.5}$

The RCSC requires the use of these values of f_t in bearing connections in which the applied shear force is greater than one-third the full design shear strength; otherwise $f_t = F_t$.

From Fig. 8-13 it is observed that the ellipse can be approximated by three straight lines. The inclined line yields the equation

$$F_t = C - C_1 f_v \qquad\qquad (8\text{-}7)$$

where f_v is the calculated shear stress (not to exceed F_v). Formulas of this type were used for many years in the AISC/ASD specification. They are still used in

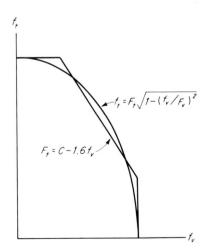

FIGURE 8-13

TABLE 8-1

AISC/ASD allowable fastener tension and shear on unthreaded nominal area—bearing-type connections

Fastener type	Tension F_t, ksi	Shear F_v, ksi	Combined tension and shear F_t, ksi*
A502 Grade 1 rivet	23	17.5	$30 - 1.3f_v \le 23$
A502 Grade 2 rivet	29	22	$38 - 1.2f_v \le 29$
A307 bolt	20	10	$26 - 1.8f_v \le 20$
A325 bolt:			
Threads excluded	44	30	$\sqrt{44^2 - 2.15f_v^2}$
Threads not excluded	44	21	$\sqrt{44^2 - 4.39f_v^2}$
A490 bolt:			
Threads excluded	54	40	$\sqrt{54^2 - 1.82f_v^2}$
Threads not excluded	54	28	$\sqrt{54^2 - 3.75f_v^2}$
Threaded parts and A449 bolts over $1\frac{1}{2}$-in diameter:			
Threads excluded	$0.33F_u$†	$0.22F_u$	$0.43F_u - 1.4f_v \le 0.33F_u$
Threads not excluded	$0.33F_u$†	$0.17F_u$	$0.43F_u - 1.8f_v \le 0.33F_u$

* When allowable stresses are increased for wind or seismic loads, the constants in these formulas shall be increased by $\frac{1}{3}$, but the coefficients of f_v shall not be changed.

† The capacity of the threaded portion of an upset rod, based upon its cross-sectional area at its major thread diameter, shall be larger than $0.6F_y$ times the nominal body area before upsetting.

TABLE 8-2

AISC/LRFD fastener tension and shear on unthreaded nominal area—bearing-type connections

Fastener type	Tension F_t, ksi*	Shear F_v, ksi†	Combined tension and shear F_t, ksi*
A502 Grade 1 rivet	45	25	$59 - 1.8f_v \le 45$
A502 Grade 2 rivet	60	33	$78 - 1.8f_v \le 60$
A307 bolt	45	24	$59 - 1.9f_v \le 45$
A325 bolt:			
Threads excluded	90	60	$117 - 1.5f_v \le 90$
Threads not excluded	90	48	$117 - 1.9f_v \le 90$
A490 bolt:			
Threads excluded	113	75	$147 - 1.5f_v \le 113$
Threads not excluded	113	60	$147 - 1.9f_v \le 113$
Threaded parts and A449 bolts over $1\frac{1}{2}$-in diameter:			
Threads excluded	$0.75F_u$‡	$0.40F_u$	$0.98F_u - 1.5f_v \le 0.75F_u$
Threads not excluded	$0.75F_u$‡	$0.50F_u$	$0.98F_u - 1.9f_v \le 0.75F_u$

* Values of F_t are nominal strengths and must be multiplied by $\phi = 0.75$ to obtain design strength.

† Values of F_v are nominal strengths and must be multiplied by $\phi = 0.75$ to obtain design strength.

‡ The nominal strength of the threaded portion of an upet rod, based upon its cross-sectional area at its major thread diameter, shall be larger than F_y times the nominal body area before upsetting.

the ASD and LRFD specifications for some fasteners but have been replaced by RCSC formulas for others. The authors think this is overly conservative in some cases. Table 8-1 gives ASD allowable stresses, while Table 8-2 gives LRFD values for fasteners in bearing-type connections.

For bolts under combined tension and shear in slip-critical connections the AISC/ASD and AISC/LRFD specify the allowable shear stresses

$$
F_v = \begin{cases} 17\left(1 - \dfrac{f_t A_b}{T_b}\right) & \text{for A325 bolts} \qquad (8\text{-}8a) \\[4mm] 21\left(1 - \dfrac{f_t A_b}{T_b}\right) & \text{for A490 bolts} \qquad (8\text{-}8b) \end{cases}
$$

where f_t is the tensile stress due to applied load and T_b the specified installation tension load of bolt. Values of T_b are given in Table 2-7.

Example 8-8-1 (AISC/ASD). Determine the number of $\frac{3}{4}$-in A325 bolts needed for the bracket shown in Fig. 8-14. The 90-kip load is 22 kips *DL* and 68 kips *LL* and acts at an angle of 50° from the horizontal.

Solution. If it is a bearing-type connection, with threads excluded from the shear plane, the allowable shear per bolt is $30 \times 0.442 = 13.26$ kips. The number of bolts required to resist the shear component of the 90-kip load is

$$
n = \frac{90 \cos 40°}{13.26} = \frac{90 \times 0.766}{13.26} = 5.2
$$

Assume three bolts per row. The shear stress on each bolt is

$$
f_v = \frac{90 \times 0.766}{6 \times 0.442} = 26.0 \text{ ksi}
$$

The tensile stress on each bolt is

$$
f_t = \frac{90 \cos 50°}{6 \times 0.442} = \frac{90 \times 0.643}{6 \times 0.442} = 21.8 \text{ ksi}
$$

From Table 8-1

$$
F_t = \sqrt{44^2 - 2.15 \times 26.0^2} = 22.0 \text{ ksi} > 21.8 \text{ ksi}
$$

The number of bolts is sufficient.

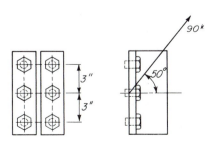

FIGURE 8-14

If the bracket is designed as a slip-critical connection, the number of bolts required is

$$n = \frac{90 \times 0.766}{17 \times 0.442} = 9.2$$

Since this number is an underestimate, we will assume six bolts per row. The tensile stress on each bolt is

$$f_t = \frac{90 \times 0.643}{12 \times 0.442} = 10.9 \text{ ksi}$$

From Eq. (8-8a), the simultaneous allowable shear stress is

$$F_v = 17\left(1 - \frac{10.9 \times 0.442}{28}\right) = 14.1 \text{ ksi}$$

The actual shear stress is

$$f_v = \frac{90 \times 0.766}{12 \times 0.442} = 13.0 < 14.1 \text{ ksi}$$

Therefore a connection with 12 bolts is adequate.

The effect of prying forces, which are discussed in Art. 8-10, has been neglected in this example.

Example 8-8-2 (AISC/LRFD). Determine the number of $\frac{3}{4}$-in A325 bolts needed for the bracket shown in Fig. 8-14. The 90-kip load is 22 kips *DL* and 68 kips *LL* and acts at an angle of 50° from the horizontal.

Solution. The required capacity is

$$P = 1.2 \, DL + 1.6 \, LL = 1.2 \times 22 + 1.6 \times 68 = 135.2 \text{ kips}$$

If it is a bearing-type connection, with threads excluded from the shear plane, the capacity per bolt is $\phi A_b F_{vu} = 0.75 \times 0.442 \times 60 = 19.89$ kips. The number of bolts required to resist the shear component of the 135.2-kip load is

$$n = \frac{135.2 \cos 40°}{19.89} = \frac{135.2 \times 0.766}{19.89} = 5.2$$

Assume three bolts per row. The shear stress on each bolt is

$$f_v = \frac{135.2 \times 0.766}{6 \times 0.442} = 39.1 \text{ ksi} < 0.75 \times 60 = 45.0$$

The tensile stress on each bolt is

$$f_t = \frac{135.2 \cos 50°}{6 \times 0.442} = \frac{135.2 \times 0.643}{6 \times 0.442} = 32.8 \text{ ksi}$$

From Table 8-2,

$$F_t = 117 - 1.5 \times 39.1 = 58.4 \text{ ksi}$$

$$\phi F_t = 0.75 \times 58.4 = 43.8 \text{ ksi} > 32.8$$

Therefore, two lines of three bolts are satisfactory.

The RCSC equation yields

$$f_t = \sqrt{90^2 - 2.25 \times 39.1} = 68.3 \text{ ksi}$$

With $\phi = 0.75$, $F_t = 0.75 \times 68.3 = 51.2$ ksi > 32.8; the connection with two lines of three bolts is sufficient.

If the bracket is designed as a slip-critical connection, the procedure is identical to that presented in Example 8-8-1, since friction connections must be checked for strength for the factored loads and for adequate resistance against slip for the service loads.

The effect of prying forces, which are discussed in Art. 8-10, has been neglected in this example.

8-9 MOMENT-RESISTANT CONNECTIONS WITH FASTENERS IN TENSION

Many connections must be designed to develop moment because the beams they support are parts of a rigid frame. For example, beams which are parts of the wind-bracing system of a tier building must resist end moments resulting from both wind forces and gravity loads. In the usual case, moment resistance of bolted or riveted connections in such frameworks depends upon tension in the fasteners.

The simplest connection of this type, which is satisfactory for small moments, is illustrated in Fig. 8-15a. On the assumption that they are unlikely to resist their proportional share of the end shear because of the flexibility of the outstanding leg of the flange angle, the fasteners in this connection which connect the angles at the flanges to the column are usually designed for their allowable value in tension, no consideration being given to a reduction because of accompanying shear. Except for the relatively small contribution of the web angles, the resisting moment of the connection is limited by the number of fasteners it is possible to put in the vertical legs of the angles at the flanges. For reasons which follow, this number should probably not exceed two. If the column flange is wide enough to accommodate four fasteners in a single gage line on the angle, the innermost fasteners may take a disproportionate share of the load (Fig. 8-16a). The same argument applies if two fasteners are used in each of two gage lines, as in Fig. 8-16b. The actual distribution of the fastener tensions is obviously a function of the stiffnesses of the angle and of the flanges of the beam and the column.

Figure 8-15b illustrates a connection in which tees connect the beam flanges to the column. This is sometimes called a *T-stub connection*. Again, the moment resisted by the web angles is relatively small and is usually neglected, in which case the fasteners connecting these angles are designed to carry only the end shear. The end moment is then assumed to be resisted by a couple furnished by the tees. The framing angles may be omitted if the fasteners in the T-stubs are adequate for both moment and shear. A seat may be used instead of framing angles (Fig. 8-15c).

Figure 8-15d shows a modification of the T-stub connection which may be

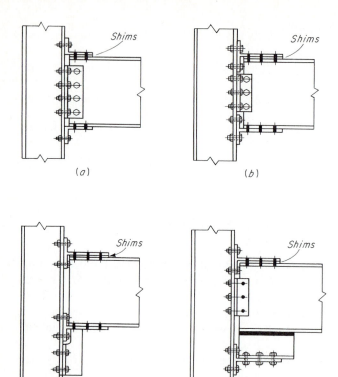

FIGURE 8-15

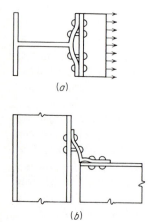

FIGURE 8-16

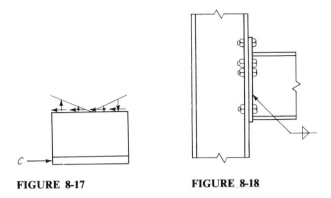

FIGURE 8-17   **FIGURE 8-18**

used if the end moment produces a pull greater than the value of four fasteners in tension. A tee is shop-welded to the bottom flange of the beam, as shown in the figure. The forces acting on the tee are shown in Fig. 8-17. The couple formed by C and the shearing forces in the welds is assumed to be resisted by bending stresses in the welds. The shear stress should also be checked.

Moment-resistant connections can also be made by using an end plate which is shop-welded to the beam (Fig. 8-18). Tests on such connections are reported in Ref. 2, where for the bolt arrangement of Fig. 8-18 it was suggested that the bolts and a portion of the end plate symmetrical about the tension flange be analyzed in the same way as for a T-stub connection. The flanges of the beam can be groove-welded or fillet-welded to the plate. The web will usually be fillet-welded. The design and analysis of an end-plate connection are illustrated in the AISC Manuals.

The parts of the connections shown in Fig. 8-15 which are attached in the fabricating shop are usually welded, rather than bolted or riveted.

8-10 PRYING FORCES IN MOMENT-RESISTANT CONNECTIONS

In Art. 8-6 we discussed initial tension in the fasteners of a connection and the resulting contact pressure between the connected parts. In this article we discuss the effect of flexibility of the connected parts. Figure 8-19 shows T-stubs which were connected with four A325 bolts to a thick plate and tested in tension.[2] In each case, failure resulted from fracture of one or more of the bolts. It will be noted that there was considerable bending of the relatively thin flange of the specimen at the left and virtually none in the thick flange of the specimen at the right. In the latter case, the analysis of Art. 8-6 could be used to determine the relationship between bolt tension and applied load. Of course, an assumption would have to be made as to the effective area over which the contact pressure is distributed.

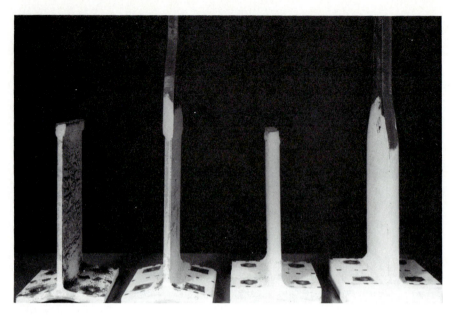

FIGURE 8-19
T-stubs tested in tension. (*From Ref. 2.*)

Behavior of the more flexible flange is shown in Fig. 8-20. The unloaded tee is shown in *a*, with the initial tensions T_0 and the equal compressive forces C_0. The latter are distributed nonuniformly over a relatively small area of contact. Figure 8-20*b* shows the tee acted upon by a force $2P$. The bolt tension is now T. The reduced compressive force, denoted by Q, has migrated toward the flange tip. This behavior has been studied in detail by a finite-element analysis of a T-stub connection, where it was found that Q may eventually be so distributed as to be virtually concentrated at the flange tip if the flange is fairly flexible.[7]

The compressive force Q is usually called a *prying force*. An approximate analysis can be made by assuming it to be concentrated at the flange tip (Fig.

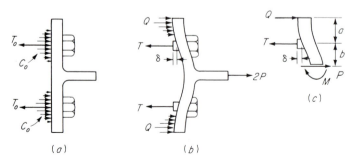

FIGURE 8-20

8-20c). The procedure followed in Art. 8-6 can then be used; i.e., the deflection δ of the flange can be equated to bolt elongation to get the relationship between the bolt tension and the applied load. Assuming the flange to remain elastic, δ is easily computed. The following equation was obtained by making some adjustments in the resulting formula for the prying force Q to simplify it and to bring it into better agreement with test results:[2]

$$\frac{Q}{P} = \frac{15ab^2 A_b - wt^4}{10a^2(a + 3b)A_b + 5wt^4} \tag{8-9}$$

where A_b = area of bolt
$\quad\quad\ w$ = length of flange tributary to bolt
$\quad\quad\ t$ = thickness of flange
$\quad a, b$ = dimensions shown in Fig. 8-20c

[Equation (8-9) is written in a form different from that in Ref. 2.]

The solution to this problem is somewhat simpler if we assume that the ultimate load is reached with the development of a plastic hinge at the junction of the flange and web; that is, $M = M_p$ in Fig. 8-20c. In this case, we have two equations of equilibrium

$$P + Q = T \tag{a}$$

$$Pb - Qa = M_p \tag{b}$$

Dividing Eq. (a) by Eq. (b) and solving the result for Q/P gives

$$\frac{Q}{P} = \frac{b - M_p/T}{a + M_p/T} \tag{c}$$

But $M_p = F_y wt^2/4$. Then, with the bolt tension at ultimate load $T_u = F_u A_b$, M_p/T in Eq. (c) becomes

$$\frac{M_p}{T} = \frac{F_y wt^2}{4} \frac{1}{F_u A_b} = \frac{F_y}{F_u} \frac{wt^2}{\pi d^2} = \beta \frac{wt^2}{d^2}$$

where d is the diameter of the bolt. Substituting this result into Eq. (c) gives[7]

$$\frac{Q}{P} = \frac{bd^2 - \beta wt^2}{ad^2 + \beta wt^2} \tag{d}$$

If the bolt fractured at or after the formation of the plastic hinge in the flange, β would be known and the prying force Q could be determined from Eq. (d). However, the finite-element analysis in Ref. 7 showed that while a substantial amount of yielding had developed in most cases, the plastic hinge was completely formed in only a few of the connections when the bolt failed. Therefore, the coefficients of the terms in Eq. (*d*) were adjusted to give better agreement with the analysis and with tests, as follows:

Connections with A325 bolts:

$$\frac{Q}{P} = \frac{100bd^2 - 18wt^2}{70ad^2 + 21wt^2}$$

(8-10*a*)

Connections with A490 bolts:

$$\frac{Q}{P} = \frac{100bd^2 - 14wt^2}{62ad^2 + 21wt^2}$$

(8-10*b*)

Figure 8-21 compares the predictions of these equations with results of the finite-element analyses and of tests. The agreement is good. In general, values of *Q* by the approximate formulas are larger than those of the tests and values by the analysis. This is conservative, since the bolt tension *T* is increased by the increase in *Q*.

According to Ref. 7, if the dimension *a* in Fig. 8-20*c* exceeds 2*t*, the value 2*t* should be used for *a* in Eqs. (8-10). Furthermore, the flange should be analyzed for bending at the bolt line and at a section $\frac{1}{16}$ in from the face of the web.

A procedure developed by Struik[8] relates the moment at the interface between the web and the flange to the moment at the bolt line. The ratio of the net area at the bolt line to the gross area at the face of the web is taken into account. The limiting moment capacity is taken as the fully plastic moment for a rectangular cross section. A comparison with experimental data indicated that this analysis overestimates the prying force.

The procedure presented by Struik was modified by Fisher.[9] The location of the force in the bolt was taken at the edge of the bolt nearest the web instead of at the bolt centerline. Thus, in Fig. 8-20*c*, *a* is increased by *d*/2 and *b* is

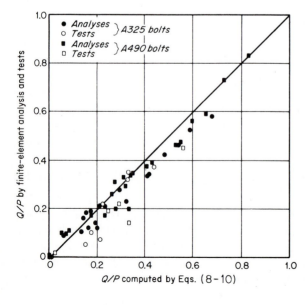

FIGURE 8-21
Prying force *Q* in T-stub connections. (*From Ref. 7.*)

decreased by $d/2$. However, the value of a is limited to $1.25b$. Details are presented in the AISC Manuals.

The proportioning of a T-stub connection must be by trial because the ratio of the prying force Q to the applied load P depends on the dimensions of the connection. The procedure is illustrated in DP8-10-1 and DP8-10-2.

DP8-10-1 (AISC/ASD) and DP8-10-2 (AISC/LRFD): T-Stub Moment Connection

A T-stub moment connection for a beam which supports both gravity and wind loads is designed in these examples. The following comments are intended to clarify computations identified by the corresponding letters on the design sheets and apply to both examples except where noted otherwise.

a. **ASD.** For loads due to wind alone or to combinations of wind and other loads, allowable stresses may be increased by one-third. Since this is equivalent to designing for three-fourths of the sum of dead load, live load, and wind load at the normal allowable stresses, we may tabulate $DL + LL$ and $\frac{3}{4}(DL + LL + WL)$ and design for the larger of these two combinations, using the normal allowable stress.

LRFD. Using the specified load factors, we tabulate $1.2\ DL + 1.6\ LL$ and $1.2\ DL + 0.5\ LL + 1.3\ WL$ and design for the larger value.

b. The connection is bearing-type, with threads excluded from the shear planes.

c. The force P on the T-stub is determined by dividing the end moment on the beam by the beam depth.

d. An estimate of the prying force must be made in order to determine the first-trial bolt size.

e. The tee used here is cut from the S24 $\times$ 106. Although a smaller tee is able to accommodate the four bolts connecting it to the flange of the beam, the section is chosen because of the additional flange thickness. A table* in the AISC Manuals facilitates the selection of the tee by giving an estimate of the required thickness in terms of the force per inch and the moment arm b of the bolt line. In this example, the length of the tee is $8\frac{1}{2}$ in, so the force is $62/8.5 = 7.29$ kli. With the $4\frac{1}{2}$-in gage shown, b will be about 2 in, in which case the AISC table shows that a $\frac{7}{8}$-in thickness is needed. The tee chosen has an average thickness $t_f = 1.09$ in.

f. The length of the tee flange tributary to each bolt is the total width of the section shared by two bolts. The authors use the designation w for this dimension. The AISC Manuals use p.

---

* See 9th ed. AISC/ASD, p. 4-89, or 1st ed. AISC/LRFD, p. 5-119.

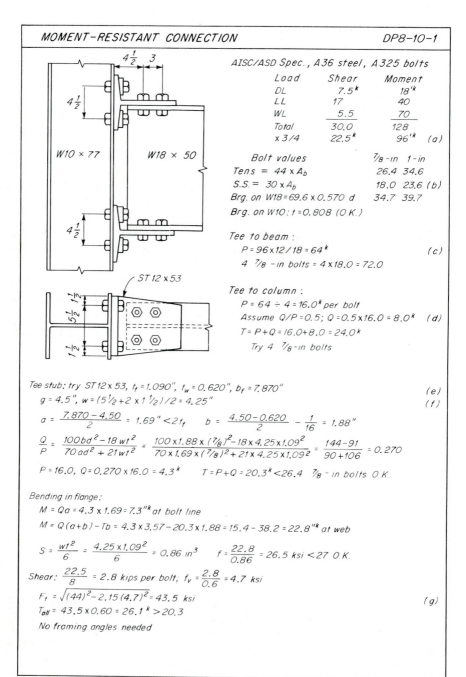

MOMENT-RESISTANT CONNECTION   *DP8-10-1*

AISC/ASD Spec., A36 steel, A325 bolts

Load	Shear	Moment
DL	7.5^k	$18^{'k}$
LL	17	40
WL	5.5	70
Total	30.0	128
× 3/4	22.5^k	$96^{'k}$ (a)

Bolt values $7/8$-in   1-in

Tens = $44 \times A_b$ 26.4   34.6

S.S.= $30 \times A_b$ 18.0   23.6 (b)

Brg. on W18 = $69.6 \times 0.570\,d$ 34.7   39.7

Brg. on W10: $t = 0.808$ (O.K.)

Tee to beam:
$$P = 96 \times 12 / 18 = 64^k \qquad (c)$$
$$4\ 7/8\text{-in bolts} = 4 \times 18.0 = 72.0$$

Tee to column:
$$P = 64 \div 4 = 16.0^k \text{ per bolt}$$
$$\text{Assume } Q/P = 0.5;\ Q = 0.5 \times 16.0 = 8.0^k \qquad (d)$$
$$T = P + Q = 16.0 + 8.0 = 24.0^k$$
$$\text{Try } 4\ 7/8\text{-in bolts}$$

Tee stub: try ST 12 × 53, $t_f = 1.090''$, $t_w = 0.620''$, $b_f = 7.870''$ (e)

$g = 4.5''$, $w = (5\,1/2 + 2 \times 1\,1/2)/2 = 4.25''$ (f)

$$a = \frac{7.870 - 4.50}{2} = 1.69'' < 2t_f \qquad b = \frac{4.50 - 0.620}{2} - \frac{1}{16} = 1.88''$$

$$\frac{Q}{P} = \frac{100bd^2 - 18\,wt^2}{70\,ad^2 + 21\,wt^2} = \frac{100 \times 1.88 \times (7/8)^2 - 18 \times 4.25 \times 1.09^2}{70 \times 1.69 \times (7/8)^2 + 21 \times 4.25 \times 1.09^2} = \frac{144 - 91}{90 + 106} = 0.270$$

$P = 16.0$, $Q = 0.270 \times 16.0 = 4.3^k$ $T = P + Q = 20.3^k < 26.4$ $7/8$-in bolts O.K.

Bending in flange:

$M = Qa = 4.3 \times 1.69 = 7.3^{''k}$ at bolt line

$M = Q(a + b) - Tb = 4.3 \times 3.57 - 20.3 \times 1.88 = 15.4 - 38.2 = 22.8^{''k}$ at web

$$S = \frac{wt^2}{6} = \frac{4.25 \times 1.09^2}{6} = 0.86\ in^3 \qquad f = \frac{22.8}{0.86} = 26.5\ ksi < 27\ O.K.$$

Shear: $\dfrac{22.5}{8} = 2.8$ kips per bolt; $f_v = \dfrac{2.8}{0.6} = 4.7$ ksi

$F_t = \sqrt{(44)^2 - 2.15\,(4.7)^2} = 43.5$ ksi   (g)

$T_{all} = 43.5 \times 0.60 = 26.1^k > 20.3$

No framing angles needed

MOMENT-RESISTANT CONNECTION

DP8-10-2

AISC/LRFD Spec., A36 steel, A325 bolts

Load	Shear	Moment
DL	7.5^k	$18'^k$
LL	17	40
WL	5.5	70
1.2 DL+1.6 LL	36.2	85.6
1.2 DL+1.3 W+0.5 LL	24.7	132.6 (a)

$W10 \times 77$ $W18 \times 50$

Bolt values $3/4$-in $7/8$-in

Tens $0.75 \times 90 \times A_b$ 29.8 40.6

Shear $0.75 \times 60 \times A_b$ 19.9 27.1 (b)

Brg: $F_p = 2.4\ F_u$, $\phi = 0.75$

W18: $0.75 \times 2.4 \times 58 \times d \times 0.570 = 44.6$ 52.1

W10: $t = 0.808$ (O.K.)

Tee to beam:

$\quad P = 132.6 \times 12/18 = 88.4^k$ (c)

$\quad 4\ 7/8$-in bolts $= 4 \times 27.1 = 108.4^k$

ST 12×53

Tee to column:

$\quad P = 88.4/4 = 22.1^k/bolt$

$\quad$ Assume $Q/P = 0.5$; $Q = 0.5 \times 22.1 = 11.1$ (d)

$\quad T = P+Q = 22.1+11.1 = 33.3^k$

$\quad$ Try $4 - 7/8$-in bolts

Tee stub try ST12 × 53, $t_f = 1.090''$, $t_w = 0.620''$, $b_f = 7.870''$ (e)

$g = 4.5''$, $w = (5^1/_2 + 2 \times 1^1/_2)/2 = 4.25''$ (f)

$a = \dfrac{7.870 - 4.50}{2} = 1.69'' < 2t_f \qquad b = \dfrac{4.50 - 0.620}{2} - \dfrac{1}{16} = 1.88''$

$\dfrac{Q}{P} = \dfrac{100bd^2 - 18\,wt^2}{70\,ad^2 + 21\,wt^2} = \dfrac{100 \times 1.88 \times (7/8)^2 - 18 \times 4.25 \times 1.09^2}{70 \times 1.69 \times (7/8)^2 + 21 \times 4.25 \times 1.09^2} = \dfrac{144 - 91}{90 + 106} = 0.270$

$P = 22.1^k$, $Q = 0.27 \times 22.1 = 5.97^k \qquad T = P+Q = 28.1^k < 40.6$ O.K.

Bending in flange:

$M = Qa = 5.97 \times 1.69 = 10.09''^k$ at bolt line

$M = Q(a+b) - Tb = 5.97 \times 3.57 - 28.1 \times 1.88 = 21.3 - 52.8 = 31.5''^k$ at web

$\phi M_n = 0.9\ \dfrac{wt^2}{4}\ F_y = 0.9 \times \dfrac{4.25 \times (1.09)^2}{4} \times 36 = 40.9''^k > 31.5$ O.K.

Shear: $36.2/8 = 4.53$ kips per bolt $\qquad f_v = \dfrac{4.53}{0.601} = 7.54$ ksi

$F_t = 117 - 1.5\ f_v = 117 - 1.5 \times 7.54 = 105.7$ ksi $> 90 \quad \phi F_t = 0.75 \times 90 = 68$ (g)

$T_{all} = 68 \times 0.6013 = 40.9^k > 28.1$ O.K.

No framing angles needed

g. The shear force per bolt turns out to be small enough to permit an allowable bolt tension which is adequate. Therefore, framing angles are not needed to provide a shear connection.

The $4\frac{1}{2}$-in gage in the flange of the tee is not large enough to give the clearance, relative to the bolts in the stem of the tee, to allow the bolts in the flange to be tightened with an impact wrench. They can be tightened with a spud wrench, howevever. Connections of this type can be made with the T-stub web shop-welded to the beam. This would allow the impact wrench to be used with the bolts at $4\frac{1}{2}$ in.

8-11   RIVETS AND A307 BOLTS IN TENSION

Hot-driven rivets develop tension upon cooling, as mentioned in Art. 8-6, which may be of a high order of magnitude. This suggests that the behavior of hot-driven riveted connections in tension can be expected to be about the same as that of high-strength bolted connections in tension. A series of 28 tests on T-stub connections with $\frac{3}{4}$-in A325 bolts and identical specimens with $\frac{3}{4}$-in A502 Grade 1 rivets showed that this is indeed the case.[10] Each specimen consisted of two T-stubs connected through the flanges, so it was similar to the bolted specimen discussed in Art. 8-9. The efficiencies of the bolted connections and their riveted counterparts were almost identical in spite of the fact that the separation of the riveted stubs was considerably greater than that of the bolted stubs because of the greater ductility of the rivets. (Efficiency was defined as the ratio of the test load to the sum of the strength of the individual fasteners in the connection.) Nevertheless, it does not follow that Eqs. (8-9) and (8-10) can be used to determine prying forces in hot-riveted connections, because there was some adjustment of the coefficients of the terms of both equations to bring the predicted values into better agreement with the results of tests on high-strength bolted connections. Therefore, in connections in which rivets will be subjected to calculated tension, some attention should be given to proportioning to control prying, e.g., by using relatively thick connection angles, T-stubs, and the like, or else by computing prying forces conservatively.

A307 bolts are rarely used in connections which subject them to calculated tension. If they are so used, there may be situations in which prying forces develop even though there may be little or no initial tension in the bolts. However, any such prying forces are likely to be small. Furthermore, no design information concerning them is available.

8-12   ANGLES IN MOMENT-RESISTANT CONNECTIONS

Proportioning of the angles in connections such as that of Fig. 8-15a can be based on an analysis similar to that of the T-stub. Deformation of such an angle

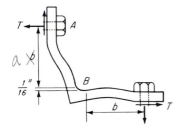

FIGURE 8-22

is shown in Fig. 8-22. If the fasteners are high-strength bolts, Eqs. (8-10) can be used to approximate the prying force, and the bolt tension and bending moments in the angle evaluated as in Art. 8-10. If rivets or A307 bolts are used and prying forces are neglected, analysis based on linearly elastic behavior, assuming complete rotational restraint at the fastener lines, give $M_A = 0.6Tb$ and $M_B = 0.4Tb$. However, if plastic hinges develop at A and B, the moments are equal and $M_A = M_B = 0.5Tb$. It would seem reasonable to take the section at B for this case at the same position as for the T-stub, as shown in the figure.

The design of a moment connection using angles instead of tees is presented in Examples 8-12-1 and 8-12-2. Such connections can be used where moments are small. However, they are classed as semirigid or partially restrained connections (Art. 8-15).

Example 8-12-1 (AISC/ASD). Design a connection of the type shown in Fig. 8-23. The beam section is a W12 × 35 and the column section a W8 × 35. Use A36 steel and $\frac{3}{4}$-in A325 bolts, threads not excluded. The end moment is 15 ft·kips *DL* and 40 ft·kips *LL*, and the end shear is 5 kips *DL* and 12 kips *LL*. As was noted in Art. 8-9, reduction in allowable bolt tension because of shear is usually neglected in connections of this type.

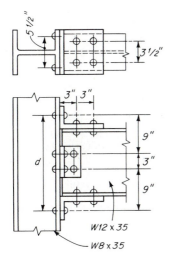

FIGURE 8-23

The properties of the sections are

W12 × 35: $d = 12.5$ $t_f = 0.520$ $t_w = 0.300$

W8 × 35: $d = 8.12$ $t_f = 0.495$ $t_w = 0.310$

Solution. Allowable stress on bolts is

$$F_t = 44.0 \text{ ksi} \qquad F_v = 21.0 \text{ ksi}$$

Allowable bearing is

$$F_p = 1.2F_u = 1.2 \times 58 = 69.6 \text{ ksi}$$

Bolt values are:

Single shear $R_v = 0.442 \times 21.0 = 9.3 \text{ kips}$
Double shear $R_v = 18.6 \text{ kips}$
Bearing, beam web $R_p = 69.6 \times \frac{3}{4} \times 0.300 = 15.7 \text{ kips}$
Bearing, beam flange $R_p = 69.6 \times \frac{3}{4} \times 0.520 = 27.1 \text{ kips}$
Tension $R_t = 0.442 \times 44.0 = 19.4 \text{ kips}$

$$d = \frac{M}{2T} = \frac{55 \times 12}{2 \times 19.4} = 17.0 \text{ in} \qquad \text{Use 18 in}$$

With $d = 18$ in

$$T = \frac{M}{d} = \frac{55 \times 12}{18} = 36.7 \text{ kips}$$

Gage on top angle $= \frac{1}{2}(18 - 12.50) = 2.75$ Use 4-in leg

Beam-flange connection

$$\text{Bolts to beam flange} = \frac{36.7}{9.3} = 3.9 \qquad \text{Use 4}$$

Try 8 × 4 × 1 angle:

$$a = 2.75 - 1 - \tfrac{1}{16} = 1.69$$

$$M = 0.5 \times 36.7 \times 1.69 = 31.0 \text{ in·kips}$$

$$b = \frac{6 \times 31.0}{27 \times 1^2} = 6.9$$

Use 8 × 4 × 1 × 8 angle to accommodate 5½-in gage in column flange.

Web connection. For two angles, 4 × 3½ × $\frac{3}{8}$ × 5½.

Double-shear value of 18.6 kips is greater than the value for bearing on the web, 15.7 kips, and therefore bearing controls.

$$R = 2 \times 15.7 = 31.4 \text{ kips} > 17 \text{ kips end reaction}$$

The bolts which connect the web angle to the column are in single shear, so $R_v = 7.7$ kips.

$$R = 4 \times 9.3 = 37.2 \text{ kips} > 17$$

Example 8-12-2 (AISC/LRFD). Design a connection of the type shown in Fig. 8-23. The beam section is a W12 × 35 and the column section is a W8 × 35. Use A36 steel and $\frac{3}{4}$-in A325 bolts, threads not excluded. The end moment is 15 ft·kips *DL* and 40 ft·kips *LL*, and the end shear is 5 kips *DL* and 12 kips *LL*. As was noted in Art. 8-9, reduction in allowable bolt tension because of shear is usually neglected in connections of this type.

The properties of the sections are

W12 × 35: $d = 12.5$ $t_f = 0.520$ $t_w = 0.300$

W8 × 35: $d = 8.12$ $t_f = 0.495$ $t_w = 0.310$

Solution. Design requirements are

$$M = 1.2 \times 15 + 1.6 \times 40 = 82.0 \text{ ft·kips}$$

$$R = 1.2 \times 5 + 1.6 \times 12 = 25.2 \text{ kips}$$

Nominal strength of bolts is

$$F_t = 90.0 \text{ ksi} \qquad \phi = 0.75$$

$$F_v = 48.0 \text{ ksi} \qquad \phi = 0.75$$

Nominal bearing is

$$F_p = 2.4 F_u = 139.2 \text{ ksi} \qquad \phi = 0.75$$

Bolt values are:

Single shear $R_v = 0.75 \times 0.442 \times 48.0 = 15.9$ kips
Double shear $R_v = 31.8$ kips
Bearing, beam web $R_p = 0.75 \times 139.2 \times \frac{3}{4} \times 0.300 = 23.5$ kips
Bearing, beam flange $R_p = 0.75 \times 139.2 \times \frac{3}{4} \times 0.520 = 40.7$ kips
Tension $R_t = 0.75 \times 90.0 \times 0.44 = 29.8$ kips

$$d = \frac{M}{2T} = \frac{82.0 \times 12}{2 \times 29.8} = 16.5 \text{ in} \qquad \text{Use 18}$$

With $d = 18$ in

$$T = \frac{M}{d} = \frac{82.0 \times 12}{18} = 54.7 \text{ kips}$$

Gage on top angle $= \frac{1}{2}(18 - 12.50) = 2.75$ Use 4-in leg

Beam-flange connection

$$\text{Bolts to beam flange} = \frac{54.7}{15.9} = 3.4 \qquad \text{Use 4}$$

Try 8 × 4 × 1 angle:

$$a = 2.75 - 1 - \tfrac{1}{16} = 1.69$$

$$M = 0.5 \times 54.7 \times 1.69 = 46.2 \text{ in·kips}$$

In the AISC/LRFD specification the nominal moment capacity of a rectangular section is $(bd^2/4)F_y$ to which $\phi = 0.9$ is applied. Therefore,

$$b = \frac{4 \times 46.2}{0.9 \times 36 \times 1^2} = 5.70$$

Use $8 \times 4 \times 1 \times 8$ angle to accommodate $5\frac{1}{2}$-in gage in column flange..

Web connection. For two angles, $4 \times 3\frac{1}{2} \times \frac{3}{8} \times 5\frac{1}{2}$.

Double-shear value of 31.8 kips is greater than the value for bearing on the web, 23.5 kips, and therefore bearing controls.

$$R = 2 \times 23.5 = 47.0 > 25.2$$

The bolts which connect the web angle to the column are in single shear, so $R_v = 15.9$ kips.

$$R = 4 \times 15.9 = 63.6 \text{ kips} > 25.2$$

8-13 TESTS OF CONNECTIONS

The beam connections that have been discussed so far in this chapter fall naturally into two groups: (1) those designed to resist only the end shear of a beam and (2) those designed to resist end moment in addition to shear. But beams are free of end moments only if they have complete freedom of rotation at the supports, and, conversely, they have end moments only if end rotation is prevented either wholly or in part. Since neither the completely free support nor the perfectly fixed one exists in fact, it is important to know how closely a given connection approximates the performance we assign to it for design purposes.

Results of three of a series of tests on the moment-resistant properties of various riveted connections are shown in Fig. 8-24. The three graphs OA, OB, and OC show the relation between the rotation ϕ and the corresponding moment M for the three types of connection shown at the right of the figure, the beam being an S12 × 31.8 in each case. The graphs are only a partial record, since ultimate moments for connections A and C were 403 and 1845 in·kips, respectively. Rotations at the ultimate moment were not reported, nor was the ultimate moment for connection B. It is helpful to interpret these graphs by observing that the moment-rotation graph for a simply supported beam coincides with the axis of ϕ, since M remains zero for any rotation. Similarly, the graph for a perfectly fixed beam coincides with the axis of M, since there is no rotation at any moment. Thus we see that the framing connection A can be classed as fairly flexible, while the T-stub connection C is quite stiff.

It is to be noted that the variation of M with ϕ is curvilinear from the beginning. Although this complicates the problem of determining the moment that will be developed by a particular connection when it is used on a beam whose span and load are given, a simple graphical procedure has been suggested.[11] If the stresses do not exceed the yield point of the material, the rotation at the end of a beam of span L supporting the total uniform load W $(W = wL)$

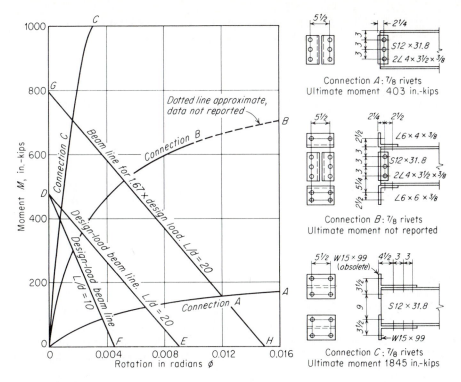

FIGURE 8-24
Comparative rigidity of connections. (*From Ref. 13.*)

and of equal end moments M is given by

$$\phi = \frac{WL^2}{24EI} - \frac{ML}{2EI} \tag{a}$$

But since the values of ϕ and M for the beam must equal the corresponding values for the connection, the intersection of the graph of this equation with that of the connection determines the solution. Furthermore, since Eq. (*a*) is linear in M and ϕ, two points are sufficient to obtain the graph. If $\phi = 0$, then $M = WL/12$, which is the end moment for a beam with built-in ends. Also, if $M = 0$, $\phi = WL^2/24EI$, the end rotation of a simply supported beam. This formula for ϕ can be put into a convenient form by substituting, in turn, M for $WL/8$ and fI/c for M to get, for a simply supported beam,

$$\phi = \frac{2}{3} \frac{f}{E} \frac{L}{d} \tag{b}$$

Thus we see that, for a given stress f, ϕ is directly proportional to the ratio L/d.

As a numerical example, consider the shape used in the tests, namely, the S12 × 31.8, as a beam spanning 20 ft so that $L/d = 20$. If this beam is supported against lateral buckling and is designed on the assumption that its end supports are simple, then, using an allowable bending stress of 20 ksi, $W - 8M/L = 8 \times 20 \times 36.4/240 = 24$ kips. Therefore, $M_F = WL/12 = 24 \times \frac{240}{12} = 480$ in·kips, which, as we have seen, corresponds to $\phi = 0$. Plotting this value on Fig. 8-24, we obtain the point D. Also, from Eq. (b), $\phi = \frac{2}{3}(20/30,000)(20) = 0.0089$ rad, which gives point E on the figure. The straight line connecting D and E, which represents the solution of Eq. (a), intersects the graph of any one of the connections at the point whose coordinates are the end moment and the corresponding end rotation *at the design load* if that connection is used on the beam we have chosen. The line DE is called the *beam line*.

The variation of end moment with the ratio L/d is easily shown. If we consider the S12 × 31.8 on a span of 10 ft so that $L/d = 10$, the allowable load $W = 8M/L$ is double that for the 20-ft span. The fixed-end moment remains the same, however, since $M_F = WL/12$. We have already seen that the end rotation for the simply supported condition is directly proportional to L/d. Thus a straight line from D to the point F midway between O and B gives us the beam line for the S12 × 31.8 on a span of 10 ft.

A significant aspect of the typical moment-rotation graph should be mentioned. Connections unload linearly, parallel to the initial slope of the loading curve. Thus, the unloaded connection retains a permanent deformation. Subsequent loadings and unloadings are elastic in the sense that they follow the original unloading line so long as the initial load is not exceeded. This behavior is analogous to that observed in the simple tension test.

8-14 BEHAVIOR OF STANDARD CONNECTIONS

The information in Fig. 8-24 enables us to determine how closely certain types of connections approximate the assumptions we make for design purposes. For example, we see that the framed-beam connection develops an end moment of about 120 in·kips when it is used on an S12 × 31.8 supporting the uniform load for an allowable stress of 20 ksi and considered as a simple beam spanning 20 ft. This is 25 percent of the end moment required to completely fix the ends of the beam. Of course, this is on the safe side as far as the beam is concerned, since the bending moment at the center is reduced by the amount of the end moment. However, it is clear that it results in uncomputed stresses in the connection itself, since it is standard procedure to design the framed-beam connections for only the end shear, in this case 12 kips. The analysis for a bolt or rivet group resisting torsion indicates that the end fasteners of the line of three connecting the angles to the web must develop a force of 20 kips to resist a moment of 120 in·kips. This combined with the vertical force of 4 kips due to the 12-kip reaction gives a resultant of 20.4 kips. Thus, the uncomputed stress in the connectors which connect the beam to the angles is considerably larger than the computed one. Furthermore, there is tension on the fasteners that connect the angle to the adjacent member which is not considered in the usual procedure for designing such a connection.

Assuming that the beam line *DE* in Fig. 8-24 is based on a factor of safety of 1.67 on yielding of the extreme fiber, the beam line at yielding is *GH* if the beam is simply supported. This line intersects the curve for connection *A* at 160 in·kips. This is only 33 percent greater than the end moment at the design load. Thus the end moment increases at a slower rate than does the moment at the center of the span.

The beam line *DE* intersects the graph for the T-stub connection *C* at the point $\phi = 0.0008$ rad, $M = 430$ in·kips. The latter value is 90 percent of the end moment for a fixed support, and the corresponding rotation is less than 3 min. Thus the uniformly loaded S12 × 31.8 spanning 20 ft is practically end-fixed if connection *C* is used.

8-15 TYPES OF CONSTRUCTION

Compared with connections *A* and *C*, connection *B* of the tests reported in Fig. 8-24 is of intermediate stiffness. It is clear that it should not be assumed to effect a rigid connection between a beam and its supporting member. On the other hand, it is uneconomical to assume it to be a moment-free connection, since it develops a resisting moment large enough to reduce the bending moment at the center well below the simple-beam value $WL/8$.

The two common assumptions as to the behavior of a building frame are (1) that its beams are free to rotate at their connections or (2) that its members are so connected that the angles they make with each other do not change under load. It is obvious that the behavior of a structure which employs connections of intermediate stiffness will be intermediate between these two extremes. Frameworks with connections of intermediate stiffness are commonly called *semirigid frames*. Computer programs which take into consideration the nonlinear characteristics of the joints, in addition to nonlinear effects as a result of yielding and the effects of joint displacement, are available for the analysis of such frames.

The AISC specifications differ somewhat in their classification of types of frames. The ASD specification recognizes the following three basic types:

Type 1: Rigid frame

Type 2: Simple framing

Type 3: Partially restrained (semirigid) framing

The LRFD specification recognizes only two types:

Type FR: Rigid frame

Type PR: Partially restrained. If connection restraint is ignored, the classification is the same as ASD Type 2, otherwise it corresponds to ASD Type 3.

Both specifications require that the connections for partially restrained construction have a dependable known moment capacity.

8-16 WELDED FRAMED BEAM CONNECTIONS

Figure 8-25 shows various ways in which a welded framed beam connection can be made. In *a* the beam web is welded directly to another member, e.g., the flange of a column. The connection can be by groove weld or by two fillet welds. The seat, which may be a plate, as shown, or an angle, is for purposes of erection. Although this is the most direct connection that can be made, it has a number of disadvantages. It requires that the gap between the end of the beam and the adjacent surface be small, otherwise an adequate connection is assured only if the size of the weld is increased. The AISC specifications require that all welded construction be in accordance with all provisions of the *Structural Welding Code,* AWS D1.1, of the American Welding Society. This specification requires that the size of fillet welds be increased by the amount of the separation if it is $\frac{1}{16}$ in or more and that in no event shall the separation exceed $\frac{3}{16}$ in. But the rolling mill allows itself a tolerance of $\pm \frac{3}{8}$ to $\frac{1}{2}$ in or more, depending on the depth and length, on the ordered length of a beam and also considers acceptable an end which may be out of square by not more than $\frac{1}{64}$ in per inch of depth of a shape. Thus a 12-in beam might show a gap which is $\frac{12}{64} = \frac{3}{16}$ in greater at one flange than at the other. These deficiencies can be corrected by flame cutting, but this is an expensive operation. Furthermore, the member to which the beam connects will be subject to tolerances. For example, the depth of a W-shape column may vary $\pm \frac{1}{8}$ in from its specified value. Also, vertical welding in the field is costly and usually should be avoided. Finally, the stiffness of such a connection may be greater than can be tolerated. Line *OC* in Fig. 8-26 shows the results of one test

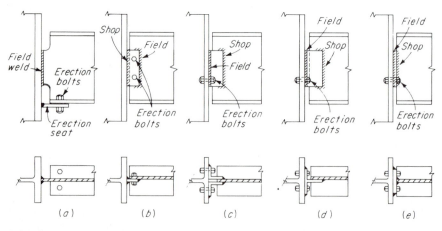

FIGURE 8-25

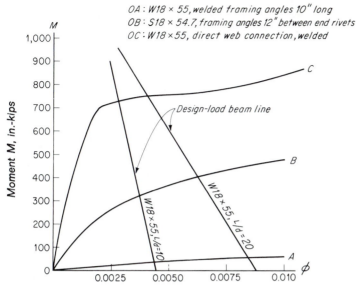

OA : W18 × 55, welded framing angles 10" long
OB : S18 × 54.7, framing angles 12" between end rivets
OC : W18 ×55, direct web connection, welded

Design-load beam line

M

1,000
900
800
700
600
500
400
300
200
100
0

C
B
A

W18×55, L/d=10
W18×55, L/d=20

Moment M, in.-kips

0.0025   0.0050   0.0075   0.010   *φ*

Rotation *φ*, radians

FIGURE 8-26

on a W18 × 55 beam connected by $\frac{1}{2}$-in fillet welds 11 in long, one on each side of the web. Initial yielding of the web at the lower end of the welds was observed at a moment of 360 in·kips. Yielding of the web along the full length of the welds occurred at 660 in·kips, and at 870 in·kips the welds cracked slightly at the top of the connection. It will be noted that for $L/d = 20$ (span 30 ft) the design-load beam line intersects curve OC at 750 in·kips. Since the web yielded full length at 660 in·kips, yielding of the connection could be expected at service loads.

The connection shown in Fig. 8-25b eliminates the problem of fit-up of the connection of Fig. 8-25a. Here, a connection plate shop-welded to the column allows field adjustment for mill tolerances in the length of the beam and depth of the column. Two side plates, one on each side of the web, may also be used instead of the single plate shown. Erection bolts take the place of a seat. This connection does not eliminate the costly vertical welding in the field, however, and is of the same order of stiffness as the connection of Fig. 8-25a. Furthermore, the plates are harder to hold in alignment during welding than angles are.

The framing angles shown in Fig. 8-25c are shop-welded to the beam web and field-welded to the column. This connection also allows for mill tolerance in the length of the beam. To provide flexibility in the connection, the angles are field-welded on the vertical edges, with short returns at the top. The returns are needed to assure a good weld with no crater at the end. The partial moment-rotation curve OA of Fig. 8-26 shows the average of data from tests on two W18 × 55 beams connected by $3\frac{1}{2} \times 2\frac{1}{2} \times \frac{1}{4}$ angles 10 in long, with the $3\frac{1}{2}$-in legs outstanding.[12] The maximum moment attained was 68 in·kips, at a rotation of about 0.03 rad. A comparison of this curve with the curve OB for an S18 × 54.7 connected by $4 \times 3\frac{1}{2} \times \frac{3}{8}$ angles, with $\frac{7}{8}$-in rivets,[13] shows the relative flexibility of the two connections. The design-load beam line for the W18 × 55 on a span of 30 ft indicates that, for this case, the welded connection develops an end moment of about 40 in·kips compared with 400 in·kips for the riveted connection.

The connection shown in Fig. 8-25d is similar to the framing-angle connection and comparable in flexibility. The end-plate connection shown in Fig. 8-25e also gives comparable flexibility and uses less connection material. However, it is more difficult to provide for mill tolerances.

The connections shown in Fig. 8-25c and e can also be bolted to the columns, rather than welded. This has the advantage of eliminating vertical welding in the field.

8-17 DESIGN OF WELDED FRAMED CONNECTIONS

Figure 8-27a shows two framing angles separated from the beam which they support. The beam reaction R is assumed to be shared equally by the two field welds (angle leg to column). The corresponding forces on the shop welds (angle leg to beam web) as they act on the angles and on the web are as shown, their lines of action intersecting the centroids of the shop welds.

If we assume the beam to be simply supported at the face of the outstanding legs of the connection angles, then the field welds can exert no moment in a plane parallel to xz. This leaves on each angle an unbalanced moment $Ra/2$, which we must then assume to be resisted by the shop weld. It is customary to compute the resulting stresses by using the torsion formula $f_v = Tr/J$, even though the formula applies only to circular cross sections. The shearing stress due to torsion must be combined with the shearing stress due to the reaction $R/2$.

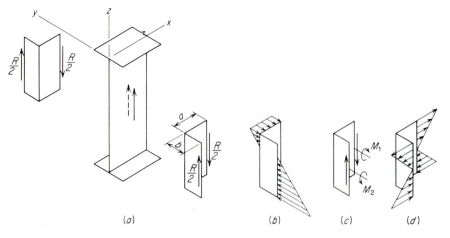

(a) (b) (c) (d)

FIGURE 8-27

There is also on each angle an unbalanced moment $Rb/2$ which tends to produce rotation about an axis parallel to x. Although this moment is undoubtedly shared by the shop weld and the field weld, it is usual practice to assume that it is resisted by the latter. The resisting couple is taken to be in the form of bearing pressures between the angles and the web at the upper ends of the angles and between the field weld and the angles over the remaining length, as is indicated in Fig. 8-27b. The analogy between this situation and that of the angle connected by rivets or bolts suggests that contact between the angles and the web be assumed to extend for about one-sixth the length of the angle. The assumption of linear distribution of stress, as shown in Fig. 8-27b, leads to a simple solution for the maximum bending stress in the weld. This stress is readily combined with the vertical shearing stress due to $R/2$, since the two are at right angles and fillet-weld stresses are assumed to be shearing stresses irrespective of their direction with respect to the cross section through the throat.

For the assumption that the shop welds furnish the couples which balance the couples $Ra/2$ in Fig. 8-27a to be true, the beam must rotate counterclockwise with respect to the angles. But this could happen only if the angles turned clockwise relative to the beam, which would mean that they help, rather than retard, the end rotation of the beam. In other words, any torsional shearing stresses on these welds result from couples which are *clockwise* on the angles and which therefore tend to increase the unbalance of moment around the y axis. Consequently, the unbalanced moment $Ra/2$ *plus the neglected clockwise moment* can be resisted only by the field weld. The situation is as shown in Fig. 8-27c, where M_1 is the clockwise moment exerted on the angle by the beam and M_2 is the balancing couple supplied by the field weld. Obviously, $M_2 = M_1 + Ra/2$. The couple M_2 is in reality the end moment which we ignored when we assumed in the beginning that the beam is simply supported at the outstanding legs of the connection angles.

Since the framing angles will not ordinarily fit snugly against the face of the member to which they connect because of variation in sizes of members, necessary erection clearances, etc., it would seem reasonable to assume that the couple M_2 is provided by the stress distribution shown in Fig. 8-27d. Therefore, we may expect the field weld to be subjected to a combination of this stress and that of Fig. 8-27b as well as a vertical shearing stress due to $R/2$.

One may ask how we achieve acceptable design with a procedure that omits consideration of the factors we have just discussed. The answer lies in the high degree of flexibility of the connection. For example, we found in Art. 8-16 an end moment of only 40 in·kips at the design load for a W18 × 55 on a span of 30 ft, so for each angle $M_2 = 20$ in·kips. Since the uniformly distributed design load for this beam is 44 kips for an allowable stress of 20 ksi, $R/2 = 11$ kips. Therefore, since a is of the order of 2 in, we see that the couple $Ra/2$ is of the same order of magnitude as is M_2. If this were not true, as would be the case if the connection were much stiffer, then the moment $Ra/2$ for which the shop weld is designed would not be adequate, nor would it be safe to neglect the effect of M_2 on the field weld.

There are several ways to arrive at a trial design. The length of this type of connection usually ranges from one-half to two-thirds the depth of the beam. Therefore, we might assume that length and then compute the required size of the weld. But we may also assume the size of the weld, which is likely to range from $\frac{3}{16}$ in for smaller beams to $\frac{3}{8}$ in for the large sizes, and then determine its length.

The following two examples illustrate the usual design procedure.

Example 8-17-1 (AISC/ASD). The beam is an A36 W21 × 62 spanning 21 ft and supporting a total uniform load of 25 kips dead load and 67 kips live load and connected at each end to the flange of a W12 × 65 column. E70 electrodes. The connection is shown in Fig. 8-28.

Solution. We will try $3\frac{1}{2} \times 2\frac{1}{2}$ connection angles, with the $2\frac{1}{2}$-in legs connected to the web of the beam. The end shear is $\frac{92}{2} = 46$ kips. Investigating first the connection to the web, we try a $\frac{3}{16}$-in shop weld. The allowable shear for a $\frac{3}{16}$-in fillet weld is

$$q = 0.3 \times 70 \times 0.707 \times \tfrac{3}{16} = 2.78 \text{ kli}$$

The length of weld required to resist the end shear is

$$l = \frac{23}{2.78} = 8.27 \text{ in}$$

where 23 kips is the shearing force per weld ($R/2$ in Fig. 8-27a). The length required for moment may be estimated by neglecting the horizontal welds and using the beam formula $f = Mc/I = 6M/l^2 t$, where t is the throat dimension. But since $ft = q$, we find from this equation that $q = 6M/l^2$. The width of the angle is $2\frac{1}{2}$ in, so $M = 23 \times 2.5 = 57.5$ in·kips and

$$L = \sqrt{\left(6 \times \frac{57.5}{2.78}\right)} = 11.1 \text{ in for each weld}$$

On the basis of these computations, we try the connection shown in the figure, whose length is about half the depth of the beam.

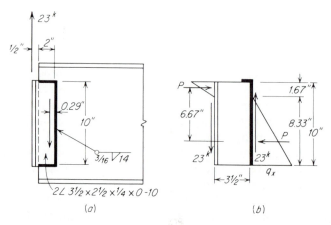

(a)   (b)

FIGURE 8-28

The distance x from the vertical weld to the centroid of the complete shop weld is

$$x = \frac{2(2 \times 1)}{14} = 0.29 \text{ in}$$

The polar moment of inertia, $J = I_x + I_y$, is

$$J = \frac{10^3}{12} + 2 \times 2 \times 5^2 + 10 \times 0.29^2 + 2\left(\frac{1.71^3}{3} + \frac{0.29^3}{3}\right) = 186 \text{ in}^4$$

The first two terms of this equation represent I_x, and since they contribute 183 in⁴, there is not much point in bothering about I_y. The size of the weld does not appear in the calculations, since we are investigating the shear per inch, not the shearing stress.

The maximum stress occurs at the free end of the horizontal weld. The two components are

$$q_x = \frac{23 \times 2.21 \times 5}{186} = 1.37 \text{ kli}$$

$$q_y = \frac{23 \times 2.21 \times 1.71}{186} = 0.47 \text{ kli}$$

The component q_y must be combined with the vertical shear resulting from the 23-kip reaction,

$$q_y = \frac{23}{14} = 1.64 \text{ kli}$$

The resultant shear is therefore $q = \sqrt{2.11^2 + 1.37^2} = 2.52$ kli. This value checks closely with the allowable value, 2.78 kli.

The stress distribution for the field weld is shown in Fig. 8-28b. Assuming that the web of the beam and the one leg of the angle are in contact for a distance equal to one-sixth the length of the angle and equating the couples, we have

$$\frac{8.33 q_x}{2} \times 6.67 = 23 \times 3.5$$

from which $q_x = 2.90$ kli. The vertical shear is

$$q_y = \frac{23}{10} = 2.30 \text{ kli}$$

The resultant $q = \sqrt{2.90^2 + 2.30^2} = 3.70$ kli. In the calculations of the horizontal shear and the direct vertical shear, the length of the short return at the top of the field weld is neglected. A field weld of $\frac{3}{16}$ in is inadequate and must therefore be $\frac{1}{4}$ in, for which the allowable $q = 0.3 \times 70 \times 0.707 \times \frac{1}{4} = 3.70$ kli. To assure flexibility of the connection, we use angles $\frac{1}{4}$ in thick, although this will require that the $\frac{1}{4}$-in field welds be built out to ensure the full throat thickness.

Example 8-17-2 (AISC/LRFD). The beam is an A36 W21 × 62 spanning 21 ft and supporting a total uniform load of 25 kips dead load and 67 kips live load and connected at each end to the flange of a W12 × 65 column. E70 electrodes. The connection is shown in Fig. 8-28.

Solution. We will try $3\frac{1}{2} \times 2\frac{1}{2}$ connection angles, with the $2\frac{1}{2}$-in legs connected to the web of the beam. The factored reaction is $R = \frac{1}{2}(1.2 \times 25 + 1.6 \times 67) = 68.6$ kips. Investigating first the connection to the web, we try a $\frac{3}{16}$-in shop weld. The factored load per angle is $\frac{1}{2} \times 68.6 = 34.3$ kips.

The design strength for a $\frac{3}{16}$-in fillet weld is

$$q = \phi \times 0.60 \times 70 \times 0.707 \times \tfrac{3}{16} = 0.75 \times 5.56 = 4.17 \text{ kli}$$

The length of weld required to resist the shear is $l = 34.3/4.17 = 8.23$ in, where 34.3 kips is the shearing force per weld ($R/2$ in Fig. 8-27a). The length required for moment may be estimated by neglecting the horizontal welds and using the beam formula $f = Mc/I = 6M/l^2t$, where t is the throat dimension. But since $ft = q$, we find from this equation that $q = 6M/l^2$. The width of the angle is $2\frac{1}{2}$ in, so $M = 34.3 \times 2.5 = 85.8$ in·kips and $L = \sqrt{6 \times 85.8/4.17} = 11.1$ in for each weld. On the basis of these computations, we try the connection shown in the figure, whose length is about half the depth of the beam.

The distance x from the vertical weld to the centroid of the complete shop weld is

$$x = \frac{2(2 \times 1)}{14} = 0.29 \text{ in}$$

The polar moment of inertia, $J = I_x + I_y$, is

$$J = \frac{10^3}{12} + 2 \times 2 \times 5^2 + 10 \times 0.29^2 + 2\left(\frac{1.71^3}{3} + \frac{0.29^3}{3}\right) = 186 \text{ in}^4$$

The first two terms of this equation represent I_x, and since they contribute 183 in⁴, there is not much point in bothering about I_y. The size of the weld does not appear in the calculations, since we are investigating the shear per inch, not the shearing stress.

The maximum stress occurs at the free end of the horizontal weld. The two components are

$$q_x = \frac{34.3 \times 2.21 \times 5}{186} = 2.04 \text{ kli}$$

$$q_y = \frac{34.3 \times 2.21 \times 1.71}{186} = 0.70 \text{ kli}$$

The component q_y must be combined with the vertical shear resulting from the 34.3-kip reaction,

$$q_y = \frac{34.3}{14} = 2.45 \text{ kli}$$

The resultant shear is therefore $q = \sqrt{3.15^2 + 2.04^2} = 3.75$ kli. This value checks closely with the design strength, 4.17 kli.

The stress distribution for the field weld is shown in Fig. 8-28b. Assuming that the web of the beam and the one leg of the angle are in contact for a distance equal to one-sixth the length of the angle and equating the couples, we have

$$\frac{8.33q_x}{2} \times 6.67 = 34.3 \times 3.5$$

from which $q_x = 4.32$ kli. The vertical shear is

$$q_y = \frac{34.2}{10} = 3.43 \text{ kli}$$

The resultant $q = \sqrt{4.32^2 + 3.43^2} = 5.52$ kli. In the calculations of the horizontal shear and the direct vertical shear, the length of the short return at the top of the field weld is neglected. A field weld of $\frac{3}{16}$ in is inadequate and must therefore be $\frac{1}{4}$ in, for which the design strength $q = 0.75 \times 0.6 \times 70 \times 0.707 \times \frac{1}{4} = 5.57$ kli. To assure flexibility of the connection, we use angles $\frac{1}{4}$ in thick, although this will require that the $\frac{1}{4}$-in field welds be built out to ensure the full throat thickness.

8-18 UNSTIFFENED WELDED BEAM SEATS

Welded seat connections can be designed so as to have about the same flexibility as welded framed connections, and where they can be used, they provide a very satisfactory and efficient support. As is the case in bolted or riveted construction, the seat may be either stiffened or unstiffened, and it must be used in conjunction with a top angle to assure stability of the beam. Typical unstiffened seats are shown in Fig. 8-29, one to a column flange, the other to the web. Two welds, one at each end of the angle, are used. These welds should be returned across the top of the seat for a distance of about $\frac{1}{2}$ in to eliminate craters at the top of the vertical welds. Although a fillet weld across the top of the seat could also be used, it is likely to interfere with erection if the beam overruns in length. The top angle

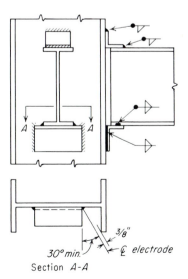

Section *A-A*   **FIGURE 8-29**

should be welded only on its toes so that it is free to bend and thus contribute to the flexibility of the connection. If the welding clearance shown in section *A-A* is not available, the web seat may consist of a plate, set out far enough to clear the web fillets of the column, fitted and welded to the inside faces of the column flanges.

The design of the welded seat involves no principles different from those of the bolted or riveted seat. The reaction is usually assumed to be uniformly distributed over a length, measured from the end of the beam, just sufficient to satisfy the web crippling and web yielding requirements of the beam. Some designers assume the stress distribution in the vertical welds to be the same as for beams, with neutral axis at midheight, while others assume a distribution similar to that of the bolted bracket so that the neutral axis is nearer the compression side. Those who hold the latter view usually take the zone of compression to be one-third the length of the weld. Either way, the design calculations are simple enough. After determining the dimensions of the horizontal leg of the seat, we assume the size of the other leg. This gives us the length of the vertical welds. It is then easy to compute the stress due to bending and combine it with the vertical shear due to the reaction, in the usual way for fillet welds. In these calculations we work with the force per inch of length of weld, as described in Examples 8-17-1 and 8-17-2, so that the size of the weld need not be known in advance. The resultant force determines the required size of the weld. If the weld turns out to be too large or too small, we change the size of the angle and try again. If we prefer, we may assume the size of the weld and compute the length required to resist the shear alone, and the moment alone, as discussed in Examples 8-17-1 and 8-17-2. This may lead to a better first guess for the size of the angle.

Since there is no computed force on the top angle, its proportions are a matter of judgment. A 4-in vertical leg and a thickness of $\frac{1}{4}$ in are suggested as minimums in the AISC Manuals.

8-19   STIFFENED WELDED BEAM SEATS

The welded, stiffened beam seat is somewhat simpler than its riveted or bolted prototype. It may consist of a tee or of two plates welded together in the form of a tee. The two types are shown in DP8-19 and Fig. 8-31. The bracket may be cut as in DP8-19 when clearance is necessary, as for fireproofing; otherwise it may be cut square as in Fig. 8-31.

The eccentricity of the beam reaction is probably greater for the stiffened seat than for the unstiffened one, since the former is stiffer. The reaction is usually assumed to lie at the midpoint of the length of bearing which is demanded by the web-yielding requirements of the beam, as in the unstiffened seat, but with this difference: the bearing length is measured from the outer end of the seat rather than from the end of the beam. The bracket is usually short enough to eliminate need for concern about local buckling of the stem.

Since the vertical welds along the stem are close together, it is advisable to weld along the underside of the flange so as to increase the torsional stiffness of the connection. This return also helps to avoid craters at the top of the vertical weld. This detail is shown in DP8-19 and Fig. 8-31. The length of each horizontal weld will usually be one-fifth to one-half that of the vertical weld, although it may be longer. The design of the stiffened beam seat is illustrated in the following example.

DP8-19-1 (AISC/ASD) and DP8-19-2 (AISC/LRFD): Welded Bracket

The required bearing length is determined by the criteria for yielding of the beam web at the web fillet and the web-crippling criteria discussed in Art. 5-17. In this case web crippling controls the required length of the stiffener plate. An end clearance, or setback, of $\frac{1}{2}$ in is provided.

In order to calculate the stresses in the weld which attaches the stiffener plate to the column, the moment is calculated on the assumption that the reaction acts at the center of the contact area. The stress in the vertical welds is computed on the assumption that the moment is resisted entirely by the welds. Furthermore, the stress due to bending moment is determined at the top horizontal weld. This is the usual practice, although theoretically the stress is higher at the lower end of the vertical weld. Tests have shown that stiffened brackets designed according to this procedure have ample factors of safety with respect to failure.

The required thickness of the web of the tee is based on the shear capacity of the tee; that is, the shear per inch of web must equal the sum of the *vertical* shear capacity per inch of the two welds. The web should also be as thick as the web of the beam supported by the seat (if both are of the same steel) in order to have the same crippling strength. According to the AISC Manuals, however, the web of stiffened seats should also be not less than twice the dimension of the weld. This is based on the idea that the web should be capable of reacting the shear strength of the welds. Since only the vertical component of the weld shear is in the direction to produce shear on the web of the seat, this would seem to be an unnecessarily severe requirement. It would require a $\frac{5}{8}$-in web, instead of $\frac{3}{8}$ in, for the seat in this example. In the same manner the flange thickness of the column should be capable of supporting the vertical shear capacity of one weld. The W8 × 31 has a flange thickness of 0.435 which is substantially greater than the $\frac{3}{16}$ in required.

8-20 MOMENT-RESISTANT WELDED BEAM CONNECTIONS

Typical moment-resistant welded connections for beams are illustrated in Fig. 8-30. The most direct connection of a beam to a column flange is shown in *a*. Here the beam flanges are groove-welded and the web fillet-welded to the column flange. In *b* the web is field-welded to a plate which is shop-welded to the column

WELDED BRACKET DP8-19-1

W8 × 31

1/4 ⌵ 6
4 × 4 × 1/4 × 0-6

W16 × 50

1/4 ⌵ 2 1/2

5/16 ⌵ 8

2   2

$\bar{y} = 3.2$

8

x

y

W16 × 50, A36 steel   AISC/ASD Spec.
Span 12'-0"
Load 3 klf DL   6 klf LL

$R = 9 \times 6 = 54^k$

<u>Brg. length</u>

Web yield: $\dfrac{54}{24 \times 0.38} - 2\frac{1}{2}\ (1^5/_{16}) = 2.64''$

Web crippling:

$$54 = 34(0.380)^2 \left[1 + 3\left(\frac{N}{16.26}\right)\left(\frac{0.380}{0.630}\right)^{1.5}\right] \sqrt{36\frac{0.630}{0.380}}$$

$N = 4.90''$

Seat length = 4.90 + 0.5 = 5.40"   <u>Use 5 1/2"</u>

$M = 54\,(5.5 - 2.5) = 162''^k$

Try vert. leg 8"
   horiz. leg 2"

$\bar{y} = \dfrac{2 \times 8 \times 4}{16 + 4} = 3.2''$

$I_x = 2\left[\dfrac{3.2^3 + 4.8^3}{3} + 2(3.2)^2\right] = 137\ in^3$

$q_z = \dfrac{162 \times 3.2}{137} = 3.78\ kli$

$q_y = \dfrac{54}{20} = 2.70\ kli$

$q = \sqrt{3.78^2 + 2.70^2} = 4.65\ kli$

Use $5/16$ – in E70 fillet weld, q = 4.64 kli

Web of tee :

$0.40 \times 36 \times t = 2 \times 2.70$
$t = 0.375''$
W16 web t = 0.380
<u>Use WT8 × 25, t = 0.380</u>

WELDED BRACKET	DP8-19-2

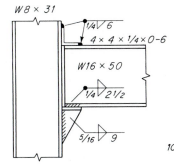

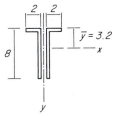

$W16 \times 50$, A36 steel   AISC/LRFD Spec.

Span $12'-0''$

Load $3\,klf$ DL $6\,klf$ LL

$1.2 \times 3 + 1.6 \times 6 = 13.2\,klf$

$R = 13.2 \times 6 = 79.2^k$

<u>Brg. length</u>

Web yield: $\dfrac{79.2}{36 \times 0.38} - 2\frac{1}{2}\ (1^5/_{16}) = 2.51\,in$

Web crippling: $\phi = 0.75$ $R = \dfrac{79.2}{0.75} = 105.6^k$

$$105.6 = 68(0.380)^2\Big[1 + 3\Big(\dfrac{N}{16.26}\Big)\Big(\dfrac{0.380}{0.630}\Big)^{1.5}\Big]\ \sqrt{36\,\dfrac{0.630}{0.380}}$$

$N = 4.5''$

Seat length $= 4.5 + 0.5 = 5.0''$ Use $5''$

$M = 79.2\,(5.0 - 2.25) = 217.8''^k$

Try vert. leg $8''$

  horiz. leg $2''$

$\bar{y} = \dfrac{2 \times 8 \times 4}{16 + 4} = 3.2''$

$I_x = 2\left[\dfrac{3.2^3 + 4.8^3}{3} + 2(3.2)^2\right] = 137\,in^3$

$q_z = \dfrac{217.8 \times 3.2}{137} = 5.09\,kli$

$q_y = \dfrac{79.2}{20} = 3.96\,kli$

$q = \sqrt{5.09^2 + 3.96^2} = 6.45\,kli$

Use $^5/_{16}$-in E70 fillet weld, $q = 6.96\,kli$

Web of tee:

    $0.60 \times 36 \times t = 2 \times 3.96$

          $t = 0.367$

    $W16$ web $t = 0.380$

    <u>Use WT8 x 25, $t = 0.380$</u>

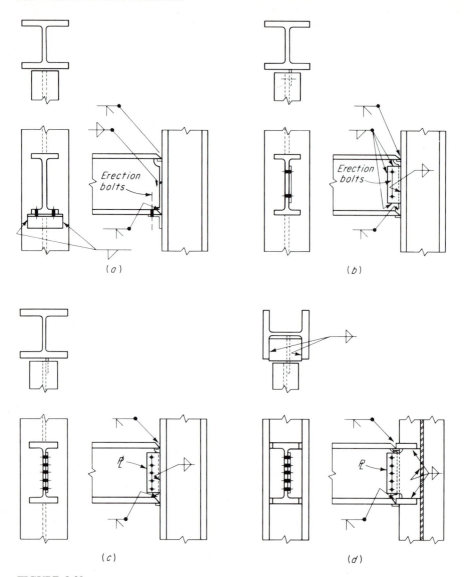

FIGURE 8-30

flange. This allows a more lenient setback of the web and also eliminates the angle seat in the connection shown in *a*. In the connection shown in *c* bolts are used instead of field fillet welds in the web connection. A similar connection of a beam to a column web is shown in *d*. Tolerances must be closely controlled in all these connections; otherwise considerable difficulty may be encountered in the field.

Less restrictive tolerances in beam length can be allowed with a connection of the type shown in Fig. 8-31. The top plate is shipped loose and positioned after

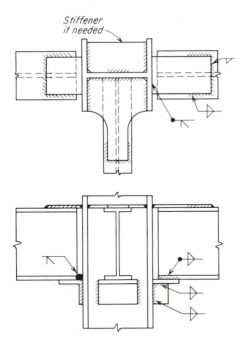

FIGURE 8-31

the beam is in place. The top plate for the beam at the left is welded full length. This connection is considered to be suitable for rigid frames [AISC/ASD Type 1 and AISC/LRFD Type FR (Art. 8-15)]. The top plate for the beam at the right is welded over only a part of its length; this connection is considered to be semi-rigid (ASD Type 3 and LRFD Type PR). In case the beam frames to the web of a column, the top plate may be widened and fillet-welded to the column web and flanges as shown. A variety of procedures, depending on the assumptions as to behavior of the connection and of the frame itself, are used for the design of top-plate connections.[14,15]

Depending on the magnitude of the reaction, the seat may be unstiffened, as at the left in Fig. 8-31, or stiffened, as at the right. The horizontal plate of the stiffened seat may extend beyond the vertical plate if this is required for a sufficient length of weld between the beam flange and its seat. If the end moment is negative, the horizontal plate may be butted against the column flange without being welded to it. But if the moment may be either positive or negative, as with wind loads, the horizontal plate must be welded to the column flange. Alternatively, the beam flange may be welded directly to the column flange, as shown in the connection at the left. If this weld is required, clearance at the end of the beam must be watched, since a minimum of $\frac{3}{16}$ in is required. The weld between the top plate and the column flange requires the same $\frac{3}{16}$-in minimum gap.

Moment-resistant beam-to-girder connections are illustrated in Fig. 8-32. If the top flanges are at the same elevation, the top plate crosses the flange of the girder, as shown in Fig. 8-32a. If the flanges are at different elevations, the top

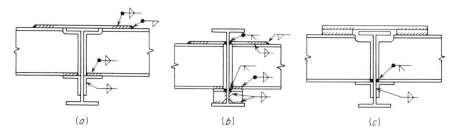

FIGURE 8-32

plates may be groove-welded to the web of the girder, as in Fig. 8-32b, or a single plate passing through a slot in the web may be used. If the difference in elevation of the flanges is small, the detail in c may be used. The seat may be an angle, as in Fig. 8-32a. If the distance between the bottom flanges of the two beams is too small for a sufficient length of weld on the seat angle, a tee may be used, as in Fig. 8-32b. The bottom flange of the beam may be groove-welded to the web of the girder, as in Fig. 8-32c, using the seat for backup, or the heel of the seat may be groove-welded in the shop to permit fillet welds in the field, as in Fig. 8-32b.

8-21   STIFFENERS IN BEAM-TO-COLUMN CONNECTIONS

The forces in the beam flanges of beam-to-column connections of the type shown in Fig. 8-30 may cause crippling and/or buckling of the column web opposite the compression flange of the beam. This phenomenon is analogous to the crippling and buckling of beam webs at concentrated loads, which was discussed in Art. 5-17.

Web buckling. The following approximate solution of the elastic buckling strength of a rectangular plate with the four edges simply supported and subjected to a concentrated compressive load P at midlength of each of two opposite sides is from Timoshenko (Ref. 16, p. 387),

$$P_{cr} = \frac{4\pi E t^3}{12(1 - v^2)b} \tag{a}$$

in which b is the width of the plate in the direction of P. It will be noted that the aspect ratio a/b of the plate does not appear in this equation, as it does (in the form of the coefficient k) in the general formula for plate buckling, Eq. (4-32). This is because it is a simplified form of the derived equation, which includes the aspect ratio. It was shown that the error in this approximation was only 2.7 percent for a plate with $a/b = 2$. The error increases for $a/b < 2$. Denoting the compressive force in the beam flange by P_{bf} and the width b of the plate by d_c, where d_c is the column-web depth between fillets, Eq. (a) yields the formula

$$\frac{d_c}{t} = \frac{33,400t^2}{P_{bf}} \qquad (b)$$

The assumption of simple supports at the fillet of the column web is conservative since the column flange will provide some rotational support if the web has not yielded at the fillet. Experiments[17-19] have shown that yielding of the web at the fillet occurs at load levels approximately equal to those obtained from Eq. (b) if the columns are made of A36 steel. For higher yield strengths yielding does not occur, so some degree of restraint is provided. If the restraint were sufficient to provide complete fixity, the strength would be twice as great as that given by Eq. (b). Chen et al.[18] suggested that fixity be accounted for by a factor represented by the ratio of the yield stress of the column to the yield stress of A36 steel. They proposed

$$\frac{d_c}{t} \le \frac{33,400t^2}{P_{bf}} \sqrt{\frac{F_{yc}}{36}} \qquad (c)$$

which produces

$$\frac{d_c}{t} \le \frac{5570t^2\sqrt{F_{yc}}}{P_{bf}} \qquad (d)$$

This formula has been adjusted to represent a lower bound for all the test results to

$$\frac{d_c}{t} \le \frac{4100t^2\sqrt{F_{yc}}}{P_{bf}} \qquad (8\text{-}11)$$

This equation is used in the AISC specifications, as follows.

AISC/ASD

$$d_c = \frac{4100t_{wc}^3\sqrt{F_{yc}}}{P_{bf}} \qquad (8\text{-}12)$$

where t_{wc} = column-web thickness. If the web depth between fillets exceeds d_c, stiffeners must be used.

AISC/LRFD. The design strength of the column web is ϕR_n, where $\phi = 0.90$ and the nominal strength R_n is given by

$$R_n = \frac{4100t_w^3\sqrt{F_{yw}}}{d_c} \qquad (8\text{-}13)$$

where t_w = web thickness and F_{yw} = yield stress of web. R_n may be exceeded if stiffeners are used.

The LRFD specification states that R_n is the limiting value for members with concentrated loads on both flanges, which is the assumption used in deriving Eq. (8-11). The ASD specification does not mention this restriction, but it is clear from the derivation that Eq. (8-12) need be used only if the column is loaded on both flanges. If the column receives load from a beam on only one flange, the web must be checked for buckling by Eqs. (5-59) for ASD and Eqs. (5-60) for LRFD.

It will be noted that Eq. (8-13) is more specific than Eq. (8-12), in that the yield stress is specified as that of the web while in Eq. (8-12) it is defined as the yield stress of the column. Of course, Eq. (8-12) can be used for built-up members with web yield stress different from that of the flange by using the web yield stress for F_{yc}.

Web crippling. According to tests reported in Ref. 20, the beam-flange force can be assumed to distribute itself into the column web as in Fig. 8-33a for an evaluation of web crippling. If the column web yields over this length, we have

$$R = F_{yw} t_w (t_{bf} + 5k_c) \tag{8-14}$$

where R is the beam-flange compressive force and the subscripts b, c, f, and w refer to the beam, column, flange, and web, respectively. Except for t_{bf} in place of N, this formula is identical to Eq. (5-57a). The AISC specifications prescribe the following.

AISC/LRFD. Column-web stiffeners must be used if the beam-flange compressive force exceeds the nominal strength ϕR_n given by Eqs. (5-57). Of course, N in this application is the thickness of the beam flange. The stiffeners, one on each side of the column web, must be placed opposite the compression flange.

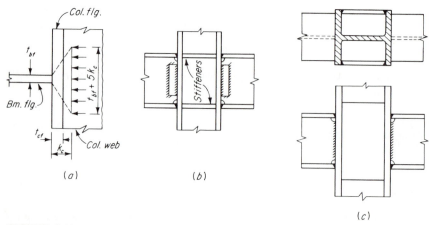

FIGURE 8-33

AISC/ASD. In this specification, instead of a formula for an allowable compressive force in the beam flange, the following formula for the required area A_{st} of the pair of column-web stiffeners is given:

$$A_{st} = \frac{P_{bf} - F_{yc}\,t_w(t_w + 5k)}{F_{yst}} \tag{8-15}$$

where P_{bf} = compressive force in beam flange or beam-flange connection plate
$\quad\;\; F_{yst}$ = stiffener yield stress

This equation may yield a negative value of A_{st}. In this case, of course, stiffeners are not required.

Local bending of column flange. In the investigation reported in Ref. 20, tests were made to determine the strength of the connection at the beam's tension flange. Some members failed by fracture of the flange weld in the vicinity of the column web, some by fracture at the fillet of the column web, and some by a tearing out of material in the column flange. A yield-line analysis of a portion of the column flange, together with observations from the tests, gave the following equation for the required thickness t_{cf} of the column flange:

$$t_{cf} = 0.4\sqrt{A_f} \tag{e}$$

AISC/ASD. Equation (e) can be extended to cover the case of differing yield stresses in beam and column by writing it in the form

$$t_{cf} = 0.4\sqrt{\frac{F_{yf}\,A_f}{F_{yc}}} = 0.4\sqrt{\frac{P_{bf}}{F_{yc}}} \tag{8-16}$$

where F_{yc} = column yield stress. P_{bf} in this equation is defined as $\frac{5}{3}$ times the dead load plus live load delivered by the flange, or $\frac{4}{3}$ times the dead load plus live load plus wind or earthquake force. The factor $\frac{5}{3}$ is needed because Eq. (e) is based on the load at which failure occurred, which is the service load multiplied by the factor of safety of $\frac{5}{3}$. Similarly, the multiplier $\frac{4}{3}$ accounts for the one-third increase in allowable stress for load combinations that include wind or earthquake forces.

    If the column flange thickness is less than t_{cf}, a pair of stiffeners must be provided opposite the tension flange of the beam.

AISC/LRFD. Solving Eq. (8-16) for P_{bf} gives $P_{bf} = 6.25 t_{cf}^2\, F_{yc}$. This is the LRFD formula, which in the LRFD notation is

$$R_n = 6.25 t_f^2\, F_{yf} \tag{8-17}$$

where R_n = nominal force and F_{yf} = yield stress of the flange. The specified resistance factor is $\phi = 0.9$.

    If the factored load exceeds ϕR_n, a pair of stiffeners must be provided opposite the tension flange of the beam.

Stiffener details. The ends of column-web stiffeners opposite the beam tension flange must be fully welded to the column flanges. Stiffeners opposite the compression flange need only be fitted against the column flanges. However, if a beam connects to only one flange, as at an exterior column, the stiffeners can terminate at middepth of the column web. Stiffeners must also be proportioned for local buckling. The same slenderness limit as for compression elements free on one unloaded edge may be used, which is $95/\sqrt{F_y}$ in the AISC specifications (Table 4-4).

Vertical stiffeners may be used instead of horizontal stiffeners (Fig. 8-33c). However, they are probably less effective than the column web, since the column flange acts somewhat as a beam continuous over three supports. They may be assumed to be only 50 percent efficient, so

$$F_{ys}\,t_s(t_{bf} + 5k_c) = P_{bf} - F_{yc}\,t_w(t_{bf} + 5k_c)$$

where t_s is the thickness of one stiffener. The stiffener slenderness limit can be determined as for a column web.

Shear reinforcement. Beam-to-column moment connections sometimes require reinforcement of the column web for shear. Consider the welded corner connection shown in Fig. 8-34a. The tensile force $T = M/d_b$ in the top flange is assumed to be resisted by a shear force V in the corner web (Fig. 8-34b). If the shear stress is uniform over the length d_c, we get

$$V = f_v\, d_c\, t_w \tag{8-18}$$

where t_w is the thickness of the corner web. In the AISC specifications d_c is defined as the clear depth between fillets. In all cases the computed shear on the panel must include shear forces resulting from moments in the beam as well as those applied by the column.

AISC/ASD. The calculated shear stress in Eq. (8-18) must not exceed the allowable shear stress F_v given by Eqs. (5-44).

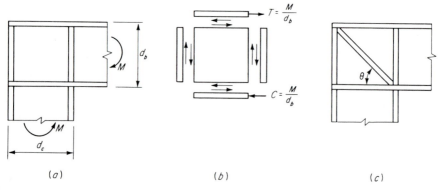

(a)   (b)   (c)

FIGURE 8-34

For plastic design, shear is assumed to be distributed uniformly over the depth $0.95d$, where d is the depth of the member. Then with the shear yield stress $F_y/\sqrt{3}$, we get

$$V = \frac{F_y}{\sqrt{3}} \times 0.95dt_w = 0.55F_y\,dt_w \tag{8-19}$$

This value of V must equal or exceed the factored shear.

AISC/LRFD. The nominal shear resistance R_v is given by the formulas

$$R_v = \begin{cases} 0.7F_y\,d_c\,t_w & P_u \le 0.75P_n \tag{8-20} \\[2ex] 0.7F_y\,d_c\,t_w\left(1.9 - 1.2\,\dfrac{P_u}{P_n}\right) & P_u > 0.75P_n \tag{8-21} \end{cases}$$

In these equations P_u and P_n are, respectively, the required axial strength and the nominal axial strength of the column.

If the web is not thick enough, the connection can be reinforced by welding a doubler plate to the web or by using a stiffener as shown in Fig. 8-34c. The area A_s of the stiffener must be sufficient for the horizontal component of the stiffener shear force to make up the deficiency in shear resistance. Therefore,

$$A_s\,f\cos\theta = T - f_v\,d_c\,t_w = \frac{M}{d_b} - f_v\,d_c\,t_w \tag{f}$$

AISC/ASD. With $f = F_t$, the allowable tension, and $f_v = F_v$, the allowable shear, Eq. (f) gives the following formula for the stiffener area:

$$A_s = \frac{1}{F_t\cos\theta}\left(\frac{M}{d_b} - F_v\,d_c\,t_w\right) \tag{8-22}$$

For plastic design, $F_t = F_y$ and $F_v = F_y/\sqrt{3}$, which gives

$$A_s = \frac{1}{F_y\cos\theta}\left(\frac{M_p}{d_b} - \frac{F_y\,d_c\,t_w}{\sqrt{3}}\right) \tag{8-23}$$

AISC/LRFD. Substituting $A_s\,f = \phi_t\,P_n$ and $f_v\,d_c\,t_w = \phi_v\,V_n$ into Eq. (f) and noting that $\phi_t = \phi_v = 0.9$, we get

$$A_s = \frac{1}{F_y\cos\theta}\left(\frac{M}{0.9d_b} - V_n\right) \tag{8-24}$$

If the moments in the members at an interior connection differ significantly in magnitude (Fig. 8-35), they may produce large shear stresses in the column web, as in the corner connection. An analysis similar to that in Fig. 8-34b shows

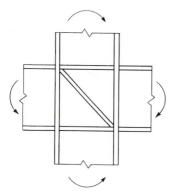

FIGURE 8-35

that the corner-connection equations can be used for this case by taking for M the algebraic sum of the moments at the connection.

DP8-21-1 (AISC/ASD) and DP8-21-2 (AISC/LRFD): Moment Connection

This example illustrates the design of the connection of a W24 × 76 beam to a W14 × 145 column. The following are clarifications of the correspondingly lettered computations on the design sheets and apply to both examples except where noted otherwise.

a. **ASD.** The $DL + LL$ shear and moment are both less than 75 percent of the total including wind, so the latter values control the design.

b. The width of the plate is $1\frac{1}{2}$ in less than the width of the beam flange to allow adequate space for the welds. In general, the difference in widths should be not less than four times the size of the weld. The required fillet weld is distributed $7\frac{1}{2}$ in across the end of the plate and 11 in on each side. The connection plate is field-welded to the column with a full-penetration groove weld.

c. The bottom flange connection plate is chosen $1\frac{1}{2}$ in wider than the beam flange to accommodate the $\frac{3}{8}$-in fillet welds. This plate is also field-welded to the column flange with a full-penetration groove weld.

d. The shear plate is shop-welded to the column flange. It is not welded full length. Some designers would weld it full length even though the 10-in welds shown give more than is required.

e. The width of the stiffener is determined by the width of the connection plate. Once the width is established, the minimum thickness follows from the b/t limitations.

f. Since a diagonal stiffener is required, a horizontal stiffener is used at the tension flange as well as at the compression flange. If only one diagonal stiffener is used, as suggested here, only one horizontal stiffener would be needed at the top flange of the beam, since it was shown that stiffeners are not needed at this flange at all so far as the column flange itself is concerned.

BEAM-TO-COLUMN MOMENT CONNECTION   DP8-21-1

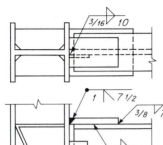

	W24×76	W14× 145	AISC/ASD Spec.
	$d_b = 23.92$	$d_c = 14.78$	A36 steel
	$b = 8.99$	$t_{cf} = 1.09$	E70 electrodes
	$t_f = 0.680$	$t_w = 0.680$	A325 bolts (slip-
		$k_c = 1.75$	critical connection)

Load	Shear	Moment	
DL	22.1	100	
LL	8.3	50	
Total	30.4^k	$150^{'k}$	
WL	24.7	280	
Total	55.1	430	
× 3/4	41.3^k	$322^{'k}$	(a)

Top (tension-flange) plate
$$T = 322 \times 12/23.92 = 162^k$$
$A_s = 162/22 = 7.35\ in^2\ 1 \times 7\tfrac{1}{2}\ pl. = 7.5\ in^2$ (b)
3/8" fillet weld $q = 21 \times 0.707 \times 3/8 = 5.56$ kli
Length of weld $= 162/5.56 = 29.1$"
Use 7½"across end and 11"each side

Bottom (compression-flange) plate
Use $3/4 \times 10\tfrac{1}{2}$ pl., $A = 7.87\ in^2$ Use 15" of 3/8" fillet weld each side   (c)

Shear plate
A325 7/8" bolts, s.s. $= 17 \times 0.6 = 10.2^k$, $n = 41.3/10.2 = 3.9$ use 4
Length of shear plate $= 3 \times 3 + 2 \times 1\tfrac{1}{2} = 12$"
$t = \dfrac{41.3}{0.4 \times 36 \times 12} = 0.24$" Use 1/4"×5"plate. $R = 1.2 \times 58 \times \tfrac{1}{4} \times \tfrac{7}{8} = 15.2^k > 10.5$
Length of 3/16"fillet weld $= 41.3/2.78 = 14.9$". Weld 10" each side   (d)

Column-flange stiffener at beam tension (top) flange
Eq. (8-16) $t_{cf} = 0.4\sqrt{A_f} = 0.4\sqrt{7.5} = 1.10 < 1.09$, stiffener not req'd.

Column-web stiffener at beam compression (bottom) flange
Eq. (5-59a)
$$R = 67.5 \times 0.680^2 \left[1 + 3\,\frac{0.680}{14.78}\left(\frac{0.680}{1.09}\right)^{1.5}\right]\sqrt{\frac{36 \times 1.09}{0.680}} = 253^k > 162\ O.K.$$
Eq. (8-14) $t_w \geq \dfrac{A_f}{t_{bf} + 5k_c} = \dfrac{7.87}{0.75 + 5 \times 1.75} = 0.828$", $t_w = 0.680$" stiffener req'd.
Eq. (8-15) $A_s = 7.87 - 0.680(0.75 + 5 \times 1.75) = 1.41\ in^2 = 0.71\ in^2$ each stiffener
Use two 5/16×5 stiffeners, $A_s = 1.57\ in^2$ each, b/t $= 16\ O.K.$ (e)

Column-web shear
Eq. (8-18) $162 = f_v \times 14.78 \times 0.680$; $f_v = 16.12\ ksi > 14.4$
Eq. (8-22) $A_s = \dfrac{1}{22 \times 0.528}\,(162 - 0.4 \times 36 \times 14.78 \times 0.680) = 1.49\ in^2$ (f)

Use one 5/16 × 5 stiffener

| | BEAM–TO–COLUMN MOMENT CONNECTION | DP8–21–2 | 1/2 |

$W\,24 \times 76$ $\quad W\,14 \times 145$ $\quad$ AISC/LRFD Spec.
$d_b = 23.92$ $\quad d_c = 14.78$ $\quad$ A36 steel
$b = 8.99$ $\quad t_{cf} = 1.09$ $\quad$ E70 electrodes
$t_f = 0.680$ $\quad t_w = 0.680$ $\quad$ A325 bolts (slip–
$\qquad\qquad\quad k_c = 1.75$ $\qquad\qquad$ critical connection)

Load	Shear, kip	Moment, ft. kips
D	22.1	100
L	8.3	50
W	24.7	280

$1.2\,D + 1.6\,L = 39.8^k$ shear
$\qquad\qquad\quad = 200^{'k}$ moment
$1.2\,D + 1.3\,W + 0.5\,L = 62.8^k$ shear
$\qquad\qquad\qquad\qquad = 509^{'k}$ moment

Top (tension–flange) plate
$\quad T = 509 \times 12/23.92 = 255^k$
$\quad 0.9 \times 36\,A_g = 255,\ A_g = 7.87\ in^2$ $\qquad$ (b)
$\quad$ Use $1\tfrac{1}{16} \times 7\tfrac{1}{2}$ pl., $A_g = 7.97\ in^2$
$\quad \tfrac{3}{8}$ fillet weld
$\qquad q = 0.75 \times 0.6 \times 70 \times 0.707 \times \tfrac{3}{8} = 8.35$ kli
$\quad$ Length of weld $= 255/8.35 = 30.5''$
$\qquad$ Use $7\tfrac{1}{2}''$ across end and $12''$ each side

Bottom (compression flange) plate
$\quad$ Use $\tfrac{3}{4} \times 10\tfrac{1}{2}$ pl., $A = 7.87\ in^2$. Use $16''$ of $\tfrac{3}{8}''$ fillet weld each side $\qquad$ (c)

Shear plate
$\quad$ A325 $\tfrac{7}{8}''$ bolts, s.s. $= 17 \times 0.6 = 10.2^k$
$\quad$ Service load $= 22.1 + 8.3 + 24.7 = 55.1^k$, $x\ \tfrac{3}{4} = 41.3$
$\quad n = 41.3/10.2 = 3.9$. Use 4

$\quad$ Check for strength, threads in shear plane
$\quad$ s.s. $= 0.75 \times 48 \times 0.6 = 21.6^k$, $4 \times 21.6 = 86.4^k < 62.8$ O.K.
$\quad$ Length of shear plate $= 3 \times 3 + 2 \times 1\tfrac{1}{2} = 12''$
$\quad t = \dfrac{62.8}{0.9 \times 0.6 \times 36 \times 12} = 0.27''$ Use $\tfrac{5}{16} \times 5$ pl.
$\quad R_n = 0.75 \times 2.4 \times \tfrac{7}{8} \times \tfrac{5}{16} \times 58 = 28.5^k > 21.1$ O.K.
$\quad$ Length of $\tfrac{3}{16}''$ fillet weld $= 62.8/4.18 = 15.0''$. Weld $10''$ each side $\qquad$ (d)

BEAM-TO-COLUMN MOMENT CONNECTION   DP8-21-2   2/2

Column-flange stiffener at beam tension (top) flange

Eq. (8-17) $\phi R_n = 0.9 \times 6.25 \, t_f^2 F_{yf} = 0.9 \times 6.25 \times 1.09^2 \times 36 = 240.6^k < 255$

Stiffener req'd.

Column-web stiffener at beam compression (bottom) flange

Eq. (5-60a)

$\phi R_n = 0.75 \times 135 \times 0.680^2 \left[1 + 3 \times \dfrac{0.750}{14.78} \left(\dfrac{0.680}{1.09}\right)^{1.5}\right] \sqrt{\dfrac{36 \times 1.09}{0.680}} = 382^k > 255$ O.K.

Eq. (5-57a) $t_w = \dfrac{\phi R_n}{F_y(N+5^k)} = \dfrac{1 \times 255}{36(0.75 + 5 \times 1.75)} = 0.746'' > 0.680$

Stiffener req'd.

$A_s = 7.87 - 0.680(0.75 + 5 \times 1.75) = 1.41 \, in^2$

Use two $5/16 \times 5$ stiffeners, $A_s = 1.57 \, in^2$ each (both flanges)   (e)

$b/t = 16$ O.K.

Column-web shear

Eq. (8-20) $R_v = V_n = 0.7 \times 36 \times 14.78 \times 0.680 = 253.3^k$

$\phi V_n = 0.9 \times 253.3 = 228 < 255$

Stiffener req'd.

Eq. (8-24) $A_s = \dfrac{1}{36 \times 0.526}\left(\dfrac{255}{0.9} - 253.3\right) = 1.59$ (f)

Use one $5/16 \times 5$ stiffener

8-22 ECCENTRICALLY LOADED BOLTED OR RIVETED SHEAR CONNECTIONS— ELASTIC ANALYSIS

The lines of action of the forces in connected members should in general pass through the centroid of the fastener group. However, it is often impracticable or impossible to arrange members so that this condition is satisfied, and as a consequence the fasteners are subjected to eccentric forces. The connections of the double-angle members of the truss of DP3-16-1 are eccentric because the centroids of the angles are not on the gage lines of the rivets. For example, the centroid of the $2\frac{1}{2} \times 1\frac{1}{2} \times \frac{3}{16}$ angles of $U_2 L_3$ is 0.85 in from the back of the angles, while the gage line of the fasteners is at a distance of $1\frac{3}{8}$ in. Eccentricities of this magnitude are usually neglected in the design of connections. Beams and girders which connect to columns but which cannot be located on or near the centerlines of the columns are sometimes supported on brackets, as shown in Fig. 8-36. The twisting moment resulting from this eccentricity must be considered in the design of the connection. This loading is sometimes called *eccentric shear*.

It is helpful to discuss the connection subjected to eccentric shear by considering first the connection which supports only a twisting couple. Let Fig. 8-37a be any arrangement of fasteners in a plate supporting the couple M. If the plate is assumed to rotate as a rigid body and the fasteners are elastic, rotation of the plate produces shearing deformations in the fasteners which are proportional to and normal to radii from the center of rotation O. Then with stress proportional to strain the shearing stress f_v on any fastener is proportional to and normal to the radius r; that is, $f_v = kr$, where k is a constant. Then, if A is the cross-sectional area of the fastener, the force R'' is

$$R'' = f_v A = krA \qquad (a)$$

In Fig. 8-37b the force R'' on an individual fastener is resolved into components R''_x and R''_y, where x, y are axes originating at the center of rotation O. By similar triangles these components are

$$R''_x = \frac{R''y}{r} \qquad R''_y = \frac{R''x}{r} \qquad (b)$$

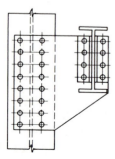

FIGURE 8-36

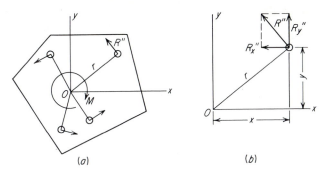

FIGURE 8-37

where x and y are the coordinates of the fastener being evaluated. Substitution of the value of R'' from Eq. (a) into Eqs. (b) gives

$$R_x'' = kAy \qquad R_y'' = kAx \qquad (c)$$

Applying the equations of equilibrium to the forces in Fig. 8-37a, and using Eqs. (a) and (c), we have

$$\sum R_x'' = k \sum Ay = 0$$

$$\sum R_y'' = k \sum Ax = 0 \qquad (d)$$

$$\sum R''r = k \sum Ar^2 = M$$

From the first two of these equations we see that the center of rotation O is at the centroid of the group of fasteners. From the third equation we find $k = M/\sum Ar^2$, which when substituted into Eq. (a) gives

$$R'' = \frac{MrA}{\sum Ar^2} \qquad (e)$$

If the fasteners are of uniform size, as is the usual case, $\sum Ar^2 = A \sum r^2$ and Eq. (e) becomes

$$R'' = \frac{Mr}{\sum r^2} \qquad (8\text{-}25)$$

Substituting the value of R from Eq. (8-25) into Eqs. (b), we get

$$R_x'' = \frac{My}{\sum r^2} \qquad R_y'' = \frac{Mx}{\sum r^2} \qquad (8\text{-}26a)$$

Since $r^2 = x^2 + y^2$, Eq. (8-26a) can be rewritten

$$R_x'' = \frac{My}{\sum (x^2 + y^2)} \qquad R_y'' = \frac{Mx}{\sum (x^2 + y^2)} \qquad (8\text{-}26b)$$

A connection supporting a force P which is eccentric with respect to the centroid of a group of fasteners (Fig. 8-38a) can be analyzed by replacing P by an equal force at the centroid (Fig. 8-38b) and a twisting couple with the value $M = Pe$ (Fig. 8-38c). Assuming again that the plate is rigid and the fasteners

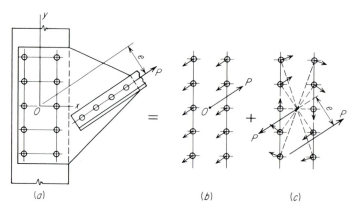

FIGURE 8-38

elastic, it follows that the fastener forces in Fig. 8-38b are equal while those in Fig. 8-38c are given by Eq. (8-25) or Eqs. (8-26). The force on any fastener in Fig. 8-38a is the resultant of the force due to P in Fig. 8-38b and the force due to the twisting moment $M = Pe$ in Fig. 8-38c.

Resolving the force P in Fig. 8-38b into its components P_x and P_y, the force on any fastener is expressed as

$$R'_x = \frac{P_x A_i}{\sum A} \qquad R'_y = \frac{P_y A_i}{\sum A} \tag{8-27a}$$

In the case where all fasteners are of the same size, Eq. (8-27a) reduces to

$$R'_x = \frac{P_x}{n} \qquad R'_y = \frac{P_y}{n} \tag{8-27b}$$

where n is the number of connectors.

The vector addition of the shear forces from the components, Eqs. (8-27), and the shear forces from the twisting moment, Eqs. (8-26), can be written in the form

$$R = \sqrt{(R'_x + R''_x)^2 + (R'_y + R''_y)^2} \tag{8-28}$$

It should be noted that the vector addition requires that the directions of the components be taken into account. It is possible to devise a sign convention so that this can be done automatically, but the authors prefer to visualize the direction of the forces and determine the direction of the components accordingly. The forces on the fasteners are shown in Figs. 8-38b and c as the resisting forces, where it can be seen that the fastener in the lower right-hand corner of the connection will be critical. It is also possible to indicate the components in terms of the acting forces. Care must be exercised that only resisting forces or only acting forces are used for all loading conditions.

The procedure is illustrated in the following example.

Example 8-22-1. The load of 20 kips in Fig. 8-39 is applied so that its line of action passes through the bolt at B. The moment of the load with respect to the centroid of

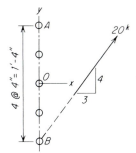

FIGURE 8-39

the fasteners can be calculated by resolving it into vertical and horizontal components at B. This gives $\frac{3}{5} \times 20 \times 8 = 96$ in·kips. Then with $\sum (x^2 + y^2) = 2(4^2 + 8^2) = 160$, the force in fasteners A and B due to the moment is

$$R_x'' = \frac{96 \times 8}{160} = 4.8 \text{ kips}$$

The components of the force in each fastener due to a 20-kip force applied at the centroid are

$$R_x' = \frac{\frac{3}{5} \times 20}{5} = 2.4 \text{ kips} \qquad R_y' = \frac{\frac{4}{5} \times 20}{5} = 3.2 \text{ kips}$$

The resultant force on the fastener at B is

$$R = \sqrt{(2.4 + 4.8)^2 + 3.2^2} = 7.88 \text{ kips}$$

Fastener B is the most highly stressed. Although bolts A and B have the same magnitudes of the individual components, it is easily verified that on bolt A the horizontal component from the moment and the horizontal component from the horizontal component of the load are in opposite directions.

The conservatism of elastic analyses was demonstrated by tests sponsored by AISC,[21] and in the seventh edition of its *Manual of Steel Construction* (1970) it recommended that inelastic behavior be accounted for, in part, in an elastic analysis by substituting an effective eccentricity e_e for the actual eccentricity e. This recommendation was not a part of the specification. For fasteners equally spaced in a single gage line the effective eccentricity is

$$e_e = e - \frac{1 + 2n}{4}$$

and for fasteners equally spaced in two or more gage lines

$$e_e = e - \frac{1 + n}{2}$$

where n is the number of fasteners in one line parallel to the direction of the applied load. These formulas may give negative values of the effective eccentricity. In this case, it is assumed to be zero. One of the test specimens consisted of two framing angles fastened to a $\frac{3}{8}$-in A36-steel plate by a single row of six $\frac{3}{4}$-in A502 Grade 1 rivets at 3-in spacing. The connection was tested under a load P

parallel to the rivet row with an eccentricity of 6.5 in. To compute the allowable force P using the effective eccentricity, we have

$$e_e = 6.5 - \frac{1 + 12}{4} = 3.25$$

$$\sum y^2 = 2(1.5^2 + 4.5^2 + 7.5^2) = 158$$

$$R_x'' = \frac{3.25P \times 7.5}{158} = 0.154P \qquad R_y' = \frac{P}{6} = 0.167P$$

$$R = \sqrt{(0.154P)^2 + (0.167P)^2}$$

from which $P = 4.40R$.

At the time this procedure was recommended, the allowable stress on A502 Grade 1 rivets was $F_v = 15$ ksi, so $R = 2F_v A_b = 2 \times 15 \times 0.44 = 13.2$ kips. This gives the allowable load $P = 4.40 \times 13.2 = 58.2$ kips. In the test, the first rivet failed in shear at $P = 181$ kips. Thus, the factor of safety based on P determined by the effective eccentricity is $181/58.2 = 3.1$. If the actual eccentricity, 6.5 in, is used, the allowable P is 37.7 kips, which gives a factor of safety of 4.80.

In the 1978 AISC/ASD specification the allowable stresses on fasteners were increased. For A502 Grade 1 rivets the allowable shear was increased from 15 to 17.5 ksi, so the value of R in the example above is 15.4 kips instead of 13.2 kips and the allowable load based on the effective eccentricity is increased from 58.2 to 67.8 kips. The factor of safety is therefore reduced from 3.1 to 2.67. Allowable stresses for other types of fasteners were increased even more significantly. For example, the allowable shear on A325 bolts with threads in the shear planes was increased from 15 to 21 ksi. With these allowables, the ratio of the factors of safety based on analyses with and without the effective eccentricity would be reduced to $3.1 \times \frac{15}{21} = 2.2$.

In the eighth edition of its ASD Manual, AISC presented an ultimate-strength analysis (Art. 8-23) and provided tables of coefficients C for several fastener patterns by which the allowable eccentric load P is determined from the formula $P = Cr_v$, where r_v is the allowable fastener shear. The factor of safety is about 2.5. The derivation of C is discussed in Art. 8-23. Elastic analysis based on the effective eccentricity was suggested as suitable for fastener geometries not covered by the tables. In the ninth edition (1990) the elastic analysis was again suggested as a suitable one for fastener patterns not covered by the tables, but without the effective eccentricity.

Since connection design by elastic analysis is always conservative compared with ultimate-strength design, it can be used safely for any eccentric-shear connection. Designers who prefer ultimate-strength design may use elastic analysis to obtain a trial design for connections not covered by ultimate-strength tables. A good estimate of the number of fasteners required for a connection such as the one in Fig. 8-36 can be obtained from Eq. (8-5), which was derived for moment connections with fasteners in tension. For connections of this type $\sum y^2$ will be predominant and x for the outermost fastener will be smaller than y so that

$R_x'' = My/\sum y^2$ and $R_y'' = 0$, approximately, and the corresponding distribution of fastener shears is the same as the distribution of the forces R and Q in Fig. 8-10e, which is the basis for Eq. (8-5). Although this neglects the component R' of Eqs. (8-27), the error is offset in part by the omission of $\sum x^2$ in Eq. (8-26b).

Example 8-22-2. Figure 8-40a shows a column bracket to support a hand-operated crane. The runway girder is supported by a plate which is shop-welded to the two bracket plates. The weight of the bridge, truck, girder rail, and lifted load produces a reaction of 7 kips *DL* and 23 kips *LL*. A bearing-type connection with $\frac{3}{4}$-in bolts, with threads not excluded from the shear plane, will be used. Determine the number of bolts required. AISC specifications.

Solution:

ASD. The load on each of the two bracket plates is $(7 + 23)/2 = 15$ kips. The allowable bolt shear $R_{ss} = 21 \times 0.44 = 9.24$ kips. To use the tables in the Manual we compute $C = P/R_{ss} = 15/9.24 = 1.62$. If two vertical rows are used, the eccentricity of the load is 11 in (Fig. 8-40a), and from table XII we find $n = 3$. If only one row of bolts is used, the eccentricity is 8.25 in (Fig. 8-40b), and from table X we find $n = 5$.

LRFD. The factored load on each of the two bracket plates is $(1.2 \times 7 + 1.6 \times 23)/2 = 22.6$ kips. The bolt design shear is $0.75 \times 48 \times 0.44 = 15.8$ kips. To use the tables in the Manual we compute $C = P/R_{ss} = 22.6/15.8 = 1.43$. If two vertical rows are used, the eccentricity of the load is 11 in (Fig. 8-40a), and from table XII we find $n = 3$. If only one row of bolts is used, the eccentricity is 8.25 in (Fig. 8-40b), and from table X we find $n = 5$.

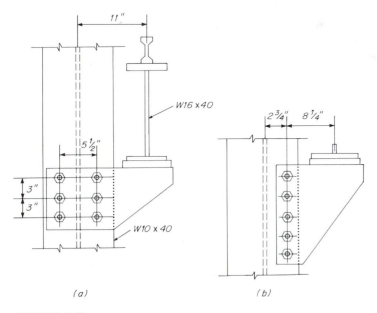

(a)   (b)

FIGURE 8-40

Elastic design. Since elastic analysis is an option if tabulated coefficients are not available for a specific connection, an elastic design of the bracket for this example will be made to demonstrate the procedure.

For the bracket with two vertical rows of bolts we have

$$P = \frac{7 + 23}{2} = 15 \text{ kips per bracket plate}$$

$$M = Pe = 15 \times 11 = 165 \text{ in·kips}$$

$$R_{ss} = 21 \times 0.44 = 9.24 \text{ kips}$$

From Eq. (8-5),

$$n = \sqrt{\frac{6 \times 165}{2 \times 3 \times 9.24} + \frac{1}{4}} - \frac{1}{2} = 3.8 \qquad \text{Try 4}$$

$$\sum r^2 = \sum x^2 + \sum y^2 = 8 \times 2.75^2 + 4(1.5^2 + 4.5^2) = 150.5$$

$$R_x'' = \frac{165 \times 4.5}{150.5} = 4.93$$

$$R_y'' = \frac{165 \times 2.75}{150.5} = 3.02$$

$$R_y' = \frac{15}{8} = 1.88$$

$$R = \sqrt{4.93^2 + (3.02 + 1.88)^2} = 6.95 \text{ kips} < 9.24$$

Although the calculated bolt shear is considerably less than the allowable value, analysis shows that three bolts per row are inadequate ($R = 10.1$ kips > 9.24). Use four bolts per row.

For the bracket with one vertical row of bolts we have

$$M = Pe = 15 \times 8.25 = 123.8 \text{ in·kips}$$

From Eq. (8-5),

$$n = \sqrt{\frac{6 \times 123.8}{1 \times 3 \times 9.24} + \frac{1}{4}} - \frac{1}{2} = 4.7 \qquad \text{Try 5}$$

$$\sum r^2 = 2(3^2 + 6^2) = 90$$

$$R_x'' = \frac{123.8 \times 6}{90} = 8.25$$

$$R_y' = \frac{15}{5} = 3$$

$$R = \sqrt{8.25^2 + 3^2} = 8.78 \text{ kips} < 9.24$$

Use one row of five bolts.

8-23 ECCENTRICALLY LOADED BOLTED OR RIVETED SHEAR CONNECTIONS— ULTIMATE-STRENGTH ANALYSIS

An ultimate-strength analysis for eccentrically loaded shear connections, in which the nonlinear characteristics of the behavior of bolts was accounted for, was developed by Crawford and Kulak.[22] The procedure retains the assumption that the plate rotates as a rigid body and that, consequently, the deformations of the bolts are in proportion to their distance from the center of rotation (refer to Fig. 8-41). The eccentric load P produces a rotation as well as a translation of the fastener group. These two displacements are reduced to a rotation about a point called the *instantaneous center of rotation.*

From experimental studies the maximum displacement at which the first bolt will fail can be established. The bolt at the greatest distance from the center of rotation will be the first to reach this maximum displacement. From the geometry of the situation the displacement of all other fasteners can be determined by simple proportion. The force acting on each fastener is then calculated from the load-versus-deformation relationship. Each fastener force is then resolved into its vertical, horizontal, and twisting-moment components. These three quantities must satisfy the equations of equilibrium.

For the nonlinear load vs. deformation behavior the relationship employed is

$$R_i = R_{ult}(1 - e^{-10\Delta_i})^{0.55} \tag{8-29}$$

where R_i = force in fastener under consideration
  R_{ult} = ultimate strength of fastener
  τ_u = ultimate strength of bolt in shear. For A325 bolts this has generally been taken as 62 percent of the tensile strength (120 ksi) or 74 ksi.
  e = natural logarithm base (2.718)
  Δ_i = deformation of the fastener under consideration

The coefficient 10 and exponent 0.55 were determined from the experimental

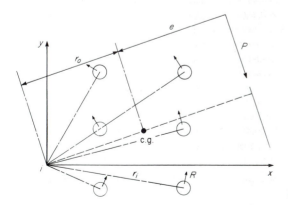

FIGURE 8-41

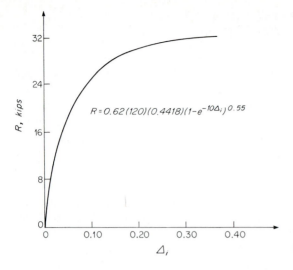

FIGURE 8-42

data. Figure 8-42 represents the result of Eq. (8-29) for a $\frac{3}{4}$-in A325 bolt with threads excluded from the shear plane. (If threads are included in the shear plane, the area of the bolt should be the root area, which is approximately 0.7 times the gross area.)

The equations of equilibrium of Fig. 8-41 are

$$\sum F_x = 0 \qquad \sum R_i \frac{y_i}{r_i} - P_x = 0 \qquad (8\text{-}30a)$$

$$\sum F_y = 0 \qquad \sum R_i \frac{x_i}{r_i} - P_y = 0 \qquad (8\text{-}30b)$$

$$\sum M = 0 \qquad \sum R_i r_i - P(e + r_0) = 0 \qquad (8\text{-}30c)$$

Because the relationship between Δ_i and R_i is nonlinear, these equations cannot be solved directly, so a location of the instantaneous center of rotation must be assumed. The coordinates x_i and y_i with respect to the assumed center are then evaluated for each fastener and the radial distances r_i calculated. The fastener farthest from the center of rotation is assigned the displacement value Δ_{max}, which is the displacement at which the first bolt fails. This value is generally taken as 0.34 in for A325 bolts. The displacement Δ_i for other fasteners in the connection is calculated from

$$\Delta_i = \frac{r}{r_{max}} \Delta_{max} = 0.34 \frac{r}{r_{max}}$$

The value of R_i for each fastener is then calculated, using Eq. (8-29), following which the quantities $R_i x_i/r_i$, $R_i y_i/r_i$, and $R_i r_i$ are calculated. These values represent the vertical component of the fastener force, its horizontal component, and its moment component, respectively. The summations of the individual contributions represent the vertical component, the horizontal component, and the twisting moment, respectively, of the force. From the direction of the load its vertical and horizontal components are converted into consistent values of P. The twisting moment is converted into a consistent value of P by dividing it by the eccentricity of the load with respect to the assumed instantaneous center of rotation. If the three values of P thus obtained are equal, the assumed location was correct. If they are not equal, a new instantaneous center must be selected and the process repeated until satisfactory agreement has been obtained. The procedure can be easily set up for a spreadsheet solution.

If this method of analysis is used in allowable-stress design, the value of P must be divided by a factor of safety. Allowable loads in the tables in the AISC/ASD Manual are based on a factor of safety of approximately 2.5. For LRFD the resistance factor ϕ must be applied.

The ultimate-strength method may also be used for slip-critical connections. In this case R_i is the same for all the fasteners and it is not necessary to calculate Δ_i.

Example 8-23-1. Determine the ultimate strength of the connection shown in Fig. 8-43. Use $\frac{3}{4}$-in-diameter A325 bolts in a bearing-type connection with threads excluded from the shear plane. Assume that the bolt deformation at failure is 0.34 in.

Solution. For $\frac{3}{4}$-in-diameter A325 bolts, Eq. (8-29) gives

$$R = 0.62 \times 120 \times 0.4418(1 - e^{-10\Delta_i})^{0.55} = 32.9(1 - e^{-10\Delta_i})^{0.55}$$

For loads parallel to the y axis, the instantaneous center of rotation will be on the x axis on the opposite side from the load. Calculations for $r_0 = 2$ in to the left of the center of gravity are given in Table 8-3 (top). From the summations in this table we

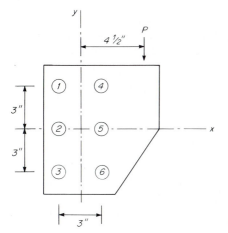

FIGURE 8-43

TABLE 8-3
Ultimate-strength calculations for connection of Fig. 8-43

Fastener	x_i	y_i	r_i	Δ_i	R_i	$\dfrac{R_i x_i}{r_i}$	$R_i r_i$
			$r_0 = 2$ in				
1	0.5	3.0	3.04	0.224	30.92	5.08	94.00
2	0.5	0.0	0.50	0.037	17.25	17.25	8.63
3	0.5	−3.0	3.04	0.224	30.92	5.08	94.00
4	3.5	3.0	4.61	0.340	32.29	24.52	148.86
5	3.5	0.0	3.50	0.258	31.50	31.50	110.25
6	3.5	−3.0	4.61	0.340	32.29	24.52	148.86
						107.95	604.60
			$r_0 = 1.65$ in				
1	0.15	3.0	3.00	0.234	31.12	1.56	93.36
2	0.15	0.0	0.15	0.012	9.92	9.92	1.49
3	0.15	−3.0	3.00	0.234	31.12	1.56	93.36
4	3.15	3.0	4.35	0.340	32.29	23.38	140.46
5	3.15	0.0	3.15	0.246	31.32	31.32	98.66
6	3.15	−3.0	4.35	0.340	32.29	23.38	140.46
						91.12	567.79

get from Eq. (8-30*b*)

$$P_u = 108.0 \text{ kips}$$

and from Eq. (8-30*c*)

$$P_u = \frac{604.60}{2 + 4.5} = 93.0 \text{ kips}$$

A new value of r_0 is selected and the process repeated. For $r_0 = 1.7$ in the result is 93.7 kips from Eq. (8-30*b*) and 92.5 kips from Eq. (8-30*c*). With $r_0 = 1.65$, calculations yield the values in Table 8-3 (bottom), from which

$$P_u = 91.1 \text{ kips}$$

$$P_u = \frac{567.79}{1.65 + 4.5} = 92.3 \text{ kips}$$

Since the differences between the two values of P_u are of opposite sign for $r_0 = 1.7$ in and $r_0 = 1.65$ in, the location of the instantaneous center of rotation has been bounded and P_u is between 92.5 and 92.3, say, $P_u = 92.4$ kips. For allowable-stress design, using a factor of safety of 2.5, the allowable value of P is $92.4/2.5 = 37.0$ kips. For LRFD design strength is obtained by multiplying computed ultimate strengths by $\phi = 0.75$ and, as noted on p. 158, by 0.8. Therefore, the design strength is $0.75 \times 0.80 \times 92.0 = 55.2$ kips. The ratio of the LRFD and ASD values $55.2/36.8 = 1.50$ corresponds to the LRFD load-factor multipliers.

In using the ultimate-strength procedure for connections in plastically designed structures it is important to note that instead of R_{ult} in Eq. (8-29) the value computed with 1.7 times the ASD allowable stress must be used, where 1.7 is the allowable-stress multiplier specified in chap. N of the specification.

Example 8-23-2. Same as Example 8-23-1 except design the connection to be slip-resistant.

Solution. Since R_i is the same for all the fasteners in a slip-resistant connection, it may be taken as unity in the calculations. The solution is shown in Table 8.4. From Table 8-4 (top)

$$P_u = 3.504 R_s$$

$$P_u = \frac{17.82}{1.6 + 4.5} R_s = 2.923 R_s$$

From Table 8-4 (bottom)

$$P_u = 2.414 R_s$$

$$P_u = \frac{17.48}{1.5 + 4.5} R_s = 2.914 R_s$$

Since the differences are reversed in sign, the value of r_0 has been bounded. Use $P_u = 2.92 R_s$.

TABLE 8-4
Slip-resistant strength calculations for connection of Fig. 8-43

Fastener	x_i	y_i	r_i	$\dfrac{x_i}{r_i}$	$R_i r_i$
		$r_0 = 1.6$ in			
1	0.10	3.0	3.00	0.033	3.00
2	0.10	0.0	0.10	1.000	0.10
3	0.10	−3.0	3.00	0.033	3.00
4	3.10	3.0	4.31	0.719	4.31
5	3.10	0.0	3.10	1.000	3.10
6	3.10	3.0	4.31	0.719	4.31
				3.504	17.82
		$r_0 = 1.5$ in			
1	0.0	3.0	3.00	0.000	3.00
2	0.0	0.0	0.00	0.000	0.00
3	0.0	−3.0	3.00	0.000	3.00
4	3.0	3.0	4.24	0.707	4.24
5	3.0	0.0	3.00	1.000	3.00
6	3.0	3.0	4.24	0.707	4.24
				2.414	17.48

The AISC/LRFD Manual contains tables of coefficients C, for a number of connections, based on the fastener-strength formula of Eq. (8-29), which enable the eccentric factored load P_u to be determined from the formula $P_u = C\phi r_v$, where r_v is the design strength of the fastener.

Based on the analysis of a large number of joints, Kulak and Crawford[22] developed the following formula for the coefficient C for joints with one line and two lines of fasteners:

$$C = \alpha' I^\beta$$

where $\quad I = I_x + I_y = \sum (x^2 + y^2)$ for $A_b = 1$
$\quad\quad I_x, I_y = $ moments of inertia of fastener areas
$\quad\quad\quad x, y = $ coordinate axes with origin at center of gravity of fastener group
$\quad\quad\quad A_b = $ fastener area

The coefficient α' is given by

$$\alpha' = \begin{cases} 0.0104 + \dfrac{0.625}{e} + \dfrac{4.719}{e^2} - \dfrac{6.750}{e^3} & \text{for one line of fasteners} \\[3mm] 0.0125 + \dfrac{0.814}{e} + \dfrac{5.550}{e^2} - \dfrac{8.220}{e^3} & \text{for two lines of fasteners} \end{cases}$$

and the exponent β by

$$\beta = \begin{cases} 0.645 - \dfrac{0.129}{e} - \dfrac{3.850}{e^2} + \dfrac{7.430}{e^3} & \text{for one line of fasteners} \\[3mm] 0.651 - \dfrac{0.183}{e} - \dfrac{3.130}{e^2} + \dfrac{6.250}{e^3} & \text{for two lines of fasteners} \end{cases}$$

Values of the load P for the connection shown in Fig. 8-43, based on the several methods of analysis discussed in Arts. 8-22 and 8-23, are given in Table 8-5. It will be noted that values by the ultimate-strength analyses are essentially the same. However, the elastic values using the reduced eccentricity of Art. 8-22 are about 42 percent larger than those based on the actual eccentricity and 23 percent larger than the average of the ultimate-strength values. Of course, these differences vary with the fastener pattern and the direction and eccentricity of the load, and the difference between the ultimate-strength values and the elastic values based on the actual eccentricity may be much larger. Also, the 23 percent larger effective-eccentricity values, compared with the ultimate-strength values, show why the reduced-eccentricity analysis was abandoned in the 1990 ASD Manual, as was mentioned in Art. 8-22.

In ultimate-strength design of eccentric-shear connections of the type shown in Fig. 8-36 for which tables are not available, Eq. (8-5) may be used to obtain an initial configuration, as was discussed in Art. 8-22.

TABLE 8-5
Load P, kips, for connection of Fig. 8-43,
A325 bolts, bearing-type connection,
threads excluded

Basis	ASD*	LRFD†
Elastic analysis:		
Actual eccentricity	32.5	48.8
Reduced eccentricity	46.4	69.5
Ultimate-strength analysis:		
Eq. (8-24)‡	37.0	55.2
AISC table§	37.5	56.2
Coefficient C¶	38.7	58.1

* Allowable value
† Design strength, $\phi = 0.75$
‡ Factor of safety = 2.5
§ Interpolation for $e = 4.5$ in
¶ $I = 49.5$ in^2, $\alpha' = 0.3773$, $\beta = 0.5244$, $C = \alpha'I^\beta = 2.92$

8-24 ECCENTRICALLY LOADED WELDED SHEAR CONNECTIONS—ELASTIC ANALYSIS

Figure 8-44 shows a fillet-welded connection of a C-shaped member which transmits the eccentric force P to the member or gusset plate to which it is welded. For purposes of analysis the weld leg is assumed to be of unit dimension and its location is defined by the edge along which it is deposited. Resolving the force P into its components P_x and P_y and the torsional moment Pe acting at the center of gravity of the weldment, we get the following for the force q per unit length of weld,

$$q'_x = \frac{P_x}{L} \tag{8-31a}$$

$$q'_y = \frac{P_y}{L} \tag{8-31b}$$

$$q''_x = \frac{Pey}{J} \tag{8-31c}$$

$$q''_y = \frac{Pex}{J} \tag{8-31d}$$

where L = length of the weld
x, y = coordinates with origin at O of point under consideration
J = polar moment of inertia

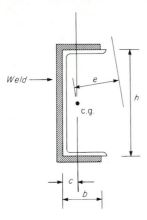

Weld

e

h

c.g.

c

b

FIGURE 8-44

The polar moment of inertia is given by

$$J = I_x + I_y = \sum I_{xx} + \sum Ay^2 + \sum I_{yy} + \sum Ax^2$$

in which I_{xx} and I_{yy} are the moments of inertia of a segment of the weldment with respect to its own controidal axes and A is its cross-sectional area. The total force in the weld is obtained from

$$q = \sqrt{(q'_x + q''_x)^2 + (q'_y + q''_y)^2} \tag{8-32}$$

The resultant force permits the weld to be sized according to procedures discussed in Chap. 3.

8-25 ECCENTRICALLY LOADED WELDED SHEAR CONNECTIONS— ULTIMATE-STRENGTH ANALYSIS

In Art. 2-12 it was pointed out that welds subject to transverse shear (shear perpendicular to the axis of the weld) are substantially stronger than welds subject to longitudinal shear. Tests on welds reveal that both strength and deformation capacity are functions of the direction of the shear in relation to the axis of the weld. Longitudinal welds are the weakest but have the greatest ductility, while transverse welds are the strongest but have the least ductility. These two effects are taken into account in the following ultimate-strength analysis by Butler of fillet-welded connections subjected to eccentric loading.[23]

Figure 8-45 shows a C-shaped weld configuration. The shear force on any element is perpendicular to the radius from the instantaneous center. Based on test data of connections made with E70 electrodes (Ref. 24) the ultimate strength can be expressed by

$$R_{i,\text{ult}} = \frac{10 + \theta}{10 + 0.582\theta} \times 0.791 F_{\text{EXX}} t \tag{8-33}$$

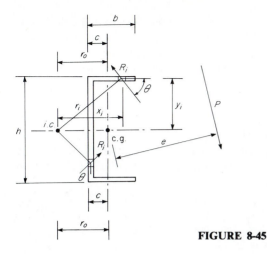

FIGURE 8-45

where $R_{i,\text{ult}}$ = ultimate shear force on element, kips per inch of length
$\quad\quad\theta$ = acute angle between shear force and axis of weld, deg
$\quad F_{\text{EXX}}$ = weld electrode strength, ksi
$\quad\quad t$ = throat dimension of weld, in

Figure 8-46 is a plot of Eq. (8-33) for E70 electrodes.
The deformation $\Delta_{i,\text{max}}$ at rupture of an element is evaluated from

$$\Delta_{i,\text{max}} = \Delta_0\left(\frac{\theta}{5} + 1\right)^{-0.47} \tag{8-34}$$

where $\Delta_0 = 0.11$ in, the deformation for $\theta = 0$. This value of Δ_0 is based on the tests of Ref. 24.

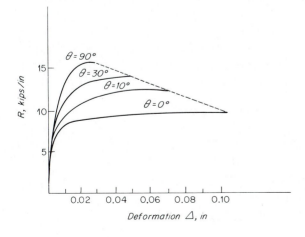

FIGURE 8-46
Load-deformation curves of E70
$\frac{1}{4}$-in fillet welds, kips/in.

It is necessary to first determine the critical element. Because the deformations of the weld segments are assumed to vary linearly with their distances r_i from the instantaneous center, the element with the smallest value of $\Delta_{i,max}/r_i$ will be critical. With the critical element thus determined, the deformation Δ_i of the other elements is given by

$$\Delta_i = \frac{r_i}{r_{i,max}} \Delta_{i,max} \tag{8-35}$$

where $\Delta_{i,max}$ is the value for the critical element and $r_{i,max}$ = radial distance to the critical element. With the displacements determined by Eq. (8-35) the force in each element is calculated from

$$R_i = R_{i,ult}(1 - e^{-k_1\Delta_i/\Delta_0})^{k_2} \tag{8-36}$$

where R_i = shear force on element i, kips per inch of length
$\quad e$ = base of natural logarithm = 2.718
$\quad k_1 = 8.274e^{0.0114\theta}$
$\quad k_2 = 0.4e^{0.0146\theta}$

The forces in the elements are then resolved into their horizontal, vertical, and moment components according to

$$R_y = R_i l_i \frac{x_i}{r_i} \tag{8-37a}$$

$$R_x = R_i l_i \frac{y_i}{r_i} \tag{8-37b}$$

$$Re = R_i r_i \tag{8-37c}$$

where l_i = length of element.

The summations of the individual contributions represent the vertical component, the horizontal component, and the twisting moment, respectively. From the direction of the load its vertical and horizontal components are converted into consistent values of P. The twisting moment is converted into a consistent value of P by dividing it by the eccentricity of the load with respect to the assumed instantaneous center of rotation. If the three values of P thus obtained are equal, the assumed location was correct. If they are not equal, a new instantaneous center must be selected and the process repeated until satisfactory agreement has been obtained. The procedure can be easily set up for a spreadsheet solution.

Steps in the procedure just described are as follows:

1. Divide the weld configuration into segments.
2. Assume the location of the instantaneous center of rotation.
3. Compute x_i, y_i, and r_i for the centroid of each segment.
4. Compute the angle θ_i for each segment.
5. Compute the deformation $\Delta_{i,max}$ of each segment [Eq. (8-34)].

6. Calculate $\Delta_{i,\max}/r_i$ for each segment.

7. With the critical segment identified (the element with the smallest value of $\Delta_{i,\max}/r_i$) calculate Δ_i for each segment [Eq. (8-35)].

8. Compute the ultimate shear strength $R_{i,\mathrm{ult}}$ for each segment [Eq. (8-33)].

9. Compute k_1 and k_2 for each segment [Eq. (8-36)].

10. Compute the resisting force R_i for each segment [Eq. (8-36)].

11. Calculate the vertical, horizontal, and moment components for each segment [Eqs. (8-37)].

12. The summations of the individual contributions represent the vertical component, the horizontal component, and the twisting moment, respectively. From the direction of the load its vertical and horizontal components are converted into consistent values of P. The twisting moment is converted into a consistent value of P by dividing it by the eccentricity of the load with respect to the assumed instantaneous center of rotation. If the three values of P thus obtained are equal, the assumed location was correct. If they are not equal, a new instantaneous center must be selected and the process repeated until satisfactory agreement has been obtained.

   The design of eccentric-shear connections by the procedure just described is facilitated for a number of weld patterns by tables of coefficients, to be discussed later, in the AISC Manuals. In developing the LRFD tables the upper limit of the resistance R from Eq. (8-36) was taken to be the value corresponding to the LRFD-specified strength $0.6F_{\mathrm{EXX}}$, while for the ASD tables the ultimate load obtained using the load-deformation curves of Fig. 8-46 was multiplied by $0.3F_{\mathrm{EXX}}\,tl/R_{i,\max}$, where $R_{i,\max}$ is from Eq. (8-36). This puts a direction-independent limit on the direction-dependent strength of an element. For example, Fig. 8-46 shows that the LRFD-specified strength of $\frac{1}{4}$-in E70 fillet welds, $0.6 \times 70 \times 0.25 \times 0.707 = 7.42$ kips/in, is about 80 percent of the average of the test results for longitudinal shear ($\theta = 0°$) and about 50 percent for transverse shear ($\theta = 90°$). Since the scatter of test results about the plots of Eq. (8-33) was about the same for all values of θ, it would seem to be more logical to account for differences between the results of laboratory tests and field performance by imposing a uniform reduction, such as is given by the LRFD resistance factor ϕ.

   Elastic analysis may be used in lieu of ultimate-strength analysis for connections not covered by the Manual tables. However, elastic analysis is conservative and may be overly so in some cases. Of course, it may always be used to obtain a trial configuration for ultimate-strength design of weldments not covered by the tables.

AISC/LRFD. Part 5 of the AISC Manual gives the factored eccentric load P_u for a variety of weld configurations in the form

$$P_u = CC_1 Dl \tag{8-38}$$

where C = tabulated coefficient

$\quad\quad C_1$ = coefficient for electrode

$\quad\quad D$ = number of sixteenths of an inch in weld size (not the throat dimension)

$\quad\quad l$ = length of a characteristic weld in the configuration

The coefficient C was obtained by multiplying the resultant P of the element components given by Eqs. (8-37) by the specified resistance factor $\phi = 0.75$ but with the stress on any weld element limited to $0.6F_{EXX}$. The coefficient C_1 is given in the following table:

Electrode	E60	E70	E80	E90	E100	E110
C_1	0.857	1	1.03	1.16	1.21	1.34

The ratio of C_1 for the electrode to the value for the E70 electrode equals the ratio of the electrode strengths. Values of the ratios for E80 and E90 electrodes were reduced by 10 percent and for the E100 and E110 electrodes by 15 percent to allow for uncertainties of extrapolation from the E70 test results.

Tables are given for several values of the inclination of P with respect to the weldment. Interpolation for intermediate angles may be unconservative, so for inclinations other than those tabulated, values for the next lower angle should be used. Procedures for interpolation have been suggested by Iwankiw.[25]

AISC/ASD. The following formulas for $R_{i,ult}$, $\Delta_{i,max}$, and R_i in the analysis recommended in part 4 of the ASD Manual are based on tests of connections made with $\frac{1}{4}$-in E60 electrodes.[26] They differ somewhat from Eqs. (8-33), (8-34), and (8-36).

$$R_{i,ult} = \frac{10 + \theta}{0.92 + 0.0603\theta} \text{ kips/in}/\tfrac{1}{4} \text{ in} \tag{8-39}$$

$$\Delta_{i,max} = 0.225(\theta + 5)^{-0.47} \tag{8-40}$$

$$R_i = R_{i,ult}(1 - e^{-\mu\Delta})^{\lambda} \tag{8-41}$$

where $\mu = 75e^{0.0114\theta}$ and $\lambda = 0.4e^{0.0146\theta}$.

The Manual gives the allowable eccentric load P for a variety of weld configurations in the form

$$P = CC_1Dl$$

where C = tabulated coefficient

$\quad\quad C_1$ = coefficient for electrode

$\quad\quad D$ = number of sixteenths of inch in weld size (not the throat dimension)

$\quad\quad l$ = length of a characteristic weld in the configuration

The coefficient C was determined by multiplying the value of $R_{i,\text{ult}}$ from Eq. (8-39) by $\frac{70}{60}$ to convert the result to E70 electrodes and by $\frac{1}{4}$ to express it in terms of a weld size of $\frac{1}{16}$ in. This result was multiplied by 0.3 to obtain the allowable stress, which yields an apparent factor of safety of 3.33. The true factor of safety is smaller, however, because evaluation of the test results was based on the theoretical throat, which, because of weld penetration and reinforcement, is always smaller than the effective throat. Furthermore a tolerance of $\frac{1}{16}$ in in fit-up is permitted by most specifications, also reducing the strength of the weld.

The coefficient C_1 is the ratio of the electrode strengths; e.g., for E90 electrodes $C_1 = \frac{90}{70} = 1.29$.

Example 8-25-1: Ultimate-strength analysis. Determine the ultimate strength of the C-shaped weldment shown in Fig. 8-47. The vertical dimension is 6 in and each horizontal leg is 2 in. The weld is a $\frac{1}{4}$-in fillet with E70 electrodes.

Solution. The weldment is symmetrical about the x axis, so only half of it need be analyzed. By inspection the summation of the horizontal components will be zero. An initial location of the instantaneous center is selected at $r_0 = 3$ in to the left of the vertical weld. Divide the weldment into five segments, as shown in Fig. 8-47. Calculations for this case are presented in Table 8-6, from which equilibrium in the y direction yields

$$P_u = 2 \times 57.15 = 114.30 \text{ kips}$$

Equilibrium of the torsional moment yields

$$P_u = \frac{2 \times 281.987}{3.0 + 3.0} = 94.0 \text{ kips}$$

Since the values of P_u are not equal, a new location of the instantaneous center must be chosen. After several iterations the following solution for $r_0 = 1.40$ in is obtained. Calculations are presented in Table 8-7, from which equilibrium in the y direction yields

$$P_u = 2 \times 45.18 = 90.36 \text{ kips}$$

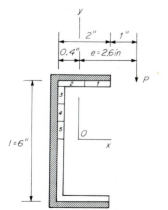

FIGURE 8-47

TABLE 8-6
Solution for $r_0 = 3$ in

Segment	l, in	x_i, in	y_i, in	r_i, in	θ_i, deg	$\Delta_{i,max}$, in	$\dfrac{\Delta_{i,max}}{r_i}$
1	1	4.5	3	5.41	56.3	0.0339	0.0063
2	1	3.5	3	4.61	49.4	0.0358	0.0078
3	1	3.0	2.5	3.91	39.8	0.0392	0.0100
4	1	3.0	1.5	3.35	26.6	0.0462	0.0138
5	1	3.0	0.5	3.04	9.5	0.0667	0.0219

Segment	Δ_i	$R_{i,ult}$	k_1	k_2	R_i	$R_i\dfrac{x_i}{r_i}$	$R_i r_i$
1	0.0339	15.173	15.720	0.9100	15.064	12.53	81.498
2	0.0289	15.002	14.531	0.8228	14.730	11.18	67.906
3	0.0245	14.697	13.025	0.7152	14.115	10.83	55.188
4	0.0210	14.058	11.205	0.5898	13.057	11.69	43.740
5	0.0190	12.290	9.220	0.4595	11.071	10.92	33.655
						$\Sigma = 57.15$	281.987

Equilibrium of the torsional moment yields

$$P_u = \frac{2 \times 199.649}{1.4 + 3.0} = 90.75 \text{ kips}$$

Therefore the ultimate capacity can be taken to be 90 kips.

TABLE 8-7
Solution for $r_0 = 1.40$ in

Segment	l, in	x_i, in	y_i, in	r_i, in	θ_i, deg	$\Delta_{i,max}$, in	$\dfrac{\Delta_{i,max}}{r_i}$
1	1	2.90	3.0	4.17	44.0	0.0376	0.0090
2	1	1.90	3.0	3.55	32.3	0.0428	0.0120
3	1	1.40	2.5	2.87	60.8	0.0328	0.0114
4	1	1.40	1.5	2.05	47.0	0.0366	0.0178
5	1	1.40	0.5	1.49	19.7	0.0519	0.0348

Segment	Δ_i	$R_{i,ult}$	k_1	k_2	R_i	$R_i\dfrac{x_i}{r_i}$	$R_i r_i$
1	0.0376	14.842	13.663	0.7604	14.736	10.25	61.450
2	0.0320	14.375	11.957	0.6410	14.089	7.54	50.016
3	0.0259	15.267	16.548	0.9718	14.965	7.30	42.951
4	0.0185	14.934	14.139	0.7945	13.823	9.44	28.337
5	0.0134	13.542	10.357	0.5333	11.339	10.65	16.895
						$\Sigma = 45.18$	199.649

Example 8-25-2 (AISC/ASD). Determine the allowable load P for the C-shaped weldment shown in Fig. 8-47. The vertical dimension is 6 in and each horizontal leg is 2 in. The weld is a $\frac{1}{4}$-in fillet with E70 electrodes.

Solution. The ASD Manual tables are entered with the following parameters:

$$k = \frac{b}{l} = \frac{2}{6} = 0.333 \qquad a = \frac{e}{l} = \frac{2.6}{6} = 0.433$$

Interpolation in table XXIII gives $C = 0.939$. For E70 electrodes $C_1 = 1.0$. Then from Eq. (8-38)

$$P = 0.939 \times 1.0 \times 4 \times 6 = 22.5 \text{ kips}$$

Example 8-25-3 (AISC/LRFD). Determine the factored load P for the C-shaped weldment shown in Fig. 8-47. The vertical dimension is 6 in and each horizontal leg is 2 in. The weld is a $\frac{1}{4}$-in fillet with E70 electrodes.

Solution. The LRFD Manual tables are entered with the following parameters:

$$k = \frac{b}{l} = \frac{2}{6} = 0.333 \qquad a = \frac{e}{l} = \frac{2.6}{6} = 0.433$$

Interpolation in table XXII gives $C = 1.505$. For E70 electrodes $C_1 = 1.0$. Then from Eq. (8-38)

$$P = 1.505 \times 1.0 \times 4 \times 6 = 36.1 \text{ kips}$$

Example 8-25-4: Elastic analysis. Determine the allowable load P for the C-shaped weldment shown in Fig. 8-47. The vertical dimension is 6 in and each horizontal leg is 2 in. The weld is a $\frac{1}{4}$-in fillet with E70 electrodes.

Solution. Compute the moment of inertia:

$$\frac{1}{12} \times 1 \times 6^3 = 18$$
$$2(\frac{1}{12} \times 2 \times 1^3) = 0.33$$
$$2(2 \times 1) \times 3^2 = 36.0$$
$$\frac{1}{12} \times 6 \times 1^3 = 0.5$$
$$(6 \times 1) \times 0.4^2 = 0.96$$
$$2(\frac{1}{12} \times 1 \times 2^3) = 1.33$$
$$2(2 \times 1)(1 - 0.4)^2 = \underline{1.44}$$
$$I = 58.56$$

Note that the sum of the first and third quantities constitutes 92 percent of the total. This will be the case for typical welds of this geometry.

$$q_y' = \frac{P}{L} = \frac{P}{10}$$

$$q_x'' = \frac{P \times 2.6 \times 3}{58.56} = \frac{7.8}{58.56} P$$

$$q_y'' = \frac{P \times 2.6 \times 1.6}{58.56} = \frac{4.16}{58.56} P$$

$$q = \left[\left(\frac{7.8}{58.56} P \right)^2 + \left(\frac{P}{10} + \frac{4.16}{58.56} P \right)^2 \right]^{0.5} = 0.2168P$$

AISC/ASD. The allowable capacity for a $\frac{1}{4}$-in fillet weld is

$$q = 0.707 \times 0.25 \times 0.3 \times 70 = 3.71 \text{ kips/in}$$

Therefore

$$3.71 = 0.2168P$$

$$P = 17.1 \text{ kips} \qquad \text{(Allowable load)}$$

AISC/LRFD. The strength of a $\frac{1}{4}$-in fillet weld, with $\phi = 0.75$, is

$$q = 0.75 \times 0.707 \times 0.25 \times 0.6 \times 70 = 5.57 \text{ kips/in}$$

Therefore

$$5.57 = 0.2168P$$

$$P = 25.7 \text{ kips} \qquad \text{(Design strength)}$$

8-26   HAUNCHED CONNECTIONS

Corner connections are sometimes tapered, as in Fig. 8-48a, or curved, as in Fig. 8-48b. This is usually done for architectural reasons. An example is shown in Fig. 2-3. Methods of analysis have been developed for both elastic design[27,28] and plastic design[29] of tapered haunches and curved haunches. Tests of elastically designed haunches show that they have adequate strength but, because of premature local buckling, may lack the rotation capacity needed for plastically designed structures.

The following procedure is recommended for plastic design of the tapered haunch.[29,30] The plastic section modulus must be adequate at all cross sections, of course, but it has been shown that it is sufficient to check it at sections 1, 2, and 3 (Fig. 8-48a). Figure 8-48c shows that the stress distribution on a cross section normal to the axis of the member is not symmetrical if both flanges are yielded and $A_c = A_t$. For symmetry, $F_y A_c \cos \beta$ must equal $F_y A_t$, from which

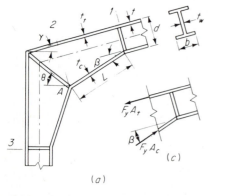

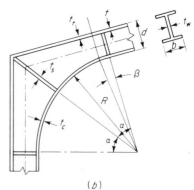

FIGURE 8-48

$A_c = A_t/\cos \beta$. This condition could be fulfilled by making $t_c = t_t/\cos \beta$. However, even if $\beta = 20°$, A_c would be only 6 percent larger than A_t, which is small enough to be neglected. Therefore, for haunches of usual proportions the flange areas can be made equal and the cross section analyzed as a symmetrical one.

Connections of this type are generally used in one-story frames, so axial compression and shear are not likely to influence proportioning for bending. Since interaction of bending and axial compression is given by Eqs. (6-11), it will be noted that the connection can be sized for bending alone if $P/P_y \leq 0.15$.

Lateral support must be provided at sections 1, 2, and 3 and the dimensions of the flange checked for stability. The required ratio b/t is the same as for beams of uniform depth (Art. 9-13). Thus, for A36 steel, the projecting-element slenderness is 8.5, so in terms of the full width b in Fig. 8-48, $b/t = 17$. An approximate solution for lateral-torsional buckling can be obtained by treating the flange as a column. For $\beta \approx 12°$, haunches of usual proportions are plastic throughout most of the length. To assure the necessary rotation capacity for plastic behavior, it is assumed that the flange is just beginning to strain harden, so $\epsilon = \epsilon_s$. Thus

$$F_{cr} = F_y = \frac{\pi^2 E_s}{(KL/r)^2} \tag{a}$$

where E_s is the strain-hardening modulus. With $E_s = 800$ ksi, $F_y = 36$ ksi, and $r = b/\sqrt{12}$, and taking $K = 0.8$ to allow for some rotational restraint, Eq. (a) gives $L/b = 5.3$ as the critical slenderness for an A36-steel haunch.[30] Tests show that this limit is not unreasonable and cannot be increased very much without a compensating increase in A_c. (For haunches in elastically designed structures, the flange need only reach ϵ_y. In this case Young's modulus applies, and $L/b = 5.3\sqrt{(30,000/800)} = 32$ for A36 steel.)

If the limit L/b exceeds 5.3, stability can be maintained by using a thicker flange. According to Ref. 29, the required increase in thickness is given by $\Delta t_c = 0.1(L/b - 6)$. However, this was based on a limiting value $L/b = 6$ and should be changed for $L/b = 5.3$ to

$$t = 0.1\left(\frac{L}{b} - 5.3\right) \tag{8-42}$$

The critical length can also be increased by proportioning the haunch with $\beta > 12°$. This results in a flange which yields over only part of its length and remains elastic over the remainder. In tests reported in Ref. 29, a haunch with $L/b = 10$ and $\beta = 21°$ developed a moment about 10 percent larger than, and rotation capacity equal to, that of a similar haunch with $L/b = 5$ and $\beta = 12°$. The flange of the haunch with $\beta = 21°$ yielded over about 20 percent of its length. Therefore, it would seem reasonable to allow values of L/b varying linearly with β within the range tested.

Since the critical length $L = 5.3b$ determined above is based on the assumption that the flange is yielded to the point of beginning of strain hardening for its full length, it may be conservative in some cases. This is because the range of

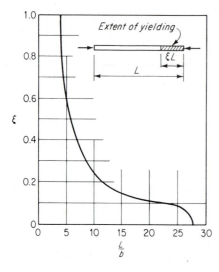

FIGURE 8-49

available sizes of standard shapes, plates, etc., is such that there is usually excess moment capacity. There is no simple way to evaluate this effect. The curve in Fig. 8-49 shows the variation of L/b with the extent of the yielded zone according to Ref. 29. By determining the distance from section 1 in Fig. 8-48a to the cross section where the haunch is at the yield moment $M_y = F_y S_x$, the extent of the yielded zone and the corresponding value of L/b can be determined. However, it will be noted that the increase in L/b over the value for a flange yielded the full length of the haunch is not significant unless the taper is such as to produce M_y at a section less than halfway from section 1 to section 2. This will usually require a value of β considerably in excess of 12°.

Stiffeners can be proportioned by assuming that they equilibrate the forces in the flanges which meet at their ends. Thus, for the stiffener at section 1,

$$F_y A_s = F_y A_c \sin \beta \qquad (8\text{-}43)$$

where A_s is the area of the two stiffeners, one on each side of the web. Equilibrium of forces at A in Fig. 8-48a leads to the following formula for the area of the pair of stiffeners at this point:[30]

$$A_s = \frac{A_{c1} \cos (\beta_1 + \gamma) - A_{c2} \sin \beta_2}{\cos \theta} \qquad (8\text{-}44)$$

where A_{c1} = area of inner flange of rafter haunch
A_{c2} = area of inner flange of column haunch
β_1 = angle of taper of rafter haunch
β_2 = angle of taper of column haunch
θ = angle of inclination of stiffener
γ = angle of inclination of rafter

An example of the design of a tapered haunch is given in DP9-15-1. A typical curved knee is shown in Fig. 8-48b. It is shown in Ref. 29 that the critical section for bending in haunches of practical proportions will be at the cross section for which $\beta = 12°$. Therefore, the thickness t_t of the outer flange can be determined from $M_p = F_y Z$ at this cross section. For a simpler solution, it may be taken conservatively as $\frac{4}{3}t$. As is the case for the tapered haunch, $A_c = A_t/\cos \beta$ if the cross section is computed as a symmetrical one. However, since $\beta \approx 12°$ at the critical section, t_c can be made equal to t_t.

The curved compression flange imposes an additional restriction on the thickness t_c. Because the radial resultant of the flange stresses at two adjacent cross sections is directed inward (Fig. 8-50a), the result is a cross bending of the flange as shown in Fig. 8-50b. This has two effects: (1) it reduces the longitudinal bending stress at a point such as a in Fig. 8-50b because of the reduced distance to the neutral axis, and (2) it produces transverse bending stresses in the flange, which are maximum at the juncture of the flange and web. The radial resultant P_R of the flange forces on a unit width of flange, taken at cross sections a unit distance apart (Fig. 8-50a), is

$$P_R = F_y \times 1 \times t_c \times \phi = \frac{F_y t_c}{R} \qquad (b)$$

Therefore, the bending moment at the web (Fig. 8-50b) is $(F_y t_c/R) \times b^2/8$. Equating this to the plastic moment of the unit strip, $F_y t^2/4$, gives

$$t_c \geq \frac{b^2}{2R} \qquad (8\text{-}45a)$$

which can also be written

$$\frac{b}{t_c} \leq \frac{2R}{b} \qquad (8\text{-}45b)$$

In this form, we have a flange slenderness limit which is in addition to the limit for local buckling.

Lateral-torsional buckling of the compression flange of the curved knee can be prevented by using the limiting length $L = 5.3b$ (for A36 steel) as for the tapered haunch, where L is the arc length of the curved flange between points of lateral support.[30]

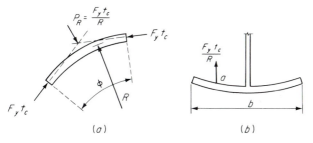

(a) (b) **FIGURE 8-50**

Although radial components of the force in the curved flange can be equili-
brated by the web of the knee, stiffeners at the points of tangency and at the
corner should be provided to guard against buckling of the web. It is conservative to proportion these stiffeners for the resultant of the radial components on
either side of the stiffener, midway to the adjacent stiffeners. This is determined as
follows. The radial component for a unit length of flange is bP_R, where P_R is the
component for a unit width given by Eq. (b). The component of this force parallel
to the stiffener is $bP_R \cos \phi$, where ϕ is the angle between the radius through the
stiffener and the radius to any element. Therefore, the force on the stiffener at the
corner is given by

$$P = 2 \int_0^{\alpha/2} \frac{bt_c F_y}{R} R \, d\phi \cos \phi = 2F_y A_f \int_0^{\alpha/2} \cos \phi \, d\phi = 2F_y A_f \sin \frac{\alpha}{2} \quad (8\text{-}46)$$

where α is half the central angle (Fig. 8-48). Of course, the force for the stiffeners
at a point of tangency is one-half the value from Eq. (8-46).

Example 8-26-1. Proportion the curved knee shown in Fig. 8-51. The adjoining
rafter is a W24 × 76 and the column a W24 × 84, both A36 steel.

Solution. The dimensions of the adjoining sections are

W24 × 76: $d = 23.92$ $b = 8.99$ $t_f = 0.680$ $t_w = 0.440$

W24 × 84: $d = 24.10$ $b = 9.02$ $t_f = 0.770$ $t_w = 0.470$

The central half angle α is $(90° - 16°40')/2 = 36°40' = 0.64$ rad. The critical
length of flange is $L = \alpha R = 5.3b$. The flange width of the knee should be the same
as that of the W24's, $b = 9$ in, so

$$0.64R = 5.3 \times 9 \qquad R = 75 \text{ in}$$

Therefore, the 68.5-in radius of the knee is satisfactory.

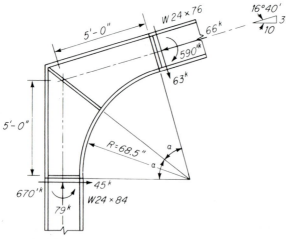

FIGURE 8-51

A $\frac{7}{16}$-in plate ($t = 0.438$ in) will be used for the web of the knee to match the webs of the W24's. The required flange area will be determined by the moment at the critical section for bending, which is at $\beta = 12°$ from the point of tangency.

The depth of the knee at the critical section adjacent to the column is

$$24.10 + R(1 - \cos 12°) = 24.10 + 68.5 \times 0.022 = 24.10 + 1.51 = 25.61 \text{ in}$$

The moment at this section is

$$M = 670 \times 12 + 45R \sin 12° - 79\left(\frac{d_{12°}}{2} - \frac{d_{0°}}{2}\right)$$

$$= 8040 + (45 \times 68.5 \times 0.208) - 39.5(25.61 - 24.10) = 8620 \text{ in·kips}$$

The depth of the knee and the moment at the critical section adjacent to the rafter are found similarly to be 25.4 in and 7930 in·kips. The required area of the flange is found from $ZF_y = M$, which gives

$$Z = A_f d_f + \frac{t_w d_w^2}{4} = \frac{M}{F_y}$$

Assuming the flange to be $\frac{7}{8}$ in thick, $d_f = 25.61 - 0.88 = 24.73$ in, and $d_w = 24.72 - 0.88 = 23.84$. Therefore

$$24.73 A_f + \frac{0.438 \times 23.84^2}{4} = \frac{8620}{36}$$

from which $A_f = 7.2$ in². A $\frac{13}{16} \times 9$ in plate gives 7.31 in². The ratio b/t for this flange is $9/0.812 = 11.1$. The permissible limits are 17 for local buckling and, from Eq. (8-45b), $2R/b = 2 \times 68.5/9 = 15.2$ for cross bending of the flange. Therefore, the $\frac{13}{16} \times 9$ in flange is satisfactory.

The stiffener force is given by Eq. (8-46). If the stiffeners are made of the same steel as the knee, the stiffener area is $A_s = 2A_f \sin(\alpha/2) = 2 \times 7.31 \times \sin 18°20' = 4.6$ in² for the stiffeners at the corner and half this amount for the stiffeners at the points of tangency. The corner stiffeners can be two $\frac{9}{16} \times 4$ in plates ($\frac{1}{2} \times 4$ should be ample) and those at the tangent point two $\frac{1}{4} \times 4$ in plates.

8-27 COLUMN SPLICES

Columns for multistory buildings are usually fabricated in two-story lengths. Although the reduction in load at successively higher stories ordinarily would permit a different size for each story, with a consequent saving in weight, the extra cost of splices and erection would more than offset any saving in cost of material. For an odd number of stories, the top section may be either one or three stories long. Columns sections are usually spliced 2 to 3 ft above the finished floor line to avoid interference with beam and girder connections. In columns with end moments this also puts the splice at a section with a smaller moment.

The ends of each section usually are finished to a plane surface for good contact. This means that, as far as the axial load is concerned, no splice at all is needed, since the load is resisted by bearing over the area in contact. However, splice plates are required because of shears and moments due to wind or other loads, and even if no shears and moments existed, it is obvious that some sort of connection is called for. The AISC specifications require columns which are finished to bear at splices or which bear on bearing plates to have enough fasteners to "hold all parts securely in place." However, splice material for other compression members which are finished to bear must be proportioned for 50 percent of the stress at the splice. Furthermore, in both these cases the connection must also be proportioned to resist the tension, if any, computed as follows:

   ASD: Tension due to lateral loads acting in conjunction with 75 percent of the dead-load stress and no live load
   LRFD: Tension due to the specification load combination A4-6 [Eq. (f) in Art. 1-13]

   Figure 8-52a shows a simple bolted or riveted splice which is sufficient if two column sections are of the same depth. If the depths are not the same, the difference must be taken up by fill plates connected to the flanges of the smaller section. However, if the two sections are of the same nominal depth, the fill plates need not provide any of the bearing area. This is because W shapes of the same nominal depth are rolled with a constant depth inside the flanges so that the flanges of two abutting sections will be flush on the inside, with the difference in depth accounted for by the difference in thickness of the flanges. However, if one column section connects to another of different nominal depth, the flanges of the upper section will not bear on those of the lower section. To provide for this condition, one or more fill plates may be fastened to the upper shaft with sufficient connection to develop their share of the load. In this case, the shaft must be finished with the fills attached (Fig. 8-52b). Alternatively, a bearing (butt) plate may be used between two sections, in which case the fills need not bear (Fig. 8-52c).

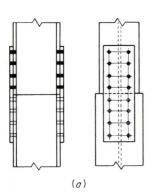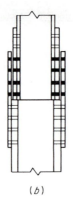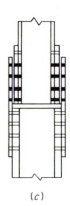

(a)   (b)   (c)

FIGURE 8-52

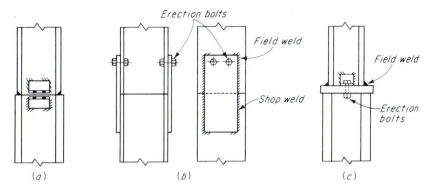

FIGURE 8-53

Typical welded splices are shown in Fig. 8-53. Columns of the same nominal depth may be spliced as shown in Fig. 8-53*a*, usually with partial-penetration groove welds, or by a splice similar to the corresponding riveted or bolted splice (Fig. 8-53*b*). If fill plates transfer a portion of the load, they must be welded to the shaft before the ends are finished for bearing. Figure 8-53*c* shows a butt plate for two columns of different nominal depths.

DP8-27-1 AISC/ASD and DP8-27-2 AISC/LRFD: Column Splice

The following comments are intended to clarify the corresponding lettered computations on the design sheets and apply to both except where noted otherwise.

a. The forces are assumed to be resisted entirely by the splice plates; this is equivalent to the assumption that the two shafts are not in contact.

   ASD. The wind moment is assumed to be counteracted by the moment due to only 75 percent of the dead load, as prescribed by the specification.

   LRFD. Load combination A4-6, $0.9D - 1.3W$, applies here.

b. The specification prescribes the shear-lag factor $U = 1$ for this case.

c. The depth of the W10 × 77 is 10.60 in, while that of the W10 × 45 is 10.10 in. Therefore, a fill plate must be used.

The splice-plate tension can also be evaluated by assuming that the plate must supply the tension that would exist at the cross section if there were no splice. This is computed as follows.

ASD. The extreme-fiber stresses are given by

$$f = -\frac{P}{A} \pm \frac{M}{S} = -\frac{\frac{3}{4} \times 42}{14.4} \pm \frac{49.5 \times 12}{54.6} = -2.19 \pm 10.88 = -13.1, +8.7 \text{ ksi}$$

COLUMN SPLICE

DP8-27-1

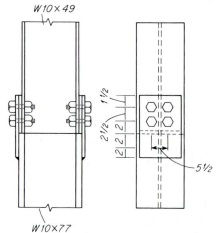

W10×49

W10×77

A 36 steel, AISC/ASD Spec.

Column Load at Point of Splice

	Axial	Moment*	Shear
DL	42^k	–	–
LL	75^k	–	–
WL	$\underline{2^k}$	$\underline{49.5^{'k}}$	$\underline{3.3^k}$
Total	119^k	$49.5^{'k}$	3.3^k

* in plane of web

$\frac{3}{4}$ – in. A325 bolts, threads not excluded from shear plane. E70 electrodes

Flange splice plates

$$\text{Tension} = \frac{49.5 \times 12}{10.62} - \frac{1}{2} \times \frac{3}{4} \times 42 = 55.9 - 15.7 = 40.2^k \tag{a}$$

$$A_g = \frac{P}{0.6F_y} = \frac{40.2}{0.6 \times 36} = 1.86 \, in^2 \qquad t = \frac{1.86}{8} = 0.123''$$

$$A_n = \frac{P}{0.5F_uU} = \frac{40.2}{0.5 \times 58 \times 1} = 1.39 \, in^2 \qquad t = \frac{1.39}{8 - 2 \times \frac{7}{8}} = 0.222'' \tag{b}$$

Use $\frac{1}{4} \times 8$ plate

s.s. $21 \times 0.44 = 9.24^k$

brg. $1.2 \times 58 \times \frac{3}{4} \times \frac{1}{4} = 13.1^k$

$$\frac{40.2}{\frac{4}{3} \times 9.24} = 3.26$$

Use 4 bolts

Weld for shop connection

$$q = 0.3 F_{Exx} \times 0.707a = 0.3 \times 70 \times 0.707 \times \frac{3}{16} = 2.78 \, kli$$

$$\frac{40.2}{\frac{4}{3} \times 2.78} = 10.8''$$

Use 11" of $\frac{3}{16}$" weld

Splice plate $\frac{1}{4} \times 8 \times 10$
Fill plate $\frac{1}{4} \times 8 \times 5\frac{1}{2}$ \hfill (c)

| COLUMN SPLICE | DP8-27-2 |

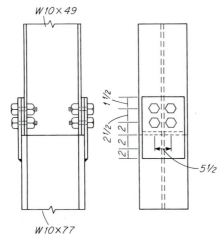

W 10 × 49

W 10 × 77

1½

2½ 2 2

5½

A 36 steel, AISC/LRFD Spec.

Column Load at Point of Splice

	Axial	Moment*	Shear
DL	42^k	–	–
LL	75^k	–	–
WL	2^k	$49.5^{'k}$	3.3^k
Total	119^k	$49.5^{'k}$	3.3^k

* in plane of web

$\frac{3}{4}$–in. A325 bolts, threads not excluded from shear plane. E70 electrodes

Flange splice plates

Load combination A4–6: 0.90D–1.3W

$$\text{Tension} = \frac{1.3 \times 49.5 \times 12}{10.62} - \frac{0.9 \times 42}{2} = 53.8^k \qquad (a)$$

$$P_n = \phi F_y A_g = 0.9 F_y A_g, \quad A_g = \frac{53.8}{0.9 \times 36} = 1.66 \text{ in}^2, \quad t = \frac{1.66}{8} = 0.21''$$

$$P_n = \phi F_u A_e = 0.75 F_u U A_n, \quad A_n = \frac{52.1}{0.75 \times 58 \times 1} = 1.24 \text{ in}^2, \quad t = \frac{1.24}{8 - 2 \times \frac{7}{8}} = 0.20'' \qquad (b)$$

Use ¼ x 8 plate

$$R_v = \phi F_{vu} A_b = 0.75 \times 48 \times 0.442 = 15.9^k$$
$$R_p = \phi \times 2.4 F_u Dt = 0.75 \times 2.4 \times 58 \times \tfrac{3}{4} \times \tfrac{1}{4} = 19.6^k$$

$$n = 53.8/15.9 = 3.4 \qquad \text{Use 4 bolts}$$

Weld for shop connection

$$q = \phi \times 0.6 F_{Exx} \times 0.707a = 0.75 \times 0.6 \times 70 \times 0.707 \times \tfrac{3}{16} = 4.18 \text{ kli}$$
$$53.8/4.18 = 12.9''$$

Use 13" of $\frac{3}{16}''$ weld

Splice plate ¼ x 8 x 10

Fill plate ¼ x 8 x 5½ $\qquad (c)$

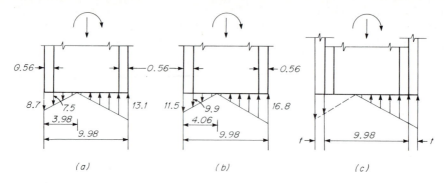

FIGURE 8-54

The resulting stress distribution, shown in Fig. 8-54a, yields the following for the splice-plate tension:

$$T = \frac{8.7 + 7.5}{2} \times 10 \times 0.56 + \frac{7.5}{2} \times 3.42 \times 0.340 = 49.7 \text{ kips}$$

This value of T is 24 percent larger than the value computed on the design sheet and would require a $\frac{5}{16}$-in splice plate.

LRFD. The extreme-fiber stresses are given by

$$f = -\frac{P}{A} \pm \frac{M}{S} = -\frac{0.9 \times 42}{14.4} \pm \frac{1.3 \times 49.5 \times 12}{54.6}$$

$$= -2.62 \pm 14.14 = -16.8, +11.5 \text{ kips}$$

The resulting stress distribution, shown in Fig. 8-54b, yields the following for the splice-plate tension:

$$T = \frac{11.5 + 9.9}{2} \times 10 \times 0.56 + \frac{9.9}{2} \times 3.50 \times 0.340 = 65.8 \text{ kips}$$

This value is 22 percent larger than the value computed on the design sheet and would require a $\frac{5}{16}$-in splice plate.

It is difficult to say which of the two values of splice-plate tension is better, in the sense that it is a good approximation of the actual tension. Since the column ends are shop-finished to provide true bearing surfaces at the splice, it would seem that the analysis that takes contact stresses into account would be more realistic. However, in this case at least, it leads to a thicker splice plate than the analysis based on the assumption that the splice plates alone provide the resistance, which appears to be a contradiction. Therefore, it is the authors' opinion that the analysis based on the splice plates alone is the better of the two.

The stress distribution shown in Fig. 8-54c is probably the best approximation that can be made of conditions at the splice. However, it requires the solution of an equation quadratic in x, and even if the distribution is simplified by assuming stress to be uniform over the splice-plate thickness, the analysis is involved.

8-28 MOMENT-RESISTANT BASES FOR COLUMNS

In the design of base plates for axially loaded columns, we assume the bearing pressure between the plate and the footing to be uniformly distributed (Art. 4-16). Anchor bolts in such a base plate are needed only to hold the column in position. Even if the column must resist a moment, however, such resistance can be developed under certain conditions without the aid of anchor bolts. If the moment is small, the bearing pressures can be assumed to be distributed as shown in Fig. 8-55a. If b is the width of the plate, the pressures f_p at the edges are given by

$$f_p = \frac{P}{A} \pm \frac{Mc}{I} = \frac{P}{bd} \pm \frac{6M}{bd^2} \tag{8-47}$$

From this equation, we see that if $M/P = d/6$, the pressures are zero at one edge and $2P/bd$ at the other. For eccentricities greater than $d/6$ a line of zero pressure lies between the edges of the plate, and the maximum pressure exceeds $2P/bd$ (Fig. 8-55b). Finally, if the eccentricity is $d/2$, the bearing pressure is concentrated at the edge of the plate, as in Fig. 8-55c. Of course, this condition can never be realized, since the reactive force must be distributed over some area. However, it is an upper bound on the eccentricity of load which can exist without anchor bolts. Thus, if $e = M/P$ exceeds $d/2$, it is clear that equilibrium requires the system of forces shown in Fig. 8-55d, where T is the anchor-bolt tension and $P + T$ the resultant bearing pressure. Neither the ASD nor the LRFD specification prescribes the distribution of the bearing pressure to be used in the analysis. The authors recommend that it be assumed to be linear.

　　The following procedure is suggested. Assume the size of the base plate. If the eccentricity M/P is more than half the assumed depth d, the plate is checked for the case shown in Fig. 8-55d, with the resultant $P + T$ distributed triangularly as in Fig. 8-55b. If the resulting anchor-bolt tension T yields anchor bolts of

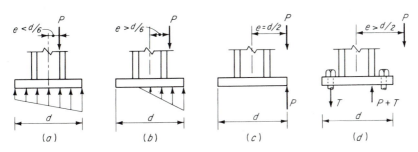

FIGURE 8-55

reasonable size, the assumed dimensions are adequate. However, if the eccentricity is less than half the assumed depth d, the bearing pressure according to the applicable Fig. 8-55a or b is computed first. If this value is less than the allowable, the assumed dimensions are adequate and only nominal anchorage is needed. If it is more than the allowable, the plate is checked for the stress distribution of Fig. 8-55d as for the case where M/P exceeds $d/2$.

The analysis for the case in Fig. 8-55d can be made by assuming that both the concrete and the steel are linearly elastic and the plate rigid, from which an equation relating bolt tension and bearing pressure follows. However, it is more realistic to assume that the anchor-bolt tension and the pressure on the concrete are independent, since this is consistent with conditions at ultimate load. Therefore, this assumption will be adopted in the following examples.

The AISC/ASD specification allowable bearing pressure is $0.35f'_c\sqrt{A_2/A_1}$, where A_2 is the maximum area of the portion of the supporting surface that is geometrically similar to and concentric with the loaded area and A_1 is the area of the steel concentrically bearing on the concrete support. The AISC/LRFD specification does not prescribe the maximum bearing pressure on the concrete but specifies instead the design bearing load in the form $P_p = \phi_c 0.85f'_c A_1\sqrt{A_2/A_1}$, where $\phi_c = 0.60$. This expression shows that the maximum pressure on the concrete is limited to $\phi_c 0.85f'_c\sqrt{A_2/A_1}$.

> **Example 8-28-1 (ASD and LRFD).** Check the adequacy of a 15×20 in base plate for the A36 W10 × 33 column of Fig. 8-56a. The footing is of 3000 psi concrete, and the plate covers one-third the area of the footing. The axial load is 15 kips *DL* and 75 kips *LL*, and the moment is 90 in·kips *DL* and 450 in·kips *LL*.

ASD solution. The eccentricity $e = \frac{540}{90} = 6$ in is less than half the assumed length of the plate. For equilibrium with no anchor-bolt tension, the base of the triangular bearing-pressure diagram must be 12 in, as shown in the figure. Therefore,

$$\tfrac{1}{2}f_c \times 12 \times 15 = 90 \text{ kips} \qquad f_c = 1.00 \text{ ksi}$$

The allowable bearing pressure is $0.35 \times 3 \times \sqrt{3} = 1.82$ ksi. Therefore, the assumed dimensions are adequate, and only nominal anchorage is required. Two $\tfrac{1}{2}$-in A36

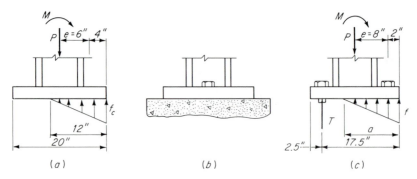

(a) (b) (c)

FIGURE 8-56

bolts,* one on each side of the web as in Fig. 8-56b, could be used, although most designers would probably use a larger bolt for a base plate the size of this one.

LRFD solution. The factored loads are $P = 1.2 \times 15 + 1.6 \times 75 = 138$ kips and $M = 1.2 \times 90 + 1.6 \times 450 = 828$ in·kips. The eccentricity $e = \frac{828}{138} = 6$ in is less than half the assumed length of the plate. For equilibrium with no anchor-bolt tension, the base of the triangular bearing-pressure diagram must be 12 in, as shown in the figure. Therefore,

$$\tfrac{1}{2}f_c \times 12 \times 15 = 138 \text{ kips} \qquad f_c = 1.53 \text{ ksi}$$

The design bearing pressure is $0.60 \times 0.85 \times 3 \times \sqrt{3} = 2.65$ ksi. Therefore, the assumed dimensions are adequate, and only nominal anchorage is required. Two $\frac{1}{2}$-in A36 bolts*, one on each side of the web as in Fig. 8-56b, could be used, although most designers would probably use a larger bolt for a base plate the size of this one.

Example 8-28-2 (ASD and LRFD). Check the adequacy of a 15×20 in base plate for the A36 W10 × 33 column of Fig. 8-56a. The footing is of 3000 psi concrete, and the plate covers one-third the area of the footing. The axial load is 26 kips DL and 79 kips LL, and the moment is 210 in·kips DL and 630 in·kips LL.

ASD solution. The eccentricity $e = \frac{840}{105} = 8$ in. The base of the triangular bearing-pressure diagram is $3(10 - 8) = 6$ in, so

$$\tfrac{1}{2}f_c \times 6 \times 15 = 105 \text{ kips} \qquad f_c = 2.33 \text{ ksi}$$

The allowable bearing pressure is $0.35 \times 3 \times \sqrt{3} = 1.82$ ksi. Since this is exceeded, we investigate the stress distribution shown in Fig. (8-56c) with $f = 1.82$ ksi. Taking moments about T, we get

$$\tfrac{1}{2} \times 1.82 \times 15a\left(17.5 - \frac{a}{3}\right) = 105 \times 15.5$$

$$a^2 - 52.5a + 358 = 0$$

This gives $a = 8.1$ in. The tension is found from

$$T = \tfrac{1}{2} \times 1.82 \times 8.1 \times 15 - 105 = 110.6 - 105 = 5.6 \text{ kips}$$

The ASD allowable load on a $\frac{3}{4}$-in A36 anchor bolt is $0.33 \times 58 \times 0.44 = 8.42$ kips. Therefore, two $\frac{3}{4}$-in bolts, placed as shown in Fig. 8-56c, are adequate.

LRFD solution. The design loads are $P = 1.2 \times 26 + 1.6 \times 79 = 157.6$ kips and $M = 1.2 \times 210 + 1.6 \times 630 = 1260$ in·kips. The eccentricity $e = 1260/157.6 = 8$ in.

---

* Nonheaded anchor bolts, straight or bent, are usually made of A36 steel.

The base of the triangular bearing-pressure diagram is $3(10 - 8) = 6$ in, so

$$\tfrac{1}{2} f_c \times 6 \times 15 = 157.6 \text{ kips} \qquad f_c = 3.50 \text{ ksi}$$

The design bearing pressure is $0.60 \times 0.85 \times 3 \times \sqrt{3} = 2.65$ ksi. Since this is exceeded, we investigate the stress distribution shown in Fig. 8-56c with $f = 2.65$ ksi. Taking moments about T, we get

$$\tfrac{1}{2} \times 2.65 \times 15a\left(17.5 - \frac{a}{3}\right) = 157.6 \times 15.5$$

$$a^2 - 52.5a + 369 = 0$$

This gives $a = 8.36$ in. The tension is found from

$$T = \tfrac{1}{2} \times 2.65 \times 8.36 \times 15 - 157.6 = 166.2 - 157.6 = 8.6 \text{ kips}$$

The LRFD design strength for an A36 anchor bolt is $\phi \times 0.75 F_u \times A_b$, where ϕ is 0.75 and A_b is the bolt area. For a $\tfrac{3}{4}$-in bolt the capacity is $0.75 \times 0.75 \times 58 \times 0.44 = 14.4$ kips. Therefore, two $\tfrac{3}{4}$-in bolts, placed as shown in Fig. 8-56c, are adequate.

8-29   BASE-PLATE DETAILS

The connection of the column shaft to its base plate may take various forms. If the moment is relatively small so that the combined stress $f = P/A + My/I$ is compressive at all points of the column cross section, the entire cross section will bear on the base plate. In this case the shaft need not be attached to the base plate to meet stress requirements, although practical considerations dictate at least a nominal connection, as in the case of columns subjected only to axial load. On the other hand, it is obvious that full-penetration groove welds (or the equivalent in fillet welds) for the entire cross section of the column would be adequate no matter how large the moment compared with the axial load. However, such a connection ordinarily is not required.

Except for the smaller columns it is usual to ship base plates unattached so that they can be leveled and grouted in place on the footings. The column can be fitted with angles attached in the shop (Fig. 8-57a). Of course, these angles are attached to the web if the anchor bolts are located as in Fig. 8-56b. Alternatively, the angles can be omitted and the column shaft welded to the base plate in the field. A direct connection between anchor bolt and column shaft, through the use of sleeves or boots attached in the shop, is usually needed for the larger moments (Fig. 8-57b). On the left in this figure is shown an angle welded to the column flange and capped by a plate welded both to the angle and to the column flange. Instead of the angle, two bars may be fillet-welded both sides to the column flange as shown at the right. This detail can be expanded to accommodate two anchor bolts. The angles or plates need not be detailed to bear on the base plate. The AISC Manuals suggest that they be cut short of the base plate by 1 in.

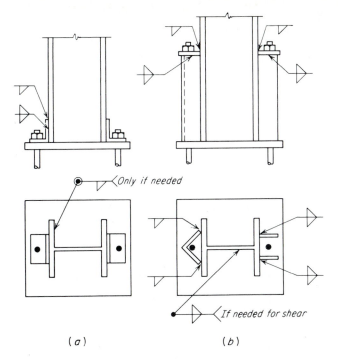

(a)   (b)

FIGURE 8-57

Example 8-29-1 (AISC/ASD). Design the base plate for the A36 W12 × 72 column shown in Fig. 8-58. The axial load P is 80 kips, and the moment is 1600 in·kips. The footing concrete is 3000 psi.

Solution. Since there is no way to make a direct determination of the size of the base plate, its dimensions must be assumed and then checked, as in Example 8-28-1. Assume the plate to be 20 × 24 in. The eccentricity of load M/P is 20 in, which exceeds $d/2$, so anchor-bolt tension is required. Assume the base plate to rest on a pedestal of the same dimensions. Therefore, $f_c = 0.35f'_c\sqrt{A_2/A_1} = 0.35f'_c = 1.05$ ksi.

With the bolt lines $2\frac{1}{2}$ in from the edges of the plate (see Fig. 8-58), summation of moments at the line of action of T gives

$$\tfrac{1}{2} \times 1.05 \times 20a\left(21.5 - \frac{a}{3}\right) = 80 \times 9\tfrac{1}{2} + 1600$$

$$a^2 - 64.5a + 522 = 0$$

from which $a = 13.1$ in. Summation of vertical forces gives

$$T + 80 = \tfrac{1}{2} \times 1.05 \times 13.1 \times 20 = 138 \text{ kips} \qquad T = 58 \text{ kips}$$

The required area for A36 anchor bolts is $58/(0.33 \times 58) = 3.33$ in². The required area can be furnished by one $2\frac{1}{4}$-in bolt.

A detail of the type shown at the right in Fig. 8-57b will be used. Assume the boot to be 12 in long, with each vertical plate fillet-welded both sides to the column

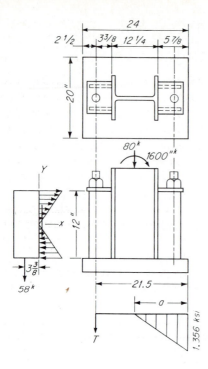

FIGURE 8-58

flange. The force per weld is $\frac{58}{4} = 14.5$ kips, and the stresses on one weld are (Fig. 8-58)

$$q_y = \frac{14.5}{12} = 1.21 \text{ kli}$$

$$q_x = \frac{14.5 \times 3.375}{12^2/6} = 2.04 \text{ kli}$$

$$q = \sqrt{1.21^2 + 2.04} = 2.37 \text{ kli}$$

The required size of E70 weld is $2.37/(21 \times 0.707) = 0.160$ or $\frac{3}{16}$ in. A $\frac{3}{8} \times 5\frac{1}{2}$ in plate will be used. Its thickness is ample for the size of the welds, and its b/t ratio is $5.5/0.375 = 14.7 \leq 16$. The top plate will be $\frac{3}{8} \times 5\frac{1}{2} \times 4$.

The thickness of the base plate must be enough to assure the stiffness needed to distribute the load. A procedure for determining the thickness of base plates for axially loaded columns was discussed in Art. 4-16. Bending of the plate in Fig. 8-58 would be critical at or near the flange on the side where the plate bears on the footing. In this case, the stiffeners complicate evaluation of such a moment, but a conservative estimate of thickness can be made by ignoring this effect. Since a in this example was found to be 13.1 in, we see that the projecting $5\frac{7}{8}$ in of base plate is acted upon by a trapezoidal stress block varying in intensity from 0.579 ksi at the column flange to 1.356 ksi at the edge of the plate. The moment at the column flange for a 1-in strip of plate is

$$M = \tfrac{1}{2} \times 1.356 \times 5.88 \times (\tfrac{2}{3} \times 5.88) + \tfrac{1}{2} \times 0.579 \times 5.88 \times (\tfrac{1}{3} \times 5.88)$$

$$= 15.63 + 3.34 = 18.96 \text{ in·kips}$$

The allowable bending stress for an A36 plate is $F_b = 0.75F_y = 27$ ksi. Therefore, from $M = F_y S_x$, we get

$$18.96 = \frac{27t^2}{6} \qquad t = 2.05 \text{ in}$$

This is a reasonable thickness for a plate with the lateral dimensions of this one. Therefore, a $2 \times 20 \times 24$ in plate is satisfactory. The design is shown in Fig. 8-58. Two $1\frac{1}{2}$-in bolts could also be used in the arrangement shown in Fig. 8-59 for Example 8-29-2.

Example 8-29-2 (AISC/LRFD). Design the base plate for the A36 W12 × 72 column shown in Fig. 8-59. The axial load P is 20 kips *DL* and 60 kips *LL*, and the moment is 400 in·kips *DL* and 1600 in·kips *LL*. The footing concrete is 3000 psi.

Solution. Since there is no way to make a direct determination of the size of the base plate, its dimensions must be assumed and then checked, as in Example 8-28-2. Assume the plate to be 20 × 24 in. The eccentricity of load is

$$e = \frac{1.2 \times 400 + 1.6 \times 1600}{1.2 \times 20 + 1.6 \times 60} = \frac{3040}{120} = 25.3 \text{ in}$$

which exceeds $d/2$, so anchor-bolt tension is required. Assume the base plate to rest on a pedestal of the same dimensions. Therefore, $f_c = 0.60 \times 0.85f'_c \sqrt{A_2/A_1} = 0.6 \times 0.85f'_c$. With $f'_c = 3$ ksi, the result is $f_c = 1.53$ ksi.

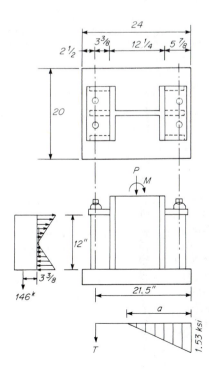

FIGURE 8-59

With the bolt lines $2\frac{1}{2}$ in from the edges of the plate (see Fig. 8-59), summation of moments at the line of action of T gives

$$\tfrac{1}{2} \times 1.53 \times 20a\left(21.5 - \frac{a}{3}\right) = 120 \times 9\tfrac{1}{2} + 3040$$

$$a^2 - 64.5a + 819.6 = 0$$

from which $a = 17.4$ in. Summation of vertical forces gives

$$T + 120 = \tfrac{1}{2} \times 1.53 \times 17.4 \times 20 = 266 \text{ kips} \qquad T = 146 \text{ kips}$$

The required tensile-stress area for A36 anchor bolts is $T/\phi F_u = T/(0.75F_u) = 146/(0.75 \times 58) = 3.36$ in². The required area can be furnished by one $2\frac{1}{4}$-in bolt or two $1\frac{1}{2}$-in bolts.

A detail of the type shown at the right in Fig. 8-57b to accommodate two bolts will be used. Three vertical plates will be required. Assume the boot to be 12 in long, with each vertical plate fillet-welded both sides to the column flange. The force per weld is $\frac{146}{6} = 24.3$ kips, and the stresses on one weld are

$$q_y = \frac{24.3}{12} = 2.03 \text{ kli}$$

$$q_x = \frac{24.3 \times 3.375}{12^2/6} = 3.42 \text{ kli}$$

$$q = \sqrt{2.03^2 + 3.42^2} = 3.98 \text{ kli}$$

The required size of E70 weld is $3.98/(\phi \times 0.707 \times 0.6 \times 70) = 3.98/(0.75 \times 0.707 \times 0.6 \times 70) = 0.179$ or $\frac{3}{16}$ in. A $\frac{3}{8} \times 5\frac{1}{2}$ in plate will be used. Its thickness is ample for the size of the welds, and its b/t ratio is $5.5/0.375 = 14.7 \le 16$. The top plate will be $\frac{3}{8} \times 5\frac{1}{2} \times 4$.

The thickness of the base plate must be enough to assure the stiffness needed to distribute the load. A procedure for determining the thickness of base plates for axially loaded columns was discussed in Art. 4-16. Bending of the plate in Fig. 8-59 would be critical at or near the flange on the side where the plate bears on the footing. In this case, the stiffeners complicate evaluation of such a moment, but a conservative estimate of thickness can be made by ignoring this effect. Since a in this example was found to be 17.4 in, we see that the projecting $5\frac{7}{8}$ in of base plate is acted upon by a trapezoidal stress block varying in intensity from 1.013 ksi at the column flange to 1.53 ksi at the edge of the plate. The moment at the column flange for a 1-in strip of plate is

$$M = \tfrac{1}{2} \times 1.53 \times 5.88 \times (\tfrac{2}{3} \times 5.88) + \tfrac{1}{2} \times 1.013 \times 5.88 \times (\tfrac{1}{3} \times 5.88)$$

$$= 17.63 + 5.84 = 23.47 \text{ in·kips}$$

The allowable capacity for an A36 plate is $\phi M_n = \phi M_p = 0.90 \times t^2/4 \times 36 = 23.47$, which gives $t = 1.70$ in. This is a reasonable thickness for a plate with the lateral dimensions of this one. Therefore, a $1\frac{3}{4} \times 20 \times 24$ in plate is satisfactory. The design is shown in Fig. 8-59.

8-30 PINNED CONNECTIONS

Pinned connections are used to permit relatively free end rotation of the connected members. Pinned joints in bascule bridges, crane booms, etc., must allow

FIGURE 8-60

relatively large rotation. Pinned joints where the rotations are relatively small are found in hinged arches (Fig. 8-60), in the links by which the suspended span of cantilever systems may be fastened to the cantilever span, in main supports of heavy trusses and girders, and in light bracing systems (clevis pins). Steel pins, which may be cast, forged, or cold-rolled and then machined, generally range in size from $1\frac{1}{2}$ to 10 in in diameter, but sizes up to 24 in are available.

Since the pin does not have parts bearing on its full length, its size is likely to be determined by bending. However, failure may occur by shearing of the pin, crushing of the plate, and, in tension members, shearing of the plate between the pinhole and the end of the plate or fracture of the plate on the net section through the pinhole. A pinned connection may also fail by dishing of the plate (Fig. 8-61).

The pin should fit snugly in the pinhole. The AISC specifications require the diameter of the hole to be not more than $\frac{1}{32}$ in larger than the diameter of the pin. The allowable bearing stress is somewhat less than for bolts and rivets. In effect, this allows freer rotation. Where large rotations are expected, bearing stresses should be reduced. The AASHTO specifications allow only 50 percent of the basic bearing stress if large rotations are expected. Since the required thickness of the parts is inversely proportional to the pin diameter, a relatively thin bearing may require an excessively large pin. To avoid this situation, members may be reinforced with pin plates at the pinhole.

In a series of 106 tests on pin-connected plate links, fracture on the net section of the plate at the pinhole did not occur until the average stress on the net section reached the ultimate tensile strength of the steel.[31] Therefore, stress concentrations at the edge of the hole had no apparent effect on the strength of the plate under static loads.

The tests also showed that the net area beyond the pinhole, on a longitudinal section of the member, must range from about 60 to 75 percent of the transverse net area at the pinhole if failure beyond the pinhole and failure on the net section at the pinhole are to be about equally probable. The smaller figure is for a member about twice as wide as its pin, while the larger figure is for one about four times as wide as its pin (this is the range of ratios of plate width to pin diameter covered by the tests).

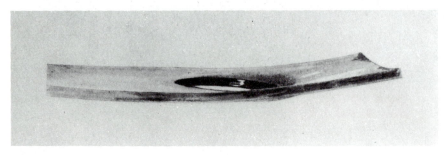

FIGURE 8-61
Buckling failure of pin plate.

Buckling of the plate beyond the pin (dishing) is a function of stability rather than strength. Therefore, dishing depends upon the ratios D/t, b/t, and a/t, where D is the diameter of the pinhole, b and a the edge and end distances, respectively, at the pinhole, and t the thickness of the plate. However, for the range of ratios of plate width to pin diameter covered by his tests, Johnston's results[31] show that if a member is designed to be equally strong on the net section through the pinhole and on the net section beyond the pin, it will be at least as strong with respect to dishing if the ratio of net width at the pinhole to thickness of the plate ranges from about 6 to 10. These ratios correspond, respectively, to the plates of Johnston's tests which were four times and two times as wide as the diameter of their pins.

PROBLEMS

8-1. Design a seat angle to support a W10 × 22 beam on the web of a W12 × 65 column. The beam reaction is 8 kips *DL* and 22 kips *LL*. There is no beam on the opposite side of the web of the column. Use $\frac{3}{4}$-in A325 bolts in a bearing-type connection with threads excluded from the shear plane. A36 steel, AISC specification.

8-2. Design seat angles to support two W12 × 50 beams, one on each side of the web of a W12 × 72 column. Each beam reaction is 4 kips *DL* and 12 kips *LL*. Use $\frac{3}{4}$-in A325 bolts in a bearing-type connection with threads not excluded from the shear plane. A36 steel, AISC specification.

8-3. A W21 × 57 beam is supported on the flange of a W8 × 31 column. The beam reaction is 15 kips *DL* and 40 kips *LL*. Detail a framed connection using A325 bolts in a bearing-type connection with threads excluded from the shear planes. A36 steel, AISC specification.

8-4. A W12 × 40 beam and a W18 × 55 beam frame on opposite sides of the web of a W21 × 62 girder. The top flanges of the beams and the girder are at the same elevation. The W12 spans 12 ft and supports dead and live loads of 1.5 and 4.0 klf, respectively. The W18 spans 13 ft and supports dead and live loads of 2.3 and 6.2 klf, respectively. Design a connection using A325 bolts. A36 steel, AISC specification.

8-5. Design the connections for the stringers to the floor beams of Prob. 5-10. Use $\frac{3}{4}$-in A325 bolts. AASHTO specification.

8-6. A W12 × 50 spandrel beam is connected to the flange of a W10 × 49 column as shown in Fig. P8-6. Design the connection for a beam reaction of 9 kips *DL* and 27

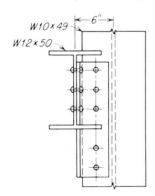

FIGURE P8-6

kips *LL*, using A325 bolts in a slip-critical connection on the standard gage line for the column. A36 steel, AISC specification.

8-7. Compute the permissible load, in terms of the permissible load *R* per bolt, for a seat stiffener whose 3-in connected leg has three bolts at 3-in pitch at $1\frac{3}{4}$-in gage, (*a*) neglecting the torsional effect discussed in Art. 8-17 and (*b*) considering the torsional effect. Also compare the permissible loads for four bolts and for five bolts at the same gage and for three, four, and five bolts if the gage is $2\frac{1}{2}$ in on a 4-in connected leg. What would you conclude about the advisability of ignoring the torsional effect?

8-8. Compute the permissible load for the following stiffened beam seats, (1) neglecting the moment M_{yz} discussed in Art. 8-17 and (2) considering the moment M_{yz}.

(*a*) Seat angle $6 \times 4 \times \frac{3}{8}$ with the 4-in leg outstanding, two $3\frac{1}{2} \times 3 \times \frac{1}{2}$ stiffener angles with the $3\frac{1}{2}$-in legs outstanding, and two rows of $\frac{3}{4}$-in A325 bolts in a bearing-type joint with six bolts in each row at 3-in pitch.

(*b*) Seat angle $6 \times 6 \times \frac{3}{8}$, two $5 \times 3\frac{1}{2} \times \frac{1}{2}$ stiffener angles with the 5-in legs outstanding, and two rows of $\frac{7}{8}$-in A325 bolts in a bearing-type joint with six bolts in each row at 3-in pitch.

(*c*) Seat angle $8 \times 6 \times \frac{7}{16}$ with the 8-in leg outstanding, two $7 \times 4 \times \frac{7}{16}$ stiffener angles with the 7-in legs outstanding, and two rows of $\frac{7}{8}$-in A490 bolts in a bearing-type joint with six bolts in each row at 3-in pitch.

Assume that the reaction is concentrated at the center of the contact area between the beam and the seat angle. What would you conclude about the advisability of ignoring the moment M_{yz}?

8-9. The load on a laterally supported beam spanning 10 ft is 3 klf *DL* and 9 klf *LL*. Design the beam and a seat to connect it to the web of a W10 × 30 column. Use $\frac{3}{4}$-in A325 bolts in a slip-critical connection. AISC specification, A36 steel.

8-10. A W21 × 132 beam connects to the web of a W16 × 57 column. The beam reaction is 36 kips *DL* and 106 kips *LL*. Design a beam seat using $\frac{7}{8}$-in A325 bolts. AISC specification, A36 steel.

8-11. Design a bracket to connect the beam to the flange of the column of Fig. P8-11, using $\frac{7}{8}$-in A325 bolts in a bearing-type joint with threads not excluded. *R* = 20 kips *DL* and 60 kips *LL*, *d* = 12 in. AISC specification, A36 steel.

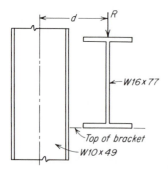

FIGURE P8-11

8-12. Design a bracket to connect the beam to the flange of the column of Fig. P8-11, using $\frac{3}{4}$-in A325 bolts. *R* = 18 kips *DL* and 52 kips *LL*, *d* = 10 in. AISC specification, A36 steel.

8-13. Design a bracket to connect the crane girder of DP5-19-1 to the flange of a W24 × 104 column, using $\frac{7}{8}$-in A325 bolts in a slip-critical connection.

8-14. Design a bracket to connect the crane girder of DP5-19-2 to the flange of a W24 × 104 column, using $\frac{7}{8}$-in A325 bolts in a slip-critical connection.

8-15. A W16 × 36 spans 15 ft and supports a uniform load of 0.8 klf *DL* and 2.4 klf *LL*. The top flange of the beam is 6 in above the top flange of the W16 × 67 supporting girder. There is no beam on the other side of the girder. Design the connection for 1-in A325 bolts in a bearing-type joint. AISC specification, A36 steel.

8-16. Design a bracket for the connection of the crane girder to the column in DP5-9-3. Use $\frac{7}{8}$-in A325 bolts.

8-17. Design a bracket for the connection of the crane girder to the column in DP5-9-4. Use $\frac{7}{8}$-in A325 bolts.

8-18. A W21 × 62 beam connects to the flange of a W14 × 109 column, A36 steel. The end shears and moments are as follows:

Load	Shear, kips	Moment, ft·kips
DL	8	26.7
LL	16	53.3
WL	6	80.0

Design a T-stub connection (Fig. 8-15*b*), bearing type with no threads in the shear planes, using A325 or A490 bolts. AISC specification.

8-19. A W24 × 84 beam connects to the flange of a W14 × 132 column, A36 steel. The end shear and moments are as follows:

Load	Shear, kips	Moment, ft·kips
DL	14	70
LL	29	175
WL	10	200

Design a T-stub connection (Fig. 8-15*d*), bearing type with no threads in the shear planes, using A325 or A490 bolts. AISC specification.

8-20. Same as Prob. 8-19, except use a connection of the type shown in Fig. 8-15*b*.

8-21. A W14 × 34 beam, whose end shear and end moment are 4 kips *DL*, 12 kips *LL* and 10 ft·kips *DL*, 30 ft·kips *LL*, connects to the flange of a W10 × 54 column. Design a semirigid connection such as that shown in Fig. 8-23, using A325 or A490 bolts. A36 steel, AISC specification.

8-22. A W14 × 53 beam, whose end shear and end moment are 3 kips *DL*, 9 kips *LL* and 18 ft·kips *DL*, 54 ft·kips *LL*, connects to the flange of a W10 × 60 column. Design a semirigid connection such as that shown in Fig. 8-23, using A325 bolts in a bearing-type joint with threads not excluded. A36 steel, AISC specification.

8-23. A W18 × 50 beam, whose end shear and end moment are 7 kips *DL*, 21 kips *LL* and 23 ft·kips *DL*, 69 ft·kips *LL*, connects to the flange of a W10 × 77 column. Design a semirigid connection such as that shown in Fig. 8-23, using A325 or A490 bolts. A36 steel, AISC specification.

8-24. A W24 × 104 beam spanning 40 ft and supporting a uniform load of 1.9 klf *DL* including its own weight and 5.6 klf *LL* connects at each end to the flange of a W12 × 72 column. Design a welded connection of the type shown in Fig. 8-25c. A36 steel, E70 electrodes, and AISC specification.

8-25. Design a welded connection of the type shown in Fig. 8-25c for the stringers to the floor beams of Prob. 5-10. A36 steel, E70 electrodes, and AASHTO specifications.

8-26. A W18 × 71 beam spanning 15 ft and supporting a uniform load of 1.8 klf *DL* including its own weight and 5.2 klf *LL* connects at each end to the flange of a W12 × 79 column. Design a welded connection of the type shown in Fig. 8-25c. A441 steel, E70 electrodes, and AISC specification.

8-27. For the data of Prob. 8-24 design a welded connection of the type shown in Fig. 8-25d.

8-28. For the data of Prob. 8-26 design a welded connection of the type shown in Fig. 8-25e.

8-29. Design a welded seat to support a W10 × 26 beam on the web of a W12 × 65 column. The beam reaction is 8 kips *DL* and 22 kips *LL*. A36 steel, E70 electrodes, and AISC specification.

8-30. Design an A36 welded seat to support an A441 W12 × 50 beam on the web of an A441 W12 × 87 column. The beam reaction is 12 kips *DL* and 38 kips *LL*. E70 electrodes, AISC specification.

8-31. Design a welded seat to support a W16 × 77 beam on the flange of a W14 × 90 column. The beam reaction is 18 kips *DL* and 52 kips *LL*. A36 steel, E70 electrodes, and AISC specification.

8-32. Design a welded bracket for the crane of Prob. 8-45. AISC specification.

8-33. Design a welded connection to support the A441 W16 × 50 beams on the A441 W12 × 72 column shown in Fig. P8-33. Each beam reaction is 13 kips *KL* and 39 kips *LL*. E70 electrodes, AISC specification.

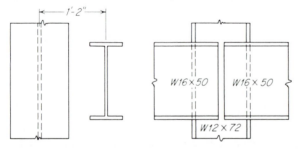

FIGURE P8-33

8-34. Design a welded connection to support the S12 × 31.8 beams on the W8 × 31 column shown in Fig. P8-34. Each beam reaction is 5 kips *DL* and 15 kips *LL*. A36 steel, E70 electrodes, and AISC specification.

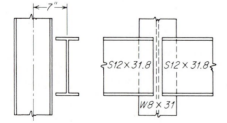

FIGURE P8-34

8-35. Design a welded connection for the beam of Prob. 8-22. E70 electrodes, AISC specification.

8-36. Design a welded connection for the beam of Prob. 8-23. E70 electrodes, AISC specification.

8-37. Design a welded connection for two W12 × 40 beams which frame opposite the web of a W18 × 50 girder. The end shear and end moment of each 12-in beam are 10 kips *DL*, 27.5 kips *LL* and 20 ft·kips *DL*, 60 ft·kips *LL*, respectively. The top flanges of the beams and girder are at the same elevation. A36 steel, E70 electrodes, AISC specification.

8-38. Design a welded connection for two W14 × 53 beams which frame opposite the web of a W21 × 62 girder. The end shear and moment of each beam are 12 kips *DL*, 36 kips *LL* and 32 ft·kips *DL*, 96 ft·kips *LL*, respectively. The top flanges of the beams are 1 in below the top flange of the girder. A441 steel, E70 electrodes, AISC specification.

8-39. Refer to Fig. 8-38. How would deformation of the plate affect the distribution of the fastener forces in Fig. 8-38*b*? How would this effect depend upon the length of the fastener rows? How would deformation of the plate affect the distribution of the fastener forces in Fig. 8-38*c*?

8-40. A line of W16 × 50 beams is offset 14 in from a line of columns. The beam-to-column connection at the end of the last beam in the line is shown in Fig. P8-40. The beam is fastened to the plate through one $4 \times 3\frac{1}{2} \times \frac{3}{8}$ angle. Steel is A36, and the $\frac{7}{8}$-in bolts are A325. Determine the allowable beam reaction *P* according to the AISC specification.

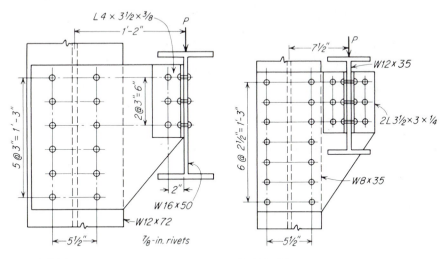

FIGURE P8-40   **FIGURE P8-41**

8-41. Determine the allowable value of *P* for the connection shown in Fig. P8-41. A36 steel, $\frac{3}{4}$-in A307 bolts, and AISC specification.

8-42. For a single row of uniformly spaced fasteners supporting an eccentric force *P* parallel to the row, the fastener force due to the moment $M = Pe$ can be found from Eq. (8-8) while that due to *P* is *P/n*. The error in Eq. (8-5) is slight if we omit the fractions $\frac{1}{4}$ and $\frac{1}{2}$. With this simplification, let the resultant of these forces equal the allowable shear *R* on a fastener, and develop a formula for *n*.

8-43. Discuss the effect on the column of the bracket with the single row vs. the bracket with the double row of bolts in Example 8-22-2.

8-44. A C12 × 25 is connected to the flange of a W8 × 40 column, as shown in Fig. P8-44. Design the connection for a moment of 330 in·kips due to wind force. Use $\frac{3}{4}$-in A325 bolts in a slip-critical connection. A36 steel, AISC specification. (In allowable-stress design the allowable stresses may be increased for wind loading.)

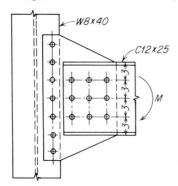

FIGURE P8-44

8-45. Design data for a 10-ton electric crane operating in a shop building are as follows: span of the bridge 20 ft, wheelbase 9.5 ft, minimum clearance to center of rail 8 in, maximum load on each wheel (not including impact) 4.5 kips *DL* and 13 kips *LL*, weight of girder and rail 0.17 klf. Columns are W10 × 60 spaced 30 ft on centers. The webs of the columns are parallel to the crane girder. Design a bracket connection using A325 bolts. Use a slip-critical connection since it is subjected to repeated stress. A36 steel, AISC specification.

8-46. Determine the ultimate strength of a C-shaped weldment with a vertical leg of 12 in and horizontal legs of 3 in. The load is applied 6 in eccentric with respect to the center of gravity of the weldment. E70 electrodes.

8-47. Determine the design strength of the weldment of Prob. 8-46, using the tables in the AISC/LRFD Manual.

8-48. Determine the allowable capacity of the weldment of Prob. 8-46, using the tables in the AISC/ASD Manual.

8-49. Design the tapered knee shown in Fig. P8-49. The axial force, shear, and moment

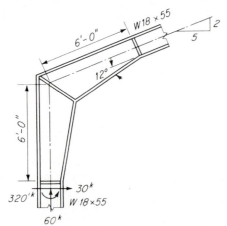

FIGURE P8-49

shown are 15 kips *DL*, 45 kips *LL*; 8 kips *DL*, 22 kips *LL*; and 80 ft·kips *DL*, 240 ft·kips *LL*, respectively. A36 steel, AISC specification.

8-50. Same as Prob. 8-49 except design a curved knee.

8-51. Design a splice between a W8 × 48 column and a W8 × 31 column which supports a concentric load of 12 kips *DL* and 38 kips *LL*, a shear of 2 kips *DL* and 6 kips *LL*, and a wind moment of 30 ft·kips in the plane of the web at the point of splice. AISC specification, A36 steel, and A325 bolts.

8-52. Design a welded splice for the column shafts of Prob. 8-51. E70 electrodes.

8-53. Design a splice between a W12 × 87 column and a W10 × 60 column which supports a concentric load of 25 kips *DL* and 75 kips *LL*, a shear of 4 kips *DL* and 11 kips *LL*, and a wind moment of 70 ft·kips in the plane of the web at the point of splice. AISC specification, A36 steel, and A325 bolts.

8-54. Design a welded splice for the column shafts of Prob. 8-53. E70 electrodes.

8-55. Design a splice to connect a W12 × 65 to a W12 × 96. The forces and moments at the splice are:

	DL	*LL*	*WL*
P, kips	133	70	10
M, ft·kips	25	15	75

A36 steel, A325 bolts, and AISC specification.

8-56. Design a welded splice for the column of Prob. 8-55. E70 electrodes.

8-57. A W8 × 31 column supports a concentric load of 12 kips *DL* and 38 kips *LL* and a moment of 8 ft·kips *DL* and 22 ft·kips *LL* in the plane of the web. Design a base plate and its connection to the column shaft. AISC specification, A36 steel, and E70 electrodes.

8-58. A W12 × 65 column supports a concentric load of 23 kips *DL* and 67 kips *LL* and a moment of 25 ft·kips *DL* and 75 ft·kips *LL* in the plane of the web. Design a base plate and its connection to the column shaft. AISC specification, A36 steel, and E70 electrodes.

8-59. A W14 × 159 column supports a concentric load of 38 kips *DL* and 112 kips *LL* and a wind moment of 275 ft·kips in the plane of the web. Design a base plate and its connection to the column shaft. AISC specification, A36 steel, and E70 electrodes.

REFERENCES

1. Astaneh, A., S. M. Call, and K. M. McMullin: Design of Single Plate Shear Connections, *AISC Eng. J.*, 1st Quarter, 1989.
2. Douty, R. T., and W. McGuire: High Strength Bolted Moment Connections, *J. Struct. Div. ASCE*, vol. 91, no. ST2, April 1965.
3. Grinter, Linton E.: "Design of Modern Steel Structures," Macmillan, New York, 1941, p. 49.
4. American Institute of Steel Construction: "Plastic Design in Steel," Chicago, 1959, p. 38.
5. Higgins, T. R., and W. H. Munse: How Much Combined Stress Can a Rivet Take, *Eng. News-Rec.*, p. 40, Dec. 4, 1952.
6. Chesson, E., Jr., N. L. Faustino, and W. H. Munse: High Strength Bolts Subjected to Tension and Shear, *J. Struct. Div. ASCE*, vol. 91, no. ST5, pp. 155–180, October 1965.

7. Nair, R. S., P. C. Birkemoe, and W. H. Munse: Behavior of Bolts in Tee-Connections Subjected to Prying Action, *Univ. Ill. Civ. Eng. Stud., Struct. Res. Ser.* 1969.
8. Struik, J. H. A., and J. deBack: Tests on Bolted T-Stubs with Respect to Bolted Beam-to-Column Connections, Report 6-69-13, Stevin Laboratory, Delft University of Technology, the Netherlands, 1969.
9. Kulak, G. L., J. W. Fisher, and J. H. Struik: "Guide to Design Criteria for Bolted and Riveted Joints," Wiley, New York, 1988.
10. Munse, W. H., K. S. Petersen, and E. Chesson, Jr.: Strength of Rivets and Bolts in Tension, *J. Struct. Div. ASCE*, March 1959.
11. Batho, Cyril: First, Second, and Final Reports, Steel Structures Committee, Department of Scientific and Industrial Research, Great Britain, 1931–1936.
12. Johnston, Bruce, and Lloyd Greene: Flexible Welded Angle Connections, *J. AWS*, October 1940.
13. Rathbun, J. C.: Elastic Properties of Riveted Connections, *Trans. ASCE*, vol. 101, p. 539, 1936.
14. Lim, Lee C., W. J. LeMessurier, and H. W. Hagen: Design of Steel Structural Members, sec. 8 in E. H. Gaylord and C. N. Gaylord (eds.), "Structural Engineering Handbook," 3d ed., McGraw-Hill, New York, 1990.
15. Blodgett, O. W.: "Design of Welded Structures," The James F. Lincoln Arc Welding Foundation, Cleveland, 1966.
16. Timoshenko, S. P., and J. M. Gere: "Theory of Elastic Stability," 2d ed., McGraw-Hill, New York, 1961.
17. Huang, J. S., W. F. Chen, and L. S. Beedle: Behavior and Design of Steel Beam-to-Column Moment Connections, *Weld. Res. Counc. Bull.* 188, October 1973.
18. Chen, W. F., and D. E. Newlin: Column Web Strength in Beam-to-Column Connections, *J. Struct. Div. ASCE*, vol. 99, ST9, September 1973.
19. Chen, W. F., and I. J. Oppenhein: Web Buckling Strength of Beam-to-Column Connections, *J. Struct. Div. ASCE*, vol. 100, ST1, January 1974.
20. Graham, J. D., A. N. Sherbourne, R. N. Khabbaz, and C. D. Jensen: "Welded Interior Beam-to-Column Connections," American Institute of Steel Construction, Chicago, 1959.
21. Higgins, T. R.: New Formulas for Fasteners Loaded Off Center, *Eng. News-Rec.*, May 21, 1964.
22. Crawford, S. F., and G. L. Kulak: Eccentrically Loaded Bolted Connections, *J. Struct. Div. ASCE*, March 1971.
23. Butler, L. J., S. Pal, and G. L. Kulak: Eccentrically Loaded Weld Connections, *J. Struct. Div. ASCE*, May 1972.
24. Kulak, G. L., and P. A. Timmler: Tests on Eccentrically Loaded Fillet Welds, Department of Civil Engineering, University of Alberta, Edmonton, Canada, December 1984.
25. Iwankiw, N. R.: Design for Eccentric and Inclined Loads on Bolt and Weld Groups, *AISC Eng. J.*, Fourth Quarter, 1987.
26. Butler, L. J., and G. L. Kulak: Strength of Fillet Welds as a Function of Direction of Load, *Weld. J.* (Welding Research Supplement), vol. 36, May 1971.
27. Bleich, F.: "Design of Rigid Frame Knees," American Institute of Steel Construction, July 1943 (reprinted March 1956).
28. Griffiths, J. D.: "Single Span Rigid Frames in Steel," American Institute of Steel Construction, 1948 (reprinted March 1956).
29. Fisher, J. W., G. C. Lee, J. A. Yura, and G. C. Driscoll, Jr.: Plastic Analysis and Tests of Haunched Corner Connections, *Weld. Res. Counc. Bull.* 91, October 1963.
30. "Plastic Design in Steel," 2d ed., ASCE Manuals and Reports on Engineering Practice no. 41, New York, 1971.
31. Johnston, Bruce G.: Pin-Connected Plate Links, *Trans. ASCE*, vol. 104, p. 314, 1939.

CHAPTER
9

PLASTIC
ANALYSIS
AND DESIGN

9-1 INTRODUCTION

It has been pointed out on several occasions in the preceding chapters that member capacity based on yield stress gives no necessary or consistent indication of the margin of safety with respect to the ultimate capacity of a structural member or the structure of which it is a part. Thus, it was shown in Art. 5-3 that, depending upon the shape of its cross section, a structural member may develop bending resistance ranging from 10 to 70 percent more than the moment at first yield, provided the metal has sufficient ductility. Furthermore, a continuous structure can usually carry a load considerably in excess of the load at which the first plastic hinge develops, as discussed in Art. 5-11.

A procedure for predicting the strength of continuous structures is discussed in this chapter. This method of design is usually called *plastic design* and, occasionally, *ultimate-strength design*. However, since the latter term has a different meaning in the design of reinforced-concrete structures, it is not commonly used as a synonym for plastic design.

9-2 DEVELOPMENT OF COLLAPSE MECHANISM

The variation of bending moment with rotation of the cross section was discussed in Art. 5-3. For beams of materials for which stress is proportional to strain, this

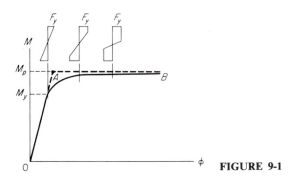

FIGURE 9-1

variation is linear until the yield moment M_y is reached (Fig. 9-1). The rate of increase of moment drops rapidly after M_y is exceeded, and the moment is very nearly equal to the plastic moment M_p at strains only several times ϵ_y, even for cross sections with large shape factors (Fig. 5-5). This variation of moment with rotation is given to good approximation by OAB in Fig. 9-1. According to this approximation, we assume that moment is proportional to rotation until M_p is reached (OA), after which rotation continues indefinitely while the moment remains constant at the value M_p (AB). A cross section in this condition is said to have developed a *plastic hinge*.

The sequence of formation of plastic hinges and the resulting redistribution of moment which leads to the peak load on a uniformly loaded fixed-ended beam was discussed in detail in Art. 5-11. It was shown that yielding develops first at the supports, following which the bending moments at these cross sections soon reach the plastic value M_p. At this stage, the bending moment at the center is $M_p/2$ if we assume the behavior OAB of Fig. 9-1. However, continued rotation at the supports under the constant moment M_p allows the moment at midspan to increase until it also reaches M_p. At this stage, rotation at midspan and at the supports can continue indefinitely with no increase in moment, provided strain hardening is neglected. Therefore, the load can increase no further. Also, with three plastic hinges, this beam is unstable and behaves like a linkage. Because of this analogy the beam is said to be a *mechanism*.

9-3 DETERMINATION OF COLLAPSE MECHANISM

In order for a beam or structure to reach its capacity load it must develop a sufficient number of plastic hinges to reduce it to a mechanism. It is evident that these hinges form at points of maximum moment, and it is immaterial whether they develop simultaneously or successively. The problem is to determine the moment diagram at collapse, which requires a knowledge of the number of plastic hinges the structure must develop to become a mechanism. The plastic-moment diagram for beams can readily be determined. Thus, the uniformly loaded beam with fixed ends (Fig. 9-2) is equivalent to a simply supported beam

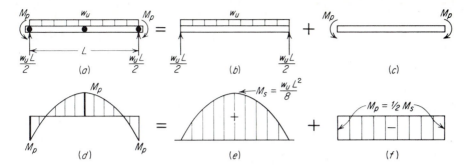

FIGURE 9-2

acted upon simultaneously by the forces shown separately in Fig. 9-2b and c. Therefore, the plastic-moment diagram of Fig. 9-2d can be found by superimposing the simple-beam moment diagrams of Fig. 9-2e and f.

The above procedure is illustrated in Fig. 9-3. Since the beam shown has a real hinge at the left support, two plastic hinges are enough to produce a mechanism (Fig. 9-3b). These hinges form at the point of application of the load and at the right support, where there are peak moments. The corresponding plastic-moment diagram is shown in Fig. 9-3c. The diagram is constructed by superimposing the simple-beam diagram ABC for the concentrated load and the simple-beam diagram ADC for the end moment. In this figure, $BE = DC = M_p$. Then since $BE = BF - EF$ and $EF = 0.6DC$, we get

$$M_p = M_s - 0.6M_p \qquad 1.6M_p = M_s$$

$$M_s = \frac{60 \times 8 \times 12}{20} = 288 \text{ ft·kips}$$

$$M_p = \frac{288}{1.6} = 180 \text{ ft·kips}$$

The location of the plastic hinges was self-evident in the preceding example. This is not always the case. For example, consider the beam shown in Fig. 9-4a. We construct the simple-beam moment diagram for the concentrated loads and

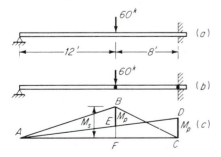

FIGURE 9-3

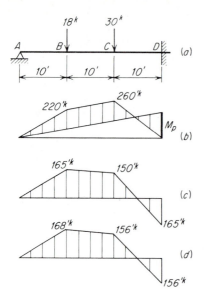

FIGURE 9-4

superimpose the simple-beam moment diagram for the unknown plastic moment at the right support (Fig. 9-4b). Since the beam has a real hinge at the left end, it will become a mechanism upon the formation of two plastic hinges. One of these hinges develops at the right support, but whether the other forms at B or at C of Fig. 9-4a is not immediately apparent. Therefore we must try both possibilities. Assuming the second hinge to be at B, we find from the geometry of the moment diagram of Fig. 9-4b

$$220 - \frac{M_p}{3} = M_p \qquad M_p = 165 \text{ ft·kips}$$

Next, assuming the second hinge to be at C, we have

$$260 - \frac{2M_p}{3} = M_p \qquad M_p = 156 \text{ ft·kips}$$

To determine which of these values is correct, consider the corresponding moment diagrams in Fig. 9-4c and d. In Fig. 9-4c there is no moment larger than 165 ft·kips, and there are two points at which the moment is 165 ft·kips, namely, at points B and D where hinges were assumed to be located in obtaining $M_p = 165$ ft·kips. On the other hand, the moment at B in Fig. 9-4d exceeds the value 156 ft·kips based on plastic hinges at C and D. Therefore, this solution cannot be correct if the beam is to be of the same cross section throughout.

A uniformly loaded beam with only one end built-in is somewhat more difficult. Since the solution is useful in dealing with continuous beams, we will develop it as a final example of the single-span beam. The beam and its plastic-moment diagram are shown in Fig. 9-5. One plastic hinge forms at the built-in end, the other at the point of maximum positive moment. The latter is not at

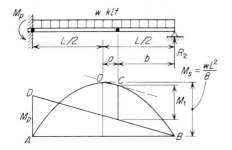

FIGURE 9-5

midspan, however, but at the section of the beam corresponding to the point C, where the tangent to the parabola AOB is parallel to the line DB. Since C is a point of maximum moment, it is also a point of zero shear in the beam. Using the notation shown in Fig. 9-5, the position of point C is found as follows:

$$R_2 = \frac{wL}{2} - \frac{M_p}{L} \tag{a}$$

$$V = R_2 - wb = \frac{wL}{2} - \frac{M_p}{L} - wb = 0$$

Therefore,

$$b = \frac{L}{2} - \frac{M_p}{wL} \tag{b}$$

The bending moment M_1 at point C is

$$M_1 = R_2 b - \frac{wb^2}{2} \tag{c}$$

Substituting into Eq. (c) the values of R_2 and b from Eqs. (a) and (b), respectively, we get

$$M_1 = \frac{wL^2}{8} - \frac{M_p}{2} + \frac{M_P^2}{2wL^2} \tag{d}$$

Since the simple-beam moment $M_s = wL^2/8$, Eq. (d) may be written

$$M_1 = M_s - \frac{M_P}{2} - \frac{M_p^2}{16M_s} \tag{9-1}$$

If there is a plastic hinge at the point of maximum positive moment as well as the built-in end, $M_1 = M_p$. Making this substitution, we get from Eq. (9-1)

$$M_p^2 - 24M_s M_p + 16M_s^2 = 0 \tag{e}$$

From Eq. (e)

$$M_p = 0.686M_s \tag{9-2}$$

The distance a from midspan to the point of maximum positive moment (Fig. 9-5) is found from Eq. (b) to be

$$a = \frac{M_p}{wL} = \frac{L}{8} \frac{M_p}{M_s} \tag{9-3}$$

In particular, if $M_p = 0.686M_s$,

$$a = \frac{L}{8} \frac{0.686M_s}{M_s} = 0.086L \tag{9-4}$$

9-4 CONTINUOUS BEAMS

The procedure described in the preceding article can be used to advantage in plastic analysis of continuous beams. For example, to determine the ultimate load P_u for the A36 W14 × 26 continuous beam of Fig. 9-6a, we superimpose the simple-beam moment diagrams for the load P_u (Fig. 9-6b) and the moment at the support (Fig. 9-6c). The result (Fig. 9-6d) shows that there are two points of peak moments at which plastic hinges can develop. Since these moments are equal, we have

$$4.8P_u - 0.4M_p = M_p$$

$$M_p = F_y Z = \frac{36 \times 40}{12} = 120 \text{ ft·kips}$$

$$P_u = \frac{1.4M_p}{4.8} = \frac{1.4 \times 120}{4.8} = 35 \text{ kips}$$

This value of P_u is the true ultimate load if there are enough plastic hinges so located as to form a mechanism and if the moment does not exceed M_p at any

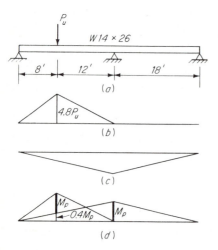

(a)

(b)

(c)

(d)   **FIGURE 9-6**

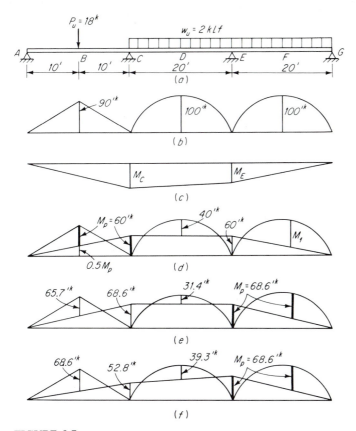

FIGURE 9-7

cross section of the beam. These conditions are fulfilled. (It is assumed that the beam has lateral support sufficient to prevent lateral-torsional buckling.)

As a second example a plastic-moment diagram for the laterally supported continuous beam of uniform cross section shown in Fig. 9-7a will be determined. Considering the structure to consist of three simple spans, we get the three moment diagrams shown in Fig. 9-7b. The moment diagram for the unknown moments at the interior supports is shown in Fig. 9-7c. The two figures must now be superimposed to produce a moment diagram that will satisfy the conditions for development of a mechanism. There are three possible mechanisms: one in span AC with plastic hinges at B and C, one in span CE with plastic hinges at C, D, and E, and one in span EG with plastic hinges at E and F. Assuming the first of these possible solutions, we get

$$90 - 0.5M_p = M_p \qquad M_p = 60 \text{ ft·kips}$$

The corresponding moment diagram for span AC is shown in Fig. 9-7d. If $M_p = 60$ ft·kips is the correct solution, it must be possible to complete the moment diagram without exceeding 60 ft·kips. This condition can be satisfied in span CE

by taking $M_E = 60$ ft·kips, which gives $M_D = 40$ ft·kips. The corresponding maximum moment in span EG is determined from Eq. (9-1):

$$M_1 = 100 - \frac{60}{2} + \frac{60^2}{16 \times 100} = 72.3 \text{ ft·kips}$$

Since this moment exceeds 60 ft·kips and cannot be reduced without increasing M_E, the assumed mechanism is not correct. This suggests that the mechanism will form in span EG. Using Eq. (9-2),

$$M_p = 0.686 \times 100 = 68.6 \text{ ft·kips}$$

Figure 9-7e shows a moment diagram corresponding to this value of M_p, for which the moment nowhere exceeds M_p. Therefore, the assumed mechanism is the correct one. However, the moment diagram of Fig. 9-7e is not the only one for which M is everywhere less than M_p. We could also assume $M_B = 68.6$ ft·kips, in which case $M_C = 2(90 - 68.6) = 52.8$ ft·kips, and $M_D = 100 - 0.5(68.6 + 52.8) = 39.3$ ft·kips (Fig. 9-7f). Thus, of the two moments M_C and M_E which were originally statically indeterminate, only M_E has been determined. For the other moment, we know only

$$52.8 \leq M_C \leq 68.6$$

Thus, the structure is still statically indeterminate, but this is immaterial so far as the determination of the required value of M_p is concerned.

9-5   MECHANISM ANALYSIS BY VIRTUAL DISPLACEMENTS

The collapse mechanism of a beam or structure can be determined by using the principle of virtual displacements. According to this principle, if a structure which is in equilibrium is given an arbitrary displacement, the work done by the external forces will equal the work done by the internal forces. In using the principle to determine the moment at collapse, the arbitrary displacement must be one for which only the internal moments at the plastic hinges contribute to the internal work. This is accomplished by allowing rotations of the structure only at points of simple support and at the points where the plastic hinges are expected to occur in producing the mechanism.

Figure 9-8a shows the beam of Fig. 9-3a, for which the value of M_p is to be determined. Two plastic hinges are sufficient to form a mechanism. They will develop at the peak-moment points B and C. Therefore, we give the beam the virtual displacement shown in Fig. 9-8b, where the only rotations permitted are those at A, B, and C. Assigning a value to any one of the hinge rotations enables the other two to be determined. Thus, with $\theta_C = \theta$, $\theta_A = 2\theta/3$ and $\theta_B = 5\theta/3$ (Fig. 9-8c). These rotations produce a displacement $\delta = 8\theta$ at the point of application of the external 60-kip load. Equating the internal work of the moments M_p to the

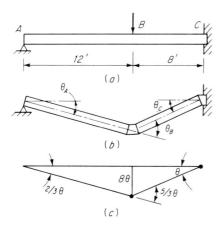

(a)

(b)

(c)

FIGURE 9-8

external work of the load, we get

$$(1 + \tfrac{5}{3})\theta M_p = 60 \times 8\theta$$

$$M_p = 180 \text{ ft·kips}$$

As a second example, the value of P_u will be determined for the beam of Fig. 9-9a, for which $M_p = 136$ ft·kips. Since two plastic hinges are enough to form a mechanism, there are two possible solutions. Assuming plastic hinges at B

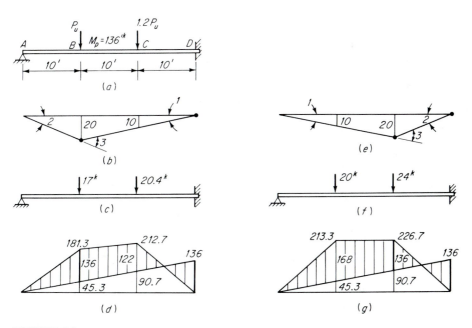

FIGURE 9-9

and D and giving the beam the virtual displacement shown in Fig. 9-9b gives

$$20 \times P_u + 10 \times 1.2P_u = (3 + 1)M_p$$

$$P_u = \frac{4M_p}{32} = \frac{5 \times 136}{32} = 17 \text{ kips}$$

This result is shown in Fig. 9-9c.

Assuming plastic hinges at C and D and giving the beam the virtual displacement shown in Fig. 9-9e gives

$$10 \times P_u + 20 \times 1.2P_u = (3 + 2)M_p$$

$$P_u = \frac{5M_p}{34} = \frac{5 \times 136}{34} = 20 \text{ kips}$$

This result is shown in Fig. 9-9f.

The moment diagrams for the two solutions are shown in Fig. 9-9d and g. It will be noted that the moment in Fig. 9-9d is nowhere larger than the specified plastic moment, 136 ft·kips. On the other hand, there are moments in excess of 136 ft·kips in the diagram for $P_u = 20$ kips (Fig. 9-9g). Therefore, P_u cannot be 20 kips. Had the diagram for $P_u = 17$ kips been constructed, it would have been unnecessary to investigate the second mechanism. Therefore, one has a choice of two procedures in using this method of analysis: (1) compute P_u for all possible mechanisms, in which case the true ultimate load is the smallest value thus found, or (2) construct the moment diagram for each P_u as it is determined and continue until the true ultimate load is identified by $M \leq M_p$ at all cross sections.

9-6   THE BOUND THEOREMS

In the analysis of the beam of the second example in Art. 9-5 it was found that only one of the two possible mechanisms gave the true ultimate load. This was the mechanism of Fig. 9-9b. Furthermore, the incorrect mechanism, Fig. 9-9e, gave a load greater than the true ultimate load. It can be proved that this is always true; i.e., of all the mechanisms that can be formed, all but the correct mechanism of collapse correspond to loads larger than the ultimate load the structure can support. This conclusion can be stated as follows.

Upper-bound theorem. The load corresponding to an assumed mechanism is greater than or equal to the true ultimate load.

A second theorem which is useful in plastic analysis can be demonstrated by using the second example of Art. 9-5, as follows. If the moments in the diagram of Fig. 9-9g are reduced in the ratio 136/168, the moment diagram in Fig. 9-10a is obtained. The corresponding reduced loads, shown in Fig. 9-10b, are less than the true ultimate loads (Fig. 9-9c). Although the moment in this diagram is nowhere larger than the prescribed value of M_p (136 ft·kips), it equals M_p at only one point. Thus, there is only one plastic hinge, which is one short of

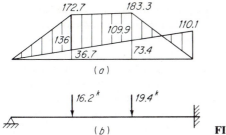

(a)

(b)   **FIGURE 9-10**

the number required to produce a mechanism. This leads to the following statement.

> **Lower-bound theorem.** The load corresponding to an assumed moment distribution which is in equilibrium with the load, and for which the moment nowhere exceeds M_p, is less than or equal to the true ultimate load.

9-7 ANALYSIS OF RECTANGULAR FRAMES

> **Example 9-7-1.** The rectangular frame shown in Fig. 9-11a is statically indeterminate. Since it is once redundant, it would be statically determinate if there were a

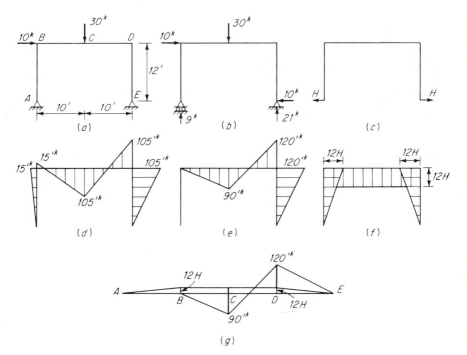

FIGURE 9-11

hinge at one other point. Therefore, if there were still another hinge, the frame would be unstable. Thus, two plastic hinges are required to form a mechanism.

Figure 9-11b shows the frame with the horizontal restraint at A removed. The resulting moment diagram is shown in Fig. 9-11e. (Moments are taken positive if the interior face of the member is in tension and are plotted positive on the tension face.) The redundant force H (whose direction is not yet known) is shown in c and the corresponding moment diagram in f. This moment diagram must be superimposed on the moment diagram of Fig. 9-11e in such a way as to produce a moment diagram for which the frame will develop the required two plastic hinges. If the three members of the frame have equal plastic resisting moments, these hinges will develop at C and D, as shown in Fig. 9-11g. Therefore,

$$120 - 12H = 90 + 12H \qquad H = \tfrac{30}{24} \text{ kips}$$

$$M_p = 90 + 12H = 90 + 15 = 105 \text{ ft·kips}$$

The resulting moment diagram is plotted on the outline of the frame in Fig. 9-11d.

If the frame of Fig. 9-11a is to be proportioned so that the plastic moment M_{pc} of the columns is only one-half the plastic moment M_{pb} of the beam, the required values of M_p are readily determined from Fig. 9-11g. Thus,

$$120 - 12H = \tfrac{1}{2}(90 + 12H) \qquad 18H = 75$$

$$M_{pc} = 120 - 12H = 120 - 50 = 70 \text{ ft·kips}$$

$$M_{pb} = 2M_{pc} = 140 \text{ ft·kips}$$

It will be noted that the final moment diagram of Fig. 9-11d can be determined once the relative moment-resisting capacities of members BD and DE have been decided. The members of the frame can then be proportioned to have resisting moments according to the requirements of the moment diagram. On the other hand, in an elastic analysis of this frame, the relative stiffnesses of the members must be assumed to effect a solution. Then, when the members are proportioned, they may have relative stiffnesses different from those assumed in advance, in which case a reanalysis is required. Thus, an advantage of plastic design is that members of a structure can be proportioned to have their resisting moments in the ratios that were assumed in advance.

Example 9-7-2. Determine the A36 W shapes for the frame of Fig. 9-12a. The three members are to have the same bending resistance.

Solution. Plastic hinges can form at B, C, and D. Should the frame collapse by forming hinges at all three of these points, the virtual displacement corresponding to the collapse mechanism would be as shown in Fig. 9-12b. This gives

$$(1 + 1\tfrac{2}{3} + \tfrac{2}{3})M_p = 12 \times 30 \qquad M_p = 108 \text{ ft·kips}$$

If the frame collapses by developing hinges at C and D, the virtual displacement corresponding to this collapse mechanism is as shown in Fig. 9-12c. This gives

$$(1\tfrac{2}{3} + 1\tfrac{2}{3})M_p = 15 \times 10 + 12 \times 30 \qquad M_p = 156 \text{ ft·kips}$$

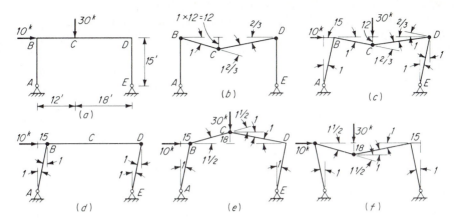

FIGURE 9-12

The frame might also collapse by developing hinges at B and D. The mechanism displacement is shown in Fig. 9-12d, for which

$$(1 + 1)M_p = 15 \times 10 \qquad M_p = 75 \text{ ft·kips}$$

In evaluating the collapse moment in the preceding cases, the virtual displacements corresponding to the collapse mechanism were taken in such a way as to make the external forces do positive work. In other words, the virtual displacement was taken in the direction in which the frame collapses. If hinges were to form at B and C, the direction in which the frame would collapse is not apparent. If the virtual displacement is taken as in Fig. 9-12e, the external work is

$$W_e = 15 \times 10 - 30 \times 18 = -390 \text{ ft·kips}$$

Therefore, if the frame were to collapse with hinges at B and C, it would collapse in the direction shown in Fig. 9-12f, for which $W_e = +390$ ft·kips:

$$(2\tfrac{1}{2} + 2\tfrac{1}{2})M_p = 390 \qquad M_p = 78 \text{ ft·kips}$$

(It is shown in the next article that it is not necessary to consider mechanisms e and f.)

Since all possible mechanisms have been investigated, the largest value of M_p found is known to be the correct one. Thus, the frame must be designed for $M_p = 156$ ft·kips, for which $Z = 156 \times \tfrac{12}{36} = 52$ in³. The W16 × 31 is the lightest section which can be used ($Z = 54$ in³), provided support against lateral-torsional buckling is adequate.

9-8 GENERAL PROCEDURE FOR MECHANISM ANALYSIS OF FRAMES

Extension of the procedure discussed in Art. 9-7 to more complex frames becomes extremely involved because of the large number of possible modes of collapse. A systematic procedure to help resolve this difficulty was suggested by Neal and Symonds.[1] The fundamentals of this procedure can be explained in terms of Example 9-7-2.

Three moments, M_B, M_C, and M_D, must be known to define the moment diagram for the frame of Example 9-7-2, Fig. 9-12a. Since the structure is once redundant, one of these moments can be prescribed independently, after which the remaining two can be determined by equations of static equilibrium. Each of these equations can be obtained by a virtual displacement corresponding to a collapse mechanism. Therefore, of all the mechanisms shown in Fig. 9-12, only two can be considered to be independent. All the others are combinations of these two. The mechanisms which are considered to be independent are called *elementary mechanisms*, and their combinations are called *combined mechanisms*. Although the elementary mechanisms can be chosen arbitrarily, there is a logical classification for rectangular frames. According to this classification, mechanisms b and d are considered to be elementary. The former is called a *beam mechanism*, the latter a *panel mechanism*. It is clear that mechanism c can be obtained by combining these two mechanisms. Mechanisms e and f are eliminated because each is a combination of a positive mechanism with a negative one.

Since the number of elementary mechanisms is equal to the number of independent equations involving the moments at points where plastic hinges can develop, a rule for the number of independent mechanisms is established. Thus

$$N = M - R \tag{9-5}$$

where N = number of independent mechanisms
M = number of possible plastic hinges
R = number of redundants

9-9 TWO-BAY FRAME—CONCENTRATED LOADS

An example illustrating analysis by combining mechanisms is given in this article, where the collapse load P for the frame of Fig. 9-13a is determined. Plastic hinges can develop at any of the seven numbered locations in the frame. The frame has three redundants. Then, from Eq. (9-5), the number of elementary mechanisms is $N = M - R = 7 - 3 = 4$. There are only two beam mechanisms and one panel mechanism, as shown in b, c, and d, so a third type of elementary mechanism must be invented. This is taken as shown in Fig. 9-13e and is called a *joint mechanism*. However, this is not a collapse mode of the frame. Since there is no external work for a virtual rotation θ of this mechanism, we get

$$(M_3 + M_4 + M_5)\theta = 0$$

This is nothing more than a statement of equilibrium of the joint.

Using the beam mechanism in Fig. 9-13b, we get

$$(1 + 2 + 1)450 = 15 \times 1.8P \qquad P = 67 \text{ kips} \tag{a}$$

The beam mechanism of Fig. 9-13c gives

$$(1 + 2\tfrac{1}{2} + 1\tfrac{1}{2})600 = 24 \times 2.25P \qquad P = 56 \text{ kips} \tag{b}$$

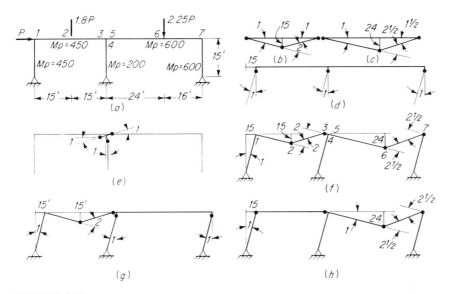

FIGURE 9-13

The panel mechanism of Fig. 9-13d gives

$$1 \times 450 + 1 \times 200 + 1 \times 600 = 15P \qquad P = 83 \text{ kips} \qquad (c)$$

According to the upper-bound theorem, we know that if any of these three values is correct, it is the smallest one. At this stage of the analysis, we could construct the moment diagram for $P = 56$ kips to determine whether the moment at any cross section in the frame exceeds the moment capacity of that cross section. However, it is usually advisable to investigate at least one combined mechanism.

Since we are seeking the smallest value of P, it is clear from an examination of the work equations (a), (b), and (c) that the elementary mechanisms must be combined in such a way as to try to decrease the internal work and/or increase the external work. This can be done by combining the work equations themselves, and for a systematic investigation of large frames this is the best procedure. However, in this example it is equally convenient to work with the combined mechanism. A combination of mechanisms b, c, and d eliminates the hinge at joint 1 but produces hinges at all the remaining points. However, it will be seen that the hinges at 4 and 5 can be eliminated by a combination with the joint mechanism of Fig. 9-13e. The result is shown in f. The work equation for this combined mechanism is

$$(2 + 2)450 + (2\tfrac{1}{2} + 2\tfrac{1}{2})600 = 15P + 15 \times 1.8P + 24 \times 2.25P$$

$$P = 50 \text{ kips}$$

Two other combined mechanisms are shown in Fig. 9-13g and h. However, instead of determining the collapse value for these, we will check the value just determined by constructing the moment diagram.

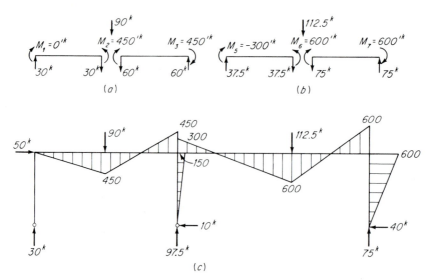

FIGURE 9-14

Figure 9-14a shows free-body diagrams for segments 1-2 and 2-3 of beam 1-3. Since there are plastic hinges at 2 and 3, M_2 and M_3 are known to be 450 ft·kips. This enables the shear for segment 2-3 to be determined, which then gives the shear for segment 1-2. With this shear known, M_1 can be determined and is found to be zero. Similarly, for segments 5-6 and 6-7 of beam 5-7, shown in Fig. 9-14b, we find $M_5 = -300$ ft·kips. The resulting moment diagram and column-base reactions are shown in Fig. 9-14c. Since the moment is nowhere larger than the prescribed values for the members, the solution $P = 50$ kips is now known to be correct.

The unknown moments at points 1 and 5 can also be determined by using the principle of virtual work. To do this, a sign convention for moment and rotation must be adopted. We take moments and rotations positive when they produce tension at the bottom of the beam. Thus, with the virtual displacement shown in Fig. 9-15, rotations at 5 and 7 are negative while that at 6 is positive. Similarly, for the mechanism in Fig. 9-13f which is being investigated, M_6 is positive while M_7 is negative. Therefore, the work equation for the virtual displacement in Fig. 9-15 is

$$-1 \times M_5 + 600 \times 2.5 + (-600)(-1.5) = 112.5 \times 24$$

from which $M_5 = -300$ ft·kips.

It will be noted that the geometry of each combined mechanism in Fig. 9-13

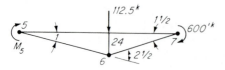

FIGURE 9-15

is determined as soon as the rotation of one of the hinges is specified; i.e., each mechanism has one degree of freedom. This is an essential characteristic of a mechanism which is to be used to compute an ultimate load or a collapse moment. Since we are restricted to mechanisms with one degree of freedom, all possible combinations of the four elementary mechanisms in Fig. 9-13 are shown in f, g, and h. Therefore, we could have computed the value of P for mechanisms g and h, in which case the true ultimate load would be the smallest value of P for the two beam mechanisms, the panel mechanism, and the three combined mechanisms. However, this method of determining the ultimate load is not generally satisfactory, because the number of possible mechanisms becomes extremely large for complex frames and because it is always possible that some combined mechanism has been overlooked. Furthermore, it is usually necessary to know the peak moments at points which were not involved in the critical mechanism, so the moment diagram must be determined in any case.

9-10   TWO-BAY FRAME—DISTRIBUTED LOADS

In frames which support distributed loads, the locations of the hinges under the distributed loads are not always self-evident. If the load is uniformly distributed over the entire span, it is convenient to assume the hinge to be at midspan for a first approximation. In many cases this first approximation will be sufficiently accurate. This technique will be illustrated in the following example.

The frame shown in Fig. 9-16 has four redundants, and there are eight points at which plastic hinges can form. Therefore, from Eq. (9-5), the number of elementary mechanisms is $N = M - R = 8 - 4 = 4$. These are the beam mechanisms in b and c, the joint mechanism (not shown), and the panel mechanism in d. If all members of the frame have the same values of M_p, we get

Mechanism b:	$(1 + 2 + 1)M_p = \frac{1}{2} \times 16 \times 32 \times 2.5$	$M_p = 160$ ft·kips
Mechanism c:	$(1 + 2 + 1)M_p = 16 \times 35$	$M_p = 140$ ft·kips
Mechanism d:	$(1 + 1 + 1 + 1)M_p = 10 \times 15$	$M_p = 37.5$ ft·kips

This combined mechanism shown in e gives

$$(2 + 2 + 1 + 2 + 2)M_p = \frac{1}{2} \times 16 \times 32 \times 2.5 + 16 \times 35 + 10 \times 15$$

$$M_p = 150 \text{ ft·kips}$$

Beam mechanism b gives the largest value of M_p. However, the value of M_p for the combined mechanism is an approximation based on formation of a plastic hinge at midspan of beam 1-3. To determine whether the combined mechanism might give a value larger than 160 ft·kips, we calculate the maximum moment for the approximate solution. A free-body diagram of segment 2-3 is shown in Fig. 9-17. With the known moments $M_p = 150$ ft·kips, the shear at section 2 is found to be $V_2 = 1.25$ kips. Since the load intensity is 2.5 klf, the point of zero shear is

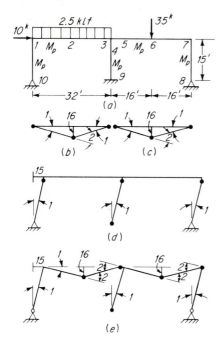

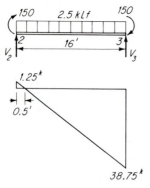

FIGURE 9-16

$1.25/2.5 = 0.5$ ft to the right of midspan. Therefore, the maximum moment is greater than M_2 by the amount

$$\Delta M = \tfrac{1}{2} \times 0.5 \times 1.25 = 0.3 \text{ ft·kips}$$

Thus, the second approximation to the moment for the combined mechanism is $M_p = 150.3$ ft·kips. A closer approximation to the theoretically correct value can be obtained by repeating the analysis, with the plastic hinge located at the point of maximum moment for the first approximation. However, it is clear that such a refinement is unnecessary in this example. This is usually the case for frames of practical proportions.

FIGURE 9-17

Instead of investigating additional mechanisms, a check is made to determine whether M is everywhere less than $M_p = 160$ ft·kips for mechanism b. M_1, M_2, and M_3 are known, leaving M_4, M_5, M_6, M_7, and M_9 to be determined. Since only three equations of equilibrium remain, the structure is twice redundant when mechanism b forms. However, we need not calculate these redundants because, according to the lower-bound theorem, if we can construct a statically admissible moment diagram for which M is everywhere less than M_p, we know that the assumed collapse mechanism is the correct one.

Although values of any two of the remaining moments can be assumed, it would seem reasonable to assume M_5, M_6, and M_7 to be equal to their mechanism values, 140 ft·kips, determined above. In this way, we get the moment diagrams for the two beams, as shown in Fig. 9-18. Moments at the column tops can then be found by joint equilibrium, which leaves only M_9 undetermined. However, with M_1 and M_7 known, the horizontal reactions at 8 and 10 are found to be 9.3 and 10.7 kips, respectively. Therefore, the horizontal reaction at 9 is 11.4 kips. The required moment at 9 is then found by moment equilibrium of column 4-9. Then, since the moment diagram for the frame satisfies $M \leq M_p$ at all points, we know that $M_p = 160$ ft·kips is correct.

Although the procedure for handling distributed loads that was used in this example is usually adequate, there are two other procedures that may be used. In one of these, the plastic hinges whose positions are unknown are located by coordinates x_1, x_2, etc. The work equation for the mechanism is then written and the correct locations of the hinges found by maximizing M_p by $\partial M_p/\partial x_1 = 0$, $\partial M_p/\partial x_2 = 0$, etc. If the structure is being analyzed to determine P, instead of M_p, the procedure is the same except that P is minimized by $\partial P/\partial x_1 = 0$, $\partial P/\partial x_2 = 0$, etc.

In the other alternative procedure the distributed load is replaced by one or more concentrated loads. The simplest replacement is a single concentrated load at midspan, but this results in considerable error. The next simplest replacement is two equal concentrated loads, one at each quarter point. This will be illustrated for the beam of Fig. 9-19a, for which the load replacements are shown in Fig. 9-19b. The two possible mechanisms for the substitute beam are shown in Fig.

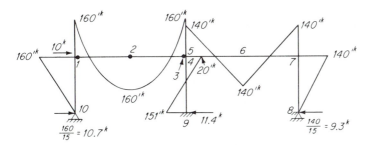

FIGURE 9-18

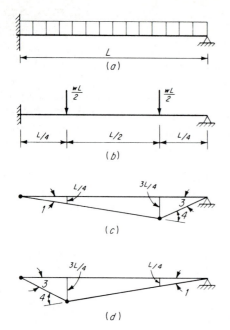

FIGURE 9-19

9-19c and d. The work equations for the two mechanisms are

Mechanism c: $\quad (4 + 1)M_p = \dfrac{wL}{2}\left(\dfrac{3L}{4} + \dfrac{L}{4}\right) \qquad M_p = \dfrac{wL^2}{10}$

Mechanism d: $\quad (4 + 3)M_p = \dfrac{wL}{2}\left(\dfrac{L}{4} + \dfrac{3L}{4}\right) \qquad M_p = \dfrac{wL^2}{14}$

Therefore $M_p = wL^2/10$. This beam was analyzed in Art. 9-3 by finding the exact location of the interior plastic hinge, which turned out to be $0.414L$ from the simply supported end of the beam. The corresponding value of M_p is given by Eq. (9-2) as

$$M_p = 0.686M_s = 0.686\,\frac{wL^2}{8} = \frac{wL^2}{11.7}$$

Thus, load replacement at the quarter points overestimates the required plastic moment by 17 percent.

Replacement of the uniform load in Fig. 9-19 by four equal concentrated loads $wL/4$ at the odd eighth points gives $M_p = wL^2/11$. This is 6 percent more than the correct value. It will be noted that a disadvantage of the load-replacement method is that each additional concentrated load increases the number of mechanisms by introducing an additional hinge. This can lead to an impractical number of mechanisms in large frames. The two procedures discussed above are covered in greater detail in Refs. 2, 3, and 4.

9-11   GABLE FRAMES

One-story buildings are often built with sloping roofs, with the structure supported by nonrectangular frames called *gable frames*. Plastic analysis of gable
frames is slightly more difficult than plastic analysis of rectangular frames
because the mechanism displacements are not as readily determined. The concept
of the instantaneous center of rotation facilitates their determination in gable
frames and other frames with sloping members. This will be shown in the following example.

The frame of Fig. 9-20a has 1 redundant and 11 points at which hinges can
form. Therefore, the number of elementary mechanisms is $N = M - R =
11 - 1 = 10$. Eight of these are beam mechanisms, two of which are shown in
Fig. 9-20b. A third elementary mechanism is the panel mechanism of Fig. 9-20c.
Since there are no joint mechanisms (joint mechanisms need be considered only
when three or more members frame in at the joint), we must invent a fourth
elementary mechanism. This is usually taken in the form shown in Fig. 9-20d. It
is essentially a variation of the panel mechanism but is sometimes called a *gable
mechanism*.

Assuming the interior hinge to form under the third purlin, the beam
mechanism of Fig. 9-20b gives

$$(1\tfrac{1}{2} + 2\tfrac{1}{2} + 1)M_p = 15(12 + 24 + 16 + 8) \qquad M_p = 180 \text{ ft·kips}$$

The same result is obtained if the hinge is assumed to act one panel farther to the
right.

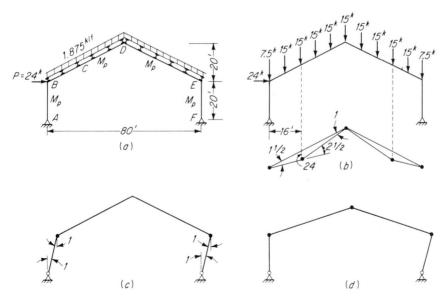

FIGURE 9-20

The panel mechanism of Fig. 9-20c gives

$$(1 + 1)M_p = 24 \times 20 \qquad M_p = 240 \text{ ft·kips}$$

The displacements for the gable mechanism will be determined by using the instantaneous center. Figure 9-21 shows the gable mechanism, where column AB rotates about A to the position AB' and rafter GC rotates about G to the position GC'. End C of rafter BC also rotates about G, but end B rotates about A. Therefore, rafter BC rotates about a point found by extending GC and AB to their intersection at O. This point is called the *instantaneous center*. It can always be found as the intersection of two straight lines, each originating at a known nontranslating point (A and G) and passing through the adjacent hinge.

To determine the external work of the purlin loads, we need the vertical component of the displacement of each purlin. The displacement of any point on a rafter, such as D in Fig. 9-21, may be found in the following manner. If the angle of rotation about O is θ, $DD' = OD \times \theta$. The vertical component of this displacement is found from the similar triangles $DD'E$ and ODF. Hence

$$\frac{D'E}{DD'} = \frac{DE}{OD}$$

so that $D'E = DF \times \theta$. Therefore, the vertical displacement of any point on rafter BC is the product of the rotation about O and the horizontal distance from ABO to that point. Similarly, the vertical displacement of any point on rafter GC is the product of the rotation about G and the horizontal distance from GH to that point.

The external work for the frame of this example is, for rafter BC rotating about O,

$$W_{e,BC} = (8 + 16 + 24 + 32 + 40)15 \times \theta = 1800\theta$$

and, for rafter GC rotating about G,

$$W_{e,GC} = (8 + 16 + 24 + 32)15 \times \theta = 1200\theta$$

The hinge rotation at G in Fig. 9-21 is θ. Since CB also rotates (about O) through the angle θ, the hinge rotation at C is 2θ. Similarly, the hinge rotation at B is

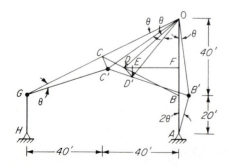

FIGURE 9-21

$\theta + 2\theta = 3\theta$. Therefore, the internal work is

$$W_i = (\theta + 2\theta + 3\theta)M_p = 6\theta M_p$$

Equating W_e and W_i, we get $M_p = 500$ ft·kips.

Although M_p is larger for the gable mechanism than for either the beam mechanism or the panel mechanism, there is a combined mechanism which, because it has only two hinges, could give a larger value. This mechanism is shown in Fig. 9-22. The hinge at H usually forms close to the ridge. In this case, we assume it to be at the first purlin to the left. After locating the instantaneous center at the intersection of GH and AB, we assume a rotation θ, about O, of the segment BDH. The corresponding rotation of AB is 3.5θ and of GCH 1.5θ. The hinge rotation at H is $1.5\theta + \theta = 2.5\theta$, and that at B is $3.5\theta + \theta = 4.5\theta$. Therefore, the internal work is

$$W_i = (2.5 + 4.5)\theta \times M_p = 7\theta M_p \tag{a}$$

The external work is found as before by determining the vertical displacements of the purlins. Thus, for the segment BD

$$W_{e,BD} = (8 + 16 + 24 + 32 + 40)\theta \times 15 = 1800\theta \tag{b}$$

For the segment CH

$$W_{e,CH} = (8 + 16 + 24 + 32)1.5\theta \times 15 = 1800\theta \tag{c}$$

Finally, the external work for the wind load at C is

$$W_{e,C} = 20 \times 1.5\theta \times 24 = 720\theta \tag{d}$$

Equating the internal work from Eq. (a) to the sum of the external work from Eqs. (b), (c), and (d), we get

$$7\theta M_p = 4320\theta \qquad M_p = 617 \text{ ft·kips}$$

Since this value is the largest so far, we check to see if it satisfies the criterion $M \le M_p$. With the moment at the two plastic hinges known, the frame is

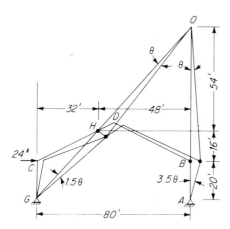

FIGURE 9-22

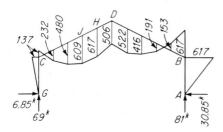

FIGURE 9-23

statically determinate and the reactions are readily computed (Fig. 9-23). A check of the moments at the purlins at J and D shows both to be less than M_p. Finally, the moment diagram shows $M \le 617$ for all points, so $M_p = 617$ ft·kips is the required plastic moment of resistance.

A detailed example of plastic design of a gable frame is given in DP9-15-1.

9-12   MEMBER STRENGTH

In the AISC Load and Resistance Factor Design Specification for Structural Steel Buildings, formulas for member strength discussed in Chaps. 3 to 6 are applicable for design by either elastic or plastic analysis, except that, if plastic analysis is used, the following restrictions must be observed:

1. Only steels for which $F_y \le 65$ ksi may be used.
2. All webs, and flanges subjected to compression involving hinge rotation, must be compact (Table 5-3).
3. Column axial forces due to factored gravity load plus factored horizontal load must not exceed $0.75F_y A_g$.
4. The column-slenderness parameter λ_c must not exceed $1.5K$. This is equivalent to a limiting value of $535/\sqrt{F_y}$ for L/r.
5. Laterally unbraced lengths of beams must not exceed the value of L_{pd} given by the following equations:

 For symmetric I-shaped members and singly symmetric I-shaped members with the compression flange larger than the tension flange, including hybrid members, loaded in the plane of the web,

$$L_{pd} = \frac{3600 + 2200M_1/M_p}{F_y} r_y$$

 For solid rectangular bars and symmetric box beams,

$$L_{pd} = \frac{5000 + 3000M_1/M_p}{F_y} r_y \ge 3000 \frac{r_y}{F_y}$$

 Members with these lengths can be expected to have hinge rotation capacities of at least 3. It should be noted that values of L_{pd} are smaller, and therefore more restrictive, than the lengths L_p discussed in Art. 5-9.

In the AISC Specification for Structural Steel Buildings, Chapter N, Plastic Design, formulas for member strength differ from those for allowable-stress design in that they are expressed as strength resultants (axial force, moment, shear, etc.) rather than as allowable stresses. The specification does not use resistance factors (ϕ) nor does it specify the variety of load combinations of the LRFD specification. Instead, only two load factors are specified: 1.7 for live load and dead load and 1.3 for live load and dead load acting together with any specified wind or earthquake forces. Consequently, plastic design according to this specification is likely to be simpler than plastic design by the LRFD specification, since it requires only that a frame which develops a collapse mechanism under factored dead load plus live load can be shown to be able to resist factored dead load plus live load plus wind or earthquake without requiring a moment larger than M_p at any section. For the LRFD specification a frame which develops a collapse mechanism for one of the load combinations of Art. 1-13 must be checked for all the other applicable load combinations to verify that M_p is nowhere exceeded.

9-13 LOCAL AND LATERAL-TORSIONAL BUCKLING

The manner in which collapse mechanisms develop was discussed in Arts. 5-11, 9-2, and 9-3. It was shown that the plastic hinges required to produce a mechanism do not, in general, form simultaneously and that rotation at the hinges which form in the early stages is assumed to continue at an essentially constant moment until the last hinge is formed. $OABC$ in Fig. 9-24 shows this necessary performance, which is usually simplified in the form $OADC$. However, the last hinge to form need only reach M_p, for which the rotation ϕ_p is sufficient.

Hinges do not develop at a point, as is assumed in the mechanism analysis. Instead, they are distributed over finite lengths of the beam. Thus, for a fixed-end beam, the strain on the extreme fiber in the vicinity of the support varies from ϵ_y at the cross section where $M = M_y$, to $\epsilon > \epsilon_y$ at the end, where $M = M_p$. For a uniformly loaded fixed-end beam with a shape factor $M_p/M_y = 1.12$, this transition occurs in the length $a = 0.015L$ (Fig. 9-25).

Rotation capacity has been investigated both theoretically and experimentally. For example, it can be shown that the average rotation in the yielded length a of Fig. 9-25 is about 11 times the rotation ϕ_p in Fig. 9-24. However, rotations of this magnitude can be developed in beams of I cross section only if adequate

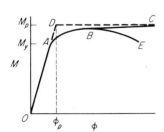

FIGURE 9-24

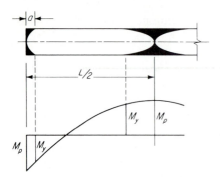

FIGURE 9-25

precaution is taken against local buckling and against lateral-torsional buckling of the member itself. Without such precaution, a reduction in moment, as in *BE* of Fig. 9-24, may occur.

An investigation of inelastic buckling of compression flanges[5] is discussed in Art. 5-6. Results of this investigation indicate that flanges supported on both unloaded edges, like the flanges of box sections, can reach strain hardening if $b/t \leq 192/\sqrt{F_y}$ [Eq. (5-10)]. In both AISC specifications, this limit is set at $190/\sqrt{F_y}$. The investigation also indicates that compression flanges supported on only one unloaded edge, as in the I cross section, can reach strain hardening if $b/t \leq 49/\sqrt{F_y}$ [Eq. (5-9)]. In chapter N of the AISC Specification for Structural Steel Buildings, a specific limit for each yield stress is set for this type of element. Thus, $b/t = 8.5$ for $F_y = 36$ ksi, 7 for $F_y = 50$ ksi, and 6 for $F_y = 65$ ksi. The latter is the highest yield stress of the steels which are permitted for plastic design.

An investigation of inelastic buckling of beam-column webs in Ref. 5 is discussed in Art. 5-15. Provisions of Chapter N are based on this investigation. Thus, slenderness of beam-column webs must not exceed the values given by

$$\frac{d}{t} = \begin{cases} \dfrac{412}{\sqrt{F_y}}\left(1 - 1.4\,\dfrac{P}{P_y}\right) & \dfrac{P}{P_y} \leq 0.27 & (9\text{-}6a) \\[4mm] \dfrac{257}{\sqrt{F_y}} & \dfrac{P}{P_y} > 0.27 & (9\text{-}6b) \end{cases}$$

The corresponding formulas in the LRFD specification are

$$\frac{h_c}{t_w} = \begin{cases} \dfrac{640}{\sqrt{F_y}}\left(1 - \dfrac{2.75 P_u}{\phi_b P_y}\right) & \dfrac{P_u}{\phi_b P_y} \leq 0.125 & (9\text{-}6c) \\[4mm] \dfrac{191}{\sqrt{F_y}}\left(2.33 - \dfrac{P_u}{\phi_b P_y}\right) \geq \dfrac{253}{\sqrt{F_y}} & \dfrac{P_u}{\phi_b P_y} > 0.125 & (9\text{-}6d) \end{cases}$$

where h_c is the clear distance between flanges less the fillet or corner radius.

Lateral-torsional buckling was discussed in Arts. 5-4 and 5-5 and specification provisions in Arts. 5-8 and 5-9. However, the objective was to determine the reduction in in-plane bending strength as a function of the unbraced length, and the limiting unbraced length which will allow the beam to reach its yield moment (point *A* of Fig. 9-24). It was shown that lateral-buckling resistance depends on the moment gradient, which is accounted for by the coefficient C_b in the lateral-buckling formulas.

There have been a number of investigations of postelastic lateral-buckling behavior to determine rotation capacity. In general, it is assumed that a beam under moment gradient has elastic properties in the portions where moments are less than about $0.90M_p$ to $0.95M_p$ and strain-hardening properties in the remainder. This assumption is in recognition of the discontinuous nature of yielding, which was discussed in Art. 2-4. Provisions of the AISC specifications are based on work reported in Ref. 6. St. Venant torsional resistance is neglected in this investigation, and lateral-torsional buckling of the beam is assumed to be equivalent to lateral buckling of the compression half of the I cross section as a column. Since the moment is M_p, this compression half of the beam is subjected to a uniform compressive stress F_y. Furthermore, with St. Venant torsion neglected, the results are expressed in terms of L/r_y, as in the simplified formula in Art. 5-8 [Eq. (5-14b)]. According to chapter N, the limiting values of L/r_y which assure the rotation capacity of a member that must develop a plastic hinge are given by

$$\frac{L}{r_y} = \begin{cases} \dfrac{1375}{F_y} + 25 & 1 \ge \dfrac{M}{M_p} > -0.5 & (9\text{-}7a) \\[3mm] \dfrac{1375}{F_y} & -0.5 \ge \dfrac{M}{M_p} \ge -1 & (9\text{-}7b) \end{cases}$$

In these formulas, M is the moment at the end opposite the plastic hinge and M/M_p is taken positive for a member bent in reversed curvature. The formulas are plotted in Fig. 9-26. It will be noted that moment gradient is not taken into account by a coefficient such as C_b. Instead, a constant value of L/r_y is specified for each of two ranges of moment gradient, which results in a discontinuity at $M/M_p = -0.5$. The corresponding formulas in the 1961 edition of the specification did not give this discontinuity. A comparison of the provisions of the two versions is shown for A36 steel in the figure.

The L/r_y limits in Fig. 9-26 need not be applied in the region of the last hinge to form in a mechanism, since rotation capacity is not required here. Instead, this segment of the frame can be analyzed as an elastic member.

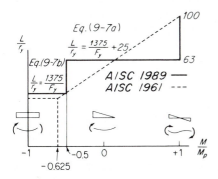

FIGURE 9-26

However, since the segment is required to develop a plastic moment, the distance from the last plastic hinge to the adjacent lateral support must satisfy the requirements for a compact section [Eqs. (5-17)]. On the other hand, the distance between lateral supports that bound a segment in which there is no plastic hinge may be checked instead for compliance with lateral-buckling requirements for noncompact section, Eqs. (5-19) and (5-20), as well as Eqs. (6-23). In the latter case, of course, the analysis must be based on service loads rather than ultimate loads. Studies of rectangular frames and gable frames show that the last hinge develops in the beam or rafter except for frames with unusually large ratios of column height to frame span (greater than about 0.6) (Refs. 4, 7). Therefore, the less severe lateral-buckling requirements will usually govern the spacing of lateral support at the hinges in beams and rafters except where they join the columns. Examples are given in the next article and in DP9-15-1.

9-14   BEAM-COLUMNS

Beam-column strength was discussed in Arts. 6-1, 6-2, and 6-6, where it was shown that values of axial load P and bending moment M which can be resisted simultaneously are given by Eqs. (6-9) and (6-11). These formulas were derived for the case of bending restricted to the plane of the end moments. However, it was shown in Arts. 5-8 and 6-5 that they can be extended to the case where lateral-torsional buckling is not prevented by using the critical moment M_m, rather than M_p, as the limiting value for bending alone in Eq. (6-19). The result is

$$\frac{P}{P_{cr}} + \frac{M}{M_m}\frac{C_m}{1 - P/P_E} \le 1 \tag{9-8}$$

$$\frac{P}{P_y} + 0.85\frac{M}{M_p} \le 1 \qquad \text{if } \frac{P}{P_y} \ge 0.15 \tag{9-9a}$$

$$M = M_p \qquad \text{if } \frac{P}{P_y} \le 0.15 \tag{9-9b}$$

P_{cr} in these equations is defined as the smaller of the critical loads for in-plane and out-of-plane buckling. Lateral-torsional buckling due to bending moment was discussed in Arts. 5-4 and 5-5. Simplified formulas for allowable-stress design, such as Eqs. (5-19) and (5-20), were discussed in Art. 5-8. The corresponding formula in chapter N of the AISC/ASD specification is

$$M_m = \left(1.07 - \frac{\sqrt{F_y}}{3160}\frac{L}{r_y}\right)M_p \le M_p \tag{9-10}$$

This formula is based on the results of tests on W shapes of the proportions ordinarily used as columns.

It should be noted that the limiting value of L/r_y which was discussed in Art. 9-12 and which is shown in Fig. 9-26 enables a beam-column to develop the fully plastic moment and adequate rotation capacity, provided $P = 0$. Therefore, where the spacing of lateral support satisfies this limitation, $M_m = M_p$.

Example 9-14-1. The W16 × 31 columns of the frame of Example 9-7-2 are checked in this example for compliance with chapter N of the AISC/ASD specification. The frame is shown in Fig. 9-27a and the moment diagram at collapse in Fig. 9-27b.

Both flange and web must be checked for local buckling. The permissible flange slenderness is $b/t = 8.5$, while the actual value is $2.76/0.442 = 6.25$. The permissible web slenderness is given by Eqs. (9-6):

$$P_y = 36 \times 9.13 = 329 \text{ kips} \qquad \frac{P}{P_y} = \frac{17}{329} = 0.05 < 0.27$$

Therefore, Eq. (9-6a) applies, and the allowable slenderness is

$$\frac{d}{t} = \frac{412}{\sqrt{36}} (1 - 1.4 \times 0.05) = 64$$

For W16 × 31, $d/t = 15.84/0.275 = 57.6$.

The lateral-bracing requirements will now be checked. Figure 9-27b shows that column DE controls. Since $M/M_p = 0$, Eq. (9-7a) applies, and the permissible slenderness ratio is

$$\frac{L}{r_y} = \frac{1375}{36} + 25 = 38 + 25 = 63$$

The actual slenderness ratio is $15 \times 12/1.17 = 154$. Therefore, intermediate support is required. In order for the limiting value 63 to apply, the moment at the intermediate braced point must satisfy $M > -0.5M_p$ (Fig. 9-26). This would require the braced point to be $L/2 = 7.5$ ft (or farther) from the column top. The slenderness ratio for a brace at this point is $7.5 \times 12/1.17 = 77$, which also exceeds the permissible value 63. Therefore, closer spacing is needed, for which Eq. (9-7b) applies, and the permissible slenderness is

$$\frac{L}{r_y} = \frac{1375}{36} = 38$$

The distance from the plastic hinge to this point is $L = 38 \times 1.17/12 = 3.7$ ft.

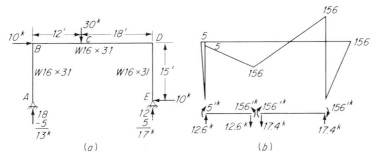

(a) (b)

FIGURE 9-27

Assuming a brace at 3.5 ft, the remaining 11.5-ft segment must be checked to determine whether additional lateral support is needed. Since there is no plastic hinge in this segment, formulas based on beginning of yield apply, as was noted in Art. 9-12. Therefore, the loads shown in Fig. 9-27a must be reduced to service values for this investigation. Assume the 10-kip load to be a wind load. The AISC load factor for a combination of wind and gravity load is 1.3, so the column axial force and moment and the corresponding stresses are

$$P = \frac{17}{1.3} = 13.1 \text{ kips} \qquad M = \frac{11.5}{15} \times \frac{156}{1.3} = 92 \text{ ft·kips}$$

$$f_a = \frac{13.1}{7.27} = 1.8 \text{ ksi} \qquad f_b = \frac{92 \times 12}{47.2} = 23.5 \text{ ksi}$$

According to the specification, allowable stresses may be increased by one-third for combinations of wind and gravity load. The value of F_a must be checked for both x- and y-axis buckling:

$$G_D = \frac{(I/L)_C}{(I/L)_B} = \frac{30}{15} = 2 \qquad G_E = 10 \qquad K = 2.1 \qquad \text{(Fig. 4-28b)}$$

$$\frac{KL}{r_x} = \frac{2.1 \times 15 \times 12}{6.40} = 59 \qquad \frac{L}{r_y} = \frac{11.5 \times 12}{1.17} = 118$$

$$F_a = 10.6 \times 1.33 = 14.1 \text{ ksi}$$

In determining the allowable bending stress, C_b must be taken equal to unity because C_m in the interaction formulas provides for the moment gradient.

$$\frac{L}{r_T} = \frac{11.5 \times 12}{1.41} = 98 > \frac{L}{r} = \sqrt{\frac{102,000}{36}} = 53$$

Therefore, Eq. (5-19b), which is the specification formula F1-6, applies. For A36 steel, this gives

$$F_b = 1.33 \left[24 - \frac{(L/r_T)^2}{1181} \right] = 1.33 \left(24 - \frac{98^2}{1181} \right) = 21.2 \text{ ksi}$$

According to Eq. (5-20b), which is the specification formula F1-8,

$$\frac{Ld}{A_f} = 11.5 \times 12 \times 6.49 = 895$$

$$F_b = 1.33 \frac{12,000}{Ld/A_f} = 1.33 \frac{12,000}{895} = 17.8 \text{ ksi}$$

The larger of these two values of F_b is the correct one. However, it is less than f_b, so an additional brace must be provided at, say, 5.75 ft from the base of the column. Had F_b been larger than f_b, the values of f_a, F_a, f_b, and F_b would have been checked for compliance with the interaction formulas Eqs. (6-23), which are the specification formulas H1-1 and H1-2.

It remains to check the columns according to Eqs. (9-8) and (9-9). Since $P/P_y = 0.05$, as determined above, $M = M_p$ [Eq. (9-9b)]. According to the specification, P_{cr} and P_E in Eq. (9-8) are determined by multiplying the allowable loads according to the formulas for allowable-stress design by the factors of safety, which are 1.7 for P_{cr} and 1.92 for P_E. The slenderness ratio for in-plane buckling was determined above, $KL/r_x = 59$. With lateral support at 5.75 ft and 11.5 ft above the base, $L/r_y = 5.75 \times 12/1.17 = 59$. Therefore $F_a = 17.5$ ksi, $F'_E = 42.9$ ksi, and

$$P_{cr} = 1.7F_a A = 1.7 \times 17.5 \times 7.67 = 229 \text{ kips}$$

$$P_E = 1.92 \times 42.9 \times 7.67 = 633 \text{ kips}$$

The specification prescribes $C_m = 0.85$ for columns in frames not braced against sidesway. Furthermore, since the column is braced in the weak direction, $M_m = M_p = 54 \times \frac{36}{12} = 162$ ft·kips. Then from Eq. (9-8)

$$\frac{17}{229} + \frac{156}{162} \frac{0.85}{1 - \frac{17}{633}} = 0.074 + 0.840 = 0.914 < 1$$

9-15 SHEAR RESISTANCE

The shear resistance of webs of beams for which the limiting load is based on first yield was discussed in Arts. 5-13 and 5-14. The shear strength of beams at cross sections where there has been some penetration of yield stress is investigated in this article.

A portion of the bending-moment diagram for a beam and the corresponding bending stresses are shown in Fig. 9-28a and b. Consider the segment below a horizontal section 1-1 which lies entirely within the yielded zone (Fig. 9-28b). Since the horizontal forces acting on this segment are in equilibrium (Fig. 9-28c), there can be no shear on section 1-1. Therefore, neither can there be shear on the vertical faces of this segment. Thus, the shear resistance of the beam must be developed entirely in the portion of the web which is still elastic, i.e., in the portion of depth a shown in Fig. 9-28b. According to this analysis, no shear resistance can exist at a cross section where there is a plastic hinge.

Consider next a cross section at which the web has yielded uniformly in shear throughout its depth (Fig. 9-29b). In this case, the yield criterion states that there can be no bending stresses in the web, so only the flanges can resist

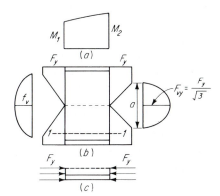

FIGURE 9-28

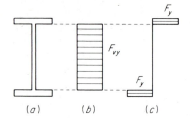

(a) (b) (c) **FIGURE 9-29**

moment. The shear resistance is given by

$$V_u = F_{vy}\, t(d - 2t_f) \tag{a}$$

where t = thickness of web
t_f = thickness of one flange
d = depth of beam

For rolled I cross sections which are used as beams, $d - 2t_f$ averages about $0.95d$. Furthermore, $F_{vy} = F_y/\sqrt{3}$ by the Mises yield criterion. Therefore, Eq. (a) can be written

$$V = 0.95dt\,\frac{F_y}{\sqrt{3}} = 0.55F_y\, dt \tag{9-11}$$

It would appear from this analysis that a fully plastic moment cannot develop at a cross section where $V = V_u$, since, according to the yield criterion, only the flanges can develop moment if the web is fully yielded in shear (Fig. 9-29c). However, tests show that this is not the case. Instead, M_p is reduced only slightly, if at all, so long as V does not exceed the value from Eq. (9-11). This is due to the effects of strain hardening. Therefore, Eq. (9-11) is prescribed in chapter N of the AISC/ASD specification.

DP9-15-1: Steel-Building Rigid Frame

In this example we design a gabled rigid frame subject to dead load, snow load, and wind load. The design will be governed by the BOCA National Building Code and the AISC Specification for Structural Steel Buildings, chap. N. The dimensions of the building and the purlin spacing are shown on sheet 1. The bases are assumed to be hinged. The following comments are identified by letters corresponding to those alongside the computations on the design sheets.

Sheet 1

a. Plastic moments are assumed to form in the rafters at the haunches and at purlin locations 8 and 12. The simple-beam moments and plastic moments are computed at sections 3 and 8. The moment diagram (sheet 2) shows that all $M \leq M_p$.

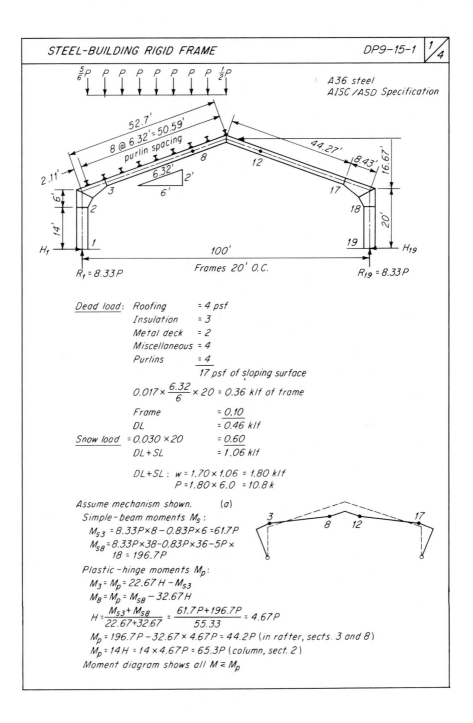

STEEL-BUILDING RIGID FRAME   DP9-15-1 1/4

A36 steel
AISC/ASD Specification

52.7'
8 @ 6.32' = 50.59' purlin spacing
2.11'
6.32'
6' 2'
44.27'
8.43'
16.67'
12
8
17
18
19
2
1
14'
6'
20'
H_1
H_{19}
100'
$R_1 = 8.33P$
Frames 20' O.C.
$R_{19} = 8.33P$
$\frac{5}{6}P$ P P P P P P P $\frac{1}{2}P$

Dead load: Roofing   = 4 psf
              Insulation   = 3
              Metal deck   = 2
              Miscellaneous   = 4
              Purlins   = 4
              _____
                               17 psf of sloping surface

$0.017 \times \dfrac{6.32}{6} \times 20 = 0.36$ klf of frame

              Frame   = 0.10
              DL   = 0.46 klf
Snow load = 0.030 × 20   = 0.60
              DL + SL   = 1.06 klf

              DL + SL : w = 1.70 × 1.06 = 1.80 klf
                         P = 1.80 × 6.0 = 10.8 k

Assume mechanism shown.   (a)
  Simple-beam moments M_s :
  $M_{s3} = 8.33P \times 8 - 0.83P \times 6 = 61.7P$
  $M_{s8} = 8.33P \times 38 - 0.83P \times 36 - 5P \times 18 = 196.7P$

  Plastic-hinge moments M_p :
  $M_3 = M_p = 22.67H - M_{s3}$
  $M_8 = M_p = M_{s8} - 32.67H$
  $H = \dfrac{M_{s3} + M_{s8}}{22.67 + 32.67} = \dfrac{61.7P + 196.7P}{55.33} = 4.67P$
  $M_p = 196.7P - 32.67 \times 4.67P = 44.2P$ (in rafter, sects. 3 and 8)
  $M_p = 14H = 14 \times 4.67P = 65.3P$ (column, sect. 2)
  Moment diagram shows all $M \leqq M_p$

3   8   12   17

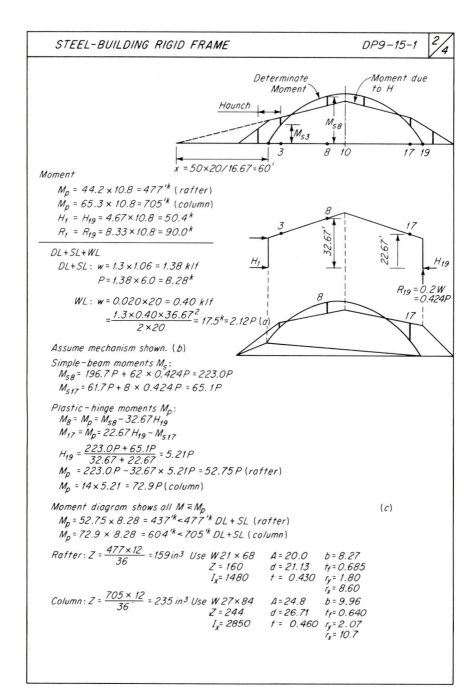

Moment

$$M_p = 44.2 \times 10.8 = 477^{'k} \ (rafter)$$
$$M_p = 65.3 \times 10.8 = 705^{'k} \ (column)$$
$$H_1 = H_{19} = 4.67 \times 10.8 = 50.4^k$$
$$R_1 = R_{19} = 8.33 \times 10.8 = 90.0^k$$

DL + SL + WL

DL+SL: $w = 1.3 \times 1.06 = 1.38 \ klf$

$$P = 1.38 \times 6.0 = 8.28^k$$

WL: $w = 0.020 \times 20 = 0.40 \ klf$

$$= \frac{1.3 \times 0.40 \times 36.67^2}{2 \times 20} = 17.5^k = 2.12P \ (a)$$

Assume mechanism shown. (b)

Simple-beam moments M_s:
$$M_{s8} = 196.7P + 62 \times 0.424P = 223.0P$$
$$M_{s17} = 61.7P + 8 \times 0.424P = 65.1P$$

Plastic-hinge moments M_p:
$$M_8 = M_p = M_{s8} - 32.67H_{19}$$
$$M_{17} = M_p = 22.67H_{19} - M_{s17}$$

$$H_{19} = \frac{223.0P + 65.1P}{32.67 + 22.67} = 5.21P$$
$$M_p = 223.0P - 32.67 \times 5.21P = 52.75P \ (rafter)$$
$$M_p = 14 \times 5.21 = 72.9P \ (column)$$

Moment diagram shows all $M \gtreqless M_p$ (c)

$$M_p = 52.75 \times 8.28 = 437^{'k} < 477^{'k} \ DL + SL \ (rafter)$$
$$M_p = 72.9 \times 8.28 = 604^{'k} < 705^{'k} \ DL + SL \ (column)$$

Rafter: $Z = \dfrac{477 \times 12}{36} = 159 \ in^3$ Use W21 × 68   A = 20.0   b = 8.27

                              Z = 160   d = 21.13 t_f = 0.685

                              I_x = 1480   t = 0.430 r_y = 1.80

                                                             r_x = 8.60

Column: $Z = \dfrac{705 \times 12}{36} = 235 \ in^3$ Use W27 × 84   A = 24.8   b = 9.96

                              Z = 244   d = 26.71 t_f = 0.640

                              I_x = 2850   t = 0.460 r_y = 2.07

                                                             r_x = 10.7

| STEEL–BUILDING RIGID FRAME | DP9–15–1 3/4 |

Combined axial force and bending (a)

Column : At top $G = \dfrac{2850}{20} \times \dfrac{2 \times 52.7}{1480} = 10.1$

At bottom $G = 10$ (hinged base)

$K = 3$ (Fig. 4–28 b)

$KL/r_x = 3 \times 14 \times 12 / 10.7 = 47$

$P_{cr} = 1.70 \times 24.8 \times 18.61 = 785^k$

$P_y = 24.8 \times 36 = 893^k$

$P_E = 1.92 \times 24.8 \times 67.51 = 3215^k$

$P = 90^k$

$M = 705^{'k}$

$M_p = 244 \times 36/12 = 732^{'k}$

$\dfrac{P}{P_y} + \dfrac{M}{1.18 M_p} = \dfrac{90}{893} + \dfrac{705}{1.18 \times 732} = 0.101 + 0.819 = 0.920 < 1.0$

$\dfrac{P}{P_{cr}} + \dfrac{C_m M}{(1 - P/P_E) M_m} = \dfrac{90}{785} + \dfrac{0.85 \times 705}{(1 - 90/3215)732} = 0.115 + 0.845 = 0.960 < 1.0$

Rafter: At column $G = \dfrac{1480}{52.7} \times \dfrac{20}{1.5 \times 2850} = 0.13$

At ridge $G = 1$

$K = 0.66$ (Fig. 4–28a)

$KL/r_x = 0.66 \times 44.27 \times 12 / 8.60 = 41$

$P_{cr} = 1.70 \times 20.0 \times 19.11 = 650^k$

$P_y = 20.0 \times 36 = 720^k$

$P_E = 1.92 \times 20.0 \times 88.71 = 3410^k$

$P = \dfrac{6}{6.32} H_1 + \dfrac{2}{6.32} (R_1 - 0.83 P)$

$\quad = \dfrac{6}{6.32} \times 50.41 + \dfrac{2}{6.32}(90 - 9) = 47.8 + 25.6 = 73.4^k$

$M = 477^{'k}$

$M_p = 160 \times 36 / 12 = 480^{'k}$

$\dfrac{P}{P_y} + \dfrac{M}{1.18 M_p} = \dfrac{73.4}{720} + \dfrac{477}{1.18 \times 480} = 0.102 + 0.844 = 0.946 < 1.0$

$\dfrac{P}{P_{cr}} + \dfrac{C_m M}{(1 - P/P_E) M_m} = \dfrac{73.4}{650} + \dfrac{0.85 \times 477}{(1 - 70/3410)480} = 0.113 + 0.865 = 0.978 < 1.0$

Shear

Column : $V_{all} = 0.55 \times 36 \times 0.463 \times 26.69 = 245^k > 50.4^k$ (b)

Rafter : $V_{all} = 0.55 \times 36 \times 0.430 \times 21.13 = 180^k$

$V_{max} = \dfrac{6}{6.32}(90 - 0.83P) - \dfrac{2}{6.32} H_1$

$\quad = \dfrac{6}{6.32}(90 - 9) - \dfrac{2}{6.32} \times 50.4 = 77.0 - 16.0 = 61.0^k < 180^k$

Local buckling

Column : flange, $b/t_f = 9.96/0.640 = 15.6 < 17$ (c)

web, $P/P_y = 90/890 = 0.101 < 0.27$

$d/t = \dfrac{412}{\sqrt{36}}(1 - 1.4 \times 0.101) = 58.8 > 26.69/0.463 = 57.7$

STEEL–BUILDING RIGID FRAME   DP9–15–1 $\frac{4}{4}$

Rafter: flange, $b/t_f = 8.27/0.685 = 12.1 < 17$
web, $P/P_y = 69.6/720 = 0.097 < 0.27$

$$d/t = \frac{412}{\sqrt{36}} (1 - 1.4 \times 0.097) = 59.1 > 21.13/0.430 = 49$$

Lateral bracing   (a)

Rafter: purlins 6.32' o.c. $\dfrac{L}{r_y} = \dfrac{6.32 \times 12}{1.80} = 42.1$

$M_4 = M_{S4} - 24 H_1 = 100.7P - 24.7 \times 4.67P$
$= -14.6P = -14.6 \times 10.8 = -158^{\prime k}$

Segment 3–4 in reverse curvature, so end moment
ratio is positive

$$\frac{M_4}{M_3} = \frac{158}{477} = 0.334$$

$$\frac{L}{r_y} = \frac{1375}{F_y} + 25 = \frac{1375}{36} + 25 = 38.2 + 25 = 63.2 > 42.1$$

Therefore lateral support OK at 3–4

Hinge at 8 forms last (Art. 9-13), so elastic-design
formulas apply

$$f_b = \frac{M}{1.7 \, S_x} = \frac{477 \times 12}{1.7 \times 140} = 24 \text{ ksi}$$

$$\frac{76 \, b_f}{\sqrt{F_y}} = \frac{76 \times 8.27}{\sqrt{36}} = 105'' = 8.8' > 6.32'$$

$$\frac{20{,}000}{(d/A_f)F_y} = \frac{20{,}000}{3.73 \times 36} = 149'' = 12.4' > 6.32'$$

Therefore lateral support OK at 7–8

Column: $\dfrac{M_1}{M_2} = 0$

$$\frac{L}{r} = \frac{1375}{36} + 25 = 63.2 < \frac{14 \times 12}{2.06} = 81.6$$

Provide brace midway between points 1 and 2

Haunch design   (b)

d = 40", $t_f = {}^{11}/_{16}$", b = 8¼", $t_w = {}^{7}/_{16}$", l = 7.17'

$Z = 10 \times 0.687(40-0.687) + \frac{1}{4}(40-1.38)^2 \times 0.438$
$= 270 + 163 = 433 \text{ in}^3$

$M_p = 433 \times 36/12 = 1299^{\prime k} > 20 \times 50.4 = 1008^{\prime k}$

Check for lateral buckling   (c)

$l/b = 86/8.25 = 10.4$

$\Delta t = 0.1(10.4 - 5.3) = 0.51$ in

$t_t = t_c = {}^{11}/_{16} + \frac{1}{2} = 1\,{}^{3}/_{16}$ in

Web stiffeners   (d)

at sections "a" and "c"

$A_{st} = A_f \sin 14°41' = 9.96 \times 1.19 \times 0.250 = 2.96 \text{ in}^2$

Use 2 stiffeners $4 \times \frac{1}{2} = 4.0 \text{ in}^2$

at section "b": $A_{st} = \dfrac{A_{C1} \cos 121°18' - A_{C2} \sin 14°41'}{\cos 35°47'}$

$$= \frac{8.25 \times 1.19(0.5195 - 0.2535)}{0.8112} = 3.22 \text{ in}^2$$

Use 2 stiffeners $4 \times \frac{1}{2} = 4.0 \text{ in}^2$

Sheet 2

a. The distributed wind load is replaced with single concentrated loads at the eaves, which produce the same moment about the base.

b. The assumed mechanism has hinges at 8 and 17. The simple-beam moments of $196.7P$ and $61.7P$ for vertical loads were computed on sheet 1.

c. The moment diagram shows all $M \leq M_p$. The moments due to $DL + SL$ at the load factor 1.7 are larger than those due to $DL + SL + WL$ at the load factor 1.3.

Sheet 3

a. The column and rafter are checked by Eqs. (9-8) and (9-9).

b. The shear resistance of the web is given by Eq. (9-11).

c. The slenderness of the column and rafter webs is checked by Eq. (9-6).

Sheet 4

a. Lateral bracing requirements are discussed in Art. 9-12; Eqs. (9-7) are applicable.

b. The design procedure for tapered haunches is discussed in Art. 8-26. The depth of 40 in was chosen so that β would be greater than $12°$. The width of the flange along the rafter portion of the haunch is made the same as the W21 $\times$ 68 rafter. The haunch is tapered to 10 in at the juncture with the W27 $\times$ 84.

c. The l/b ratio of 10.4 requires that the flange thickness be increased to $1\frac{3}{16}$ in Eq. (8-42).

d. Stiffener areas are determined from Eqs. (8-43) and (8-44). An elastic design of the frame of this example is given in Ref. 8.

9-16   DEFLECTIONS

As a rule, it is the service-load deflections of a structure which are of concern. However, plastic design is based on loads at collapse, so there is a question how service-load deflections may be determined, other than by an elastic analysis at service-load intensity. Sometimes it may be expedient to determine collapse-load deflections, from which a conservative estimate of service-load deflection can always be made. This will be shown for the uniformly loaded fixed-end beam whose load-deflection plot was determined in Art. 5-11 (Fig. 5-18). If only the deflection at ultimate load were known, the service-load deflection for this beam could be estimated by assuming linear load-deflection behavior from O to B. Then, if the load factor were 1.7, the service-load deflection would be $0.82/1.7 = 0.48$ in. However, with this load factor the service load is $153/1.7 = 90$ kips, and the correct service-load deflection is given by a point on OA in Fig. 5-18, that is, $\Delta = 0.31 \times \frac{90}{115} = 0.24$ in. Therefore, the approximate procedure overestimates the deflection by 100 percent in this case. While this is indeed a large error, the estimated value may still be useful, since if it is in itself acceptable, no further calculations are needed.

Although the service-load deflection can be computed closely by determining the load-deflection history, as in Fig. 5-18, this procedure is limited in application because a deflection computation is required at the formation of each additional plastic hinge until the mechanism is formed. However, collapse-load deflections can be determined without a hinge-by-hinge analysis if the location of the last hinge to form is known. The slope-deflection equations can be used for this analysis,[4] although other methods, such as the virtual-displacement method,[3] can also be used. Elastic continuity of the frame at the last hinge to form is essential to the solution, since it is the basis for one of the necessary equations. If the location of the last hinge to form is not known, each hinge of the mechanism can be assumed to be last to form, and the largest deflection so calculated is the true deflection.

As pointed out in Art. 5-7, deflection of beams in floors can be easily evaluated in terms of the ratio L/d of span to depth. Therefore, in most practical applications, deflection of floors can be approximated closely enough without the deflection analyses discussed above. An upper bound for the deflection of a beam in a frame can be obtained by assuming the beam to be simply supported, in which case Δ/L is readily determined.

9-17 MOMENT BALANCING

A scheme for plastic analysis of structures, called *moment balancing*, is described in this article. It is based on the two bound theorems discussed in Art. 9-6.

If one constructs for a frame any moment diagram which satisfies requirements for equilibrium and then proportions the frame to this moment diagram so that there are enough plastic hinges to form a mechanism and so that M nowhere exceeds M_p, the lower-bound and upper-bound theorems are both satisfied. The lower-bound theorem is satisfied because the assumed moment diagram is in equilibrium with the loads and the moment nowhere exceeds M_p, and it follows that the corresponding load is less than, or at best equal to, the ultimate load the structure can support. The upper-bound theorem is satisfied because there are enough plastic hinges to form a mechanism, and it follows that the corresponding load is greater than, or at best equal to, the ultimate load the structure can support. Thus, such a structure will just collapse at the load for which it is proportioned.

Figure 9-30 shows simple adjustments which can be made in a trial moment diagram for the purpose of developing a moment diagram that yields a collapse mechanism. Interior moments are taken positive if they produce tension on the bottom fiber; end moments are positive when they are clockwise on the member. Each of these distributions can be thought of as a shift of an initial base line. In

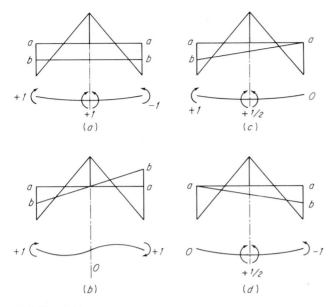

FIGURE 9-30

Fig. 9-30a base a-a of the beam-mechanism moment diagram for a concentrated load is shifted to b-b by adding uniform moment, i.e., moments in the ratio $+1$, $+1$, -1. Figure 9-30b shows the base line a-a rotated about its midpoint to b-b. In this case, the distribution of moment that is added to the initial distribution is in the ratio $+1$, 0, $+1$. The base may also be rotated about either end, as in Fig. 9-30c and d.

A simple example is shown in Fig. 9-31a (Ref. 9). The frame is to be designed in A36 steel for a gravity load of 1.3 klf and a wind load of 0.6 klf. The beam-mechanism moment for gravity load alone at a load factor of 1.7 is

$$M_p = \frac{1.7 \times 1.3 \times 96^2}{16} = 1275 \text{ ft·kips}$$

The required section modulus is $Z = 1275 \times \frac{12}{36} = 425$ in³. The lightest W shape is the W33 × 130, for which $Z = 467$ in³ and $M_p = 1401$ ft·kips. However, if this shape is used for both beam and columns, the frame will not form a mechanism at the specified ultimate load. Instead, it will support a service load of 1.30 × $\frac{1401}{1275} = 1.43$ klf at a load factor of 1.7.

To see whether a lighter frame can be designed, we revise the assumed distribution of moments, -1275, $+1275$, $+1275$, which is shown in Fig. 9-31b, so as to produce a plastic hinge at midspan. This is accomplished by superimposing the set of moments $+126$, $+126$, -126, which corresponds to Fig. 9-30a, on the initial values. The resulting moments at the ends of the beam are -1149 and $+1149$, which require moments at the column tops of $+1149$ and -1149, as

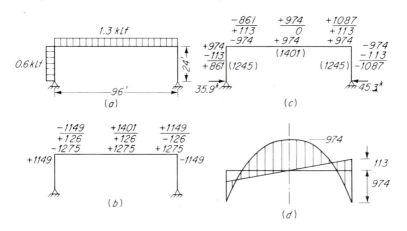

FIGURE 9-31

shown on the figure. Therefore, a mechanism will form if the columns can be sized to a plastic moment of 1149 ft·kips. However, the lightest column which furnishes a plastic moment of at least 1149 ft·kips is the W33 × 118, for which $M_p = 1245$ ft·kips. Although no mechanism will form, the resulting frame is the lightest that can be built in A36 steel with standard rolled shapes and is 500 lb lighter than the frame with W33 × 130 members for both beam and columns.

The proposed frame is checked in Fig. 9-31c for adequacy against wind and gravity load. The load factor for this combination is 1.3. The gravity-load moments and sway moment due to wind are

Gravity: $$1.3 \times 1.3 \times \frac{96^2}{16} = 974 \text{ ft·kips}$$

Wind: $$1.3 \times 0.6 \times 12 \times 24 = 226 \text{ ft·kips}$$

The analysis begins with the gravity-load moments, as shown in the figure. Since gravity and wind load together tend to produce a combination of beam and panel mechanism, the frame will tend to develop two plastic hinges, one near midspan of the beam and the other at the top of the leeward column. The wind moments will be counterclockwise on the column tops. If these moments are assumed to be equal, equilibrium is achieved with the beam-moment distribution shown in Fig. 9-30b. Therefore, the moments +113, 0, +113 are added to the beam-mechanism moments, with moments of −113 at the column tops for equilibrium, as shown in Fig. 9-31c. The resulting horizontal reactions on the frame are shown in the figure. Although it is not needed in the solution, the starting moment and the subsequent adjustment are shown in Fig. 9-31d. Since the moments nowhere exceed the plastic-moment capacity of the members, the frame is adequate, provided local buckling, lateral-torsional buckling, and beam-column requirements are satisfied. Neither shape need be checked for local buckling of the flange, because the AISC/ASD Manual's plastic-design selection table excludes shapes for which the flange b/t exceeds 8.5. The Manual denotes with an asterisk those shapes for which local buckling of the web must be checked [by Eqs. (9-6)] if there is axial load in addition to bending. The W33 × 118 column does require this check. It must also be checked against Eqs. (9-7) to (9-9).

It should be noted that the final moments in Fig. 9-31c are not those which would exist under the assumed loading. In fact, one could find any number of moment distributions which would be in equilibrium with these loads and for which the moment would nowhere exceed M_p. However, we are interested only in determining whether the frame is adequate for the specified loads, and the precise moment distribution is not of interest.

If the required load factor for wind and gravity load were 1.6, the gravity-load beam moments for the frame of Fig. 9-31a would be 1200 ft·kips, as shown in Fig. 9-32. The required wind-load moment is 276 ft·kips. However, only 45 ft·kips of this moment can be developed at the leeward column, since $M_p = 1245$ ft·kips for that member. [If P/P_y exceeds 0.15, this column-top moment must be reduced to satisfy Eqs. (9-8) and (9-9).] Adding the distribution +45, 0, +45 to the starting moments gives 90 ft·kips of wind moment, which is 186 ft·kips short of the 276 ft·kips needed. This moment must be carried by the windward column. The joint-balancing beam moment is +186 ft·kips, which produces the set of moments +186, +93, 0 in the beam. The final moment distribution is one in which the moment is nowhere larger than M_p, except possibly for the beam, for which the maximum moment occurs to the left of midspan. The location of this point is easily found, as shown in the shear diagram, and the maximum moment determined by computing the increment $\Delta M = 1.5$ ft·kips. Thus, the maximum moment is only 1295 ft·kips. Therefore, $M \le M_p$ at all points of the frame. Furthermore, there is only one plastic hinge, instead of the two required for a mechanism. Therefore, the frame is more than adequate for these loads at a load factor of 1.6.

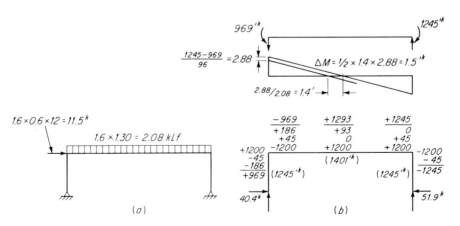

FIGURE 9-32

9-18   TWO-BAY FRAME BY MOMENT BALANCING

The two-bay frame in Fig. 9-33a is to be designed in A36 steel for a roof load of 1.5 klf at a load factor of 1.7. The initial beam moments, assuming beam mechanisms in each span, and the balancing column moments are shown in Fig. 9-33b (Ref. 9). The required section moduli are given in Table 9-1, for which the sections shown are chosen. The columns are restricted to not more than 12 in wide in the plane of the frame. All the members satisfy local-buckling requirements. Each column is checked against the beam-column interaction formulas, as in Example 9-14-1, to determine the reduction in M_p, if any, because of the axial force P. The reduced moments are shown in the table.

Figure 9-33c shows how the initial distribution of moments of Fig. 9-33b can be improved to take advantage of the excess capacities of the members shown in Table 9-1. A midspan hinge is developed in each beam by adding the distributions $+18$, $+18$, -18, and $+14$, $+14$, -14. These do not upset the sway balance. Were it possible to choose columns with precisely the required moments, the resulting frame would develop plastic hinges at the points indicated in Fig. 9-33c. Although these are enough hinges to produce a mechanism, the possible displacements, one of which is shown in Fig. 9-33d, involve rotations at certain hinges which are opposed in sense to the moments at these points. Therefore, this system of hinges does not produce a collapse mechanism, and it may be possible to reduce the column moments still further.

The collapse configuration in Fig. 9-33d suggests that a hinge is needed in at least one of the beams at the interior column. This is easily accomplished by using the distribution of Fig. 9-30b. However, the off-center location of the interior hinge of each beam must be anticipated. Therefore, the adjustment -2, -2, $+2$ is made in each span. This does not alter the sway balance. Furthermore, the $+$, 0, $+$ distribution which is added to one beam must be accompanied by a $-$, 0, $-$ distribution, with the same absolute values, in the other span in order to maintain equilibrium of sway moments. It turns out that the right span controls.

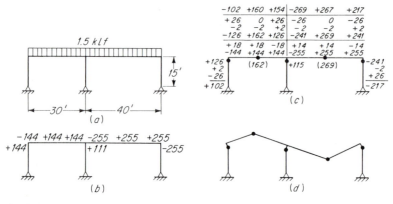

FIGURE 9-33

TABLE 9-1

Member	M	Z required	Section	M_p	Reduced M	Revised M_p	Revised Section
1	144	48	W16 × 31	162			
2	255	85	W18 × 46	269			
3	144	48	W12 × 35	155	153	102	W12 × 27
4	111	37	W12 × 40	173	138	115	
5	255	85	W12 × 58	260	260	217	W12 × 50

That is, there cannot be a midspan hinge and one at the interior column in the left span without exceeding the moment capacity of the W18 × 45 in the right span. Therefore, the moment set $+26$, 0, $+26$ is added to the left span and -26, 0, -26 to the right span to produce the final set of moments shown in Fig. 9-33c. This gives a beam mechanism in the right span. A shear-diagram check for maximum moment in the right span, as made in Fig. 9-32, shows that M_p is not exceeded. The revised column moments are entered in Table 9-1. It will be noted that columns 3 and 5 can be reduced in size to save 9 and 8 lb/ft, respectively.

Moment balancing is also called moment distribution. However, it is significant that it bears little or no resemblance to moment distribution based on elastic behavior. In elastic design one must fit the moment diagram to the structure because the distribution of moment depends on relative stiffnesses and cannot be determined until the frame has been proportioned. On the other hand, plastic design allows one to construct a moment diagram and then proportion a frame to fit it; this can be done because the distribution of moments is according to plastic-moment capacities rather than relative stiffnesses. Thus, whether computations are by hand or by computer, plastic design offers greater freedom in the design of frameworks.

Additional examples of moment balancing are given in Refs. 2, 9, and 10.

9-19 FRAME BUCKLING

Buckling of frames was discussed in Art. 6-4. It was shown that frames which are braced against sidesway are not subject to overall buckling and that only the stability of the individual members need be considered. Unbraced frames, however, even if they are symmetrical and symmetrically loaded, may become unstable and buckle in a sidewise mode at loads much less than they can support in the braced condition (Fig. 6-13). A procedure for predicting the critical load for this case, based on column effective-length coefficients K as functions of the relative stiffnesses $G = \sum (I/L)_c / \sum (I/L)_b$, is discussed in that article. Although the same procedure can be used for plastically designed frames, it is more difficult because buckling will occur after plastic hinges are partially or fully developed in some of the beams. As a result, stiffnesses of the beam cross section vary along the beam, and its overall stiffness is difficult to evaluate.[11]

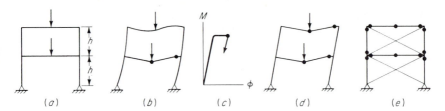

FIGURE 9-34

The resistance of a frame to sidesway buckling depends on its stiffness in sidewise bending, which is successively reduced with the formation of each additional plastic hinge. For example, a plastic hinge at one end of a beam reduces its effective stiffness at the opposite end from I/L to $0.75I/L$, as is known from moment-distribution theory. Formation of a second hinge at or near midspan reduces the effective stiffness to zero. Thus, there is a progressive deterioration of stiffness of the beams in a frame.

A symmetrically loaded symmetrical frame may become unstable prior to the development of a collapse mechanism. If a mechanism develops in the first-floor beam of the two-story frame shown in Fig. 9-34a, the sidesway buckling shape will be as shown in Fig. 9-34b. The plastic hinge at the left end of the beam is not shown in Fig. 9-34b because the moment at this point at the beginning of buckling is opposite to the moment due to the load. Therefore, the beam unloads elastically at this end, as shown in Fig. 9-34c. It will be seen that, because of the beam mechanism, the frame buckles as a one-story frame $2h$ in height. If both beams develop mechanisms, the sidesway stiffness vanishes, as shown in Fig. 9-34d. A detailed investigation of an unbraced four-story one-bay frame with both gravity load and wind load is given in Ref. 3.

There is a further complication in the analysis of unbraced high-rise frames because sidesway causes additional gravity-load moments. Thus, if there is a horizontal displacement Δ at the roof line of a one-story frame, there is a moment $P\Delta$ which is not taken into account in the examples in this chapter. This effect is negligible for frames of a few stories, but it becomes significant in high-rise frames.

PROBLEMS

9-1. The loads shown on the laterally supported beam of Fig. P9-1 are service loads. Determine the required A36 beam for a load factor of 1.5.

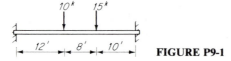

FIGURE P9-1

9-2. The loads shown on the laterally supported beam of Fig. P9-2 are service loads. Determine the required A36 beam for a load factor of 1.5.

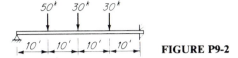

FIGURE P9-2

9-3. Determine P_u for the A36 laterally supported W16 × 36 continuous beam of Fig. P9-3.

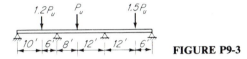

FIGURE P9-3

9-4. The loads shown on the laterally supported continuous beam of Fig. P9-4 are service loads. Determine the required A36 beam for a load factor of 1.6.

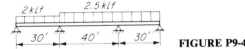

FIGURE P9-4

9-5. The loads shown on the laterally supported continuous beam of Fig. P9-5 are service loads. Determine the required A36 beam for a load factor of 1.6.

FIGURE P9-5

9-6. The loads shown on the laterally supported beam of Fig. P9-6 are service loads. Determine the required A36 beam for a load factor of 1.6.

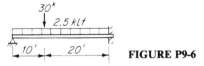

FIGURE P9-6

9-7. Compute the required plastic moment for the frame of Fig. 9-11 supporting the 30-kip vertical load and a horizontal load of 5 kips at B. The three members are to have equal resisting moments M_p.

9-8. Compute the required plastic moment for the frame of Fig. P9-8 with $P_u = 60$ kips. The three members have equal values of M_p.

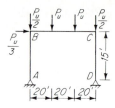

FIGURE P9-8

9-9. Compute the value of P_u for the frame of Fig. P9-8 with $M_p = 240$ ft·kips for the beam and 180 ft·kips for each column.

9-10. Same as Prob. 9-8 except that the column bases A and D are fixed.

9-11. Compute the required plastic moment for the frame of Fig. P9-11. The three members have equal values of M_p.

FIGURE P9-11

9-12. Same as Prob. 9-11 with a horizontal force $P_u = 8$ kips at B, in addition to the uniform load.

9-13. Compute w_u for the frame of Fig. P9-13. Given $M_{pAB} = M_{pBC} = M_{pCD} = 160$ ft·kips.

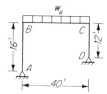

FIGURE P9-13

9-14. Compute the required value of M_p for the frame of Fig. P9-14. The loads shown are ultimate loads. Given $M_{pBC} = M_{pCD}$ and $M_{pAB} = 1.2M_{pBC}$.

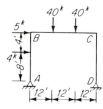

FIGURE P9-14

9-15. Compute the value of w_u for the frame of Fig. P9-15, with $M_p = 200$ ft·kips for AB, BCD, and DE and 50 ft·kips for CF.

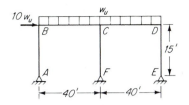

FIGURE P9-15

9-16. Compute the value of P_u for the frame of Fig. P9-16, with $M_{pAB} = M_{pBc} = 100$ ft·kips, $M_{pCD} = M_{pDE} = 300$ ft·kips, $M_{pCF} = 200$ ft·kips.

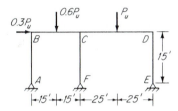

FIGURE P9-16

9-17. Same as Prob. 9-16 except that the horizontal load is $0.1P_u$.

9-18. The loads shown on the frame of Fig. P9-18 are service loads. Determine the required value of M_p for load factors of 1.7 on gravity load alone and 1.3 on gravity load combined with wind load. The wind can act from either direction.

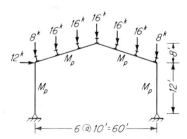

FIGURE P9-18

9-19. The loads shown in the frame of Fig. P9-19 are service loads. Determine the required value of M_p for load factors of 1.5 on gravity load and 1.2 on gravity load combined with wind load.

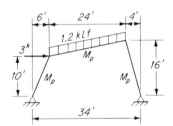

FIGURE P9-19

9-20. Determine the value of P_u for the frame of Fig. P9-20. All the members are the same size, with $M_p = 180$ ft·kips.

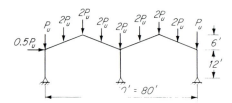

FIGURE P9-20

9-21. Design a one-bay, one-story A36-steel frame which spans 60 ft and is 18 ft high. The column bases are hinged. The frame carries concentrated vertical loads of 30 kips at midspan and each quarter point, 15 kips vertical at each column top, and a wind load of 12 kips at the roof line. Use a load factor of 1.7 for gravity load alone and 1.3 for gravity load plus wind load.

9-22. Determine whether the frame which was designed in Art. 9-18 can support the specified gravity loads together with a concentrated wind load of 8 kips at the roof line. The load factor is 1.5 for both wind and gravity load. The loads shown on the laterally supported continuous beam are service loads.

REFERENCES

1. Neal, B. G., and P. S. Symonds: The Rapid Calculation of the Plastic Collapse Load of a Framed Structure, *Proc. Inst. Civ. Eng. (London)*, vol. 1, 1952.
2. Hodge, P. G., Jr.: "Plastic Analysis of Structures," McGraw-Hill, New York, 1959.
3. Massonnet, C. E., and M. A. Save: "Plastic Analysis and Design," Blaisdell, New York, 1965.
4. Beedle, L. S.: "Plastic Design of Steel Frames," Wiley, New York, 1958.
5. Haaijer, G.: Plate Buckling in the Strain-Hardening Range, *Trans. ASCE*, col. 124, 1959.
6. Lay, M. G., and T. V. Galambos: Inelastic Beams under Moment Gradient, *J. Struct. Div. ASCE*, February 1967.
7. "Plastic Design in Steel," 2d ed., ASCE Manuals and Reports on Practice no. 41, New York, 1971.
8. Kavanagh, T. C., and R. C. Y. Young: Arches and Rigid Frames, sec. 17 in E. H. Gaylord and C. N. Gaylord (eds.), 3d ed., "Structural Engineering Handbook," McGraw-Hill, New York, 1990.
9. Gaylord, E. H.: Plastic Design by Moment Balancing, *AISC Eng. J.*, October 1967.
10. Horne, M. R.: A Moment Distribution Method for the Analysis and Design of Structures by the Plastic Theory, *Proc. Inst. Civ. Eng.*, vol. 3, pt. 3, April 1954.
11. Lu, Le-Wu: Inelastic Buckling of Steel Frames, *J. Struct. Div. ASCE*, December 1965.

CHAPTER
10

STABILITY
AND
STRENGTH
OF FLAT
PLATES

10-1 STABILITY OF FLAT PLATES

Buckling of flat plates with various in-plane force systems acting on the edges has been discussed at several points in preceding chapters. The solution to all such problems derives from a single equation of equilibrium relating the edge forces to the displacement w normal to the plate.

Figure 10-1 shows a rectangular flat plate with stresses f_x and f_y (tension positive) and shear stresses f_v distributed along the middle line at the edges. The equation of equilibrium is

$$\frac{EI}{1-\mu^2}\left(\frac{\partial^4 w}{\partial x^4} + 2\frac{\partial^4 w}{\partial x^2\,\partial y^2} + \frac{\partial^4 w}{\partial y^4}\right) = t\left(f_x\frac{\partial^2 w}{\partial x^2} + 2f_v\frac{\partial^2 w}{\partial x\,\partial y} + f_y\frac{\partial^2 w}{\partial y^2}\right) \quad (10\text{-}1)$$

where $I = t^3/12$ = moment of inertia of cross-sectional area of a unit strip of plate

t = thickness of plate

μ = Poisson's ratio

w = deflection of a point in the middle plane of plate

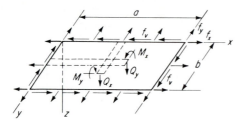

FIGURE 10-1

The bending moments are given by

$$M_x = -\frac{EI}{1-\mu^2}\left(\frac{\partial^2 w}{\partial x^2} + \mu \frac{\partial^2 w}{\partial y^2}\right) \tag{10-2a}$$

$$M_y = -\frac{EI}{1-\mu^2}\left(\frac{\partial^2 w}{\partial y^2} + \mu \frac{\partial^2 w}{\partial x^2}\right) \tag{10-2b}$$

where M_x and M_y are the moments per unit of width of sections parallel to the y and x axes, respectively (Fig. 10-1). The shearing resultants Q_x and Q_y shown in Fig. 10-1 are

$$Q_x = -\frac{EI}{1-\mu^2}\frac{\partial}{\partial x}\left(\frac{\partial^2 w}{\partial x^2} + \frac{\partial^2 w}{\partial y^2}\right) \tag{10-3a}$$

$$Q_y = -\frac{EI}{1-\mu^2}\frac{\partial}{\partial y}\left(\frac{\partial^2 w}{\partial x^2} + \frac{\partial^2 w}{\partial y^2}\right) \tag{10-3b}$$

Details of the derivation can be found elsewhere.[1,2]

If f_x is compressive (negative) and w is independent of y, Eq. (10-1) reduces to

$$\frac{EI}{1-\mu^2}\frac{d^4 w}{dx^4} + f_x t \frac{d^2 w}{dx^2} = 0 \tag{a}$$

This is the differential equation for bending of a bar of unit width and thickness t acted upon by a compressive force $f_x t$. Except for the term $1 - \mu^2$, Eq. (a) is the fourth-order form of Eq. (g) of Art. 4-2. The solution for hinged ends is

$$f_x t = \frac{\pi^2 EI}{(1-\mu^2)a^2} \tag{10-4}$$

where a is the length of the strip in the direction of x (Fig. 10-1). This corresponds to Eq. (4-1) for the centrally loaded column. Similarly, with w independent of x, the third and sixth terms of Eq. (10-1) give the critical load for a strip of length b in the direction of y. The second term in Eq. (10-1) results from distortion of an element of the plate by twisting moments acting on the element.

FIGURE 10-2

Figure 10-2 shows a flat plate, hinged on all four edges, which has buckled under the uniform edge compression f_x. For this case, Eq. (10-1) reduces to

$$\frac{EI}{1-\mu^2}\left(\frac{\partial^4 w}{\partial x^4} + 2\frac{\partial^4 w}{\partial x^2\,\partial y^2} + \frac{\partial^4 w}{\partial y^4}\right) + f_x t\,\frac{\partial^2 w}{\partial x^2} = 0 \qquad (10\text{-}5)$$

Equation (10-5) can be satisfied for certain values of f_x by

$$w = w_{mn} \sin\frac{m\pi x}{a}\,\sin\frac{n\pi y}{b} \qquad \begin{array}{l} m = 1, 2, 3, \ldots \\ n = 1, 2, 3, \ldots \end{array} \qquad (10\text{-}6)$$

It is clear that this solution also satisfies the specified boundary conditions since $w = 0$ at the four edges and, from Eqs. (10-2), bending moments are zero at the four edges. Substituting w from Eq. (10-6) into Eq. (10-5) gives

$$\frac{EI}{1-\mu^2}\left(\frac{m^4\pi^4}{a^4} + 2\frac{m^2 n^2\pi^4}{a^2 b^2} + \frac{n^4\pi^4}{b^4}\right) - f_x t\,\frac{m^2\pi^2}{a^2} = 0$$

from which

$$f_x t = \frac{\pi^2 EI}{1-\mu^2}\,\frac{(m^2/a^2 + n^2/b^2)^2}{m^2/a^2} = \frac{\pi^2 EI}{1-\mu^2}\left(\frac{m}{a} + \frac{n^2}{m}\frac{a}{b^2}\right)^2$$

This equation gives an infinite number of values of the compressive force $f_x t$. However, we are interested in the smallest value at which a buckled configuration can exist. It is clear that $f_x t$ is smallest when $n = 1$, which means that the plate buckles in one half wave transverse to the direction of loading. Therefore,

$$f_x t = \frac{\pi^2 EI}{(1-\mu^2)a^2}\left(m + \frac{1}{m}\frac{a^2}{b^2}\right)^2 \qquad (10\text{-}7)$$

where m is the number of half waves in the direction of f_x. If $m = 1$,

$$f_x t = \frac{\pi^2 EI}{(1-\mu^2)a^2}\left(1 + \frac{a^2}{b^2}\right)^2 \qquad (10\text{-}8)$$

This equation is identical to Eq. (10-4) except for the factor in parentheses. Furthermore, $f_x t$ in Eq. (10-8) approaches the value given by Eq. (10-4) as a/b decreases. Thus, the second term in parentheses measures the stiffening of the plate which results from support of the unloaded edges.

It would appear from Eq. (10-8) that $f_x t$ increases without limit as the width b of the plate decreases. This would be true if the plate buckled in only one longitudinal half wave. However, the possibility of multiple-wave buckling modes must be investigated. For this purpose, it is convenient to rewrite Eq. (10-7) in the form

$$f_x t = \frac{\pi^2 E I}{(1 - \mu^2) b^2} \left(m \frac{b}{a} + \frac{1}{m} \frac{a}{b} \right)^2 \tag{10-9}$$

Substituting $I = t^3/12$ into this equation and using the notation

$$k = \left(m \frac{b}{a} + \frac{1}{m} \frac{a}{b} \right)^2 \tag{10-10}$$

and denoting the critical value of f_x by F_{cr}, we get

$$F_{cr} = \frac{k \pi^2 E}{12(1 - \mu^2)(b/t)^2} \tag{10-11}$$

The ratio of length a to width b of a plate is called its *aspect ratio*. Values of k from Eq. (10-10) are shown in curve A of Fig. 10-3. It will be noted that k has a minimum value of 4 for $a/b = 1, 2, 3, \ldots, n$. The plate buckles in one longitudinal half wave ($m = 1$) if $a/b \le \sqrt{2}$, two if $\sqrt{2} \le a/b \le \sqrt{6}$, etc. Except for the unlikely case of the extremely short plate (a/b less than about 0.5) the error in using $k = 4$ for all values of a/b is at most about 10 percent, and in the usual case, for which a/b is of the order of 10 or more, it is extremely small.

Values of k for the plate of Fig. 10-2 with the loaded edges clamped

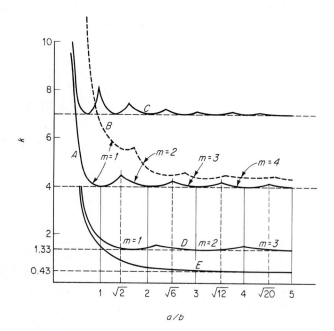

FIGURE 10-3
Plate-buckling coefficients.

(unloaded edges hinged) are shown by the dashed line B in Fig. 10-3. This is also a family of intersecting curves. In this case, the miminum values of k for the various branches are not equal. However, it is clear that $k = 4$ is satisfactory for the usual case of large a/b.

Values of k for the plate of Fig. 10-2 with the unloaded edges clamped (loaded edges hinged) are shown in curve C of Fig. 10-3. Here there is a substantial increase in k; the minimum value for each curve of the system is 7. The effect of clamping the loaded edges in this case is similar to that of the preceding case, and can be ignored for plates of practical proportions.

Values of k for plates with one unloaded edge free are given by D and E of Fig. 10-3. For curve D the unloaded edge that is supported is clamped, while for curve E it is hinged. The minimum value of k for curve D is 1.33. The buckling behavior of the plate with the supported unloaded edge hinged differs from that of the other cases shown in this figure, in that such a plate buckles in only one longitudinal half wave regardless of the aspect ratio. The value of k decreases with increase in a/b and approaches the limiting value 0.43. However, even for a plate as short as $a = 5b$, k is only 9 percent larger than the minimum value. Therefore, except for very short plates, $k = 0.43$ is a very good approximation.

Equation (10-11) is valid only if stress is proportional to strain. Modification of the equation for the case where the critical stress exceeds the proportional limit is discussed in Art. 4-12.

Critical stresses for plates with two opposite edges subjected to bending stresses $f_x = My/I$ can also be determined from Eq. (10-1). This is discussed in Art. 5-15. The critical stress f_v for a plate subjected to shear stress on its edges is discussed in Art. 5-14.

Local buckling of plate elements in axially loaded compression members is shown in Fig. 4-32.

10-2 POSTBUCKLING STRENGTH OF FLAT PLATES

It was pointed out in Art. 4-2 that the difference between the buckling load and the postbuckling strength of the axially loaded column is so small that the buckling load is a practical measure of strength. In contrast, the postbuckling strength of a flat plate can be considerably larger than the buckling load. Figure 10-4a shows a uniformly compressed flat plate, simply supported on all edges, at the onset of buckling. At this state, the stress is given by Eq. (10-11) with $k = 4$. If the critical stress is less than the yield stress, further shortening of the plate increases the stress at the edges because they must remain straight. On the other hand, this shortening produces little or no increase in strain on a vertical strip at the middle, because such shortening is more easily accommodated by an increase in the amplitude of the buckles. The result is a stress distribution such as that shown in Fig. 10-4b. The value of P corresponding to this stress distribution is more difficult to determine than the buckling strength. Equation (10-1) is not applicable because it neglects the effect of membrane stresses in the middle plane

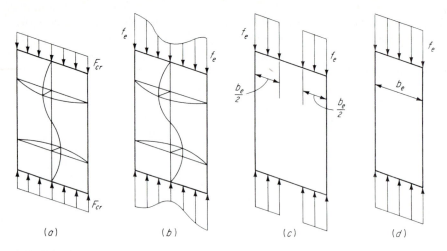

FIGURE 10-4

of the plate; these become significant for large deflections. The following approximate procedure was given by Karman[3] in 1932. It is assumed that the nonuniform postbuckling stress distribution can be replaced by the two rectangular stress blocks of intensity f_e and width $b_e/2$, where f_e is the edge stress of Fig. 10-4b and b_e is the *effective width* of the plate (Fig. 10-4c). Therefore,

$$P = f_e b_e t \qquad (a)$$

To determine the effective width, we assume that it is the same as the width b_e of a plate which buckles at the uniform stress f_e (Fig. 10-4d). Then, using Eq. (10-11),

$$f_e = \frac{4\pi^2 E}{12(1 - \mu^2)(b_e/t)^2} \qquad (b)$$

from which

$$\frac{b_e}{t} = 1.9\sqrt{\frac{E}{f_e}} \qquad (10\text{-}12a)$$

The edge stress f_e continues to increase with increase in strain of the plate until a limiting value is reached. In the case of a flat-yield steel, this limit is F_y for practical purposes. For a gradually yielding steel the offset-yield stress is usually taken as the limiting stress. Therefore, the effective width at ultimate load is given by

$$\frac{b_{ey}}{t} = 1.9\sqrt{\frac{E}{F_y}} \qquad (10\text{-}12b)$$

Figure 10-5 shows a comparison of Eq. (10-12b) with results of tests.[4] The ordinate in this figure is such that the equation plots as a straight line at 1.9. A test that checks the formula exactly plots on this line. It will be seen that most of

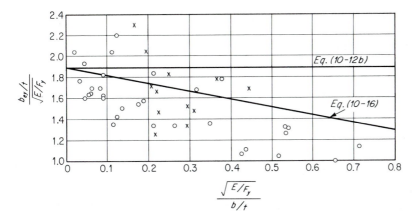

FIGURE 10-5
Postbuckling strength of uniformly compressed plates with both unloaded edges supported.

the tests plot below, which means that Eq. (10-12b) overestimates the effective width, except for plates at the left in the figure, which are those with large b/t. Because of this, other formulas, one of which is shown in the figure, have been developed. These are discussed in Art. 10-3.

Assuming that the Karman formulation for effective width can be used for uniformly compressed plates with other boundary conditions, Eq. (b) becomes

$$f_e = \frac{k\pi^2 E}{12(1 - \mu^2)(b_e/t)^2} \qquad (c)$$

which gives the effective width

$$\frac{b_e}{t} = 0.95\sqrt{\frac{kE}{f_e}} \qquad (10\text{-}13a)$$

Similarly, at ultimate load

$$\frac{b_{ey}}{t} = 0.95\sqrt{\frac{kE}{F_y}} \qquad (10\text{-}13b)$$

With $k = 4$ Eqs. (10-13) reduce to Eqs. (10-12).

For a plate with one unloaded edge free and the other hinged, $k = 0.43$ (Fig. 10-3), for which Eqs. (10-13) give

$$\frac{b_e}{t} = 0.64\sqrt{\frac{E}{f_e}} \qquad (10\text{-}14a)$$

$$\frac{b_{ey}}{t} = 0.64\sqrt{\frac{E}{F_y}} \qquad (10\text{-}14b)$$

Postbuckling strength according to the effective width from Eq. (10-14b) is compared in Fig. 10-6 with results of tests. The test results in this figure are from two

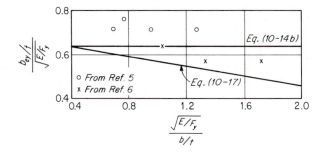

FIGURE 10-6
Postbuckling strength of uniformly compressed plates with one unloaded edge free.

sources. The specimens reported in Ref. 5 were of cruciform cross section, fabricated by welding three $\frac{1}{4}$-in A514-steel plates for which $F_y \approx 100$ ksi. The four flanges were identical. Thus, they tended to buckle simultaneously, so each acted as a single plate simply supported on one unloaded edge and free on the other. The b/t ratios of the six specimens were 4, 8, 12, 16, 20, and 22. The specimen with flanges of $b/t = 4$ failed by bend buckling, the other five by local buckling. However, only four of these five are shown in the figure because the specimen with $b/t = 8$ did not fail (by local buckling) until after it had reached yield stress. Each of the three specimens reported in Ref. 6 was composed of two cold-formed channels joined back to back by epoxy glue to form an I. The average yield stress was 78.6 ksi. The members were fabricated from 16-gage carbon steel ($t = 0.06$ in), with b/t values of 11.40, 15.40, and 20.75. The L/r ratio was less than 20, and all three failed by local buckling of the flanges.

10-3 ADDITIONAL FORMULAS FOR EFFECTIVE WIDTH

Equations (10-13) can be brought into better agreement with results of tests by using a reduction factor, as follows. For Eq. (10-13b)

$$\frac{b_{ey}}{t} = 0.95 \sqrt{\frac{kE}{F_y}} \left(1 - C \frac{\sqrt{kE/F_y}}{b/t} \right) \tag{10-15}$$

where C is a coefficient to be determined by tests. With $C = 0.21$, Eq. (10-15) yields for the plate supported on both unloaded edges ($k = 4$)

$$\frac{b_{ey}}{t} = 1.9 \sqrt{\frac{E}{F_y}} \left(1 - 0.42 \frac{\sqrt{E/F_y}}{b/t} \right) \tag{10-16}$$

and for the plate with one unloaded edge free ($k = 0.43$)

$$\frac{b_{ey}}{t} = 0.62 \sqrt{\frac{E}{F_y}} \left(1 - 0.14 \frac{\sqrt{E/F_y}}{b/t} \right) \tag{10-17}$$

Equation (10-16) is plotted in Fig. 10-5 and Eq. (10-17) in Fig. 10-6.

Formulas for the ultimate average stress F_u on the gross cross section are found from Eqs. (10-16) and (10-17) by using $F_u = F_y b_e t/bt$, which gives for the plate supported on both unloaded edges

$$\frac{F_u}{F_y} = \frac{b_e}{b} = \frac{1.9\sqrt{E/F_y}}{b/t}\left(1 - 0.42\,\frac{\sqrt{E/F_y}}{b/t}\right) \le 1 \tag{10-18}$$

and for the plate with one unloaded edge free

$$\frac{F_u}{F_y} = \frac{0.62\sqrt{E/F_y}}{b/t}\left(1 - 0.14\,\frac{\sqrt{E/F_y}}{b/t}\right) \le 1 \tag{10-19}$$

Equation (10-18) is plotted in Fig. 10-7. The following additional formula,[2] which is also based on curve fitting to test results, is also shown in the figure:

$$\frac{F_u}{F_y} = 1.42\left(\frac{\sqrt{E/F_y}}{b/t}\right)^{0.85} \le 1 \tag{10-20}$$

Equations (10-18) and (10-20) for the compressed plate supported on both unloaded edges are compared in Fig. 10-8, where values of F_u for an A36 plate are plotted as functions of plate slenderness b/t. Also shown is the critical stress, curve A. Note that Eq. (10-20) gives $b/t = 44$ as the limiting value to enable an A36-steel plate to just reach yield stress without buckling. This agrees very well with the AISC value 42 (Table 4-4). The limiting value $b/t = 32$, which enables

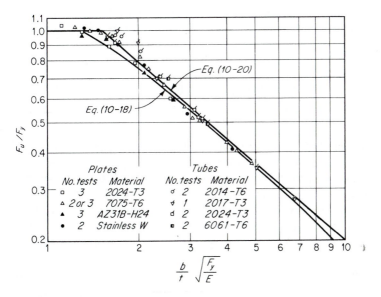

FIGURE 10-7
Postbuckling strength of uniformly compressed plates with both unloaded edges supported. (*Adapted from "Structural Stability Theory" by George Gerard, 1962. Used with permission of McGraw-Hill, Inc.*)

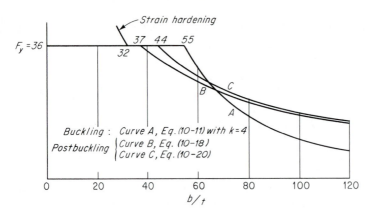

FIGURE 10-8

strain hardening to begin, is also shown in the figure. This value was established in Ref. 7. It was adopted by AISC as a requirement for plastic design, as shown in Table 5-4; that is, $190/\sqrt{F_y} = 190/\sqrt{36} = 32$.

An important aspect of the nature of the support at the unloaded edges of plates supported on all four edges remains to be discussed. If these unloaded edges are free to move in the plane of the plate, the plate contracts in width as it buckles and the unloaded edges remain free of stress in the transverse direction. On the other hand, if they resist contraction, reactive forces develop. These effects can be evaluated by using the large-deflection theory of plates (Ref. 1, p. 411). Most test results are on specimens in which lateral contraction is not restrained appreciably.

10-4 SPECIFICATION PROVISIONS FOR POSTBUCKLING BEHAVIOR OF PLATE ELEMENTS

Forces in members of steel frames in which hot-rolled shapes are commonly used are usually large enough to require plate elements thick enough to preclude local buckling at stresses less than the yield stress. Thus, there is no provision in the AASHTO specifications for taking postbuckling strength of plates into account; instead, upper limits of slenderness b/t are specified, as discussed in Art. 4-14. AREA also specifies upper limits for b/t, but it allows the limit for plates supported on only one unloaded edge to be exceeded if the area corresponding to the excess width is excluded in computations having to do with stress on the member. Of course, this is an application of the Karman effective width. On the other hand, this option is not permitted for plates supported on both unloaded edges. However, the limiting b/t for such plates may be increased for columns in which the actual stress f_a is less than the allowable stress F_a by multiplying the limiting value of b/t by $\sqrt{F_a/f_a}$.

In both the AISC and the AISI specifications plates supported on both unloaded edges are called *stiffened elements*, while those supported on only one unloaded edge are called *unstiffened elements*. Specification requirements for the two types are discussed in the following paragraphs. Since in some case yield stress in a member cross section may be attained while a particular element of the cross section is stressed below yield, effective-width formulas are given in terms of the calculated stress f in the element under consideration instead of the yield stress F_y.

Noticeable waviness of unstiffened elements with b/t greater than about 30 and of stiffened elements with b/t greater than about 250 may develop at the allowable load permitted by the AISC and AISI specifications.[8] Therefore, if protection is required against unserviceability because of excessive waviness of elements with b/t larger than these values, advantage of the full postbuckling strength should not be taken and service-load stresses should not be significantly larger than the local-buckling stress of the weakest element.

AISI. Effective widths of uniformly compressed stiffened elements are given by Eq. (10-16) and of uniformly compressed unstiffened elements by Eq. (10-17), except that the format and notation differ from that used here. With $b_{ey} = b_e$, $F_y = f$, and $E = 29,000$ ksi, Eq. (10-16) for stiffened elements reduces to

$$b_e = 324 \frac{t}{\sqrt{f}} \left(1 - \frac{71.2}{(b/t)\sqrt{f}} \right) \leq b \qquad (10\text{-}21)$$

and Eq. (10-17) for unstiffened elements to

$$b_e = 106 \frac{t}{\sqrt{f}} \left(1 - \frac{23.4}{(b/t)\sqrt{f}} \right) \leq b \qquad (10\text{-}22)$$

The width b in these equations, which is denoted by w in the AISI specification, is defined as the *flat width*, that is, the width of the element exclusive of the radii at its junction with adjoining elements.

The value of f in Eqs. (10-21) and (10-22) is not the service-load stress. Instead, it is the stress F_n by Eqs. (10-36), which are discussed in Art. 10-6, for compression members and the stress in the element at initial yield of the effective cross section for flexural members.

AISC/LRFD. The effective-width concept is not used for unstiffened elements in this specification. Instead, a limiting stress F_L on the element, which is between the critical stress and the postbuckling strength, is used. For the single angle, whose legs have little or no rotational restraint at their juncture, the limiting stress is given by

$$F_L = F_y \left(1.340 - 0.00447 \sqrt{F_y}\, \frac{b}{t} \right) \qquad \frac{76}{\sqrt{F_y}} < \frac{b}{t} < \frac{155}{\sqrt{F_y}} \qquad (a)$$

in the inelastic range and

$$F_L = \frac{15,500}{(b/t)^2} \qquad\qquad \frac{b}{t} \geq \frac{155}{\sqrt{F_y}} \qquad (b)$$

in the elastic range. The limiting stresses are given in the specification in the form $F_L = Q_s F_y$. The following formulas are specified.

For single angles,

$$Q_s = \begin{cases} 1.340 - 0.00447\sqrt{F_y}\,\dfrac{b}{t} & \dfrac{76}{\sqrt{F_y}} < \dfrac{b}{t} < \dfrac{155}{\sqrt{F_y}} & (10\text{-}23) \\[4mm] \dfrac{15,500}{F_y(b/t)^2} & \dfrac{b}{t} \geq \dfrac{155}{\sqrt{F_y}} & (10\text{-}24) \end{cases}$$

For angles or plates projecting from columns or other compression members and for projecting elements of compression flanges of beams and girders,

$$Q_s = \begin{cases} 1.415 - 0.00437\sqrt{F_y}\,\dfrac{b}{t} & \dfrac{95}{\sqrt{F_y}} < \dfrac{b}{t} < \dfrac{195}{\sqrt{F_y}} & (10\text{-}25) \\[4mm] \dfrac{20,000}{F_y(b/t)^2} & \dfrac{b}{t} \geq \dfrac{195}{\sqrt{F_y}} & (10\text{-}26) \end{cases}$$

For stems of tees,

$$Q_s = \begin{cases} 1.908 - 0.00715\sqrt{F_y}\,\dfrac{b}{t} & \dfrac{127}{\sqrt{F_y}} < \dfrac{b}{t} < \dfrac{176}{\sqrt{F_y}} & (10\text{-}27) \\[4mm] \dfrac{20,000}{F_y(b/t)^2} & \dfrac{b}{t} \geq \dfrac{176}{\sqrt{F_y}} & (10\text{-}28) \end{cases}$$

The limiting $b/t = 95/\sqrt{F_y}$ for Eq. (10-25) is the upper limit of slenderness for projecting compression flanges of beams and columns (Table 4-4).

The effective widths of uniformly compressed stiffened elements are given by the following formulas.

For flanges of square and rectangular box sections of uniform thickness,

$$b_e = \frac{326t}{\sqrt{f}}\left(1 - \frac{64.9}{(b/t)\sqrt{f}}\right) \leq b \qquad (10\text{-}29)$$

For other uniformly compressed stiffened elements,

$$b_e = \frac{326t}{\sqrt{f}}\left(1 - \frac{57.2}{(b/t)\sqrt{f}}\right) \leq b \qquad (10\text{-}30)$$

The stress f in Eqs. (10-29) and (10-30) is the compressive stress in the element. For axially loaded compression members it is obtained by dividing the load P by the actual cross-sectional area, rather than the effective area, while for flexural members it is computed for the effective cross section. Furthermore, if the members have unstiffened elements, f must be such that the accompanying stress in any unstiffened element does not exceed $\phi_b Q_s F_y$ for flexural members or $\phi_c F_{cr}$ for compression members, where ϕ_b and ϕ_c are the resistance factors 0.90 for flexure and 0.85 for compression, respectively.

The width b in Eqs. (10-29) and (10-30) is not the flat width w as in the AISI formulas because of differences between rolled shapes and cold-formed shapes. Definitions of b are given for flanges, webs, legs of angles, stems of tees, and various other section elements.

AISC/ASD. The effective width of stiffened elements is given in terms of the service-load stress f. To allow for the fact that the load on which the factor of safety is based depends on the effective width at that load, rather than on the effective width at the service load, the service-load stress must be multiplied by the factor of safety before substituting into Eq. (10-15). Therefore, formulas corresponding to the LRFD formulas, Eqs. (10-29) and (10-30), are obtained by dividing the numerical coefficients in those equations by $\sqrt{1.67}$, where 1.67 is the factor of safety. The results are

$$b_e = \frac{253t}{\sqrt{f}}\left(1 - \frac{50.3}{(b/t)\sqrt{f}}\right) \le b \tag{10-31}$$

for flanges of square and rectangular box sections of uniform thickness, and

$$b_e = \frac{253t}{\sqrt{f}}\left(1 - \frac{44.3}{(b/t)\sqrt{f}}\right) \le b \tag{10-32}$$

The stress f in Eqs. (10-31) and (10-32) is the compressive stress in the element. For axially loaded compression members it is determined by dividing the load P by the actual cross-sectional area, rather than the effective area, while for flexural members it is computed for the effective cross section. Furthermore, if the member has unstiffened elements, f must be such that the stress in any unstiffened element does not exceed $Q_s F_b$ for flexural members or $Q_s F_a$ for compression members, where F_b and F_a are the allowable stresses for flexure and axial compression, respectively.

The limiting stresses F_L and the corresponding formulas for Q_s are the same as in the AISC/LRFD specification, except that the following equations are used instead of Eqs. (10-25) and (10-26)

$$Q_s = \begin{cases} 1.293 - 0.00309\sqrt{\dfrac{F_y}{k_c}}\dfrac{b}{t} & \dfrac{95}{\sqrt{F_y/k_c}} < \dfrac{b}{t} < \dfrac{195}{\sqrt{F_y/k_c}} \tag{10-33} \\[4mm] \dfrac{26{,}200k_c}{F_y(b/t)^2} & \dfrac{b}{t} \ge \dfrac{195}{\sqrt{F_y/k_c}} \tag{10-34} \end{cases}$$

in which $k_c = 1$ if $h/t \le 70$ and $4.05/(h/t)^{0.46}$ if $h/t > 70$, where $h =$ clear distance between flanges of the beam or girder at the section under investigation. How these limiting stresses are used is discussed in Art. 10-6.

10-5 INTERACTION OF LOCAL BUCKLING AND COLUMN BEND BUCKLING

The A36-steel box column of Fig. 10-9 will be used to illustrate the interaction of local buckling and column bend buckling. The local buckling stress is given by Eq. (10-11) with $k = 4$:

$$\frac{b}{t} = \frac{20}{\frac{1}{4}} = 80$$

$$F_{cr} = \frac{4\pi^2 \times 29{,}000}{12(1 - 0.3^2)80^2} = 16.3 \text{ ksi}$$

Since $F_{cr} < \frac{36}{2}$, it is in the elastic range of bend buckling. The corresponding slenderness ratio is found from the Euler formula:

$$\frac{L}{r} = \pi\sqrt{\frac{29{,}000}{16.3}} = 133$$

This gives point A in Fig. 10-10. Thus, bend buckling and local buckling occur simultaneously for this column if $L/r = 133$, while failure by bend buckling alone would be expected for $L/r > 133$.

The postbuckling strength of the plate element will be computed for the effective width according to Eq. (10-16):

$$\frac{b_e}{t} = 1.9\sqrt{\frac{29{,}000}{36}}\left(1 - 0.42\frac{\sqrt{29{,}000/36}}{80}\right) = 45.9$$

$$b_e = 45.9 \times \tfrac{1}{4} = 11.5 \text{ in}$$

$$A_e = 4 \times 11.5 \times \tfrac{1}{4} = 11.5 \text{ in}^2$$

$$P_u = 36 \times 11.5 = 414 \text{ kips}$$

$$F_u = \tfrac{414}{20} = 20.7 \text{ ksi}$$

The post-local-buckling strength can be counted on only if the column is short enough to preclude bend buckling. Of course, this condition is certain to be satis-

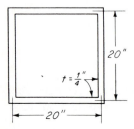

FIGURE 10-9

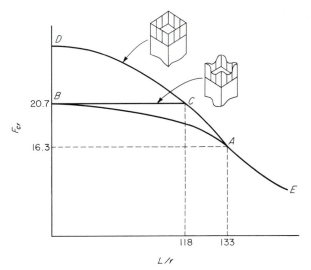

FIGURE 10-10

fied if $L/r = 0$. Therefore, $F_u = 20.7$ ksi gives point B in Fig. 10-10. Thus, it is clear that a column for which $0 < L/r < 133$ will fail at $20.7 > F_u > 16.3$ ksi. Although the horizontal line BC might be taken as the ultimate stress for $0 < L/r < 118$, this leads to an inconsistency at C because the stress distribution corresponding to any point on BC is the nonuniform postbuckling distribution shown in the figure, while the distribution corresponding to any point on the bend-buckling curve $DCAE$ is uniform, as shown. Thus, point C represents two incompatible stress distributions. Therefore, the strength of this particular column must be represented by a line BA which is a function of both L/r and b/t. Except for whatever information is available from tests, the shape of BA is unknown.

10-6 SPECIFICATION PROVISIONS FOR INTERACTION OF LOCAL BUCKLING AND COLUMN BEND BUCKLING

AISI. This specification prescribes the same formulas for compression members as the AISC/ASD specification but in different form and with some differences in the factor of safety. The allowable axial load P is given by

$$P_a = \frac{F_n A_e}{\Omega} \tag{10-35}$$

where F_n = nominal buckling stress
A_e = effective area (sum of effective areas of all elements of the cross section)
Ω = factor of safety

The nominal buckling stress is given by

$$F_n = \begin{cases} F_y\left(1 - \dfrac{F_y}{4F_e}\right) & F_e > \dfrac{F_y}{2} & \text{(10-36a)} \\[2ex] F_e & F_e \le \dfrac{F_y}{2} & \text{(10-36b)} \end{cases}$$

F_e in Eqs. (10-36) is the elastic (Euler) buckling stress, based on the radius of gyration of the gross area of the cross section, rather than the effective area. The factor of safety is 1.92 except for fully effective sections having wall thicknesses greater than 0.09 in and not subject to torsional or torsional flexural buckling, for which Ω is the same as the factor of safety in the AISC/ASD specification [denominator of Eq. (4-17)].

Equations (10-36) are identical to the AISC/ASD formulas, Eqs. (4-17), with the factor of safety omitted, as can be shown by substituting $(\pi^2 E)/(KL/r^2)$ for F_e.

AISC. For the case of the column short enough not to fail by bend buckling, the compressive strength of a member containing both stiffened and unstiffened elements is taken to be the product of the effective area of the cross section, which is the sum of the effective areas of the stiffened elements and the full areas of the unstiffened elements, and the critical stress F_L of the weakest unstiffened element. For the channel of Fig. 10-11 as an example,

$$P = F_L(2b_1 t_1 + b_{2e} t_2) \tag{a}$$

where $F_L = Q_s F_y$ with Q_s from Eqs. (10-25) and (10-26). From Eq. (a), the average stress on the cross section is

$$f_{av} = \frac{P}{A} = \frac{F_L(2b_1 t_1 + b_{2e} t_2)}{2b_1 t_1 + b_2 t_2} \tag{b}$$

The ratio of the effective area to the gross area is denoted by Q_a:

$$Q_a = \frac{\text{effective area}}{\text{gross area}} \tag{c}$$

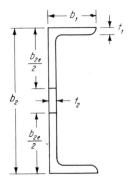

FIGURE 10-11

With this notation and using $F_L = Q_s F_y$, Eq. (b) gives

$$f_{av} = Q_a Q_s F_y = QF_y \tag{10-37}$$

where $Q = Q_a Q_s$.

Since QF_y in Eq. (10-37) is the average stress on the column short enough not to bend buckle, it gives a point at $L/r = 0$ on the f-L/r curve (point B of Fig. 10-10). However, instead of a formula for the range of L/r from B to A, interaction of local buckling and bend buckling is determined by substituting QF_y for F_y in the column formulas, as discussed in following paragraphs.

AISC/LRFD. Substitution of QF_y for F_y in Eq. (4-27) yields

$$F_{cr} = 0.658^{Q\lambda_c^2} QF_y \qquad \lambda_c\sqrt{Q} \le 1.5 \tag{10-38a}$$

Equation (4-28) remains unchanged. This is because it is the Euler buckling stress F_E, as is shown in the discussion of that equation. Therefore,

$$F_{cr} = \frac{0.877F_y}{\lambda_c^2} \qquad \lambda_c\sqrt{Q} > 1.5 \tag{10-38b}$$

In Eqs. (10-38), $\lambda_c = (KL/r\pi)\sqrt{F_y/E}$.

AISC/ASD. Substitution of QF_y for F_y in Eq. (4-17) yields

$$F_a = \frac{QF_y\left[1 - \frac{1}{2}\left(\frac{KL/r}{C_{cQ}}\right)^2\right]}{\frac{5}{3} + \frac{3}{8}\frac{KL/r}{C_{cQ}} - \frac{1}{8}\left(\frac{KL/r}{C_{cQ}}\right)^3} \qquad \frac{KL}{r} \le C_{cQ} \tag{10-39a}$$

in which $C_{cQ} = \pi\sqrt{2E/QF_y}$. Since Eq. (4-18) does not contain F_y, it remains unchanged. Therefore,

$$F_a = \frac{149,000}{(KL/r)^2} \qquad \frac{KL}{r} > C_{cQ} \tag{10-39b}$$

Discussion of LRFD and ASD formulas. Since the factor Q_a in $Q = Q_a Q_s$ was obtained by computing the unit stress on the full cross-sectional area, F_{cr} in Eqs. (10-38) and F_a in Eqs. (10-39) are multiplied by A_g to obtain the corresponding nominal load P_n and allowable load P, and the radius of gyration of the gross cross section is used to compute L/r.

Equation (10-38a) is plotted in Fig. 10-12 for $Q = 1$ (fully effective cross section) and $Q = 0.7$. These plots intersect the curve for Eq. (10-38b) at $\lambda_c = 1.5$ and 1.79, respectively. The corresponding ASD formulas, Eqs. (10-39), plot similarly, with intersections at $L/r = 126$ and 151. It will be noted that the logic in locating point A in Fig. 10-10 at the local-buckling stress of an element of the

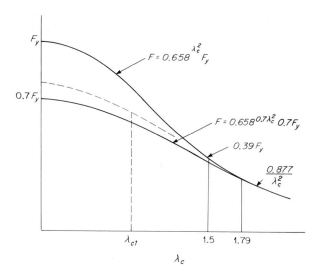

FIGURE 10-12

cross section is missing in the derivation of these equations. Thus it is possible for this point to be to the right of point B on the CD curve in Fig. 10-12. Although such a cross section is likely to be rare, this does suggest that there could be cases where a member element may buckle prematurely or, in extreme cases, even at service load.

Figure 10-12 shows that the Q_a component of Q should be calculated for $L/r = 0$; that is, the effective widths of stiffened elements of the member should be computed for F_y in LRFD and $0.6F_y$ in ASD, except where the value of Q_s for an unstiffened element reduces the value of Q, in which case effective widths should be computed for $\phi_c Q_s F_y$ and $0.6Q_s F_y$, respectively. If, for example, Q_a is based instead on the axial stress for a column with $\lambda_c = \lambda_{c1}$, the resulting effective widths are larger and Q is larger because of the larger Q_a, the result being a curve indicated by the dashed line in Fig. 10-12. Thus there would be an infinite number of formulas for F_{cr}, each of which would be valid for only one λ_c (or one L/r).

In the 1980 edition of the AISI specification effective widths were calculated as described above; that is, for a cross section containing only stiffened elements, the effective widths and the corresponding values of Q_a were computed for the basic design stress $0.6F_y$, irrespective of the value of L/r, while for one containing both stiffened and unstiffened elements, Q_a was based on the stress F_c used to compute Q_s, which, of course, is also independent of L/r. But in the AISC/LRFD specification (1986) effective widths are computed for the stress f based on the full cross-sectional area, that is, P/A_g, unless the member contains unstiffened elements, in which case f must not exceed $\phi_c F_{cr}$ by Eqs. (10-38) with $Q = Q_s$. In the AISC/ASD specification (1989) f is also computed for the full cross-sectional area unless the member contains unstiffened elements, in which case f must not exceed F_a by Eqs. (10-39) with $Q = Q_s$. Thus, with the AISC specifications effective widths of stiffened elements of a member of given length and cross section must be evaluated for the value of f corresponding to L/r or λ and, therefore, require trial-and-error solution.

Example 10-6-1. Compute the AISC/ASD allowable load P for an $8 \times 8 \times \frac{3}{16}$ structural-tube pin-ended column 20 ft long (Fig. 10-13). $F_y = 50$ ksi.

Solution
   Trial 1. For an estimate of the stress f for determining the effective width, compute b_e for the stress $f = 0.6 \times 50 = 30$ ksi at $L/r = 0$.

$$\frac{b}{t} = \frac{7.44}{\frac{3}{16}} = 39.7 \qquad \frac{KL}{r} = \frac{240}{3.18} = 75.5$$

From Eq. (10-31)

$$\frac{b_e}{t} = \frac{253}{\sqrt{30}}\left(1 - \frac{50.3}{39.7\sqrt{30}}\right) = 35.5 \qquad b_e = 35.5 \times \tfrac{3}{16} = 6.66 < 7.44$$

$$A_e = 5.77 - 4(7.44 - 6.66) \times \tfrac{3}{16} = 5.18 \text{ in}^2$$

$$Q_a = \frac{5.18}{5.77} = 0.898$$

$$C_{cQ} = \pi\sqrt{\frac{2E}{QF_y}} = 113$$

From Eq. (10-39a)

$$\text{F.S.} = \frac{5}{3} + \frac{3}{8} \times \frac{75.5}{113} - \frac{1}{8}\left(\frac{75.5}{113}\right)^3 = 1.88$$

$$F_a = \left[1 - \frac{1}{2}\left(\frac{75.5}{113}\right)^2\right] \times \frac{50}{\text{F.S.}} = 20.7 \text{ ksi}$$

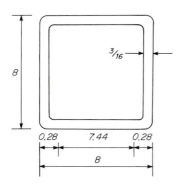

FIGURE 10-13

Trial 2. Based on $F_a = 20.7$ ksi from trial 1, try $f = 21$ ksi

$$\frac{b_e}{t} = \frac{253}{\sqrt{21}}\left(1 - \frac{50.3}{39.7\sqrt{21}}\right) = 39.9 \qquad b_e = 39.9 \times \tfrac{3}{16} = 7.48 \text{ in} > 7.44$$

Since $b_e > b$, the cross section is fully effective, so $Q_a = 1$ and $C_{cq} = C_c$:

$$C_c = \pi\sqrt{\frac{2E}{F_y}} = 107.0$$

$$\text{F.S.} = \frac{5}{3} + \frac{3}{8} \times \frac{75.5}{107} - \frac{1}{8}\left(\frac{75.5}{107}\right)^3 = 1.89$$

$$F_a = \left[1 - \frac{1}{2}\left(\frac{75.5}{107}\right)^2\right] \times \frac{50}{\text{F.S.}} = 19.9 \text{ ksi}$$

Trial 3. Based on $F_a = 19.9$ ksi from trial 2, try $f = 19.9$ ksi

$$\frac{b_e}{t} = \frac{253}{\sqrt{19.9}}\left(1 - \frac{50.3}{39.7\sqrt{19.9}}\right) = 40.6 \qquad b_e = 40.6 \times \tfrac{3}{16} = 7.61 \text{ in} > 7.44$$

Therefore, Q_a and C_c are the same as in trial 2, so $F_a = 19.9$ and $P = 19.9 \times 5.77 = 115$ kips.

Example 10-6-2. Compute the AISC/LRFD nominal load P_n for an $8 \times 8 \times \tfrac{3}{16}$ structural-tube pin-ended column 20 ft long (Fig. 10-13). $F_y = 50$ ksi.

Solution

   Trial 1. For an estimate of the stress F_{cr} for determining the effective width, compute b_e for $f = F_{cr} = 50$ ksi at $L/r = 0$.

$$\frac{b}{t} = \frac{7.44}{\tfrac{3}{16}} = 39.7 \qquad \frac{KL}{r} = \frac{240}{3.18} = 75.5$$

From Eq. (10-29)

$$\frac{b_e}{t} = \frac{326}{\sqrt{50}}\left(1 - \frac{64.9}{39.7\sqrt{50}}\right) = 35.4 \qquad b_e = 35.4 \times \tfrac{3}{16} = 6.64 \text{ in} < 7.44$$

$$A_{\text{eff}} = 5.77 - 4(7.44 - 6.64) \times \tfrac{3}{16} = 5.17 \text{ in}^2$$

$$Q_a = \frac{5.17}{5.77} = 0.896 \qquad \lambda_c = \frac{75.5}{\pi}\sqrt{\frac{50}{29,000}} = 0.998$$

$$\lambda_c\sqrt{Q} = 0.998\sqrt{0.896} = 0.945 < 1.5$$

From Eq. (10-38a) with $Q\lambda_c^2 = 0.945^2 = 0.893$,

$$F_{cr} = 0.658^{0.893} \times 0.896 \times 50 = 30.8 \text{ ksi}$$

Trial 2. Based on $F_{cr} = 30.8$ ksi from trial 1, try $F_{cr} = 31$ ksi.

$$\frac{b_e}{t} = \frac{326}{\sqrt{31}} \left(1 - \frac{64.9}{39.7\sqrt{31}} \right) = 41.4 \qquad b_e = 41.4 \times \tfrac{3}{16} = 7.76 \text{ in} > 7.44$$

Since $b_e > b$, the cross section is fully effective, so $Q_a = 1$ and $\lambda_c\sqrt{Q} = \lambda_c = 0.998$. From Eq. (10-38a) with $Q = 1$,

$$F_{cr} = 0.658^{0.998} \times 50 = 33.0 \text{ ksi}$$

Trial 3. Based on $F_{cr} = 33.0$ ksi from trial 2, try $f = 33$ ksi

$$\frac{b_e}{t} = \frac{326}{\sqrt{33}} \left(1 - \frac{64.9}{39.7\sqrt{33}} \right) = 40.6 \qquad b_e = 40.6 \times \tfrac{3}{16} = 7.61 \text{ in} > 7.44$$

Therefore, Q_a and λ_c are the same as in trial 2, so $F_{cr} = 33.0$ ksi and $P_n = 33.0 \times 5.77 = 190$ kips.

Example 10-6-3. Compute the AISI allowable load P for an $8 \times 8 \times \tfrac{3}{16}$ structural-tube pin-ended column 20 ft long (Fig. 10-13). $F_y = 50$ ksi.

Solution

$$\frac{b}{t} = \frac{744}{\tfrac{3}{16}} = 39.7 \qquad \frac{KL}{r} = \frac{240}{3.18} = 75.5$$

From Eq. (10-21)

$$\frac{b_e}{t} = \frac{324}{\sqrt{50}} \left(1 - \frac{71}{39.7\sqrt{50}} \right) = 34.2 \qquad b_e = 34.2 \times \tfrac{3}{16} = 6.42 \text{ in} < 7.44$$

$$A_e = 5.77 - 4(7.44 - 6.42) \times \tfrac{3}{16} = 5.00 \text{ in}^2$$

From Eqs. (10-35) and (10-36a)

$$F_e = \frac{\pi^2 E}{(KL/r)^2} = \frac{29{,}000\pi^2}{75.5^2} = 50.2 \text{ ksi} > \frac{F_y}{2}$$

$$F_n = 50 \left(1 - \frac{50}{4 \times 50.2} \right) = 37.5 \text{ ksi}$$

$$P = \frac{37.5 \times 5.00}{1.92} = 97.7 \text{ kips}$$

Example 10-6-4. Compute the AISC/ASD allowable load P for the column shown in cross section in Fig. 10-14. $L = 8$ ft, $K = 1$, $F_y = 50$ ksi.

Solution

$$A = (2 \times 3.906 + 9.813) \times 0.1875 = 3.30 \text{ in}^2$$

$$I_y = 2 \times 0.1875 \times \frac{3.906^3}{3} = 7.45 \text{ in}^4$$

$$r_y = \sqrt{\frac{7.45}{3.30}} = 1.50 \text{ in} \qquad \frac{KL}{r} = \frac{1 \times 96}{1.50} = 64.0$$

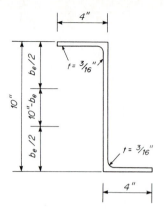

FIGURE 10-14

Flange. The specification defines the width b of unstiffened plates to be the distance from the free edge to the first line of fasteners or welds. For this section, $b = 4 - 0.1875 = 3.81$ in. Then from Eq. (10-25)

$$\frac{b}{t} = \frac{3.81}{\frac{3}{16}} = 20.3 \qquad \frac{95}{\sqrt{50}} < \frac{b}{t} < \frac{195}{\sqrt{50}} \qquad 13.4 < 20.3 < 27.6$$

$$Q_s = 1.293 - 0.00309 \times 20.3\sqrt{50} = 0.850$$

Trial 1. Assume cross section to be fully effective. Then $Q_a = 1$ and $Q = Q_a Q_s = 1 \times 0.850 = 0.850$, and from Eq. (10-39$a$)

$$C_{cQ} = \pi\sqrt{\frac{58,000}{0.850 \times 50}} = 116$$

$$F_a = \frac{0.850 \times 50[1 - \frac{1}{2}(\frac{64}{116})^2]}{\frac{5}{3} + \frac{3}{8} \times \frac{64}{116} - \frac{1}{8}(\frac{64}{116})^3} = 19.4 \text{ ksi}$$

The width of the web will be taken to be the clear width, $10 - 2 \times 0.1875 = 9.63$ in.

$$\frac{b}{t} = \frac{9.63}{0.1875} = 51.4$$

and from Eq. (10-32)

$$\frac{b_e}{t} = \frac{253}{\sqrt{19.4}}\left(1 - \frac{44.3}{51.4\sqrt{19.4}}\right) = 46.2 \qquad b_e = 8.66 \text{ in} < 9.63$$

$$A_e = 3.30 - (9.63 - 8.66) \times 0.1875 = 3.12 \text{ in}^2$$

$$Q_a = \frac{3.12}{3.30} = 0.946 \qquad Q = Q_a Q_s = 0.946 \times 0.850 = 0.804$$

Trial 2. Assume $Q = 0.804$ from trial 1.

$$C_{cQ} = \pi \sqrt{\frac{58,000}{0.804 \times 50}} = 119$$

$$F_a = \frac{0.804 \times 50[1 - \frac{1}{2}(\frac{64}{119})^2]}{\frac{5}{3} + \frac{3}{8} \times \frac{64}{119} - \frac{1}{8}(\frac{64}{119})^3} = 18.6 \text{ ksi}$$

$$\frac{b_e}{t} = \frac{253}{\sqrt{18.6}}\left(1 - \frac{44.3}{51.4\sqrt{18.6}}\right) = 46.9 \qquad b_e = 8.79 \text{ in} < 9.63$$

$$A_e = 3.30 - (9.63 - 8.79) \times 0.1875 = 3.14 \text{ in}^2$$

$$Q_a = \frac{3.14}{3.30} = 0.952 \qquad Q = Q_a Q_s = 0.952 \times 0.850 = 0.809$$

Trial 3. Assume $Q = 0.809$ from trial 2.

$$C_{cQ} = \pi \sqrt{\frac{58,000}{0.809 \times 50}} = 119$$

$$F_a = \frac{0.809 \times 50[1 - \frac{1}{2}(\frac{64}{119})^2]}{\frac{5}{3} + \frac{3}{8} \times \frac{64}{119} - \frac{1}{8}(\frac{64}{119})^3} = 18.7 \text{ ksi}$$

$$\frac{b_e}{t} = \frac{253}{\sqrt{18.6}}\left(1 - \frac{44.3}{51.4\sqrt{18.7}}\right) = 46.8 \qquad b_e = 8.78 \text{ in} < 9.63$$

$$A_e = 3.30 - (9.63 - 8.78) \times 0.1875 = 3.14 \text{ in}^2$$

Since A_e in trial 3 is the same as in trial 2, Q is also the same. Therefore, $F_a = 18.7$ ksi and $P = F_a A_g = 18.7 \times 3.30 = 61.7$ kips.

Example 10-6-5. Compute the AISC/LRFD nominal compression P_n for the column shown in cross section in Fig. 10-14. $L = 8$ ft, $K = 1$, $F_y = 50$ kips.

Solution. The following AISC/ASD quantities computed in Example 10-6-4 for this column are the same in AISC/LRFD:

$$A = 3.30 \text{ in}^2 \qquad r_y = 1.50 \text{ in} \qquad \frac{KL}{r} = 64.0 \qquad Q_s = 0.850$$

Trial 1. Assume cross section to be fully effective. Then $Q_a = 1$ and $Q = Q_a Q_s = 0.850$, and from Eq. (10-38a)

$$\lambda_c \sqrt{Q} = \frac{KL}{r\pi} \sqrt{\frac{F_y Q}{E}} = \frac{64}{\pi} \sqrt{\frac{50 \times 0.850}{29,000}} = 0.780 < 1.5$$

$$F_{cr} = 0.658^{Q\lambda_c^2} Q F_y = 0.658^{0.608} \times 0.850 \times 50 = 33.0 \text{ ksi}$$

The width of the web will be taken to be the clear width, $10 - 2 \times 0.1875 = 9.63$ in. To compute the effective width, par. 3b of sec. B5 defines

f as $\phi_c F_{cr} = 0.85 F_{cr}$, with F_{cr} computed for $Q = Q_s$. Since $Q_a = 1$ for this trial, $Q_s = 0.850$ as computed above, so $F_{cr} = 33.0$ ksi. Then $f = 0.85 \times 33.0 = 28.0$ ksi, and from Eq. (10-30) with $b/t = 9.63/0.1875 = 51.4$,

$$\frac{b_e}{t} = \frac{326}{\sqrt{28.0}}\left(1 - \frac{57.2}{51.4\sqrt{28.8}}\right) = 48.7 \qquad b_e = 9.13 \text{ in} < 9.63$$

$$A_e = 3.30 - (9.63 - 9.13) \times 0.1875 = 3.21 \text{ in}^2$$

$$Q_a = \frac{3.21}{3.30} = 0.973 \qquad Q = Q_a Q_s = 0.973 \times 0.850 = 0.827$$

Trial 2. Assume $Q = 0.827$ from trial 1.

$$\lambda_c\sqrt{Q} = \frac{64}{\pi}\sqrt{\frac{50 \times 0.827}{29,000}} = 0.781 < 1.5$$

$$F_{cr} = 0.658^{0.610} \times 0.827 \times 50 = 32.0 \text{ ksi}$$

$$\frac{b_e}{t} = \frac{326}{\sqrt{32.0}}\left(1 - \frac{57.2}{51.4\sqrt{32.0}}\right) = 46.3 \qquad b_e = 8.68 \text{ in} < 9.63$$

$$A_e = 3.30 - (9.63 - 8.68) \times 0.1875 = 3.12 \text{ in}^2$$

$$Q_a = \frac{3.12}{3.30} = 0.946 \qquad Q = Q_a Q_s = 0.964 \times 0.850 = 0.804$$

Trial 3. Assume $Q = 0.804$ from trial 2.

$$\lambda_c\sqrt{Q} = \frac{64}{\pi}\sqrt{\frac{50 \times 0.804}{29,000}} = 0.759 < 1.5$$

$$F_{cr} = 0.658^{0.576} \times 0.804 \times 50 = 31.6 \text{ ksi}$$

$$\frac{b_e}{t} = \frac{326}{\sqrt{31.6}}\left(1 - \frac{57.2}{51.4\sqrt{31.6}}\right) = 46.5 \qquad b_e = 8.72 \text{ in} < 9.63$$

$$A_e = 3.30 - (9.63 - 8.72) \times 0.1875 = 3.13 \text{ in}^2$$

Since A_e in trial 3 is the same as in trial 2, Q is also the same. Therefore, $F_{cr} = 31.6$ ksi and $P_n = 31.6 \times 3.30 = 104$ kips.

Example 10-6-6. Compute the AISI allowable compression P for the column shown in cross section in Fig. 10-15. $L = 8$ ft, $K = 1$, $F_y = 50$ ksi.

Solution. Properties will be computed for a section with square corners. Therefore,

$$A = (2 \times 3.906 + 9.813) \times 0.1875 = 3.30 \text{ in}^2$$

$$I_y = 2 \times 0.1875 \times \frac{3.906^3}{3} = 7.45 \text{ in}^4$$

$$r_y = \sqrt{\frac{7.45}{3.30}} = 1.50 \text{ in} \qquad \frac{KL}{r} = \frac{1 \times 96}{1.50} = 64.0$$

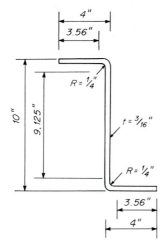

FIGURE 10-15

From Eqs. (10-36)

$$F_e = \frac{\pi^2 E}{(KL/r)^2} = \frac{29,000\pi^2}{64^2} = 69.9 \text{ ksi} > \frac{F_y}{2}$$

$$F_n = 50\left(1 - \frac{50}{4 \times 69.9}\right) = 41.0 \text{ ksi}$$

Effective width of web [Eq. (10-21)],

$$\frac{b}{t} = \frac{9.125}{0.1875} = 48.7 \qquad \frac{b_e}{t} = \frac{324}{\sqrt{41.0}}\left(1 - \frac{71.2}{48.7\sqrt{41.0}}\right) = 39.0$$

$$b_e = 7.32 \text{ in} < 9.125$$

Effective width of flange [Eq. (10-22)],

$$\frac{b}{t} = \frac{3.56}{0.1875} = 19.0 \qquad \frac{b_e}{t} = \frac{106}{\sqrt{41.0}}\left(1 - \frac{23.4}{19.0\sqrt{41.0}}\right) = 13.4$$

$$b_e = 2.51 \text{ in} < 3.56$$

$$A_e = 3.30 - [2(3.56 - 2.51) + (9.125 - 7.32)] \times 0.1875 = 2.57 \text{ in}^2$$

From Eq. (10-35)

$$P = \frac{41.0 \times 2.57}{1.92} = 54.9 \text{ kips}$$

Example 10-6-7. Compute the allowable compression P for the column shown in cross section in Fig. 10-15 according to the AISC/ASD specification, except use $f = 0.6 Q_s F_y$ to compute effective widths (see Art. 10-6 for reason). $L = 8$ ft, $K = 1$, $F_y = 50$ ksi.

Solution. The following quantities computed for this column in Example 10-6-4 are the same for this example:

$$A = 3.30 \text{ in}^2 \qquad r_y = 1.50 \text{ in} \qquad \frac{KL}{r_y} = 64.0 \qquad Q_s = 0.850 \qquad \text{Web } \frac{b}{t} = 51.4$$

Effective width of web is given by Eq. (10-32) with $f = 0.6 \times 0.850 \times 50 = 25.5$ ksi:

$$\frac{b_e}{t} = \frac{253}{\sqrt{25.5}} \left(1 - \frac{44.3}{51.4\sqrt{25.5}}\right) = 41.6 \qquad b_e = 7.80 \text{ in} < 10$$

$$A_e = 3.30(9.63 - 7.80) \times 0.1875 = 2.96 \text{ in}^2$$

$$Q_a = \frac{2.96}{3.30} = 0.897 \qquad Q = 0.897 \times 0.850 = 0.762$$

$$C_{cQ} = \pi \sqrt{\frac{2E}{QF_y}} = \pi \sqrt{\frac{58,000}{0.762 \times 50}} = 123$$

Then from Eq. (10-39a)

$$F_a = \frac{[1 - \frac{1}{2}(\frac{64}{123})^2] \times 0.762 \times 50}{\frac{5}{3} + \frac{3}{8} \times \frac{64}{123} - \frac{1}{8}(\frac{64}{123})^3} = 17.6 \text{ ksi}$$

$$P = 17.6 \times 3.30 = 58.1 \text{ kips}$$

10-7 DISCUSSION OF EXAMPLES OF ART. 10-6

If the effective width in Example 10-6-1 is computed for the value of f at $L/r = 0$, which the authors believe is the correct procedure (Art. 10-6), the value of F_a determined in trial 1 is correct and $P = 18.5 \times 5.77 = 107$ kips. Although this is only 7 percent less than the value of $P = 115$ kips in trial 3, the difference can be considerably larger for sections with larger values of b/t. In Example 10-6-2, P_n for the trial 1 value of F_{cr} is $30.8 \times 5.77 = 178$ kips, which is 6.3 percent less than the value of trial 3.

The AISI value of P in Example 10-6-3, 97.7 kips, is 8.7 percent less than the AISC/ASD trial 1 value in Example 10-6-1. Since the AISI formulas, Eqs. (10-36), are identical to the AISC formulas with the factor of safety omitted, as can be shown by substituting for F_E in the AISI formulas, the difference in these results lies in the difference in the effective widths.

In Example 10-6-7 the effective width of the web of the column is computed for the value of f at $L/r = 0$, namely, 25.5 ksi, rather than for $f = F_a$ at $L/r = 64$, as in Example 10-6-4. The authors believe this to be the correct procedure (Art. 10-6). The resulting value of P is 58.1 kips, which is 5.8 percent less than the value 61.7 kips of Example 10-6-4. There is a comparable difference between the value of P in Example 10-6-5 and the value based on the effective width of web for $L/r = 0$.

The AISI value of P in Example 10-6-6, 54.9 kips, is 5.5 percent less than the modified AISC/ASD value 58.1 kips of Example 10-6-7. Since the AISI formulas, Eqs. (10-36), are identical to the AISC/ASD formulas with the factor of safety omitted, as was pointed out in Art. 10-6, the difference in these results lies in the differences in effective widths, which are due largely to the AISI procedure of basing element slenderness on the flat width rather than on overall widths as is the case for most elements in the AISC specification.

10-8 POSTBUCKLING STRENGTH OF BEAMS

The bending strength of beam cross sections with compression-flange components which buckle locally is discussed in this article.

 If the compression flange of the box shown in Fig. 10-16a buckles at a stress less than F_y, the bending strength of the cross section is attained with the stress distribution shown in Fig. 10-16b. The equivalent stress distribution on the effective cross section c is shown in d. Since the neutral axis of the effective cross section lies below middepth, the compression flange yields before the tension flange does. Therefore, the edge stress f_e is known, and the effective width b_e can be determined. On the other hand, if the cross section is one in which the tension flange yields first, as would be the case for the trapezoidal box of Fig. 10-17, the edge stress f_e on the compression flange is not known, so either it or the effective

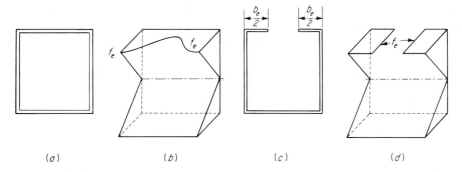

(a)   (b)   (c)   (d)

FIGURE 10-16

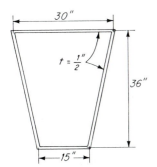

FIGURE 10-17

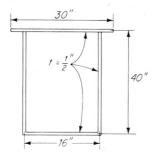

FIGURE 10-18

width must be assumed and the resisting moment determined by successive approximations. Ordinarily, one would assume $f_e = F_y$ for the first approximation.

If the compression flange consists of or contains one or more unstiffened elements, the analyses according to the AISC and AISI specifications differ because of the difference in the treatment of such elements in these specifications, as is discussed in the following.

Using the AISC specifications, one may begin by computing the critical stress for the unstiffened elements, $\phi_b Q_s F_y$ for LRFD, $0.6 Q_s F_y$ for ASD. If in the resulting stress distribution the stress at any point exceeds F_y, the distribution is revised proportionately to reduce that stress to F_y. Then, if there are no stiffened compression elements, the cross section is fully effective and the section moduli and corresponding bending moment can be computed. If there are also stiffened compression elements, as in the section shown in Fig. 10-18, one may determine their effective widths for the stresses of the assumed stress distribution, determine the section moduli of the resulting effective cross section, and recompute the bending moment for which the stress nowhere exceeds F_y and the compressive stress on any unstiffened element does not exceed F_{cr}. Of course, iteration must then proceed until satisfactory convergence is reached.

Since the AISI specification considers effective widths of unstiffened elements rather than their critical stresses, analysis will usually begin with a determination of the effective widths of both stiffened and unstiffened compression elements of the cross section, based on a stress F_y on the extreme fiber. The section modulus of the resulting effective section is then determined, and if it shows that the stress at any other point of the cross section does not exceed F_y, the initial assumption is proved correct and the bending moment can be calculated. Of course, if this condition is not satisfied, a second assumption must be made and iteration continued until satisfactory convergence is achieved.

Example 10-8-1. Compute the AISC/LRFD nominal moment M_n and the AISC/ASD allowable moment M for the $12 \times 12 \times \frac{1}{4}$ structural tube shown in Fig. 10-19a. $F_y = 50$ ksi.

Solution. Since the compression-flange width will be reduced if local buckling controls, the neutral axis of the effective cross section will lie below middepth. Therefore, compression-flange stress controls.

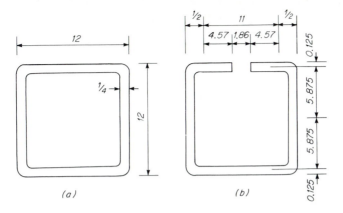

FIGURE 10-19

AISC/LRFD. From Eq. (10-29), with $b/t = 11/0.25 = 44$ and $f = F_y$,

$$\frac{b_e}{t} = \frac{326}{\sqrt{50}}\left(1 - \frac{64.9}{44\sqrt{50}}\right) = 36.5 \qquad b_e = 9.13 \text{ in} \le 11$$

AISC/ASD. From Eq. (10-31), with $b/t = 11/0.25 = 44$ and $f = 0.6F_y$,

$$\frac{b_e}{t} = \frac{253}{\sqrt{30}}\left(1 - \frac{50.3}{44\sqrt{30}}\right) = 36.6 \qquad b_e = 9.14 \text{ in} \le 11$$

LRFD and ASD. From Fig. 10-19b,

$$A = 0.25(4 \times 11.75 - 1.86) = 11.3 \text{ in}^2$$

$$e = \frac{0.25 \times 1.86 \times 5.88}{11.3} = 0.242 \text{ in}$$

$$\frac{I}{t} = (11.75 - 1.86) \times 6.12^2 + 11.75 \times 5.63^2 + 2 \times \frac{6.12^3}{3} + 2 \times \frac{5.63^3}{3}$$

$$= 1015 \text{ in}^3 \qquad I = 254 \text{ in}^4$$

LRFD:
$$M_n = F_y \frac{I}{c} = 50 \times \frac{254}{6.12} = 2075 \text{ in·kips}$$

ASD:
$$M = 0.6F_y \frac{I}{c} = 0.6 \times 50 \times \frac{254}{6.12} = 1245 \text{ in·kips}$$

PROBLEMS

10-1. Compute the short-column strength of the A36-steel welded member shown in Fig. P10-1 (*a*) with full postbuckling of both flange and web and (*b*) with the useful strength limited to that at which the flange buckles.

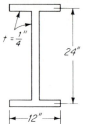

FIGURE P10-1

10-2. Same as Prob. 10-1 except that the cross section is that shown in Fig. P10-2.

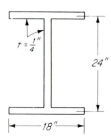

FIGURE P10-2

10-3. Compute the short-column strength of the cold-formed A570 Grade 40 steel hat section of Fig. P10-3 (*a*) with full postbuckling of all components and (*b*) with the useful strength limited to that at which the projecting flange buckles. Given $B = 12$ in, $D = 10$ in, $d = 1.50$ in, $t = 0.06$ in, $R = \frac{3}{16}$ in.

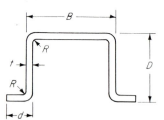

FIGURE P10-3

10-4. Compute the AISC allowable load for a 16-ft A36-steel column with the cross section shown in Fig. P10-2.

10-5. Compute the allowable load for a 10-ft A570 Grade 40 steel column with the cross section shown in Fig. P10-3 with $B = 4$, $D = 4$, $d = 0.915$, $t = 0.075$, $R = \frac{3}{32}$, all in inches, and with a 5.68×0.06-in plate spot-welded to the hat to form a closed section. Use the AISI specification.

10-6. Compute the allowable load for a 10-ft pin-ended A36-steel column with the cross section shown in Fig. P10-6 for a factor of safety of 1.8 based on accounting for the full postbuckling strengths of the components.

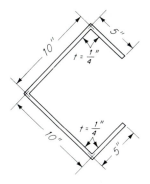

FIGURE P10-6

10-7. Compute the allowable bending moment for the A36-steel cross section of Fig. P10-1 according to the AISC/ASD specification. What factor of safety does this allowable moment have with respect to the bending resistance taking into account full postbuckling of the flange?

10-8. Compute the nominal moment resistance M_n for the A36-steel cross section of Fig. P10-1 according to the AISC/LRFD specification.

10-9. Compute the allowable bending moment for the A570 Grade 40 cross section of Fig. P10-3, with the top flange in compression, according to the AISI specification.

10-10. Compute for a factor of safety of 1.75 the allowable bending moment of the A441-steel cross section shown in Fig. P10-10.

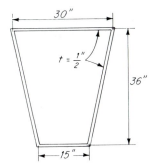

FIGURE P10-10

10-11. Compute for a factor of safety of 1.75 the allowable bending moment of the A441-steel cross section shown in Fig. P10-11.

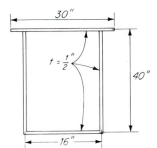

FIGURE P10-11

10-12. Compute the resisting moment at extreme-fiber yield of the $20 \times 20 \times \frac{1}{4}$ in steel box shown in Fig. P10-12. $F_y = 42$ ksi.

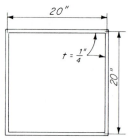

FIGURE P10-12

REFERENCES

1. Timoshenko, S., and J. M. Gere: "Theory of Elastic Stability," 3d ed., McGraw-Hill, New York, 1969.
2. Gerard, G.: "Introduction to Structural Stability Theory," McGraw-Hill, New York, 1962.
3. Karman, T. von, E. E. Sechler, and L. H. Donnell: The Strength of Thin Plates in Compression, *Trans. ASME, APM*, vol. 54, no. 2, January 1932.
4. Winter, G.: Strength of Light-Gage Steel Compression Flanges, *Trans. ASCE*, vol. 112, 1947.
5. Haaijer, G.: Selection and Application of Constructional Steels, in E. D. Verink, Jr. (ed.), *Methods of Materials Selection, Metall. Soc. Conf.*, vol. 40, Gainesville, Fla., May 1966.
6. Dhalla, A. K.: Influence of Ductility on Structural Behavior of Cold-Formed Steel Members, *Cornell Univ. Dept. Struct. Eng. Rep. 336*, 1971.
7. Haaijer, G.: Plate Buckling in the Strain-Hardening Range, *Trans. ASCE*, vol. 124, 1959.
8. American Iron and Steel Institute: Specification for the Design of Cold-Formed Steel Structural Members, August 1986.

CHAPTER

11

STEEL BRIDGES

11-1 INTRODUCTION

The factors that must be considered in the design of a bridge may be grouped into three interdependent categories: economic, functional, and physical. In addition, there are governmental regulations to be met if the bridge crosses navigable waters. There are often conflicts in requirements that can be resolved only by compromise, and judgment, skill, and broad experience of a high order are essential to the development of a sound plan. Economics plays an important role. Not only are there questions of economy with respect to the type of structure to be built, the materials to be used, the number of spans, the method of erection, and the like, but there are questions that have to do with the economic feasibility of the project itself. The functional planning involves considerations of grade and alignment, number of tracks or traffic lanes, approach facilities for collecting and dispersing traffic of highway bridges, and appearance. Conditions at the site have a considerable influence on grade and alignment. Although beauty is not prerequisite to efficient performance, an ugly bridge is not functional in the broad sense of the word. The bridge should be in harmony with its setting, and in many cases this in itself can well determine the type that should be built. The physical planning involves consideration of the foundation materials, the character of the stream if one is involved, the type of bridge, the number of spans, and questions of similar nature. Borings to determine the character and depth of foundation materials are an obvious necessity. Information on the stream's flood stages and low-water stages, on its scouring propensities, and on the nature and amount of drift carried by floods is also vital. Both foundation and stream characteristics have a direct influence on the layout of the bridge. For example, the more expensive the pier, the longer will be the economic span, and it is evident that foundation materials at considerable depths and high flood stages both call for taller and therefore more expensive piers. Furthermore, as the distance between piers increases, the limit of the simple-span bridge is eventually passed so that a structure suitable for long spans, say the cantilever or the suspension bridge, becomes a necessity.

The federal government has authority to regulate the bridging of navigable waters; permits for the construction of such bridges (except those over streams which have been placed in the "advanced approval" category by the Commandant, U.S. Coast Guard) must be obtained from the U.S. Coast Guard and other appropriate agencies.

The discussion in this article is intended only to highlight the problems involved in planning a bridge. Bridge design is treated in detail in Ref. 1. Except for the fact that certain elements such as floors are more or less independent of the type of bridge, discussion in the articles to follow is limited to simple-span beam bridges and truss bridges.

11-2   ECONOMICS OF SIMPLE-SPAN BRIDGES

Simple-span bridges were described and discussed in Art. 2-2. The rolled-beam bridge is likely to be an economical choice for railroad bridges of spans up to 50 ft, while the highway beam bridge may be economical for spans up to about 60 ft and the composite beam bridge for spans up to about 100 ft. The plate-girder bridge becomes economical for spans of about 60 ft and is commonly used for spans to 300 ft or more. Welded girders made up of three plates compete with rolled beams in all but the shortest spans. The plate-girder bridge is likely to be cheaper than truss bridges up to at least the limit for shipment in one piece. The economical limiting span for both the beam bridge and the plate-girder bridge is greater for continuous structures than it is for simple spans. Continuous plate-girder bridges with spans exceeding 950 ft have been built.

Although trusses are usually used in highway bridges only for very long spans, they may be economical for shorter spans where aesthetics and (in the case of through bridges) safety with high-speed traffic are not critical. Deck truss bridges are preferable. The use of welding, in conjunction with H sections and box sections for truss members, produces a clean, light, cheap, and easy-to-maintain structure.[1]

The depth of simple-span bridge trusses usually ranges from about one-fifth to one-eighth the span, shorter spans being relatively deeper. The depth/span ratio is also somewhat dependent upon the live load, so highway-bridge trusses are usually shallower than railroad-bridge trusses of comparable span. Trusses for deck bridges are often relatively shallower than trusses for through bridges. Both the AASHTO and the AREA specifications prescribe one-tenth the span as the preferable minimum depth of truss. Trusses of economical proportions usually result if the angle between diagonals and verticals is between 35 and 40°. Thus, panel lengths increase with the span of the truss and eventually lead to excessively heavy floor systems unless subdivided trusses are adopted. Panel lengths of 16 to 32 ft are usually economical for the highway-bridge truss. For spans greater than about 320 ft, the K truss is advisable to reduce floor weight and inclination of the diagonals.

The relative economy of the parallel-chord truss and the curved-chord truss is not easy to evaluate. In the curved-chord truss, chord stresses are essentially uniform, and their vertical components relieve the web members. Thus, the curved-chord truss is lighter than the parallel-chord truss, but costs of fabrication and erection may be slightly higher. It should be noted, however, that for through bridges the curved-chord truss is more graceful. On the other hand, the lines of the parallel-chord truss are more in harmony with the deck bridge.

11-3 BRACING

Lateral bracing for the deck truss bridge usually consists of horizontal trusses in the planes of each of the two chords of the vertical trusses. Since lateral forces resulting from live load are resisted almost entirely by the lateral truss in the plane of the floor, the top lateral truss is more important than the bottom lateral truss. However, the top lateral truss is not as important for the deck highway bridge as for the deck railroad bridge, since the former usually has a concrete or steel floor, which, with the stringers and floor beams, can take over the function of the lateral truss. Nevertheless, a top lateral truss must be provided in any case to help in the erection of the bridge and to furnish wind resistance until the floor is in place. Except for the half-through (pony-truss) bridge, which is virtually obsolete, lateral bracing for through bridges also consists of two trusses, but the relative importance of the two systems is reversed. Two diagonals in each panel are used ordinarily, but single diagonals are common in single-track plate-girder railroad bridges.

Members of the lateral truss take various forms. Single angles are quite common for the relatively unimportant bottom lateral truss of the deck bridge, and it is usual to assume that the shear is resisted entirely by the diagonal that is in tension. Of course, this means that the member connecting opposite panel points must be designed as a strut, so it may need to be a double-angle member or perhaps an H. Diagonals of the bottom lateral truss in through bridges are usually single or double angles connected to gusset plates on the bottom flanges of the chords. This truss is often designed on the assumption that one diagonal in a panel resists half the shear in tension while the other resists the other half in compression. The top laterals of both deck and through bridges are usually the same depth as the chord so as to connect to both its flanges. A separate system of

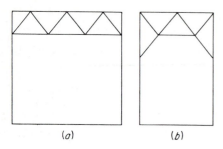

      (*a*)   (*b*)   **FIGURE 11-1**

lateral bracing is usually employed to connect the stringers of an open-floor rail-road bridge to relieve them of bending due to lateral forces from the train. A single system in the plane of the top flanges is sufficient.

  Bracing in the transverse vertical planes is called *sway bracing*. In the deck truss bridge, two diagonals in the transverse planes at each panel point are used. The sway frames at the ends of the bridge transmit the end reactions of the top lateral truss to the abutment, and must be designed accordingly. Lateral forces on the intermediate frames are not usually calculated, since the lateral trusses are designed to transmit these forces to the abutments. Therefore, sizes of members of the intermediate frames are a matter of judgment, except for limitations as to slenderness ratio.

  The end posts of the through bridge must be tied together to form a rigid frame capable of transferring the end reaction of the top lateral truss to the abutments. This combination of end posts and bracing is called a *portal frame*. In order to minimize bending stresses in the end posts and provide a maximum of rigidity, portal bracing should be as deep as headroom allows. The portal frame shown in Fig. 11-1*a*, or some modification of it, is quite common for highway bridges and double-track railroad bridges. The frame shown in Fig. 11-1*b*, or some modification of it, is common for single-track railroad bridges. The frame is almost invariably a two-plane structure connecting to both flanges of the end posts. Its members are usually of the same type as the top lateral diagonals.

11-4 WEIGHT OF BRIDGES

The dead-load force is often a large percentage of the total force in a bridge-truss member. For this reason, it is helpful to have a good estimate of the weight of a bridge before its members are designed. The weight is dependent on the span, depth, width of roadway, number of panels, and loading as well as on the design specifications and the individuality of the designer. Many rules and formulas for estimating weights of bridges have been devised. Probably the most complete data were published by Waddell.[2] A simple and quite accurate method of estimating the weight per foot of two trusses and their bracing was developed by Hudson and is given by the equation

$$w = \frac{100A_n}{3} \tag{11-1}$$

where w is the weight per foot of bridge of two trusses and their bracing and A_n is the required net area, in square inches, of the largest member of the tension chord. The net area A_n is calculated for the total force due to live load, impact, and dead load, including a guessed weight of trusses and their bracing.

11-5 BRIDGE FLOORS

The most common floor system for the steel highway bridge consists of a reinforced-concrete slab supported on steel stringers parallel to the direction of traffic. The stringers are supported by floor beams connecting to girders or trusses. In the beam bridge, the beams themselves perform the function of the stringers, and since the beams rest on abutments or piers, no floor beams are needed. The concrete slab may be bonded mechanically to the top flanges of the stringers by using connectors to develop horizontal shear between the slab and the stringer. This is called *composite construction* and is discussed in Chap. 5 and Art. 11-11.

Since the floor constitutes a major part of the dead load of a bridge, several forms of lightweight floor construction have been developed. The battle-deck floor consists of steel plate welded to the top flanges of the stringers. The plate is usually less than 1 in thick, and the stringers are usually spaced 18 to 32 in apart. The plate not only distributes the wheel load over several stringers but also serves as part of the compression flange of each stringer. Unless it is covered with a bituminous surfacing, battle-deck flooring is likely to be slippery when wet. Another type of steel flooring is made by riveting together alternate straight and crimped bars to form an open grid. The straight bars are the main load-carrying members and are braced laterally by the crimped bars. The top edges of the bars are flush. This type of open-grid flooring is welded to a secondary system of structural members (called *sills*) placed transverse to, and supported by, stringers. In another type of open-grid floor the sill is eliminated by special carrying beams that are an integral part of the grid. Several other types of grid flooring are manufactured. In some cases the grid is filled with concrete. Orthotropic steel-deck-plate construction is described in Art. 2-2 (Fig. 2-12) and discussed in detail in Ref. 1.

The most common type of floor for the railroad bridge consists of timber crossties resting on stringers which frame into floor beams. Since this is an open floor, it can be used only for stream and secondary highway crossings; over city streets and main highways a ballasted roadway on a solid floor is necessary. The solid floor may consist of an all-metal deck or of a concrete or timber trough supported on stringers and floor beams or on floor beams alone. In addition to the protection it offers, this type of floor provides a continuous ballasted roadbed.

11-6 DESIGN OF FLOOR SLABS

The principal moment in the bridge-floor slab is the positive moment in the transverse direction midway between stringers. The design procedure prescribed by the AASHTO specifications is based on theoretical studies by Westergaard.[3] For a slab whose span is perpendicular to the flow of traffic, the live-load moment for simple spans in foot·kips per foot width of slab is given by

$$M = \frac{S + 2}{32} P \tag{11-2}$$

where S is the effective span length (for continuous slabs the center-to-center distance between stringers minus half the width of the flange) and P is the load on the rear wheel. The positive moment for slabs continuous over three or more supports is assumed to be 80 percent of the simple-span moment. According to the specifications, Eq. (11-2) applies to both composite and noncomposite construction.

In addition to the positive bending moments, there are, of course, negative transverse moments at the supports (stringers). Furthermore, certain positions of the truck wheels produce negative transverse moments in the midsection of the slab between stringers, while other positions produce positive transverse moments over the supports. All these moments have been found to be less than the positive transverse moments at the midsection of the slab panel. The ratios of these moments to the positive transverse moment vary along the span of the bridge, and experimental results show that they are smaller than theory would indicate. The AASHTO specifications prescribe a negative moment at the support equal in magnitude to the positive moment at midpanel.

A wheel load in the central portion of a slab panel produces not only transverse bending moments but longitudinal bending moments as well. The existence of these moments in the longitudinal direction is easy to see if one visualizes the saucerlike depression surrounding the wheel. For this reason, and also to control cracking of the slab due to shrinkage and temperature change, longitudinal reinforcement is needed at both the top and the bottom surfaces of the slab. AASHTO specifications prescribe a percentage of the positive transverse reinforcement of $220/\sqrt{S}$, with a maximum of 67 percent. This amount is placed in the bottom in the middle half of the slab span; in the outer quarter of the span an amount of not less than 50 percent of that required in the middle half must be provided.

Shear and bond stresses in reinforced-concrete floor slabs that meet the requirements for moment discussed in this article can be depended upon to be within allowable limits, so they need not be investigated.

11-7   DESIGN OF STRINGERS AND FLOOR BEAMS

A wheel load applied directly over an interior stringer of a bridge floor is shared by the several stringers in the panel because of the stiffness of the slab in the direction transverse to the stringers. Of course, the load is not distributed equally, and the distribution depends upon the relative stiffnesses of the slab and the stringers. However, since at least two wheels (on the same axle) occupy a given position on the bridge, and since the maximum moment in a given stringer results when both lanes of a two-lane bridge are loaded, the maximum moments for the various stringers do not differ appreciably. The maximum moment for one stringer can be determined with sufficient accuracy by assuming that it supports the portion kP of a single wheel load P, where k is given by

$$k = \frac{b}{s} \tag{a}$$

where b is the center-to-center spacing of stringers and s is a constant that depends upon the span of the stringer and the relative stiffnesses of the stringer and the slab. Within practical limits for bridge floors of the type under consideration, values of s range from 5 to 6 ft.

For bridges of two or more traffic lanes, the AASHTO specifications require that the live-load moment for one interior stringer be computed for the portion kP of a single wheel load P given by

$$k = \frac{S}{5.5} \qquad S < 14 \text{ ft} \tag{11-3}$$

where S is the average stringer spacing in feet. No distinction is made between composite and noncomposite construction. If S exceeds 14 ft, the load on one stringer is to be determined by assuming that the floor slab acts as a series of simple beams supported by the stringers. The live load on the outside stringer is to be determined by assuming the slab to act as a simple beam between stringers unless the floor is supported on four or more stringers, in which case the fraction of the wheel load must not be less than

$$\frac{S}{5.5} \qquad S \le 6 \text{ ft}$$

$$\frac{S}{4.0 + 0.25S} \qquad 6 < S < 14 \text{ ft} \tag{11-4}$$

where S is the distance in feet between the outside stringer and the adjacent interior stringer. When $S > 14$ ft, the slab is assumed to act as a simple beam between stringers.

In determining the dead-load moment for one stringer, the stringer can be assumed to support a strip of floor extending halfway to the adjacent stringer on each side. Curbs, railings, and wearing surface, if placed after the slab has cured, may be considered equally distributed to all stringers.

The live-load moment in a floor beam is determined according to the type of load (lane or truck) that produces the larger moment. According to the AASHTO specifications, no distribution of wheel loads on floor beams is to be assumed; i.e., wheel loads over the floor beam are considered to be concentrated loads. The dead-load moment can be determined by treating the weight of the slab, stringers, and floor beam as a load distributed uniformly along the floor beam or as a series of concentrated loads acting at the points of connection of the stringers.

11-8 END BEARINGS

Bridge bearings are designed to transmit the loads to the foundation and to provide for expansion of the superstructure. They are of two general types, fixed and expansion. Fixed bearings act as hinges in that they permit rotation but not expansion. Expansion bearings permit rotation as well as movements of the superstructure resulting from temperature change, deflection, etc.

The span beyond which the simple bearing plate is unsatisfactory is largely a question of judgment and experience. According to the AASHTO specifications, spans of less than 50 ft may be arranged to slide upon metal plates with smooth surfaces, and no provisions for deflection of the spans need be made. The AREA specifications set the limit at 70 ft. AASHTO permits the use of elastomeric pads for both fixed and expansion bearings for all types of bridges. It is the least expensive bearing for light and intermediate reactions. Figure 11-2 shows a bearing that makes use of a rocker between the bearing plate and the beam or girder. A similar detail in which the anchor bolts do not pass through the rocker is shown in Fig. 11-3. In this case, the beam is held in position by means of pintles shaped like gear teeth. This type of support may be used where resistance to uplift need not be provided. For example, it may be used for the inside beams of the beam bridge, with the outside beams supported by bearings of the type shown in Fig. 11-2.

Figure 11-4a shows an expansion bearing for larger bridges. Several variations are shown in the view at the right. The soleplate may be bolted to the girder, as at the left of the centerline, or welded, as shown at the right. Resistance to uplift may be provided by using a hinge plate, as at the left; if such resistance

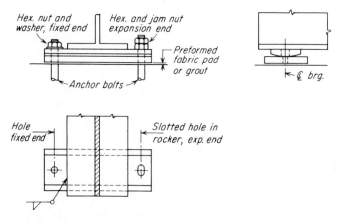

FIGURE 11-2

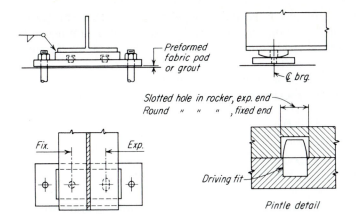

FIGURE 11-3

is not needed, lateral movement is prevented by a plate such as that shown at the right. A corresponding fixed end bearing is shown in Fig. 11-4*b*.

Although there is only a line of contact between an unloaded rocker and its bearing plate, deformation under load distributes the reaction over a finite area. Evidently, at a given load this area increases with increase in the radius of the

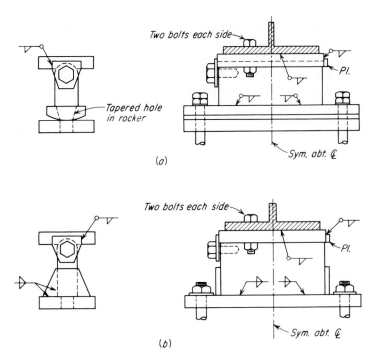

FIGURE 11-4

rocker, since a rocker of infinitely large radius would have a plane surface to begin with. The allowable load must be evaluated in terms of a limiting permanent deformation. Thus the yield point of the material is also a factor. Empirical formulas based on the results of tests are used for purposes of design. According to the AASHTO specifications, the allowable bearing pressure p in pounds per lineal inch between rocker and bearing plate is given by

$$
p = \begin{cases}
\dfrac{F_y - 13,000}{20,000}\, 600d & d \leq 25 \text{ in} \\[3ex]
\dfrac{F_y - 13,000}{20,000}\, 3000\sqrt{d} & 25 \leq d \leq 125 \text{ in}
\end{cases}
\tag{11-5}
$$

where F_y is the yield point of the metal in the rocker or the bearing plate, whichever is smaller, and d is the diameter of the rocker in inches.

The AREA specification uses

$$
p = \begin{cases}
690d & d \leq 25 \text{ in} \\
3450\sqrt{d} & 25 \leq d \leq 125 \text{ in}
\end{cases}
\tag{11-6}
$$

Since the necessary radius and length of a given rocker depend upon the load to be supported, it is obvious that for a very large reaction the required radius may be too large for satisfactory results, or else the rocker may be too long if the radius is held within reasonable bounds. This dilemma is resolved by using a series of rollers. Segmental rollers (Fig. 11-5) are ordinarily used since they occupy less space than cylindrical rollers. The rollers may be coupled with the sidebars shown and the entire nest held in position by tooth guides which engage slots in the shoe and in the bearing plate. Sidebars may be omitted if each roller is held by teeth. Lateral movement is prevented by the tongues shown in the view at the right. Resistance to uplift may be provided by lugs that have projections extending over the upper surface of the base of the shoe or by enlarging the base of the shoe and providing slotted holes for the anchor bolts. The

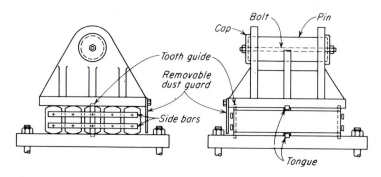

FIGURE 11-5

FIGURE 11-6
Eldersburg–Louisville Road Bridge. (*J. E. Greiner Company, Inc., Consulting Engineers.*)

roller assembly may be enclosed with removable dust guards; they are shown on only two sides in Fig. 11-5 to indicate that they are optional. A detailed example of the design of bearings is given in the next article.

11-9 DP11-9-1: ELDERSBURG–LOUISVILLE ROAD BRIDGE

The Eldersburg–Louisville Road Bridge (Figs. 11-6 and 11-7), which crosses Morgan Run in Carroll County, Maryland, consists of two 216-ft truss spans and two 70-ft beam spans. It was designed for the city of Baltimore by J. E. Greiner Company, Consulting Engineers, of Baltimore. Except for some of the joints and splices, the complete calculations for the design of the truss-span superstructure are presented here through the courtesy and cooperation of the consulting engineers and the Baltimore Department of Public Works. The authors have made some changes in notation and have revised the design to conform to the 1989

(*text continues on page 738*)

FIGURE 11-7
Eldersburg–Louisville Road Bridge. (*J. E. Greiner Company, Inc., Consulting Engineers.*)

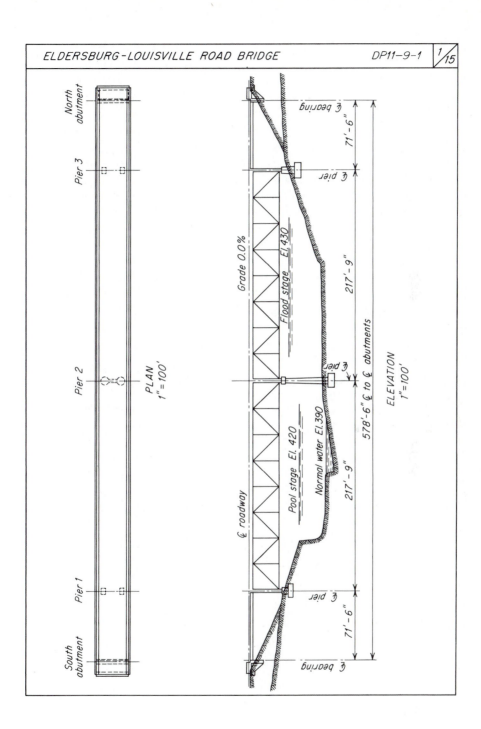

ELDERSBURG-LOUISVILLE ROAD BRIDGE
DP11-9-1 1/15

PLAN
1" = 100'

ELEVATION
1" = 100'

ELDERSBURG-LOUISVILLE ROAD BRIDGE DP11-9-1 2/15

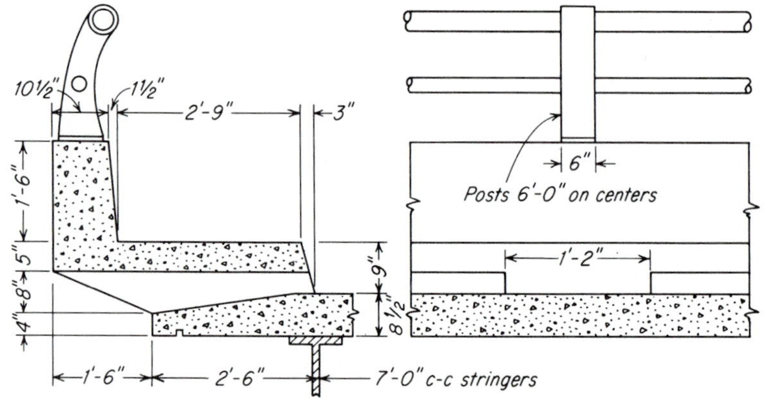

10½"
1½"
2'-9"
3"
1'-6"
5"
8"
4"
9"
8½"
1'-6"
2'-6"
7'-0" c-c stringers
6"
Posts 6'-0" on centers
1'-2"

Section			Weight	Arm	Moment	(a)
Top rail	(3½ std. steel pipe)		9.2	3.4	31	
Bott. rail	(2½ std. steel pipe)		5.8	3.7	22	
Post	65 × 1/6 (cast iron)		10.8	3.6	39	
Parapet	0.875 × 1.5 × 150	=	197.5	3.56	703	
	½ × 0.125 × 1.5 × 150	=	14.0	3.08	43	
Sidewalk	0.42 × 3.82 × 150	=	241.0	2.09	504	
Sidewalk support	½ × 0.67 × 1.5 × 1.17 × 150 × 1/6	=	14.6	3.00	44	
	0.33 × 2.5 × 1.17 × 150 × 1/6	=	24.3	1.25	30	
	½ × 0.33 × 2.17 × 1.17 × 150 × 1/6	=	10.5	1.78	19	
			527.7	2.72	1435	

SIDEWALK Span = 6.0 − 1.17 = 4.83' (b)

DL 197.5 + 14.0 + 241 = 452.5#/' × 4.83²/10 = 1055

LL 85 × 3 = 255.0#/' × 4.83²/10 = 595

1650'#

$d = 5 - 2 - 0.31 = 2.69$

$$A_s = \frac{1650 \times 12}{20{,}000 \times 0.88 \times 2.69} = 0.42 \text{ in}^2$$

#5 @ 8" $A_s = 0.46 \text{ in}^2$

ELDERSBURG-LOUISVILLE ROAD BRIDGE DP11-9-1 3/15

ROADWAY SLAB

Stringers 7'-0" c.c.

$S = 7.0 - 0.37 = 6.63'$ (a)

$M_D = \frac{1}{10} \times 0.1 \times 6.63^2 \quad = 0.44$ (b)

$M_L = 0.8 \times 16 \times (6.63+2)/32 = 3.46$ (b)

$M_I = 0.30 \times 3.46 \qquad = \underline{1.04}$ (c)

$\qquad\qquad\qquad\qquad\qquad\qquad 4.94^{'k}$

8-in slab $\qquad d = 8.0 - 0.75 - 1.50 - 0.31 = 5.44''$ (d)

#5 @ 6" $\qquad A_s = 0.62 \ in^2 \quad p = \dfrac{0.62}{12 \times 5.44} = 0.0095$

$\qquad k = 0.351 \ ; \quad j = 0.882$

$f_s = \dfrac{M}{A_s jd} = \dfrac{4.94 \times 12}{0.62 \times 0.882 \times 5.44} = 19.9 \ ksi$

$f_c = \dfrac{2pf_s}{k} = \dfrac{2 \times 0.0095 \times 19.9}{0.351} = 1.08 \ ksi$

Section over ₵ of stringer at face of curb
(carried by 4-ft section of slab) (e)

		Shear	Arm	Moment	
DL	0.528×6	3.17	2.72	$8.62^{'k}$	(f)
	$0.1 \times 2.5 \times 4$	1.00	1.25	1.25	(g)
LL sdwk	$85 \times 3 \times 6$	1.53	1.50	2.31	
LL curb	0.5×6	3.00	0.75	$\underline{2.25}$	(h)
				$14.43^{'k}$	

$d = 8 - 2 = 6''$ #5 @ 6" $A_s = 8 \times 0.31 = 2.48 \ in^2$ (i)

$p = \dfrac{2.48}{48 \times 6} = 0.00861 \qquad k = 0.338 \quad j = 0.887$

$f_s = \dfrac{14.43 \times 12}{2.48 \times 0.887 \times 6.0} = 13.1 \ ksi$

$f_c = \dfrac{2 \times 0.00861 \times 13.1}{0.35} = 0.67 \ ksi$

ELDERSBURG-LOUISVILLE ROAD BRIDGE   DP11-9-1   4/15

EXTERIOR STRINGER 0.33 ⟋ 2.17

$$0.33 \times \tfrac{1}{2} \times 2.17 \times 150 \times 4.83/6.0 = 44.5 \,\#/'$$

Sdwk & parapet $528 \times 9.72/7$ $= 734$ (a)
Fl. slab $(100 \times 9.5 \times 4.75 - 44.5 \times 8.78)/7 = 587$
Stringer $= \underline{82}$
                    1403

Sidewalk LL $= 85 \times 3 \times 8.5/7 = 310\,\#/'$
Fraction of wheel load to stringer $= 7/(4 + 0.25 \times 7) = 1.22$ (b)

		Shear		Moment	
DL	1.403×13.5	$= 19.0$	$\tfrac{1}{8} \times 1.403 \times 27^2$	$= 128$	(c)
Sdwk LL	310×13.5	$= 4.2$	$\tfrac{1}{8} \times 0.310 \times 27^2$	$= 28$	
LL	$1.22 \times 47.4 \times \tfrac{1}{2}$	$= 28.9$ (d)	$1.22 \times 237 \times \tfrac{1}{2}$	$= 145$	(d)
I	0.30×28.9	$= \underline{8.7}$	0.30×145	$= \underline{43}$	
		V 60.8^k		M $344^{'k}$	

$$\frac{I}{c} = \frac{344 \times 12}{20 \times 1.25} = 165 \, in^3 \qquad \underline{W24 \times 76} \qquad (e)$$

$\tfrac{7}{8}$A325 bolts Friction-type connection: ss $= 8.12^k$
$60.8/8.12 = 7.5$ req'd.

$$DL \, defl. = \frac{5ML^2}{48EI} = \frac{5 \times 128 \times 27^2 \times 1728}{48 \times 29,000 \times 2100} = 0.276''$$

no camber req'd.   (f)

INTERIOR STRINGER

Fl. slab $100 \times 7 = 700$
Stringer $\underline{90}$
                    790
Fraction of wheel load to stringer $= 7/5.5 = 1.27$ (g)

		Shear		Moment	
DL	0.79×13.5	$= 10.7$	$\tfrac{1}{8} \times 0.79 \times 27^2$	$= 72$	
LL	$1.27 \times 47.4 \times \tfrac{1}{2}$	$= 30.1$	$1.27 \times 237 \times \tfrac{1}{2}$	$= 151$	
I	0.30×30.1	$= \underline{9.0}$	0.30×151	$= \underline{45}$	
		V 49.8^k		M $268^{'k}$	

$$\frac{I}{c} = \frac{268 \times 12}{20} = 161 \, in^3 \qquad \underline{W24 \times 76}$$

$\tfrac{7}{8}$A325 bolts $49.8/8.12 = 6.2$ req'd.

Effect of cantilevered sidewalk on first interior stringer
Use 90% DL
    $0.9 \times 528 \times 2.72/7 = 185\,\#/'$ uplift   (h)
    $M = 0.185 \times 27^2/8 = 17^{'k}$
    $M = 268 - 17 = 251^{'k}$
    $\dfrac{I}{c} = \dfrac{251 \times 12}{20} = 151 \, in^3 \qquad \underline{W24 \times 68}$

ELDERSBURG-LOUISVILLE ROAD BRIDGE   DP11-9-1 $\dfrac{5}{15}$

INTERIOR FLOOR BEAM

|←—7'—→|←—7'—→|←—7'—→|←—7'—→|
|←4'→|←——20' c-c trusses——→|←4'→|

LL per lane
$32 + (8 + 32)\,{}^{13}\!/_{27} = 51.3^k$ (a)

DL ext. stringer	$1.40 \times 27 + 0.11 \times 2$	$= 38.0^k$	(b)
DL int. stringer	$(0.79 - 0.20)\,27 + 0.11 \times 5$	$= 16.5^k$	(c)
DL ctr. stringer	$0.79 \times 27 + 0.11 \times 7$	$= 22.1^k$	
Sdwk LL	$= 0.085 \times 3 \times 27 \times 8.5/7.0$	$= 8.4^k$	

Max. neg. moment

DL	38.0×4	$= 152$
Sdwk	8.4×4	$= 34$
LL	$51.3 \times \frac{1}{2} \times 1.22 \times 4.0$	$= 125$
I	0.30×74	$= \underline{22}$
		$333^{'k}$

LL to ext. stringer	$51.3 \times \frac{1}{2} \times \frac{1}{7}$	$= 3.7^k$	(d)
LL to int. stringer	$51.3 \times \frac{1}{2} \times \frac{8}{7}$	$= 29.3^k$	
LL to ctr. stringer	$51.3 \times \frac{5}{7}$	$= 36.7^k$	

Max. pos. moment

DL	$38.0\,(10-14) + 16.5\,(10-7) + 11.05 \times 10 =$	8
LL	$3.7\,(10-14) + 29.3\,(10-7) + 18.35 \times 10 =$	257
I	0.30×257	$= \underline{77}$
		$342^{'k}$

$\dfrac{I}{c} = \dfrac{342 \times 12}{20} = 205\ in.^3$ W27×84

Net I $= 2830 - 0.490\,(2^2 + 6^2)\,2 = 2790\ in^4$

Net I/c $= 2790/13.35 = 208\ in^3$

END FLOOR BEAM

LL per lane	${}^{1}\!/_{27}\,(32 \times 28.25 + 32 \times 14.25 + 8 \times 0.25)$	$= 50.6^k$	(e)
DL ext. stringer	$1.40 \times 28.25 \times 14.12/27 + 0.11 \times 2$	$= 20.9^k$	
DL int. stringer	$(0.79 - 0.20) \times 28.25 \times 14.12/27 + 0.11 \times 5$	$= 9.2^k$	
DL ctr. stringer	$0.79 \times 28.25 \times 14.12/27 + 0.11 \times 7$	$= 12.5^k$	
Sdwk LL	$\dfrac{0.085 \times 3 \times 28.25 \times 14.12}{27} \times \dfrac{8.5}{7.0}$	$= 4.6^k$	

Max. neg. moment

DL	20.9×4	$= 83.6$
Sdwk	4.6×4	$= 18.4$
LL	$50.6 \times \frac{1}{2} \times 1.22 \times 4.0$	$= 123.5$
I	0.30×72.5	$= \underline{21.8}$
		$247.3^{'k}$

END FLOOR BEAM (continued)

LL to ext. stringer $50.6 \times \frac{1}{2} \times \frac{1}{7}$ = 3.6^k
LL to int. stringer $50.6 \times \frac{1}{2} \times \frac{8}{7}$ = 28.9^k
LL to ctr. stringer $50.6 \times \frac{5}{7}$ = 36.2^k

Max. pos. moment

DL $20.9 \times (-4) + 9.2 \times 3 + 6.25 \times 10$ = 6.4
LL $3.5 \times (-4) + 28.9 \times 3 + 18.1 \times 10$ = 253.7
I 0.30×253.7 = $\underline{76.1}$
$336.2^{\prime k}$

$\dfrac{I}{c} = \dfrac{336 \times 12}{20} = 202 \ in^3$ $\underline{W27 \times 84}$

TRUSS

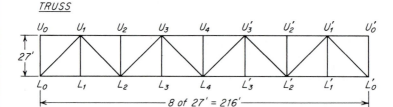

8 of 27' = 216'

DL per truss

	plf	Panel load (kips)
Sdwk., parapet, railing	528	14.3
Fl. slab (100 × 16.5) − 44	1606	43.4
Stringers (76 + 76 + 38) 1.02 (a)	190	5.1
Fl. bms. 84 × 1.20 × 14.5/27	54	1.5
Truss (assumed)	580	15.8
Bracing (assumed)	150	4.1
	3108	84.2

Dead load stresses   (b)

Panel pt.	Panel load	V	ΣV	Diagonal	Top chd.	Bott. chd.
0	42.0	336				
		294		−416	0	+294
1	84.0		294			
		210		+298	−504	+294
2	84.0		504			
		126		−178	−504	+630
3	84.0		630			
		42		+60	−672	+630
4	84.0		672			

ELDERSBURG-LOUISVILLE ROAD BRIDGE   DP11-9-1 $\frac{7}{15}$

<u>TRUSS</u> (continued)

   <u>Sidewalk live load</u>

     Load per ft. on truss $P \times 3 \times 25.5/20 = 3.83\,P$ (a)

$$P = \left(30 + \frac{3000}{216}\right)\left(\frac{55-3}{50}\right) = 45.6\,psf \times 3.83 = 175\,plf$$

Panel load $= 0.175 \times 27 = 4.72^{k}$

$V = 4.72 \times 3.5 = 16.5^{k}$

$$P = \left(30 + \frac{3000}{189}\right)(1.04) = 47.6\,psf \times 3.83 \times 27 = 4.93^{k}$$

$V = 4.93 \times 6 \times {}^{7}\!/_{16} = 13.0^{k}$

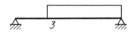

$$P = \left(30 + \frac{3000}{162}\right)(1.04) = 50.5\,psf \times 3.83 \times 27 = 5.22^{k}$$

$V = 5.22 \times 5 \times {}^{3}\!/_{8} = 9.8^{k}$

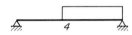

$$P = \left(30 + \frac{3000}{135}\right)(1.04) = 54.3\,psf \times 3.83 \times 27 = 5.60^{k}$$

$V = 5.60 \times 4 \times {}^{5}\!/_{16} = 7.0^{k}$

Top chord
    $U_0\,U_1 = 0$
    $U_1\,U_3 = -16.5 \times 2 - 4.72 \times 1 = -28.3^{k}$
    $U_3\,U_3' = -16.5 \times 4 - 4.72 \times 6 = -37.7^{k}$

Bottom chord
    $L_0\,L_2 = 16.5 \times 1 = +16.5^{k}$
    $L_2\,L_4 = 16.5 \times 3 - 4.72 \times 3 = +35.4^{k}$

Diagonals
    $L_0\,U_1 = 16.5\,\sqrt{2} = -23.4^{k}$
    $U_1\,L_2 = 13.0\,\sqrt{2} = +18.4^{k}$
    $L_2\,U_3 = 9.8\,\sqrt{2} = -13.9^{k}$
    $U_3\,L_4 = 7.0\,\sqrt{2} = +9.9^{k}$

Verticals
    $U_2\,L_2$ & $U_4\,L_4 = 60 \times 3.83 \times 27 = -6.2^{k}$
    $U_0\,L_0 = {}^{1}\!/_{2} \times 6.2 = -3.1^{k}$

TRUSS _(continued)_

Live loads

Fraction of lane load to truss $= (19+5)/20 = 1.2$ (a)

$$0.64 \times 1.2 = 0.768 \times 27 = 20.7^k$$
$$26 \times 1.2 = \qquad\qquad 31.2^k$$ (b)
$$18 \times 1.2 = \qquad\qquad 21.6^k$$

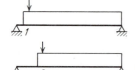

$V = 20.7 \times 3.5 + 31.2 \times 7/8 = 72.5 + 27.3 = 99.8^k$
$I = 50/(189+125) = 0.159$

$V = 20.7 \times 6 \times 7/16 + 31.2 \times 3/4 = 54.3 + 23.4 = 77.7^k$
$I = 50/(162+125) = 0.174$

$V = 20.7 \times 5 \times 3/8 + 31.2 \times 5/8 = 38.8 + 19.5 = 58.3^k$
$I = 50/(135+125) = 0.192$

$V = 20.7 \times 4 \times 5/16 + 31.2 \times 1/2 = 25.9 + 15.6 = 41.5^k$
$I = 50/(108+125) = 0.215$

Truck

$V = 72 \times 1.2 \times 71.67/216 = 28.7^k$ (c)
$I = 50/(81+125) = 0.243$

Uniform load over entire span: $I = 50/(216+125) = 0.147$

Top chords
$U_0 U_1 = 0$
$U_1 U_3 = 72.5 \times 2 - 20.7 \times 1 + 21.6 \times 3/4 \times 2 = -157^k$
$U_3 U_3' = 72.5 \times 4 - 20.7 \times 6 + 21.6 \times 1/2 \times 4 = -209^k$

Bottom chords
$L_0 L_2 = 72.5 \times 1 + 21.6 \times 7/8 \times 1 = +92^k$
$L_2 L_4 = 72.5 \times 3 - 20.7 \times 3 + 21.6 \times 5/8 \times 3 = +196^k$

Diagonals
$L_0 U_1 = 99.8 \sqrt{2} = -142^k$
$U_1 L_2 = 77.7 \sqrt{2} = +110^k$
$L_2 U_3 = 58.3 \sqrt{2} = -83^k$
$U_3 L_4 = 41.5 \sqrt{2} = +59^k$

Verticals
$U_0 L_0 = 32 + 32 \times 13/27 = 47.4 \times 1.2 = -57^k$
$U_2 L_2 = 32 + 40 \times 13/27 = 51.3 \times 1.2 = -62^k$

ELDERSBURG-LOUISVILLE ROAD BRIDGE — DP11-9-1 — 9/15

TRUSS (continued)

Mem.	DL	LL	I	Sdwk LL	Total	L	r	L/r	Allow. stress	Area req'd	Gross	Net*	Eff.†	Section
$U_0\,U_1$					Nom.	27.0								W14×61
$U_1\,U_3$	−504	−157	−23	−28	−712	27.0	4.02	81	14.0	50.9	51.8			W14×176
$U_3\,U_3'$	−672	−209	−31	−38	−950	27.0	4.10	79	14.1	67.3	68.5			W14×233
$L_0\,L_2$	+294	+92	+14	+17	+417	27.0		88	20	20.9	26.5	22.8		W14×90
$L_2\,L_4$	+630	+196	+29	+36	+891	27.0		81	20	44.6	51.8	44.9		W14×176
$L_0\,U_1$	−416	−142	−23	−24	−605	38.18	4.02	114	12.1	50.0	51.8			W14×176
$U_1\,L_2$	+298	+110	+19	+19	+446	38.18		124	20	22.3	26.5	23.7		W14×90
$L_2\,U_3$	−178	−83	−16	−14	−291	38.18	3.81 / 3.71	120 / 124	11.7 / 11.4	24.9 / 25.5	29.1		27.6	W14×99
$U_3\,L_4$	+60	+59	+13	+10	+142	38.18	2.45	187	20	7.1	17.9	15.3		W14×61
$U_0\,L_0$	−46	−57	−17	−3	−119	27.0	2.70 / 2.45	120 / 132	11.7 / 10.7	10.5 / 11.1	17.9		14.8	W14×61
$U_1\,L_1$					Nom.	27.0								W14×30
$U_2\,L_2$	−84	−62	−19	−6	−171	27.0	2.70 / 2.45	120 / 132	11.7 / 10.7	14.6 / 16.0	17.9		14.8	W14×61
$U_3\,L_3$					Nom.	27.0								W14×30
$U_4\,L_4$	−84	−62	−19	−6	−171	27.0	2.70 / 2.45	120 / 132	11.7 / 10.7	14.6 / 16.0	17.9		14.8	W14×61

*Deductions for two 1-in holes in each flange and two 1-in holes in web. No holes in webs of diagonals.

†The actual radius of gyration of members corresponding to the entries in this column is less than that required to give maximum allowable L/r. AASHO specifications allow this provided the required area is not more than an effective area based on the actual value of r (10.7.2). Thus for $L_2\,U_3$, $L/r = 120$ if $r = 3.81$. But for the W14×95, $r = 3.71$. Therefore, the effective area $= 29.1\,(3.71/3.81)^2 = 27.6$ in.² This applies only to compression members, furthermore, it is also required that the allowable load based on properties of the actual area be adequate.

LATERAL BRACING

Wind loads (a)

Railing, parapet & floor $0.29 + 0.21 + 1.92 + 0.67 = 3.09 \ ft^2/ft$
Railing posts $(0.5 \times 2.0 + 1.17 \times 0.33)/6 = 0.23$
Stringers $= 2.0$
½ truss $= \underline{3.0}$ (b)
  8.32

Wind on top chord $= W = 8.32 \times 75 = 624 \ plf$
" " bott. " $= W = 3.0 \times 75 = 225 \ plf$
" " live load $= WL$ $= 100 \ plf$ (c)

Chords

$M = \frac{1}{8} \times 216^2 (0.30 \times 624 + 100) = 1670^{'k}$ (d)
$U_3 U_3' = 1670/20 = 84^k$
$DL + LL^k + I + 84 = 950 + 84 = 1034^k < 1.25 \times 14.1 \times 69.7 = 1230^k$ (e)
$M = \frac{1}{8} \times 216^2 \times 624 = 3630^{'k}$
$U_3 U_3' = 3630/20 = 182^k$
$DL + 182 = 672 + 182 = 854^k < 1230^k$ (e)

Top laterals

20'

D1 Panel shear $= 624 \times 27 \times 3.5 = 59.2^k$ $l = 33.6'$
Diag. stress $= 59.2 \times 33.6/20 = 100^k$ @ $20 = 5.00 \ in^2$ net (f)
  or 50^k @ $11.4 = 4.90 \ in^2$ gross
Use W8×28 : $8.23 - 1.85 = 6.38 \ in^2$ net 12 bolts
For struts $r = 20 \times 12/140 = 1.72$ Use W8×31 12 bolts

Bottom laterals

D1 Stress $= 100 \times 225/624 = 36^k$ @ $20 = 1.80 \ in^2$ net
  $r = 33.6 \times 0.5 \times 12/240 = 0.84$ req'd
  $5 \times 5 \times \frac{5}{16}$ ∠ $3.03 - 0.31 - 0.78 = 1.94 \ in^2$ net 3 bolts (g)
Bottom struts W8×31

Sway frames (at panel points 2, 4, 2')

$l = 33.6'$ $r = 33.6 \times 0.5 \times 12/240 = 0.84$ req'd
  Use $5 \times 5 \times \frac{5}{16}$ ∠

End cross frames

Diag. stress $= 0.624 \times 108 \times 33.6/20 = 113^k$ @ $20 = 5.65 \ in^2$ net
Use W8×28 12 bolts

ELDERSBURG-LOUISVILLE ROAD BRIDGE   DP11-9-1   11/15

TRUSS SHOES

Shoe reaction
1. $DL + LL + I$
   DL 3.11×108 $= 336$ (sheet 6)
   Sdwk $LL = 0.175 \times 108$ $= 19$ (sheet 7)
   LL $(0.64 \times 108 + 18) \times 1.2 = 105$ (sheet 8)
   I 0.147×105 $= \underline{15}$
   475^k/shoe at 100% all. stress

2. $DL + LL + I + 30\% W + WL$
   Wind top chord and WL $0.624 \times 0.3 + 100 = 0.287 \times 29.75 = 8.5$ (a)
   Wind bott. chord 0.225×0.3 $= \underline{0.068} \times 2.75 = \underline{0.2}$
                                      $0.355^k/ft$ $8.7^{'k}/ft$

   Lat. shear $= 0.355 \times 108 = 38.4^k$/shoe
   Mom. $= 8.7 \times 108 = 940^k$
   Shoe reaction $= 475 \pm 940/20 = 522^k$/shoe at 125% all. stress   (b)
                              $= 428^k$/shoe (no uplift)

3. $DL + W$
   Wind top chord $0.624 \times 29.75 = 18.6^k/ft$
   Wind bott. chord $\underline{0.225} \times 2.75 = \underline{0.6}$
                   0.849 $19.2^{'k}/ft$
   Lat. shear $= 0.849 \times 108 = 91.8^k$/shoe
   Mom. $= 19.2 \times 108 = 2070^{'k}$
   Shoe reaction $= 336 \pm 2070/20 = 440^k$/shoe at 125% all. stress
                              $= 232^k$/shoe (no uplift)

4. Long. forces (applied to fixed shoes)
   Traction $0.05 (18 + 0.64 \times 216) = 7.8^k$/shoe   (c)

   $45°$ wind $(DL + LL + I + 30\% W + WL) = \dfrac{0.355}{2} \times \dfrac{216}{2} = 19.2^k$ (d)

   $45°$ wind $(DL + W) = \dfrac{0.849}{2} \times \dfrac{216}{2} = 45.9^k$

Expansion shoes (see dwg. on Sheet 12)
   Assume rocker radius $= 1' - 5''$ Dia. $= 34''$
   All. brg. stress $= 3000 \sqrt{34} (36 - 13)/20 = 20.1^{k/''}$ (e)
   Req'd. lgth. brg. $= 475/20.1 = 23.6''$
   Shear area req'd. $= 91.8 / (14 \times 1.25) = 5.25$ in^2 (f)
   Use $2 - 2'' \phi$ dowels   Area $= 6.28$ in^2
   Req'd. pin brg. area $= 475/14 = 34.0$ in^2
   Req'd. pin dia. $= 34.0/(18 - 3) = 2.26$ in^2 (g)
   Use $4'' \phi$ bearing surface (see figure Sheet 12)
   Req'd. allowance for exp. and contr. $= 1.25 \times 2.16 = 2.7''$ (h)
   Use $7''$ billet for shoe

Expansion shoes   (continued)

   Bearing plate

     Req'd. area = 475/1 = 475 in.² Req'd. width = 23.6 + 4.25 + 8 = 35.9"   (a)

     Try 36 × 20 pl. I = 24,000 in⁴

     Assume max. eccentricity due to contraction = 1.6"   (b)

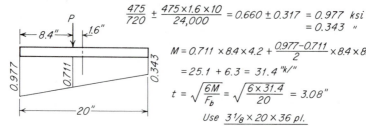

$$\frac{475}{720} \pm \frac{475 \times 1.6 \times 10}{24,000} = 0.660 \pm 0.317 = 0.977 \text{ ksi}$$
$$= 0.343 \text{ "}$$

$$M = 0.711 \times 8.4 \times 4.2 + \frac{0.977 - 0.711}{2} \times 8.4 \times 8.4 \times \tfrac{2}{3}$$

$$= 25.1 + 6.3 = 31.4 \text{ "k/"}$$

$$t = \sqrt{\frac{6M}{F_b}} = \sqrt{\frac{6 \times 31.4}{20}} = 3.08"$$

Use $3\tfrac{1}{8} \times 20 \times 36$ pl.

2∠ 4 × 4 × ⅜

1/2∇

3" shear key

¾" pl.

7" billet

1'-6"

2'-4"

2"⌀ dowels

1'-1¼" to ℄ chord

1'-4½"

3⅛"

¾" pl.

2" rad.

4 × 4 × ½ ∠

17" rad.

Brg. pl. 3⅛ × 20 × 36

Fixed shoes

   Bearing plate

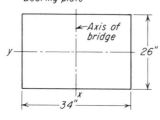

←Axis of bridge

y

26"

x

34"

Trial area 475/0.6 = 792 in²   (c)

Try 26 × 34 pl.   A = 884 in²

$$S_x = \frac{26 \times 34^2}{6} = 5009 \text{ in}^3$$

$$S_y = \frac{34 \times 26^2}{6} = 3831 \text{ in}^3$$

1. DL + LL + I + 30%W + WL + Tr. + Fr. @ 125% all. = 1.25 ksi brg.   (d)

$$\frac{522}{884} \pm \frac{38.4 \times 19.6}{5009} \pm \frac{17.9 \times 19.6}{3831} = 0.591 \pm 0.151 \pm 0.092 = 0.842 \text{ksi}$$ (e)

$$\frac{428}{884} \pm \quad " \quad \pm \quad " \quad = 0.486 \pm 0.151 \pm 0.092 = 0.243 \text{ ksi}$$ (f)

Fixed shoes   (continued)

2. $DL + W$

$$\frac{440}{884} \pm \frac{91.8 \times 19.6}{5009} \pm \frac{10.1 \times 19.6}{3831} = 0.498 + 0.360 + 0.052 = +0.910\,ksi$$

$$\frac{232}{884} \pm \quad '' \quad \pm \quad '' \quad = 0.262 \pm 0.360 \pm 0.052 = +0.674\,ksi$$

$$= -0.150\,ksi \quad (a)$$

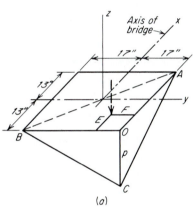

(a)

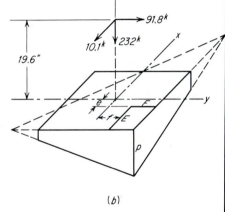

(b)

$$E = \frac{26}{4} = 6.5''$$

$$F = \frac{34}{4} = 8.5''$$

$$p = \frac{3V}{8EF} = \frac{3 \times 232}{8 \times 6.5 \times 8.5} = 1.57\,ksi$$

$$e = \frac{10.1 \times 19.6}{232} = 0.9, \quad f = \frac{91.8 \times 19.6}{232} = 7.8$$

$$E = 13 - 0.9 = 12.1, \quad F = 17 - 7.8 = 9.2$$

$$p = \frac{3 \times 232}{8 \times 12.1 \times 9.2} = 0.780\,ksi$$

3. $45°\ wind\,(DL+LL+I+30\%W+WL+Tr+Fr)$

$\quad$ Shoe react. $= 475 \pm \frac{470}{20} = \begin{array}{l} +499 \\ +451 \end{array}$

$W = 19.2$

$Tr. = 7.8$

$Fr. = \underline{10.1}$

Long. force $= 37.1^k/shoe$

$$\frac{499}{884} \pm \frac{19.2 \times 19.6}{5009} \pm \frac{37.1 \times 19.6}{3831} = 0.565 + 0.075 + 0.190 = +0.830\ ksi$$

$$\frac{451}{884} \pm \quad '' \quad \pm \quad '' \quad = 0.510 - 0.075 - 0.190 = +0.245\ ksi$$

ELDERSBURG - LOUISVILLE ROAD BRIDGE   DP11-9-1 $\frac{14}{15}$

Fixed shoes (continued)

4. 45° wind ($DL + W + Fr.$)

$$\text{Shoe react.} = 336 \pm \frac{1035}{20} = \begin{array}{l} +388 \\ +284 \end{array}$$

$$\begin{array}{r} W = 45.9 \\ Fr. = \underline{10.1} \\ \text{Long. force} = 56\ ^k/\text{shoe} \end{array}$$

$$\frac{388}{884} \pm \frac{45.9 \times 19.6}{5009} \pm \frac{56 \times 19.6}{3831} = 0.439 + 0.180 + 0.287 = +0.906\ ksi$$

$$\frac{284}{884} \pm\quad '' \quad\pm\quad '' \quad = 0.322 \pm 0.180 \pm 0.287 = +0.789\ ksi$$

$$= -0.145\ ksi$$

Since uplift occurs on only one corner, maximum pressure will not exceed +0.789 ksi by enough to approach the allowable pressure of 1.25 ksi   (a)

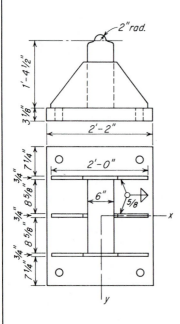

Billet stresses on section at bottom

$$A = 6 \times 18 = 108\ in^2$$

$$S_x = \frac{6 \times 18^2}{6} = 324\ in^3$$

$$S_y = \frac{18 \times 6^2}{6} = 108\ in^3$$

All. stress = $1.25 \times 20 = 25\ ksi$

1. $DL + LL + I + 30\% W + WL + Tr. + Fr.$

$$\frac{522}{108} \pm \frac{38.4 \times 16.5}{324} \pm \frac{17.9 \times 16.5}{108}$$

$$4.83 \pm 1.96 \pm 2.74 = +9.53, +0.13\ ksi$$

3. 45° wind ($DL + LL + I + 30\% W + WL$)

$$\frac{499}{108} \pm \frac{19.2 \times 16.5}{324} \pm \frac{37.1 \times 16.5}{108}$$

$$4.62 \pm 0.98 \pm 5.66 = +11.26, -2.02\ ksi$$

Overturning moment due to longitudinal force taken by diaphragm.

$$I\ billet = 18 \times 6^3/12 \qquad\qquad = 324$$

$$I\ diaphragm = \frac{3 \times 3/4 \times 24^3}{12} - \frac{3/4 \times 6^3}{12} = \underline{2578}$$

$$2902$$

$$\pm \frac{37.1 \times 16.5 \times 12}{2902} = \pm 2.53\ ksi$$

The −2.53 ksi represents uplift on welds at base of diaphragm.

All. stress on welds $2 \times 0.27 \times 58 \times 1.25 \times 0.707 \times 0.625 = 17.3\ kli$

Force per inch of diaphragm = $2.53 \times 1 \times 3/4 = 1.90\ kli < 17.3$

ELDERSBURG-LOUISVILLE ROAD BRIDGE   DP11-9-1 | 15/15 |

TRUSS DETAILS

Joint L_0 (Fig. 11-15) $7/8$ A325 bolts   ss = 8.12^k (friction-type connection)
  $L_0 U_1$ W14×176, A = 51.8 in^2, F_a = 12.1 ksi, d = 15.25"
    P = -605^k, P_{all} = -626^k, 616/8.12 = 76 bolts

  $L_0 L_2$ W14×90, A_g = 26.5 in^2, A_n = 22.8 in^2, F_t = 20 ksi, d = 14.0"
    P = 417^k, P_{all} = 456^k, P_{av} = 437^k, 437/8.12 = 54 bolts
    1-$11/16$ fill and 1-$5/8$ fill
    2 × 0.688 × 20 = 27.5^k @ 8.12 = 4 bolts required before
        4 holes can be deducted from flange   (a)

  $U_0 L_0$ W14×61, A = 17.9 in^2, A_{eff} = 14.8 in^2, F_a = 11.7 ksi, d = 13.91"
    P = -119^k, P_{all} = -173^k, P_{av} = 149^k, 149/8.12 = 19 bolts
    2-$11/16$ fills

          Bolts to W14×61 stub   (b)
  Vert. comp. $L_0 U_1$ 605 × 0.707 = 430^k
  Approx. load from $U_0 L_0$ 62^k (c)
                                           ────
                                           492^k
  Gusset plates in brg. = 2 × 10 × $5/8$ × 20 = 250
                                          ────────
                                          242^k/8.12 = 30 bolts

  Stress in $5/8$ gusset plate
    Shear on vertical section 430/(0.625 × 2 × 43) = 8.0 ksi   (d)

  Ecc. load on horizontal section at end of diagonal   (e)
    P = 430 + 62 - 12 × 8.12 = 395^k
    A = 40 × 0.625 × 2 = 50.0 in^2
    I = 2 × 0.625 × 40^3/12 = 6667 in^4 e = 4"
    $\frac{395}{50} \pm \frac{395 \times 4 \times 20}{6667}$ = 7.9 ± 4.8 = 12.7 ksi

Joint U_1 (Fig. 11-16)
  $U_1 U_3$ W14×176, A = 51.8 in^2, F_a = 14.0 ksi, d = 15.25"
    P = -712^k, P_{all} = -726^k, P_{av} = 719^k, 719/8.12 = 89 bolts

  $L_0 U_1$ W14×176, d = 15.25", 76 bolts

  $U_1 L_2$ W14×99, A_g = 29.1 in^2, A_n = 26.0 in^2, F_t = 20 ksi, d = 14.12"
    P = 446^k, P_{all} = 520^k, 483/8.12 = 59 bolts, 2-$9/16$ fills

  $U_0 U_1$ W14×61, A_g = 17.9 in^2, A_{eff} = 14.8 in^2, F_a = 11.7 ksi, d = 13.91"
    P = 0, P_{all} = 17.9 × 11.7 × 0.75 = 155^k, 155/8.12 = 20 bolts   (f)
    1-$5/8$ fill, 1-$11/16$ fill

  $U_1 L_1$ W14×61, A_g = 17.9 in^2, A_n = 15.3 in^2, F_t = 20 ksi, d = 13.91"
    P = 0, P_{all} = 15.3 × 20 × 0.75 = 230^k, 230/8.12 = 28 bolts   (g)
    1-$5/8$ fill, 1-$11/16$ fill

edition of the AASHTO specifications, but otherwise the calculations are substantially the same as those of the Greiner Company. The following comments are identified by letters corresponding to those alongside the computations on the design sheets. Pertinent clauses in the AASHTO specifications are noted in parentheses.

Sheet 2

a. These calculations determine the location of the center of gravity and the weight of the structure that overhangs the outside stringer. Moment arms are measured (in feet) from the centerline of the stringer.
b. The sidewalk is designed as a continuous slab, using the clear span between supports. The dead load consists of the weights of the parapet and sidewalk. The live load is 85 psf (3.14.1.1). The minimum concrete cover measured from the top of the slab is 2 in (8.22.1).

Sheet 3

a. Spans of roadway slab were discussed in Art. 11-6. A 9-in flange width for the stringer was assumed.
b. The dead-load and live-load moments are taken to be 80 percent of the corresponding moments for a simply supported slab. The formula for the live-load moment [Eq. (11-2)] is given by the specifications (3.24.3.1).
c. The allowance for impact is the fraction of the live load given by $I = 50/(L + 125)$, in which L is the length in feet of the portion of the span that is loaded to produce the maximum stress in the member. The maximum value of I is 0.3 (3.8.2.1).
d. The roadway slab is 8 in thick and is reinforced for positive moment with no. 5 bars 6 in on centers. Allowances of $\frac{3}{4}$ in for wearing surface and at least $1\frac{1}{2}$ in of protective covering for the reinforcement are provided. The calculated stresses compare favorably with the allowable values, 20 ksi for the reinforcement and 1.2 ksi for the concrete.
e. The sidewalk and parapet are supported on concrete pedestals 14 in wide on 6-ft centers, as shown in the sketch on sheet 2. The pedestals are supported in turn on the cantilevered portion of the roadway slab. The width of slab over which the stresses can be considered to be distributed uniformly is not known; however, it is certainly more than the width of the pedestal but less than the distance between pedestals. The effective width is assumed to be 4 ft.
f. This is the dead load computed on sheet 2.
g. This is the weight of the 4-ft section of slab which is assumed to support the pedestal.
h. The live load on the curb is a lateral force representing the effect of a vehicle striking the curb and is assumed to act at the top of the curb (3.14.2.1). It should be noted that since the curb load is lateral, the shear on the section of

slab under consideration is only $3.17 + 1.00 + 1.53 = 5.70$ kips. This is so small that the shearing stress need not be computed.

i. The slab is reinforced for negative moment by bending up alternate positive-moment bars and supplementing them with no. 5 bars 12 in on centers.

Sheet 4

a. To calculate the dead load supported by the exterior stringer, the slab is assumed to act as a simple beam supported by the exterior stringer and the first interior stringer. The sketch and other information on sheet 2 will help to clarify these computations.

b. This is the wheel-load distribution formula of 3.23.2.3.1.5.

c. The stringers span 27 ft (see sketch on sheet 6).

d. The quantities 47.4 and 237 are taken from the table of maximum moments, shears, and reactions per lane of load (AASHTO specifications, appendix A). These values are easy to compute. For shear (Fig. 11-8*a*) $R = 32 + 32 \times 13/27 = 47.4$ kips. For moment (Fig. 11-8*b*) $M = 64 \times 10 \times 10/27 = 237$ ft·kips. Since the wheels on only one side of the truck are effective for the exterior stringer, the shear and moment for this stringer are one-half the values for the lane load.

e. Since the outside stringer supports sidewalk live load as well as traffic live load and impact, the allowable stress may be increased 25 percent (3.23.2.3.1.3).

f. Camber is secured by cold-gagging the beam in the fabricating shop. Since small cambers may not be permanent, camber is usually not specified if the dead-load deflection is less than the minimum camber that is likely to remain permanent. According to the AISC Manuals, camber less than about $\frac{3}{4}$ in is not likely to be permanent for this beam.

g. The distribution of wheel loads to stringers was discussed in Art. 11-7. In this case, the fraction of one wheel load supported by one stringer is given by Eq. (11-3) [(3.23.2.3.1.5)].

h. Since the sidewalk produces an uplift on the first interior stringer, a check is made to determine whether the reduction in bending moment on this stringer is enough to justify a lighter shape. The design of the stringers assuming the weight of the sidewalk, curb, and railing to be equally distributed to all four stringers (3.23.2.3.1.5) is as follows.

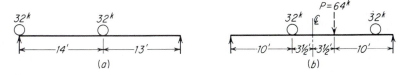

FIGURE 11-8

Interior stringer:

Floor slab	$100 \times 7 = 700$
Sidewalk and parapet	$528/4 = 132$
Stringer	$= \ \ 80$
	$\overline{912}$

Fraction of wheel load to stringer $= \dfrac{7}{5.5} = 1.27$

Shear		**Moment**	
DL:	$0.9 \times 13.5 \qquad = 12.3$	$\frac{1}{8} \times 0.91 \times 27^2 = \ \ 83$
LL:	$1.27 \times 47.4 \times \frac{1}{2} = 30.1$	$1.27 \times 237 \times \frac{1}{2} = 151$
I:	$0.30 \times 30.1 \qquad = \ \ 9.0$	$0.30 \times 151 \qquad = \ \ 45$
	$\overline{V = 51.4 \text{ kips}}$	$\overline{M = 279 \text{ ft·kips}}$

$$\frac{I}{c} = \frac{279 \times 12}{20} = 167 \text{ in}^3 \qquad \text{W24} \times 76$$

Exterior stringer:

Sidewalk and parapet		$528/4 \ = 132$
Floor slab	$\dfrac{100 \times 9.5 \times 4.75 - 44.5 \times 8.87}{7}$	$= 587$
Stringer		$= \ \ 82$
		$\overline{801}$

Sidewalk $LL = 310$ lb/ft

Fraction of wheel load to stringer $= 1.22$

DL	$0.801 \times 13.5 \qquad = 10.8$	$\frac{1}{8} \times 0.801 \times 27^2 = \ \ 73$
Sidewalk *LL*	$0.310 \times 13.5 \qquad = \ \ 4.2$	$\frac{1}{8} \times 0.310 \times 27^2 = \ \ 28$
LL	$1.22 \times 47.4 \times \frac{1}{2} = 28.9$	$1.22 \times 237 \times \frac{1}{2} = 145$
I	$0.30 \times 28.9 \qquad = \ \ 8.7$	$0.30 \times 145 \qquad = \ \ 43$
	$\overline{V = 52.6 \text{ kips}}$	$\overline{M = 289 \text{ ft·kips}}$

$$\frac{I}{c} = \frac{289 \times 12}{20 \times 1.25} = 138.7 \text{ in}^3$$

A W21 × 68 provides sufficient strength. However, AASHTO specifications require that the outside stringer provide a carrying capacity not less than that of the interior stringer. Therefore a W24 × 76 is required.

Sheet 5

a. The part of the live load in each lane that is supported by the floor beam consists of the 32-kip rear axle, directly over the floor beam, and an 8-kip front axle and a 32-kip trailer axle each 14 ft from the floor beam.

b. In this calculation the number 1.40 is the combined weight, in kips, of the sidewalk, parapet, floor slab, and stringer, taken from sheet 4. The floor beam is assumed to weigh 0.11 klf. Figure 11-9 shows how the weight of the floor beam is converted to a statically equivalent system of forces acting at the points of attachment of the stringers.

c. In the computation for this stringer the uplift from the cantilevered sidewalk is taken into account.

d. Figure 11-10 explains the calculations for the live-load reactions of the stringers on the floor beam. The floor slab is assumed to act as a series of 7-ft simple beams.

e. The slab overhangs the end floor beam a distance of 1.25 ft. Therefore, the maximum live load on the end floor beam will result with the truck placed so that the trailer axle is at the tip of the overhang.

Sheet 6

a. In this calculation the factor 1.02 provides an allowance of 2 percent for the weight of bolt heads, nuts, details, paint, etc. In the next line, the factor 1.20

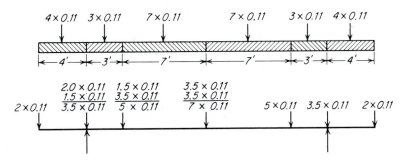

FIGURE 11-9

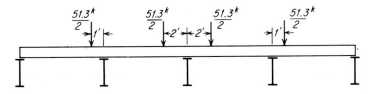

FIGURE 11-10

provides an allowance of 20 percent for the weight of stringer connection angles and floor-beam details, paint, etc.

b. The forces in the bars of the truss are computed by the method of index stresses.

Sheet 7

a. Since the structure supports cantilevered sidewalks, maximum stresses in the truss members will occur with only one sidewalk loaded. The specifications allow a reduction in the intensity of live load if a long stretch of sidewalk is to be loaded (3.24.1.1). This is because of the improbability that it will be fully loaded. For loaded lengths ranging from 26 to 100 ft the live load is 60 psf, while for loaded lengths in excess of 100 ft it is given by the equation

$$P = \left(30 + \frac{3000}{L}\right)\frac{55 - W}{50}$$

where P = load, psf (not to exceed 60 psf)
   L = loaded length, ft
   W = width of sidewalk, ft

The various lengths of load considered here are chosen so as to give maximum stresses. The approximate method, based on the assumption that full panel loads exist at all panel points to the right of a given panel, with none to the left, is used. For example, the load extending from the right end of the bridge leftward to panel point 1 gives full panel loads at joints 2 to 1' inclusive and half panel loads at 1 and 0'. The half panel load at joint 1 is neglected. This is the position of load for maximum stress in $U_1 L_2$.

Sheet 8

a. For the purpose of determining the live load on the truss, the roadway is assumed to be divided into two traffic lanes of equal width (3.6.2). The truck or lane loads are assumed to occupy a width of 10 ft (3.6.1) and are placed each within its own traffic lane but in such a position as to produce the maximum load on the truss. The resulting position of load for the 28-ft roadway is shown in Fig. 11-11.

b. The AASHTO specifies that either the truck load or the lane load be used, whichever produces the larger stress. The lane load consists of a uniform load of 0.64 klf together with a concentrated load to be positioned for maximum effect. A concentrated load of 26 kips must be used if a shearing force is being determined, while for moment a concentrated load of 18 kips is to be used.

c. The truck load is shown here in position to produce a maximum compressive force in $L_4 U_3'$. The object is to determine whether there can be a reversal of stress in this member. Since the live-load shear including impact is less than

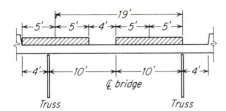

FIGURE 11-11

the dead-load shear for this panel, which was computed on sheet 6, no reversal occurs.

Sheet 9. The W14's chosen for this truss range in depth from 13.86 to 16.12 in. Differences are taken care of at the joints by fillers (sheet 15). Three of the members have only nominal loads; i.e., their calculated loads are zero. The lightest available W is used for all these members except in the case of $U_0 U_1$. The flange of the W14 × 30 is only 6.73 in wide; the difference between it and the adjacent 15.65 in flange of $U_1 U_3$ would have been considerable. Hence the lightest shape in the 14 × 10 series, the W14 × 61, is used for $U_0 U_1$.

Sheet 10

a. AASHTO specifications require that bridge trusses be designed for a wind pressure of 75 psf. The specifications further require total forces of not less than 300 plf and 150 plf in the plane of the loaded chord and the plane of the unloaded chord, respectively. Since gusts can be relatively concentrated, it is assumed that only part of the structure may be subject to wind pressure. Therefore, the wind is assumed to act on whatever area will result in the maximum force in a particular member. For this reason, wind pressure is usually referred to as a "moving" load (3.15).

b. The area of the truss is estimated by considering the exposed area of its members plus an allowance for gusset plates.

c. Wind pressure on the live load is 100 psf (3.15.1.2).

d. Only 30 percent of the wind force on the structure need be taken in combination with wind on the live load.

e. Allowable stresses may be increased 25 percent for combinations of dead load, live load, impact, and wind. Thus, if the sum of $DL + LL + I +$ wind or of $DL +$ wind is less than 1.25 times the allowable force in the member at the nominal allowable stress, the member is acceptable.

f. Here the lateral truss is assumed to act as a single-diagonal truss, with only the diagonal member that is subjected to tension considered to be active. In the next line, the truss is assumed to be a double-diagonal system, with each diagonal resisting half the shear in the panel. The allowable compressive stress is taken to be that for $L/r = 120$. Although the wind loads for D2, D3, and D4 will be successively smaller than that in D1, the W8 × 28 is used throughout.

g. To determine the net area, deduction is made for one bolt hole in the connected leg and for half the area of the unconnected leg (10.9.1).

Sheet 11

a. Resultant wind forces are assumed to act at the centerlines of the chords. The base of the bearing plate is 2 ft $8\frac{7}{8}$ in, or 2.75 ft, below the centerline of the bottom chord (see sketch on sheet 12).

b. The trusses are spaced 20 ft apart.

c. Fixed shoes are designed for a longitudinal force of 5 percent of the live load in all lanes, using the uniform lane loads plus the 18-kip concentrated load, with no impact (3.9).

d. Although it is not required by the specifications, a quarterly wind is assumed to act as shown in Fig. 11-12. The component parallel to the bridge is resisted by the fixed shoes.

e. The allowable bearing pressure on rollers and rockers is given by Eqs. (11-5).

f. The dowels which hold the rocker in place on the base plate must transmit the lateral shear of 91.8 kips.

g. The length of the bearing surface is 18 in, as shown in the sketch on sheet 12. Deduction is made for the 3-in shear key shown in the figure. Note that a pin is not used; instead, the billet is machined to a semicylindrical surface.

h. The specifications require an allowance for expansion and contraction (10.11) unless provision for thermal induced stresses are made. Allowance is made here for 1.25 in per 100 ft of span.

Sheet 12

a. The required bearing length of the rocker is 23.6 in (sheet 11). The slots in the rocker for the 2-in dowels are $2\frac{1}{8}$ in, and 4 × 4 angles are used to fasten the rocker to the base plate, as shown on the sketch.

b. Since it is assumed that the reaction of the truss on the shoe is centered on the base plate at an approximate mean temperature, the 2.7-in allowance for expansion and contraction determined on sheet 11 is assumed to be about equally divided between expansion and contraction.

c. A trial area of the bearing plate is found by using the reaction for the first load combination on sheet 11. Since this is not the worst condition of loading, the bearing pressure on the concrete is assumed at only 0.6 ksi instead of the

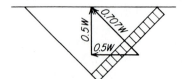

FIGURE 11-12

allowable value 1 ksi. The guessed size of the plate is then checked for various combinations of load.

d. The load combination here is that of the second group on sheet 11 together with traction and roller friction from the fourth group. The 38.4-kip force from the second group is a lateral force; i.e., it is parallel to the y axis of the bearing plate. This lateral force and the longitudinal force from traction and roller friction are assumed to act at the centerline of the pin, which is $19\frac{5}{8}$ in above the base. Note that these forces have the same value for the shoe on the leeward side of the bridge as for the windward shoe, while the vertical reaction from group 2 is 522 kips on the leeward shoe but only 428 kips on the windward shoe.

e. This is the largest bearing pressure under the leeward shoe. However, we must check to see that the combination of the plus and the two minus signs does not result in a minus value, since this would mean that only part of the area of the plate bears on the masonry and this is contrary to the assumption on which the calculation is based. Inspection of the figures shows that there is no uplift.

f. The only reason for investigating the windward shoe is that uplift is more likely here, so that even though the vertical reaction is smaller, the bearing pressure might be larger than for the leeward shoe. Using both minus signs, we get +0.243 ksi. Therefore no uplift occurs, and there is no need to compute the maximum bearing pressure on this shoe.

Sheet 13

a. The load combination considered here produces uplift. Computing the bearing pressures at the four corners of the plate (Fig. 11-13), we find uplift indicated to the left of AB. Since this represents a sizable inactive area, the maximum bearing pressure may exceed the value 0.674 ksi by a considerable margin. Assume that a line of zero pressure extends diagonally across the plate, as in Fig. a of sheet 13. The resultant pressure passes through the centroid of the

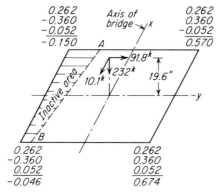

FIGURE 11-13

pressure pyramid $OABC$. But for a pyramid whose edges OA, OB, and OC are mutually perpendicular, the coordinates E and F of the centroid are one-fourth of the distances OA and OB, respectively. In terms of these coordinates, the volume of the pyramid is given by $V = 8pEF/3$. For the reaction of 232 kips, we find from this equation $p = 1.57$ ksi, as calculated on sheet 13. The required location of the 232-kip resultant bearing pressure is found by computing the eccentricities e and f in Fig. b of sheet 13. Then $E = 12.1$ in, and $F = 9.2$ in. Since both these values are larger than those computed previously, we know that the resultant force in Fig. a is too far from the center of the plate. Therefore, the actual maximum bearing pressure must be less than 1.57 ksi. Since a pressure pyramid corresponding to $E = 12.1$ and $F = 9.2$ extends beyond the corners of the plate, as shown in Fig. b, the actual maximum bearing pressure must be more than the value of p corresponding to this pyramid. We assume then that the maximum bearing pressure lies between 0.780 and 1.57 ksi, and since the allowable value is 1.25 ksi, we decide that the bearing plate is adequate for this combination of forces.

Sheet 14

a. The pressures at the four corners of the plate for this combination of forces are shown in Fig. 11-14.

Sheet 15

a. There are four rows of bolts in each flange (Fig. 11-15). Two holes were deducted from each flange in determining the net section of the tension members (sheet 9).

b. The calculation here is to determine the number of bolts needed to connect the gusset plates at L_0 to the short piece of W14 × 61 that bears on the soleplate (Fig. 11-15).

c. Since the positions of live load for maximum effect are not the same for $U_0 L_0$ and $L_0 U_1$, the 119-kip force in $U_0 L_0$ does not occur simultaneously with the

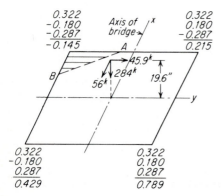

FIGURE 11-14

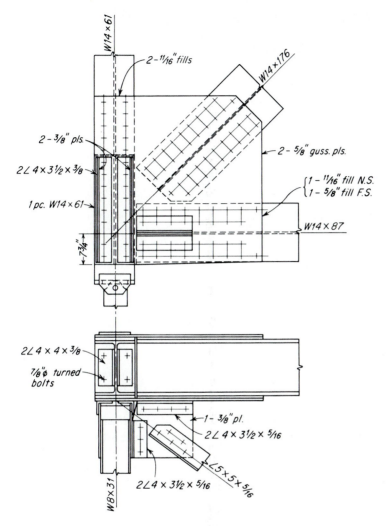

FIGURE 11-15
Detail at L_0, Eldersburg–Louisville Road Bridge.

605-kip force in $L_0 U_1$. The value here is estimated, although it could be determined by calculating the force in $U_0 L_0$ with the live load in position for maximum stress in $L_0 U_1$.

d. This is the calculated shearing stress on a vertical section through the gusset plates just to the left of $L_0 L_1$ (Fig. 11-15). A discussion of the assumptions that are usually made in analyzing gusset plates is given in Art. 3-17.

e. The section here is taken horizontally through the end of $L_0 U_1$ at its centerline (Fig. 11-15). The load on this section from the upper portion of the gusset plates is the vertical component of $L_0 U_1$ plus the 62-kip load in $U_0 L_0$.

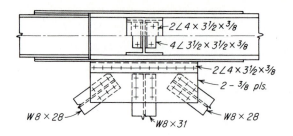

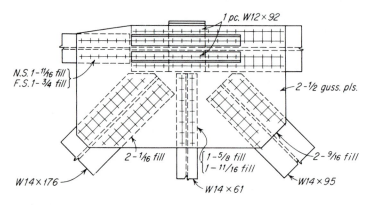

FIGURE 11-16
Detail at U_1, Eldersburg–Louisville Road Bridge.

f. Since there is no calculated load in this member, the number of bolts must satisfy the requirement that no connection be designed for less than 75 percent of the allowable load (10.19.1.1).

Joint U_1 is shown in Fig. 11-16. The splice of $L_0 L_2$ to $L_2 L_4$ is designed in DP3-15-3 and shown in Fig. 3-35.

11-10 BEAM BRIDGES

The highway beam bridge is widely used because of its simplicity of design and construction. The bridge consists of a series of parallel steel beams (stringers) supporting a continuous reinforced-concrete slab. The construction may be either composite or noncomposite. The stringers may be W's, W's reinforced with cover plates, or plate girders. They are usually spaced 5 to 8 ft on centers. The multiple-span beam bridge may be continuous over its piers or may consist of a series of simply supported spans. The two-lane bridge usually has at least four stringers. Since the beam bridge is essentially a bridge floor in which abutments and piers replace the floor beams of the truss bridge, the procedures discussed in Art. 11-7 apply also to it. Thus, unless the construction is composite, all the information needed for the design of the beam bridge has already been covered. The remainder of this chapter will be devoted to a discussion of design procedures for the composite-beam bridge and, as an illustrative example, the design of the beams for the 70-ft approach spans of the Eldersburg–Louisville Road Bridge.

11-11 COMPOSITE-BEAM BRIDGES

The behavior and design of composite beams is discussed in Chap. 5, where it is shown that a reinforced-concrete floor supported on steel beams can be designed as a system of parallel T beams, provided the slab is mechanically bonded to the beam. This bond is provided by stud or channel shear connectors, which are discussed in Art. 5-22. With the beam spacing and slab thickness common to highway bridges, considerable savings in weight of steel may be realized by reinforcing the bottom flange with a cover plate or by using a welded unsymmetrical I.

Since the spacing of the beams of a beam bridge is a function of the width of the roadway and the number of beams, and since the thickness of the slab depends in turn upon the spacing of the beams, this much is known when the proportioning of the beam itself is begun. Except for tables of cross-sectional properties and allowable loads, however, there is no direct procedure for determining the size of a composite beam. Procedures for preliminary design are given in Ref. 4.

In the usual case of the beam bridge built without shoring, the dead load of the beams and slab is supported by the steel beam alone. Therefore, there is no stress in the concrete due to this load, and the section modulus of the beam itself determines the stresses. Since the live load is supported by composite action, the stresses from this source are determined from the modulus of the transformed section. Properties of the transformed section are determined in the usual way, assuming elastic behavior. According to the AASHTO specifications, the effective width of the slab as a T-beam flange is as follows.

For an interior beam, the smallest of:

1. One-fourth of the span of the beam
2. The center-to-center distance of beams
3. Twelve times the least thickness of the slab

For a beam having a flange on only one side, the smallest of:

1. One-twelfth of the span of the beam
2. Half the center-to-center distance of the adjacent beam
3. Six times the thickness of the slab

Sidewalks, curbs, railings, and wearing surface are usually added after the slab is built, and the weight of this additional construction produces a sustained compressive stress that may result in plastic flow of the slab. An allowance for this effect can be made by using a section modulus based on an increased value of the modular ratio n; the value $3n$ is usually recommended.

11-12   LENGTH OF COVER PLATES

A formula for the length of cover plates for a uniformly loaded composite beam can be determined as follows. The bending stresses f at midspan and f' at the cross section where the cover plate ends are

$$f = \frac{wL^2}{8S_c} \qquad f' = \frac{w(L^2 - L'^2)}{8S'_c}$$

where L = span
  L' = length of cover plate
  S_c = section modulus of composite beam at midspan
  S'_c = section modulus of composite beam without cover plate

Assuming both cross sections stressed to their allowable values, $f = f'$, and dividing the second equation by the first and simplifying the result, we get

$$\frac{L'}{L} = \sqrt{1 - \frac{S'_c}{S_c}} \tag{11-7}$$

Equation (11-7) is on the unsafe side for beams that support moving concentrated loads. For this case, the equation may be modified as explained in Art. 7-6. However, the following procedure is more conservative. Figure 11-17a shows the wheels of an H truck of the AASHTO specifications placed in position for maximum moment. The corresponding moment diagram, including the effect of a uniform dead load, is $ABCD$ in Fig. 11-17b. If we assume that the segment AB is a parabola with vertex at B, Eq. (11-7) may be used to determine the distance from B to the left end of the cover plate. To this must be added the distance $a/2$ from B to the midpoint of the span. Thus, to get the half length $L'/2$ of the cover

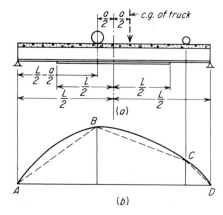

(b)   **FIGURE 11-17**

TABLE 11-1

H load		HS load	
Span, ft	a, ft	Span, ft	a, ft
Less than 26.5	0	Less than 23.9	0
Greater than 26.5	2.8	Between 23.9 and 33.8	7
		Greater than 33.8	4.7

plate, we add $a/2$ to the value obtained by substituting $L/2 - a/2$ for L in Eq. (11-7). The resulting value of L' is given by

$$L' = a + (L - a)\sqrt{1 - \frac{S_c'}{S_c}} \qquad (11\text{-}8)$$

Values of a for the truck loads of the AASHTO specifications are given in Table 11-1. For spans shorter than 26.5 ft, maximum moment occurs under the rear wheel of the H truck, so the wheel is at midspan and $a = 0$. For spans longer than 26.5 ft, maximum moment occurs with the loads in the position shown in Fig. 11-17a, and $a = 2.8$ ft. The three axles of the HS truck result in three possibilities. For spans less than 23.9 ft, maximum moment occurs with one wheel at midspan and $a = 0$. For spans ranging from 23.9 to 33.8 ft, maximum moment occurs with the two equally heavy trailer axles on the span, and $a = 7$ ft. For spans longer than 33.8 ft, maximum moment occurs when three axles are on the span, and $a = 4.7$ ft.

The cover plate must be extended beyond the theoretical cutoff point and attached adequately. According to AASHTO, this extension must be at least twice the width of the plate if it is not welded across the end and $1\frac{1}{2}$ times the width if it is so welded. The weld connecting the plate within the length of this extension must be sufficient to develop the force in the plate corresponding to the computed stress at the theoretical cutoff point, where the stress is computed for the cross section including the cover plate. Thus, if M is the bending moment at the theoretical cutoff point, we have

$$M = F_b S_c' \qquad (a)$$

where F_b is the allowable bending stress and S_c' is the section modulus without the cover plate. The stress f at this cross section, with the cover plate included, is

$$f = \frac{M}{S_c} \qquad (b)$$

where S_c is the modulus of the cross section with the cover plate. Therefore, the force P on which the required weld is based is

$$P = fA = \frac{M}{S_c} A = F_b A \frac{S_c'}{S_c} \qquad (11\text{-}9)$$

ELDERSBURG-LOUISVILLE ROAD BRIDGE   DP11–14–1   1/4

Span 70'-0". Beams spaced 7'-0" on centers
    BEAM   B   (See plan Sheet 4)
 Dead load
    Slab (7¼") = 7 × 150 × 7.25/12 = 0.634 klf
    Beam $\underline{0.226\ klf}$
                         0.860 klf
    Wearing surface (2"bituminous) = 0.175 klf
 Live load
    Fraction wheel load to beam = 7/5.5 = 1.27
    $I = \dfrac{50}{125 + 70} = 0.256$

	Shear		Moment	

  LL 1.27× 62.4 × ½ = 39.7ᵏ   1.27× 985.6 × ½ = 626 ᵏ
  I   0.256 × 39.7 $=\underline{\ 10.2\ }$ 0.256 × 626 $=\underline{\ 160\ }$ᵏ
                     49.9ᵏ   786 × 12 = 9,450"ᵏ
  DL 0.86 × 35   = 30.1ᵏ   ⅛ × 0.86 × 70² = 527 × 12 = 6,320"ᵏ
  Wear. sur. 0.175 × 35 = 6.1ᵏ   ⅛ × 0.175 × 70² = 107 × 12 = 1280"ᵏ

  Properties of section

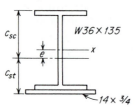

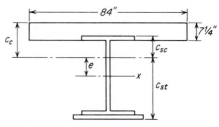

                        14 × ¾

 Beam and flange plate

Section	Area	Mom. abt. x	I_x	
W36 × 135	39.8	0	× 3.80² =	574
14 × ¾	$\underline{10.5}$	×(−18.15) = $\underline{-191}$	× 14.35² =	2160
	50.3	$\underline{\|-191}$		$\underline{7820}$
		e = −3.80in		10,554 in⁴

    C_{sc} = 3.80 + 35.55/2 = 21.58 in C_{st} = 17.78 − 3.80 + 0.75 = 14.73 in

 Beam, flange plate and slab (n = 10)

Section	Area	Mom. abt. x	I_x	
W36 × 135	39.8		× 9.58² = 3650	
14 × ¾	10.5	×(−18.15) = − 191	× 27.73² = 8060	
84 × 7.25/10	$\underline{60.9}$	×(+20.60) = $\underline{+1254}$	× 11.03² = 7400	
	111.2	$\underline{\|+1063}$	7820	
		e = + 9.58 in	$\underline{\ 268\ }$	
			27,198 in⁴	

    C_{sc} = 17.78 − 9.58 = 8.20in C_{st} = 17.78 + 9.58 + 0.75 = 28.11 in
    C_c = 8.20 + 7.25 − 0.79 = 14.66in

ELDERSBURG-LOUISVILLE ROAD BRIDGE   DP11-14-1 2/4

Properties of section (continued)

Beam, flange plate and slab (n = 30)

Section	Area	Mom. abt. x	I_x
W36 × 135	39.8		× 3.22^2 = 411
14 × 3/4	10.5	× (− 18.15) = − 191	× 21.37^2 = 4780
84 × 7.25/30	20.3	× (+ 20.60) = +418	× 17.39^2 = 6120
	70.6	$\boxed{+227}$	7820
		e = +3.22 in	89
			19,220 in^4

$c_{sc} = 17.78 - 3.22 = 14.56$ in $c_{st} = 17.78 + 3.22 + 0.75 = 21.75$ in
$c_c = 14.56 + 7.25 - 0.79 = 21.02$ in

Beam and slab (n = 10)

Section	Area	Mom. abt. x	I_x
W36 × 135	39.8		× 12.48^2 = 6183
84 × 7.25/10	60.9	× (+20.60) = +1254	× 8.13^2 = 4025
	100.7	$\boxed{+1254}$	7820
		e = 12.48 in	268
			18,296 in^4

$c_{sc} = 17.78 - 12.48 = 5.30$ in
$c_c = 5.30 + 7.25 - 0.79 = 11.76$ in $c_{st} = 17.78 + 12.48 = 30.26$ in

Maximum bending stresses

$$f_{sc} = \frac{9450 \times 8.20}{27,198} + \frac{6320 \times 21.58}{10,554} + \frac{1280 \times 14.56}{19,220} = 16.72 \, ksi$$

$$f_{st} = \frac{9450 \times 28.11}{27,198} + \frac{6320 \times 14.73}{10,554} + \frac{1280 \times 21.75}{19,220} = 20.03 \, ksi$$

$$f_c = \frac{9450 \times 14.66}{10 \times 27,198} + \frac{1280 \times 21.02}{30 \times 19,220} = 0.56 \, ksi$$

Length of cover plate

$$l = a + (L-a) \sqrt{1 - \frac{S_c'}{S_c}}$$

$a = 4.67$ ft $S_c' = 18,296/30.26 = 607$ in^3 $S_c = 27,198/28.11 = 967$ in^3

$$l = 4.67 + (70 - 4.67) \sqrt{1 - \frac{607}{967}} = 44.7 \, ft$$

Force in cover plate at theoretical end

$$P = F_b A \frac{S_c'}{S_c} = 20 \times 10.5 \times \frac{607}{967} = 132^k$$

Length 5/16-in fillet weld

$$l = \frac{132}{0.27 \times 58 \times 0.707 \times 5/16} = 39''$$

Use cover plate 3/4 × 14 × 47'-3"

ELDERSBURG-LOUISVILLE ROAD BRIDGE $\qquad$ *DP11-14-1* $\frac{3}{4}$

Shear connectors
  Vertical shear

$\qquad$ End: $I = \dfrac{50}{70+125} = 0.256$

$\qquad V_{max} = \left[16 + \dfrac{7.0}{5.5}\left(16 + \dfrac{70-14}{70} + 4 \times \dfrac{70-28}{70}\right)\right] \times 1.256 = 44.3^k$

$\qquad V_{min} = Q$

$\qquad$ 10 ft from end: $I = \dfrac{50}{60+125} = 0.27$

$\qquad V_{max} = \dfrac{7.0}{5.5}\left(16 \times \dfrac{60}{70} + 16 \times \dfrac{60-14}{70} + 4 \times \dfrac{60-28}{70}\right) \times 1.27 = 42.1^k$

$\qquad V_{min} = -\dfrac{7.0}{5.5} \times 4 \times \dfrac{10}{70} \times 1.30 = -0.90^k$

$\qquad$ 20 ft from end: $I = \dfrac{50}{50+125} = 0.286$

$\qquad V_{max} = \dfrac{7.0}{5.5}\left(16 \times \dfrac{50}{70} + 16 \dfrac{50-14}{70} + 4 \times \dfrac{50-28}{70}\right) \times 1.286 = 34.2^k$

$\qquad V_{min} = -\dfrac{7.0}{5.5}\left(4 \times \dfrac{20}{70} + 16 \times \dfrac{6}{70}\right) \times 1.30 = -4.2^k$

$\qquad$ 30 ft from end: $I = \dfrac{50}{40+125} = 0.30$

$\qquad V_{max} = \dfrac{7.0}{5.5}\left(16 \times \dfrac{40}{70} + 16 \times \dfrac{40-14}{70} + 4 \times \dfrac{40-28}{70}\right) 1.30 = 26.1^k$

$\qquad V_{min} = -\dfrac{7.0}{5.5}\left(4 \times \dfrac{30}{70} + 16 \times \dfrac{16}{70} + 16 \times \dfrac{2}{70}\right) 1.30 = -9.6^k$

Use groups of two 7/8-in. diameter studs
$\qquad Z_r = 2 \times 10.6 \times 0.875^2 = 16.2^k$

$\qquad$ For beam and slab: $\dfrac{Z_r I}{Q} = \dfrac{16.2 \times 18,296 \times 10}{7.25 \times 84\,(11.76 - 3.62)} = 550$

$\qquad$ For beam, flange plate and slab: $\dfrac{Z_r I}{Q} = \dfrac{16.2 \times 27,198 \times 10}{7.25 \times 84\,(14.66 - 3.62)} = 654$

Spacing
$\qquad$ End $= S = \dfrac{550}{44.3} = 12.4''$

$\qquad$ 10 ft from end: $S = \dfrac{598}{42.1 + 0.9} = 13.9''$

$\qquad$ 20 ft from end: $S = \dfrac{654}{34.2 + 4.2} = 17.1''$

$\qquad$ 30 ft from end: $S = \dfrac{654}{26.1 + 9.6} = 18.3''$

Number connectors for ultimate strength
$\qquad P = A_s F_y = 50.20 \times 36 = 1810^k \quad P = 0.85 f_c' bc = 0.85 \times 3 \times 84 \times 7.25 = 1550^k$
$\qquad S_u = 930 d_s^2 \sqrt{f_c'} = 930 \times 0.875^2 \sqrt{3000} = 39^k$
$\qquad N = \dfrac{P}{0.85\,S_u} = \dfrac{1550}{0.85 \times 39} = 47$ studs
$\qquad$ *Fatigue strength governs*

Spacing
$\qquad$ 20 @ 12 + 10 @ 16 + 2 @ 18 + 10 @ 16 + 20 @ 12
$\qquad$ *Place first row of studs 2in inside span*

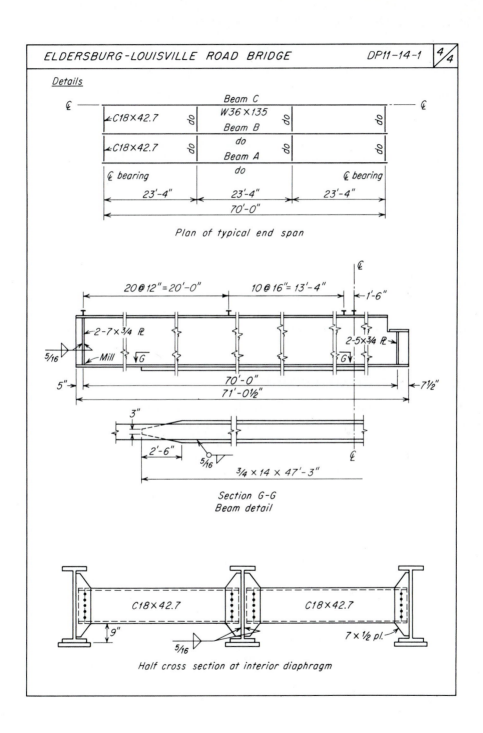

ELDERSBURG-LOUISVILLE ROAD BRIDGE   DP11–14–1   4/4

Details

Plan of typical end span

Section G-G
Beam detail

Half cross section at interior diaphragm

11-13 SHEAR-CONNECTOR SPACING

Shear connectors and their spacing were discussed in Art. 5-24. AASHTO requires connectors equal in number to the smaller of T by Eq. (5-81) and C_1 by Eq. (5-82) divided by 85 percent of the ultimate strength of one connector. The reason for the smaller value was explained in Art. 5-24. Shear-connector strengths are given by Eqs. (5-87a) and (5-87b). AASHTO also requires that shear connectors be spaced so as to protect them from fatigue failure. The range of shear to be considered at any cross section is the difference between the maximum shear and the minimum shear, exclusive of dead load, at the section. The fatigue strengths of channel connectors and of welded studs, in pounds, are:

Number of cycles	Channel	Welded stud
100,000	$4,000w$	$13,000d^2$
500,000	$3,000w$	$10,600d^2$
2,000,000	$2,400w$	$7,850d^2$

An example is given in DP11-14-1.

11-14 DP11-14-1: ELDERSBURG– LOUISVILLE ROAD BRIDGE

The two 70-ft approach spans of the Eldersburg–Louisville Road Bridge (DP11-14-1, sheet 1) are composite-beam bridges. Each span has five beams spaced 7 ft on centers and supporting a concrete slab $7\frac{1}{4}$ in thick topped with a 2-in bituminous wearing surface. Computations for the design of the slab are omitted, since the procedure is a repetition of that for the slab of the truss spans.

Calculations for the bearing stiffeners and the bearing plates shown on the elevation on sheet 4 are omitted in this example.

REFERENCES

1. Elliott, A. L.: Steel and Concrete Bridges, sec. 18, and Wolchuk, R., Steel-Plate-Deck Bridges, sec. 19 in E. H. Gaylord and C. N. Gaylord (eds.), "Structural Engineering Handbook," 3d ed., McGraw-Hill, New York, 1990.
2. Waddell, J. A. L.: Weights of Metal in Steel Trusses, *Trans. ASCE*, vol. 101, 1936.
3. Westergaard, H. M.: Computation of Stresses in Bridge Slabs due to Wheel Loads, *Public Roads*, vol. 11, no. 1, March 1930.
4. Hooper, I., M. A. Grubb, and I. M. Viest: Design of Composite Members, sec. 14 in E. H. Gaylord and C. N. Gaylord (eds.), "Structural Engineering Handbook," 3d ed., McGraw-Hill, New York, 1990.

CHAPTER
12

BUILDINGS

12-1 INDUSTRIAL BUILDINGS

The function of an industrial building is to support and house a manufacturing process or to store the raw materials for (or products of) a manufacturing process. Many industrial plants are located in small population centers because of cheaper land, adequate space for parking and future expansion, and the opportunity for providing a pleasing environment away from congested city areas. Other factors which must be considered in the site selection are topography, subsoil conditions, transportation, and utilities.

With the site selected, the planning of the production process and the structure to house it can proceed. Using the total area and volume requirements established for the preliminary planning, the exterior dimensions can be developed. Square or nearly square areas are usually more economical because they require less exterior wall length. Dimensions of individual bays within the structure are often dictated by the manufacturing process. Large, clear areas unobstructed by columns and partitions are desirable so as to provide sufficient flexibility and to facilitate later changes in the production layout without major building alterations. The plan must also allow for future expansion, preferably by expanding the plant on any or all of its four sides without shifting existing production layouts. The single-story industrial building, consisting of a floor slab on grade and a flat-roof superstructure, is the most economical from the standpoint of first cost and maintenance. In most industrial manufacturing processes and

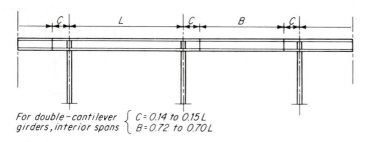

For double-cantilever { C = 0.14 to 0.15 L
girders, interior spans { B = 0.72 to 0.70 L

FIGURE 12-1

warehousing, it is also the most economical from the standpoint of operating cost.

The structural framing scheme may be developed somewhat as described in the following paragraphs. These steps are not dissociated but closely interrelated.

Column rows are located to provide adequate clearance for the production layout. The height of the building will partly determine the economical spacing of column rows, since several tall, closely spaced columns with short-span trusses may require more steel than fewer columns with trusses of longer span. For a structure 180 ft wide, for example, two 90-ft aisles may be more economical than three 60-ft aisles. Wider aisles also allow greater flexibility in future modification of the arrangement of the plant.

For buildings without cranes, bays about 40 × 40 ft are likely to be economical for large square buildings, but for rectangular buildings with a large ratio of perimeter to area, bays about 30 × 30 ft may be better. For buildings with light and medium cranes, bays of about 25 to 30 ft will likely be more economical because of the cost of the crane-runway steel.[1]

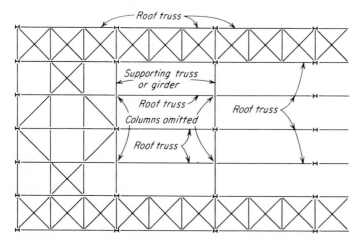

FIGURE 12-2

Steel frames are primarily of two basic types. The first, which is common for short-span layouts, consists of a frame composed of continuous or double-cantilevered girders over the columns in one direction with simple-span bar joists in the other direction (Fig. 12-1). The second consists of trusses framed in the long dimension of the bay with purlins framing between trusses in the short dimension. This system is often used where a long span, say 70 ft or more, is required in one direction while a much shorter span is acceptable in the other direction. Trusses are not likely to be economical for spans less than about 70 ft. If a large bay is needed in only some areas of the building, a bay may be enlarged for the full width of the building or by an arrangement such as the one shown in Fig. 12-2 in which the roof trusses in one or more aisles are supported by transverse girders or trusses instead of by columns.

12-2 RIGID-FRAME BUILDINGS

The rigid-frame bent may be used for the main structural framing of industrial buildings, auditoriums, gymnasiums, churches, and other structures which require large areas unobstructed by columns. The framing is simple to erect and pleasing in appearance. Several types of rigid-frame bents are shown in Fig. 12-3. The moments developed at the connections in these frames reduce the moment at midspan of the transverse members, resulting in lighter and shallower transverse members but heavier column sections. Therefore a rigid frame may require a greater amount of steel than a braced bent of equal rise and span.

Economical spans for single-story single-span rigid frames may range from 30 to about 200 ft. For buildings with average roof load the following spacing of frames will usually prove economical:

Span, ft	Frame spacing, ft
30–40	16
40–60	18
60–100	20
Over 100	$\frac{1}{5}-\frac{1}{6}$ span

Columns of rigid frames may be designed with rotationally restrained (fixed) or rotationally free (hinged) bases. Pin-connected bases are rarely required; instead, a flat base plate with a single line of anchor bolts on the neutral axis of the column is common and is usually considered to act as a hinge. The horizontal reaction in smaller frames can be developed by the footing, but for spans greater than 60 to 80 ft a tie between the column bases or the footings may be necessary. Such a tie is usually located under the floor slab.

The design of a rigid frame is illustrated in DP9-15-1.

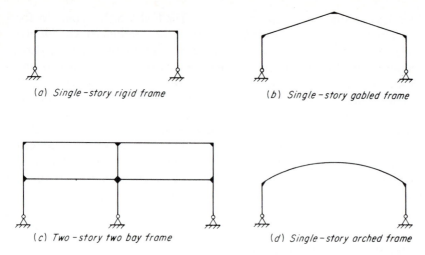

(a) Single-story rigid frame   (b) Single-story gabled frame

(c) Two-story two bay frame   (d) Single-story arched frame

FIGURE 12-3

12-3 FLOOR CONSTRUCTION

The one-way reinforced-concrete slab is one of the heaviest floor decks, but it makes a stiff floor and has a good fire rating. The minimum thickness is $3\frac{1}{2}$ to 4 in. Lightweight aggregates may be used to reduce the weight. Composite construction, in which the steel beam is encased in concrete or else bonded to the slab by means of shear connectors, may be advantageous for heavily loaded floors. The design of composite beams is discussed in Chap. 5.

A floor system consisting of a reinforced-concrete slab $2\frac{1}{2}$ to 3 in thick, supported by, and cast with, reinforced-concrete joists spaced 24 to 36 in, is economical for spans up to 30 ft (Fig. 12-4). The joists are formed by using removable metal pans. A similar two-way system is made by using small, square pans. Both systems may also be built using lightweight filler blocks of clay tile, gypsum tile, etc., instead of metal pans. This system provides an excellent surface for plastering, and no metal lath is required except on the bottom flanges of the steel beams if they are to be fireproofed with concrete or plaster. Most floors of this type require substantial forms and shoring during construction.

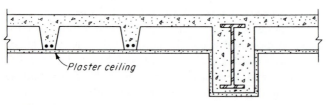

Plaster ceiling

FIGURE 12-4
Concrete joist floor.

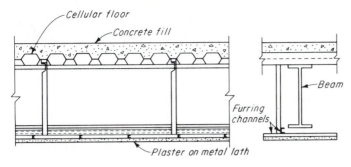

FIGURE 12-5
Cellular steel floor.

Cellular floor decking of light-gage steel, which may be used for spans up to about 25 ft, is available from a number of manufacturers. In one form, the unit for this type of floor consists of a flat sheet of steel spot-welded to a second sheet bent into a series of alternating troughs. Almost any kind of floor covering, e.g., asphalt tile, may be applied to the flat surface. Other forms consist of two sheets of steel both bent into a series of alternating troughs and spot-welded together (Fig. 12-5). These units must be topped with concrete or other material to produce the floor surface. Either form gives parallel, lengthwise cells which are useful as electrical raceways. If a fire-rated floor is required, at least 2 in of concrete topping must be used in conjunction with a suspended, plastered ceiling.

Open-web steel joists produce the lightest floor system (Fig. 2-1). These joists may be welded or bolted to the top flange of the supporting beam or attached by anchor rods fastened over the beam flange. A concrete slab 2 to $2\frac{1}{2}$ in thick and cast in place over steel mesh or welded wire fabric backed by heavy paper is ordinarily used. Standard open-web joists are available in depths ranging in 2-in increments from 8 to 24 in. The 24-in joist may be used on spans up to 48 ft. Longspan steel joists, with depths of 18 and 20 in and 24 to 48 in in 4-in increments are available for clear spans of 25 to 96 ft. Deep longspan joists with depths of 52, 56, and 60 in can span up to 120 ft.

There are many variations and adaptations of the floor systems described above, some of which are proprietary. Precast planks of gypsum or concrete are also used.

A comprehensive comparison of floor systems is given in Ref. 2.

12-4 ROOF SYSTEMS

The structural systems described previously for floors can be used for flat roofs. The long-span open-web joist is available with the top chord sloped to give either a single or a double pitch, but not exceeding $\frac{1}{8}$ in/ft, where roof drainage is required. In addition to these systems, corrugated cement-asbestos board, corrugated metal, and patented steel roof-deck materials should be considered. Corrugated cement-asbestos board is surfaced with a rigid insulating material and a built-up covering consisting of several layers of roofing felt cemented together with coal-tar pitch or asphalt and topped with slag or gravel. Corrugated metal may also be insulated and surfaced with a built-up covering.

Metal plates formed with interlocking ribs which increase strength and stiffness are manufactured in many different styles. These decks are usually covered with a vapor seal, a rigid insulating board, and a built-up roofing. They are installed either with ribs up or with ribs down. With ribs up there results a smooth ceiling which may be shop-painted with a baked-on enamel. If the appearance is objectionable with ribs down, an acoustical material may be applied to the lower surface.

A variety of precast units in the form of flat slabs, channel sections, and interlocking tiles, with or without glass insert panels, is used for pitched roofs as well as for flat roofs. These units may be manufactured from portland cement and lightweight aggregate, chemically expanded concrete, gypsum, and portland cement and asbestos fiber. Corrugated sheets of metal, cement-asbestos board, and wire glass are particularly adaptable to industrial buildings.

12-5 EXTERIOR WALLS

Many forms of exterior wall construction are available. Walls must be structurally sound, have adequate fire-resistance and insulating properties, offer protection against condensation of water vapor, be durable and easily maintained, and be pleasing in appearance.

Bearing walls must be strong enough to support, in addition to their own weight, any loads from floors and the roof which frame into them. According to the Uniform Building Code, bearing walls of plain masonry must be not less than 12 in thick, except that walls of one-story business buildings and residential buildings not over three stories high may be 8 in thick. Each successive 35-ft height of wall below the topmost 35 ft must be increased 4 in in thickness. The minimum thickness of unreinforced, grouted, brick masonry walls may be 2 in less than that required for plain masonry walls. Similar, but less severe, limitations are prescribed for reinforced-concrete bearing walls. Panel walls (also called curtain walls) in skeleton frame construction are usually specified in terms of their fire-resistance rating. For example, the BOCA National Building Code requires that the fire-resistance rating of panel walls be not less than 4 h for both fireproof and semifireproof construction. Except for reinforced-concrete walls, this requirement necessitates masonry walls ranging in thickness from 8 to 12 in.

Corrugated cement-asbestos board and corrugated-metal siding are used extensively for walls of industrial buildings. Wall sections consisting of two steel sheets with a layer of insulation between have also been widely accepted. Very attractive architectural effects are produced with fluted metal wall panels, which may be aluminum, stainless steel, galvanized copper-bearing steel, or porcelain-enameled iron or steel.

Structural glass blocks, which are hollow, colorless, and translucent, are appropriate for exterior walls when ventilating sash are not required or when clear glass is not needed for visibility. Since their coefficient of heat transfer is less than one-half that of single-thickness common glass, heating costs are reduced and air conditioning improved. Glass blocks should not be subjected to vertical loads other than their own weight.

12-6 PARTITIONS

Some of the factors to be considered in selecting partitions are appearance, weight, acoustical properties, and ease of erection. Although they usually carry no load other than their own weight, partitions for a building of only a few stories may be designed as bearing walls.

Clay tile, cinder block, and gypsum tile are used extensively, but for certain types of occupancy, such as general office areas, hollow partitions and other lightweight assemblies are more popular. Prefabricated hollow partitions may consist of metal lath and plaster supported on steel channel studs. Solid metal lath and plaster partitions offer the advantage of increased floor area because of their 2-in thickness. Metal and wire glass are adaptable to conditions requiring lightweight partitions which can be removed, altered, and relocated easily.

12-7 CRANEWAYS

Crane girders for industrial buildings may be supported on column brackets, as in Fig. 12-6*a*, but heavy cranes are supported as in Fig. 12-6*b* or *c*. The column

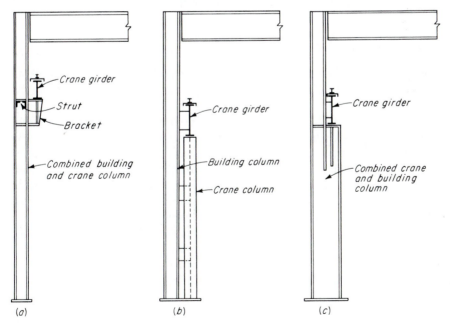

FIGURE 12-6
Crane girder columns.

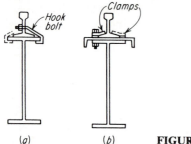

FIGURE 12-7

shown in Fig. 12-6b has the advantage of being fabricated from rolled sections and has good stiffness in both principal directions. The crane girder may be a rolled shape or plate girder, depending upon the span and the load. The section shown in Fig. 12-7b, which consists of a channel attached to the top flange of a W shape, is also used. Crane rails are attached to the girder with bolted clamps, but hook bolts are used with the lighter rails if the girder flanges are too narrow for clamps (Fig. 12-7a).

Large industrial buildings sometimes require craneways located at two or three levels in the same aisle and one or more runways in adjacent aisles. Crane girders in adjacent aisles can be supported on brackets connected to a single line of columns for the lighter cranes, but the heavier ones require separate columns.

The design of crane girders is illustrated in Arts. 5-9 and 5-19.

12-8   BRACING

The bent of Fig. 12-8a can resist vertical loads and lateral loads in its plane without dependence upon adjacent bents. However, it has little resistance to forces normal to its plane, and bracing such as *ABCD* in the plane of the top chord (Fig. 12-8b) and *BCEF* in the plane of the columns (Fig. 12-8c) is required. Two adjacent bents and their bracing form a braced bay, which, through the purlins and eave struts, supports adjacent bents. However, supplementary bracing such as that shown in Fig. 12-8b is usually provided for additional stiffness and to facilitate erection. The number and spacing of the braced bents depends to some extent on the magnitude of the horizontal forces to be resisted. There should be at least one braced bay between adjacent expansion joints in the building.

Different arrangements of bracing may be used in the wall panel *BCEF*. For example, the wall strut *GHIJ* is usually omitted in a building with girts, in which case the bay may be braced with diagonals from *C* to *F* and from *B* to *E* or, depending on the height of the building, with one or more intermediate lines of struts dividing *BCEF* into equal panels, with two diagonals in each panel. In some cases knee braces from *H* and *I* to the eave strut *CB* are used instead of diagonal bracing.

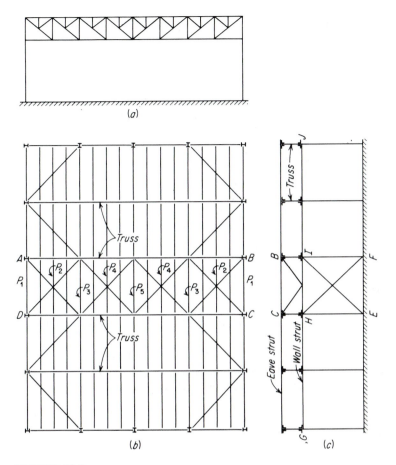

FIGURE 12-8

In addition to the bracing just described, the bottom chords of the trusses should be tied together at occasional panel points by lines of struts parallel to the wall strut *GHIJ*. As a general rule, these lines of struts should be spaced so that the slenderness ratio of the bottom chord, with respect to bending in the horizontal plane, does not exceed the specification limit. If the spacing of the trusses is too large for a single strut, cross frames similar to *BCHI* are used instead, with the purlins and the verticals of the main trusses forming part of the system.

A system of bracing like that described above will, in general, be sufficient to produce a stable structure. Bracing is expensive and should not be overdone. Just what is necessary in a given situation is, to a considerable extent, a question of judgment that depends on the engineer's qualitative evaluation. Forces in the members of the bracing system are rarely large enough to control their design. Therefore, except for whatever guidance is offered by slenderness-ratio limitations, their size is largely a question of judgment.

Trusses at the ends of a building are not necessary unless future extensions are to be provided for. Purlins in the end bays can be supported on rafters and other gable framing attached to the columns in the end walls. End walls without trusses must also have X- or knee-braced panels.

Bracing for simpler steel buildings that contain beams continuous over columns, with rolled-section purlins or open-web joists framing between, usually consists of bridging between joists to stiffen the roof system and knee braces or moment-resistant beam-to-column connections.

Craneways must be braced to resist the longitudinal forces from starting and stopping the crane. If the girder is supported as in Fig. 12-6*b* or *c*, knee braces at the crane column will be adequate for all but the heaviest cranes. Runways for the latter may require occasional X-braced panels. If the girder is supported on brackets (Fig. 12-6*a*), a strut consisting of two angles, laced or battened, may be used, as shown. This strut may be a part of the bracing system in the braced bays.

12-9 TRUSSES

It is impossible to formulate rules which will automatically determine the most economical truss for a given set of conditions. Certain principles which are helpful are discussed in this article.

The slope of a roof is determined principally by considerations of climate, drainage, and the type of roofing. Slopes must be 20 percent or more for lapped shingles, such as wood, asphalt, or clay tile. Flat roofs should be built with a slope of at least $\frac{1}{8}$ in/ft to facilitate drainage.

The depth of the Fink truss and similar types is determined largely by the slope requirements of the roofing. Since they are not ordinarily suitable for slopes less than about 5 in/ft, their depths will be at least one-fifth the span, which is ample for stiffness. Trusses for roofs of lesser slope and for flat roofs will usually be of the Pratt or Warren triangulation. The economical depth for these trusses is likely to be one-twelfth to one-eighth the span. The former figure is probably ample for continuous trusses, but simply supported trusses ordinarily should be somewhat deeper, perhaps about one-tenth the span as a minimum. However, clearance for shipping must be taken into consideration. It may be impossible to ship a truss deeper than about 10 ft, depending of course upon clearances on the route it must travel. Thus, if a truss with a span of, say, 120 ft and a depth of 11 or 12 ft cannot be shipped shop-fabricated in one or two sections, a depth of 10 ft—even though it is only one-twelfth the span—will almost certainly prove to be more economical.

The depth of a truss must also be considered in relation to the length of the panels. The panel length depends in turn upon the spacing of the purlins and upon the necessity of getting a favorable slope for the diagonal web members. Spacing of the purlins is governed, of course, by the type of roof deck. In general, the slope of the diagonals should be 40 to 50° with the horizontal. A slope of more than 50° may require an excessive number of diagonals, while a slope of less than 40° is likely to result in needlessly large stresses in the web system. Steep diagonals can be avoided in deep trusses with relatively close-spaced purlins by using a subdivided truss, such as that of Fig. 12-8a.

The spacing of long-span trusses (longer than about 150 ft) should be carefully considered. Such trusses may be more economical on 40- to 50-ft centers, rather than 20- to 25-ft, with the purlins supported on longitudinal trusses framing into the longspan trusses at 20- to 25-ft intervals.

Before the stresses in the members can be determined, the weight of the truss must be estimated and added to the dead load of the purlins, roof deck, and roofing. The weight of a truss is influenced by its pitch and span, by the spacing of the trusses, by the magnitude and distribution of loading, by differences in specifications, and by the ingenuity of the designer. The weight of a truss of ordinary span, together with the lateral bracing, may be estimated at about 10 percent of the load it supports. Long-span trusses, especially those supporting other trusses, are likely to be heavier. Many formulas for estimating the weight of a truss have been published, but because of the factors just mentioned, they cannot be depended upon for accurate estimates. The weight of a truss should be computed after it has been designed to make sure that it is close enough to the assumed weight.

12-10 WIND BRACING FOR TALL BUILDINGS

Wind forces are of no consequence in the design of the structural frame for multi-story buildings that have a small ratio of height to width. The inherent stiffness of the standard framing connection produces a frame which has the strength to resist lateral forces of considerable magnitude without the help of special wind bracing.

If a building must be braced for wind or other lateral force, the obvious solution is a system of diagonal bracing, called an *X-brace system*, that forms with the columns and beams a series of vertical trusses (Fig. 12-9a). Architectural requirements usually relegate it to walls enclosing shaft or service areas where there are few or no openings to interfere. However, X-bracing has been used, exposed, in the exterior walls of several buildings; Fig. 12-10 is an example. The John Hancock building (Chicago) is also braced in this manner.

The K-brace system (Fig. 12-9b), in which the horizontal member (the floor beam) is supported at midspan, is more efficient in weight of steel because it

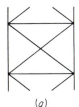 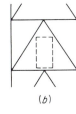 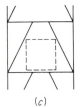 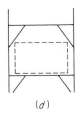

(a)   (b)   (c)   (d)

FIGURE 12-9

furnishes an interior support for the floor beam, even though the saving in weight of the floor beam is partially offset by the heavier bracing members. The K-brace also allows greater freedom in the use of aisle space, since it is possible to fit doors beneath its apex. Larger openings may necessitate a modified form of the K-braced bent (Fig. 12-9c), which is sometimes called a *full-story knee-braced bent*. Still larger openings can be provided by using the knee braces shown in Fig. 12-9d. If aisles must be free of bracing, moment-resistant beam-to-column connections must be used. A bent that is provided with any form of bracing is called a *braced bent*. A bent that is designed to resist wind forces is called a *wind bent*. A wind bent may be a braced bent, a rigid frame, or a combination of the two. Since the floors are usually of a type that serve as horizontal diaphragms, not every bent in a tier building need be a wind bent. In some cases wind bents in the outside walls may be sufficient. If the plan provides a sufficiently large, centrally located service area, this area may be surrounded with braced bents to form a core through which wind forces are delivered to the ground. An example is shown in Fig. 12-11, where full-story knee-braced bents are used in section *A-A* and truss-type panels in section *B-B*. Service areas may sometimes be enclosed by shear walls so as to eliminate braced bents altogether. The shear wall is nothing more than a substantial wall, usually of reinforced concrete or masonry. It need not be a monolithic wall—it may consist of securely anchored panels built into the spaces framed by the columns and girders of the frame.

Where full usable aisle space is required in wind bents, moment-resistant beam-to-column connections must be used instead of bracing. However, rigid-frame bents cannot always be used in the modern multistory building. Ducts for mechanical systems occupy a considerable portion of the depth allowed for floor construction, so beams and girders must be as shallow as possible to minimize story height. Furthermore, where large column-free space is required, beam spans are long. Under these conditions, it is difficult and sometimes impossible to design efficient rigid-frame bents. Although this problem can be solved by using deep beams or girders with web openings for mechanical ducts, such openings generally require reinforcement, which also increases the cost of the framing system.

The braced bent is generally stiffer than the rigid frame and requires little or no increase in the sizes of beams and columns (over that which is required for gravity loads) to achieve acceptable horizontal deflection. On the other hand, moment-resistant frames usually require large member sizes, at the lower levels of the building, to limit these deflections. Braced frames of different configurations may be required in the same system, and in many cases braced frames must be combined with rigid frames.

For buildings over about 60 stories, the optimum bracing system is the box-type frame, in which all the structural elements of the exterior walls act like walls of a tube. This can be accomplished by making the exterior framing an X-braced bent the full width of the building (Fig. 12-10), by using closely spaced diagonals on the exterior walls (Fig. 12-12), or by using closely spaced exterior columns with relatively stiff spandrels (Fig. 12-13).

FIGURE 12-10
Alcoa Building, San Francisco. (*American Institute of Steel Construction.*)

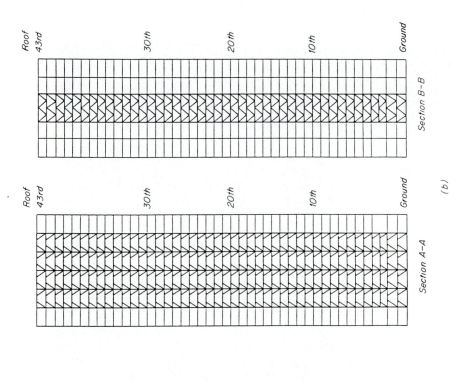

Section B-B

(b)

Section A-A

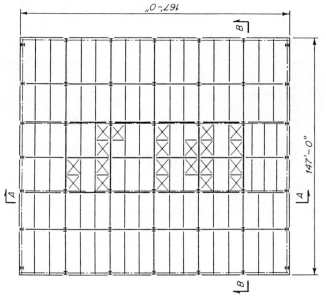

167'-0"

147'-0"

(a)

FIGURE 12-11
(*From Ref. 3.*)

770

FIGURE 12-12
IBM Building, Pittsburgh, Pa. (*United States Steel Corporation.*)

FIGURE 12-13
World Trade Center, New York City, under construction. (*Port of New York Authority.*)

12-11   WIND-BENT ANALYSIS

Wind-bracing systems of tall buildings are highly statically indeterminate. However, many computer programs are available, and there is virtually no limit to the size and complexity of structures that can be programmed and solved in reasonable machine time.[3] A first approximation of the frame may be made by basing member sizes on gravity loads alone. The preliminary design is then modified as needed and reanalyzed.

There are two approximate methods of analysis, described in the following two articles, which may be used to obtain a trial design of frames that are reasonably symmetrical. Ordinarily, however, it is probably better to proceed as described in the preceding paragraph.

12-12   THE PORTAL METHOD

The simple portal of Fig. 12-14a is statically indeterminate to the third degree, so three assumptions are needed to make an analysis by statics alone. If we assume (1) the magnitude of one of the horizontal reactions, (2) the location of the point of inflection of the left-hand column, and (3) the location of the point of inflection of the right-hand column, we can solve for the remaining horizontal reaction, the vertical reactions, and the end moments. Figure 12-14a shows the reactions, Fig. 12-14b the deflected shape of the portal, and Fig. 12-14c the bending-moment diagrams, assuming points of inflection to lie at the midpoint of each column and the horizontal reactions to be equal.

Consider next the single-story, three-bay bent shown in Fig. 12-15a. If we had instead three independent portals (Fig. 12-15b) and were to make for each the same assumptions as were described for Fig. 12-14, each bent would be statically determinate. The portal method of analysis is based on the assumption that the lateral force P acting on the multibay bent of Fig. 12-15a is divided equally among the corresponding number of independent portals (Fig. 12-15b) and that

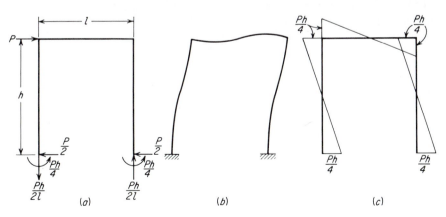

FIGURE 12-14

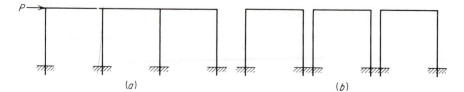

FIGURE 12-15

the reactive forces are those which are obtained by simple superposition of the forces acting on the independent portals. This leads to the conclusion that the interior columns of a multibay bent carry twice the shear of the exterior columns and that each column and each girder has a point of inflection at midpoint. By a simple extension of this idea, we assume for a multistory, multibay bent that the shear in each story is distributed in the same manner as for a single-story, multibay bent and that every column and every girder has a point of inflection at midpoint.

The portal method is easy to use. Once the shears in the columns of each story are known, moments at the top and bottom of each column in a story are found by multiplying the shear by the half length of the column. This follows from the assumption that the point of inflection is at midheight. Next, the end moment in a girder connecting to an outside column is equal to the sum of the column moments at that joint, as is evident from Fig. 12-16a. But if there is a point of inflection at the midpoint of the girder, the end moments on the girder are numerically equal, so that the moment at the interior end of the girder is also known (Fig. 12-16b). Next, the end moment for the first interior girder is found from the condition that the sum of the girder moments must equal the sum of the column moments at an interior joint (Fig. 12-16c). The shear in any girder is found by dividing the sum of the end moments on the girder by the span (Fig. 12-16b). Evidently, the axial force in any column of any story is equal to the sum of the shears on all the girders connecting to it above the story in question.

The portal method is considered to be generally satisfactory for buildings of moderate height/width ratio and not over about 25 stories high. Story heights and girder spans should be approximately equal and the configuration reasonably symmetrical.

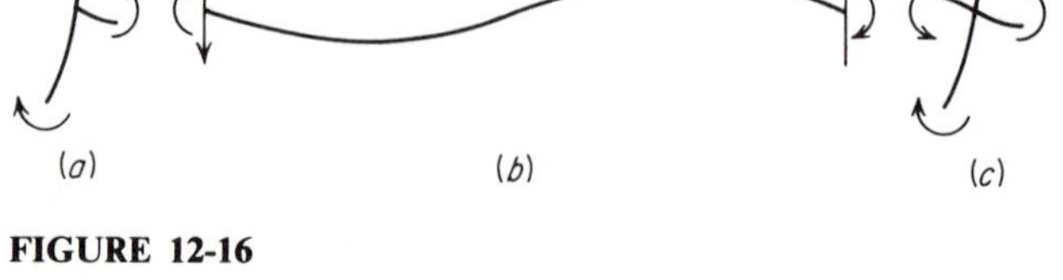

(a)   (b)   (c)

FIGURE 12-16

12-13   THE CANTILEVER METHOD

In the cantilever method of analysis, points of inflection of all the columns and girders of a building frame are assumed to lie at midpoint, just as in the portal method. However, instead of an assumption about the distribution of the shear among the columns of a given story, in the cantilever method an assumption is made about the distribution of the axial stresses in the columns of a given story. It is assumed that the bent acts as a cantilever beam and that in resisting the bending moments produced by the lateral forces it develops in its columns axial stresses distributed linearly about a neutral axis, as in beams. Since it is the stresses rather than the forces that are distributed linearly, the axial forces in the columns cannot be determined without an estimate of the relative cross-sectional areas. However, some users of this method assume that the axial forces, rather than the axial stresses, are distributed linearly, which is another way of saying that they assume the columns to have equal cross-sectional areas.

As an example, assume that the columns of a three-bay framework are spaced 20 ft on centers and that the story height, measured between centerlines of floor beams, is 14 ft. Isolating the portion that lies above the points of inflection of the columns in the top story, we get Fig. 12-17a. The wind force at the roof is 8 kips. Assume that the cross-sectional area of each interior column is 1.5 times the cross-sectional area A_1 of the exterior column. Let the axial stress on the exterior column be f. Then on each interior column the axial stress is $f/3$. The corresponding forces P_1 and P_2 are shown on the figure. From the equation of moments about the neutral axis O, we get

$$60P_1 + 20P_2 = 60fA_1 + 20 \times 0.5fA_1 = 8 \times 7$$

$$fA_1 = 0.8$$

Therefore, $P_1 = fA_1 = 0.8$ kip, and $P_2 = 0.5fA_1 = 0.4$ kip.

If Fig. 12-17a represents the top story of a multistory frame, we can find by proportion the axial forces in the columns of any other story for which the cross-sectional areas of the columns are in the same ratio as are those in the top story.

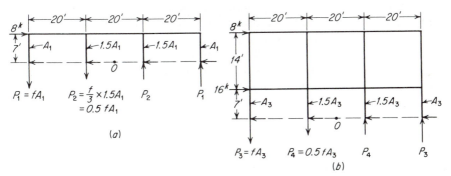

FIGURE 12-17

Thus if we write the equation for moments at point O of Fig. 12-17b, we get the same equation as before except that A_3 replaces A_1 and the right member, $8 \times 7 = 56$ ft·kips, becomes $8 \times 21 + 16 \times 7 = 280$ ft·kips. Then, since $\frac{280}{56} = 5$, we have $P_3 = 5P_1 = 4$ kips and $P_4 = 5P_2 = 2$ kips.

Once the axial forces in the columns are known, the shears in the girders are easy to determine. Thus in Fig. 12-17a it is evident that the shear in the outside girder at the roof is equal to the axial force P_1 in the outside column while that in the interior girder is equal to the sum of the forces P_1 and P_2. Similarly, the shear in the outside girder at the top floor (Fig. 12-17b) is equal to the difference between the axial forces P_3 and P_1 in the adjacent outside columns. With the shears in the girders known, end moments in the girders are determined by multiplying each shearing force by the half span of the corresponding girder. This follows from the assumption that the points of inflection are at midspan. Moments in the columns may be found next, starting at the roof and taking advantage of the assumed equality of the end moments in each column of each story. Following this, determination of the shears in the columns and the axial forces in the girders completes the analysis.

The cantilever method is used less often than the portal method. In the opinion of a committee of the ASCE, it is suitable for buildings of moderate height/width ratio and not more than 25 to 35 stories high. It is considered to be superior to the portal method for high, narrow buildings.[4] Story heights and girder spans should be approximately equal and the configuration reasonably symmetrical. A more detailed explanation of the portal and the cantilever methods may be found in Ref. 5.

12-14   LIMITATIONS OF PORTAL AND CANTILEVER METHODS

The deflection of a frame is a combination of flexural and shear distortions. Since the portal method is based on a distribution of lateral shear to the columns of a bent, it tends to produce a result which is primarily the effect of shear distortion. The distortion of frames with low height/width ratio is primarily that of shear. Therefore, the portal analysis is appropriate for such frames. On the other hand, the cantilever method is based on a distribution of column axial forces similar to the distribution of bending stress in a flexural member, so it tends to produce a result which is primarily a result of flexural distortion. The primary distortion of building frames with a high height/width ratio is due to bending as a cantilever. Therefore, the cantilever method is appropriate for such frames.

REFERENCES

1. Fisher, J. M.: Industrial Buildings, sec. 22 in E. H. Gaylord and C. N. Gaylord (eds.), "Structural Engineering Handbook," 3d ed., McGraw-Hill, New York, 1990.

2. Tang, S. J. Y., and I. R. Chin: Buildings—General Design Considerations, sec. 21 in E. H. Gaylord and C. N. Gaylord (eds.), "Structural Engineering Handbook," 3d ed., McGraw-Hill, New York, 1990.
3. Eligator, M. H., S. L. Chu, and L. A. Occhicone: Tall Buildings, sec. 23 in E. H. Gaylord and C. N. Gaylord (eds.), "Structural Engineering Handbook," 3d ed., McGraw-Hill, New York, 1990.
4. Wind Bracing in Steel Buildings, Final Report of Subcommittee 31, *Trans. ASCE*, vol. 105, p. 1713, 1940.
5. Norris, E. H., J. B. Wilbur, and S. Utku: "Elementary Structural Analysis," 4th ed., p. 231, McGraw-Hill, New York, 1991.

TABLE A-1

Approximate radii of gyration

Section	Formula	Section	Formula	Section	Formula
	$r_x = 0.29h$ $r_y = 0.29b$		$r_x = 0.42h$ $r_y = 0.42b$		$r_x = 0.31h$ $r_y = 0.48b$
	$r_x = 0.40h$ $h = $ mean h		$r_y = $ same as for 2 L		$r_x = 0.37h$ $r_y = 0.28b$
	$r_x = 0.25h$		$r_x = 0.42h$ $r_y = $ same as for 2 L		$r_x = 0.31h$
	$r = \sqrt{\dfrac{H^2+h^2}{16}}$ $r = 0.35 H_m$		$r_x = 0.39h$ $r_y = 0.21b$		$r_x = 0.31h$
	$r_x = 0.31h$ $r_y = 0.31h$ $r_z = 0.197h$		$r_x = 0.45h$ $r_y = 0.235b$		$r_x = 0.40h$ $r_y = 0.21b$
	$r_x = 0.29h$ $r_y = 0.32h$ $r_z = 0.18\dfrac{h+b}{2}$		$r_x = 0.36h$ $r_y = 0.45b$		$r_x = 0.38h$ $r_y = 0.22b$
	$r_x = 0.31h$ $r_y = 0.215b$ $= b(0.21+0.02s)$		$r_x = 0.36h$ $r_y = 0.60b$		$r_x = 0.39h$
	$r_x = 0.32h$ $r_y = 0.21b$ $= b(0.19+0.02s)$		$r_x = 0.36h$ $r_y = 0.53b$		$r_x = 0.35h$
	$r_x = 0.29h$ $r_y = 0.24b$ $= b(0.23+0.02s)$		$r_x = 0.39h$ $r_y = 0.55b$		$r_x = 0.435h$ $r_y = 0.25b$
	$r_x = 0.30h$ $r_y = 0.17b$		$r_x = 0.42h$ $r_y = 0.32b$		$r_x = 0.42h$
	$r_x = 0.25h$ $r_y = 0.21b$		$r_x = 0.44h$ $r_y = 0.28b$		$r_x = 0.42h$
	$r_x = 0.21h$ $r_y = 0.21b$ $r_z = 0.19h$		$r_x = 0.50h$ $r_y = 0.28b$		$r_x = 0.285h$ $r_y = 0.37b$
	$r_x = 0.38h$ $r_y = 0.19b$		$r_x = 0.39h$ $r_y = 0.21b$		$r_x = 0.42h$ $r_y = 0.23b$

Source: J. A. L. Waddell, "Bridge Engineering," Wiley, New York, 1925.

TABLE A-2
SI Conversion Factors

Item	Multiply	By	To obtain
Acceleration	foot per square second (ft/s^2)	0.3048	meter per square second (m/s^2)
Area	square inch (in^2)	645.2	square millimeter (mm^2)
	square foot (ft^2)	0.09290	square meter (m^2)
	square mile (U.S.) (mi^2)	2.590	square kilometer (km^2)
Density	pound-mass per cubic inch	27,680	kilogram per cubic meter (kg/m^3)
	pound-mass per cubic foot	16.02	kg/m^3
Force	pound (lb)	4.448	newton (N)
	kilopound (kip)	4.448	kilonewton (kN)
	ton (2000 lb)	8.896	kN
Length	inch (in)	25.40	millimeter (mm)
	foot (ft)	0.3048	meter (m)
	mile (mi)	1.609	kilometer (km)
Mass	pound (av.) (lb)	0.4536	kilogram (kg)
	kip	453.6	kg
	ton (2000 lb)	907.2	kg
Pressure, stress	pound-force/in^2 (psi)	6.895	kilopascal (kPa)
	kip-force/in^2 (ksi)	6895	kPa
	pound-force/ft^2 (psf)	992.9	kPa
	feet of water (at 39.2°F)	2.989	kPa
Speed	mi (U.S.)/h	4.470	m/s
Temperature	degree Fahrenheit (°F)	$(t° - 32)/1.8$	degree Celsius (°C)
Volume	cubic inch (in^3)	16,387	cubic millimeter (mm^3)
	cubic foot (ft^3)	0.02832	cubic meter (m^3)

NAME INDEX

Page numbers in *italic* indicate references.

SUBJECT INDEX